UG

MATH 100

Custom Edition for the University of Massachusetts Amherst

Thinking Mathematically

Robert Blitzer

Taken from:

Thinking Mathematically, Fourth Edition
by Robert Blitzer

Custom Publishing

New York Boston San Francisco
London Toronto Sydney Tokyo Singapore Madrid
Mexico City Munich Paris Cape Town Hong Kong Montreal

Cover Art: Boston Skyline-Streak, by Kay Canavino and Minuteman (246)

Taken from:

Thinking Mathematically, Fourth Edition
by Robert Blitzer

Published by Prentice Hall
Upper Saddle River, New Jersey 07458

This special edition published in cooperation with Pearson Custom Publishing.

Printed in the United States of America

10 9 8 7 6 5 4 3 2 1

2008360591

WH

Pearson
Custom Publishing
is a division of

PEARSON

www.pearsonhighered.com

ISBN 10: 0-536-24644-0
ISBN 13: 978-0-536-24644-8

Contents

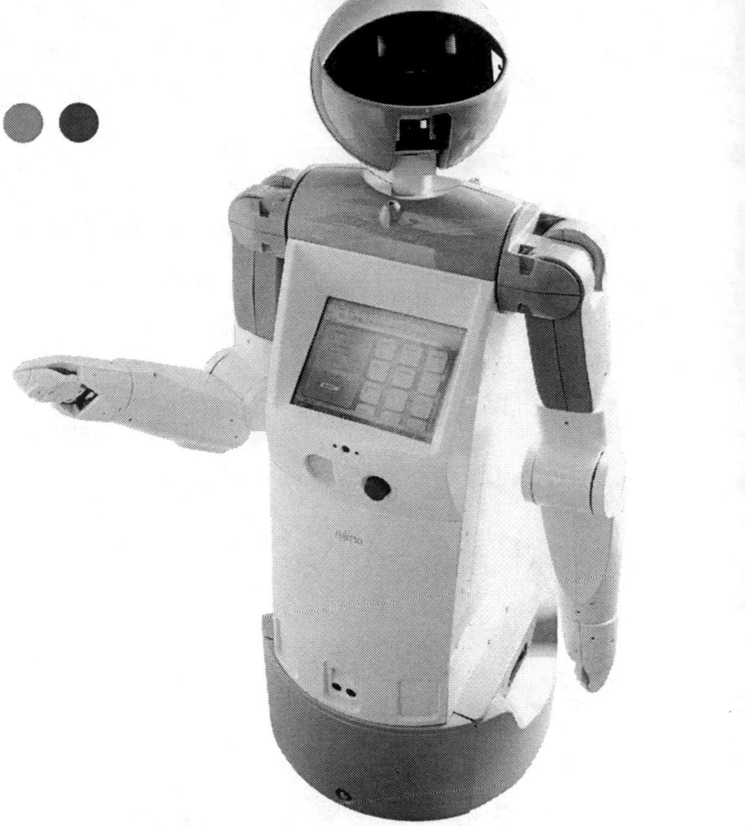

6

Algebra: Equations and Inequalities 303

7

Algebra: Graphs, Functions, and Linear Systems 367

8

Consumer Mathematics and Financial Management 443

9

Measurement 507

10

Geometry 537

11

Counting Methods and Probability Theory 607

12

Statistics 679

About the Author

Bob and his horse Jerid

Bob Blitzer is a native of Manhattan and received a Bachelor of Arts degree with dual majors in mathematics and psychology (minor: English Literature) from the City College of New York. His unusual combination of academic interests led him toward a Master of Arts in mathematics from the University of Miami and a doctorate in behavioral sciences from Nova University. Bob is most energized by teaching mathematics and has taught a variety of mathematics courses at Miami Dade College for nearly 30 years. He has received numerous teaching awards, including Innovator of the Year from the League for Innovations in the Community College, and was among the first group of recipients at Miami Dade College for an endowed chair based on excellence in the classroom. In addition to *Thinking Mathematically*, Bob has written textbooks covering introductory algebra, intermediate algebra, algebra and trigonometry, and precalculus, all published by Prentice Hall.

Preface

Thinking Mathematically, Fourth Edition provides a general survey of mathematical topics that are useful in our contemporary world. My primary purpose in writing the book was to show students how mathematics can be applied to their lives in interesting, enjoyable, and meaningful ways. The book's variety of topics and flexibility of sequence make it appropriate for a one- or two-term course in liberal arts mathematics, quantitative reasoning, finite mathematics, mathematics for education majors, as well as for courses specifically designed to meet state-mandated requirements in mathematics.

I wrote the book to help diverse students, with different backgrounds and career plans, to succeed. **Thinking Mathematically, Fourth Edition**, has four major goals:

1. To help students acquire knowledge of fundamental mathematics.
2. To show students how mathematics can solve authentic problems that apply to their lives.
3. To enable students to understand and reason with quantitative issues and mathematical ideas they are likely to encounter in college, career, and life.
4. To enable students to develop problem-solving skills, while fostering critical thinking, within an interesting setting.

One major obstacle in the way of achieving these goals is the fact that very few students actually read their textbook. This has been a regular source of frustration for me and my colleagues in the classroom. Anecdotal evidence gathered over years highlights two basic reasons why students do not take advantage of their textbook:

"I'll never use this information."

"I can't follow the explanations."

I've written every page of the Fourth Edition with the intent of eliminating these two objections. The ideas and tools I've used to do so are described for the student in "A Brief Guide to Getting the Most from This Book," which appears inside the front cover.

What's New in the Fourth Edition?

- **Practice Plus Exercises.** More challenging practice exercises that often require students to combine several skills or concepts have been added to the exercise sets. The 442 Practice Plus Exercises in the Fourth Edition provide instructors with the option of creating assignments that take practice exercises to a more challenging level than in the previous edition.
- **New Applications and Real-World Data.** I researched hundreds of books, magazines, almanacs, and online data sites to prepare the Fourth Edition. The Fourth Edition contains more new, innovative, applications, supported by data that extend as far up to the present as possible, than any previous revisions of this book. There are 453 new exercises in the application category of the exercise sets, as well as 54 titled, worked-out examples that are based on new applications.
- **More Than 1400 New Examples and Exercises.** In addition to the 442 Practice Plus Exercises and the 507 new application examples and exercises, the Fourth Edition contains more than 500 new exercises that appear in the practice category of the exercise sets.

- **Integration of Graphs and Mathematical Models.** Mathematical modeling is introduced in Chapter 1. The integrated use of graphs and models is provided so that students can interpret and reason with information involving numbers and mathematical ideas.
- **Increased Study Tip Boxes.** The book's Study Tip boxes offer suggestions for problem solving, point out common errors to avoid, and provide informal hints and suggestions. These invaluable hints appear in greater abundance in the Fourth Edition.
- **New Enrichment Essays ("Blitzer Bonuses").** The Fourth Edition contains a variety of new, but optional, enrichment essays.
- **Chapter Test Prep Video CD.** Found within MyMathLab, these videos provide students with step-by-step solutions for each of the exercises in the book's chapter tests.

What Content and Organizational Changes Have Been Made to the Fourth Edition?

- Section 1.1 (Inductive and Deductive Reasoning) contains a greater variety of examples and exercises that require students to identify patterns and engage in inductive reasoning.
- Section 1.2 (Estimation, Graphs, and Mathematical Models) includes a new discussion on rounding the decimal part of a decimal number. Also included is an early discussion of mathematical modeling and mathematical models. Students are shown how to reason with quantitative information presented graphically by developing linear models that estimate relationships between variables.
- Section 2.1 (Basic Set Concepts) reviews inequality notation and uses this notation to represent various sets containing natural numbers. Following the discussion of one-to-one correspondences and equivalent sets, the section concludes with a new, but brief, introduction to infinite sets. This "tease" on infinite sets is developed in more detail at the conclusion of Section 2.2 and in the Blitzer Bonus at the end of that section.
- Section 2.2 (Subsets) is now devoted exclusively to ideas about subsets. Venn diagrams are no longer introduced in this section.
- Section 2.3 (Venn Diagrams and Set Operations) contains a new discussion on sets and precise use of everyday English. The words *or* and *and* are related to set operations through practical contexts involving graphs and real-world data. The formula for the cardinal number of the union of two finite sets was moved from the section on surveys to this section.
- Section 2.4 (Set Operations and Venn Diagrams with Three Sets) contains a new example explaining how to determine a Venn diagram from three sets and a universal set. Graphics with clarifying voice balloons illustrate the process in a step-by-step manner.
- Section 2.5 (Survey Problems) uses new graphics with clarifying voice balloons to illustrate how to determine a Venn diagram for a survey. A new follow-up example involving the use of a survey's Venn diagram places English words and phrases such as *neither*, *none*, *exactly one*, *at least two*, *and*, *or*, and *but* into the context of mathematical ideas about sets.
- Section 3.2 (Compound Statements and Connectives) now contains translations of $p \rightarrow q$ and $p \leftrightarrow q$ that involve the words *necessary* and *sufficient*. The section concludes with a new discussion on dominance of connectives.
- Section 3.3 (Truth Tables for Negation, Conjunction, and Disjunction) emphasizes truth tables that require four cases, but now includes tables with two cases, as well as those with eight cases. There is a new example on

determining the truth value of a compound statement for a specific case within the context of graphical data.

- Section 3.6 (Arguments and Truth Tables) contains new applications that span the gamut from the Menendez brothers' criminal case to Nixon's resignation. The exercise set contains a brief discussion, with exercises, of common fallacies in everyday reasoning.
- Chapter 4 (Number Representation and Calculation) contains new discussions of digital technology, including a Blitzer Bonus that relates base two and truth tables to computers. There are new application exercises in Exercise Set 4.3 based on these ideas.
- Chapter 6 (Algebra: Equations and Inequalities) now opens with a discussion of mathematical modeling and mathematical models, repeated from Chapter 1 for those who did not cover that chapter. The mathematical models that appear throughout Chapter 6 range from how responses to negative life events vary with sense of humor to how blood pressure varies with age.
- Chapter 7 (Algebra: Graphs, Functions, and Linear Systems) has been reorganized. After functions are introduced in the first section, the next four sections are devoted to linear models, including linear functions and their graphs, systems of linear equations in two variables, linear inequalities in two variables, and linear programming. The last section of the chapter focuses on approximating reality with nonlinear models.
- Section 7.1 (Graphing and Functions) contains new examples involving data presented graphically and functions that model the data.
- Section 7.3 (Systems of Linear Equations in Two Variables) contains new applications involving revenue functions, cost functions, break-even points, and profit functions.
- Section 7.6 (Approximating Reality with Nonlinear Models) is a new section in which the shape of data presented in scatter plots suggests modeling with exponential functions, logarithmic functions, and quadratic functions.
- Section 8.1 (Percent, Sales Tax, and Income Tax) contains a new objective on computing income tax.
- Section 8.3 (Compound Interest) now discusses formulas for compound interest subject to n compoundings per year, as well as to continuous compounding.
- Section 8.4 (Annuities, Stocks, and Bonds) is a new section on determining the value of an annuity, as well as determining regular annuity payments needed to achieve a financial goal. Stocks and bonds, presented as a separate section in the previous edition, have been moved to this section following the discussion of annuities.
- Section 8.6 (Amortization and the Cost of Home Ownership) now develops the loan payment formula for installment loans using formulas for compound interest and the value of an annuity. As in the previous edition, the loan payment formula is used to compute the monthly payment and interest costs for a mortgage. However, the Fourth Edition also applies the formula to determine payments and interest for other kinds of installment loans, including car loans and student loans.
- Section 10.3 (Polygons, Perimeter, and Tessellations) relates geometric ideas to the visual arts with a new discussion of tessellations and their angle requirements.
- Section 11.4 (Fundamentals of Probability) contains an early introduction to contingency tables, or two-way tables that relate two categories of data using row variables and column variables. New contingency tables with real-world data are used in Section 11.4, Section 11.6 (Events Involving *Not* and *Or*; Odds), and Section 11.7 (Events Involving *And*; Conditional Probability).

- Section 12.1 (Sampling, Frequency Distributions, and Graphs) has new and more current examples illustrating misleading visual displays.
- Section 12.4 (The Normal Distribution) contains new applications that can be modeled by the normal distribution. There is also a new, but brief, discussion of quartiles as commonly encountered percentiles.

I hope that my love for learning, as well as my respect for the diversity of students I have taught and learned from over the years, is apparent throughout this new edition. By connecting mathematics to the whole spectrum of learning, it is my intent to show students that their world is profoundly mathematical, and indeed, π is in the sky.

Robert Blitzer

To the Student

I have written this book to give you control over the part of your life that involves numbers and mathematical ideas. Gaining an understanding and appreciation of mathematics will help you participate fully in the twenty-first century. In some ways, you cannot get along in life without the mathematics in this book. For example, if you do not understand the basic ideas of investment, you may find it impossible to achieve your financial goals. If you do not have at least a rudimentary understanding of logic, you may not be able to analyze information objectively, possibly arriving at conclusions hastily without a method for considering all the evidence.

This book has been written so that you can learn about the power of mathematics directly from its pages. All concepts are carefully explained, important definitions and procedures are set off in boxes, and worked-out examples that present solutions in a step-by-step manner appear in every section. Each example is followed by a similar matched problem, called a Check Point, for you to try so that you can actively participate in the learning process as you read the book. (Answers to all Check Points appear in the back of the book.) Study Tip boxes offer hints and suggestions and often point out common errors to avoid. A great deal of attention has been given to applying mathematics to your life to make your learning experience both interesting and relevant.

As you begin your studies, I would like to offer some specific suggestions for using this book and for being successful in this course:

1. **Read the book.** Read each section with pen (or pencil) in hand. Move through the worked-out examples with great care. These examples provide a model for doing exercises in the exercise sets. As you proceed through the reading, do not give up if you do not understand every single word. Things will become clearer as you read on and see how various procedures are applied to specific worked-out examples.
2. **Work problems every day and check your answers.** The way to learn mathematics is by doing mathematics, which means working the Check Points and assigned exercises in the exercise sets. The more exercises you work, the better you will understand the material.
3. **Review for quizzes and tests.** After completing a chapter, study the two-column review chart, work the exercises in the Chapter Review, and work the exercises in the Chapter Test. Answers to all these exercises are given in the back of the book.

> The methods that I've used to help you read the book, work the problems, and review for tests are described in "A Brief Guide to Getting the Most from This Book," which appears inside the front cover. Spend a few minutes reviewing the guide to familiarize yourself with the book's features and their benefits.

4. **Use the resources available with this book.** Additional resources to aid your study are described on page xvi. These resources include a Solutions Manual, a Chapter Test Prep Video CD, MyMathLab, an online version of the book with links to multimedia resources, MathXL®, an online homework, tutorial, and assessment system of the text, and tutorial support at the PH Tutor Center.

5. **Attend all lectures.** No book is intended to be a substitute for valuable insights and interactions that occur in the classroom. In addition to arriving for lecture on time and being prepared, you will find it useful to read a section before it is covered in lecture. This will give you a clear idea of the new material that will be discussed.

I wrote this book in Point Reyes National Seashore, 40 miles north of San Francisco. The park consists of 75,000 acres with miles of pristine surf-washed beaches, forested ridges, and bays bordered by white cliffs. It was my hope to convey the beauty and excitement of mathematics using nature's unspoiled beauty as a source of inspiration and creativity. Enjoy the pages that follow as you empower yourself with the mathematics needed to succeed in college, your career, and in your life.

Regards,

Bob

Robert Blitzer

Acknowledgments

I wish to express my appreciation to all the reviewers for their helpful feedback, frequently transmitted with wit, humor, and intelligence. Every change to this edition is the result of their thoughtful comments and suggestions. In particular, I would like to thank:

Laurel Berry, *Bryant and Stratton College*
Kris Bowers, *Florida State University*
Gerard Buskes, *University of Mississippi*
Fred Butler, *West Virginia University*
Jimmy Chang, *St. Petersburg College*
Jerry Chen, *Suffolk County Community College*
Ivette Chuca, *El Paso Community College*
David Cochener, *Austin Peay State University*
Elizabeth T. Dameron, *Tallahassee Community College*
Tristen Denley, *University of Mississippi*
Suzanne Feldberg, *Nassau Community College*
Margaret Finster, *Erie Community College*
Lyn Geisler III, *Randolph-Macon College*
Dale Grussing, *Miami Dade College*
Cindy Gubitose, *Southern Connecticut State University*
Virginia Harder, *College at Oneonta*
Joseph Lloyd Harris, *Gulf Coast Community College*
Julia Hassett, *Oakton Community College*
Sonja Hensler, *St. Petersburg College*
Larry Hoehn, *Austin Peay State University*
Alec Ingraham, *New Hampshire College*
Linda Kuroski, *Erie Community College—City Campus*
Jamie Langille, *University of Nevada, Las Vegas*
Veronique Lanuqueitte, *St. Petersburg College*
Mitzi Logan, *Pitt Community College*
Linda Lohman, *Jefferson Community College*
Mike Marcozzi, *University of Nevada, Las Vegas*
Diana Martelly, *Miami Dade College*
Jim Matovina, *Community College of Southern Nevada*
Erik Matsuoka, *Leeward Community College*
Marcel Maupin, *Oklahoma State University*
Diana McCammon, *Delgado Community College*
Mex McKinley, *Florida Keys Community College*
Paul Mosbos, *State University of New York—Cortland*
Tammy Muhs, *University of Central Florida*
Cornelius Nelan, *Quinnipiac University*
Lawrence S. Orilia, *Nassau Community College*
Richard F. Patterson, *University of North Florida*
Frank Pecchioni, *Jefferson Community College*
Stan Perrine, *Charleston Southern University*
Anthony Pettofrezzo, *University of Central Florida*
Val Pinciu, *Southern Connecticut State University*
Evelyn Popplo-Cody, *Marshall University*
Virginia S. Powell, *University of Louisiana at Monroe*
Kim Query, *Lindenwood College*
Anne Quinn, *Edinboro University of Pennsylvania*
Bill Quinn, *Frederick Community College*
Sharonda Ragland, *ECPI College of Technology*
Shawn Robinson, *Valencia Community College*
Gary Russell, *Brevard Community College*
Mary Lee Seitz, *Erie Community College*
Laurie A. Stahl, *State University of New York—Fredonia*
Abolhassan Taghavy, *Richard J. Daley College & Chicago State University*
Ann Thrower, *Kilgore College*
Mike Tomme, *Community College of Southern Nevada*
Sherry Tornwall, *University of Florida*
Christopher Scott Vaughen, *Miami Dade College*
Bill Vaughters, *Valencia Community College*
Karen Villareal, *University of New Orleans*
Don Warren, *Edison Community College*
Shirley Wilson, *North Central College*
James Wooland, *Florida State University*
Cindy Zarske, *Fullerton College*
Marilyn Zopp, *McHenry County College*

Additional acknowledgments are extended to Dan Miller, for preparing the solutions manuals, Brad Davis, for preparing the answer section and serving as accuracy checker, the Preparè, Inc. formatting team, for the book's brilliant paging, Aaron Darnall at Scientific Illustrators, for superbly illustrating the book, Rachel Lucas, photo researcher, for obtaining the book's new photographs, Rebecca Muller, for preparing the CD Lecture series, including the Chapter Test Prep Video CDs, Liz Dameron, for preparing the *CLAST Manual*, and Barbara Mack, whose talents as production editor kept every aspect of this complex project moving through its many stages.

I would like to thank my editors at Prentice Hall, Sally Yagan and Chuck Synovec, and Project Manager, Michael Bell, who guided and coordinated the book from manuscript through production. Thanks to John Christiana, for the beautiful cover and interior design, Wayne Parkins and Patrice Jones, for their innovative marketing efforts, and to the entire Prentice Hall sales force, for their confidence and enthusiasm about the book.

Resources to Help You Study

Student Resources

Student Study Pack

Everything a student needs to succeed in one place. Packaged with the book or available for purchase stand-alone, the Study Pack contains:

Student Solutions Manual

Fully worked solutions to odd-numbered exercises and all check points.

Pearson Tutor Center

Tutors provide one-on-one tutoring for any problem with an answer at the back of the book. Students access the Tutor Center via toll-free phone, fax, or e-mail.

CD Lecture Series

A comprehensive set of CD-ROMs tied to the textbook, containing short video clips of an instructor working key book examples.

CLAST Manual

The *CLAST Manual* helps build students' proficiency in 55 mathematical skills in the fields of Arithmetic, Geometry, Algebra, Statistics, and Logic. Written as an additional supplement for students who are required to take the CLAST (students in the State of Florida), the first part of the *CLAST Manual* focuses on the skill-by-skill description of each of the 55 skills required in the exam, including worked out examples. The second part of this manual is a collection of CLAST-style homework exercises linked to various sections of *Thinking Mathematically 4e*.

Instructor Resources

Instructor Resource Distribution

All instructor resources can be downloaded from the Web site, *www.prenhall.com*. Select "Browse our catalog," then, click on "Mathematics;" select your course and choose your text. Under "Resources," on the left side, select "instructor" and choose the supplement you need to download. You will be required to run through a one time registration before you can complete this process.

Instructor Solutions Manual

Fully worked solutions to all textbook exercises and chapter projects.

TestGen

Easily create tests from textbook section objectives. Questions are algorithmically generated allowing for unlimited versions. Edit problems or create your own.

Test Item File

A printed test bank derived from TestGen.

PowerPoint Lecture Slides

Fully editable slides that follow the textbook. Project in class or post to a Web site in an online course.

Mini-Lectures

Mini-Lectures are provided for the Teaching Assistant, adjunct, part-time instructor, or even full-time instructor for lecture preparation by providing learning objectives, examples not found in the text, teaching notes, and the answers to said examples. Mini-Lectures are available from the Instructor's Resource Center and MyMathLab.

Instructor's Edition

Provides answers to all exercises in the back of the text.

MathXL®

MathXL® is a powerful online homework, tutorial, and assessment system that accompanies your textbook. Instructors can create, edit, and assign online homework and tests using algorithmically generated exercises correlated at the objective level to the textbook. Student work is tracked in an online gradebook. Students can take chapter tests and receive personalized study plans based on their results. The study plan diagnoses weaknesses and links students to tutorial exercises for objectives they need to study. Students can also access video clips from selected exercises. MathXL® is available to qualified adopters. For more information, visit our Web site at *www.mathxl.com*, or contact your Prentice Hall sales representative for a demonstration.

MyMathLab

MyMathLab is a text-specific, customizable online course for your textbooks. MyMathLab is powered by CourseCompass™—Pearson Education's online teaching and learning environment—and by MathXL®—our online homework, tutorial, and assessment system. MyMathLab gives you the tools you need to deliver all or a portion of your course online, whether your students are in a lab setting or working from home.

MyMathLab provides a rich and flexible set of course materials, featuring free-response exercises that are algorithmically generated for unlimited practice. Students can use online tools such as video lectures and a multimedia textbook to improve their performance. Instructors can use MyMathLab's homework and test managers to select and assign online exercises correlated to the textbook, and can import TestGen tests for added flexibility. The online gradebook—designed specifically for mathematics—automatically tracks students' homework and test results and gives the instructor control over how to calculate final grades. MyMathLab is available to qualified adopters. For more information, visit our Web site at *www.mymathlab.com* or contact your Prentice Hall sales representative for a product demonstration.

CHAPTER 4

Number Representation and Calculation

Adorable on the outside and clever on the inside, it's not hard to imagine friendly robots as our home-helping buddies. Built-in microchips with extraordinary powers based on ancient numeration systems enable your robot to recognize you, engage in (meaningful?) conversation, and perform household chores. If you find the idea of a friendship with a sophisticated machine a bit unsettling, consider a robot dog or cat. Scientists have designed these critters to blend computer technology with the cuddly appeal of animals. They move, play, and sleep like real pets, and can even be programmed to sing and dance. Without an understanding of how we represent numbers, none of this technology could exist.

Connections between binary numeration systems and computer technology are discussed in "Letters and Words in Base Two" on page 205, "Music in Base Two" on page 207, and "Base Two, Logic, and Computers" on page 214.

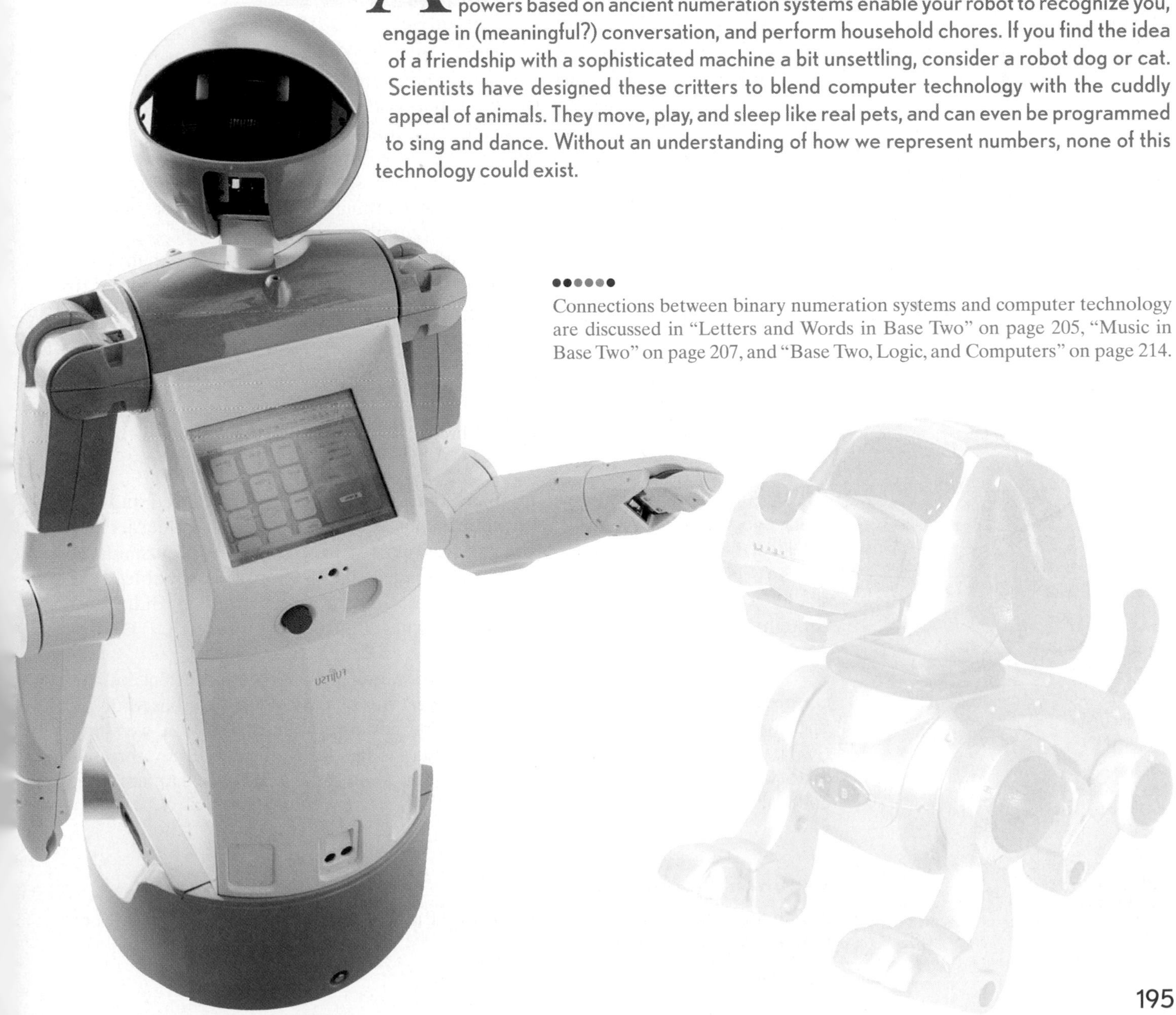

SECTION 4.1 • OUR HINDU-ARABIC SYSTEM AND EARLY POSITIONAL SYSTEMS

OBJECTIVES

1. Evaluate an exponential expression.
2. Write a Hindu-Arabic numeral in expanded form.
3. Express a number's expanded form as a Hindu-Arabic numeral.
4. Understand and use the Babylonian numeration system.
5. Understand and use the Mayan numeration system.

All of us have an intuitive understanding of *more* and *less*. As humanity evolved, this sense of more and less was used to develop a system of counting. A tribe needed to know how many sheep it had, and whether the flock was increasing or decreasing in number. The earliest way of keeping count probably involved some tally method, using one vertical mark on a cave wall for each sheep. Later, a variety of vocal sounds developed as a tally for the number of things in a group. Finally, written symbols, or numerals, were used to represent numbers.

A **number** is an abstract idea that addresses the question, "How many?" A **numeral** is a symbol used to represent a number. Different symbols may be used to represent the same number. Numerals used to represent how many buffalo are shown in Figure 4.1 include

FIGURE 4.1

𝍸 ||||	IX	9.
Tally method	Roman numeral	Hindu-Arabic numeral

We take numerals and the numbers that they represent for granted and use them every day. A **system of numeration** consists of a set of basic numerals and rules for combining them to represent numbers. It took humanity thousands of years to invent numeration systems that made computation a reasonable task. Today we use a system of writing numerals that was invented in India and brought to Europe by the Arabs. Our numerals are therefore called **Hindu-Arabic numerals**.

Like literature or music, a numeration system has a profound effect on the culture that created it. Computers, which affect our everyday lives, are based on an understanding of our Hindu-Arabic system of numeration. In this section, we study the characteristics of our numeration system. We also take a brief journey through history to look at two numeration systems that pointed the way toward an amazing cultural creation, our Hindu-Arabic system.

1 Evaluate an exponential expression.

Exponential Notation

An understanding of *exponents* is important in understanding the characteristics of our numeration system.

EXPONENTIAL NOTATION

If n is a natural number (1, 2, 3, and so on),

Exponent or Power

$$b^n = \underbrace{b \cdot b \cdot b \cdot \cdots \cdot b}_{\text{b appears as a factor n times.}}$$

Base

b^n is read "the nth power of b" or "b to the nth power." Thus, the nth power of b is defined as the product of n factors of b. The expression b^n is called an **exponential expression**. Furthermore, $b^1 = b$.

STUDY TIP

Powers of 10 play an important role in our system of numeration. Notice the following relationship.

$$10^8 = \underbrace{100{,}000{,}000}$$

Exponent is 8. There are 8 zeros.

In general, the number of zeros appearing to the right of the 1 in any numeral that represents a power of 10 is the same as the exponent on that power of 10.

EXAMPLE 1 UNDERSTANDING EXPONENTIAL NOTATION

Evaluate the following:

a. 10^2 **b.** 10^3 **c.** 10^4 **d.** 2^6 **e.** 1^7 **f.** 7^1.

SOLUTION

a. $10^2 = 10 \times 10 = 100$

b. $10^3 = 10 \times 10 \times 10 = 1000$

c. $10^4 = 10 \times 10 \times 10 \times 10 = 10{,}000$

d. $2^6 = 2 \times 2 \times 2 \times 2 \times 2 \times 2 = 64$

e. $1^7 = 1 \times 1 \times 1 \times 1 \times 1 \times 1 \times 1 = 1$

f. $7^1 = 7$

CHECK POINT 1 Evaluate the following:

a. 7^2 **b.** 5^3 **c.** 1^4 **d.** 10^5 **e.** 10^6 **f.** 18^1.

2 Write a Hindu-Arabic numeral in expanded form.

Our Hindu-Arabic Numeration System

An important characteristic of our Hindu-Arabic system is that we can write the numeral for any number, large or small, using only ten symbols. The ten symbols that we use are

$$0, 1, 2, 3, 4, 5, 6, 7, 8, \text{ and } 9.$$

These symbols are called **digits**, from the Latin word for fingers.

With the use of exponents, Hindu-Arabic numerals can be written in **expanded form** in which the value of the digit in each position is made clear. In a Hindu-Arabic numeral, the place value of the first digit on the right is 1. The place value of the second digit from the right is 10. The place value of the third digit from the right is 100, or 10^2. For example, we can write 663 in expanded form by thinking of 663 as six 100s plus six 10s plus three 1s. This means that 663 in expanded form is

$$\begin{aligned} 663 &= (6 \times 100) + (6 \times 10) + (3 \times 1) \\ &= (6 \times 10^2) + (6 \times 10^1) + (3 \times 1). \end{aligned}$$

Because the value of a digit varies according to the position it occupies in a numeral, the Hindu-Arabic numeration system is called a **positional-value**, or **place-value**, system. The positional values in the system are based on powers of ten and are

$$\ldots, 10^5, 10^4, 10^3, 10^2, 10^1, 1.$$

BLITZER BONUS

Tally Sticks

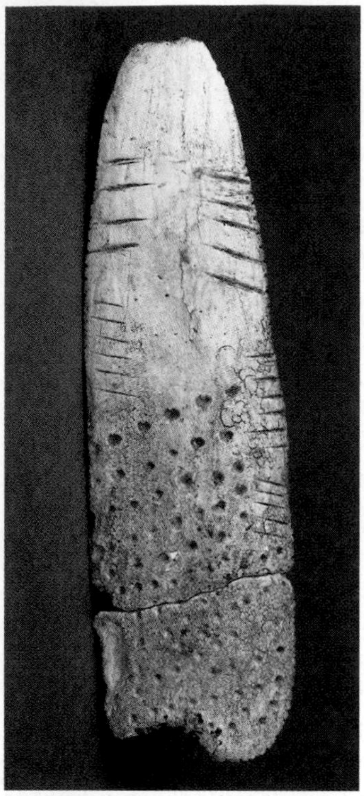

This notched reindeer antler dates from 15,000 B.C. Humans learned how to keep track of numbers by tallying notches on bones with the same intelligence that led them to preserve and use fire, and at around the same time. Using tally sticks, early people grasped the idea that nine buffalo and nine sheep had something in common: the abstract idea of *nine*. As the human mind conceived of numbers separately from the things they represented, systems of numeration developed.

EXAMPLE 2 WRITING HINDU-ARABIC NUMERALS IN EXPANDED FORM

Write each of the following in expanded form:

a. 3407 **b.** 53,525.

SOLUTION

a. $3407 = (3 \times 10^3) + (4 \times 10^2) + (0 \times 10^1) + (7 \times 1)$

or $= (3 \times 1000) + (4 \times 100) + (0 \times 10) + (7 \times 1)$

Because $0 \times 10^1 = 0$, this term could be left out, but the expanded form is clearer when it is included.

b. $53{,}525 = (5 \times 10^4) + (3 \times 10^3) + (5 \times 10^2) + (2 \times 10^1) + (5 \times 1)$

or $= (5 \times 10{,}000) + (3 \times 1000) + (5 \times 100) + (2 \times 10) + (5 \times 1)$

CHECK POINT 2 Write each of the following in expanded form:

a. 4026 **b.** 24,232.

3 Express a number's expanded form as a Hindu-Arabic numeral.

EXAMPLE 3 EXPRESSING A NUMBER'S EXPANDED FORM AS A HINDU-ARABIC NUMERAL

Express each expanded form as a Hindu-Arabic numeral:

a. $(7 \times 10^3) + (5 \times 10^1) + (4 \times 1)$

b. $(6 \times 10^5) + (8 \times 10^1)$.

SOLUTION For clarification, we begin by showing all powers of ten, starting with the highest exponent given. Any power of ten that is left out is expressed as 0 times that power of ten.

a. $(7 \times 10^3) + (5 \times 10^1) + (4 \times 1)$

$= (7 \times 10^3) + (0 \times 10^2) + (5 \times 10^1) + (4 \times 1)$

$= 7054$

b. $(6 \times 10^5) + (8 \times 10^1)$

$= (6 \times 10^5) + (0 \times 10^4) + (0 \times 10^3) + (0 \times 10^2) + (8 \times 10^1) + (0 \times 1)$

$= 600{,}080$

CHECK POINT 3 Express each expanded form as a Hindu-Arabic numeral:

a. $(6 \times 10^3) + (7 \times 10^1) + (3 \times 1)$

b. $(8 \times 10^4) + (9 \times 10^2)$.

Examples 2 and 3 show how there would be no Hindu-Arabic system without an understanding of zero and the invention of a symbol to represent nothingness. The system must have a symbol for zero to serve as a placeholder in case one or more powers of ten are not needed. The concept of zero was a new and radical invention, one that changed our ability to think about the world.

"It took men about five thousand years, counting from the beginning of number symbols, to think of a symbol for nothing."

ISAAC ASIMOV,
Asimov on Numbers

Early Positional Systems

Our Hindu-Arabic system developed over many centuries. Its digits can be found carved on ancient Hindu pillars over 2200 years old. In 1202, the Italian mathematician Leonardo Fibonacci (1170–1250) introduced the system to Europe, writing of its special characteristic: "With the nine Hindu digits and the Arab symbol 0, any number can be written." The Hindu-Arabic system came into widespread use only when printing was invented in the fifteenth century.

Jasper Johns, "*Zero*". © Jasper Johns/ Licensed by VAGA, New York, NY.

The Hindu-Arabic system uses powers of ten. However, positional systems can use powers of any number, not just 10. Think about our system of time, based on powers of 60:

$$1 \text{ minute} = 60 \text{ seconds}$$
$$1 \text{ hour} = 60 \text{ minutes} = 60 \times 60 \text{ seconds} = 60^2 \text{ seconds.}$$

What is significant in a positional system is position and the powers that positions convey. The first early positional system that we will discuss uses powers of 60, just like those used for units of time.

4 Understand and use the Babylonian numeration system.

The Babylonian Numeration System

The city of Babylon, 55 miles south of present-day Baghdad, was the center of Babylonian civilization that lasted for about 1400 years between 2000 B.C. and 600 B.C. The Babylonians used wet clay as a writing surface. Their clay tablets were heated and dried to give a permanent record of their work, which we are able to decipher and read today. Table 4.1 gives the numerals of this civilization's numeration system.

TABLE 4.1 BABYLONIAN NUMERALS

Babylonian numerals	∨	<
Hindu-Arabic numerals	1	10

The place values in the Babylonian system use powers of 60. The place values are

$$\ldots,\quad 60^3,\quad 60^2,\quad 60^1,\quad 1.$$

$60^3 = 60 \times 60 \times 60 = 216{,}000$

$60^2 = 60 \times 60 = 3600$

The Babylonians left a space to distinguish the various place values in a numeral from one another. For example,

∨ < ∨∨

means

$$\downarrow \qquad \downarrow \qquad \downarrow$$
$$(1 \times 60^2) + (10 \times 60^1) + (1 + 1) \times 1$$
$$= (1 \times 3600) + (10 \times 60) + (2 \times 1)$$
$$= 3600 + 600 + 2 = 4202.$$

EXAMPLE 4 CONVERTING FROM A BABYLONIAN NUMERAL TO A HINDU-ARABIC NUMERAL

Write

∨∨ <∨ <<∨∨

as a Hindu-Arabic numeral.

SOLUTION From left to right, the place values are 60^2, 60^1, and 1. Represent the numeral in each place as a familiar Hindu-Arabic numeral using Table 4.1. Multiply each Hindu-Arabic numeral by its respective place value. Then find the sum of these products.

∨∨   <∨   <<∨∨

means

↓   ↓   ↓

$$
\begin{aligned}
& (1 + 1) \times 60^2 + (10 + 1) \times 60^1 + (10 + 10 + 1 + 1) \times 1 \\
&= (2 \times 60^2) + (11 \times 60^1) + (22 \times 1) \\
&= (2 \times 3600) + (11 \times 60) + (22 \times 1) \\
&= 7200 + 660 + 22 = 7882.
\end{aligned}
$$

This sum indicates that the given Babylonian numeral is 7882 when written as a Hindu-Arabic numeral.

A major disadvantage of the Babylonian system is that it did not contain a symbol for zero. Some Babylonian tablets have a larger gap between the numerals or the insertion of the symbol ⪡ to indicate a missing place value, but this led to some ambiguity and confusion.

CHECK POINT 4 Write

∨∨∨   <<   <<<∨

as a Hindu-Arabic numeral.

5 Understand and use the Mayan numeration system.

The Mayan Numeration System

The Maya, a tribe of Central American Indians, lived on the Yucatan Peninsula. At its peak, between 300 and 1000 A.D., their civilization covered an area including parts of Mexico, all of Belize and Guatemala, and part of Honduras. They were famous for their magnificent architecture, their astronomical and mathematical knowledge, and their excellence in the arts. Their numeration system was the first to have a symbol for zero. Table 4.2 gives the Mayan numerals.

TABLE 4.2 MAYAN NUMERALS

0	1	2	3	4	5	6	7	8	9
⬭	•	••	•••	••••	—	• —	•• —	••• —	•••• —
10	**11**	**12**	**13**	**14**	**15**	**16**	**17**	**18**	**19**
— —	• — —	•• — —	••• — —	•••• — —	— — —	• — — —	•• — — —	••• — — —	•••• — — —

The place values in the Mayan system are

$$\ldots, \quad 18 \times 20^3, \quad 18 \times 20^2, \quad 18 \times 20, \quad 20, \quad 1$$

18 × 20 × 20 × 20 = 144,000   18 × 20 × 20 = 7200   18 × 20 = 360

Notice that instead of giving the third position a place value of 20^2, the Mayans used 18×20. This was probably done so that their calendar year of 360 days would be a basic part of the numeration system.

Numerals in the Mayan system are expressed vertically. The place value at the bottom of the column is 1.

BLITZER BONUS

Numbers and Bird Brains

Birds have large, well-developed brains and are more intelligent than is suggested by the slur "bird brain." Parakeets can learn to count to seven. They have been taught to identify a box of food by counting the number of small objects in front of the box. Some species of birds can tell the difference between two and three. If a nest contains four eggs and one is taken, the bird will stay in the nest to protect the remaining three eggs. However, if two of the four eggs are taken, the bird recognizes that only two remain and will desert the nest, leaving the remaining two eggs unprotected.

Birds easily master complex counting problems. The sense of *more* and *less* that led to the development of numeration systems is not limited to the human species.

EXAMPLE 5 USING THE MAYAN NUMERATION SYSTEM

Write

as a Hindu-Arabic numeral.

SOLUTION The given Mayan numeral has four places. From top to bottom, the place values are 7200, 360, 20, and 1. Represent the numeral in each row as a familiar Hindu-Arabic numeral using Table 4.2. Multiply each Hindu-Arabic numeral by its respective place value. Then find the sum of these products.

Mayan numeral		Hindu-Arabic numeral		Place value		
	=	14	×	7200	=	100,800
	=	0	×	360	=	0
	=	7	×	20	=	140
	=	12	×	1	=	12
						100,952

The sum on the right indicates that the given Mayan numeral is 100,952 when written as a Hindu-Arabic numeral.

CHECK POINT 5 Write

as a Hindu-Arabic numeral.

EXERCISE SET 4.1

• Practice Exercises

In Exercises 1–8, evaluate the expression.

1. 5^2 **2.** 6^2 **3.** 2^3 **4.** 4^3

5. 3^4 **6.** 2^4 **7.** 10^5 **8.** 10^6

In Exercises 9–22, write each Hindu-Arabic numeral in expanded form.

9. 36 **10.** 65 **11.** 249 **12.** 698

13. 703 **14.** 902 **15.** 4856 **16.** 5749

17. 3070 **18.** 9007 **19.** 34,569 **20.** 67,943

21. 230,007,004 **22.** 909,006,070

In Exercises 23–32, express each expanded form as a Hindu-Arabic numeral.

23. $(7 \times 10^1) + (3 \times 1)$

24. $(9 \times 10^1) + (4 \times 1)$

25. $(3 \times 10^2) + (8 \times 10^1) + (5 \times 1)$

26. $(7 \times 10^2) + (5 \times 10^1) + (3 \times 1)$

27. $(5 \times 10^5) + (2 \times 10^4) + (8 \times 10^3) + (7 \times 10^2) + (4 \times 10^1) + (3 \times 1)$

28. $(7 \times 10^6) + (4 \times 10^5) + (2 \times 10^4) + (3 \times 10^3) + (1 \times 10^2) + (9 \times 10^1) + (6 \times 1)$

29. $(7 \times 10^3) + (0 \times 10^2) + (0 \times 10^1) + (2 \times 1)$

30. $(9 \times 10^4) + (0 \times 10^3) + (0 \times 10^2) + (4 \times 10^1) + (5 \times 1)$

31. $(6 \times 10^8) + (2 \times 10^3) + (7 \times 1)$

32. $(3 \times 10^8) + (5 \times 10^4) + (4 \times 1)$

In Exercises 33–40, use Table 4.1 on page 199 to write each Babylonian numeral as a Hindu-Arabic numeral.

33. <<∨∨∨∨ **34.** <<<∨∨

35. <<∨ ∨∨ **36.** << <∨∨

37. ∨∨∨ <∨∨ ∨∨∨ **38.** ∨∨ <∨ <<∨∨

39. <∨ <∨ <∨ <∨ **40.** << << <∨∨ <∨∨

In Exercises 41–50, use Table 4.2 on page 200 to write each Mayan numeral as a Hindu-Arabic numeral.

41.  **42.**  **43.**  **44.** 

45.  **46.**  **47.**  **48.** 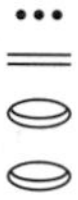

49.  **50.** 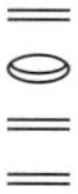

• Practice Plus

In Exercises 51–54, express the result of each addition as a Hindu-Arabic numeral in expanded form.

51. ∨ << <<∨ + <∨ <<< ∨∨∨∨

52. <∨ < <∨∨∨ + ∨∨∨ << ∨∨

53. 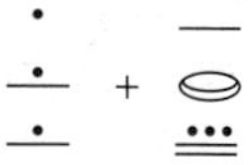 **54.** 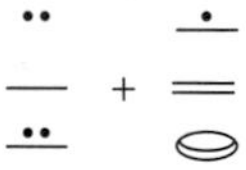

If n is a natural number, then $10^{-n} = \frac{1}{10^n}$. *Negative powers of 10 can be used to write the decimal part of Hindu-Arabic numerals in expanded form. For example,*

$$\begin{aligned} 0.8302 &= (8 \times 10^{-1}) + (3 \times 10^{-2}) + (0 \times 10^{-3}) + (2 \times 10^{-4}) \\ &= \left(8 \times \frac{1}{10^1}\right) + \left(3 \times \frac{1}{10^2}\right) + \left(0 \times \frac{1}{10^3}\right) + \left(2 \times \frac{1}{10^4}\right) \\ &= \left(8 \times \frac{1}{10}\right) + \left(3 \times \frac{1}{100}\right) + \left(0 \times \frac{1}{1000}\right) + \left(2 \times \frac{1}{10{,}000}\right). \end{aligned}$$

In Exercises 55–62, express each expanded form as a Hindu-Arabic numeral.

55. $(4 \times 10^{-1}) + (7 \times 10^{-2}) + (5 \times 10^{-3}) + (9 \times 10^{-4})$

56. $(6 \times 10^{-1}) + (8 \times 10^{-2}) + (1 \times 10^{-3}) + (2 \times 10^{-4})$

57. $(7 \times 10^{-1}) + (2 \times 10^{-4}) + (3 \times 10^{-6})$

58. $(8 \times 10^{-1}) + (3 \times 10^{-4}) + (7 \times 10^{-6})$

59. $(5 \times 10^3) + (3 \times 10^{-2})$

60. $(7 \times 10^4) + (5 \times 10^{-3})$

61. $(3 \times 10^4) + (7 \times 10^2) + (5 \times 10^{-2}) + (8 \times 10^{-3}) + (9 \times 10^{-5})$

62. $(7 \times 10^5) + (3 \times 10^2) + (2 \times 10^{-1}) + (2 \times 10^{-3}) + (1 \times 10^{-5})$

• Application Exercises

The Chinese "rod system" of numeration is a base ten positional system. The digits for 1 through 9 are shown as follows:

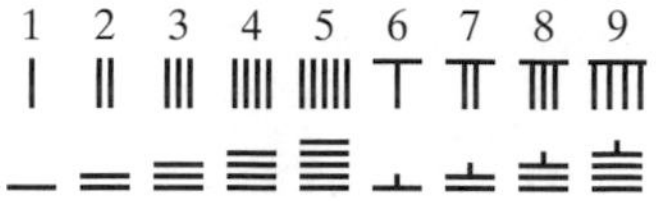

The vertical digits in the second row are used for place values of 1, 10^2, 10^4, *and all even powers of 10. The horizontal digits in the third row are used for place values of* 10^1, 10^3, 10^5, 10^7, *and all odd powers of 10. A blank space is used for the digit zero. In Exercises 63–66, write each Chinese "rod system" numeral as a Hindu-Arabic numeral.*

63. 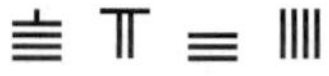 **64.** 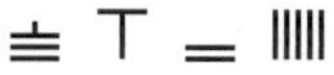

65. 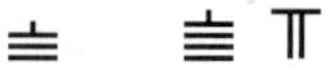 **66.** 

67. Humans have debated for decades about what messages should be sent to the stars to grab the attention of extraterrestrials and demonstrate our mathematical prowess. In the 1970s, Soviet scientists suggested we send the exponential message

$$10^2 + 11^2 + 12^2 = 13^2 + 14^2.$$

The Soviets called this equation "mind-catching." Evaluate the exponential expressions and verify that the sums on the two sides are equal. What is the significance of this sum?

• Writing in Mathematics

68. Describe the difference between a number and a numeral.

69. Explain how to evaluate 7^3.

70. What is the base in our Hindu-Arabic numeration system? What are the digits in the system?

71. Why is a symbol for zero needed in a positional system?

72. Explain how to write a Hindu-Arabic numeral in expanded form.

73. Describe one way that the Babylonian system is similar to the Hindu-Arabic system and one way that it is different from the Hindu-Arabic system.

74. Describe one way that the Mayan system is similar to the Hindu-Arabic system and one way that it is different from the Hindu-Arabic system.

75. **Research activity** Write a report on the history of the Hindu-Arabic system of numeration. Useful references include history of mathematics books, encyclopedias, and the World Wide Web.

• Critical Thinking Exercises

76. Write ∨ <∨∨ <∨ as a Mayan numeral.

77. Write  as a Babylonian numeral.

78. Use Babylonian numerals to write the numeral that precedes and the numeral that follows:

<∨ <<<<<∨∨∨∨∨∨∨∨∨.

• Group Exercise

79. Your group task is to create an original positional numeration system that is different from the three systems discussed in this section.

a. Construct a table showing your numerals and the corresponding Hindu-Arabic numerals.

b. Explain how to represent numbers in your system, and express a three-digit and a four-digit Hindu-Arabic numeral in your system.

SECTION 4.2 • NUMBER BASES IN POSITIONAL SYSTEMS

OBJECTIVES

1. Change numerals in bases other than ten to base ten.
2. Change base ten numerals to numerals in other bases.

You are being drawn deeper into cyberspace, spending more time online each week. With constantly improving high-resolution images, cyberspace is reshaping your life by nourishing shared enthusiasms. The people who built your computer talk of "incredible bandwidth" that will give you the visual experience, in high-definition 3-D format, of being in the same room with a person who is actually in another city.

Because of our ten fingers and ten toes, the base ten Hindu-Arabic system seems to be an obvious choice. However, it is not base ten that computers use to process information and communicate with one another. Your experiences in cyberspace are sustained with a binary, or base two, system. In this section, we study numeration systems with bases other than ten. An understanding of such systems will help you to appreciate the nature of a positional system. You will also attain a better understanding of the computations you have used all of your life. You will even get to see how the world looks from a computer's point of view.

1 | Change numerals in bases other than ten to base ten.

Changing Numerals in Bases Other Than Ten to Base Ten

The base of a positional numeration system refers to the number of individual digit symbols that can be used in that system as well as to the number whose powers define the place values. For example, the digit symbols in a base five system are 0, 1, 2, 3, and 4. The place values in a base five system are powers of 5:

$$\begin{aligned} &\ldots, 5^4, 5^3, 5^2, 5^1, 1 \\ = &\ldots, 5 \times 5 \times 5 \times 5, 5 \times 5 \times 5, 5 \times 5, 5, 1 \\ = &\ldots, 625, 125, 25, 5, 1. \end{aligned}$$

When a numeral appears without a subscript, it is assumed that the base is ten. Bases other than ten are indicated with a spelled-out subscript, as in the numeral

$$122_{\text{five}}.$$

This numeral is read "one two two base five." Do not read it as "one hundred twenty two" because that terminology implies a base ten numeral, naming 122 in base ten.

We can convert 122_{five} to a base ten numeral by following the same procedure used in Section 4.1 to change the Babylonian and Mayan numerals to base ten Hindu-Arabic numerals. In the case of 122_{five}, the numeral has three places. From left to right, the place values are 5^2, 5^1, and 1. Multiply each digit in the numeral by its respective place value. Then add these products.

$$\begin{aligned} 122_{\text{five}} &= (1 \times 5^2) + (2 \times 5^1) + (2 \times 1) \\ &= (1 \times 25) + (2 \times 5) + (2 \times 1) \\ &= 25 + 10 + 2 \\ &= 37 \end{aligned}$$

Thus,

$$122_{\text{five}} = 37.$$

In base five, we do not need a digit symbol for 5 because

$$10_{\text{five}} = (1 \times 5^1) + (0 \times 1) = 5.$$

Likewise, the base ten numeral 6 is represented as 11_{five}, the base ten numeral 7 as 12_{five}, and so on. Table 4.3 shows base ten numerals from 0 through 20 and their base five equivalents.

TABLE 4.3

Base Ten	Base Five
0	0
1	1
2	2
3	3
4	4
5	10
6	11
7	12
8	13
9	14
10	20
11	21
12	22
13	23
14	24
15	30
16	31
17	32
18	33
19	34
20	40

In any base, the digit symbols begin at 0 and go up to one less than the base. In base b, the digit symbols begin at 0 and go up to $b - 1$. The place values in a base b system are powers of b:

$$\ldots, b^4, b^3, b^2, b, 1.$$

Table 4.4 shows the digit symbols and place values in various bases.

TABLE 4.4 DIGIT SYMBOLS AND PLACE VALUES IN VARIOUS BASES

Base	Digit Symbols	Place Values
two	0, 1	$\ldots, 2^4, 2^3, 2^2, 2^1, 1$
three	0, 1, 2	$\ldots, 3^4, 3^3, 3^2, 3^1, 1$
four	0, 1, 2, 3	$\ldots, 4^4, 4^3, 4^2, 4^1, 1$
five	0, 1, 2, 3, 4	$\ldots, 5^4, 5^3, 5^2, 5^1, 1$
six	0, 1, 2, 3, 4, 5	$\ldots, 6^4, 6^3, 6^2, 6^1, 1$
seven	0, 1, 2, 3, 4, 5, 6	$\ldots, 7^4, 7^3, 7^2, 7^1, 1$
eight	0, 1, 2, 3, 4, 5, 6, 7	$\ldots, 8^4, 8^3, 8^2, 8^1, 1$
nine	0, 1, 2, 3, 4, 5, 6, 7, 8	$\ldots, 9^4, 9^3, 9^2, 9^1, 1$
ten	0, 1, 2, 3, 4, 5, 6, 7, 8, 9	$\ldots, 10^4, 10^3, 10^2, 10^1, 1$

We have seen that in base five, 10_{five} represents one group of 5 and no groups of 1. Thus, $10_{\text{five}} = 5$. Similarly, in base six, 10_{six} represents one group of 6 and no groups of 1. Thus, $10_{\text{six}} = 6$. In general $10_{\text{base } b}$ represents one group of b and no groups of 1. This means that $10_{\text{base } b} = b$.

Here is the procedure for changing a numeral in a base other than ten to base ten:

CHANGING TO BASE TEN

To change a numeral in a base other than ten to a base ten numeral,

1. Find the place value for each digit in the numeral.
2. Multiply each digit in the numeral by its respective place value.
3. Find the sum of the products in step 2.

TECHNOLOGY

You can use a calculator to convert to base ten. For example, to convert 4726_{eight} to base ten, press the following keys:

MANY SCIENTIFIC CALCULATORS

4 [×] 8 [y^x] 3 [+] 7 [×] 8 [y^x] 2 [+] 2 [×] 8 [+] 6 [=]

MANY GRAPHING CALCULATORS

4 [×] 8 [∧] 3 [+] 7 [×] 8 [∧] 2 [+] 2 [×] 8 [+] 6 [ENTER].

EXAMPLE 1 CONVERTING TO BASE TEN

Convert 4726_{eight} to base ten.

SOLUTION The given base eight numeral has four places. From left to right, the place values are

$$8^3, 8^2, 8^1, \text{ and } 1.$$

Multiply each digit in the numeral by its respective place value. Then find the sum of these products.

Place value: 8^3	Place value: 8^2	Place value: 8^1	Place value: 1
4	7	2	6_{eight}

$$\begin{aligned} 4726_{\text{eight}} &= (4 \times 8^3) + (7 \times 8^2) + (2 \times 8^1) + (6 \times 1) \\ &= (4 \times 8 \times 8 \times 8) + (7 \times 8 \times 8) + (2 \times 8) + (6 \times 1) \\ &= 2048 + 448 + 16 + 6 \\ &= 2518 \end{aligned}$$

CHECK POINT 1 Convert 3422_{five} to base ten.

EXAMPLE 2 CONVERTING TO BASE TEN

Convert 100101_{two} to base ten.

SOLUTION Multiply each digit in the numeral by its respective place value. Then find the sum of these products.

Place value: 2^5	Place value: 2^4	Place value: 2^3	Place value: 2^2	Place value: 2^1	Place value: 1
1	0	0	1	0	1_{two}

$$\begin{aligned} 100101_{\text{two}} &= (1 \times 2^5) + (0 \times 2^4) + (0 \times 2^3) + (1 \times 2^2) + (0 \times 2^1) + (1 \times 1) \\ &= (1 \times 32) + (0 \times 16) + (0 \times 8) + (1 \times 4) + (0 \times 2) + (1 \times 1) \\ &= 32 + 0 + 0 + 4 + 0 + 1 \\ &= 37 \end{aligned}$$

CHECK POINT 2 Convert 110011_{two} to base ten.

The word *digital* in computer technology refers to a method of encoding numbers, letters, visual images, and sounds using a **binary**, or base two, **system** of 0s and 1s. Because computers use electrical signals that are groups of on–off pulses of electricity, the digits in base two are convenient. In binary code, 1 indicates the passage of an electrical pulse ("on") and 0 indicates its interruption ("off"). For example, the number 37 (100101_{two}) becomes the binary code on–off–off–on–off–on. Microchips in a computer store and process these binary signals.

BLITZER BONUS

Letters and Words in Base Two

Wilhelm Leibniz (1646–1716)

Letters are converted into base two numbers for computer processing. A through Z are assigned 65 through 90, with each number expressed in base two. Thus, the binary code for A(65) is 1000001. Similarly, a through z are assigned 97 through 122 in base two.

The German mathematician Wilhelm Leibniz was the first modern thinker to promote the base two system. He never imagined that one day the base two system would enable computers to process information and communicate with one another.

In addition to base two, computer applications often involve base eight, called an **octal system**, and base sixteen, called a **hexadecimal system**. Base sixteen presents a problem because digit symbols are needed from 0 up to one less than the base. This means that we need more digit symbols than the ten (0, 1, 2, 3, 4, 5, 6, 7, 8, and 9) used in our base ten system. Computer programmers use the letters A, B, C, D, E, and F as base sixteen digit symbols for the numbers ten through fifteen, respectively.

Additional digit symbols in base sixteen:

A = 10	B = 11
C = 12	D = 13
E = 14	F = 15

EXAMPLE 3 CONVERTING TO BASE TEN

Convert $EC7_{\text{sixteen}}$ to base ten.

SOLUTION From left to right, the place values are

$$16^2, 16^1, \text{ and } 1.$$

The digit symbol E represents 14 and the digit symbol C represents 12. Although this numeral looks a bit strange, follow the usual procedure: Multiply each digit in the numeral by its respective place value. Then find the sum of these products.

Place value: 16^2 — Place value: 16^1 — Place value: 1

$$E \quad C \quad 7_{\text{sixteen}}$$

E = 14 — C = 12

$$\begin{aligned} EC7_{\text{sixteen}} &= (14 \times 16^2) + (12 \times 16^1) + (7 \times 1) \\ &= (14 \times 16 \times 16) + (12 \times 16) + (7 \times 1) \\ &= 3584 + 192 + 7 \\ &= 3783 \end{aligned}$$

CHECK POINT 3 Convert $AD4_{\text{sixteen}}$ to base ten.

2 Change base ten numerals to numerals in other bases.

Changing Base Ten Numerals to Numerals in Other Bases

To convert a base ten numeral to a numeral in a base other than ten, we need to find how many groups of each place value are contained in the base ten numeral. When the base ten numeral consists of one or two digits, we can do this mentally. For example, suppose that we want to convert the base ten numeral 6 to a base four numeral. The place values in base four are

$$\ldots, 4^3, 4^2, 4, 1.$$

The place values that are less than 6 are 4 and 1. We can express 6 as one group of four and two ones:

$$6_{\text{ten}} = (1 \times 4) + (2 \times 1) = 12_{\text{four}}.$$

EXAMPLE 4 A MENTAL CONVERSION FROM BASE TEN TO BASE FIVE

Convert the base ten numeral 8 to a base five numeral.

SOLUTION The place values in base five are

$$\ldots, 5^3, 5^2, 5, 1.$$

The place values that are less than 8 are 5 and 1. We can express 8 as one group of five and three ones:

$$8_{\text{ten}} = (1 \times 5) + (3 \times 1) = 13_{\text{five}}.$$

CHECK POINT 4 Convert the base ten numeral 6 to a base five numeral.

BLITZER BONUS

Music in Base Two

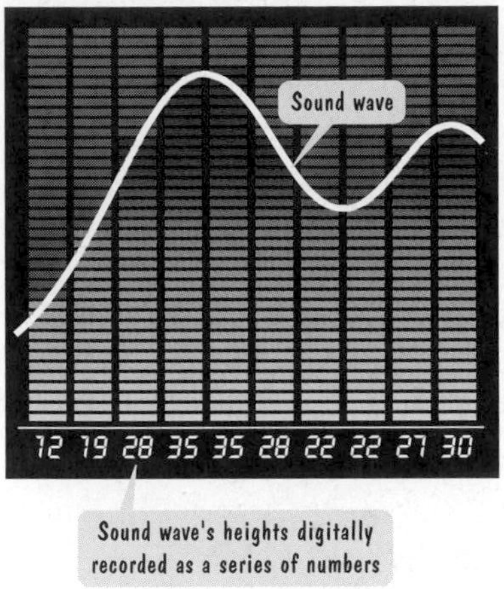

Digital technology can represent musical sounds as a series of numbers in binary code. The music is recorded by a microphone that converts it into an electric signal in the form of a sound wave. The computer measures the height of the sound wave thousands of times per second, converting each discrete measurement into a base two number. The resulting series of binary numbers is used to encode the music. Compact discs store these digital sequences using millions of bumps (1) and spaces (0) on a tiny spiral that is just one thousand-millionth of a meter wide and almost 3 miles (5 kilometers) long. A CD player converts the digital data back into sound.

If a conversion cannot be performed mentally, you can use divisions to determine how many groups of each place value are contained in a base ten numeral.

EXAMPLE 5 USING DIVISIONS TO CONVERT FROM BASE TEN TO BASE EIGHT

Convert the base ten numeral 299 to a base eight numeral.

SOLUTION The place values in base eight are

$$\ldots, 8^3, 8^2, 8^1, 1, \quad \text{or} \quad \ldots, 512, 64, 8, 1.$$

The place values that are less than 299 are 64, 8, and 1. We can use divisions to show how many groups of each of these place values are contained in 299. Divide 299 by 64. Divide the remainder by 8.

$$\begin{array}{r} 4 \\ 64\overline{)299} \\ \underline{256} \\ 43 \end{array} \qquad \begin{array}{r} 5 \\ 8\overline{)43} \\ \underline{40} \\ 3 \end{array}$$

4 groups of 64

5 groups of 8

3 ones left over

These divisions show that 299 can be expressed as 4 groups of 64, 5 groups of 8, and 3 ones:

$$\begin{aligned} 299 &= (4 \times 64) + (5 \times 8) + (3 \times 1) \\ &= (4 \times 8^2) + (5 \times 8^1) + (3 \times 1) \\ &= 453_{\text{eight}}. \end{aligned}$$

CHECK POINT 5 Convert the base ten numeral 365 to a base seven numeral.

EXAMPLE 6 USING DIVISIONS TO CONVERT FROM BASE TEN TO BASE SIX

Convert the base ten numeral 3444 to a base six numeral.

SOLUTION The place values in base six are

$$\ldots, 6^5, 6^4, 6^3, 6^2, 6^1, 1, \quad \text{or} \quad \ldots, 7776, 1296, 216, 36, 6, 1.$$

We use the powers of 6 that are less than 3444 and perform successive divisions by these powers.

$$\begin{array}{r} 2 \\ 1296\overline{)3444} \\ \underline{2592} \\ 852 \end{array} \qquad \begin{array}{r} 3 \\ 216\overline{)852} \\ \underline{648} \\ 204 \end{array} \qquad \begin{array}{r} 5 \\ 36\overline{)204} \\ \underline{180} \\ 24 \end{array} \qquad \begin{array}{r} 4 \\ 6\overline{)24} \\ \underline{24} \\ 0 \end{array}$$

2 groups of 1296

3 groups of 216

5 groups of 36

4 groups of 6

0 ones left over

Using these four quotients and the final remainder, we can immediately write the answer.

$$3444 = 23540_{\text{six}}$$

CHECK POINT 6 Convert the base ten numeral 2763 to a base five numeral.

EXERCISE SET 4.2

• Practice Exercises

In Exercises 1–18, convert the numeral to a numeral in base ten.

1. 43_{five} **2.** 34_{five} **3.** 52_{eight}

4. 67_{eight} **5.** 132_{four} **6.** 321_{four}

7. 1011_{two} **8.** 1101_{two} **9.** 2035_{six}

10. 2073_{nine} **11.** 70355_{eight} **12.** 41502_{six}

13. 2096_{sixteen} **14.** 3104_{fifteen} **15.** 110101_{two}

16. 101101_{two} **17.** $ACE5_{\text{sixteen}}$ **18.** $EDF7_{\text{sixteen}}$

In Exercises 19–28, mentally convert each base ten numeral to a numeral in the given base.

19. 7 to base five **20.** 9 to base five

21. 11 to base seven **22.** 12 to base seven

23. 2 to base two **24.** 3 to base two

25. 13 to base four **26.** 19 to base four

27. 37 to base six **28.** 25 to base six

In Exercises 29–40, use divisions to convert each base ten numeral to a numeral in the given base.

29. 87 to base five **30.** 85 to base seven

31. 108 to base four **32.** 199 to base four

33. 19 to base two **34.** 23 to base two

35. 138 to base three **36.** 129 to base three

37. 386 to base six **38.** 428 to base nine

39. 1599 to base seven **40.** 1346 to base eight

• Practice Plus

In Exercises 41–44, use Table 4.1 on page 199 to write each Hindu-Arabic numeral as a Babylonian numeral.

41. 3052 **42.** 6704 **43.** 23,546 **44.** 41,265

In Exercises 45–48, use Table 4.2 on page 200 to write each Hindu-Arabic numeral as a Mayan numeral.

45. 9307 **46.** 8703 **47.** 28,704 **48.** 34,847

49. Convert 34_{five} to base seven.

50. Convert 46_{eight} to base five.

51. Convert 110010011_{two} to base eight.

52. Convert 101110001_{two} to base eight.

• Application Exercises

Read the Blitzer Bonus on page 205. Then use the information in the essay to solve Exercises 53–60.

In Exercises 53–56, write the binary representation for each letter.

53. F **54.** Y **55.** m **56.** p

In Exercises 57–58, break each binary sequence into groups of seven digits and write the word represented by the sequence.

57. 10100001000001100110 0

58. 1001100101010110000111001011

In Exercises 59–60, write a sequence of binary digits that represents each word.

59. Mom **60.** Dad

• Writing in Mathematics

61. Explain how to determine the place values for a four-digit numeral in base six.

62. Describe how to change a numeral in a base other than ten to a base ten numeral.

63. Describe how to change a base ten numeral to a numeral in another base.

• Critical Thinking Exercises

In Exercises 64–65, write in the indicated base the counting numbers that precede and follow the number expressed by the given numeral.

64. 888_{nine}

65. $EC5_{\text{sixteen}}$

66. Arrange from smallest to largest:

$$11111011_{\text{two}},\ 3A6_{\text{twelve}},\ 673_{\text{eight}}.$$

• Group Exercises

The following topics are appropriate for either individual or group research projects. A report should be given to the class on the researched topic. Useful references include history of mathematics books, books whose purpose is to excite the reader about mathematics, encyclopedias, and the World Wide Web.

67. Societies that Use Numeration Systems with Bases Other Than Ten

68. The Use of Fingers to Represent Numbers

69. Applications of Bases Other Than Ten

70. Binary, Octal, Hexadecimal Bases and Computers

71. Babylonian and Mayan Civilizations and Their Contributions

SECTION 4.3 • COMPUTATION IN POSITIONAL SYSTEMS

OBJECTIVES

1. Add in bases other than ten.
2. Subtract in bases other than ten.
3. Multiply in bases other than ten.
4. Divide in bases other than ten.

People have always looked for ways to make calculations faster and easier. The Hindu-Arabic system of numeration made computation simpler and less mysterious. More people were able to perform computation with ease, leading to the widespread use of the system.

All computations in bases other than ten are performed exactly like those in base ten. However, when a computation is equal to or exceeds the given base, use the mental conversions discussed in the previous section to convert from the base ten numeral to a numeral in the desired base.

1 Add in bases other than ten.

Addition

EXAMPLE 1 ADDITION IN BASE FOUR

Add:

$$\begin{array}{r} 33_{\text{four}} \\ +\ 13_{\text{four}} \\ \hline \end{array}.$$

The 4^1, or fours' column

The ones' column

$$\begin{array}{r} 33_{\text{four}} \\ +\ 13_{\text{four}} \\ \hline \end{array}$$

SOLUTION We will begin by adding the numbers in the right-hand column. In base four, the digit symbols are 0, 1, 2, and 3. If a sum in this, or any, column exceeds 3, we will have to convert this base ten number to base four. We begin by adding the numbers in the right-hand, or ones', column:

$$3_{\text{four}} + 3_{\text{four}} = 6.$$

6 is not a digit symbol in base four. However, we can express 6 as one group of four and two ones left over:

$$3_{\text{four}} + 3_{\text{four}} = 6_{\text{ten}} = (1 \times 4) + (2 \times 1) = 12_{\text{four}}.$$

Now we record the sum of the right-hand column, 12_{four}:

We place the digit on the left above the fours' column.

12_{four}

$$\begin{array}{r} 1\ \ \\ 33_{\text{four}} \\ +\ 13_{\text{four}} \\ \hline 2\ \ \end{array}$$

We place the digit on the right under the ones' column.

Next, we add the three digits in the fours' column:

$$1_{\text{four}} + 3_{\text{four}} + 1_{\text{four}} = 5.$$

5 is not a digit symbol in base four. However, we can express 5 as one group of four and one left over:

$$1_{\text{four}} + 3_{\text{four}} + 1_{\text{four}} = 5_{\text{ten}} = (1 \times 4) + (1 \times 1) = 11_{\text{four}}.$$

Record the 11_{four}.

$$\begin{array}{r} {\scriptstyle 1} \\ 33_{\text{four}} \\ +\ 13_{\text{four}} \\ \hline 112_{\text{four}} \end{array}$$

This is the desired sum.

You can check the sum by converting 33_{four}, 13_{four}, and 112_{four} to base ten: $33_{\text{four}} = 15$, $13_{\text{four}} = 7$, and $112_{\text{four}} = 22$. Because $15 + 7 = 22$, our work is correct.

CHECK POINT 1 Add:

$$\begin{array}{r} 32_{\text{five}} \\ +\ 44_{\text{five}} \\ \hline \end{array}.$$

EXAMPLE 2 ADDITION IN BASE TWO

Add:

$$\begin{array}{r} 111_{\text{two}} \\ +\ 101_{\text{two}} \\ \hline \end{array}.$$

The 2^2, or fours' column

The 2^1, or twos' column

The ones' column

$$\begin{array}{r} 111_{\text{two}} \\ +\ 101_{\text{two}} \\ \hline \end{array}$$

SOLUTION We begin by adding the numbers in the right-hand, or ones', column:

$$1_{\text{two}} + 1_{\text{two}} = 2.$$

2 is not a digit symbol in base two. We can express 2 as one group of 2 and zero ones left over:

$$1_{\text{two}} + 1_{\text{two}} = 2_{\text{ten}} = (1 \times 2) + (0 \times 1) = 10_{\text{two}}.$$

Now we record the sum of the right-hand column, 10_{two}:

$$\begin{array}{r} {\scriptstyle 1} \\ 111_{\text{two}} \\ +\ 101_{\text{two}} \\ \hline 0\phantom{_{\text{two}}} \end{array} \qquad 10_{\text{two}}$$

We place the digit on the left above the twos' column.

We place the digit on the right under the ones' column.

Next, we add the three digits in the twos' column:

$$1_{\text{two}} + 1_{\text{two}} + 0_{\text{two}} = 2_{\text{ten}} = (1 \times 2) + (0 \times 1) = 10_{\text{two}}.$$

Now we record the sum of the middle column, 10_{two}:

$$\begin{array}{r} {\scriptstyle 11} \\ 111_{\text{two}} \\ +\ 101_{\text{two}} \\ \hline 00\phantom{_{\text{two}}} \end{array} \qquad 10_{\text{two}}$$

We place the digit on the left above the fours' column.

We place the digit on the right under the twos' column.

Finally, we add the three digits in the fours' column:

$$1_{\text{two}} + 1_{\text{two}} + 1_{\text{two}} = 3.$$

3 is not a digit symbol in base two. We can express 3 as one group of 2 and one 1 left over:

$$1_{\text{two}} + 1_{\text{two}} + 1_{\text{two}} = 3_{\text{ten}} = (1 \times 2) + (1 \times 1) = 11_{\text{two}}.$$

Record the 11_{two}.

$$\begin{array}{r} {\scriptstyle 1\,1} \\ 111_{two} \\ +\ 101_{two} \\ \hline 1100_{two} \end{array}$$

This is the desired sum.

You can check the sum by converting to base ten: $111_{two} = 7$, $101_{two} = 5$, and $1100_{two} = 12$. Because $7 + 5 = 12$, our work is correct.

CHECK POINT 2 Add:

$$\begin{array}{r} 111_{two} \\ +\ 111_{two}. \end{array}$$

2 Subtract in bases other than ten.

Subtraction

To subtract in bases other than ten, we line up the digits with the same place values and subtract column by column, beginning with the column on the right. If "borrowing" is necessary to perform the subtraction, borrow the amount of the base. For example, when we borrow in base ten subtraction, we borrow 10s. Likewise, we borrow 2s in base two, 3s in base three, 4s in base four, and so on.

EXAMPLE 3 SUBTRACTION IN BASE FOUR

Subtract:

$$\begin{array}{r} 31_{four} \\ -\ 12_{four}. \end{array}$$

SOLUTION We start by performing subtraction in the right column, $1_{four} - 2_{four}$. Because 2_{four} is greater than 1_{four}, we need to borrow from the preceding column. We are working in base four, so we borrow one group of 4. This gives a sum of $4 + 1$, or 5, in base ten. Now we subtract 2 from 5, obtaining a difference of 3:

We borrow one group of 4. Now there are 2 groups of 4 for this place value, not 3.

$$\begin{array}{r} {\scriptstyle 2\,5} \\ \not{3}\not{1}_{four} \\ -\ 12_{four} \\ \hline 3_{four} \end{array}$$

We add the borrowed group of 4 to 1 in base ten: $1 + 4 = 5$.

Now we perform the subtraction in the second column from the right:

We subtract 1 from 2.

$$\begin{array}{r} {\scriptstyle 2\,5} \\ \not{3}\not{1}_{four} \\ -\ 12_{four} \\ \hline 13_{four} \end{array}$$

This is the desired difference.

You can check the difference by converting to base ten: $31_{four} = 13$, $12_{four} = 6$, and $13_{four} = 7$. Because $13 - 6 = 7$, our work is correct.

CHECK POINT 3 Subtract:

$$\begin{array}{r} 41_{five} \\ -\ 23_{five}. \end{array}$$

BLITZER BONUS

A Revolution at the Supermarket

0 76950 45026 4

Computerized scanning registers "read" the universal product code on packaged goods and convert it to a base two numeral that is sent to the scanner's computer. The computer calls up the appropriate price and subtracts the sale from the supermarket's inventory.

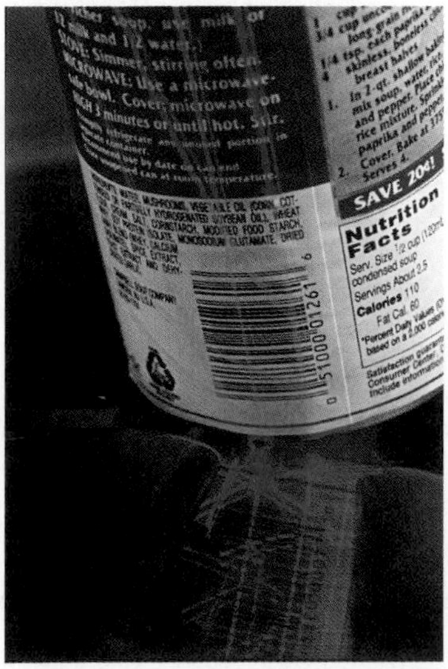

BLITZER BONUS

Mechanical Computing

In 1944, scientists at IBM produced Mark I (shown here), the world's biggest calculator. Mark I performed basic arithmetic, multiplying and dividing huge numbers in mere seconds. Its greatest drawback was its size: 50 feet long and 35 tons!

Calculating without thought and skill was the motivating factor in the history of mechanical computing. Today's handheld calculators provide the mathematical power of a computer, allowing the user to perform computations, graph equations, analyze data, write and use original programs, and even perform algebra's symbolic manipulations. Also, the World Wide Web now offers virtual calculators that simulate the format of actual calculators.

3 | Multiply in bases other than ten.

EXAMPLE 4 SUBTRACTION IN BASE FIVE

Subtract:

$$3431_{\text{five}} - 1242_{\text{five}}.$$

SOLUTION

Step 1. Borrow a group of 5 from the preceding column. This gives a sum of 5 + 1, or 6, in base ten.

$$\begin{array}{r} 3431_{\text{five}} \\ -\,1242_{\text{five}} \\ \hline 4_{\text{five}} \end{array}$$

Step 2. 6 − 2 = 4

Step 3. Borrow a group of 5 from the preceding column. This gives a sum of 5 + 2, or 7, in base ten.

$$\begin{array}{r} 3431_{\text{five}} \\ -\,1242_{\text{five}} \\ \hline 34_{\text{five}} \end{array}$$

Step 4. 7 − 4 = 3

Step 5. No borrowing is needed for these two columns.

$$\begin{array}{r} 3431_{\text{five}} \\ -\,1242_{\text{five}} \\ \hline 2134_{\text{five}} \end{array}$$

Step 6. 3 − 2 = 1

Step 7. 3 − 1 = 2

Thus, $3431_{\text{five}} - 1242_{\text{five}} = 2134_{\text{five}}$.

CHECK POINT 4 Subtract: $5144_{\text{seven}} - 3236_{\text{seven}}$.

Multiplication

EXAMPLE 5 MULTIPLICATION IN BASE SIX

Multiply:

$$\begin{array}{r} 34_{\text{six}} \\ \times\, 2_{\text{six}}. \\ \hline \end{array}$$

SOLUTION We multiply just as we do in base ten. That is, first we will multiply the digit 2 by the digit 4 directly above it. Then we will multiply the digit 2 by the digit 3 in the left column. Keep in mind that only the digit symbols 0, 1, 2, 3, 4, and 5 are permitted in base six. We begin with

$$2_{\text{six}} \times 4_{\text{six}} = 8_{\text{ten}} = (1 \times 6) + (2 \times 1) = 12_{\text{six}}.$$

Record the 2 and carry the 1:

$$\begin{array}{r} {}^{1} \\ 34_{\text{six}} \\ \times\, 2_{\text{six}} \\ \hline 2_{\text{six}}. \end{array}$$

Our next computation involves both multiplication and addition:

$$(2_{\text{six}} \times 3_{\text{six}}) + 1_{\text{six}} = 6 + 1 = 7_{\text{ten}} = (1 \times 6) + (1 \times 1) = 11_{\text{six}}.$$

Record the 11_{six}.

$$\begin{array}{r} 34_{\text{six}} \\ \times\, 2_{\text{six}} \\ \hline 112_{\text{six}} \end{array}$$

This is the desired product.

Let's check the product by converting to base ten: $34_{\text{six}} = 22$, $2_{\text{six}} = 2$, and $112_{\text{six}} = 44$. Because $22 \times 2 = 44$, our work is correct.

CHECK POINT 5 Multiply:

$$\begin{array}{r} 45_{\text{seven}} \\ \times\, 3_{\text{seven}}. \\ \hline \end{array}$$

4 Divide in bases other than ten.

Division

The answer in a division problem is called a **quotient**. A multiplication table showing products in the same base as the division problem is helpful.

EXAMPLE 6 DIVISION IN BASE FOUR

Use Table 4.5, showing products in base four, to perform the following division:

$$3_{\text{four}}\overline{)222_{\text{four}}}.$$

TABLE 4.5 MULTIPLICATION: BASE FOUR

×	0	1	2	3
0	0	0	0	0
1	0	1	2	3
2	0	2	10	12
3	0	3	12	21

SOLUTION We can use the same method to divide in base four that we use in base ten. Begin by dividing 22_{four} by 3_{four}. Use Table 4.5 to find in the vertical column headed by 3 the largest product that is less than or equal to 22_{four}. This product is 21_{four}. Because $3_{\text{four}} \times 3_{\text{four}} = 21_{\text{four}}$, the first number in the quotient is 3_{four}.

$$\begin{array}{r} 3 \\ 3_{\text{four}}\overline{)222_{\text{four}}} \end{array}$$

First digit in the quotient

Divisor

Dividend

Now multiply $3_{\text{four}} \times 3_{\text{four}}$ and write the product, 21_{four}, under the first two digits of the dividend.

$$\begin{array}{rl} & 3 \\ 3_{\text{four}} & \overline{)222_{\text{four}}} \\ & \underline{21} \end{array}$$

Subtract: $22_{\text{four}} - 21_{\text{four}} = 1_{\text{four}}$.

$$\begin{array}{rl} & 3 \\ 3_{\text{four}} & \overline{)222_{\text{four}}} \\ & \underline{21} \\ & 1 \end{array}$$

Bring down the next digit in the dividend, 2_{four}.

$$\begin{array}{rl} & 3 \\ 3_{\text{four}} & \overline{)222_{\text{four}}} \\ & \underline{21} \\ & 12 \end{array}$$

We now return to Table 4.5. Find in the vertical column headed by 3 the largest product that is less than or equal to 12_{four}. Because $3_{\text{four}} \times 2_{\text{four}} = 12_{\text{four}}$, the next numeral in the quotient is 2_{four}. We use this information to finish the division.

$$\begin{array}{rl} & 32_{\text{four}} \\ 3_{\text{four}} & \overline{)222_{\text{four}}} \\ & \underline{21} \\ & 12 \\ & \underline{12} \\ & 0 \end{array}$$

This is the desired quotient.

Let's check the quotient by converting to base ten: $3_{\text{four}} = 3$, $222_{\text{four}} = 42$, and $32_{\text{four}} = 14$. Because $3\overline{)42}^{\,14}$, our work is correct.

CHECK POINT 6 Use Table 4.5, showing products in base four, to perform the following division:

$$2_{\text{four}}\overline{)112_{\text{four}}}.$$

BLITZER BONUS

Base Two, Logic, and Computers

Smaller than a fingernail, a computer's microchip operates like a tiny electronic brain. The microchip in Figure 4.2 is magnified almost 1200 times, revealing transistors with connecting tracks positioned above them. These tiny transistors switch on and off to control electronic signals, processing thousands of pieces of information per second. Since 1971, the number of transistors that can fit onto a single chip has increased from over 2000 to a staggering 500 million.

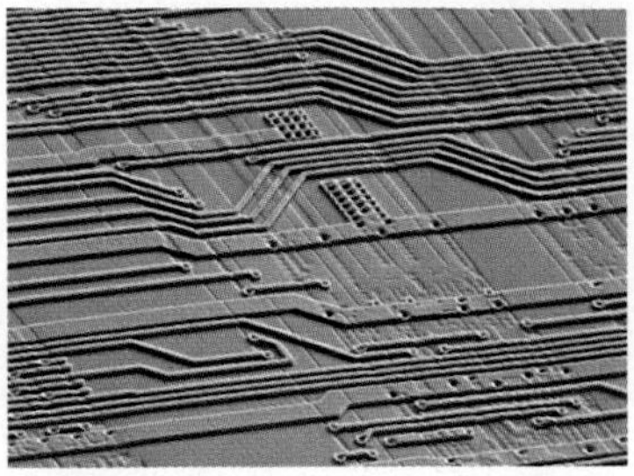

FIGURE 4.2

We have seen that communication inside a computer takes the form of sequences of on–off electric pulses that digitally represent numbers, words, sounds, and visual images. These binary streams are manipulated when they pass through the microchip's gates, shown in Figure 4.3. The **not gate** takes a digital sequence and changes all the 0s to 1s and all the 1s to 0s.

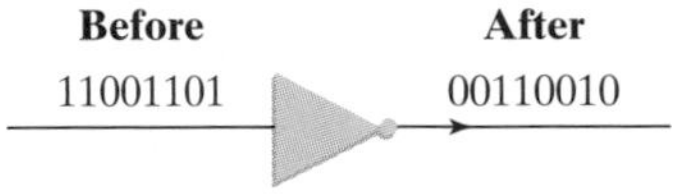

The *and* and *or gates* take two input sequences and produce one output sequence. The **and gate** outputs a 1 if both sequences have a 1; otherwise, it outputs a 0.

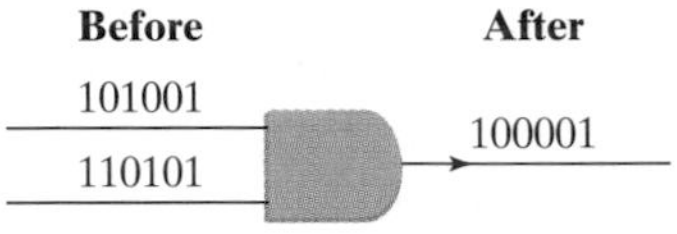

The **or gate** outputs a 1 if either sequence has a 1; otherwise, it outputs a 0.

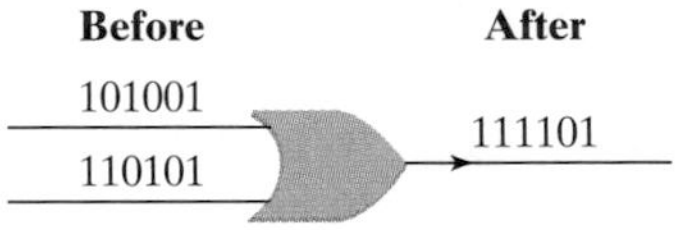

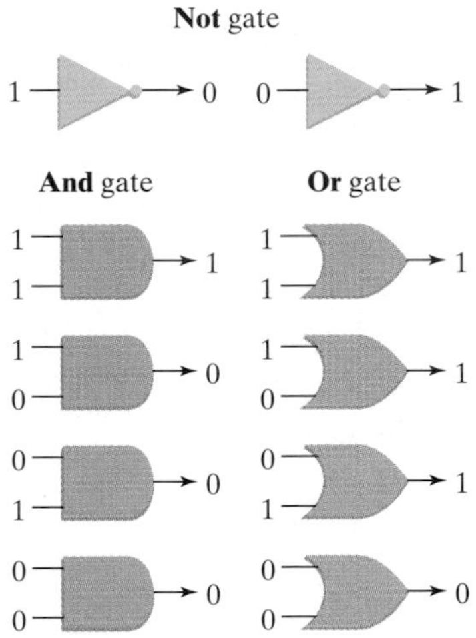

FIGURE 4.3

These gates are at the computational heart of a computer. They should remind you of negation, conjunction, and disjunction in logic, except that T is now 1 and F is now 0. Without the merging of base two and logic, computers as we know them would not exist.

EXERCISE SET 4.3

• Practice Exercises

In Exercises 1–12, add in the indicated base.

1. $23_{four} + 13_{four}$
2. $31_{four} + 22_{four}$
3. $11_{two} + 11_{two}$
4. $101_{two} + 11_{two}$
5. $342_{five} + 413_{five}$
6. $323_{five} + 421_{five}$
7. $645_{seven} + 324_{seven}$
8. $632_{seven} + 564_{seven}$
9. $6784_{nine} + 7865_{nine}$
10. $1021_{three} + 2011_{three}$
11. $14632_{seven} + 5604_{seven}$
12. $53B_{sixteen} + 694_{sixteen}$

In Exercises 13–24, subtract in the indicated base.

13. $32_{four} - 13_{four}$
14. $21_{four} - 12_{four}$
15. $23_{five} - 14_{five}$
16. $32_{seven} - 16_{seven}$
17. $475_{eight} - 267_{eight}$
18. $712_{nine} - 483_{nine}$
19. $563_{seven} - 164_{seven}$
20. $462_{eight} - 177_{eight}$
21. $1001_{two} - 111_{two}$
22. $1000_{two} - 101_{two}$
23. $1200_{three} - 1012_{three}$
24. $4C6_{sixteen} - 198_{sixteen}$

In Exercises 25–34, multiply in the indicated base.

25. $25_{six} \times 4_{six}$
26. $34_{five} \times 3_{five}$
27. $11_{two} \times 1_{two}$
28. $21_{four} \times 3_{four}$
29. $543_{seven} \times 5_{seven}$
30. $243_{nine} \times 6_{nine}$
31. $623_{eight} \times 4_{eight}$
32. $543_{six} \times 5_{six}$
33. $21_{four} \times 12_{four}$
34. $32_{four} \times 23_{four}$

In Exercises 35–38, use the multiplication tables shown below to divide in the indicated base.

MULTIPLICATION: BASE FOUR

×	0	1	2	3
0	0	0	0	0
1	0	1	2	3
2	0	2	10	12
3	0	3	12	21

MULTIPLICATION: BASE FIVE

×	0	1	2	3	4
0	0	0	0	0	0
1	0	1	2	3	4
2	0	2	4	11	13
3	0	3	11	14	22
4	0	4	13	22	31

35. $2_{\text{four}}\overline{)100_{\text{four}}}$

36. $2_{\text{four}}\overline{)321_{\text{four}}}$

37. $3_{\text{five}}\overline{)224_{\text{five}}}$

38. $4_{\text{five}}\overline{)134_{\text{five}}}$

• Practice Plus

In Exercises 39–46, perform the indicated operations.

39. $10110_{\text{two}} + 10100_{\text{two}} + 11100_{\text{two}}$

40. $11100_{\text{two}} + 11111_{\text{two}} + 10111_{\text{two}}$

41. $11111_{\text{two}} + 10110_{\text{two}} - 101_{\text{two}}$

42. $10111_{\text{two}} + 11110_{\text{two}} - 111_{\text{two}}$

43. $1011_{\text{two}} \times 101_{\text{two}}$

44. $1101_{\text{two}} \times 110_{\text{two}}$

45. $D3_{\text{sixteen}} \times 8A_{\text{sixteen}}$

46. $B5_{\text{sixteen}} \times 2C_{\text{sixteen}}$

• Application Exercises

Read the Blitzer Bonus on page 214. Then use the information in the essay to solve Exercises 47–52. Each exercise shows the binary sequences 10011 and 11001 about to be manipulated by passing through a microchip's series of gates. Provide the result(s) of these computer manipulations, designated by ? *in each diagram.*

47.

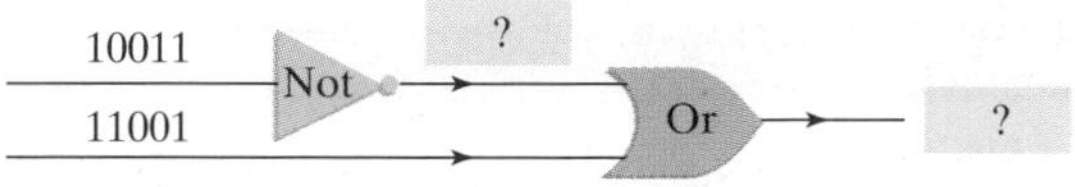

48.

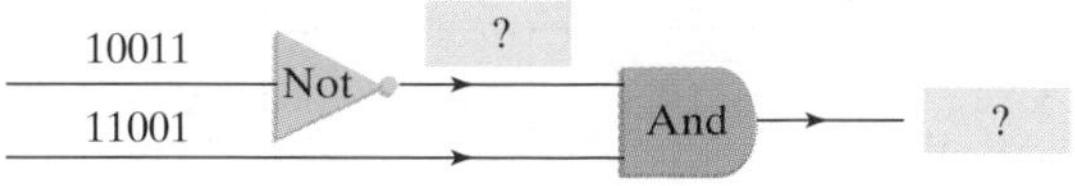

49.

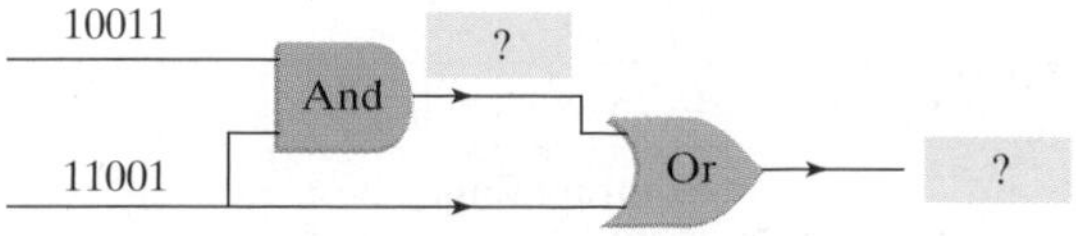

50.

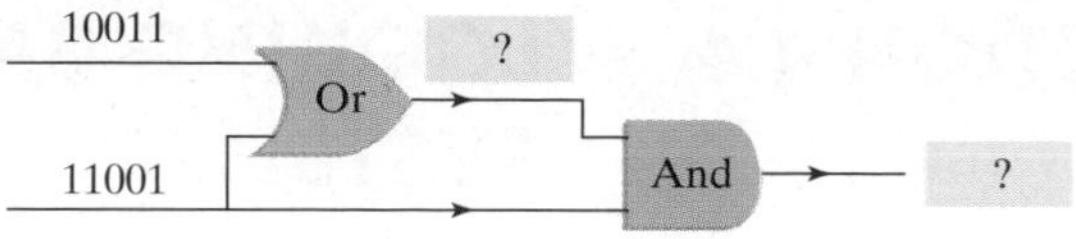

51.

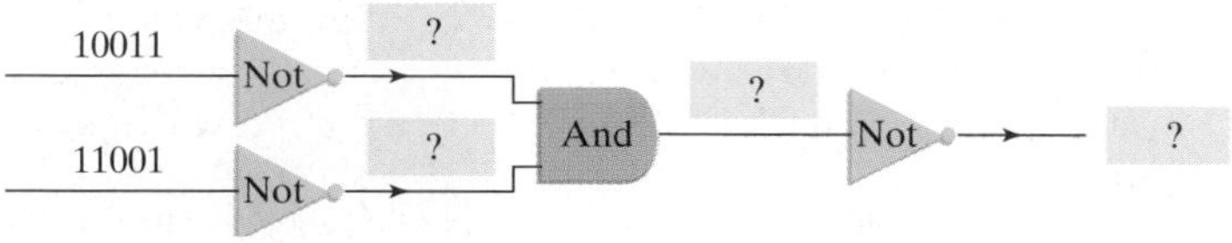

52.

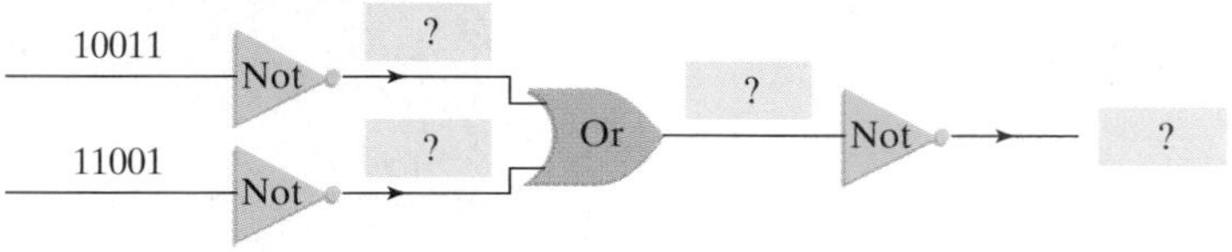

53. Use the equivalence $p \rightarrow q \equiv \sim p \vee q$ to select the circuit in Exercises 47–52 that illustrates a conditional gate.

• Writing in Mathematics

54. Describe how to add two numbers in a base other than ten. How do you express and record the sum of numbers in a column if that sum exceeds the base?

55. Describe how to subtract two numbers in a base other than ten. How do you subtract a larger number from a smaller number in the same column?

56. Describe two difficulties that youngsters encounter when learning to add, subtract, multiply, and divide using Hindu-Arabic numerals. Base your answer on difficulties that are encountered when performing these computations in bases other than ten.

• Critical Thinking Exercises

57. Divide: $31_{\text{seven}}\overline{)2426_{\text{seven}}}$.

58. Use the Mayan numerals in Table 4.2 on page 200 to solve this exercise. Add  and  without converting to Hindu-Arabic numerals.

• Group Exercises

59. Group members should research various methods that societies have used to perform computations. Include finger multiplication, the galley method (sometimes called the Gelosia method), Egyptian duplation, subtraction by complements, Napier's bones, and other methods of interest in your presentation to the entire class.

60. Organize a debate. One side represents people who favor performing computations by hand, using the methods and procedures discussed in this section, but applied to base ten numerals. The other side represents people who favor the use of calculators for performing all computations. Include the merits of each approach in the debate.

SECTION 4.4 • LOOKING BACK AT EARLY NUMERATION SYSTEMS

OBJECTIVES

1. Understand and use the Egyptian system.
2. Understand and use the Roman system.
3. Understand and use the traditional Chinese system.
4. Understand and use the Ionic Greek system.

Super Bowl XXV, played on January 27, 1991, resulted in the closest score of all time: NY Giants: 20; Buffalo: 19. If you are intrigued by sports facts and figures, you are probably aware that major sports events, such as the Super Bowl, are named using Roman numerals. Perhaps you have seen the use of Roman numerals in dating movies and television shows, or on clocks and watches.

In this section, we embark on a brief journey through time and numbers. Our Hindu-Arabic numeration system, the focus of this chapter, is successful because it expresses numbers with just ten symbols and makes computation with these numbers relatively easy. By these standards, the early numeration systems discussed in this section, such as Roman numerals, are unsuccessful. By looking briefly at these systems, you will see that our system is outstanding when compared with other historical systems.

1 Understand and use the Egyptian system.

The Egyptian Numeration System

Like most great civilizations, ancient Egypt had several numeration systems. The oldest is hieroglyphic notation, which developed around 3400 B.C. Table 4.6 lists the Egyptian hieroglyphic numerals with the equivalent Hindu-Arabic numerals. Notice that the numerals are powers of ten. Their numeral for 1,000,000, or 10^6, looks like someone who just won the lottery!

STUDY TIP

It is not necessary to memorize the symbols for the four numeration systems discussed in this section. Focus your attention on understanding the idea behind each system and how these ideas have been incorporated into our Hindu-Arabic system.

TABLE 4.6 EGYPTIAN HIEROGLYPHIC NUMERALS

Hindu-Arabic Numeral	Egyptian Numeral	Description
1	𓏺	Staff
10	𓎆	Heel bone
100	𓍢	Spiral
1000	𓆼	Lotus blossom
10,000	𓂭	Pointing finger
100,000	𓆐	Tadpole
1,000,000	𓁨	Astonished person

It takes far more space to represent most numbers in the Egyptian system than in our system. This is because a number is expressed by repeating each numeral the required number of times. However, no numeral, except perhaps the astonished person, should be repeated more than nine times. If we were to use the Egyptian system to represent 764, we would need to write

100 100 100 100 100 100 100 10 10 10 10 10 10 1 1 1 1

and then represent each of these symbols with the appropriate hieroglyphic numeral from Table 4.6. Thus, 764 as an Egyptian numeral is

The ancient Egyptian system is an example of an **additive system**, one in which the number represented is the sum of the values of the numerals.

EXAMPLE 1 USING THE EGYPTIAN NUMERATION SYSTEM

Write the following numeral as a Hindu-Arabic numeral:

SOLUTION Using Table 4.6, find the value of each of the Egyptian numerals. Then add them.

$$1{,}000{,}000 + 10{,}000 + 10{,}000 + 10 + 10 + 10 + 1 + 1 + 1 + 1 = 1{,}020{,}034$$

CHECK POINT 1 Write the following numeral as a Hindu-Arabic numeral:

EXAMPLE 2 USING THE EGYPTIAN NUMERATION SYSTEM

Write 1752 as an Egyptian numeral.

SOLUTION First break down the Hindu-Arabic numeral into quantities that match the Egyptian numerals:

$$1752 = 1000 + 700 + 50 + 2$$
$$= 1000 + 100 + 100 + 100 + 100 + 100 + 100 + 100$$
$$+ 10 + 10 + 10 + 10 + 10 + 1 + 1.$$

Now, use Table 4.6 to find the Egyptian symbol that matches each quantity. For example, the lotus blossom, , matches 1000. Write each of these symbols and leave out the addition signs. Thus, the number 1752 can be expressed as

CHECK POINT 2 Write 2563 as an Egyptian numeral.

BLITZER BONUS

Hieroglyphic Numerals on Ancient Egyptian Tombs

Egyptian tombs from as early as 2600 B.C. contained hieroglyphic numerals. The funeral rites of ancient Egypt provided the dead with food and drink. The numerals showed how many of each item were included in the offering. Thus, the deceased had nourishment in symbolic form even when the offerings of the rite itself were gone.

2 Understand and use the Roman system.

The Roman Numeration System

The Roman numeration system was developed between 500 B.C. and 100 A.D. It evolved as a result of tax collecting and commerce in the vast Roman Empire. The Roman numerals shown in Table 4.7 were used throughout Europe until the eighteenth century. They are still commonly used in outlining, on clocks, for certain copyright dates, and in numbering some pages in books. Roman numerals are selected letters from the Roman alphabet.

STUDY TIP

Here's a sentence to help remember the letters used for Roman numerals in increasing order:

If **V**al's **X**-ray **L**ooks **C**lear, **D**on't **M**edicate.

TABLE 4.7 ROMAN NUMERALS

Roman numeral	I	V	X	L	C	D	M
Hindu-Arabic numeral	1	5	10	50	100	500	1000

If the symbols in Table 4.7 decrease in value from left to right, then add their values to obtain the value of the Roman numeral as a whole. For example, CX = 100 + 10 = 110. On the other hand, if symbols increase in value from left to right, then subtract the value of the symbol on the left from the symbol on the right. For example, IV means 5 − 1 = 4 and IX means 10 − 1 = 9.

Only the Roman numerals representing 1, 10, 100, 1000, . . . , can be subtracted. Furthermore, they can be subtracted only from their next two greater Roman numerals.

Roman numeral (values that can be subtracted are shown in red)	I	V	X	L	C	D	M
Hindu-Arabic numeral	1	5	10	50	100	500	1000

I can be subtracted only from V and X.

X can be subtracted only from L and C.

C can be subtracted only from D and M.

EXAMPLE 3 USING ROMAN NUMERALS

Write CLXVII as a Hindu-Arabic numeral.

SOLUTION Because the numerals decrease in value from left to right, we add their values to find the value of the Roman numeral as a whole.

$$\text{CLXVII} = 100 + 50 + 10 + 5 + 1 + 1 = 167$$

CHECK POINT 3 Write MCCCLXI as a Hindu-Arabic numeral.

EXAMPLE 4 USING ROMAN NUMERALS

Write MCMXCVI as a Hindu-Arabic numeral.

SOLUTION

$$\begin{aligned} &\text{M} \quad \text{CM} \quad \text{XC} \quad \text{V} \quad \text{I} \\ &= 1000 + (1000 - 100) + (100 - 10) + 5 + 1 \\ &= 1000 + 900 + 90 + 5 + 1 = 1996 \end{aligned}$$

CHECK POINT 4 Write MCDXLVII as a Hindu-Arabic numeral.

BLITZER BONUS

Do Not Offend Jupiter

Have you ever noticed that clock faces with Roman numerals frequently show the number 4 as IIII instead of IV? One possible reason is that IIII provides aesthetic balance when visually paired with VIII on the other side. A more intriguing reason (although not necessarily true) is that the Romans did not want to offend the god Jupiter (spelled IVPITER) by daring to place the first two letters of his name on the face of a clock.

Because Roman numerals involve subtraction as well as addition, it takes far less space to represent most numbers than in the Egyptian system. It is never necessary to repeat any symbol more than three consecutive times. For example, we write 46 as a Roman numeral using

XLVI rather than XXXXVI.

XL = 50 − 10 = 40

EXAMPLE 5 USING ROMAN NUMERALS

Write 249 as a Roman numeral.

SOLUTION

$$\begin{aligned} 249 &= 200 + 40 + 9 \\ &= 100 + 100 + (50 - 10) + (10 - 1) \\ &\quad\downarrow \quad\;\; \downarrow \qquad\quad \downarrow \qquad\qquad \downarrow \\ &= \text{C} \quad \text{C} \quad\;\; \text{XL} \qquad\quad \text{IX} \end{aligned}$$

Thus, 249 = CCXLIX.

CHECK POINT 5 Write 399 as a Roman numeral.

The Roman numeration system uses bars above numerals or groups of numerals to show that the numbers are to be multiplied by 1000. For example,

$$\overline{\text{L}} = 50 \times 1000 = 50{,}000 \quad \text{and} \quad \overline{\text{CM}} = 900 \times 1000 = 900{,}000.$$

Placing bars over Roman numerals reduces the number of symbols needed to represent large numbers.

3 Understand and use the traditional Chinese system.

The Traditional Chinese Numeration System

The numerals used in the traditional Chinese numeration system are given in Table 4.8. At least two things are missing—a symbol for zero and a surprised lottery winner!

TABLE 4.8 TRADITIONAL CHINESE NUMERALS

Traditional Chinese numerals	一	二	三	四	五	六	七	八	九	十	百	千
Hindu-Arabic numerals	1	2	3	4	5	6	7	8	9	10	100	1000

3
1000
2
100
6
10
4

Representing 3264 vertically is the first step in expressing it as a Chinese numeral.

So, how are numbers represented with this set of symbols? Chinese numerals are written vertically. Using our digits, the number 3264 is expressed as shown in the margin.

The next step is to replace each of these seven symbols with a traditional Chinese numeral from Table 4.8. Our next example illustrates this procedure.

3000:	3	三
	1000	千
200:	2	二
	100	百
60:	6	六
	10	十
4:	4	四

Writing 3264 as a Chinese numeral

EXAMPLE 6 USING THE TRADITIONAL CHINESE NUMERATION SYSTEM

Write 3264 as a Chinese numeral.

SOLUTION First, break down the Hindu-Arabic numeral into quantities that match the Chinese numerals. Represent each quantity vertically. Then, use Table 4.8 on the previous page to find the Chinese symbol that matches each quantity. This procedure, with the resulting Chinese numeral, is shown in the margin.

The Chinese system does not need a numeral for zero because it is not positional. For example, we write 8006, using zeros as placeholders, to indicate that two powers of ten, namely 10^2, or 100, and 10^1, or 10, are not needed. The Chinese leave this out, writing

8		八
1000		千
6 ,	or	六.

CHECK POINT 6 Write 2693 as a Chinese numeral.

4 Understand and use the Ionic Greek system.

The Ionic Greek Numeration System

The ancient Greeks, masters of art, architecture, theater, literature, philosophy, geometry, and logic, were not masters when it came to representing numbers. The Ionic Greek numeration system, which can be traced back as far as 450 B.C., used letters of their alphabet for numerals. Table 4.9 shows the many symbols (too many symbols!) used to represent numbers.

TABLE 4.9 IONIC GREEK NUMERALS

1	α	alpha	10	ι	iota	100	ρ	rho
2	β	beta	20	κ	kappa	200	σ	sigma
3	γ	gamma	30	λ	lambda	300	τ	tau
4	δ	delta	40	μ	mu	400	υ	upsilon
5	ϵ	epsilon	50	ν	nu	500	ϕ	phi
6	ϛ	vau	60	ξ	xi	600	χ	chi
7	ζ	zeta	70	o	omicron	700	ψ	psi
8	η	eta	80	π	pi	800	ω	omega
9	θ	theta	90	Q	koph	900	ᴨ	sampi

To represent a number from 1 to 999, the appropriate symbols are written next to one another. For example, the number $21 = 20 + 1$. When 21 is expressed as a Greek numeral, the plus sign is left out:

$$21 = \kappa\alpha.$$

Similarly, the number 823 written as a Greek numeral is $\omega\kappa\gamma$.

EXAMPLE 7 USING THE IONIC GREEK NUMERATION SYSTEM

Write $\psi\lambda\delta$ as a Hindu-Arabic numeral.

SOLUTION $\psi = 700$, $\lambda = 30$, and $\delta = 4$. Adding these numbers gives 734.

CHECK POINT 7 Write $\omega\pi\epsilon$ as a Hindu-Arabic numeral.

One of the many unsuccessful features of the Greek numeration system is that new symbols have to be added to represent higher numbers. It is like an alphabet that gets bigger each time a new word is used and has to be written.

EXERCISE SET 4.4

• Practice Exercises

Use Table 4.6 on page 216 to solve Exercises 1–12.

In Exercises 1–6, write each Egyptian numeral as a Hindu-Arabic numeral.

1. 
2. 
3. 
4. 
5. 
6. 

In Exercises 7–12, write each Hindu-Arabic numeral as an Egyptian numeral.

7. 423 **8.** 825 **9.** 1846
10. 1425 **11.** 23,547 **12.** 2,346,031

Use Table 4.7 on page 218 to solve Exercises 13–36.

In Exercises 13–28, write each Roman numeral as a Hindu-Arabic numeral.

13. XI **14.** CL **15.** XVI
16. LVII **17.** XL **18.** CM
19. LIX **20.** XLIV **21.** CXLVI
22. CLXI **23.** MDCXXI **24.** MMCDXLV
25. MMDCLXXVII **26.** MDCXXVI **27.** $\overline{\text{IX}}$CDLXVI
28. $\overline{\text{V}}$MCCXI

In Exercises 29–36, write each Hindu-Arabic numeral as a Roman numeral.

29. 43 **30.** 96 **31.** 129 **32.** 469
33. 1896 **34.** 4578 **35.** 6892 **36.** 5847

Use Table 4.8 on page 219 to solve Exercises 37–48.

In Exercises 37–42, write each traditional Chinese numeral as a Hindu-Arabic numeral.

37. 八十八 **38.** 七百五 **39.** 五百二十七 **40.** 三千八十一 **41.** 二千七百七十六 **42.** 八千二百三十六

In Exercises 43–48, write each Hindu-Arabic numeral as a traditional Chinese numeral.

43. 43 **44.** 269 **45.** 583
46. 2965 **47.** 4870 **48.** 7605

Use Table 4.9 on page 220 to solve Exercises 49–56.

In Exercises 49–52, write each Ionic Greek numeral as a Hindu-Arabic numeral.

49. $\iota\beta$ **50.** $\phi\epsilon$ **51.** $\sigma\lambda\delta$ **52.** $\psi o\theta$

In Exercises 53–56, write each Hindu-Arabic numeral as an Ionic Greek numeral.

53. 43 **54.** 257 **55.** 483 **56.** 895

• Practice Plus

57. Write  as a Roman numeral and as a traditional Chinese numeral.

58. Write  as a Roman numeral and as a traditional Chinese numeral.

59. Write MDCCXLI as an Egyptian numeral and as a traditional Chinese numeral.

60. Write MMCCXLV as an Egyptian numeral and as a traditional Chinese numeral.

In Exercises 61–64, write each numeral as a numeral in base five.

61.  **62.** 

63. CXCII **64.** CMLXXIV

In Exercises 65–66, perform each subtraction without converting to Hindu-Arabic numerals.

65. 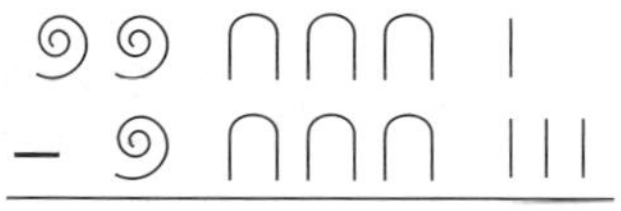

66. 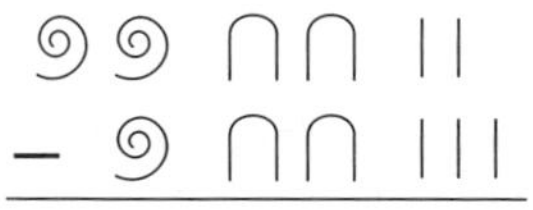

• Application Exercises

67. Look at the back of a U.S. one dollar bill. What date is written in Roman numerals along the base of the pyramid with an eye? What is this date's significance?

68. A construction crew demolishing a very old building was surprised to find the numeral MCMLXXXIX inscribed on the cornerstone. Explain why they were surprised.

The Braille numeration system is a base ten positional system that uses raised dots in 2-by-3 cells as digit symbols.

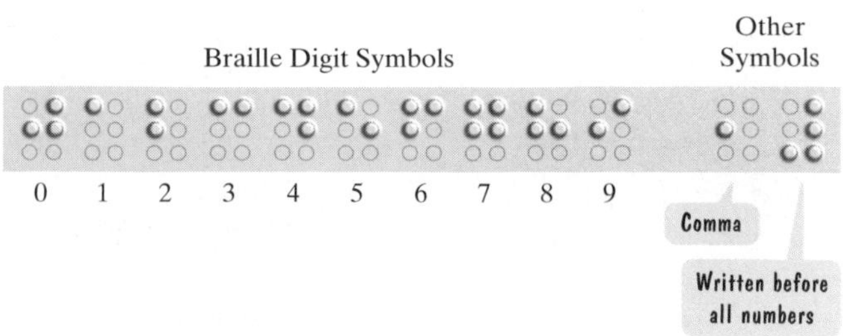

In Exercises 69–70, use the digit symbols at the bottom of the previous page to express each Braille numeral as a Hindu-Arabic numeral and as a Roman numeral.

69. 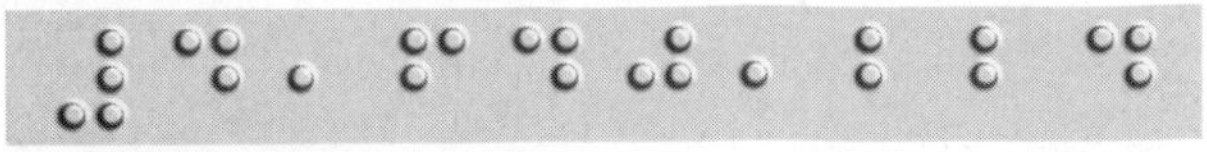

70. 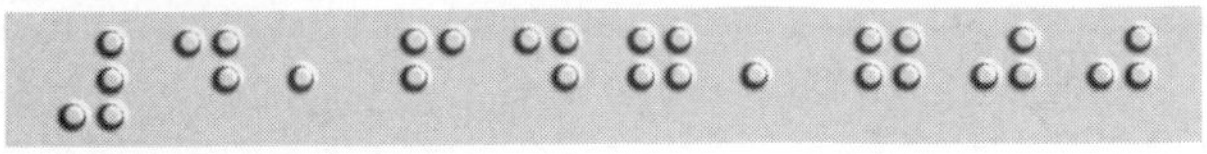

• Writing in Mathematics

71. Describe how a number is represented in the Egyptian numeration system.

72. If you are interpreting a Roman numeral, when do you add values and when do you subtract them? Give an example to illustrate each case.

73. Describe how a number is represented in the traditional Chinese numeration system.

74. Describe one disadvantage of the Ionic Greek numeration system.

75. If you could use only one system of numeration described in this section, which would you prefer? Discuss the reasons for your choice.

• Critical Thinking Exercises

76. Arrange these three numerals from smallest to largest.

四
百
二
十
八

CCCCXLIX 

77. Use Egyptian numerals to write the numeral that precedes and the numeral that follows

78. After reading this section, a student had a numeration nightmare about selling flowers in a time-warped international market. She started out with 200 flowers, selling XLVI of them to a Roman,

to an Egyptian,

二
十

to a traditional Chinese family, and the remainder to a Greek. How many flowers were sold to the Greek? Express the answer in the Ionic Greek numeration system.

• Group Exercises

Take a moment to read the introduction to the group exercises on page 208. Exercises 79–83 list some additional topics for individual or group research projects.

79. A Time Line Showing Significant Developments in Numeration Systems

80. Animals and Number Sense

81. The Hebrew Numeration System (or any system not discussed in this chapter)

82. The Rhind Papyrus and What We Learned from It

83. Computation in an Early Numeration System

CHAPTER SUMMARY, REVIEW, AND TEST

• SUMMARY DEFINITIONS AND CONCEPTS — EXAMPLES

4.1 Our Hindu-Arabic System and Early Positional Systems

a. In a positional-value, or place-value, numeration system, the value of each symbol, called a digit, varies according to the position it occupies in the number.

b. The Hindu-Arabic numeration system is a base ten system with the digits 0, 1, 2, 3, 4, 5, 6, 7, 8, and 9. The place values in the system are

$$\ldots, 10^5, 10^4, 10^3, 10^2, 10^1, 1.$$

Ex. 2, p. 198;
Ex. 3, p. 198

c. The Babylonian numeration system is a base 60 system, with place values given by

$$\ldots,\ 60^3,\ 60^2,\ 60^1,\ 1.$$
$$\text{or}\quad \text{or}\quad \text{or}$$
$$216{,}000\quad 3600\quad 60$$

Babylonian numerals are given in Table 4.1 on page 199.

Ex. 4, p. 199

d. The Mayan numeration system has place values given by

$$\ldots,\ 18\times 20^3,\ 18\times 20^2,\ 18\times 20,\ 20,\ 1.$$
$$\text{or}\quad \text{or}\quad \text{or}$$
$$144{,}000\quad 7200\quad 360$$

Mayan numerals are given in Table 4.2 on page 200.

Ex. 5, p. 201

4.2 Number Bases in Positional Systems

a. The base of a positional numeration system refers to the number of individual digit symbols used in the system as well as to the powers of the numbers used in place values. In base b, there are b digit symbols (from 0 through $b - 1$ inclusive) with place values given by

$$\ldots, b^4, b^3, b^2, b^1, 1.$$

b. To change a numeral in a base other than ten to a base ten numeral,

1. Multiply each digit in the numeral by its respective place value.
2. Find the sum of the products in step 1.

Ex. 1, p. 205; Ex. 2, p. 205; Ex. 3, p. 206

c. To change a base ten numeral to a base b numeral, use mental conversions or repeated divisions by powers of b to find how many groups of each place value are contained in the base ten numeral.

Ex. 4, p. 206; Ex. 5, p. 207; Ex. 6, p. 207

4.3 Computation in Positional Systems

a. Computations in bases other than ten are performed using the same procedures as in ordinary base ten arithmetic. When a computation is equal to or exceeds the given base, use mental conversions to convert from the base ten numeral to a numeral in the desired base.

Ex. 1, p. 209; Ex. 2, p. 210; Ex. 3, p. 211; Ex. 4, p. 212; Ex. 5, p. 212

b. To divide in bases other than ten, it is convenient to use a multiplication table for products in the required base.

Ex. 6, p. 213

4.4 Looking Back at Early Numeration Systems

a. A successful numeration system expresses numbers with relatively few symbols and makes computation with these numbers fairly easy.

b. By the standard in (a), the Egyptian system (Table 4.6 on page 216), the Roman system (Table 4.7 on page 218), the Chinese system (Table 4.8 on page 219), and the Greek system (Table 4.9 on page 220) are all unsuccessful. Unlike our Hindu-Arabic system, these systems are not positional and contain no symbol for zero.

Ex. 1, p. 217; Ex. 2, p. 217; Ex. 3, p. 218; Ex. 4, p. 218; Ex. 5, p. 219; Ex. 6, p. 220; Ex. 7, p. 220

REVIEW EXERCISES

4.1

In Exercises 1–2, evaluate the expression.

1. 11^2 **2.** 7^3

In Exercises 3–5, write each Hindu-Arabic numeral in expanded form.

3. 472 **4.** 8076 **5.** 70,329

In Exercises 6–7, express each expanded form as a Hindu-Arabic numeral.

6. $(7 \times 10^5) + (0 \times 10^4) + (6 \times 10^3) + (9 \times 10^2) + (5 \times 10^1) + (3 \times 1)$

7. $(7 \times 10^8) + (4 \times 10^7) + (3 \times 10^2) + (6 \times 1)$

Use Table 4.1 on page 199 to write each Babylonian numeral in Exercises 8–9 as a Hindu-Arabic numeral.

8. < ∨   < ∨ ∨ ∨

9. ∨ ∨   < <   < < <

Use Table 4.2 on page 200 to write each Mayan numeral in Exercises 10–11 as a Hindu-Arabic numeral.

10. 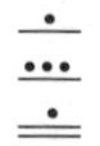

11. 

12. Describe how a positional system is used to represent a number.

4.2

In Exercises 13–18, convert the numeral to a numeral in base ten.

13. 34_{five} **14.** 110_{two} **15.** 643_{seven}

16. 1084_{nine} **17.** $\text{FD3}_{\text{sixteen}}$ **18.** 202202_{three}

In Exercises 19–24, convert each base ten numeral to a numeral in the given base.

19. 89 to base five **20.** 21 to base two

21. 473 to base three **22.** 7093 to base seven

23. 9348 to base six **24.** 554 to base twelve

4.3

In Exercises 25–28, add in the indicated base.

25. $\begin{array}{r} 46_{\text{seven}} \\ +53_{\text{seven}} \\ \hline \end{array}$ **26.** $\begin{array}{r} 574_{\text{eight}} \\ +605_{\text{eight}} \\ \hline \end{array}$ **27.** $\begin{array}{r} 11011_{\text{two}} \\ +10101_{\text{two}} \\ \hline \end{array}$ **28.** $\begin{array}{r} 43\text{C}_{\text{sixteen}} \\ +694_{\text{sixteen}} \\ \hline \end{array}$

In Exercises 29–32, subtract in the indicated base.

29. $\begin{array}{r} 34_{\text{six}} \\ -25_{\text{six}} \\ \hline \end{array}$ **30.** $\begin{array}{r} 624_{\text{seven}} \\ -246_{\text{seven}} \\ \hline \end{array}$ **31.** $\begin{array}{r} 1001_{\text{two}} \\ -\ 110_{\text{two}} \\ \hline \end{array}$ **32.** $\begin{array}{r} 4121_{\text{five}} \\ -1312_{\text{five}} \\ \hline \end{array}$

In Exercises 33–35, multiply in the indicated base.

33. $32_{\text{four}} \times 3_{\text{four}}$

34. $43_{\text{seven}} \times 6_{\text{seven}}$

35. $123_{\text{five}} \times 4_{\text{five}}$

In Exercises 36–37, divide in the indicated base. Use the multiplication tables on page 215.

36. $2_{\text{four}}\overline{)332_{\text{four}}}$

37. $4_{\text{five}}\overline{)103_{\text{five}}}$

4.4

Use Table 4.6 on page 216 to solve Exercises 38–41.

In Exercises 38–39, write each Egyptian numeral as a Hindu-Arabic numeral.

38. 

39. 

In Exercises 40–41, write each Hindu-Arabic numeral as an Egyptian numeral.

40. 2486

41. 34,573

In Exercises 42–43, assume a system that represents numbers exactly like the Egyptian system, but with different symbols. In particular, A = 1, B = 10, C = 100, *and* D = 1000.

42. Write DDCCCBAAAA as a Hindu-Arabic numeral.

43. Write 5492 as a numeral in terms of A, B, C, and D.

44. Describe how the Egyptian system or the system in Exercises 42–43 is used to represent a number. Discuss one disadvantage of such a system when compared to our Hindu-Arabic system.

Use Table 4.7 on page 218 to solve Exercises 45–49.

In Exercises 45–47, write each Roman numeral as a Hindu-Arabic numeral.

45. CLXIII

46. MXXXIV

47. MCMXC

In Exercises 48–49, write each Hindu-Arabic numeral as a Roman numeral.

48. 49

49. 2965

50. Explain when to subtract the value of symbols when interpreting a Roman numeral. Give an example.

Use Table 4.8 on page 219 to solve Exercises 51–54.

In Exercises 51–52, write each traditional Chinese numeral as a Hindu-Arabic numeral.

51. 五
百
五
十
四

52. 八
千
二
百
五
十
三

In Exercises 53–54, write each Hindu-Arabic numeral as a traditional Chinese numeral.

53. 274

54. 3587

In Exercises 55–58, assume a system that represents numbers exactly like the traditional Chinese system, but with different symbols. The symbols are shown as follows:

Numerals in the System	A	B	C	D	E	F	G	H	I	X	Y	Z
Hindu-Arabic Numerals	1	2	3	4	5	6	7	8	9	10	100	1000

Express each numeral in Exercises 55–56 as a Hindu-Arabic numeral.

55. C
Y
F
X
E

56. D
Z
E
Y
B
X

Express each Hindu-Arabic numeral in Exercises 57–58 as a numeral in the system used for Exercises 55–56.

57. 793

58. 6854

59. Describe how the Chinese system or the system in Exercises 55–58 is used to represent a number. Discuss one disadvantage of such a system when compared to our Hindu-Arabic system.

Use Table 4.9 on page 220 to solve Exercises 60–63.

In Exercises 60–61, write each Ionic Greek numeral as a Hindu-Arabic numeral.

60. $\chi\nu\gamma$

61. $\chi o\eta$

In Exercises 62–63, write each Hindu-Arabic numeral as an Ionic Greek numeral.

62. 453

63. 902

In Exercises 64–68, assume a system that represents numbers exactly like the Greek Ionic system, but with different symbols. The symbols are shown as follows:

Decimal	**1**	**2**	**3**	**4**	**5**	**6**	**7**	**8**	**9**
Ones	A	B	C	D	E	F	G	H	I
Tens	J	K	L	M	N	O	P	Q	R
Hundreds	S	T	U	V	W	X	Y	Z	a
Thousands	b	c	d	e	f	g	h	i	j
Ten thousands	k	l	m	n	o	p	q	r	s

In Exercises 64–66, express each numeral as a Hindu-Arabic numeral.

64. UNG

65. mhZRD

66. rXJH

In Exercises 67–68, express each Hindu-Arabic numeral as a numeral in the system used for Exercises 64–66.

67. 597

68. 25,483

69. Discuss one disadvantage of the Greek Ionic system or the system described in Exercises 64–68 when compared to our Hindu-Arabic system.

CHAPTER 4 TEST

1. Evaluate 9^3.
2. Write 567 in expanded form.
3. Write 63,028 in expanded form.
4. Express as a Hindu-Arabic numeral:

$$(7 \times 10^3) + (4 \times 10^2) + (9 \times 10^1) + (3 \times 1).$$

5. Express as a Hindu-Arabic numeral:

$$(4 \times 10^5) + (2 \times 10^2) + (6 \times 1).$$

6. What is the difference between a number and a numeral?
7. Explain why a symbol for zero is needed in a positional system.
8. Place values in the Babylonian system are

$$\ldots, 60^3, 60^2, 60^1, 1.$$

Use the numerals shown to write the following Babylonian numeral as a Hindu-Arabic numeral:

<< <vv <v.

Babylonian	v	<
Hindu-Arabic	1	10

9. Place values in the Mayan system are

$$\ldots, 18 \times 20^3, 18 \times 20^2, 18 \times 20, 20, 1.$$

Use the numerals shown to write the following Mayan numeral as a Hindu-Arabic numeral:

𝋤
𝋦
𝋠 .

Mayan	𝋠	•	••	•••	••••	—	𝋦
Hindu-Arabic	0	1	2	3	4	5	6

In Exercises 10–12, convert the numeral to a numeral in base ten.

10. 423_{five} 11. 267_{nine} 12. 110101_{two}

In Exercises 13–15, convert each base ten numeral to a numeral in the given base.

13. 77 to base three
14. 56 to base two
15. 1844 to base five

In Exercises 16–18, perform the indicated operation.

16. $\begin{array}{r} 234_{\text{five}} \\ +\ 423_{\text{five}} \\ \hline \end{array}$
17. $\begin{array}{r} 562_{\text{seven}} \\ -\ 145_{\text{seven}} \\ \hline \end{array}$
18. $\begin{array}{r} 54_{\text{six}} \\ \times\ \ 3_{\text{six}} \\ \hline \end{array}$

19. Use the multiplication table shown to perform this division: $3_{\text{five}}\overline{)1213_{\text{five}}}$.

A MULTIPLICATION TABLE FOR BASE FIVE

×	0	1	2	3	4
0	0	0	0	0	0
1	0	1	2	3	4
2	0	2	4	11	13
3	0	3	11	14	22
4	0	4	13	22	31

Use the symbols in the tables shown below to solve Exercises 20–23.

Hindu-Arabic Numeral	Egyptian Numeral
1	𓏺
10	𓎆
100	𓍢
1000	𓆼
10,000	𓂭
100,000	𓆐
1,000,000	𓁨

Hindu-Arabic Numeral	Roman Numeral
1	I
5	V
10	X
50	L
100	C
500	D
1000	M

20. Write the following numeral as a Hindu-Arabic numeral:

𓂭𓂭𓍢𓍢𓍢|||.

21. Write 32,634 as an Egyptian numeral.
22. Write the Roman numeral MCMXCIV as a Hindu-Arabic numeral.
23. Express 459 as a Roman numeral.
24. Describe one difference between how a number is represented in the Egyptian system and the Roman system.

CHAPTER 5

Number Theory and the Real Number System

While listening to the radio, you hear politicians discussing the problem of the $8.6 trillion national debt. They state that it's more than the gross domestic product of China, the world's second-richest nation, and four times greater than the combined net worth of America's 691 billionaires. They make it seem like the national debt is a real problem, but later you realize that you don't really know what a number like 8.6 trillion means. If the national debt were evenly divided among all citizens of the country, how much would every man, woman, and child have to pay?

Literacy with numbers, called *numeracy*, is a prerequisite for functioning in a meaningful way personally, professionally, and as a citizen. In this chapter, our focus is on understanding numbers, their properties, and their applications. The problem of placing the $8.6 trillion national debt in perspective appears as Example 9 in Section 5.6.

SECTION 5.1 • NUMBER THEORY: PRIME AND COMPOSITE NUMBERS

OBJECTIVES

1. Determine divisibility.
2. Write the prime factorization of a composite number.
3. Find the greatest common divisor of two numbers.
4. Solve problems using the greatest common divisor.
5. Find the least common multiple of two numbers.
6. Solve problems using the least common multiple.

Number Theory and Divisibility

You are organizing an intramural league at your school. You need to divide 40 men and 24 women into all-male and all-female teams so that each team has the same number of people. The men's teams should have the same number of players as the women's teams. What is the largest number of people that can be placed on a team?

This problem can be solved using a branch of mathematics called **number theory**. Number theory is primarily concerned with the properties of numbers used for counting, namely 1, 2, 3, 4, 5, and so on. The set of counting numbers is also called the set of **natural numbers**. We represent this set by the letter **N**.

THE SET OF NATURAL NUMBERS

$$\mathbf{N} = \{1, 2, 3, 4, 5, 6, 7, 8, 9, 10, 11, \dots\}$$

We can solve the intramural league problem. However, to do so we must understand the concept of divisibility. For example, there are a number of different ways to divide the 24 women into teams, including

1 team with all 24 women:	$1 \times 24 = 24$
2 teams with 12 women per team:	$2 \times 12 = 24$
3 teams with 8 women per team:	$3 \times 8 = 24$
4 teams with 6 women per team:	$4 \times 6 = 24$
6 teams with 4 women per team:	$6 \times 4 = 24$
8 teams with 3 women per team:	$8 \times 3 = 24$
12 teams with 2 women per team:	$12 \times 2 = 24$
24 teams with 1 woman per team:	$24 \times 1 = 24.$

The natural numbers that are multiplied together resulting in a product of 24 are called *factors* of 24. Any natural number can be expressed as a product of two or more natural numbers. The natural numbers that are multiplied are called the **factors** of the product. Notice that a natural number may have many factors.

$$2 \times 12 = 24 \qquad 3 \times 8 = 24 \qquad 6 \times 4 = 24$$

Factors of 24   Factors of 24   Factors of 24

The numbers 1, 2, 3, 4, 6, 8, 12, and 24 are all factors of 24. Each of these numbers divides 24 without a remainder.

In general, let a and b represent natural numbers. We say that a is **divisible** by b if the operation of dividing a by b leaves a remainder of 0.

A natural number is divisible by all of its factors. Thus, 24 is divisible by 1, 2, 3, 4, 6, 8, 12, and 24. Using the factor 8, we can express this divisibility in a number of ways:

24 is **divisible** by 8.
8 is a **divisor** of 24.
8 **divides** 24.

Mathematicians use a special notation to indicate divisibility.

STUDY TIP

The words *factor* and *divisor* mean the same thing. Thus, 8 is a factor and a divisor of 24.

STUDY TIP

Do not confuse the notations $b|a$ and b/a. The symbol $b|a$ means b divides a. The symbol b/a means b divided by a (that is $b \div a$, the quotient of b and a). For example, $5|35$ means 5 divides 35, whereas $5/35$ means 5 divided by 35, which is the fraction $\frac{1}{7}$.

DIVISIBILITY

If a and b are natural numbers, a is **divisible** by b if the operation of dividing a by b leaves a remainder of 0. This is the same as saying that b is a **divisor** of a, or b **divides** a. All three statements are symbolized by writing

$$b|a.$$

Using this new notation, we can write

$$12|24.$$

Twelve divides 24 because 24 divided by 12 leaves a remainder of 0. By contrast, 13 does not divide 24 because 24 divided by 13 does not leave a remainder of 0. The notation

$$13\nmid 24$$

means that 13 does not divide 24.

1 Determine divisibility.

Table 5.1 shows some common rules for divisibility. Divisibility rules for 7 and 11 are difficult to remember and are not included in the table.

TABLE 5.1 RULES OF DIVISIBILITY

Divisible By	Test	Example
2	The last digit is 0, 2, 4, 6, or 8.	5,892,796 is divisible by 2 because the last digit is 6.
3	The sum of the digits is divisible by 3.	52,341 is divisible by 3 because the sum of the digits is $5 + 2 + 3 + 4 + 1 = 15$, and 15 is divisible by 3.
4	The last two digits form a number divisible by 4.	3,947,136 is divisible by 4 because 36 is divisible by 4.
5	The number ends in 0 or 5.	28,160 and 72,805 end in 0 and 5, respectively. Both are divisible by 5.
6	The number is divisible by both 2 and 3. (In other words, the number is even and the sum of its digits is divisible by 3.)	954 is divisible by 2 because it ends in 4. 954 is also divisible by 3 because the digit sum is 18, which is divisible by 3. Because 954 is divisible by both 2 and 3, it is divisible by 6.
8	The last three digits form a number that is divisible by 8.	593,777,832 is divisible by 8 because 832 is divisible by 8.
9	The sum of the digits is divisible by 9.	5346 is divisible by 9 because the sum of the digits, 18, is divisible by 9.
10	The last digit is 0.	998,746,250 is divisible by 10 because the number ends in 0.
12	The number is divisible by both 3 and 4. (In other words, the sum of the digits is divisible by 3 and the last two digits form a number divisible by 4.)	614,608,176 is divisible by 3 because the digit sum is 39, which is divisible by 3. It is also divisible by 4 because the last two digits form 76, which is divisible by 4. Because 614,608,176 is divisible by both 3 and 4, it is divisible by 12.

EXAMPLE 1 USING THE RULES OF DIVISIBILITY

Which one of the following statements is true?

a. $4 \mid 3{,}754{,}086$ **b.** $9 \nmid 4{,}119{,}706{,}413$ **c.** $8 \mid 677{,}840$

SOLUTION

a. $4 \mid 3{,}754{,}086$ states that 4 divides 3,754,086. Table 5.1 indicates that for 4 to divide a number, the last two digits must form a number that is divisible by 4. Because 86 is not divisible by 4, the given statement is false.

b. $9 \nmid 4{,}119{,}706{,}413$ states that 9 does *not* divide 4,119,706,413. Based on Table 5.1, if the sum of the digits is divisible by 9, then 9 does indeed divide this number. The sum of the digits is $4 + 1 + 1 + 9 + 7 + 0 + 6 + 4 + 1 + 3 = 36$, which is divisible by 9. Because 4,119,706,413 is divisible by 9, the given statement is false.

c. $8 \mid 667{,}840$ states that 8 divides 677,840. Table 5.1 indicates that for 8 to divide a number, the last three digits must form a number that is divisible by 8. Because 840 is divisible by 8, then 8 divides 677,840, and the given statement is true.

The statement given in part (c) is the only true statement.

CHECK POINT 1 Which one of the following statements is true?

a. $8 \mid 48{,}324$ **b.** $6 \mid 48{,}324$ **c.** $4 \nmid 48{,}324$

TECHNOLOGY

CALCULATORS AND DIVISIBILITY

You can use a calculator to verify each result in Example 1. Consider part (a):

$$4 \mid 3{,}754{,}086.$$

Divide 3,754,086 by 4 using the following keystrokes:

3754086 [÷] 4.

Press [=] or [ENTER]. The number displayed is 938521.5. This is not a natural number. The 0.5 shows that the division leaves a nonzero remainder. Thus, 4 does not divide 3,754,086. The given statement is false.

Now consider part (b):

$$9 \nmid 4{,}119{,}706{,}413.$$

Use your calculator to divide the number on the right by 9:

4119706413 [÷] 9.

Press [=] or [ENTER]. The display is 457745157. This is a natural number. The remainder of the division is 0, so 9 does divide 4,119,706,413. The given statement is false.

Prime Factorization

2 Write the prime factorization of a composite number.

By developing some other ideas of number theory, we will be able to solve the intramural league problem. We begin with the definition of a prime number.

PRIME NUMBERS

A **prime number** is a natural number greater than 1 that has only itself and 1 as factors.

Using this definition, we see that the number 7 is a prime number because it has only 1 and 7 as factors. Said in another way, 7 is prime because it is divisible by only 1 and 7. The first ten prime numbers are 2, 3, 5, 7, 11, 13, 17, 19, 23, and 29. Each number in this list has exactly two divisors, itself and 1. By contrast, 9 is not a prime number; in addition to being divisible by 1 and 9, it is also divisible by 3. The number 9 is an example of a *composite number.*

STUDY TIP

The number 2 is the only even prime number. Every other even number has at least three factors: 1, 2, and the number itself.

COMPOSITE NUMBERS

A **composite number** is a natural number greater than 1 that is divisible by a number other than itself and 1.

Using this definition, the first ten composite numbers are 4, 6, 8, 9, 10, 12, 14, 15, 16, and 18. Each number in this list has at least three divisors.

Every composite number can be expressed as the product of prime numbers. For example, the composite number 45 can be expressed as

$$45 = 3 \times 3 \times 5.$$

Note that 3 and 5 are prime numbers. Expressing a composite number as the product of prime numbers is called **prime factorization**. The prime factorization of 45 is $3 \times 3 \times 5$. The order in which we write these factors does not matter. This means that

$$45 = 3 \times 3 \times 5$$
$$\text{or } 45 = 5 \times 3 \times 3$$
$$\text{or } 45 = 3 \times 5 \times 3.$$

In Chapter 1, we defined a **theorem** as a statement that can be proved using deductive reasoning. The ancient Greeks proved that if the order of the factors is disregarded, there is only one prime factorization possible for any given composite number. This statement is called the **Fundamental Theorem of Arithmetic**.

THE FUNDAMENTAL THEOREM OF ARITHMETIC
Every composite number can be expressed as a product of prime numbers in one and only one way (if the order of the factors is disregarded).

One method used to find the prime factorization of a composite number is called a **factor tree**. To use this method, begin by selecting any two numbers whose product is the number to be factored. If one or both of the factors are not prime numbers, continue to factor each composite number. Stop when all numbers are prime.

STUDY TIP

It does not matter how you begin a factor tree. For example, in Example 2 you can factor 700 by starting with 5 and 140. ($5 \times 140 = 700$)

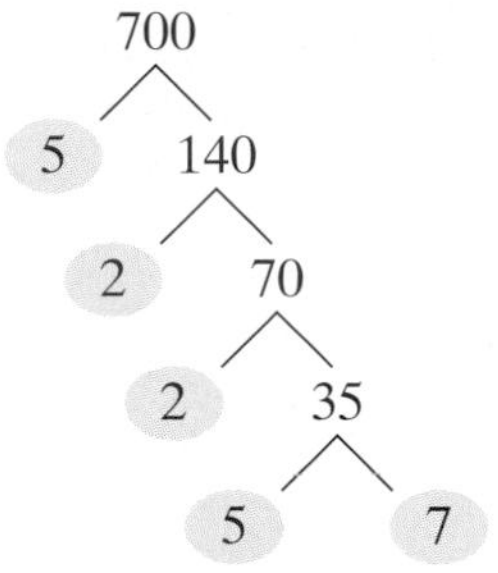

The prime factorization of 700 is

$$700 = 5 \times 2 \times 2 \times 5 \times 7$$
$$= 2^2 \times 5^2 \times 7.$$

This is the same prime factorization we obtained in Example 2.

EXAMPLE 2 PRIME FACTORIZATION USING A FACTOR TREE

Find the prime factorization of 700.

SOLUTION Start with any two numbers whose product is 700, such as 7 and 100. This forms the first branch of the tree. Continue factoring the composite number or numbers that result (in this case 100), branching until the end of each branch contains a prime number.

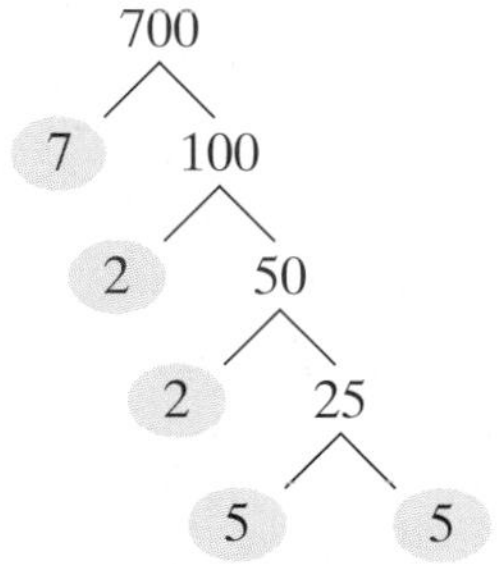

The prime factors are circled. Thus, the prime factorization of 700 is

$$700 = 7 \times 2 \times 2 \times 5 \times 5.$$

We can use exponents to show the repeated prime factors:

$$700 = 7 \times 2^2 \times 5^2.$$

Using a dot to indicate multiplication and arranging the factors from least to greatest, we can write

$$700 = 2^2 \cdot 5^2 \cdot 7.$$

CHECK POINT 2 Find the prime factorization of 120.

3 Find the greatest common divisor of two numbers.

Greatest Common Divisor

The greatest common divisor of two or more natural numbers is the largest number that is a divisor (or factor) of all the numbers. For example, 8 is the greatest common divisor of 32 and 40 because it is the largest natural number that divides both 32 and 40. Some pairs of numbers have 1 as their greatest common divisor. Such number pairs are said to be **relatively prime**. For example, the greatest common divisor of 5 and 26 is 1. Thus, 5 and 26 are relatively prime.

The greatest common divisor can be found using prime factorizations.

FINDING THE GREATEST COMMON DIVISOR OF TWO OR MORE NUMBERS USING PRIME FACTORIZATIONS

To find the greatest common divisor of two or more numbers,

1. Write the prime factorization of each number.
2. Select each prime factor with the smallest exponent that is common to each of the prime factorizations.
3. Form the product of the numbers from step 2. The greatest common divisor is the product of these factors.

EXAMPLE 3 FINDING THE GREATEST COMMON DIVISOR

Find the greatest common divisor of 216 and 234.

SOLUTION

Step 1. Write the prime factorization of each number. Begin by writing the prime factorizations of 216 and 234.

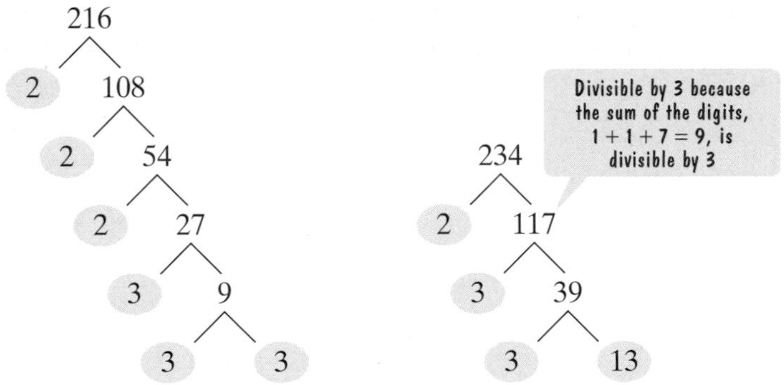

The factor tree at the left indicates that

$$216 = 2^3 \times 3^3.$$

The factor tree at the right indicates that

$$234 = 2 \times 3^2 \times 13.$$

Step 2. Select each prime factor with the smallest exponent that is common to each of the prime factorizations. Look at the factorizations of 216 and 234 from step 1. Can you see that 2 is a prime number common to the factorizations of 216 and 234? Likewise, 3 is also a prime number common to the two factorizations. By contrast, 13 is a prime number that is not common to both factorizations.

$$216 = 2^3 \times 3^3$$
$$234 = 2 \times 3^2 \times 13$$

2 is a prime number common to both factorizations.

3 is a prime number common to both factorizations.

Now we need to use these prime factorizations to determine which exponent is appropriate for 2 and which exponent is appropriate for 3. The appropriate exponent is the smallest exponent associated with the prime number in the factorizations. The exponents associated with 2 in the factorizations are 1 and 3, so we select 1. Therefore, one factor for the greatest common divisor is 2^1, or 2. The exponents associated with 3 in the factorizations are 2 and 3, so we select 2. Therefore, another factor for the greatest common divisor is 3^2.

$$216 = 2^3 \times 3^3$$

Smallest exponent on 2 is 1.

Smallest exponent on 3 is 2.

$$234 = 2^1 \times 3^2 \times 13$$

BLITZER BONUS

Simple Questions with No Answers

In number theory, a good problem is one that can be stated quite simply, but whose solution turns out to be particularly difficult, if not impossible.

In 1742, the mathematician Christian Goldbach (1690–1764) wrote a letter to Leonhard Euler (1707–1783) in which he proposed, without a proof, that every even number greater than 2 is the sum of two primes. For example,

Even number		Sum of two primes
4	=	2 + 2
6	=	3 + 3
8	=	3 + 5
10	=	5 + 5
12	=	7 + 5

and so on.

Two and a half centuries later, it is still not known if this conjecture is true or false. Inductively, it appears to be true; computer searches have written even numbers as large as 400 trillion as the sum of two primes. Deductively, no mathematician has been able to prove that the conjecture is true. Even a reward of one million dollars for a proof offered by the publishing house Farber and Farber in 2000 to help publicize the novel *Uncle Petros and Goldbach's Conjecture* went unclaimed.

Step 3. Form the product of the numbers from step 2. The greatest common divisor is the product of these factors.

$$\text{Greatest common divisor} = 2 \times 3^2 = 2 \times 9 = 18$$

The greatest common divisor of 216 and 234 is 18.

CHECK POINT 3 Find the greatest common divisor of 225 and 825.

4 Solve problems using the greatest common divisor.

BLITZER BONUS

GIMPS

A prime number of the form $2^p - 1$, where p is prime, is called a **Mersenne prime**, named for the seventeenth-century monk Marin Mersenne (1588–1648), who stated that $2^p - 1$ is prime for $p = 2, 3, 5, 7, 13, 17, 19, 31, 67,$ 127, and 257. Without calculators and computers, it is not known how Mersenne arrived at these assertions, although it is now known that $2^p - 1$ is *not* prime for $p = 67$ and 257; it *is* prime for $p = 61$, 89, and 107. In 2006, there were 43 known Mersenne primes: $2^p - 1$ is prime for $p = 2; 3; 5; 7; 13; 17; 19; 31; 61; 89;$ 107; 127; 521; 607; 1279; 2203; 2281; 3217; 4253; 4423; 9689; 9941; 11,213; 19,937; 21,701; 23,209; 44,497; 86,243; 110,503; 132,049; 216,091; 756,839; 859,433; 1,257,787; 1,398,269; 2,976,221; 3,021,377; 6,972,593; 13,466,917; 20,996,011; 24,036,583; 25,964,951; and 30,402,457.

In 1995, the American computer scientist George Woltman began the *Great Internet Mersenne Prime Search* (*GIMPS*). By pooling the combined efforts of thousands of people interested in finding new Mersenne primes, GIMPS's participants have yielded several important results, including the record prime $2^{30,402,457} - 1$, a number with 9,152,052 digits that was discovered in 2006. As of December 2006, there was a $100,000 award to the first person to find a prime number with at least ten million digits.

EXAMPLE 4 SOLVING A PROBLEM USING THE GREATEST COMMON DIVISOR

For an intramural league, you need to divide 40 men and 24 women into all-male and all-female teams so that each team has the same number of people. What is the largest number of people that can be placed on a team?

SOLUTION Because 40 men are to be divided into teams, the number of men on each team must be a divisor of 40. Because 24 women are to be divided into teams, the number of women placed on a team must be a divisor of 24. Although the teams are all-male and all-female, the same number of people must be placed on each team. The largest number of people that can be placed on a team is the largest number that will divide into 40 and 24 without a remainder. This is the greatest common divisor of 40 and 24.

To find the greatest common divisor of 40 and 24, begin with their prime factorizations.

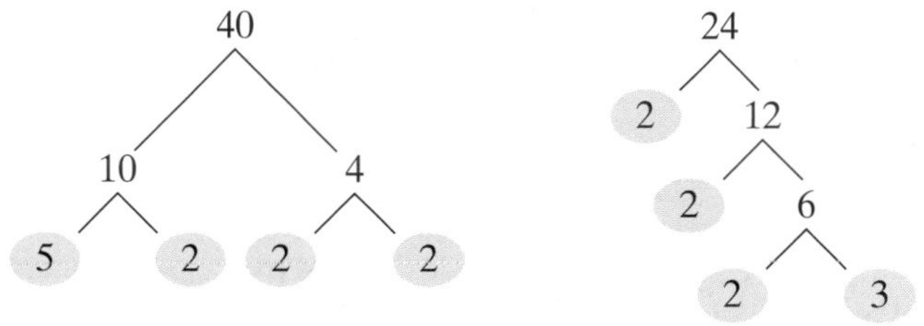

The factor trees indicate that

$$40 = 2^3 \times 5 \quad \text{and} \quad 24 = 2^3 \times 3.$$

We see that 2 is a prime number common to both factorizations. The exponents associated with 2 in the factorizations are 3 and 3, so we select 3.

$$\text{Greatest common divisor} = 2^3 = 2 \times 2 \times 2 = 8$$

The largest number of people that can be placed on a team is 8. Thus, the 40 men can form five teams with 8 men per team. The 24 women can form three teams with 8 women per team.

CHECK POINT 4 A choral director needs to divide 192 men and 288 women into all-male and all-female singing groups so that each group has the same number of people. What is the largest number of people that can be placed in each singing group?

5 Find the least common multiple of two numbers.

Least Common Multiple

The **least common multiple** of two or more natural numbers is the smallest natural number that is divisible by all of the numbers. One way to find the least common multiple is to make a list of the numbers that are divisible by each number. This list represents the **multiples** of each number. For example, if we wish to find the least common multiple of 15 and 20, we can list the sets of multiples of 15 and multiples of 20.

Numbers Divisible by 15:
Multiples of 15: {15, 30, 45, 60, 75, 90, 105, 120, . . . }

Numbers Divisible by 20:
Multiples of 20: {20, 40, 60, 80, 100, 120, 140, 160, . . . }

Some common multiples of 15 and 20 are 60 and 120. The least common multiple is 60. Equivalently, 60 is the smallest number that is divisible by both 15 and 20.

Sometimes a partial list of the multiples for each of two numbers does not reveal the smallest number that is divisible by both given numbers. A more efficient method for finding the least common multiple is to use prime factorizations.

FINDING THE LEAST COMMON MULTIPLE USING PRIME FACTORIZATIONS

To find the least common multiple of two or more numbers,

1. Write the prime factorization of each number.
2. Select every prime factor that occurs, raised to the greatest power to which it occurs, in these factorizations.
3. Form the product of the numbers from step 2. The least common multiple is the product of these factors.

EXAMPLE 5 FINDING THE LEAST COMMON MULTIPLE

Find the least common multiple of 144 and 300.

SOLUTION

Step 1. Write the prime factorization of each number. Write the prime factorizations of 144 and 300.

$$144 = 2^4 \times 3^2$$
$$300 = 2^2 \times 3 \times 5^2$$

Step 2. Select every prime factor that occurs, raised to the greatest power to which it occurs, in these factorizations. The prime factors that occur are 2, 3, and 5. The greatest exponent that appears on 2 is 4, so we select 2^4. The greatest exponent that appears on 3 is 2, so we select 3^2. The greatest exponent that occurs on 5 is 2, so we select 5^2. Thus, we have selected 2^4, 3^2, and 5^2.

Step 3. Form the product of the numbers from step 2. The least common multiple is the product of these factors.

$$\text{Least common multiple} = 2^4 \times 3^2 \times 5^2 = 16 \times 9 \times 25 = 3600$$

The least common multiple of 144 and 300 is 3600. The smallest natural number divisible by 144 and 300 is 3600.

CHECK POINT 5 Find the least common multiple of 18 and 30.

BLITZER BONUS

Palindromic Primes

May a moody baby doom a yam? Leaving aside the answer to this question, what makes the sentence interesting is that it reads the same from left to right and from right to left! Such a sentence is called a **palindrome**. Some prime numbers are also palindromic. For example, the prime number 11 reads the same forward and backward, although a more provocative example containing all ten digits is

1,023,456,987,896,543,201.

In the following pyramid of palindromic primes, each number is obtained by adding two digits to the beginning and end of the previous prime.

2
30203
133020331
1713302033171
12171330203317121
151217133020331712151
1815121713302033171215181
16181512171330203317121518161

The largest known palindromic prime was discovered in 2003 by David Broadhurst, a retired electrical engineer. The number contains 30,803 digits (and, yes, 30,803 is also a palindromic prime!).

Source: Clifford A. Pickover, *A Passion for Mathematics*, John Wiley and Sons, Inc., 2005.

6 Solve problems using the least common multiple.

EXAMPLE 6 SOLVING A PROBLEM USING THE LEAST COMMON MULTIPLE

A movie theater runs its films continuously. One movie runs for 80 minutes and a second runs for 120 minutes. Both movies begin at 4:00 P.M. When will the movies begin again at the same time?

SOLUTION The shorter movie lasts 80 minutes, or 1 hour, 20 minutes. It begins at 4:00, so it will be shown again at 5:20. The longer movie lasts 120 minutes, or 2 hours. It begins at 4:00, so it will be shown again at 6:00. We are asked to find when the movies will begin again at the same time. Therefore, we are looking for the least common multiple of 80 and 120. Find the least common multiple and then add this number of minutes to 4:00 P.M.

Begin with the prime factorizations of 80 and 120:

$$80 = 2^4 \times 5$$
$$120 = 2^3 \times 3 \times 5.$$

Now select each prime factor, with the greatest exponent from each factorization.

$$\text{Least common multiple} = 2^4 \times 3 \times 5 = 16 \times 3 \times 5 = 240$$

Therefore, it will take 240 minutes, or 4 hours, for the movies to begin again at the same time. By adding 4 hours to 4:00 P.M., they will start together again at 8:00 P.M.

STUDY TIP

Example 6 can also be solved by making a partial list of starting times for each movie.

Shorter Movie (Runs 1 hour, 20 minutes):

4:00, 5:20, 6:40, 8:00, . . .

Longer Movie (Runs 2 hours):

4:00, 6:00, 8:00, . . .

The list reveals that both movies start together again at 8:00 P.M.

CHECK POINT 6 A movie theater runs two documentary films continuously. One documentary runs for 40 minutes and a second documentary runs for 60 minutes. Both movies begin at 3:00 P.M. When will the movies begin again at the same time?

EXERCISE SET 5.1

• Practice Exercises

Use rules of divisibility to determine whether each number given in Exercises 1–10 is divisible by

a. 2 **b.** 3 **c.** 4 **d.** 5 **e.** 6
f. 8 **g.** 9 **h.** 10 **i.** 12.

1. 6944 **2.** 7245 **3.** 21,408 **4.** 25,025
5. 26,428 **6.** 89,001 **7.** 374,832 **8.** 347,712
9. 6,126,120 **10.** 5,941,221

In Exercises 11–24, use a calculator to determine whether each statement is true or false. If the statement is true, explain why this is so using one of the rules of divisibility in Table 5.1 on page 229.

11. $3|5958$ **12.** $3|8142$ **13.** $4|10{,}612$
14. $4|15{,}984$ **15.** $5|38{,}814$ **16.** $5|48{,}659$
17. $6|104{,}538$ **18.** $6|163{,}944$ **19.** $8|20{,}104$
20. $8|28{,}096$ **21.** $9|11{,}378$ **22.** $9|23{,}772$
23. $12|517{,}872$ **24.** $12|785{,}172$

In Exercises 25–44, find the prime factorization of each composite number.

25. 75 **26.** 45 **27.** 56 **28.** 48
29. 105 **30.** 180 **31.** 500 **32.** 360
33. 663 **34.** 510 **35.** 885 **36.** 999
37. 1440 **38.** 1280 **39.** 1996 **40.** 1575
41. 3675 **42.** 8316 **43.** 85,800 **44.** 30,600

In Exercises 45–56, find the greatest common divisor of the numbers.

45. 42 and 56 **46.** 25 and 70 **47.** 16 and 42
48. 66 and 90 **49.** 60 and 108 **50.** 96 and 212
51. 72 and 120 **52.** 220 and 400 **53.** 342 and 380
54. 224 and 430 **55.** 240 and 285 **56.** 150 and 480

In Exercises 57–68, find the least common multiple of the numbers.

57. 42 and 56 **58.** 25 and 70 **59.** 16 and 42
60. 66 and 90 **61.** 60 and 108 **62.** 96 and 212
63. 72 and 120 **64.** 220 and 400 **65.** 342 and 380
66. 224 and 430 **67.** 240 and 285 **68.** 150 and 480

• Practice Plus

In Exercises 69–74, determine all values of d that make each statement true.

69. $9|12{,}34d$ **70.** $9|23{,}42d$ **71.** $8|76{,}523{,}45d$
72. $8|88{,}888{,}82d$ **73.** $4|963{,}23d$ **74.** $4|752{,}67d$

A **perfect number** *is a natural number that is equal to the sum of its factors, excluding the number itself. In Exercises 75–78, determine whether or not each number is perfect.*

75. 28 **76.** 6 **77.** 20 **78.** 50

A prime number is an **emirp** *("prime" spelled backward) if it becomes a different prime number when its digits are reversed. In Exercises 79–82, determine whether or not each prime number is an emirp.*

79. 41 **80.** 43 **81.** 107 **82.** 113

A prime number p such that $2p + 1$ is also a prime number is called a **Germain prime**, *named after the German mathematician Sophie Germain (1776–1831), who made major contributions to number theory. In Exercises 83–86, determine whether or not each prime number is a Germain prime.*

83. 13 **84.** 11 **85.** 241 **86.** 97

87. Find the product of the greatest common divisor of 24 and 27 and the least common multiple of 24 and 27. Compare this result to the product of 24 and 27. Write a conjecture based on your observation.

88. Find the product of the greatest common divisor of 48 and 72 and the least common multiple of 48 and 72. Compare this result to the product of 48 and 72. Write a conjecture based on your observation.

• Application Exercises

89. In Carl Sagan's novel *Contact*, Ellie Arroway, the book's heroine, has been working at SETI, the Search for Extraterrestrial Intelligence, listening to the crackle of the cosmos. One night, as the radio telescopes are turned toward Vega, they suddenly pick up strange pulses through the background noise. Two pulses are followed by a pause, then three pulses, five, seven,

11, 13, 17, 19, 23, 29, 31, . . .

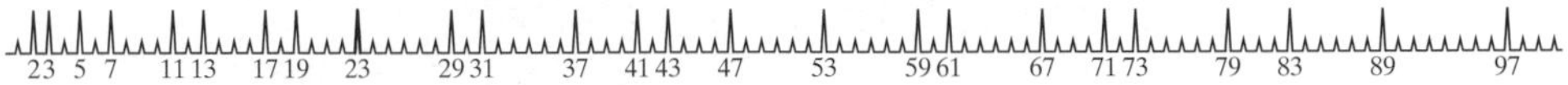

continuing through 97. Then it starts all over again. Ellie is convinced that only intelligent life could generate the structure in the sequence of pulses. "It's hard to imagine some radiating plasma sending out a regular set of mathematical signals like this." What is it about the structure of the pulses that the book's heroine recognizes as the sign of intelligent life? Asked in another way, what is significant about the number of pulses?

90. There are two species of insects, *Magicicada septendecim* and *Magicicada tredecim*, that live in the same environment. They have a life cycle of exactly 17 and 13 years, respectively. For all but their last year, they remain in the ground feeding on the sap of tree roots. Then, in their last year, they emerge en masse from the ground as fully formed cricketlike insects, taking over the forest in a single night. They chirp loudly, mate, eat, lay eggs, then die six weeks later.

(*Source:* Marcus du Sautoy, *The Music of the Primes*, HarperCollins, 2003)

a. Suppose that the two species have life cycles that are not prime, say 18 and 12 years, respectively. List the set of multiples of 18 that are less than or equal to 216. List the set of multiples of 12 that are less than or equal to 216. Over a 216-year period, how many times will the two species emerge in the same year and compete to share the forest?

b. Recall that both species have evolved prime-number life cycles, 17 and 13 years, respectively. Find the least common multiple of 17 and 13. How often will the two species have to share the forest?

c. Compare your answers to parts (a) and (b). What explanation can you offer for each species having a prime number of years as the length of its life cycle?

91. A relief worker needs to divide 300 bottles of water and 144 cans of food into groups that each contain the same number of items. Also, each group must have the same type of item (bottled water or canned food). What is the largest number of relief supplies that can be put in each group?

92. A choral director needs to divide 180 men and 144 women into all-male and all-female singing groups so that each group has the same number of people. What is the largest number of people that can be placed in each singing group?

93. You have in front of you 310 five-dollar bills and 460 ten-dollar bills. Your problem: Place the five-dollar bills and the ten-dollar bills in stacks so that each stack has the same number of bills, and each stack contains only one kind of bill (five-dollar or ten-dollar). What is the largest number of bills that you can place in each stack?

94. Harley collects sports cards. He has 360 football cards and 432 baseball cards. Harley plans to arrange his cards in stacks so that each stack has the same number of cards. Also, each stack must have the same type of card (football or baseball). Every card in Harley's collection is to be placed in one of the stacks. What is the largest number of cards that can be placed in each stack?

95. You and your brother both work the 4:00 P.M. to midnight shift. You have every sixth night off. Your brother has every tenth night off. Both of you were off on June 1. Your brother would like to see a movie with you. When will the two of you have the same night off again?

96. A movie theater runs its films continuously. One movie is a short documentary that runs for 40 minutes. The other movie is a full-length feature that runs for 100 minutes. Each film is shown in a separate theater. Both movies begin at noon. When will the movies begin again at the same time?

97. Two people are jogging around a circular track in the same direction. One person can run completely around the track in 15 minutes. The second person takes 18 minutes. If they both start running in the same place at the same time, how long will it take them to be together at this place if they continue to run?

98. Two people are in a bicycle race around a circular track. One rider can race completely around the track in 40 seconds. The other rider takes 45 seconds. If they both begin the race at a designated starting point, how long will it take them to be together at this starting point again if they continue to race around the track?

• Writing in Mathematics

99. If a is a factor of c, what does this mean?

100. Why is 45 divisible by 5?

101. What does "a is divisible by b" mean?

102. Describe the difference between a prime number and a composite number.

103. What does the Fundamental Theorem of Arithmetic state?

104. What is the greatest common divisor of two or more natural numbers?

105. Describe how to find the greatest common divisor of two numbers.

106. What is the least common multiple of two or more natural numbers?

107. Describe how to find the least common multiple of two natural numbers.

108. The process of finding the greatest common divisor of two natural numbers is similar to finding the least common multiple of the numbers. Describe how the two processes differ.

109. What does the Blitzer Bonus on page 232 have to do with Gödel's discovery about mathematics and logic, described on page 163?

• Critical Thinking Exercises

110. Write a four-digit natural number that is divisible by 4 and not by 8.

111. Find the greatest common divisor and the least common multiple of $2^{17} \cdot 3^{25} \cdot 5^{31}$ and $2^{14} \cdot 3^{37} \cdot 5^{30}$. Express answers in the same form as the numbers given.

112. A middle-age man observed that his present age was a prime number. He also noticed that the number of years in which his age would again be prime was equal to the number of years ago in which his age was prime. How old is the man?

113. A movie theater runs its films continuously. One movie runs for 85 minutes and a second runs for 100 minutes. The theater has a 15-minute intermission after each movie, at which point the movie is shown again. If both movies start at noon, when will the two movies start again at the same time?

114. The difference between consecutive prime numbers is always an even number, except for two particular prime numbers. What are those numbers?

• Technology Exercises

Use the divisibility rules listed in Table 5.1 on page 229 to answer the questions in Exercises 115–117. Then, using a calculator, perform the actual division to determine whether your answer is correct.

115. Is 67,234,096 divisible by 4?

116. Is 12,541,750 divisible by 3?

117. Is 48,201,651 divisible by 9?

• Group Exercises

The following topics from number theory are appropriate for either individual or group research projects. A report should be given to the class on the researched topic. Useful references include liberal arts mathematics textbooks, books about numbers and number theory, books whose purpose is to excite the reader about mathematics, history of mathematics books, encyclopedias, and the World Wide Web.

118. Euclid and Number Theory

119. An Unsolved Problem from Number Theory

120. Perfect Numbers

121. Deficient and Abundant Numbers

122. Formulas that Yield Primes

123. The Sieve of Eratosthenes

SECTION 5.2 • THE INTEGERS; ORDER OF OPERATIONS

OBJECTIVES

1. Define the integers.
2. Graph integers on a number line.
3. Use the symbols < and >.
4. Find the absolute value of an integer.
5. Perform operations with integers.
6. Use the order of operations agreement.

From the political left and right, watchdogs of the federal budget are warning of fiscal trouble. David Walker, Comptroller General of the United States and the nation's top auditor, admits to being "terrified" about the budget deficit in coming decades. To hear him tell it, the United States can be likened to Rome before the fall of the empire. America's financial condition is "worse than advertised," he says. It has a "broken business model. It faces deficits in its budget, its balance of payments, and its savings." In this section, we use operations on a set of numbers called the *integers* to describe numerically the sad state of the nation's finances.

1 Define the integers.

Defining the Integers

In Section 5.1, we applied some ideas of number theory to the set of natural, or counting, numbers:

$$\text{Natural numbers} = \{1, 2, 3, 4, 5, \ldots\}.$$

When we combine the number 0 with the natural numbers, we obtain the set of **whole numbers**:

$$\text{Whole numbers} = \{0, 1, 2, 3, 4, 5, \ldots\}.$$

The whole numbers do not allow us to describe certain everyday situations. For example, if the balance in your checking account is \$30 and you write a check for \$35, your checking account is overdrawn by \$5. We can write this as −5, read *negative* 5. The set consisting of the natural numbers, 0, and the negatives of the natural numbers is called the set of **integers**.

$$\text{Integers} = \{\underbrace{\ldots, -4, -3, -2, -1}_{\substack{\text{Negative}\\ \text{integers}}}, 0, \underbrace{1, 2, 3, 4, \ldots}_{\substack{\text{Positive}\\ \text{integers}}}\}$$

Notice that the term *positive integers* is another name for the natural numbers. The positive integers can be written in two ways:

1. Use a "+" sign. For example, +4 is "positive four."
2. Do not write any sign. For example, 4 is assumed to be "positive four."

The Number Line; The Symbols < and >

The **number line** is a graph we use to visualize the set of integers, as well as sets of other numbers. The number line is shown in Figure 5.1.

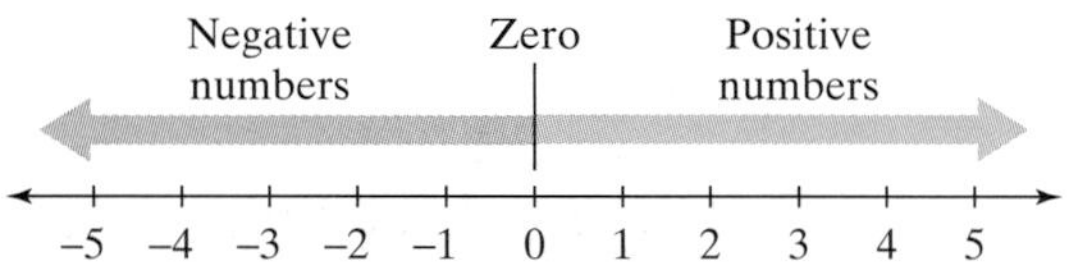

FIGURE 5.1 The number line

The number line extends indefinitely in both directions, shown by the arrows on the left and the right. Zero separates the positive numbers from the negative numbers on the number line. The positive integers are located to the right of 0 and the negative integers are located to the left of 0. **Zero is neither positive nor negative.** For every positive integer on a number line, there is a corresponding negative integer on the opposite side of 0.

2 Graph integers on a number line.

Integers are graphed on a number line by placing a dot at the correct location for each number.

EXAMPLE 1 GRAPHING INTEGERS ON A NUMBER LINE

Graph: **a.** −3 **b.** 4 **c.** 0.

SOLUTION Place a dot at the correct location for each integer.

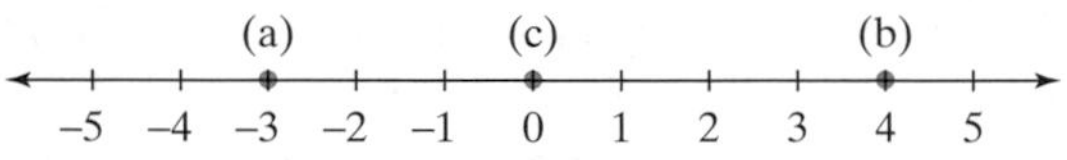

CHECK POINT 1 Graph:

a. −4 **b.** 0 **c.** 3.

3 Use the symbols $<$ and $>$.

We will use the following symbols for comparing two integers:

$<$ means "is less than."

$>$ means "is greater than."

On the number line, the integers increase from left to right. The *lesser* of two integers is the one farther to the *left* on a number line. The *greater* of two integers is the one farther to the *right* on a number line.

Look at the number line in Figure 5.2. The integers -4 and -1 are graphed.

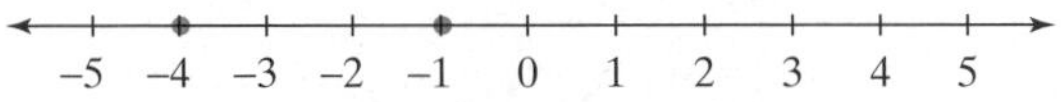

FIGURE 5.2

Observe that -4 is to the left of -1 on the number line. This means that -4 is less than -1.

$$-4 < -1$$

-4 is less than -1 because -4 is to the **left** of -1 on the number line.

In Figure 5.2, we can also observe that -1 is to the right of -4 on the number line. This means that -1 is greater than -4.

$$-1 > -4$$

-1 is greater than -4 because -1 is to the **right** of -4 on the number line.

The symbols $<$ and $>$ are called **inequality symbols**. These symbols always point to the lesser of the two real numbers when the inequality statement is true.

-4 is less than -1. $\quad -4 < -1 \quad$ The symbol points to -4, the lesser number.

-1 is greater than -4. $\quad -1 > -4 \quad$ The symbol still points to -4, the lesser number.

EXAMPLE 2 USING THE SYMBOLS $<$ AND $>$

Insert either $<$ or $>$ in the shaded area between the integers to make each statement true:

a. -4 ■ 3 **b.** -1 ■ -5 **c.** -5 ■ -2 **d.** 0 ■ -3.

SOLUTION The solution is illustrated by the number line in Figure 5.3.

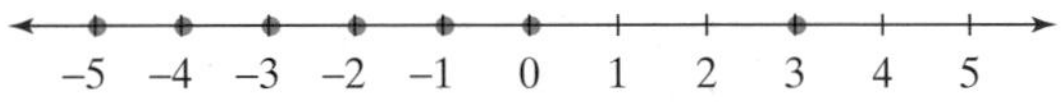

FIGURE 5.3

a. $-4 < 3$ (negative 4 is less than 3) because -4 is to the left of 3 on the number line.

b. $-1 > -5$ (negative 1 is greater than negative 5) because -1 is to the right of -5 on the number line.

c. $-5 < -2$ (negative 5 is less than negative 2) because -5 is to the left of -2 on the number line.

d. $0 > -3$ (zero is greater than negative 3) because 0 is to the right of -3 on the number line.

STUDY TIP

You can think of negative integers as amounts of money that you *owe*. It's better to owe less, so

$$-1 > -5.$$

CHECK POINT 2 Insert either $<$ or $>$ in the shaded area between the integers to make each statement true:

a. 6 ■ -7 **b.** -8 ■ -1 **c.** -25 ■ -2 **d.** -14 ■ 0.

The symbols $<$ and $>$ may be combined with an equal sign, as shown in the following table:

This inequality is true if either the < part or the = part is true.

This inequality is true if either the > part or the = part is true.

Symbols	Meaning	Examples	Explanation
$a \le b$	a is less than or equal to b.	$2 \le 9$ $9 \le 9$	Because $2 < 9$ Because $9 = 9$
$b \ge a$	b is greater than or equal to a.	$9 \ge 2$ $2 \ge 2$	Because $9 > 2$ Because $2 = 2$

4 Find the absolute value of an integer.

Absolute Value

Absolute value describes distance from 0 on a number line. If a represents an integer, the symbol $|a|$, represents its absolute value, read "the absolute value of a." For example,

$$|-5| = 5.$$

The absolute value of -5 is 5 because -5 is 5 units from 0 on a number line.

ABSOLUTE VALUE

The **absolute value** of an integer a, denoted by $|a|$, is the distance from 0 to a on the number line. Because absolute value describes a distance, it is never negative.

EXAMPLE 3 FINDING ABSOLUTE VALUE

Find the absolute value:

a. $|-3|$ **b.** $|5|$ **c.** $|0|$.

SOLUTION

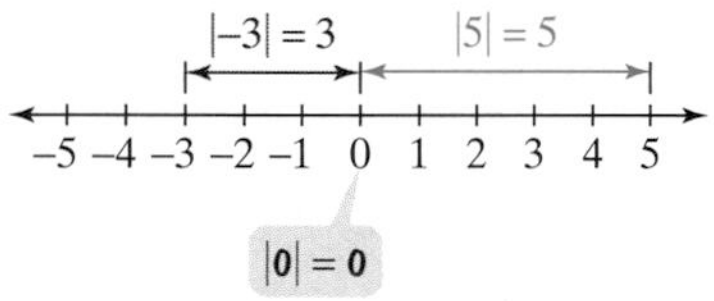

a. $|-3| = 3$ The absolute value of -3 is 3 because -3 is 3 units from 0.

b. $|5| = 5$ 5 is 5 units from 0.

c. $|0| = 0$ 0 is 0 units from itself.

Example 3 illustrates that the absolute value of a positive integer or 0 is the number itself. The absolute value of a negative integer, such as -3, is the number without the negative sign. Zero is the only real number whose absolute value is 0: $|0| = 0$. **The absolute value of any integer other than 0 is always positive.**

CHECK POINT 3 Find the absolute value:

a. $|-8|$ **b.** $|6|$.

5 Perform operations with integers.

Addition of Integers

It has not been a good day! First, you lost your wallet with \$30 in it. Then, you borrowed \$10 to get through the day, which you somehow misplaced. Your loss of \$30 followed by a loss of \$10 is an overall loss of \$40. This can be written

$$-30 + (-10) = -40.$$

The result of adding two or more numbers is called the **sum** of the numbers. The sum of -30 and -10 is -40.

You can think of gains and losses of money to find sums. For example, to find $17 + (-13)$, think of a gain of \$17 followed by a loss of \$13. There is an overall gain of \$4. Thus, $17 + (-13) = 4$. In the same way, to find $-17 + 13$, think of a loss of \$17 followed by a gain of \$13. There is an overall loss of \$4, so $-17 + 13 = -4$.

Using gains and losses, we can develop the following rules for adding integers:

RULES FOR ADDITION OF INTEGERS

Rule | **Examples**

If the integers have the same sign,

1. Add their absolute values.
2. The sign of the sum is the same as the sign of the two numbers.

$-11 + (-15) = -26$

Add absolute values: $11 + 15 = 26$.

Use the common sign.

If the integers have different signs,

1. Subtract the smaller absolute value from the larger absolute value.
2. The sign of the sum is the same as the sign of the number with the larger absolute value.

$-13 + 4 = -9$

Subtract absolute values: $13 - 4 = 9$.

Use the sign of the number with the greater absolute value.

$13 + (-6) = 7$

Subtract absolute values: $13 - 6 = 7$.

Use the sign of the number with the greater absolute value.

TECHNOLOGY

CALCULATORS AND ADDING INTEGERS

You can use a calculator to add integers. Here are the keystrokes for finding $-11 + (-15)$:

SCIENTIFIC CALCULATOR

11 [+/−] [+] 15 [+/−] [=]

GRAPHING CALCULATOR

[(−)] 11 [+] [(−)] 15 [ENTER].

Here are the keystrokes for finding $-13 + 4$:

SCIENTIFIC CALCULATOR

13 [+/−] [+] 4 [=]

GRAPHING CALCULATOR

[(−)] 13 [+] 4 [ENTER].

STUDY TIP

In addition to gains and losses of money, another good analogy for adding integers is temperatures above and below zero on a thermometer. Think of the thermometer as a number line standing straight up. For example,

$$-11 + (-15) = -26$$

If it's 11 below zero and the temperature falls 15 degrees, it will then be 26 below zero.

$$-13 + 4 = -9$$

If it's 13 below zero and the temperature rises 4 degrees, the new temperature will be 9 below zero.

$$13 + (-6) = 7.$$

If it's 13 above zero and the temperature falls 6 degrees, it will then be 7 above zero.

Using the analogies of gains and losses of money or temperatures can make the formal rules for addition of integers easy to use.

Can you guess what number is displayed if you use a calculator to find a sum such as $18 + (-18)$? If you gain 18 and then lose 18, there is neither an overall gain or loss. Thus,

$$18 + (-18) = 0.$$

We call 18 and -18 **additive inverses**. Additive inverses have the same absolute value, but lie on opposite sides of zero on the number line. Thus, -7 is the additive inverse of 7, and 5 is the additive inverse of -5. In general, the sum of any integer and its additive inverse is 0:

$$a + (-a) = 0.$$

Subtraction of Integers

Suppose that a computer that normally sells for \$1500 has a price reduction of \$600. The computer's reduced price, \$900, can be expressed in two ways:

$$1500 - 600 = 900 \quad \text{or} \quad 1500 + (-600) = 900.$$

This means that

$$1500 - 600 = 1500 + (-600).$$

To subtract 600 from 1500, we add 1500 and the additive inverse of 600. Generalizing from this situation, we define subtraction as follows:

> **DEFINITION OF SUBTRACTION**
> For all integers a and b,
> $$a - b = a + (-b).$$
> In words, to subtract b from a, add the additive inverse of b to a. The result of subtraction is called the **difference**.

EXAMPLE 4 SUBTRACTING INTEGERS

Subtract:

a. $17 - (-11)$ **b.** $-18 - (-5)$ **c.** $-18 - 5$.

SOLUTION

a. $17 - (-11) = 17 + 11 = 28$

Change the subtraction to addition. Replace −11 with its additive inverse.

b. $-18 - (-5) = -18 + 5 = -13$

Change the subtraction to addition. Replace −5 with its additive inverse.

c. $-18 - 5 = -18 + (-5) = -23$

Change the subtraction to addition. Replace 5 with its additive inverse.

CHECK POINT 4 Subtract:

a. $30 - (-7)$ **b.** $-14 - (-10)$ **c.** $-14 - 10$.

STUDY TIP

You can think of subtracting a negative integer as taking away a debt. Let's apply this analogy to $17 - (-11)$. Your checking account balance is \$17 after an erroneous \$11 charge was made against your account. When you bring this error to the bank's attention, they will take away the \$11 debit and your balance will go up to \$28:

$$17 - (-11) = 28.$$

TECHNOLOGY

CALCULATORS AND SUBTRACTING INTEGERS

You can use a calculator to subtract integers. Here are the keystrokes for finding $17 - (-11)$:

SCIENTIFIC CALCULATOR

17 [−] 11 [+/−] [=]

GRAPHING CALCULATOR

17 [−] [(−)] 11 [ENTER].

Here are the keystrokes for finding $-18 - (-5)$:

SCIENTIFIC CALCULATOR

18 [+/−] [−] 5 [+/−] [=]

GRAPHING CALCULATOR

[(−)] 18 [−] [(−)] 5 [ENTER].

Don't confuse the subtraction key on a graphing calculator, [−], with the sign change or additive inverse key, [(−)]. What happens if you do?

Subtraction is used to solve problems in which the word *difference* appears. The difference between integers a and b is expressed as $a - b$.

EXAMPLE 5 AN APPLICATION OF SUBTRACTION USING THE WORD *DIFFERENCE*

The bar graph in Figure 5.4 shows the budget surplus or deficit for the United States government from 2000 through 2005. What is the difference between the 2000 surplus and the 2005 deficit?

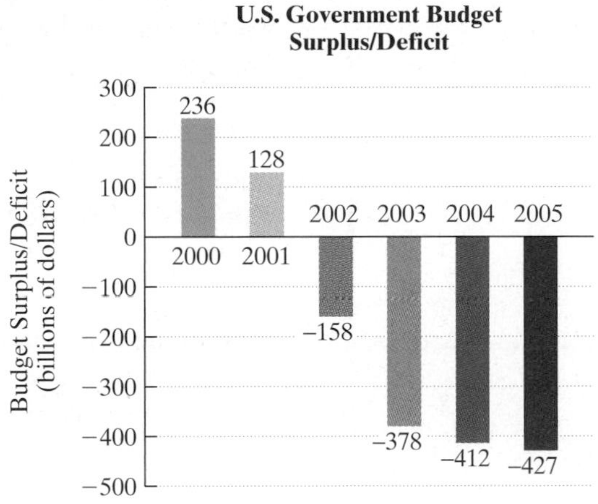

FIGURE 5.4
Source: Budget of the U.S. Government

SOLUTION

The difference | is | the 2000 surplus | minus | the 2005 deficit.

$$= 236 - (-427)$$
$$= 236 + 427 = 663$$

The difference between the 2000 surplus and the 2005 deficit is \$663 billion.

CHECK POINT 5 Use Figure 5.4 to find the difference between the 2004 deficit and the 2005 deficit.

Multiplication of Integers

The result of multiplying two or more numbers is called the **product** of the numbers. You can think of multiplication as repeated addition or subtraction that starts at 0. For example,

$$3(-4) = 0 + (-4) + (-4) + (-4) = -12$$

The numbers have different signs and the product is negative.

and

$$(-3)(-4) = 0 - (-4) - (-4) - (-4) = 0 + 4 + 4 + 4 = 12.$$

The numbers have the same sign and the product is positive.

These observations give us the following rules for multiplying integers:

RULES FOR MULTIPLYING INTEGERS

Rule	Examples
1. The product of two integers with different signs is found by multiplying their absolute values. The product is negative.	• $7(-5) = -35$
2. The product of two integers with the same sign is found by multiplying their absolute values. The product is positive.	• $(-6)(-11) = 66$
3. The product of 0 and any integer is 0: $a \cdot 0 = 0$ and $0 \cdot a = 0$.	• $-17(0) = 0$
4. If no number is 0, a product with an odd number of negative factors is found by multiplying absolute values. The product is negative.	• $-2(-3)(-5) = -30$ Three (odd) negative factors
5. If no number is 0, a product with an even number of negative factors is found by multiplying absolute values. The product is positive.	• $-2(3)(-5) = 30$ Two (even) negative factors

Exponential Notation

Because exponents indicate repeated multiplication, rules for multiplying real numbers can be used to evaluate exponential expressions.

EXAMPLE 6 EVALUATING EXPONENTIAL EXPRESSIONS

Evaluate: **a.** $(-6)^2$ **b.** -6^2 **c.** $(-5)^3$ **d.** $(-2)^4$.

SOLUTION

a. $(-6)^2 = (-6)(-6) = 36$

Base is −6. Same signs give positive product.

b. $-6^2 = -(6 \cdot 6) = -36$

Base is 6. The negative is not inside parentheses and is not taken to the second power.

c. $(-5)^3 = (-5)(-5)(-5) = -125$

An odd number of negative factors gives a negative product.

d. $(-2)^4 = (-2)(-2)(-2)(-2) = 16$

An even number of negative factors gives a positive product.

CHECK POINT 6 Evaluate:

a. $(-5)^2$ **b.** -5^2 **c.** $(-4)^3$ **d.** $(-3)^4$.

BLITZER BONUS

Exponential Representations of the Beast

The New Testament book of Revelation designates 666 as the Number of the Beast (the Antichrist):

> "Here is wisdom. Let him that hath understanding count the number of the beast: for it is the number of a man; and his number is six hundred threescore and six." (Revelation 13:18)

Although your author has no idea of what this actually means, he is intrigued by the beast's curious exponential representations:

$$666 = 6 + 6 + 6 + 6^3 + 6^3 + 6^3$$

$$666 = 1^3 + 2^3 + 3^3 + 4^3 + 5^3 + 6^3 + 5^3 + 4^3 + 3^3 + 2^3 + 1^3$$

$$666 = 2^2 + 3^2 + 5^2 + 7^2 + 11^2 + 13^2 + 17^2$$

Sum of the squares of the first seven prime numbers

$$666 = 1^6 - 2^6 + 3^6.$$

The beast is even interesting in Roman numerals:

$$666 = \text{DCLXVI}.$$

Contains all Roman numerals from D(500) to I (1) in decending order

Division of Integers

The result of dividing the integer a by the nonzero integer b is called the **quotient** of the numbers. We can write this quotient as $a \div b$ or $\frac{a}{b}$.

A relationship exists between multiplication and division. For example,

$$\frac{-12}{4} = -3 \text{ means that } 4(-3) = -12.$$

$$\frac{-12}{-4} = 3 \text{ means that } -4(3) = -12.$$

Because of the relationship between multiplication and division, the rules for obtaining the sign of a quotient are the same as those for obtaining the sign of a product.

RULES FOR DIVIDING INTEGERS

Rule	Examples
1. The quotient of two integers with different signs is found by dividing their absolute values. The quotient is negative.	• $\frac{80}{-4} = -20$ • $\frac{-15}{5} = -3$
2. The quotient of two integers with the same sign is found by dividing their absolute values. The quotient is positive.	• $\frac{27}{9} = 3$ • $\frac{-45}{-3} = 15$
3. Zero divided by any nonzero integer is zero.	• $\frac{0}{-5} = 0$ (because $-5(0) = 0$)
4. Division by 0 is undefined.	• $\frac{-8}{0}$ is undefined (because 0 cannot be multiplied by an integer to obtain -8).

TECHNOLOGY

MULTIPLYING AND DIVIDING ON A CALCULATOR

Example: $(-173)(-256)$

SCIENTIFIC CALCULATOR

173 [+/−] [×] 256 [+/−] [=]

GRAPHING CALCULATOR

[(−)] 173 [×] [(−)] 256 [ENTER]

The number 44288 should be displayed.

Division is performed in the same manner, using [÷] instead of [×]. What happens when you divide by 0? Try entering

8 [÷] 0

and pressing [=] or [ENTER].

6 Use the order of operations agreement.

Order of Operations

Suppose that you want to find the value of $3 + 7 \cdot 5$. Which procedure shown below is correct?

$$3 + 7 \cdot 5 = 3 + 35 = 38 \quad \text{or} \quad 3 + 7 \cdot 5 = 10 \cdot 5 = 50$$

If you know the answer, you probably know certain rules, called the **order of operations**, to make sure that there is only one correct answer. One of these rules states that if a problem contains no parentheses, perform multiplication before addition. Thus, the procedure on the left is correct because the multiplication of 7 and 5 is done first. Then the addition is performed. The correct answer is 38.

Here are the rules for determining the order in which operations should be performed:

STUDY TIP

Here's a sentence to help remember the order of operations: "Please excuse my dear Aunt Sally."

Please	**P**arentheses
Excuse	**E**xponents
My	**M**ultiplication
Dear	**D**ivision
Aunt	**A**ddition
Sally	**S**ubtraction

ORDER OF OPERATIONS

1. Perform all operations within grouping symbols.
2. Evaluate all exponential expressions.
3. Do all multiplications and divisions in the order in which they occur, working from left to right.
4. Finally, do all additions and subtractions in the order in which they occur, working from left to right.

In the third step, be sure to do all multiplications and divisions *as they occur* from left to right. For example,

$$8 \div 4 \cdot 2 = 2 \cdot 2 = 4$$

Do the division first because it occurs first.

$$8 \cdot 4 \div 2 = 32 \div 2 = 16.$$

Do the multiplication first because it occurs first.

EXAMPLE 7 USING THE ORDER OF OPERATIONS

Simplify: $6^2 - 24 \div 2^2 \cdot 3 + 1$.

SOLUTION There are no grouping symbols. Thus, we begin by evaluating exponential expressions. Then we multiply or divide. Finally, we add or subtract.

$6^2 - 24 \div 2^2 \cdot 3 + 1$

$= 36 - 24 \div 4 \cdot 3 + 1$ — Evaluate exponential expressions: $6^2 = 6 \cdot 6 = 36$ and $2^2 = 2 \cdot 2 = 4$.

$= 36 - 6 \cdot 3 + 1$ — Perform the multiplications and divisions from left to right. Start with $24 \div 4 = 6$.

$= 36 - 18 + 1$ — Now do the multiplication: $6 \cdot 3 = 18$.

$= 18 + 1$ — Finally, perform the additions and subtractions from left to right. Subtract: $36 - 18 = 18$.

$= 19$ — Add: $18 + 1 = 19$.

CHECK POINT 7 Simplify: $7^2 - 48 \div 4^2 \cdot 5 + 2$.

EXAMPLE 8 USING THE ORDER OF OPERATIONS

Simplify: $(-6)^2 - (5 - 7)^2(-3)$.

SOLUTION Because grouping symbols appear, we perform the operation within parentheses first.

$(-6)^2 - (5 - 7)^2(-3)$

$= (-6)^2 - (-2)^2(-3)$ Work inside parentheses first: $5 - 7 = 5 + (-7) = -2$.

$= 36 - 4(-3)$ Evaluate exponential expressions: $(-6)^2 = (-6)(-6) = 36$ and $(-2)^2 = (-2)(-2) = 4$.

$= 36 - (-12)$ Multiply: $4(-3) = -12$.

$= 48$ Subtract: $36 - (-12) = 36 + 12 = 48$.

CHECK POINT 8 Simplify $(-8)^2 - (10 - 13)^2(-2)$.

EXERCISE SET 5.2

• Practice Exercises

In Exercises 1–4, start by drawing a number line that shows integers from −5 to 5. Then graph each of the following integers on your number line.

1. 3 **2.** 5 **3.** −4 **4.** −2

In Exercises 5–12, insert either < or > in the shaded area between the integers to make the statement true.

5. −2 ■ 7 **6.** −1 ■ 13 **7.** −13 ■ −2 **8.** −1 ■ −13
9. 8 ■ −50 **10.** 7 ■ −9 **11.** −100 ■ 0 **12.** 0 ■ −300

In Exercises 13–18, find the absolute value.

13. $|-14|$ **14.** $|-16|$ **15.** $|14|$
16. $|16|$ **17.** $|-300{,}000|$ **18.** $|-1{,}000{,}000|$

In Exercises 19–30, find each sum.

19. $-7 + (-5)$ **20.** $-3 + (-4)$ **21.** $12 + (-8)$
22. $13 + (-5)$ **23.** $6 + (-9)$ **24.** $3 + (-11)$
25. $-9 + (+4)$ **26.** $-7 + (+3)$ **27.** $-9 + (-9)$
28. $-13 + (-13)$ **29.** $9 + (-9)$ **30.** $13 + (-13)$

In Exercises 31–42, perform the indicated subtraction.

31. $13 - 8$ **32.** $14 - 3$ **33.** $8 - 15$
34. $9 - 20$ **35.** $4 - (-10)$ **36.** $3 - (-17)$
37. $-6 - (-17)$ **38.** $-4 - (-19)$ **39.** $-12 - (-3)$
40. $-19 - (-2)$ **41.** $-11 - 17$ **42.** $-19 - 21$

In Exercises 43–52, find each product.

43. $6(-9)$ **44.** $5(-7)$ **45.** $(-7)(-3)$
46. $(-8)(-5)$ **47.** $(-2)(6)$ **48.** $(-3)(10)$
49. $(-13)(-1)$ **50.** $(-17)(-1)$ **51.** $0(-5)$
52. $0(-8)$

In Exercises 53–66, evaluate each exponential expression.

53. 5^2 **54.** 6^2 **55.** $(-5)^2$ **56.** $(-6)^2$
57. 4^3 **58.** 2^3 **59.** $(-5)^3$ **60.** $(-4)^3$
61. $(-5)^4$ **62.** $(-4)^4$ **63.** -3^4 **64.** -1^4
65. $(-3)^4$ **66.** $(-1)^4$

In Exercises 67–80, find each quotient, or, if applicable, state that the expression is undefined.

67. $\frac{-12}{4}$ **68.** $\frac{-40}{5}$ **69.** $\frac{21}{-3}$ **70.** $\frac{60}{-6}$
71. $\frac{-90}{-3}$ **72.** $\frac{-66}{-6}$ **73.** $\frac{0}{-7}$ **74.** $\frac{0}{-8}$
75. $\frac{-7}{0}$ **76.** $\frac{0}{0}$
77. $(-480) \div 24$ **78.** $(-300) \div 12$
79. $(465) \div (-15)$ **80.** $(-594) \div (-18)$

In Exercises 81–98, use the order of operations to find the value of each expression.

81. $7 + 6 \cdot 3$ **82.** $-5 + (-3) \cdot 8$
83. $(-5) - 6(-3)$ **84.** $-8(-3) - 5(-6)$
85. $6 - 4(-3) - 5$ **86.** $3 - 7(-1) - 6$
87. $3 - 5(-4 - 2)$ **88.** $3 - 9(-1 - 6)$
89. $(2 - 6)(-3 - 5)$ **90.** $9 - 5(6 - 4) - 10$
91. $3(-2)^2 - 4(-3)^2$ **92.** $5(-3)^2 - 2(-2)^3$
93. $(2 - 6)^2 - (3 - 7)^2$ **94.** $(4 - 6)^2 - (5 - 9)^3$
95. $6(3 - 5)^3 - 2(1 - 3)^3$
96. $-3(-6 + 8)^3 - 5(-3 + 5)^3$
97. $8^2 - 16 \div 2^2 \cdot 4 - 3$
98. $10^2 - 100 \div 5^2 \cdot 2 - (-3)$

• Practice Plus

In Exercises 99–104, use the order of operations to find the value of each expression.

99. $8 - 3[-2(2 - 5) - 4(8 - 6)]$

100. $8 - 3[-2(5 - 7) - 5(4 - 2)]$

101. $-2^2 + 4[16 \div (3 - 5)]$

102. $-3^2 + 2[20 \div (7 - 11)]$

103. $4|10 - (8 - 20)|$

104. $-5|7 - (20 - 8)|$

In Exercises 105–108, express each sentence as a single numerical expression. Then use the order of operations to simplify the expression.

105. Cube -2. Subtract this exponential expression from -10.

106. Cube -5. Subtract this exponential expression from -100.

107. Subtract 10 from 7. Multiply this difference by 2. Square this product.

108. Subtract 11 from 9. Multiply this difference by 2. Raise this product to the fourth power.

• Application Exercises

The bar graph shows the U.S. trade balance in goods and services, in billions of dollars, from 2000 through 2005. The most complete scorecard of the U.S. international trade performance deteriorated to a record \$805 billion deficit in 2005. Use the information shown by the graph to solve Exercises 109–112. Express answers in billions of dollars.

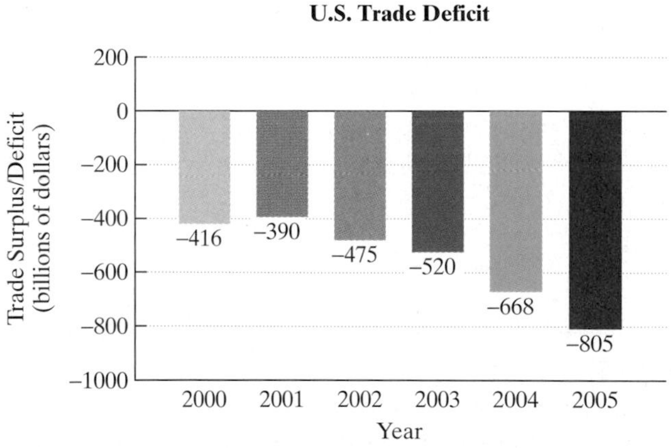

Source: Bureau of Economic Analysis

109. Find the difference between the 2000 trade deficit and the 2005 trade deficit.

110. Find the difference between the 2001 trade deficit and the 2005 trade deficit.

111. By how much did the 2005 deficit exceed twice the 2001 deficit?

112. Find the average trade deficit for 2003 and 2004 combined. By how much did the 2005 deficit exceed this average?

113. The peak of Mount Kilimanjaro, the highest point in Africa, is 19,321 feet above sea level. Qattara Depression, Egypt, the lowest point in Africa, is 436 feet below sea level. What is the difference in elevation between the peak of Mount Kilimanjaro and the Qattara Depression?

114. The peak of Mount Everest is 8848 meters above sea level. The Marianas Trench, on the floor of the Pacific Ocean, is 10,915 meters below sea level. What is the difference in elevation between the peak of Mount Everest and the Marianas Trench?

The following table shows the amount of money, in billions of dollars, collected and spent by the U.S. government from 2001 through 2005. Use the information from the table to solve Exercises 115–118. Express answers in billions of dollars.

Year	Money Collected (billions of dollars)	Money Spent (billions of dollars)
2001	\$1991	\$1863
2002	\$1853	\$2011
2003	\$1782	\$2160
2004	\$1880	\$2292
2005	\$2053	\$2479

Source: Budget of the U.S. Government

115. In 2002, what was the difference between the amount of money collected and the amount spent? Was there a budget surplus or deficit in 2002?

116. In 2003, what was the difference between the amount of money collected and the amount spent? Was there a budget surplus or deficit in 2003?

117. What is the difference between the 2001 surplus and the 2005 deficit?

118. What is the difference between the 2001 surplus and the 2004 deficit?

The way that we perceive the temperature on a cold day depends on both air temperature and wind speed. The windchill is what the air temperature would have to be with no wind to achieve the same chilling effect on the skin. In 2002, the National Weather Service issued new windchill temperatures, shown in the table below. Use the information from the table to solve Exercises 119–122.

New Windchill Temperature Index

Air Temperature (°F)

Wind Speed (miles per hour)	30	25	20	15	10	5	0	−5	−10	−15	−20	−25
5	25	19	13	7	1	−5	−11	−16	−22	−28	−34	−40
10	21	15	9	3	−4	−10	−16	−22	−28	−35	−41	−47
15	19	13	6	0	−7	−13	−19	−26	−32	−39	−45	−51
20	17	11	4	−2	−9	−15	−22	−29	−35	−42	−48	−55
25	16	9	3	−4	−11	−17	−24	−31	−37	−44	−51	−58
30	15	8	1	−5	−12	−19	−26	−33	−39	−46	−53	−60
35	14	7	0	−7	−14	−21	−27	−34	−41	−48	−55	−62
40	13	6	−1	−8	−15	−22	−29	−36	−43	−50	−57	−64
45	12	5	−2	−9	−16	−23	−30	−37	−44	−51	−58	−65
50	12	4	−3	−10	−17	−24	−31	−38	−45	−52	−60	−67
55	11	4	−3	−11	−18	−25	−32	−39	−46	−54	−61	−68
60	10	3	−4	−11	−19	−26	−33	−40	−48	−55	−62	−69

(Shaded) Frostbite occurs in 15 minutes or less.

Source: National Weather Service

119. What is the difference between how cold the temperature feels with winds at 10 miles per hour and 25 miles per hour when the air temperature is 15°F?

120. What is the difference between how cold the temperature feels with winds at 5 miles per hour and 30 miles per hour when the air temperature is 10°F?

121. What is the difference in the windchill temperature between an air temperature of 5°F with winds at 50 miles per hour and an air temperature of −10°F with winds at 5 miles per hour?

122. What is the difference in the windchill temperature between an air temperature of 5°F with winds at 55 miles per hour and an air temperature of −5°F with winds at 10 miles per hour?

• Writing in Mathematics

123. How does the set of integers differ from the set of whole numbers?

124. Explain how to graph an integer on a number line.

125. If you are given two integers, explain how to determine which one is smaller.

126. Explain how to add integers.

127. Explain how to subtract integers.

128. Explain how to multiply integers.

129. Explain how to divide integers.

130. Describe what it means to raise a number to a power. In your description, include a discussion of the difference between -5^2 and $(-5)^2$.

131. Why is $\frac{0}{4}$ equal to 0, but $\frac{4}{0}$ undefined?

• Critical Thinking Exercises

In Exercises 132–133, insert one pair of parentheses to make each calculation correct.

132. $8 - 2 \cdot 3 - 4 = 10$

133. $8 - 2 \cdot 3 - 4 = 14$

• Technology Exercises

Scientific calculators that have parentheses keys allow for the entry and computation of relatively complicated expressions in a single step. For example, the expression $15 + (10 - 7)^2$ can be evaluated by entering the following keystrokes:

15 [+] [(] 10 [−] 7 [)] [y^x] 2 [=].

Find the value of each expression in Exercises 134–136 in a single step on your scientific calculator.

134. $8 - 2 \cdot 3 - 9$

135. $(8 - 2) \cdot (3 - 9)$

136. $5^3 + 4 \cdot 9 - (8 + 9 \div 3)$

SECTION 5.3 • THE RATIONAL NUMBERS

OBJECTIVES

1. Define the rational numbers.
2. Reduce rational numbers.
3. Convert between mixed numbers and improper fractions.
4. Express rational numbers as decimals.
5. Express decimals in the form $\frac{a}{b}$.
6. Multiply and divide rational numbers.
7. Add and subtract rational numbers.
8. Apply the density property of rational numbers.
9. Solve problems involving rational numbers.

You are making eight dozen chocolate chip cookies for a large neighborhood block party. The recipe lists the ingredients needed to prepare five dozen cookies, such as $\frac{3}{4}$ cup sugar. How do you adjust the amount of sugar, as well as each of the other ingredients, given in the recipe?

Adapting a recipe to suit a different number of portions usually involves working with numbers that are not integers. For example, the number describing the amount of sugar, $\frac{3}{4}$ (cup), is not an integer, although it consists of the quotient of two integers, 3 and 4. Before returning to the problem of changing the size of a recipe, we study a new set of numbers consisting of the quotient of integers.

1 | Define the rational numbers.

Defining the Rational Numbers

If two integers are added, subtracted, or multiplied, the result is always another integer. This, however, is not always the case with division. For example, 10 divided by 5 is the integer 2. By contrast, 5 divided by 10 is $\frac{1}{2}$, and $\frac{1}{2}$ is not an integer. To permit divisions such as $\frac{5}{10}$, we enlarge the set of integers, calling the new collection the *rational numbers*. The set of **rational numbers** consists of all the numbers that can be expressed as a quotient of two integers, with the denominator not 0.

THE RATIONAL NUMBERS

The set of **rational numbers** is the set of all numbers which can be expressed in the form $\frac{a}{b}$, where a and b are integers and b is not equal to 0. The integer a is called the **numerator** and the integer b is called the **denominator**.

STUDY TIP

We know that the quotient of two numbers with different signs is a negative number. Thus,

$$\frac{-3}{4} = -\frac{3}{4} \text{ and } \frac{3}{-4} = -\frac{3}{4}.$$

The following numbers are examples of rational numbers:

$$\frac{1}{2}, \frac{-3}{4}, 5, 0.$$

The integer 5 is a rational number because it can be expressed as the quotient of integers: $5 = \frac{5}{1}$. Similarly, 0 can be written as $\frac{0}{1}$.

In general, every integer a is a rational number because it can be expressed in the form $\frac{a}{1}$.

2 Reduce rational numbers.

Reducing Rational Numbers

A rational number is **reduced to its lowest terms**, or **simplified**, when the numerator and denominator have no common divisors other than 1. Reducing rational numbers to lowest terms is done using the **Fundamental Principle of Rational Numbers**.

THE FUNDAMENTAL PRINCIPLE OF RATIONAL NUMBERS

If $\frac{a}{b}$ is a rational number and c is any number other than 0,

$$\frac{a \cdot c}{b \cdot c} = \frac{a}{b}.$$

The rational numbers $\frac{a}{b}$ and $\frac{a \cdot c}{b \cdot c}$ are called **equivalent fractions**.

When using the Fundamental Principle to reduce a rational number, the simplification can be done in one step by finding the greatest common divisor of the numerator and the denominator, and using it for c. Thus, **to reduce a rational number to its lowest terms, divide both the numerator and the denominator by their greatest common divisor.**

For example, consider the rational number $\frac{12}{100}$. The greatest common divisor of 12 and 100 is 4. We reduce to lowest terms as follows:

$$\frac{12}{100} = \frac{3 \cdot \cancel{4}}{25 \cdot \cancel{4}} = \frac{3}{25} \quad \text{or} \quad \frac{12}{100} = \frac{12 \div 4}{100 \div 4} = \frac{3}{25}.$$

EXAMPLE 1 REDUCING A RATIONAL NUMBER

Reduce $\frac{130}{455}$ to lowest terms.

SOLUTION Begin by finding the greatest common divisor of 130 and 455.

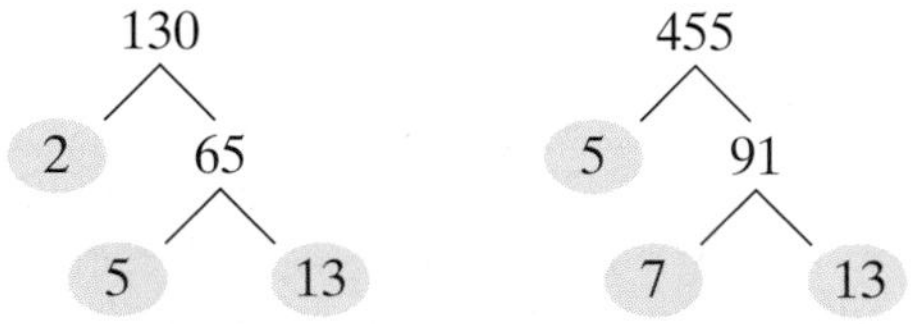

Thus, $130 = 2 \cdot 5 \cdot 13$ and $455 = 5 \cdot 7 \cdot 13$. The greatest common divisor is $5 \cdot 13$, or 65. Divide the numerator and the denominator of the given rational number by $5 \cdot 13$ or by 65.

$$\frac{130}{455} = \frac{2 \cdot \cancel{5} \cdot \cancel{13}}{\cancel{5} \cdot 7 \cdot \cancel{13}} = \frac{2}{7} \quad \text{or} \quad \frac{130}{455} = \frac{130 \div 65}{455 \div 65} = \frac{2}{7}$$

There are no common divisors of 2 and 7 other than 1. Thus, the rational number $\frac{2}{7}$ is in its lowest terms.

CHECK POINT 1 Reduce $\frac{72}{90}$ to lowest terms.

3 Convert between mixed numbers and improper fractions.

STUDY TIP

The mixed number $3\frac{4}{5}$ is read "three and four-fifths."

Mixed Numbers and Improper Fractions

A **mixed number** consists of the sum of an integer and a rational number, expressed without the use of an addition sign. Here is an example of a mixed number:

$$3\frac{4}{5}.$$

The integer is 3 and the rational number is $\frac{4}{5}$. $3\frac{4}{5}$ means $3 + \frac{4}{5}$.

An **improper fraction** is a rational number whose numerator is greater than its denominator. An example of an improper fraction is $\frac{19}{5}$.

The mixed number $3\frac{4}{5}$ can be converted to the improper fraction $\frac{19}{5}$ using the following procedure:

CONVERTING A POSITIVE MIXED NUMBER TO AN IMPROPER FRACTION

1. Multiply the denominator of the rational number by the integer and add the numerator to this product.
2. Place the sum in step 1 over the denominator in the mixed number.

EXAMPLE 2 CONVERTING FROM A MIXED NUMBER TO AN IMPROPER FRACTION

Convert $3\frac{4}{5}$ to an improper fraction.

SOLUTION

$$3\frac{4}{5} = \frac{5 \cdot 3 + 4}{5}$$

Multiply the denominator by the integer and add the numerator.

Place the sum over the mixed number's denominator.

$$= \frac{15 + 4}{5} = \frac{19}{5}$$

CHECK POINT 2 Convert $2\frac{5}{8}$ to an improper fraction.

When converting a negative mixed number to an improper fraction, copy the negative sign and then follow the previous procedure. For example,

$$-2\frac{3}{4} = -\frac{4 \cdot 2 + 3}{4} = -\frac{8 + 3}{4} = -\frac{11}{4}.$$

Copy the negative sign from step to step and convert $2\frac{3}{4}$ to an improper fraction.

A positive improper fraction can be converted to a mixed number using the following procedure:

CONVERTING A POSITIVE IMPROPER FRACTION TO A MIXED NUMBER

1. Divide the denominator into the numerator. Record the quotient and the remainder.
2. Write the mixed number using the following form:

$$\text{quotient}\ \frac{\text{remainder}}{\text{original denominator}}.$$

integer part (quotient); rational number part (remainder over original denominator)

EXAMPLE 3 CONVERTING FROM AN IMPROPER FRACTION TO A MIXED NUMBER

Convert $\frac{42}{5}$ to a mixed number.

SOLUTION

Step 1. Divide the denominator into the numerator.

$$\begin{array}{r} 8 \\ 5\overline{)42} \\ \underline{40} \\ 2 \end{array}$$

quotient: 8; remainder: 2

Step 2. Write the mixed number using quotient $\dfrac{\text{remainder}}{\text{original denominator}}$. Thus,

$$\frac{42}{5} = 8\frac{2}{5}.$$

(quotient: 8; remainder: 2; original denominator: 5)

CHECK POINT 3 Convert $\frac{5}{3}$ to a mixed number.

STUDY TIP

In applied problems, answers are usually expressed as mixed numbers, which many people find more meaningful than improper fractions. Improper fractions are often easier to work with when performing operations with fractions.

When converting a negative improper fraction to a mixed number, copy the negative sign and then follow the previous procedure. For example,

$$-\frac{29}{8} = -3\frac{5}{8}.$$

Copy the negative sign.

Convert $\frac{29}{8}$ to a mixed number.

$$\begin{array}{r} 3 \leftarrow \text{quotient} \\ 8\overline{)29} \\ \underline{24} \\ 5 \leftarrow \text{remainder} \end{array}$$

4 Express rational numbers as decimals.

Rational Numbers and Decimals

We have seen that a rational number is the quotient of integers. Rational numbers can also be expressed as decimals. As shown in the place-value chart in the margin, it is convenient to represent rational numbers with denominators of 10, 100, 1000, and so on as decimals. For example,

$$\frac{7}{10} = 0.7, \quad \frac{3}{100} = 0.03, \quad \text{and} \quad \frac{8}{1000} = 0.008.$$

Tens	Ones	Tenths	Hundredths	Thousandths	Ten-Thousandths	Hundred-Thousandths
10	1	$\frac{1}{10}$	$\frac{1}{100}$	$\frac{1}{1000}$	$\frac{1}{10,000}$	$\frac{1}{100,000}$

decimal point

Any rational number $\frac{a}{b}$ can be expressed as a decimal by dividing the denominator, b, into the numerator, a.

EXAMPLE 4 EXPRESSING RATIONAL NUMBERS AS DECIMALS

Express each rational number as a decimal:

a. $\frac{5}{8}$ **b.** $\frac{7}{11}$.

SOLUTION In each case, divide the denominator into the numerator.

a.
$$\begin{array}{r} 0.625 \\ 8\overline{)5.000} \\ \underline{4\,8} \\ 20 \\ \underline{16} \\ 40 \\ \underline{40} \\ 0 \end{array}$$

b.
$$\begin{array}{r} 0.6363\ldots \\ 11\overline{)7.0000\ldots} \\ \underline{6\,6} \\ 40 \\ \underline{33} \\ 70 \\ \underline{66} \\ 40 \\ \underline{33} \\ 70 \\ \vdots \end{array}$$

In Example 4, the decimal for $\frac{5}{8}$, namely 0.625, stops and is called a **terminating decimal**. Other examples of terminating decimals are

$$\frac{1}{4} = 0.25, \quad \frac{2}{5} = 0.4, \quad \text{and} \quad \frac{7}{8} = 0.875.$$

By contrast, the division process for $\frac{7}{11}$ results in $0.6363\ldots$, with the digits 63 repeating over and over indefinitely. To indicate this, write a bar over the digits that repeat. Thus,

$$\frac{7}{11} = 0.\overline{63}.$$

The decimal for $\frac{7}{11}$, $0.\overline{63}$, is called a **repeating decimal**. Other examples of repeating decimals are

$$\frac{1}{3} = 0.333\ldots = 0.\overline{3} \quad \text{and} \quad \frac{2}{3} = 0.666\ldots = 0.\overline{6}.$$

RATIONAL NUMBERS AND DECIMALS

Any rational number can be expressed as a decimal. The resulting decimal will either terminate (stop), or it will have a digit that repeats or a block of digits that repeat.

CHECK POINT 4 Express each rational number as a decimal:

a. $\frac{3}{8}$ **b.** $\frac{5}{11}$.

5 Express decimals in the form $\frac{a}{b}$.

Reversing Directions: Expressing Decimals as a Quotient of Two Integers

Terminating decimals can be expressed with denominators of 10, 100, 1000, 10,000, and so on. Use the place-value chart shown in the margin. The digits to the right of the decimal point are the numerator of the rational number. To find the denominator, observe the last digit to the right of the decimal point. The place-value of this digit will indicate the denominator.

Tens	Ones	Tenths	Hundredths	Thousandths	Ten-Thousandths	Hundred-Thousandths
10	1	$\frac{1}{10}$	$\frac{1}{100}$	$\frac{1}{1000}$	$\frac{1}{10{,}000}$	$\frac{1}{100{,}000}$

decimal point

EXAMPLE 5 EXPRESSING TERMINATING DECIMALS IN $\frac{a}{b}$ FORM

Express each terminating decimal as a quotient of integers:

a. 0.7 **b.** 0.49 **c.** 0.048.

SOLUTION

a. $0.7 = \frac{7}{10}$ because the 7 is in the tenths position.

b. $0.49 = \frac{49}{100}$ because the digit on the right, 9, is in the hundredths position.

c. $0.048 = \frac{48}{1000}$ because the digit on the right, 8, is in the thousandths position. Reducing to lowest terms, $\frac{48}{1000} = \frac{48 \div 8}{1000 \div 8} = \frac{6}{125}$.

CHECK POINT 5 Express each terminating decimal as a quotient of integers, reduced to lowest terms:

a. 0.9 **b.** 0.86 **c.** 0.053.

If you are given a rational number as a repeating decimal, there is a technique for expressing the number as a quotient of integers. Although we will not be discussing algebra until Chapter 6, the basic algebra used in this technique should be familiar to you. We begin by illustrating the technique with an example. Then we will summarize the steps in the procedure and apply them to another example.

EXAMPLE 6 EXPRESSING A REPEATING DECIMAL IN $\frac{a}{b}$ FORM

Express $0.\overline{6}$ as a quotient of integers.

SOLUTION

Step 1. Let n equal the repeating decimal. Let $n = 0.\overline{6}$, so that $n = 0.66666\ldots$.

Step 2. If there is one repeating digit, multiply both sides of the equation in step 1 by 10.

$$n = 0.66666\ldots \quad \text{This is the equation from step 1.}$$

$$10n = 10(0.66666\ldots) \quad \text{Multiply both sides by 10.}$$

$$10n = 6.66666\ldots \quad \text{Multiplying by 10 moves the decimal point one place to the right.}$$

STUDY TIP

In step 3, be sure to line up the decimal points before subtracting.

Step 3. Subtract the equation in step 1 from the equation in step 2.

Remember from algebra that n means $1n$. Thus, $10n - 1n = 9n$.

$$10n = 6.66666\ldots \quad \text{This is the equation from step 2.}$$

$$-\;\; n = 0.66666\ldots \quad \text{This is the equation from step 1.}$$

$$9n = 6$$

Step 4. Divide both sides of the equation in step 3 by the number in front of n and solve for n. We solve $9n = 6$ for n by dividing both sides by 9.

$$9n = 6 \quad \text{This is the equation from step 3.}$$

$$\frac{9n}{9} = \frac{6}{9} \quad \text{Divide both sides by 9.}$$

$$n = \frac{6}{9} = \frac{2}{3} \quad \text{Reduce } \tfrac{6}{9} \text{ to lowest terms: } \frac{6}{9} = \frac{2 \cdot \cancel{3}}{3 \cdot \cancel{3}} = \frac{2}{3}.$$

We began the solution process with $n = 0.\overline{6}$, and now we have $n = \frac{2}{3}$. Therefore,

$$0.\overline{6} = \frac{2}{3}.$$

Here are the steps for expressing a repeating decimal as a quotient of integers. Assume that the repeating digit or digits begin directly to the right of the decimal point.

EXPRESSING A REPEATING DECIMAL AS A QUOTIENT OF INTEGERS

Step 1. Let n equal the repeating decimal.

Step 2. Multiply both sides of the equation in step 1 by 10 if one digit repeats, by 100 if two digits repeat, by 1000 if three digits repeat, and so on.

Step 3. Subtract the equation in step 1 from the equation in step 2.

Step 4. Divide both sides of the equation in step 3 by the number in front of n and solve for n.

CHECK POINT 6 Express $0.\overline{2}$ as a quotient of integers.

EXAMPLE 7 EXPRESSING A REPEATING DECIMAL IN $\frac{a}{b}$ FORM

Express $0.\overline{53}$ as a quotient of integers.

SOLUTION

Step 1. Let n equal the repeating decimal. Let $n = 0.\overline{53}$, so that $n = 0.535353\ldots$.

Step 2. If there are two repeating digits, multiply both sides of the equation in step 2 by 100.

$$n = 0.535353\ldots \qquad \text{This is the equation from step 1.}$$
$$100n = 100(0.535353\ldots) \qquad \text{Multiply both sides by 100.}$$
$$100n = 53.535353\ldots \qquad \text{Multiplying by 100 moves the decimal point two places to the right.}$$

Step 3. Subtract the equation in step 1 from the equation in step 2.

$$100n = 53.535353\ldots \qquad \text{This is the equation from step 2.}$$
$$-\quad n = 0.535353\ldots \qquad \text{This is the equation from step 1.}$$
$$99n = 53$$

Step 4. Divide both sides of the equation in step 3 by the number in front of n and solve for n. We solve $99n = 53$ for n by dividing both sides by 99.

$$99n = 53 \qquad \text{This is the equation from step 3.}$$
$$\frac{99n}{99} = \frac{53}{99} \qquad \text{Divide both sides by 99.}$$
$$n = \frac{53}{99}$$

Because n equals $0.\overline{53}$ and n equals $\frac{53}{99}$,

$$0.\overline{53} = \frac{53}{99}.$$

CHECK POINT 7 Express $0.\overline{79}$ as a quotient of integers.

6 Multiply and divide rational numbers.

Multiplying and Dividing Rational Numbers

The product of two rational numbers is found as follows:

MULTIPLYING RATIONAL NUMBERS

The product of two rational numbers is the product of their numerators divided by the product of their denominators.

If $\frac{a}{b}$ and $\frac{c}{d}$ are rational numbers, then $\frac{a}{b} \cdot \frac{c}{d} = \frac{a \cdot c}{b \cdot d}$.

EXAMPLE 8 MULTIPLYING RATIONAL NUMBERS

Multiply. If possible, reduce the product to its lowest terms:

a. $\frac{3}{8} \cdot \frac{5}{11}$ **b.** $\left(-\frac{2}{3}\right)\left(-\frac{9}{4}\right)$ **c.** $\left(3\frac{2}{3}\right)\left(1\frac{1}{4}\right)$.

SOLUTION

a. $\frac{3}{8} \cdot \frac{5}{11} = \frac{3 \cdot 5}{8 \cdot 11} = \frac{15}{88}$

b. $\left(-\frac{2}{3}\right)\left(-\frac{9}{4}\right) = \frac{(-2)(-9)}{3 \cdot 4} = \frac{18}{12} = \frac{3 \cdot \cancel{6}}{2 \cdot \cancel{6}} = \frac{3}{2}$ or $1\frac{1}{2}$

c. $\left(3\frac{2}{3}\right)\left(1\frac{1}{4}\right) = \frac{11}{3} \cdot \frac{5}{4} = \frac{11 \cdot 5}{3 \cdot 4} = \frac{55}{12}$ or $4\frac{7}{12}$

CHECK POINT 8 Multiply. If possible, reduce the product to its lowest terms:

a. $\frac{4}{11} \cdot \frac{2}{3}$ **b.** $\left(-\frac{3}{7}\right)\left(-\frac{14}{4}\right)$ **c.** $\left(3\frac{2}{5}\right)\left(1\frac{1}{2}\right)$.

STUDY TIP

You can divide numerators and denominators by common factors *before* performing multiplication. Then multiply the remaining factors in the numerators and multiply the remaining factors in the denominators. For example,

$$\frac{7}{15} \cdot \frac{20}{21} = \frac{\overset{1}{\cancel{7}}}{\underset{3}{\cancel{15}}} \cdot \frac{\overset{4}{\cancel{20}}}{\underset{3}{\cancel{21}}} = \frac{1 \cdot 4}{3 \cdot 3} = \frac{4}{9}.$$

Two numbers whose product is 1 are called **reciprocals**, or **multiplicative inverses**, of each other. Thus, the reciprocal of 2 is $\frac{1}{2}$ and the reciprocal of $\frac{1}{2}$ is 2 because $2 \cdot \frac{1}{2} = 1$. In general, if $\frac{c}{d}$ is a nonzero rational number, its reciprocal is $\frac{d}{c}$ because $\frac{c}{d} \cdot \frac{d}{c} = 1$.

Reciprocals are used to find the quotient of two rational numbers.

DIVIDING RATIONAL NUMBERS

The quotient of two rational numbers is the product of the first number and the reciprocal of the second number.

If $\frac{a}{b}$ and $\frac{c}{d}$ are rational numbers and $\frac{c}{d}$ is not 0, then $\frac{a}{b} \div \frac{c}{d} = \frac{a}{b} \cdot \frac{d}{c} = \frac{a \cdot d}{b \cdot c}$.

EXAMPLE 9 DIVIDING RATIONAL NUMBERS

Divide. If possible, reduce the quotient to its lowest terms:

a. $\frac{4}{5} \div \frac{1}{10}$ **b.** $-\frac{3}{5} \div \frac{7}{11}$ **c.** $4\frac{3}{4} \div 1\frac{1}{2}$.

SOLUTION

a. $\frac{4}{5} \div \frac{1}{10} = \frac{4}{5} \cdot \frac{10}{1} = \frac{4 \cdot 10}{5 \cdot 1} = \frac{40}{5} = 8$

b. $-\frac{3}{5} \div \frac{7}{11} = -\frac{3}{5} \cdot \frac{11}{7} = \frac{-3(11)}{5 \cdot 7} = -\frac{33}{35}$

c. $4\frac{3}{4} \div 1\frac{1}{2} = \frac{19}{4} \div \frac{3}{2} = \frac{19}{4} \cdot \frac{2}{3} = \frac{19 \cdot 2}{4 \cdot 3} = \frac{38}{12} = \frac{19 \cdot \cancel{2}}{6 \cdot \cancel{2}} = \frac{19}{6}$ or $3\frac{1}{6}$

CHECK POINT 9 Divide. If possible, reduce the quotient to its lowest terms:

a. $\frac{9}{11} \div \frac{5}{4}$ **b.** $-\frac{8}{15} \div \frac{2}{5}$ **c.** $3\frac{3}{8} \div 2\frac{1}{4}$.

7 Add and subtract rational numbers.

Adding and Subtracting Rational Numbers

Rational expressions with identical denominators are added and subtracted using the following rules:

ADDING AND SUBTRACTING RATIONAL NUMBERS WITH IDENTICAL DENOMINATORS

The sum or difference of two rational numbers with identical denominators is the sum or difference of their numerators over the common denominator.

If $\frac{a}{b}$ and $\frac{c}{b}$ are rational numbers, then $\frac{a}{b} + \frac{c}{b} = \frac{a+c}{b}$ and $\frac{a}{b} - \frac{c}{b} = \frac{a-c}{b}$.

EXAMPLE 10 ADDING AND SUBTRACTING RATIONAL NUMBERS WITH IDENTICAL DENOMINATORS

Perform the indicated operations:

a. $\frac{3}{7} + \frac{2}{7}$ **b.** $\frac{11}{12} - \frac{5}{12}$ **c.** $-5\frac{1}{4} - \left(-2\frac{3}{4}\right)$.

SOLUTION

a. $\frac{3}{7} + \frac{2}{7} = \frac{3+2}{7} = \frac{5}{7}$

b. $\frac{11}{12} - \frac{5}{12} = \frac{11-5}{12} = \frac{6}{12} = \frac{1 \cdot \cancel{6}}{2 \cdot \cancel{6}} = \frac{1}{2}$

c. $-5\frac{1}{4} - \left(-2\frac{3}{4}\right) = -\frac{21}{4} - \left(-\frac{11}{4}\right) = -\frac{21}{4} + \frac{11}{4} = \frac{-21+11}{4} = \frac{-10}{4} = -\frac{5}{2}$ or $-2\frac{1}{2}$

CHECK POINT 10 Perform the indicated operations:

a. $\frac{5}{12} + \frac{3}{12}$ **b.** $\frac{7}{4} - \frac{1}{4}$ **c.** $-3\frac{3}{8} - \left(-1\frac{1}{8}\right)$.

If the rational numbers to be added or subtracted have different denominators, we use the least common multiple of their denominators to rewrite the rational numbers. The least common multiple of the denominators is called the **least common denominator**.

Rewriting rational numbers with a least common denominator is done using the Fundamental Principle of Rational Numbers, discussed at the beginning of this section. Recall that if $\frac{a}{b}$ is a rational number and c is a nonzero number, then

$$\frac{a}{b} = \frac{a}{b} \cdot \frac{c}{c} = \frac{a \cdot c}{b \cdot c}.$$

Multiplying the numerator and the denominator of a rational number by the same nonzero number is equivalent to multiplying by 1, resulting in an equivalent fraction.

EXAMPLE 11 ADDING RATIONAL NUMBERS WITH UNLIKE DENOMINATORS

Find the sum: $\frac{3}{4} + \frac{1}{6}$.

SOLUTION The smallest number divisible by both 4 and 6 is 12. Therefore, 12 is the least common multiple of 4 and 6, and will serve as the least common denominator. To obtain a denominator of 12, multiply the denominator and the numerator of the first rational number, $\frac{3}{4}$, by 3. To obtain a denominator of 12, multiply the denominator and the numerator of the second rational number, $\frac{1}{6}$, by 2.

$$\frac{3}{4} + \frac{1}{6} = \frac{3}{4} \cdot \frac{3}{3} + \frac{1}{6} \cdot \frac{2}{2}$$

Rewrite each rational number as an equivalent fraction with a denominator of 12. $\frac{3}{3} = 1$ and $\frac{2}{2} = 1$, and multiplying by 1 does not change a number's value.

$$= \frac{9}{12} + \frac{2}{12}$$

Multiply.

$$= \frac{11}{12}$$

Add numerators and put this sum over the least common denominator.

CHECK POINT 11 Find the sum: $\frac{1}{5} + \frac{3}{4}$.

If the least common denominator cannot be found by inspection, use prime factorizations of the denominators and the method for finding their least common multiple, discussed in Section 5.1.

EXAMPLE 12 SUBTRACTING RATIONAL NUMBERS WITH UNLIKE DENOMINATORS

Perform the indicated operation: $\frac{1}{15} - \frac{7}{24}$.

SOLUTION We need to first find the least common denominator, which is the least common multiple of 15 and 24. What is the smallest number divisible by both 15 and 24? The answer is not obvious, so we begin with the prime factorization of each number.

$$15 = 5 \cdot 3$$
$$24 = 8 \cdot 3 = 2^3 \cdot 3$$

The different factors are 5, 3, and 2. Using the greatest number of times each factor appears in any factorization, the least common multiple is $5 \cdot 3 \cdot 2^3 = 5 \cdot 3 \cdot 8 = 120$. We will now express each rational number with a denominator of 120, which is the least common denominator. For the first rational number, $\frac{1}{15}$, 120 divided by 15 is 8. Thus, we will multiply the numerator and denominator by 8. For the second rational number, $\frac{7}{24}$, 120 divided by 24 is 5. Thus, we will multiply the numerator and denominator by 5.

$$\frac{1}{15} - \frac{7}{24} = \frac{1}{15} \cdot \frac{8}{8} - \frac{7}{24} \cdot \frac{5}{5}$$ Rewrite each rational number as an equivalent fraction with a denominator of 120.

$$= \frac{8}{120} - \frac{35}{120}$$ Multiply.

$$= \frac{8 - 35}{120}$$ Subtract the numerators and put this difference over the least common denominator.

$$= \frac{-27}{120}$$ Perform the subtraction.

$$= \frac{-9 \cdot \cancel{3}}{40 \cdot \cancel{3}}$$ Reduce to lowest terms.

$$= -\frac{9}{40}$$

TECHNOLOGY

Here is a possible keystroke sequence on a graphing calculator for the subtraction problem in Example 12:

1 [÷] 15 [−] 7 [÷] 24

[▶Frac] [ENTER].

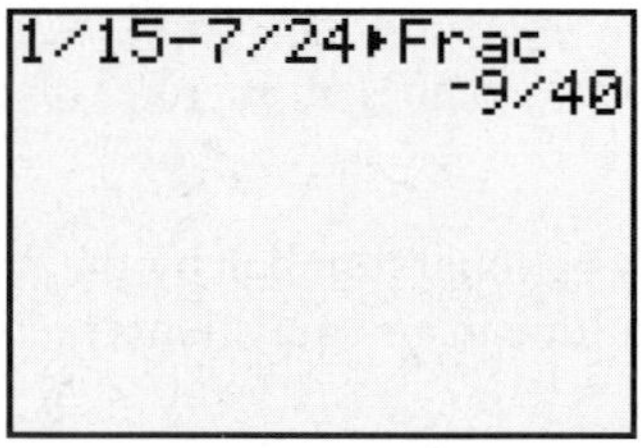

The calculator display reads −9/40, serving as a check for our answer in Example 12.

CHECK POINT 12 Perform the indicated operation: $\frac{3}{10} - \frac{7}{12}$.

8 Apply the density property of rational numbers.

Density of Rational Numbers

It is always possible to find a rational number between any two given rational numbers. Mathematicians express this idea by saying that the set of rational numbers is **dense**.

DENSITY OF THE RATIONAL NUMBERS

If r and t represent rational numbers, with $r < t$, then there is a rational number s such that s is between r and t:

$$r < s < t.$$

One way to find a rational number between two given rational numbers is to find the rational number halfway between them. Add the given rational numbers and divide their sum by 2, thereby finding the average of the numbers.

EXAMPLE 13 ILLUSTRATING THE DENSITY PROPERTY

Find a rational number halfway between $\frac{1}{2}$ and $\frac{3}{4}$.

SOLUTION First, add $\frac{1}{2}$ and $\frac{3}{4}$.

$$\frac{1}{2}+\frac{3}{4}=\frac{2}{4}+\frac{3}{4}=\frac{5}{4}$$

Next, divide this sum by 2.

$$\frac{5}{4}\div\frac{2}{1}=\frac{5}{4}\cdot\frac{1}{2}=\frac{5}{8}$$

The number $\frac{5}{8}$ is halfway between $\frac{1}{2}$ and $\frac{3}{4}$. Thus,

$$\frac{1}{2}<\frac{5}{8}<\frac{3}{4}.$$

STUDY TIP

The inequality $\frac{1}{2}<\frac{5}{8}<\frac{3}{4}$ is more obvious if all denominators are changed to 8:

$$\frac{4}{8}<\frac{5}{8}<\frac{6}{8}.$$

We can repeat the procedure of Example 13 and find a rational number halfway between $\frac{1}{2}$ and $\frac{5}{8}$. Repeated application of this procedure implies the following surprising result:

Between any two given rational numbers are *infinitely many* rational numbers.

CHECK POINT 13 Find a rational number halfway between $\frac{1}{3}$ and $\frac{1}{2}$.

9 Solve problems involving rational numbers.

Problem Solving with Rational Numbers

A common application of rational numbers involves preparing food for a different number of servings than what the recipe gives. The amount of each ingredient can be found as follows:

Amount of ingredient needed

$$=\frac{\text{desired serving size}}{\text{recipe serving size}}\times\text{ingredient amount in the recipe.}$$

EXAMPLE 14 CHANGING THE SIZE OF A RECIPE

A chocolate-chip cookie recipe for five dozen cookies requires $\frac{3}{4}$ cup sugar. If you want to make eight dozen cookies, how much sugar is needed?

SOLUTION Amount of sugar needed

$$=\frac{\text{desired serving size}}{\text{recipe serving size}}\times\text{sugar amount in recipe}$$

$$=\frac{8\text{ }\cancel{\text{dozen}}}{5\text{ }\cancel{\text{dozen}}}\times\frac{3}{4}\text{ cup}$$

The amount of sugar, in cups, needed is determined by multiplying the rational numbers:

$$\frac{8}{5}\times\frac{3}{4}=\frac{8\cdot 3}{5\cdot 4}=\frac{24}{20}=\frac{6\cdot\cancel{4}}{5\cdot\cancel{4}}=1\frac{1}{5}.$$

Thus, $1\frac{1}{5}$ cups of sugar is needed. (Depending on the measuring cup you are using, you may need to round the sugar amount to $1\frac{1}{4}$ cups.)

CHECK POINT 14 A chocolate-chip cookie recipe for five dozen cookies requires two eggs. If you want to make seven dozen cookies, exactly how many eggs are needed? Now round your answer to a realistic number that does not involve a fractional part of an egg.

EXERCISE SET 5.3

• Practice Exercises

In Exercises 1–12, reduce each rational number to its lowest terms.

1. $\frac{10}{15}$ **2.** $\frac{18}{45}$ **3.** $\frac{15}{18}$ **4.** $\frac{16}{64}$

5. $\frac{24}{42}$ **6.** $\frac{32}{80}$ **7.** $\frac{60}{108}$ **8.** $\frac{112}{128}$

9. $\frac{342}{380}$ **10.** $\frac{210}{252}$ **11.** $\frac{308}{418}$ **12.** $\frac{144}{300}$

In Exercises 13–18, convert each mixed number to an improper fraction.

13. $2\frac{3}{8}$ **14.** $2\frac{7}{9}$ **15.** $-7\frac{3}{5}$

16. $-6\frac{2}{5}$ **17.** $12\frac{7}{16}$ **18.** $11\frac{5}{16}$

In Exercises 19–24, convert each improper fraction to a mixed number.

19. $\frac{23}{5}$ **20.** $\frac{47}{8}$ **21.** $-\frac{76}{9}$

22. $-\frac{59}{9}$ **23.** $\frac{711}{20}$ **24.** $\frac{788}{25}$

In Exercises 25–36, express each rational number as a decimal.

25. $\frac{3}{4}$ **26.** $\frac{3}{5}$ **27.** $\frac{7}{20}$ **28.** $\frac{3}{20}$

29. $\frac{7}{8}$ **30.** $\frac{5}{16}$ **31.** $\frac{9}{11}$ **32.** $\frac{3}{11}$

33. $\frac{22}{7}$ **34.** $\frac{20}{3}$ **35.** $\frac{2}{7}$ **36.** $\frac{5}{7}$

In Exercises 37–48, express each terminating decimal as a quotient of integers. If possible, reduce to lowest terms.

37. 0.3 **38.** 0.9 **39.** 0.4 **40.** 0.6

41. 0.39 **42.** 0.59 **43.** 0.82 **44.** 0.64

45. 0.725 **46.** 0.625 **47.** 0.5399 **48.** 0.7006

In Exercises 49–56, express each repeating decimal as a quotient of integers. If possible, reduce to lowest terms.

49. $0.\overline{7}$ **50.** $0.\overline{1}$ **51.** $0.\overline{9}$ **52.** $0.\overline{3}$

53. $0.\overline{36}$ **54.** $0.\overline{81}$ **55.** $0.\overline{257}$ **56.** $0.\overline{529}$

In Exercises 57–92, perform the indicated operations. If possible, reduce the answer to its lowest terms.

57. $\frac{3}{8}\cdot\frac{7}{11}$ **58.** $\frac{5}{8}\cdot\frac{3}{11}$ **59.** $\left(-\frac{1}{10}\right)\left(\frac{7}{12}\right)$

60. $\left(-\frac{1}{8}\right)\left(\frac{5}{9}\right)$ **61.** $\left(-\frac{2}{3}\right)\left(-\frac{9}{4}\right)$ **62.** $\left(-\frac{5}{4}\right)\left(-\frac{6}{7}\right)$

63. $\left(3\frac{3}{4}\right)\left(1\frac{3}{5}\right)$ **64.** $\left(2\frac{4}{5}\right)\left(1\frac{1}{4}\right)$ **65.** $\frac{5}{4}\div\frac{3}{8}$

66. $\frac{5}{8}\div\frac{4}{3}$ **67.** $-\frac{7}{8}\div\frac{15}{16}$ **68.** $-\frac{13}{20}\div\frac{4}{5}$

69. $6\frac{3}{5}\div 1\frac{1}{10}$ **70.** $1\frac{3}{4}\div 2\frac{5}{8}$ **71.** $\frac{2}{11}+\frac{3}{11}$

72. $\frac{5}{13}+\frac{2}{13}$ **73.** $\frac{5}{6}-\frac{1}{6}$ **74.** $\frac{7}{12}-\frac{5}{12}$

75. $\frac{7}{12}-\left(-\frac{1}{12}\right)$ **76.** $\frac{5}{16}-\left(-\frac{5}{16}\right)$ **77.** $\frac{1}{2}+\frac{1}{5}$

78. $\frac{1}{3}+\frac{1}{5}$ **79.** $\frac{3}{4}+\frac{3}{20}$ **80.** $\frac{2}{5}+\frac{2}{15}$

81. $\frac{5}{24}+\frac{7}{30}$ **82.** $\frac{7}{108}+\frac{55}{144}$ **83.** $\frac{13}{18}-\frac{2}{9}$

84. $\frac{13}{15}-\frac{2}{45}$ **85.** $\frac{4}{3}-\frac{3}{4}$ **86.** $\frac{3}{2}-\frac{2}{3}$

87. $\frac{1}{15}-\frac{27}{50}$ **88.** $\frac{4}{15}-\frac{1}{6}$ **89.** $3\frac{3}{4}-2\frac{1}{3}$

90. $3\frac{2}{3}-2\frac{1}{2}$ **91.** $\left(\frac{1}{2}-\frac{1}{3}\right)\div\frac{5}{8}$ **92.** $\left(\frac{1}{2}+\frac{1}{4}\right)\div\left(\frac{1}{2}+\frac{1}{3}\right)$

In Exercises 93–98, find a rational number halfway between the two numbers in each pair.

93. $\frac{1}{4}$ and $\frac{1}{3}$ **94.** $\frac{2}{3}$ and $\frac{5}{6}$ **95.** $\frac{1}{2}$ and $\frac{2}{3}$

96. $\frac{3}{5}$ and $\frac{2}{3}$ **97.** $-\frac{2}{3}$ and $-\frac{5}{6}$ **98.** -4 and $-\frac{7}{2}$

Different operations with the same rational numbers usually result in different answers. Exercises 99–100 illustrate some curious exceptions.

99. Show that $\frac{13}{4}+\frac{13}{9}$ and $\frac{13}{4}\times\frac{13}{9}$ give the same answer.

100. Show that $\frac{169}{30}+\frac{13}{15}$ and $\frac{169}{30}\div\frac{13}{15}$ give the same answer.

• Practice Plus

In Exercises 101–106, perform the indicated operations. If possible, reduce the answer to its lowest terms.

101. $-\frac{9}{4}\left(\frac{1}{2}\right)+\frac{3}{4}\div\frac{5}{6}$

102. $\left[-\frac{4}{7}-\left(-\frac{2}{5}\right)\right]\left[-\frac{3}{8}+\left(-\frac{1}{9}\right)\right]$

103. $\dfrac{\frac{7}{9}-3}{\frac{5}{6}}\div\frac{3}{2}+\frac{3}{4}$

104. $\dfrac{\frac{17}{25}}{\frac{3}{5}-4}\div\frac{1}{5}+\frac{1}{2}$

105. $\frac{1}{4}-6(2+8)\div\left(-\frac{1}{3}\right)\left(-\frac{1}{9}\right)$

106. $\frac{3}{4}-4(2+7)\div\left(-\frac{1}{2}\right)\left(-\frac{1}{6}\right)$

In Exercises 107–110, perform the indicated operations. Leave denominators in prime factorization form.

107. $\dfrac{5}{2^2\cdot 3^2}-\dfrac{1}{2\cdot 3^2}$ **108.** $\dfrac{7}{3^2\cdot 5^2}-\dfrac{1}{3\cdot 5^3}$

109. $\dfrac{1}{2^4\cdot 5^3\cdot 7}+\dfrac{1}{2\cdot 5^4}-\dfrac{1}{2^3\cdot 5^2}$

110. $\dfrac{1}{2^3\cdot 17^8}+\dfrac{1}{2\cdot 17^9}-\dfrac{1}{2^2\cdot 3\cdot 17^8}$

In Exercises 111–114, express each rational number as a decimal. Then insert either < or > in the shaded area between the rational numbers to make the statement true.

111. $\frac{6}{11}$ ■ $\frac{7}{12}$ **112.** $\frac{29}{36}$ ■ $\frac{28}{35}$

113. $-\frac{5}{6}$ ■ $-\frac{8}{9}$ **114.** $-\frac{1}{125}$ ■ $-\frac{3}{500}$

• Application Exercises

The circle graph shows the breakdown of the number of countries in the world that are free, partly free, or not free. Use the information in the graph to solve Exercises 115–116.

World's Countries by Status of Freedom

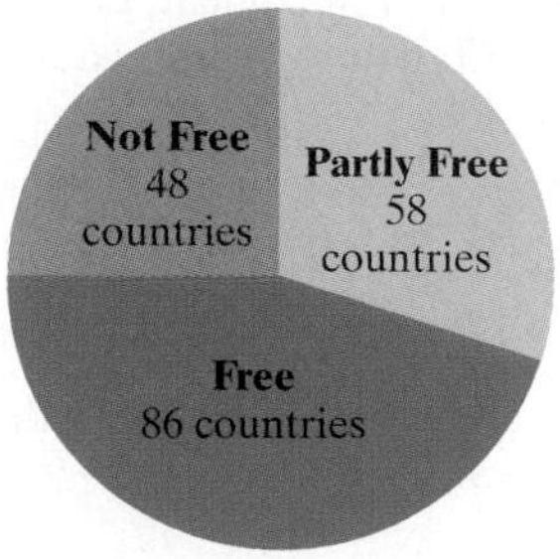

Source: Larry Berman and Bruce Murphy, *Approaching Democracy*, 4th Edition, Prentice Hall, 2003

115. What fractional part of the world's countries is free? Reduce the answer to its lowest terms.

116. What fractional part of the world's countries is not free? Reduce the answer to its lowest terms.

Use the following list of ingredients for chocolate brownies to solve Exercises 117–122.

Ingredients for 16 Brownies

$\frac{2}{3}$ cup butter, 5 ounces unsweetened chocolate, $1\frac{1}{2}$ cups sugar, 2 teaspoons vanilla, 2 eggs, 1 cup flour

117. How much of each ingredient is needed to make 8 brownies?

118. How much of each ingredient is needed to make 12 brownies?

119. How much of each ingredient is needed to make 20 brownies?

120. How much of each ingredient is needed to make 24 brownies?

121. With only one cup of butter, what is the greatest number of brownies that you can make? (Ignore part of a brownie.)

122. With only one cup of sugar, what is the greatest number of brownies that you can make? (Ignore part of a brownie.)

A mix for eight servings of instant potatoes requires $2\frac{2}{3}$ cups of water. Use this information to solve Exercises 123–124.

123. If you want to make 11 servings, how much water is needed?

124. If you want to make six servings, how much water is needed?

In most societies, women say they prefer to marry men who are older than themselves, whereas men say they prefer women who are younger. Evolutionary psychologists attribute these preferences to female concern with a partner's material resources and male concern with a partner's fertility (Source: David M. Buss, Psychological Inquiry, *6, 1–30). The graph shows the preferred age in a mate in five selected countries. Use the information in the graph to solve Exercises 125–128. Express each answer as a mixed number.*

Preferred Age in a Mate

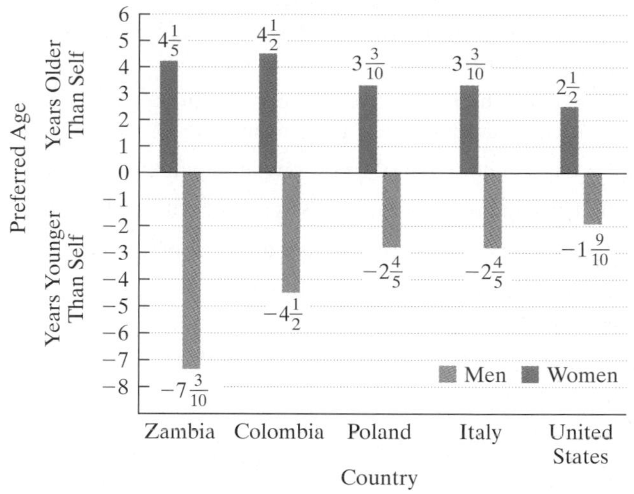

Source: Carole Wade and Carol Tavris, *Psychology*, 6th Edition, Prentice Hall, 2000

125. What is the difference between the preferred age in a mate for women in Italy and women in the United States?

126. What is the difference between the preferred age in a mate for women in Zambia and women in the United States?

127. What is the difference between the preferred age in a mate for men in Italy and men in the United States?

128. What is the difference between the preferred age in a mate for men in Colombia and men in the United States?

129. A franchise is owned by three people. The first owns $\frac{5}{12}$ of the business and the second owns $\frac{1}{4}$ of the business. What fractional part of the business is owned by the third person?

130. At a workshop on enhancing creativity, $\frac{1}{4}$ of the participants are musicians, $\frac{2}{5}$ are artists, $\frac{1}{10}$ are actors, and the remaining participants are writers. What fraction of the people attending the workshop are writers?

131. If you walk $\frac{3}{4}$ mile and then jog $\frac{2}{5}$ mile, what is the total distance covered? How much farther did you walk than jog?

132. Some companies pay people extra when they work more than a regular 40-hour work week. The overtime pay is often $1\frac{1}{2}$ times the regular hourly rate. This is called time and a half. A summer job for students pays $12 an hour and offers time and a half for the hours worked over 40. If a student works 46 hours during one week, what is the student's total pay before taxes?

133. A will states that $\frac{3}{5}$ of the estate is to be divided among relatives. Of the remaining estate, $\frac{1}{4}$ goes to the National Foundation for AIDS Research. What fraction of the estate goes to the National Foundation for AIDS Research?

134. The legend of a map indicates that 1 inch = 16 miles. If the distance on the map between two cities is $2\frac{3}{8}$ inches, how far apart are the cities?

• Writing in Mathematics

135. What is a rational number?

136. Explain how to reduce a rational number to its lowest terms.

137. Explain how to convert from a mixed number to an improper fraction. Use $7\frac{2}{3}$ as an example.

138. Explain how to convert from an improper fraction to a mixed number. Use $\frac{47}{5}$ as an example.

139. Explain how to write a rational number as a decimal.

140. Explain how to write 0.083 as a quotient of integers.

141. Explain how to write $0.\overline{9}$ as a quotient of integers.

142. Explain how to multiply rational numbers. Use $\frac{5}{6} \cdot \frac{1}{2}$ as an example.

143. Explain how to divide rational numbers. Use $\frac{5}{6} \div \frac{1}{2}$ as an example.

144. Explain how to add rational numbers with different denominators. Use $\frac{5}{6} + \frac{1}{2}$ as an example.

145. What does it mean when we say that the set of rational numbers is dense?

146. Explain what is wrong with this statement. "If you'd like to save some money, I'll be happy to sell you my computer system for only $\frac{3}{2}$ of the price I originally paid for it."

• Critical Thinking Exercises

147. Shown in the next column is a short excerpt from "The Star-Spangled Banner." The time is $\frac{3}{4}$, which means that each measure must contain notes that add up to $\frac{3}{4}$. The values of the different notes tell musicians how long to hold each note.

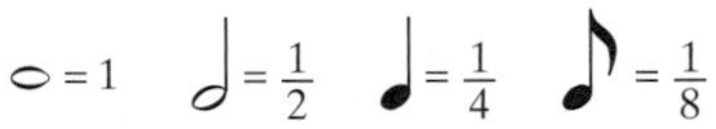

Use vertical lines to divide this line of "The Star-Spangled Banner" into measures.

148. Use inductive reasoning to predict the addition problem and the sum that will appear in the fourth row. Then perform the arithmetic to verify your conjecture.

$$\frac{1}{1\cdot 2}+\frac{1}{2\cdot 3}=\frac{2}{3}$$

$$\frac{1}{1\cdot 2}+\frac{1}{2\cdot 3}+\frac{1}{3\cdot 4}=\frac{3}{4}$$

$$\frac{1}{1\cdot 2}+\frac{1}{2\cdot 3}+\frac{1}{3\cdot 4}+\frac{1}{4\cdot 5}=\frac{4}{5}$$

• Technology Exercises

149. Use a calculator to express the following rational numbers as decimals.

a. $\frac{197}{800}$ **b.** $\frac{4539}{3125}$ **c.** $\frac{7}{6250}$

150. Some calculators have a fraction feature. This feature allows you to perform operations with fractions and displays the answer as a fraction reduced to its lowest terms. If your calculator has this feature, use it to verify any five of the answers that you obtained in Exercises 57–92.

• Group Exercise

151. Each member of the group should present an application of rational numbers. The application can be based on research or on how the group member uses rational numbers in his or her life. If you are not sure where to begin, ask yourself how your life would be different if fractions and decimals were concepts unknown to our civilization.

SECTION 5.4 • THE IRRATIONAL NUMBERS

OBJECTIVES

1. Define the irrational numbers.
2. Simplify square roots.
3. Perform operations with square roots.
4. Rationalize the denominator.

Shown here is Renaissance artist Raphael Sanzio's (1483–1520) image of Pythagoras from *The School of Athens* mural. Detail of left side.
Stanza della Segnatura, Vatican Palace, Vatican State. Scala/Art Resource, NY.

For the followers of the Greek mathematician Pythagoras in the sixth century B.C., numbers took on a life-and-death importance. The "Pythagorean Brotherhood" was a secret group whose members were convinced that properties of whole numbers were the key to understanding the universe. Members of the Brotherhood (which admitted women) thought that all numbers that were not whole numbers could be

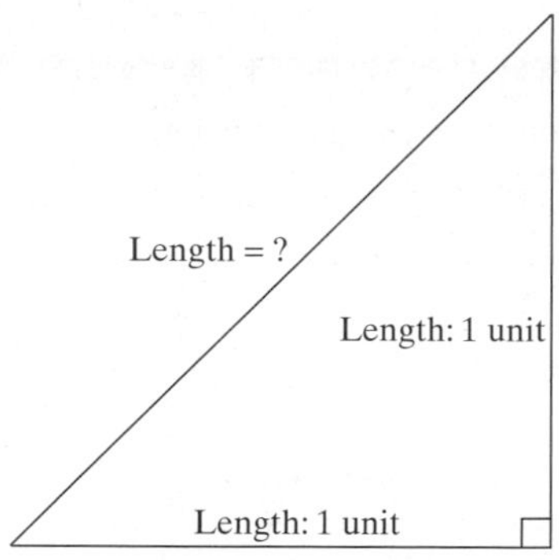

FIGURE 5.5

represented as the ratio of whole numbers. A crisis occurred for the Pythagoreans when they discovered the existence of a number that was not rational. Because the Pythagoreans viewed numbers with reverence and awe, the punishment for speaking about this number was death. However, a member of the Brotherhood revealed the secret of the number's existence. When he later died in a shipwreck, his death was viewed as punishment from the gods.

The triangle in Figure 5.5 led the Pythagoreans to the discovery of a number that could not be expressed as the quotient of integers. Based on their understanding of the relationship among the sides of this triangle, they knew that the length of the side shown in red had to be a number that, when squared, is equal to 2. The Pythagoreans discovered that this number seemed to be close to the rational numbers

$$\frac{14}{10}, \frac{141}{100}, \frac{1414}{1000}, \frac{14{,}141}{10{,}000}, \text{ and so on.}$$

However, they were shocked to find that there is no quotient of integers whose square is equal to 2.

The positive number whose square is equal to 2 is written $\sqrt{2}$. We read this "the square root of 2," or "radical 2." The symbol $\sqrt{\ }$ is called the **radical sign**. The number under the radical sign, in this case 2, is called the **radicand**. The entire symbol $\sqrt{2}$ is called a **radical**.

Using deductive reasoning, mathematicians have proved that $\sqrt{2}$ cannot be represented as a quotient of integers. This means that there is no terminating or repeating decimal that can be multiplied by itself to give 2. We can, however, give a decimal approximation for $\sqrt{2}$. We use the symbol $\approx$, which means "is approximately equal to." Thus,

$$\sqrt{2} \approx 1.414214.$$

We can verify that this is only an approximation by multiplying 1.414214 by itself. The product is not exactly 2:

$$1.414214 \times 1.414214 = 2.000001237796.$$

1 Define the irrational numbers.

A number like $\sqrt{2}$, whose decimal representation does not come to an end and does not have a block of repeating digits, is an example of an **irrational number**.

> **THE IRRATIONAL NUMBERS**
> The set of **irrational numbers** is the set of numbers whose decimal representations are neither terminating nor repeating.

Perhaps the best known of all the irrational numbers is π (pi). This irrational number represents the distance around a circle (its circumference) divided by the diameter of the circle. In the *Star Trek* episode "Wolf in the Fold," Spock foils an evil computer by telling it to "compute the last digit in the value of π." Because π is an irrational number, there is no last digit in its decimal representation:

$$\pi = 3.14159265358979323846264338327 95\ldots.$$

The nature of the irrational number π has fascinated mathematicians for centuries. Amateur and professional mathematicians have taken up the challenge of calculating π to more and more decimal places. Although such an exercise may seem pointless, it serves as the ultimate stress test for new high-speed computers and also as a test for the long-standing, but still unproven, conjecture that the distribution of digits in π is completely random.

BLITZER BONUS

The Best and Worst of π

In 2002, Japanese mathematicians at Tokyo University calculated π to 1.24 trillion decimal places. The calculations used 400 hours of computer time, beating their previous record, set in 1999, of 206 billion places.

The most inaccurate version of π came from the 1897 General Assembly of Indiana. Bill No. 246 stated that "π was by law 4."

TECHNOLOGY

You can obtain decimal approximations for irrational numbers using a calculator. For example, to approximate $\sqrt{2}$, use the following keystrokes:

Scientific Calculator	Graphing Calculator
2 [√] or 2 [2ND/INV] [x^2]	[√] 2 [ENTER] or [2ND/INV] [x^2] 2 [ENTER]

Some graphing calculators show an open parenthesis after displaying √‾. In this case, enter a closed parenthesis, [ )], after 2.

The display may read 1.41421356237, although your calculator may show more or fewer digits. Between which two integers would you graph $\sqrt{2}$ on a number line?

The U.N. building is designed with three golden rectangles.

Square Roots

The United Nations Building in New York was designed to represent its mission of promoting world harmony. Viewed from the front, the building looks like three rectangles stacked upon each other. In each rectangle, the width divided by the height is $\sqrt{5} + 1$ to 2, approximately 1.618 to 1. The ancient Greeks believed that such a rectangle, called a **golden rectangle**, was the most pleasing of all rectangles. The comparison 1.618 to 1 is approximate because $\sqrt{5}$ is an irrational number.

The **principal square root** of a nonnegative number n, written $\sqrt{n}$, is the positive number that when multiplied by itself gives n. Thus,

$$\sqrt{36} = 6 \text{ because } 6 \cdot 6 = 36$$

and

$$\sqrt{81} = 9 \text{ because } 9 \cdot 9 = 81.$$

Notice that both $\sqrt{36}$ and $\sqrt{81}$ are rational numbers because 6 and 9 are terminating decimals. Thus, **not all square roots are irrational.**

Numbers such as 36 and 81 are called *perfect squares*. A **perfect square** is a number that is the square of a whole number. The first few perfect squares are listed below.

$\mathbf{0} = 0^2$	$\mathbf{16} = 4^2$	$\mathbf{64} = 8^2$	$\mathbf{144} = 12^2$
$\mathbf{1} = 1^2$	$\mathbf{25} = 5^2$	$\mathbf{81} = 9^2$	$\mathbf{169} = 13^2$
$\mathbf{4} = 2^2$	$\mathbf{36} = 6^2$	$\mathbf{100} = 10^2$	$\mathbf{196} = 14^2$
$\mathbf{9} = 3^2$	$\mathbf{49} = 7^2$	$\mathbf{121} = 11^2$	$\mathbf{225} = 15^2$

The principal square root of a perfect square is a whole number. For example,

$$\sqrt{0} = 0, \sqrt{1} = 1, \sqrt{4} = 2, \sqrt{9} = 3, \sqrt{16} = 4, \sqrt{25} = 5, \sqrt{36} = 6,$$

and so on.

2 Simplify square roots.

Simplifying Square Roots

A rule for simplifying square roots can be generalized by comparing $\sqrt{25 \cdot 4}$ and $\sqrt{25} \cdot \sqrt{4}$. Notice that

$$\sqrt{25 \cdot 4} = \sqrt{100} = 10 \quad \text{and} \quad \sqrt{25} \cdot \sqrt{4} = 5 \cdot 2 = 10.$$

Because we obtain 10 in both situations, the original radicals must be equal. That is,

$$\sqrt{25 \cdot 4} = \sqrt{25} \cdot \sqrt{4}.$$

STUDY TIP

There are no addition or subtraction rules for square roots:

$$\sqrt{a+b} \neq \sqrt{a} + \sqrt{b}$$
$$\sqrt{a-b} \neq \sqrt{a} - \sqrt{b}.$$

For example, if $a = 9$ and $b = 16$,

$$\sqrt{9+16} = \sqrt{25} = 5$$

and

$$\sqrt{9} + \sqrt{16} = 3 + 4 = 7.$$

Thus,

$$\sqrt{9+16} \neq \sqrt{9} + \sqrt{16}.$$

This result is a particular case of the **product rule for square roots** that can be generalized as follows:

THE PRODUCT RULE FOR SQUARE ROOTS

If a and b represent nonnegative numbers, then

$$\sqrt{ab} = \sqrt{a}\cdot\sqrt{b} \quad \text{and} \quad \sqrt{a}\cdot\sqrt{b} = \sqrt{ab}.$$

The square root of a product is the product of the square roots.

Example 1 shows how the product rule is used to remove from the square root any perfect squares that occur as factors.

EXAMPLE 1 SIMPLIFYING SQUARE ROOTS

Simplify, if possible:

a. $\sqrt{75}$ **b.** $\sqrt{500}$ **c.** $\sqrt{17}$.

SOLUTION

a. $\sqrt{75} = \sqrt{25\cdot 3}$ 25 is the greatest perfect square that is a factor of 75.

$= \sqrt{25}\cdot\sqrt{3}$ $\sqrt{ab} = \sqrt{a}\cdot\sqrt{b}$

$= 5\sqrt{3}$ Write $\sqrt{25}$ as 5.

b. $\sqrt{500} = \sqrt{100\cdot 5}$ 100 is the greatest perfect square factor of 500.

$= \sqrt{100}\cdot\sqrt{5}$ $\sqrt{ab} = \sqrt{a}\cdot\sqrt{b}$

$= 10\sqrt{5}$ Write $\sqrt{100}$ as 10.

c. Because 17 has no perfect square factors (other than 1), $\sqrt{17}$ cannot be simplified.

CHECK POINT 1 Simplify, if possible:

a. $\sqrt{12}$ **b.** $\sqrt{60}$ **c.** $\sqrt{55}$.

3 Perform operations with square roots.

Multiplying Square Roots

If a and b are nonnegative, then we can use the product rule

$$\sqrt{a}\cdot\sqrt{b} = \sqrt{a\cdot b}$$

to multiply square roots. The product of the square roots is the square root of the product. Once the square roots are multiplied, simplify the square root of the product when possible.

EXAMPLE 2 MULTIPLYING SQUARE ROOTS

Multiply:

a. $\sqrt{2}\cdot\sqrt{5}$ **b.** $\sqrt{7}\cdot\sqrt{7}$ **c.** $\sqrt{6}\cdot\sqrt{12}$.

SOLUTION

a. $\sqrt{2}\cdot\sqrt{5} = \sqrt{2\cdot 5} = \sqrt{10}$

b. $\sqrt{7}\cdot\sqrt{7} = \sqrt{7\cdot 7} = \sqrt{49} = 7$

It is possible to multiply irrational numbers and obtain a rational number for the product.

c. $\sqrt{6}\cdot\sqrt{12} = \sqrt{6\cdot 12} = \sqrt{72} = \sqrt{36\cdot 2} = \sqrt{36}\cdot\sqrt{2} = 6\sqrt{2}$

CHECK POINT 2 Multiply:

a. $\sqrt{3}\cdot\sqrt{10}$ **b.** $\sqrt{10}\cdot\sqrt{10}$ **c.** $\sqrt{6}\cdot\sqrt{2}$.

BLITZER BONUS

A Radical Idea: Time Is Relative

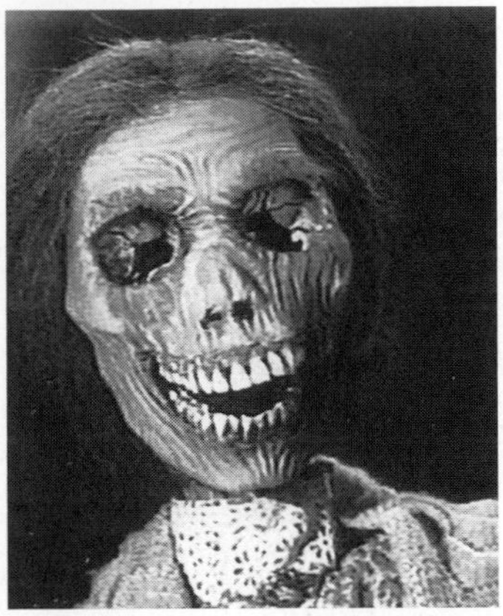

What does travel in space have to do with square roots? Imagine that in the future we will be able to travel at velocities approaching the speed of light (approximately 186,000 miles per second). According to Einstein's theory of relativity, time would pass more quickly on Earth than it would in the moving spaceship. The square root expression

$$R_f\sqrt{1-\left(\frac{v}{c}\right)^2}$$

gives the aging rate of an astronaut relative to the aging rate of a friend on Earth, R_f. In the expression, v is the astronaut's speed and c is the speed of light. As the astronaut's speed approaches the speed of light, we can substitute c for v:

$$R_f\sqrt{1-\left(\frac{v}{c}\right)^2} \quad \text{Let } v = c.$$
$$= R_f\sqrt{1-\left(\frac{c}{c}\right)^2}$$
$$= R_f\sqrt{1-1^2}$$
$$= R_f\sqrt{0} = 0.$$

Close to the speed of light, the astronaut's aging rate relative to a friend on Earth is nearly 0. What does this mean? As we age here on Earth, the space traveler would barely get older. The space traveler would return to a futuristic world in which friends and loved ones would be long dead.

Dividing Square Roots

Another property for square roots involves division.

THE QUOTIENT RULE FOR SQUARE ROOTS

If a and b represent nonnegative numbers and $b \neq 0$, then

$$\frac{\sqrt{a}}{\sqrt{b}} = \sqrt{\frac{a}{b}} \quad \text{and} \quad \sqrt{\frac{a}{b}} = \frac{\sqrt{a}}{\sqrt{b}}.$$

The quotient of two square roots is the square root of the quotient.

Once the square roots are divided, simplify the square root of the quotient when possible.

EXAMPLE 3 DIVIDING SQUARE ROOTS

Find the quotient:

a. $\frac{\sqrt{75}}{\sqrt{3}}$ **b.** $\frac{\sqrt{90}}{\sqrt{2}}$.

SOLUTION

a. $\frac{\sqrt{75}}{\sqrt{3}} = \sqrt{\frac{75}{3}} = \sqrt{25} = 5$

b. $\frac{\sqrt{90}}{\sqrt{2}} = \sqrt{\frac{90}{2}} = \sqrt{45} = \sqrt{9 \cdot 5} = \sqrt{9} \cdot \sqrt{5} = 3\sqrt{5}$

CHECK POINT 3 Find the quotient:

a. $\frac{\sqrt{80}}{\sqrt{5}}$ **b.** $\frac{\sqrt{48}}{\sqrt{6}}$.

Adding and Subtracting Square Roots

The number that multiplies a square root is called the square root's **coefficient**. For example, in $3\sqrt{5}$, 3 is the coefficient of the square root.

Square roots with the same radicand can be added or subtracted by adding or subtracting their coefficients:

$$a\sqrt{c} + b\sqrt{c} = (a+b)\sqrt{c} \qquad a\sqrt{c} - b\sqrt{c} = (a-b)\sqrt{c}.$$

Sum of coefficients times the common square root

Difference of coefficients times the common square root

EXAMPLE 4 ADDING AND SUBTRACTING SQUARE ROOTS

Add or subtract as indicated:

a. $7\sqrt{2} + 5\sqrt{2}$ **b.** $2\sqrt{5} - 6\sqrt{5}$ **c.** $3\sqrt{7} + 9\sqrt{7} - \sqrt{7}$.

SOLUTION

a. $7\sqrt{2} + 5\sqrt{2} = (7+5)\sqrt{2}$
$= 12\sqrt{2}$

b. $2\sqrt{5} - 6\sqrt{5} = (2-6)\sqrt{5}$
$= -4\sqrt{5}$

c. $3\sqrt{7} + 9\sqrt{7} - \sqrt{7} = 3\sqrt{7} + 9\sqrt{7} - 1\sqrt{7}$ Write $\sqrt{7}$ as $1\sqrt{7}$.
$= (3 + 9 - 1)\sqrt{7}$
$= 11\sqrt{7}$

CHECK POINT 4 Add or subtract as indicated:

a. $8\sqrt{3} + 10\sqrt{3}$ **b.** $4\sqrt{13} - 9\sqrt{13}$ **c.** $7\sqrt{10} + 2\sqrt{10} - \sqrt{10}$.

In some situations, it is possible to add and subtract square roots that do not contain a common square root by first simplifying.

EXAMPLE 5 ADDING AND SUBTRACTING SQUARE ROOTS BY FIRST SIMPLIFYING

Add or subtract as indicated:

a. $\sqrt{2} + \sqrt{8}$ **b.** $4\sqrt{50} - 6\sqrt{32}$.

SOLUTION

a. $\sqrt{2} + \sqrt{8}$

$= \sqrt{2} + \sqrt{4 \cdot 2}$ Split 8 into two factors such that one is a perfect square.

$= 1\sqrt{2} + 2\sqrt{2}$ $\sqrt{4 \cdot 2} = \sqrt{4} \cdot \sqrt{2} = 2\sqrt{2}$

$= (1 + 2)\sqrt{2}$ Add coefficients and retain the common square root.

$= 3\sqrt{2}$ Simplify.

b. $4\sqrt{50} - 6\sqrt{32}$

$= 4\sqrt{25 \cdot 2} - 6\sqrt{16 \cdot 2}$ 25 is the greatest perfect square factor of 50 and 16 is the greatest perfect square factor of 32.

$= 4 \cdot 5\sqrt{2} - 6 \cdot 4\sqrt{2}$ $\sqrt{25 \cdot 2} = \sqrt{25}\sqrt{2} = 5\sqrt{2}$ and $\sqrt{16 \cdot 2} = \sqrt{16}\sqrt{2} = 4\sqrt{2}$.

$= 20\sqrt{2} - 24\sqrt{2}$ Multiply.

$= (20 - 24)\sqrt{2}$ Subtract coefficients and retain the common square root.

$= -4\sqrt{2}$ Simplify.

STUDY TIP

Sums or differences of square roots that cannot be simplified and that do not contain a common square root cannot be combined into one term by adding or subtracting coefficients. Some examples:

- $5\sqrt{3} + 3\sqrt{5}$ cannot be combined by adding coefficients. The square roots, $\sqrt{3}$ and $\sqrt{5}$, are different.
- $28 + 7\sqrt{3}$, or $28\sqrt{1} + 7\sqrt{3}$, cannot be combined by adding coefficients. The square roots, $\sqrt{1}$ and $\sqrt{3}$, are different.

CHECK POINT 5 Add or subtract as indicated:

a. $\sqrt{3} + \sqrt{12}$ **b.** $4\sqrt{8} - 7\sqrt{18}$.

4 Rationalize the denominator.

Rationalizing the Denominator

You can use a calculator to compare the approximate values for $\frac{1}{\sqrt{3}}$ and $\frac{\sqrt{3}}{3}$. The two approximations are the same. This is not a coincidence:

$$\frac{1}{\sqrt{3}} = \frac{1}{\sqrt{3}} \cdot \boxed{\frac{\sqrt{3}}{\sqrt{3}}} = \frac{\sqrt{3}}{\sqrt{9}} = \frac{\sqrt{3}}{3}$$

Any number divided by itself is 1. Multiplication by 1 does not change the value of $\frac{1}{\sqrt{3}}$.

This process involves rewriting a radical expression as an equivalent expression in which the denominator no longer contains any radicals. The process is called

rationalizing the denominator. If the denominator contains the square root of a natural number that is not a perfect square, **multiply the numerator and the denominator by the smallest number that produces the square root of a perfect square in the denominator.**

EXAMPLE 6 RATIONALIZING DENOMINATORS

Rationalize the denominator:

a. $\frac{15}{\sqrt{6}}$ **b.** $\sqrt{\frac{3}{5}}$ **c.** $\frac{12}{\sqrt{8}}$.

SOLUTION

a. If we multiply numerator and denominator of $\frac{15}{\sqrt{6}}$ by $\sqrt{6}$, the denominator becomes $\sqrt{6}\cdot\sqrt{6} = \sqrt{36} = 6$. Therefore, we multiply by 1, choosing $\frac{\sqrt{6}}{\sqrt{6}}$ for 1.

$$\frac{15}{\sqrt{6}} = \frac{15}{\sqrt{6}}\cdot\frac{\sqrt{6}}{\sqrt{6}} = \frac{15\sqrt{6}}{\sqrt{36}} = \frac{15\sqrt{6}}{6} = \frac{5\sqrt{6}}{2}$$

Multiply by 1.

Simplify: $\frac{15}{6} = \frac{5\cdot\not{3}}{2\cdot\not{3}} = \frac{5}{2}$.

b. $$\sqrt{\frac{3}{5}} = \frac{\sqrt{3}}{\sqrt{5}} = \frac{\sqrt{3}}{\sqrt{5}}\cdot\frac{\sqrt{5}}{\sqrt{5}} = \frac{\sqrt{15}}{\sqrt{25}} = \frac{\sqrt{15}}{5}$$

Multiply by 1.

c. The *smallest* number that will produce a perfect square in the denominator of $\frac{12}{\sqrt{8}}$ is $\sqrt{2}$, because $\sqrt{8}\cdot\sqrt{2} = \sqrt{16} = 4$. We multiply by 1, choosing $\frac{\sqrt{2}}{\sqrt{2}}$ for 1.

$$\frac{12}{\sqrt{8}} = \frac{12}{\sqrt{8}}\cdot\frac{\sqrt{2}}{\sqrt{2}} = \frac{12\sqrt{2}}{\sqrt{16}} = \frac{12\sqrt{2}}{4} = 3\sqrt{2}$$

CHECK POINT 6 Rationalize the denominator:

a. $\frac{25}{\sqrt{10}}$ **b.** $\sqrt{\frac{2}{7}}$ **c.** $\frac{5}{\sqrt{18}}$.

BLITZER BONUS

Golden Rectangles

The early Greeks believed that the most pleasing of all rectangles were **golden rectangles**, whose ratio of width to height is

$$\frac{w}{h} = \frac{2}{\sqrt{5}-1}.$$

The Parthenon at Athens fits into a golden rectangle once the triangular pediment is reconstructed.

STUDY TIP

You can rationalize the denominator of $\frac{12}{\sqrt{8}}$ by multiplying by $\frac{\sqrt{8}}{\sqrt{8}}$. However, it takes more work to simplify the result.

Irrational Numbers and Other Kinds of Roots

Irrational numbers appear in roots other than square roots. The symbol $\sqrt[3]{\ }$ represents the **cube root** of a number. For example,

$$\sqrt[3]{8} = 2 \text{ because } 2\cdot2\cdot2 = 8 \quad\text{and}\quad \sqrt[3]{64} = 4 \text{ because } 4\cdot4\cdot4 = 64.$$

Although these cube roots are rational numbers, most cube roots are not. For example,

$$\sqrt[3]{217} \approx 6.0092 \text{ because } (6.0092)^3 \approx 216.995, \text{ not exactly } 217.$$

There is no end to the kinds of roots for numbers. For example, $\sqrt[4]{\ }$ represents the **fourth root** of a number. Thus, $\sqrt[4]{81} = 3$ because $3\cdot3\cdot3\cdot3 = 81$. Although the fourth root of 81 is rational, most fourth roots, fifth roots, and so on tend to be irrational.

EXERCISE SET 5.4

• Practice Exercises

Evaluate each expression in Exercises 1–10.

1. $\sqrt{9}$ **2.** $\sqrt{16}$ **3.** $\sqrt{25}$ **4.** $\sqrt{49}$
5. $\sqrt{64}$ **6.** $\sqrt{100}$ **7.** $\sqrt{121}$ **8.** $\sqrt{144}$
9. $\sqrt{169}$ **10.** $\sqrt{225}$

In Exercises 11–16, use a calculator with a square root key to find a decimal approximation for each square root. Round the number displayed to the nearest **a.** *tenth,* **b.** *hundredth,* **c.** *thousandth.*

11. $\sqrt{173}$ **12.** $\sqrt{3176}$ **13.** $\sqrt{17{,}761}$
14. $\sqrt{779{,}264}$ **15.** $\sqrt{\pi}$ **16.** $\sqrt{2\pi}$

In Exercises 17–24, simplify the square root.

17. $\sqrt{20}$ **18.** $\sqrt{50}$ **19.** $\sqrt{80}$ **20.** $\sqrt{12}$
21. $\sqrt{250}$ **22.** $\sqrt{192}$ **23.** $7\sqrt{28}$ **24.** $3\sqrt{52}$

In Exercises 25–56, perform the indicated operation. Simplify the answer when possible.

25. $\sqrt{7}\cdot\sqrt{6}$ **26.** $\sqrt{19}\cdot\sqrt{3}$ **27.** $\sqrt{6}\cdot\sqrt{6}$
28. $\sqrt{5}\cdot\sqrt{5}$ **29.** $\sqrt{3}\cdot\sqrt{6}$ **30.** $\sqrt{12}\cdot\sqrt{2}$
31. $\sqrt{2}\cdot\sqrt{26}$ **32.** $\sqrt{5}\cdot\sqrt{50}$ **33.** $\frac{\sqrt{54}}{\sqrt{6}}$
34. $\frac{\sqrt{75}}{\sqrt{3}}$ **35.** $\frac{\sqrt{90}}{\sqrt{2}}$ **36.** $\frac{\sqrt{60}}{\sqrt{3}}$
37. $\frac{-\sqrt{96}}{\sqrt{2}}$ **38.** $\frac{-\sqrt{150}}{\sqrt{3}}$ **39.** $7\sqrt{3} + 6\sqrt{3}$
40. $8\sqrt{5} + 11\sqrt{5}$ **41.** $4\sqrt{13} - 6\sqrt{13}$
42. $6\sqrt{17} - 8\sqrt{17}$ **43.** $\sqrt{5} + \sqrt{5}$
44. $\sqrt{3} + \sqrt{3}$ **45.** $4\sqrt{2} - 5\sqrt{2} + 8\sqrt{2}$
46. $6\sqrt{3} + 8\sqrt{3} - 16\sqrt{3}$ **47.** $\sqrt{5} + \sqrt{20}$
48. $\sqrt{3} + \sqrt{27}$ **49.** $\sqrt{50} - \sqrt{18}$
50. $\sqrt{63} - \sqrt{28}$ **51.** $3\sqrt{18} + 5\sqrt{50}$
52. $4\sqrt{12} + 2\sqrt{75}$ **53.** $\frac{1}{4}\sqrt{12} - \frac{1}{2}\sqrt{48}$
54. $\frac{1}{5}\sqrt{300} - \frac{2}{3}\sqrt{27}$ **55.** $3\sqrt{75} + 2\sqrt{12} - 2\sqrt{48}$
56. $2\sqrt{72} + 3\sqrt{50} - \sqrt{128}$

In Exercises 57–66, rationalize the denominator.

57. $\frac{5}{\sqrt{3}}$ **58.** $\frac{12}{\sqrt{5}}$ **59.** $\frac{21}{\sqrt{7}}$
60. $\frac{30}{\sqrt{5}}$ **61.** $\frac{12}{\sqrt{30}}$ **62.** $\frac{15}{\sqrt{50}}$
63. $\frac{15}{\sqrt{12}}$ **64.** $\frac{13}{\sqrt{40}}$ **65.** $\sqrt{\frac{2}{5}}$ **66.** $\sqrt{\frac{5}{7}}$

• Practice Plus

In Exercises 67–74, perform the indicated operations. Simplify the answer when possible.

67. $3\sqrt{8} - \sqrt{32} + 3\sqrt{72} - \sqrt{75}$
68. $3\sqrt{54} - 2\sqrt{24} - \sqrt{96} + 4\sqrt{63}$
69. $3\sqrt{7} - 5\sqrt{14}\cdot\sqrt{2}$
70. $4\sqrt{2} - 8\sqrt{10}\cdot\sqrt{5}$
71. $\frac{\sqrt{32}}{5} + \frac{\sqrt{18}}{7}$ **72.** $\frac{\sqrt{27}}{2} + \frac{\sqrt{75}}{7}$
73. $\frac{\sqrt{2}}{\sqrt{3}} + \frac{\sqrt{3}}{\sqrt{2}}$ **74.** $\frac{\sqrt{2}}{\sqrt{7}} + \frac{\sqrt{7}}{\sqrt{2}}$

• Application Exercises

The formula

$$d = \sqrt{\frac{3h}{2}}$$

models the distance, d, in miles, that a person h feet high can see to the horizon. Use this formula to solve Exercises 75–76.

75. The pool deck on a cruise ship is 72 feet above the water. How far can passengers on the pool deck see? Write the answer in simplified radical form. Then use the simplified radical form and a calculator to express the answer to the nearest tenth of a mile.

76. The captain of a cruise ship is on the star deck, which is 120 feet above the water. How far can the captain see? Write the answer in simplified radical form. Then use the simplified radical form and a calculator to express the answer to the nearest tenth of a mile.

Police use the formula $v = 2\sqrt{5L}$ to estimate the speed of a car, v, in miles per hour, based on the length, L, in feet, of its skid marks upon sudden braking on a dry asphalt road. Use the formula to solve Exercises 77–78.

77. A motorist is involved in an accident. A police officer measures the car's skid marks to be 245 feet long. Estimate the speed at which the motorist was traveling before braking. If the posted speed limit is 50 miles per hour and the motorist tells the officer he was not speeding, should the officer believe him? Explain.

78. A motorist is involved in an accident. A police officer measures the car's skid marks to be 45 feet long. Estimate the speed at which the motorist was traveling before braking. If the posted speed limit is 35 miles per hour and the motorist tells the officer she was not speeding, should the officer believe her? Explain.

79. The graph shows the median heights for boys of various ages in the United States from birth through 60 months, or five years old.

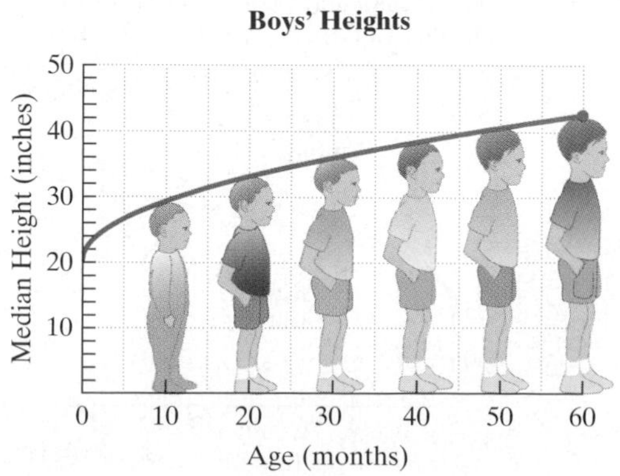

Source: Laura Walther Nathanson, *The Portable Pediatrician for Parents*

a. Use the graph at the bottom of the previous page to estimate the median height, to the nearest inch, of boys who are 50 months old.

b. The formula $h = 2.9\sqrt{x} + 20.1$ models the median height, h, in inches, of boys who are x months of age. According to the formula, what is the median height of boys who are 50 months old? Use a calculator and round to the nearest tenth of an inch. How well does your estimate from part (a) describe the median height obtained from the formula?

80. The graph shows the median heights for girls of various ages in the United States from birth through 60 months, or five years old.

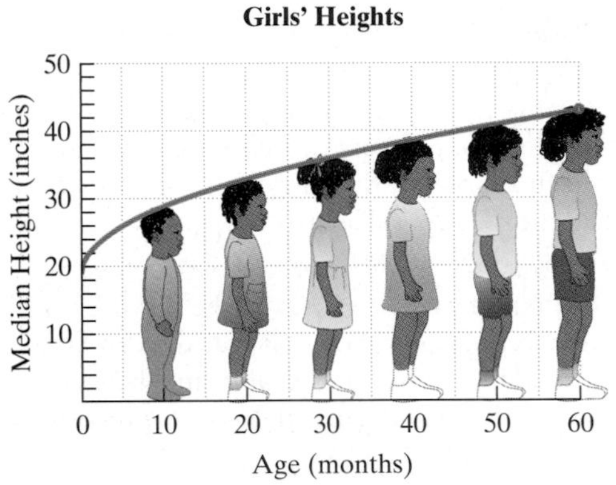

Source: Laura Walther Nathanson, *The Portable Pediatrician for Parents*

a. Use the graph to estimate the median height, to the nearest inch, of girls who are 50 months old.

b. The formula $h = 3.1\sqrt{x} + 19$ models the median height, h, in inches, of girls who are x months of age. According to the formula, what is the median height of girls who are 50 months old? Use a calculator and round to the nearest tenth of an inch. How well does your estimate from part (a) describe the median height obtained from the formula?

Autism is a neurological disorder that impedes language and derails social and emotional development. New findings suggest that the condition is not a sudden calamity that strikes children at the age of 2 or 3, but a developmental problem linked to abnormally rapid brain growth during infancy. The graphs show that the heads of severely autistic children start out smaller than average and then go through a period of explosive growth. Exercises 81–82 involve mathematical models for the data shown by the graphs.

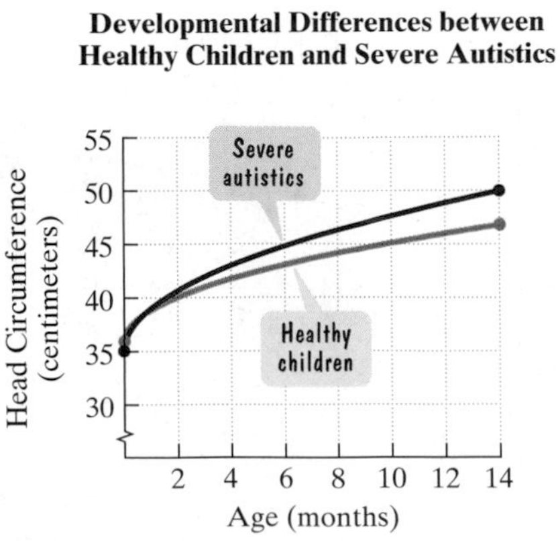

Source: The Journal of the American Medical Association

81. The data for one of the two groups shown by the graphs in the previous column can be modeled by

$$H = 2.9\sqrt{x} + 36,$$

where H is the head circumference, in centimeters, at age x months, $0 \leq x \leq 14$.

a. According to the model, what is the head circumference at birth?

b. According to the model, what is the head circumference at 9 months?

c. According to the model, what is the head circumference at 14 months? Use a calculator and round to the nearest tenth of a centimeter.

d. Use the values that you obtained in parts (a) through (c) and the graphs shown at the bottom of the previous column to determine if the given model describes healthy children or severe autistics.

82. The data for one of the two groups shown by the graphs in the previous column can be modeled by

$$H = 4\sqrt{x} + 35,$$

where H is the head circumference, in centimeters, at age x months, $0 \leq x \leq 14$.

a. According to the model, what is the head circumference at birth?

b. According to the model, what is the head circumference at 9 months?

c. According to the model, what is the head circumference at 14 months? Use a calculator and round to the nearest centimeter.

d. Use the values that you obtained in parts (a) through (c) and the graphs shown at the bottom of the previous column to determine if the given model describes healthy children or severe autistics.

The Blitzer Bonus on page 266 gives the square root expression

$$R_f\sqrt{1 - \left(\frac{v}{c}\right)^2}$$

for the aging rate of an astronaut relative to the aging rate of a friend on Earth, R_f, where v is the astronaut's speed and c is the speed of light. Take a few minutes to read the essay and then solve Exercises 83–84.

83. You are moving at 80% of the speed of light. Substitute $0.8c$ in the expression shown above. What is your aging rate relative to a friend on Earth? If 100 weeks have passed for your friend, how long were you gone?

84. You are moving at 90% of the speed of light. Substitute $0.9c$ in the expression shown above. What is your aging rate, correct to two decimal places, relative to a friend on Earth? If 100 weeks have passed for your friend, how long, to the nearest week, were you gone?

• Writing in Mathematics

85. Describe the difference between a rational number and an irrational number.

86. Describe what is wrong with this statement: $\pi = \frac{22}{7}$.

87. Using $\sqrt{50}$, explain how to simplify a square root.

88. Describe how to multiply square roots.

89. Explain how to add square roots with the same radicand.

90. Explain how to add $\sqrt{3} + \sqrt{12}$.

91. Describe what it means to rationalize a denominator. Use $\frac{2}{\sqrt{5}}$ in your explanation.

• Critical Thinking Exercises

92. Which one of the following is true?

a. The product of any two irrational numbers is always an irrational number.

b. $\sqrt{9} + \sqrt{16} = \sqrt{25}$

c. $\sqrt{\sqrt{16}} = 2$

d. $\frac{\sqrt{64}}{2} = \sqrt{32}$

In Exercises 93–95, insert either < or > in the shaded area between the numbers to make each statement true.

93. $\sqrt{2}$ ▒ 1.5 **94.** $-\pi$ ▒ -3.5 **95.** $-\frac{3.14}{2}$ ▒ $-\frac{\pi}{2}$

96. How does doubling a number affect its square root?

97. Between which two consecutive integers is $-\sqrt{47}$?

98. Simplify: $\sqrt{2} + \sqrt{\frac{1}{2}}$.

99. Create a counterexample to show that the following statement is false: The difference between two irrational numbers is always an irrational number.

• Group Exercises

The following topics related to irrational numbers are appropriate for either individual or group research projects. A report should be given to the class on the researched topic.

100. A History of How Irrational Numbers Developed

101. Pi: Its History, Applications, and Curiosities

102. Proving That $\sqrt{2}$ Is Irrational

103. Imaginary Numbers: Their History, Applications, and Curiosities

104. The Golden Rectangle in Art and Architecture

SECTION 5.5 • REAL NUMBERS AND THEIR PROPERTIES

OBJECTIVES

1. Recognize subsets of the real numbers.
2. Recognize properties of real numbers.

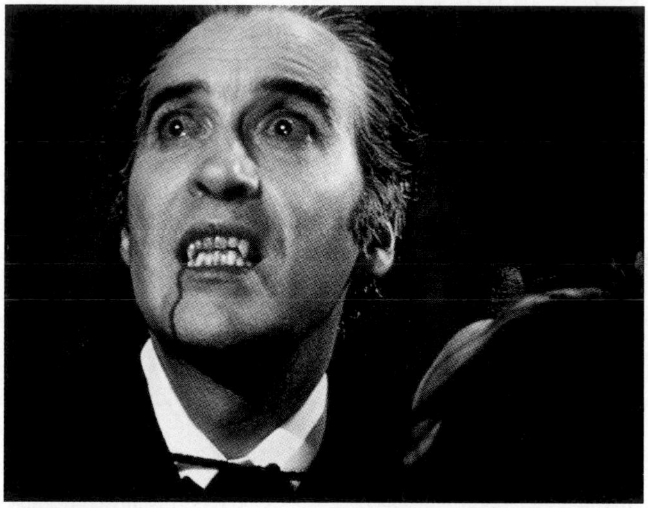

Horror films offer the pleasure of vicarious terror, of being safely scared.

1 Recognize subsets of the real numbers.

The Set of Real Numbers

The vampire legend is death as seducer; he/she sucks our blood to take us to a perverse immortality. The vampire resembles us, but appears only at night, hidden among mortals. In this section, you will find vampires in the world of numbers. Mathematicians even use the labels *vampire* and *weird* to describe sets of numbers. However, the label that appears most frequently is *real*. The union of the rational numbers and the irrational numbers is the set of **real numbers**.

The sets that make up the real numbers are summarized in Table 5.2 on the next page. We refer to these sets as **subsets** of the real numbers, meaning that all elements in each subset are also elements in the set of real numbers.

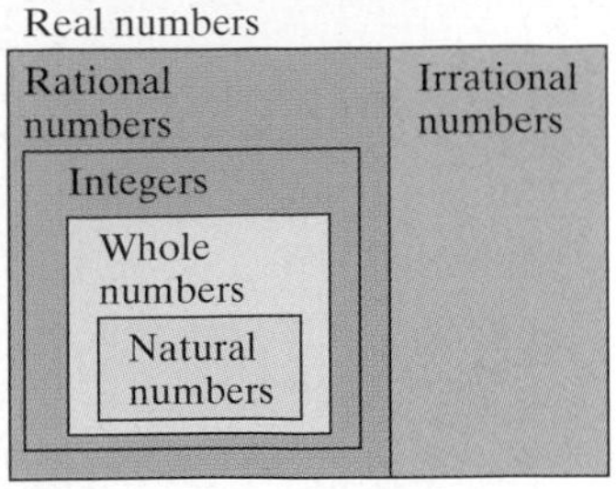

This diagram shows that every real number is rational or irrational.

TABLE 5.2 IMPORTANT SUBSETS OF THE REAL NUMBERS

Name	Description	Examples
Natural numbers	$\{1, 2, 3, 4, 5, \ldots\}$ These are the numbers that we use for counting.	$2, 3, 5, 17$
Whole numbers	$\{0, 1, 2, 3, 4, 5, \ldots\}$ The set of whole numbers includes 0 and the natural numbers.	$0, 2, 3, 5, 17$
Integers	$\{\ldots, -5, -4, -3, -2, -1, 0, 1, 2, 3, 4, 5, \ldots\}$ The set of integers includes the negatives of the natural numbers and the whole numbers.	$-17, -5, -3, -2, 0, 2, 3, 5, 17$
Rational numbers	$\left\{\frac{a}{b} \,\middle\vert\, a \text{ and } b \text{ are integers and } b \neq 0\right\}$ The set of rational numbers is the set of all numbers that can be expressed as a quotient of two integers, with the denominator not 0. Rational numbers can be expressed as terminating or repeating decimals.	$-17 = \frac{-17}{1}, -5 = \frac{-5}{1}, -3, -2,$ $0, 2, 3, 5, 17,$ $\frac{2}{5} = 0.4,$ $\frac{-2}{3} = -0.6666\ldots = -0.\overline{6}$
Irrational numbers	The set of irrational numbers is the set of all numbers whose decimal representations are neither terminating nor repeating. Irrational numbers cannot be expressed as a quotient of integers.	$\sqrt{2} \approx 1.414214$ $-\sqrt{3} \approx -1.73205$ $\pi \approx 3.142$ $-\frac{\pi}{2} \approx -1.571$

EXAMPLE 1 CLASSIFYING REAL NUMBERS

Consider the following set of numbers:

$$\left\{-7, -\frac{3}{4}, 0, 0.\overline{6}, \sqrt{5}, \pi, 7.3, \sqrt{81}\right\}.$$

List the numbers in the set that are

a. natural numbers. **b.** whole numbers. **c.** integers.
d. rational numbers. **e.** irrational numbers. **f.** real numbers.

SOLUTION

a. Natural numbers: The natural numbers are the numbers used for counting. The only natural number in the set is $\sqrt{81}$ because $\sqrt{81} = 9$. (9 multiplied by itself, or 9^2, is 81.)

b. Whole numbers: The whole numbers consist of the natural numbers and 0. The elements of the set that are whole numbers are 0 and $\sqrt{81}$.

c. Integers: The integers consist of the natural numbers, 0, and the negatives of the natural numbers. The elements of the set that are integers are $\sqrt{81}$, 0, and -7.

d. Rational numbers: All numbers in the set that can be expressed as the quotient of integers are rational numbers. These include $-7\left(-7 = \frac{-7}{1}\right), -\frac{3}{4}, 0\left(0 = \frac{0}{1}\right)$, and $\sqrt{81}\left(\sqrt{81} = \frac{9}{1}\right)$. Furthermore, all numbers in the set that are terminating or repeating decimals are also rational numbers. These include $0.\overline{6}$ and 7.3.

e. Irrational numbers: The irrational numbers in the set are $\sqrt{5}\,(\sqrt{5} \approx 2.236)$ and $\pi\,(\pi \approx 3.14)$. Both $\sqrt{5}$ and π are only approximately equal to 2.236 and 3.14, respectively. In decimal form, $\sqrt{5}$ and π neither terminate nor have blocks of repeating digits.

f. Real numbers: All the numbers in the given set are real numbers.

CHECK POINT 1 Consider the following set of numbers:

$$\left\{-9, -1.3, 0, 0.\overline{3}, \frac{\pi}{2}, \sqrt{9}, \sqrt{10}\right\}.$$

BLITZER BONUS

Weird Numbers

Mathematicians use the label **weird** to describe a number if

1. The sum of its factors, excluding the number itself, is greater than the number.
2. No partial collection of the factors adds up to the number.

The number 70 is weird. Its factors are 1, 2, 5, 7, 10, 14, and 35. The sum of these factors is 74, which is greater than 70. Two or more numbers in the list of factors cannot be added to obtain 70.

Weird numbers are rare. Below 10,000, the weird numbers are 70, 836, 4030, 5830, 7192, 7912, and 9272. It is not known whether an odd weird number exists.

List the numbers in the set that are

a. natural numbers. **b.** whole numbers. **c.** integers.
d. rational numbers. **e.** irrational numbers. **f.** real numbers.

BLITZER BONUS

Vampire Numbers

Like legendary vampires that lie concealed among humans, vampire numbers lie hidden within the set of real numbers, mostly undetected. By definition, vampire numbers have an even number of digits. Furthermore, they are the product of two numbers whose digits all survive, in scrambled form, in the vampire. For example, 1260, 1435, and 2187 are vampire numbers.

$$21 \times 60 = 1260 \qquad 35 \times 41 = 1435 \qquad 27 \times 81 = 2187$$

The digits 2, 1, 6, and 0 lie scrambled in the vampire number.

The digits 3, 5, 4, and 1 lurk within the vampire number.

The digits 2, 7, 8, and 1 survive in the vampire number.

As the real numbers grow increasingly larger, is it necessary to pull out a wooden stake with greater frequency? How often can you expect to find vampires hidden among the giants? And is it possible to find a weird vampire?

On the right of the equal sign is a 40-digit vampire number that was discovered using a Pascal program on a personal computer:

$$98{,}765{,}432{,}198{,}765{,}432{,}198 \times 98{,}765{,}432{,}198{,}830{,}604{,}534 = 9{,}754{,}610{,}597{,}415{,}368{,}368{,}844{,}499{,}268{,}390{,}128{,}385{,}732.$$

Source: Clifford Pickover, *Wonders of Numbers*, Oxford University Press, 2001

2 Recognize properties of real numbers.

Properties of the Real Numbers

When you use your calculator to add two real numbers, you can enter them in either order. The fact that two real numbers can be added in either order is called the **commutative property of addition**. You probably use this property, as well as other properties of real numbers listed in Table 5.3, without giving it much thought. The properties of the real numbers are especially useful in algebra, as we shall see in Chapter 6.

BLITZER BONUS

The Associative Property and the English Language

In the English language, phrases can take on different meanings depending on the way the words are associated with commas. Here are three examples.

- Woman, without her man, is nothing.
  Woman, without her, man is nothing.
- What's the latest dope?
  What's the latest, dope?
- Population of Amsterdam broken down by age and sex
  Population of Amsterdam, broken down by age and sex

TABLE 5.3 PROPERTIES OF THE REAL NUMBERS

Name	Meaning	Examples
Closure Property of Addition	The sum of any two real numbers is a real number.	$4\sqrt{2}$ is a real number and $5\sqrt{2}$ is a real number, so $4\sqrt{2}+5\sqrt{2}$, or $9\sqrt{2}$, is a real number.
Closure Property of Multiplication	The product of any two real numbers is a real number.	10 is a real number and $\frac{1}{2}$ is a real number, so $10 \cdot \frac{1}{2}$, or 5, is a real number.
Commutative Property of Addition	Changing order when adding does not affect the sum. $a+b=b+a$	$13+7=7+13$
Commutative Property of Multiplication	Changing order when multiplying does not affect the product. $ab=ba$	$13 \cdot 7 = 7 \cdot 13$ $\sqrt{2}\cdot\sqrt{5}=\sqrt{5}\cdot\sqrt{2}$
Associative Property of Addition	Changing grouping when adding does not affect the sum. $(a+b)+c=a+(b+c)$	$(7+2)+5=7+(2+5)$ $9+5=7+7$ $14=14$
Associative Property of Multiplication	Changing grouping when multiplying does not affect the product. $(ab)c=a(bc)$	$(7\cdot 2)\cdot 5 = 7\cdot(2\cdot 5)$ $14\cdot 5 = 7\cdot 10$ $70=70$
Distributive Property of Multiplication over Addition	Multiplication distributes over addition. $a\cdot(b+c)=a\cdot b+a\cdot c$	$7(4+\sqrt{3})=7\cdot 4+7\cdot\sqrt{3}$ $=28+7\sqrt{3}$

STUDY TIP

Commutative: Changes *order*.
Associative: Changes *grouping*.

EXAMPLE 2 IDENTIFYING PROPERTIES OF THE REAL NUMBERS

Name the property illustrated:

a. $\sqrt{3}\cdot 7 = 7\cdot\sqrt{3}$
b. $(4 + 7) + 6 = 4 + (7 + 6)$
c. $2(3 + \sqrt{5}) = 6 + 2\sqrt{5}$
d. $\sqrt{2} + (\sqrt{3} + \sqrt{7}) = \sqrt{2} + (\sqrt{7} + \sqrt{3})$.

SOLUTION

a. $\sqrt{3}\cdot 7 = 7\cdot\sqrt{3}$ — Commutative property of multiplication
b. $(4 + 7) + 6 = 4 + (7 + 6)$ — Associative property of addition
c. $2(3 + \sqrt{5}) = 6 + 2\sqrt{5}$ — Distributive property of multiplication over addition
d. $\sqrt{2} + (\sqrt{3} + \sqrt{7}) = \sqrt{2} + (\sqrt{7} + \sqrt{3})$ — The only change between the left and the right sides is in the order that $\sqrt{3}$ and $\sqrt{7}$ are added. The order is changed from $\sqrt{3} + \sqrt{7}$ to $\sqrt{7} + \sqrt{3}$ using the commutative property of addition.

CHECK POINT 2 Name the property illustrated:

a. $(4\cdot 7)\cdot 3 = 4\cdot(7\cdot 3)$
b. $3(\sqrt{5} + 4) = 3(4 + \sqrt{5})$
c. $3(\sqrt{5} + 4) = 3\sqrt{5} + 12$
d. $2(\sqrt{3} + \sqrt{7}) = (\sqrt{3} + \sqrt{7})2$.

Although the entire set of real numbers is closed with respect to addition and multiplication, some of the subsets of the real numbers do not satisfy the closure property for a given operation. If an operation on a set results in just one number that is not in that set, then the set is not closed for that operation.

EXAMPLE 3 VERIFYING CLOSURE

a. Are the integers closed with respect to multiplication?
b. Are the irrational numbers closed with respect to multiplication?
c. Are the natural numbers closed with respect to division?

SOLUTION

a. Consider some examples of the multiplication of integers:

$$3\cdot 2 = 6 \qquad 3(-2) = -6 \qquad -3(-2) = 6 \qquad -3\cdot 0 = 0.$$

The product of any two integers is always a positive integer, a negative integer, or zero, which is an integer. Thus, the integers are closed under the operation of multiplication.

b. If we multiply two irrational numbers, must the product always be an irrational number? The answer is no. Here is an example:

$$\sqrt{7}\cdot\sqrt{7} = \sqrt{49} = 7.$$

Both irrational — Not an irrational number

This means that the irrational numbers are not closed under the operation of multiplication.

c. If we divide any two natural numbers, must the quotient always be a natural number? The answer is no. Here is an example:

$$4 \div 8 = \tfrac{1}{2}.$$

Both natural numbers — Not a natural number

Thus, the natural numbers are not closed under the operation of division.

CHECK POINT 3

a. Are the natural numbers closed with respect to multiplication?
b. Are the integers closed with respect to division?

The commutative property involves a change in order with no change in the final result. However, changing the order in which we subtract and divide real numbers can produce different answers. For example,

$$7 - 4 \neq 4 - 7 \quad \text{and} \quad 6 \div 2 \neq 2 \div 6.$$

Because the real numbers are not commutative with respect to subtraction and division, it is important that you enter numbers in the correct order when using a calculator to perform these operations.

The associative property does not hold for the operations of subtraction and division. The examples below show that if we change groupings when subtracting or dividing three numbers, the answer may change.

$$(6-1) - 3 \neq 6 - (1-3) \qquad (8 \div 4) \div 2 \neq 8 \div (4 \div 2)$$
$$5 - 3 \neq 6 - (-2) \qquad 2 \div 2 \neq 8 \div 2$$
$$2 \neq 8 \qquad 1 \neq 4$$

BLITZER BONUS

Beyond the Real Numbers

Only real numbers greater than or equal to zero have real number square roots. The square root of -1, $\sqrt{-1}$, is not a real number. This is because there is no real number that can be multiplied by itself that results in -1. Multiplying any real number by itself can never give a negative product. In the sixteenth century, mathematician Girolamo Cardano wrote that square roots of negative numbers would cause "mental tortures." In spite of these "tortures," mathematicians invented a new number, called i, to represent $\sqrt{-1}$. The number i is not a real number; it is called an **imaginary number**. Thus, $\sqrt{9} = 3$, $-\sqrt{9} = -3$, but $\sqrt{-9}$ is not a real number. However, $\sqrt{-9}$ is an imaginary number, represented by $3i$. The adjective *real* as a way of describing what we now call the real numbers was first used by the French mathematician and philosopher René Descartes (1596–1650) in response to the concept of imaginary numbers.

EXERCISE SET 5.5

• Practice Exercises

In Exercises 1–4, list all numbers from the given set that are

a. *natural numbers.* **b.** *whole numbers.* **c.** *integers.*

d. *rational numbers.* **e.** *irrational numbers.* **f.** *real numbers.*

1. $\{-9, -\frac{4}{5}, 0, 0.25, \sqrt{3}, 9.2, \sqrt{100}\}$

2. $\{-7, -0.\overline{6}, 0, \sqrt{49}, \sqrt{50}\}$

3. $\{-11, -\frac{5}{6}, 0, 0.75, \sqrt{5}, \pi, \sqrt{64}\}$

4. $\{-5, -0.\overline{3}, 0, \sqrt{2}, \sqrt{4}\}$

5. Give an example of a whole number that is not a natural number.

6. Give an example of an integer that is not a whole number.

7. Give an example of a rational number that is not an integer.

8. Give an example of a rational number that is not a natural number.

9. Give an example of a number that is an integer, a whole number, and a natural number.

10. Give an example of a number that is a rational number, an integer, and a real number.

11. Give an example of a number that is an irrational number and a real number.

12. Give an example of a number that is a real number, but not an irrational number.

Complete each statement in Exercises 13–15 to illustrate the commutative property.

13. $3 + (4 + 5) = 3 + (5 + \_\_\_)$

14. $\sqrt{5} \cdot 4 = 4 \cdot \_\_\_$

15. $9 \cdot (6 + 2) = 9 \cdot (2 + \_\_\_)$

Complete each statement in Exercises 16–17 to illustrate the associative property.

16. $(3 + 7) + 9 = \_\_\_ + (7 + \_\_\_)$

17. $(4 \cdot 5) \cdot 3 = \_\_\_ \cdot (5 \cdot \_\_\_)$

Complete each statement in Exercises 18–20 to illustrate the distributive property.

18. $3 \cdot (6 + 4) = 3 \cdot 6 + 3 \cdot \_\_\_$

19. $\_\_\_ \cdot (4 + 5) = 7 \cdot 4 + 7 \cdot 5$

20. $2 \cdot (\_\_\_ + 3) = 2 \cdot 7 + 2 \cdot 3$

Use the distributive property to simplify the radical expressions in Exercises 21–28.

21. $5(6 + \sqrt{2})$

22. $4(3 + \sqrt{5})$

23. $\sqrt{7}(3 + \sqrt{2})$

24. $\sqrt{6}(7 + \sqrt{5})$

25. $\sqrt{3}(5 + \sqrt{3})$

26. $\sqrt{7}(9 + \sqrt{7})$

27. $\sqrt{6}(\sqrt{2} + \sqrt{6})$

28. $\sqrt{10}(\sqrt{2} + \sqrt{10})$

In Exercises 29–38, state the name of the property illustrated.

29. $6 + (-4) = (-4) + 6$

30. $11 \cdot (7 + 4) = 11 \cdot 7 + 11 \cdot 4$

31. $6 + (2 + 7) = (6 + 2) + 7$

32. $6 \cdot (2 \cdot 3) = 6 \cdot (3 \cdot 2)$

33. $(2 + 3) + (4 + 5) = (4 + 5) + (2 + 3)$

34. $7 \cdot (11 \cdot 8) = (11 \cdot 8) \cdot 7$

35. $2(-8 + 6) = -16 + 12$

36. $-8(3 + 11) = -24 + (-88)$

37. $(2\sqrt{3}) \cdot \sqrt{5} = 2(\sqrt{3} \cdot \sqrt{5})$

38. $\sqrt{2}\pi = \pi\sqrt{2}$

In Exercises 39–43, use two numbers to show that

39. the natural numbers are not closed with respect to subtraction.

40. the natural numbers are not closed with respect to division.

41. the integers are not closed with respect to division.

42. the irrational numbers are not closed with respect to subtraction.

43. the irrational numbers are not closed with respect to multiplication.

• Practice Plus

In Exercises 44–47, determine if each statement is true or false. Do not use a calculator.

44. $468(787 + 289) = 787 + 289(468)$

45. $468(787 + 289) = 787(468) + 289(468)$

46. $58 \cdot 9 + 32 \cdot 9 = (58 + 32) \cdot 9$

47. $58 \cdot 9 \cdot 32 \cdot 9 = (58 \cdot 32) \cdot 9$

In Exercises 48–49, name the property used to go from step to step each time that (why?) *occurs.*

48. $7 + 2(x + 9)$

$= 7 + (2x + 18)$ (why?)

$= 7 + (18 + 2x)$ (why?)

$= (7 + 18) + 2x$ (why?)

$= 25 + 2x$

$= 2x + 25$ (why?)

49. $5(x + 4) + 3x$

$= (5x + 20) + 3x$ (why?)

$= (20 + 5x) + 3x$ (why?)

$= 20 + (5x + 3x)$ (why?)

$= 20 + (5 + 3)x$ (why?)

$= 20 + 8x$

$= 8x + 20$ (why?)

• Application Exercises

In Exercises 50–53, use the definition of vampire numbers from the Blitzer Bonus on page 273 to determine which products are vampires.

50. $15 \times 93 = 1395$

51. $80 \times 86 = 6880$

52. $20 \times 51 = 1020$

53. $146 \times 938 = 136{,}948$

A **narcissistic number** *is an n-digit number equal to the sum of each of its digits raised to the nth power. Here's an example:*

$$153 = 1^3 + 5^3 + 3^3.$$

Three digits, so exponents are 3

In Exercises 54–57, determine which real numbers are narcissistic.

54. 370 **55.** 371 **56.** 372 **57.** 9474

58. Closure illustrates that a characteristic of a set is not necessarily a characteristic of all of its subsets. The real numbers are closed with respect to multiplication, but the irrational numbers, a subset of the real numbers, are not. Give an example of a set that is not mathematical that has a particular characteristic, but which has a subset without this characteristic.

59. The algebraic expressions

$$\frac{D(A+1)}{24} \quad \text{and} \quad \frac{DA+D}{24}$$

describe the drug dosage for children between the ages of 2 and 13. In each algebraic expression, D stands for an adult dose and A represents the child's age.

a. Name the property that explains why these expressions are equal for all values of D and A.

b. If an adult dose of ibuprofen is 200 milligrams, what is the proper dose for a 12-year-old child? Use both forms of the algebraic expressions to answer the question. Which form is easier to use?

• Writing in Mathematics

60. What does it mean when we say that the rational numbers are a subset of the real numbers?

61. What does it mean if we say that a set is closed under a given operation?

62. State the commutative property of addition and give an example.

63. State the commutative property of multiplication and give an example.

64. State the associative property of addition and give an example.

65. State the associative property of multiplication and give an example.

66. State the distributive property of multiplication over addition and give an example.

67. Does $7 \cdot (4 \cdot 3) = 7 \cdot (3 \cdot 4)$ illustrate the commutative property or the associative property? Explain your answer.

• Critical Thinking Exercises

68. Which one of the following statements is true?

a. Every rational number is an integer.

b. Some whole numbers are not integers.

c. Some rational numbers are not positive.

d. Irrational numbers cannot be negative.

69. Which one of the following statements is true?

a. Subtraction is a commutative operation.

b. $(24 \div 6) \div 2 = 24 \div (6 \div 2)$

c. $7 \cdot a + 3 \cdot a = a \cdot (7 + 3)$

d. $2 \cdot a + 5 = 5 \cdot a + 2$

SECTION 5.6 • EXPONENTS AND SCIENTIFIC NOTATION

OBJECTIVES

1. Use properties of exponents.
2. Convert from scientific notation to decimal notation.
3. Convert from decimal notation to scientific notation.
4. Perform computations using scientific notation.
5. Solve applied problems using scientific notation.

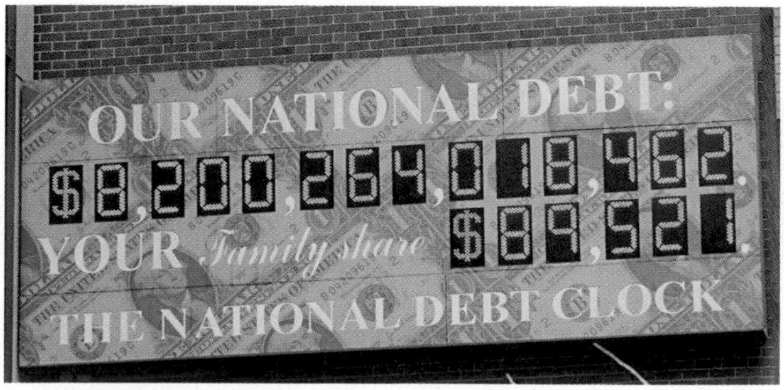

We frequently encounter very large and very small numbers. Governments throughout the world are concerned about the billions of tons of carbon dioxide that the global population of 6.5 billion people release into the atmosphere each year. In the photo shown above, the national debt of the United States was about \$8.2 trillion. A typical atom has a diameter of about one-ten-billionth of a meter. Exponents provide a way of putting these large and small numbers in perspective.

1 Use properties of exponents.

Properties of Exponents

We have seen that exponents are used to indicate repeated multiplication. Now consider the multiplication of two exponential expressions, such as $b^4 \cdot b^3$. We are multiplying 4 factors of b and 3 factors of b. We have a total of 7 factors of b:

4 factors of b 3 factors of b

$$b^4 \cdot b^3 = (b \cdot b \cdot b \cdot b)(b \cdot b \cdot b) = b^7.$$

Total: 7 factors of b

The product is exactly the same if we add the exponents:

$$b^4 \cdot b^3 = b^{4+3} = b^7.$$

Properties of exponents allow us to perform operations with exponential expressions without having to write out long strings of factors. Three such properties are given in Table 5.4.

TABLE 5.4 PROPERTIES OF EXPONENTS

Property	Meaning	Examples
The Product Rule $b^m \cdot b^n = b^{m+n}$	When multiplying exponential expressions with the same base, add the exponents. Use this sum as the exponent of the common base.	$9^6 \cdot 9^{12} = 9^{6+12} = 9^{18}$
The Power Rule $(b^m)^n = b^{m \cdot n}$	When an exponential expression is raised to a power, multiply the exponents. Place the product of the exponents on the base and remove the parentheses.	$(3^4)^5 = 3^{4 \cdot 5} = 3^{20}$ $(5^3)^8 = 5^{3 \cdot 8} = 5^{24}$
The Quotient Rule $\frac{b^m}{b^n} = b^{m-n}$	When dividing exponential expressions with the same base, subtract the exponent in the denominator from the exponent in the numerator. Use this difference as the exponent of the common base.	$\frac{5^{12}}{5^4} = 5^{12-4} = 5^8$ $\frac{9^{40}}{9^5} = 9^{40-5} = 9^{35}$

The third property in Table 5.4, the quotient rule, can lead to a zero exponent when subtracting exponents. Here is an example:

$$\frac{4^3}{4^3} = 4^{3-3} = 4^0.$$

We can see what this zero exponent means by evaluating 4^3 in the numerator and the denominator:

$$\frac{4^3}{4^3} = \frac{4 \cdot 4 \cdot 4}{4 \cdot 4 \cdot 4} = \frac{64}{64} = 1.$$

This means that 4^0 must equal 1. This example illustrates the zero exponent rule.

THE ZERO EXPONENT RULE

If b is any real number other than 0,

$$b^0 = 1.$$

EXAMPLE 1 USING THE ZERO EXPONENT RULE

Use the zero exponent rule to simplify:

a. 7^0 **b.** π^0 **c.** $(-5)^0$ **d.** -5^0.

SOLUTION

a. $7^0 = 1$ **b.** $\pi^0 = 1$ **c.** $(-5)^0 = 1$ **d.** $-5^0 = -1$

Only 5 is raised to the 0 power.

CHECK POINT 1 Use the zero exponent rule to simplify:

a. 19^0 **b.** $(3\pi)^0$ **c.** $(-14)^0$ **d.** -14^0.

The quotient rule can result in a negative exponent. Consider, for example, $4^3 \div 4^5$:

$$\frac{4^3}{4^5} = 4^{3-5} = 4^{-2}.$$

We can see what this negative exponent means by evaluating the numerator and the denominator:

$$\frac{4^3}{4^5} = \frac{\cancel{4}\cdot\cancel{4}\cdot\cancel{4}}{\cancel{4}\cdot\cancel{4}\cdot\cancel{4}\cdot 4\cdot 4} = \frac{1}{4^2}.$$

Notice that $\frac{4^3}{4^5}$ equals both 4^{-2} and $\frac{1}{4^2}$. This means that 4^{-2} must equal $\frac{1}{4^2}$. This example is a particular case of the negative exponent rule.

STUDY TIP

$\frac{4^3}{4^5}$ and $\frac{4^5}{4^3}$ represent different numbers:

$$\frac{4^3}{4^5} = 4^{3-5} = 4^{-2} = \frac{1}{4^2} = \frac{1}{16}$$

$$\frac{4^5}{4^3} = 4^{5-3} = 4^2 = 16.$$

THE NEGATIVE EXPONENT RULE

If b is any real number other than 0 and m is a natural number,

$$b^{-m} = \frac{1}{b^m}.$$

EXAMPLE 2 USING THE NEGATIVE EXPONENT RULE

Use the negative exponent rule to simplify:

a. 8^{-2} **b.** 5^{-3} **c.** 7^{-1}.

SOLUTION

a. $8^{-2} = \frac{1}{8^2} = \frac{1}{8\cdot 8} = \frac{1}{64}$

b. $5^{-3} = \frac{1}{5^3} = \frac{1}{5\cdot 5\cdot 5} = \frac{1}{125}$

c. $7^{-1} = \frac{1}{7^1} = \frac{1}{7}$

CHECK POINT 2 Use the negative exponent rule to simplify:

a. 9^{-2} **b.** 6^{-3} **c.** 12^{-1}.

John Scott "*Invoking the Googolplex*" 1981, watercolour on paper, 24 × 18 in. *Source*: Photo courtesy of The Gallery, Stratford, Ontario.

Powers of Ten

Exponents and their properties allow us to represent and compute with numbers that are large or small. For example, one billion, or 1,000,000,000 can be written as 10^9. In terms of exponents, 10^9 might not look very large, but consider this: If you can count to 200 in one minute and decide to count for 12 hours a day at this rate, it would take you in the region of 19 years, 9 days, 5 hours, and 20 minutes to count to 10^9!

Powers of ten follow two basic rules:

1. **A positive exponent tells how many 0s follow the 1.** For example, 10^9 (one billion) is a 1 followed by nine zeros: 1,000,000,000. A googol, 10^{100}, is a 1 followed by one hundred zeros. (A googol far exceeds the number of protons, neutrons, and electrons in the universe.) A googol is a veritable pipsqueak compared to the googolplex, 10 raised to the googol power, or $10^{10^{100}}$; that's a 1 followed by a googol zeros. (If each zero in a googolplex were no larger than a grain of sand, there would not be enough room in the universe to represent the number.)
2. **A negative exponent tells how many places there are to the right of the decimal point.** For example, 10^{-9} (one billionth) has nine places to the right of the decimal point. The nine places contain eight 0s and the 1.

$$10^{-9} = 0.\underbrace{000000001}_{\text{nine places}}$$

BLITZER BONUS

Earthquakes and Powers of Ten

The earthquake that ripped through northern California on October 17, 1989, measured 7.1 on the Richter scale, killed more than 60 people, and injured more than 2400. Shown here is San Francisco's Marina district, where shock waves tossed houses off their foundations and into the street.

The Richter scale is misleading because it is not actually a 1 to 8, but rather a 1 to 10 million scale. Each level indicates a tenfold increase in magnitude from the previous level, making a 7.0 earthquake a million times greater than a 1.0 quake.

The following is a translation of the Richter scale:

Richter number (R)	**Magnitude (10^{R-1})**
1	$10^{1-1} = 10^0 = 1$
2	$10^{2-1} = 10^1 = 10$
3	$10^{3-1} = 10^2 = 100$
4	$10^{4-1} = 10^3 = 1000$
5	$10^{5-1} = 10^4 = 10{,}000$
6	$10^{6-1} = 10^5 = 100{,}000$
7	$10^{7-1} = 10^6 = 1{,}000{,}000$
8	$10^{8-1} = 10^7 = 10{,}000{,}000$

TABLE 5.5 NAMES OF LARGE NUMBERS

10^2	hundred
10^3	thousand
10^6	million
10^9	billion
10^{12}	trillion
10^{15}	quadrillion
10^{18}	quintillion
10^{21}	sextillion
10^{24}	septillion
10^{27}	octillion
10^{30}	nonillion
10^{100}	googol
10^{googol}	googolplex

Scientific Notation

As of December 2006, the national debt of the United States was about \$8.6 trillion. This is the amount of money the government has had to borrow over the years, mostly by selling bonds, because it has spent more than it has collected in taxes. A stack of \$1 bills equaling the national debt would rise to twice the distance from Earth to the moon. Because a trillion is 10^{12} (see Table 5.5), the national debt can be expressed as

$$8.6 \times 10^{12}.$$

The number 8.6×10^{12} is written in a form called *scientific notation*.

SCIENTIFIC NOTATION

A positive number is written in **scientific notation** when it is expressed in the form

$$a \times 10^n,$$

where a is a number greater than or equal to 1 and less than 10 ($1 \le a < 10$) and n is an integer.

It is customary to use the multiplication symbol, $\times$, rather than a dot, when writing a number in scientific notation.

Here are two examples of numbers in scientific notation:

- Each day, 2.6×10^7 pounds of dust from the atmosphere settle on Earth.
- The length of the AIDS virus is 1.1×10^{-4} millimeter.

2 Convert from scientific notation to decimal notation.

We can use n, the exponent on the 10 in $a \times 10^n$, to change a number in scientific notation to decimal notation. If n is **positive**, move the decimal point in a to the **right** n places. If n is **negative**, move the decimal point in a to the **left** $|n|$ places.

EXAMPLE 3 CONVERTING FROM SCIENTIFIC TO DECIMAL NOTATION

Write each number in decimal notation:

a. 2.6×10^7 **b.** 1.1×10^{-4}.

SOLUTION In each case, we use the exponent on the 10 to move the decimal point. In part (a), the exponent is positive, so we move the decimal point to the right. In part (b), the exponent is negative, so we move the decimal point to the left.

a. $2.6 \times 10^7 = 26{,}000{,}000$

$n = 7$

Move the decimal point 7 places to the right.

b. $1.1 \times 10^{-4} = 0.00011$

$n = -4$

Move the decimal point $|-4|$ places, or 4 places, to the left.

CHECK POINT 3 Write each number in decimal notation:

a. 7.4×10^9 **b.** 3.017×10^{-6}.

3 Convert from decimal notation to scientific notation.

To convert a positive number from decimal notation to scientific notation, we reverse the procedure of Example 3.

CONVERTING FROM DECIMAL TO SCIENTIFIC NOTATION

Write the number in the form $a \times 10^n$.

- Determine a, the numerical factor. Move the decimal point in the given number to obtain a number greater than or equal to 1 and less than 10.
- Determine n, the exponent on 10^n. The absolute value of n is the number of places the decimal point was moved. The exponent n is positive if the given number is greater than 10 and negative if the given number is between 0 and 1.

EXAMPLE 4 CONVERTING FROM DECIMAL NOTATION TO SCIENTIFIC NOTATION

Write each number in scientific notation:

a. 4,600,000 **b.** 0.000023.

TECHNOLOGY

You can use your calculator's EE (enter exponent) or EXP key to convert from decimal to scientific notation. Here is how it's done for 0.000023:

MANY SCIENTIFIC CALCULATORS

Keystrokes	Display
.000023 EE =	2.3 − 05

MANY GRAPHING CALCULATORS

Use the mode setting for scientific notation.

Keystrokes	Display
.000023 ENTER	2.3E − 5

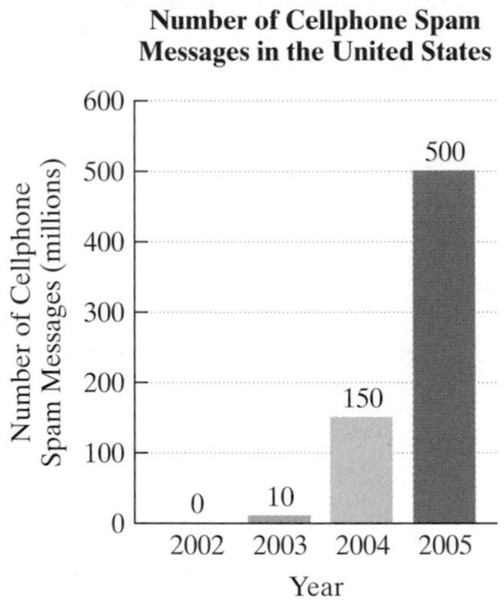

FIGURE 5.6
Source: Ferris Research

SOLUTION

a. $4{,}600{,}000 = 4.6 \times 10^6$

This number is greater than 10, so n is positive in $a \times 10^n$.

Move the decimal point in 4,600,000 to get $1 \le a < 10$.

The decimal point moved 6 places from 4,600,000 to 4.6.

b. $0.000023 = 2.3 \times 10^{-5}$

This number is less than 1, so n is negative in $a \times 10^n$.

Move the decimal point in 0.000023 to get $1 \le a < 10$.

The decimal point moved 5 places from 0.000023 to 2.3.

CHECK POINT 4 Write each number in scientific notation:

a. 7,410,000,000 **b.** 0.000000092.

EXAMPLE 5 EXPRESSING THE NUMBER OF CELLPHONE SPAM MESSAGES IN SCIENTIFIC NOTATION

As feature-rich cellphones function more like PCs, digital intruders are targeting them with viruses, spam, and phishing scams. The bar graph in Figure 5.6 shows the number of cellphone spam messages, in millions, from 2002 through 2005. Express the number of spam messages in 2005 in scientific notation.

SOLUTION Because a million is 10^6, the number of cellphone spam messages in 2005 can be expressed as

$$500 \times 10^6.$$

This factor is not between 1 and 10, so the number is not in scientific notation.

The voice balloon indicates that we need to convert 500 to scientific notation.

$$500 \times 10^6 = (5 \times 10^2) \times 10^6 = 5 \times (10^2 \times 10^6) = 5 \times 10^{2+6} = 5 \times 10^8$$

There were 5×10^8 cellphone spam messages in 2005.

STUDY TIP

Many of the large numbers we encounter in newspapers, magazines, and almanacs are expressed in millions (10^6), billions (10^9), and trillions (10^{12}). We can use exponential properties to describe the number of cellphone spam messages in 2005 using millions or billions.

$$500 \times 10^6 = 5 \times 10^8 = 0.5 \times 10^9$$

There were 500 million messages.

This expresses the number of messages in scientific notation.

There were half a billion messages.

CHECK POINT 5 In 2005, the federal cost of social security was \$519 billion. Express this amount in scientific notation.

4 Perform computations using scientific notation.

Computations with Scientific Notation

We use the product rule for exponents to multiply numbers in scientific notation:

$$(a \times 10^n) \times (b \times 10^m) = (a \times b) \times 10^{n+m}.$$

Add the exponents on 10 and multiply the other parts of the numbers separately.

TECHNOLOGY

$(3.4 \times 10^9)(2 \times 10^{-5})$ on a Calculator:

MANY SCIENTIFIC CALCULATORS

3.4 [EE] 9 [×] 2 [EE] 5 [+/−] [=]

Display: 6.8 04

MANY GRAPHING CALCULATORS

3.4 [EE] 9 [×] 2 [EE] [(−)] 5 [ENTER]

Display: 6.8 E 4

EXAMPLE 6 MULTIPLYING NUMBERS IN SCIENTIFIC NOTATION

Multiply: $(3.4 \times 10^9)(2 \times 10^{-5})$. Write the product in decimal notation.

SOLUTION

$(3.4 \times 10^9)(2 \times 10^{-5}) = (3.4 \times 2) \times (10^9 \times 10^{-5})$ Regroup factors.

$= 6.8 \times 10^{9+(-5)}$ Add the exponents on 10 and multiply the other parts.

$= 6.8 \times 10^4$ Simplify.

$= 68{,}000$ Write the product in decimal notation.

CHECK POINT 6 Multiply: $(1.3 \times 10^7)(4 \times 10^{-2})$. Write the product in decimal notation.

We use the quotient rule for exponents to divide numbers in scientific notation:

$$\frac{a \times 10^n}{b \times 10^m} = \left(\frac{a}{b}\right) \times 10^{n-m}.$$

Subtract the exponents on 10 and divide the other parts of the numbers separately.

EXAMPLE 7 DIVIDING NUMBERS IN SCIENTIFIC NOTATION

Divide: $\frac{8.4 \times 10^{-7}}{4 \times 10^{-4}}$. Write the quotient in decimal notation.

SOLUTION

$\frac{8.4 \times 10^{-7}}{4 \times 10^{-4}} = \left(\frac{8.4}{4}\right) \times \left(\frac{10^{-7}}{10^{-4}}\right)$ Regroup factors.

$= 2.1 \times 10^{-7-(-4)}$ Subtract the exponents on 10 and divide the other parts.

$= 2.1 \times 10^{-3}$ Simplify: $-7 - (-4) = -7 + 4 = -3$.

$= 0.0021$ Write the quotient in decimal notation.

CHECK POINT 7 Divide: $\frac{6.9 \times 10^{-8}}{3 \times 10^{-2}}$. Write the quotient in decimal notation.

Multiplication and division involving very large or very small numbers can be performed by first converting each number to scientific notation.

EXAMPLE 8 USING SCIENTIFIC NOTATION TO MULTIPLY

Multiply: $0.00064 \times 9{,}400{,}000{,}000$. Express the product in **a.** scientific notation and **b.** decimal notation.

SOLUTION

a. $0.00064 \times 9{,}400{,}000{,}000$

$= 6.4 \times 10^{-4} \times 9.4 \times 10^{9}$ — Write each number in scientific notation.

$= (6.4 \times 9.4) \times (10^{-4} \times 10^{9})$ — Regroup factors.

$= 60.16 \times 10^{-4+9}$ — Add the exponents on 10 and multiply the other parts.

$= 60.16 \times 10^{5}$ — Simplify.

$= (6.016 \times 10) \times 10^{5}$ — Express 60.16 in scientific notation.

$= 6.016 \times 10^{6}$ — Add exponents on 10: $10^{1} \times 10^{5} = 10^{1+5} = 10^{6}$.

b. The answer in decimal notation is obtained by moving the decimal point in 6.016 six places to the right. The product is 6,016,000.

CHECK POINT 8 Multiply: $0.0036 \times 5{,}200{,}000$. Express the product in **a.** scientific notation and **b.** decimal notation.

5 Solve applied problems using scientific notation.

Applications: Putting Numbers in Perspective

Due to tax cuts and spending increases, the United States began accumulating large deficits in the 1980s. To finance the deficit, the government had borrowed \$8.6 trillion as of December 2006. The graph in Figure 5.7 shows the national debt increasing over time.

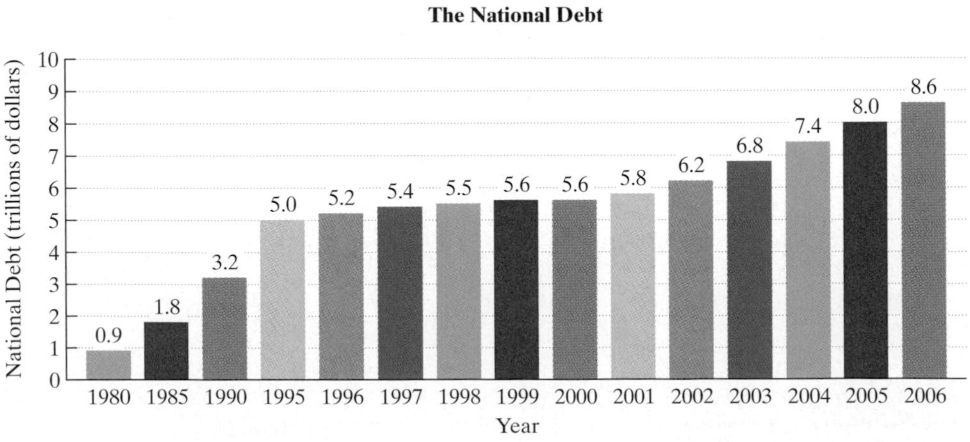

FIGURE 5.7
Source: Office of Management and Budget

Example 9 shows how we can use scientific notation to comprehend the meaning of a number such as 8.6 trillion.

TECHNOLOGY

Here is the keystroke sequence for solving Example 9 using a calculator:

8.4 [EE] 12 [÷] 3 [EE] 8.

The quotient is displayed by pressing [=] on a scientific calculator or [ENTER] on a graphing calculator. The answer can be displayed in scientific or decimal notation. Consult your manual.

EXAMPLE 9 THE NATIONAL DEBT

As of December 2006, the national debt was \$8.6 trillion, or 8.6×10^{12} dollars. At that time, the U.S. population was approximately 300,000,000 (300 million), or 3×10^8. If the national debt was evenly divided among every individual in the United States, how much would each citizen have to pay?

SOLUTION The amount each citizen must pay is the total debt, 8.6×10^{12} dollars, divided by the number of citizens, 3×10^8.

$$\frac{8.6 \times 10^{12}}{3 \times 10^8} = \left(\frac{8.6}{3}\right) \times \left(\frac{10^{12}}{10^8}\right)$$
$$\approx 2.87 \times 10^{12-8}$$
$$= 2.87 \times 10^4$$
$$= 28{,}700$$

Every U.S. citizen would have to pay approximately \$28,700 to the federal government to pay off the national debt.

CHECK POINT 9 Pell Grants help low-income undergraduate students pay for college. In 2006, the federal cost of this program was \$13 billion ($\$13 \times 10^9$) and there were 5.1 million (5.1×10^6) grant recipients. How much, to the nearest hundred dollars, was the average grant?

BLITZER BONUS

Fermat's Last Theorem

Pierre de Fermat (1601–1665) was a lawyer who enjoyed studying mathematics. In a margin of one of his books, he claimed that no natural numbers satisfy

$$a^n + b^n = c^n$$

if n is an integer greater than or equal to 3.

If $n = 2$, we can find numbers satisfying $a^n + b^n = c^n$, or $a^2 + b^2 = c^2$. For example,

$$3^2 + 4^2 = 5^2.$$

However, Fermat claimed that no natural numbers satisfy

$$a^3 + b^3 = c^3, \quad a^4 + b^4 = c^4, \quad a^5 + b^5 = c^5,$$

and so on.

Fermat claimed to have a proof of his conjecture, but added, "The margin of my book is too narrow to write it down." Some believe that he never had a proof and intended to frustrate his colleagues.

In June 1993, 40-year-old Princeton math professor Andrew Wiles claimed that he discovered a proof of the theorem. Subsequent study revealed flaws, but Wiles corrected them. In 1995, his final proof served as a classic example of how great mathematicians accomplish great things: a combination of genius, hard work, frustration, and trial and error.

(Andrew Wiles 1953–)

EXERCISE SET 5.6

• Practice Exercises

In Exercises 1–12, use properties of exponents to simplify each expression. First express the answer in exponential form. Then evaluate the expression.

1. $2^2 \cdot 2^3$ **2.** $3^3 \cdot 3^2$ **3.** $4 \cdot 4^2$ **4.** $5 \cdot 5^2$

5. $(2^2)^3$ **6.** $(3^3)^2$ **7.** $(1^4)^5$ **8.** $(1^3)^7$

9. $\frac{4^7}{4^5}$ **10.** $\frac{6^7}{6^5}$ **11.** $\frac{2^8}{2^4}$ **12.** $\frac{3^8}{3^4}$

In Exercises 13–24, use the zero and negative exponent rules to simplify each expression.

13. 3^0 **14.** 9^0 **15.** $(-3)^0$ **16.** $(-9)^0$

17. -3^0 **18.** -9^0 **19.** 2^{-2} **20.** 3^{-2}

21. 4^{-3} **22.** 2^{-3} **23.** 2^{-5} **24.** 2^{-6}

In Exercises 25–30, use properties of exponents to simplify each expression. First express the answer in exponential form. Then evaluate the expression.

25. $3^4 \cdot 3^{-2}$ **26.** $2^5 \cdot 2^{-2}$ **27.** $3^{-3} \cdot 3$

28. $2^{-3} \cdot 2$ **29.** $\frac{2^3}{2^7}$ **30.** $\frac{3^4}{3^7}$

In Exercises 31–46, express each number in decimal notation.

31. 2.7×10^2 **32.** 4.7×10^3 **33.** 9.12×10^5

34. 8.14×10^4 **35.** 8×10^7 **36.** 7×10^6

37. 1×10^5 **38.** 1×10^8 **39.** 7.9×10^{-1}

40. 8.6×10^{-1} **41.** 2.15×10^{-2} **42.** 3.14×10^{-2}

43. 7.86×10^{-4} **44.** 4.63×10^{-5} **45.** 3.18×10^{-6}

46. 5.84×10^{-7}

In Exercises 47–66, express each number in scientific notation.

47. 370 **48.** 530 **49.** 3600 **50.** 2700

51. 32,000 **52.** 64,000 **53.** 220,000,000

54. 370,000,000,000 **55.** 0.027 **56.** 0.014

57. 0.0037 **58.** 0.00083 **59.** 0.00000293

60. 0.000000647 **61.** 820×10^5 **62.** 630×10^8

63. 0.41×10^6 **64.** 0.57×10^9 **65.** 2100×10^{-9}

66. $97{,}000 \times 10^{-11}$

In Exercises 67–80, perform the indicated operation and express each answer in decimal notation.

67. $(2 \times 10^3)(3 \times 10^2)$ **68.** $(5 \times 10^2)(4 \times 10^4)$

69. $(2 \times 10^9)(3 \times 10^{-5})$ **70.** $(4 \times 10^8)(2 \times 10^{-4})$

71. $(4.1 \times 10^2)(3 \times 10^{-4})$ **72.** $(1.2 \times 10^3)(2 \times 10^{-5})$

73. $\frac{12 \times 10^6}{4 \times 10^2}$ **74.** $\frac{20 \times 10^{20}}{10 \times 10^{15}}$

75. $\frac{15 \times 10^4}{5 \times 10^{-2}}$ **76.** $\frac{18 \times 10^2}{9 \times 10^{-3}}$

77. $\frac{6 \times 10^3}{2 \times 10^5}$ **78.** $\frac{8 \times 10^4}{2 \times 10^7}$

79. $\frac{6.3 \times 10^{-6}}{3 \times 10^{-3}}$ **80.** $\frac{9.6 \times 10^{-7}}{3 \times 10^{-3}}$

In Exercises 81–90, perform the indicated operation by first expressing each number in scientific notation. Write the answer in scientific notation.

81. (82,000,000)(3,000,000,000)

82. (94,000,000)(6,000,000,000)

83. (0.0005)(6,000,000) **84.** (0.000015)(0.004)

85. $\frac{9{,}500{,}000}{500}$ **86.** $\frac{30{,}000}{0.0005}$

87. $\frac{0.00008}{200}$ **88.** $\frac{0.0018}{0.0000006}$

89. $\frac{480{,}000{,}000{,}000}{0.00012}$ **90.** $\frac{0.000000096}{16{,}000}$

• Practice Plus

In Exercises 91–94, perform the indicated operations. Express each answer as a fraction reduced to its lowest terms.

91. $\frac{2^4}{2^5} + \frac{3^3}{3^5}$ **92.** $\frac{3^5}{3^6} + \frac{2^3}{2^6}$

93. $\frac{2^6}{2^4} - \frac{5^4}{5^6}$ **94.** $\frac{5^6}{5^4} - \frac{2^4}{2^6}$

In Exercises 95–98, perform the indicated computations. Express answers in scientific notation.

95. $(5 \times 10^3)(1.2 \times 10^{-4}) \div (2.4 \times 10^2)$

96. $(2 \times 10^2)(2.6 \times 10^{-3}) \div (4 \times 10^3)$

97. $\frac{(1.6 \times 10^4)(7.2 \times 10^{-3})}{(3.6 \times 10^8)(4 \times 10^{-3})}$

98. $\frac{(1.2 \times 10^6)(8.7 \times 10^{-2})}{(2.9 \times 10^6)(3 \times 10^{-3})}$

• Application Exercises

The graph shows the net worth, in billions of dollars, of the five richest Americans. Use 10^9 for one billion and the figures shown to solve Exercises 99–102. Express all answers in scientific notation.

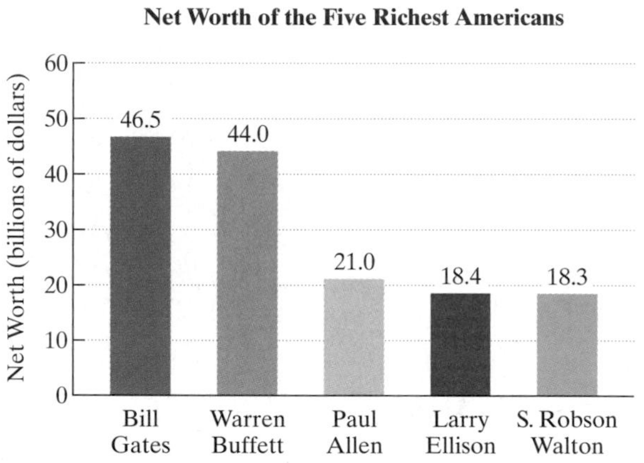

Source: Forbes Billionaires List, 2005

99. How much is Bill Gates worth?

100. How much is Warren Buffett worth?

101. By how much does Larry Ellison's worth exceed that of S. Robson Walton?

102. If each person doubled his net worth, by how much would Larry Ellison's worth exceed that of S. Robson Walton?

Our ancient ancestors hunted for their meat and expended a great deal of energy chasing it down. Today, our animal protein is raised in cages and on feedlots, delivered in great abundance nearly to our door. Use the numbers shown below to solve Exercises 103–106. Use 10^6 for one million and 10^9 for one billion.

Source: Time, October 20, 2003

In Exercises 103–104, use 300 million, or 3×10^8, for the U.S. population. Express answers in decimal notation, rounded to the nearest whole number.

103. Find the number of hot dogs consumed by each American in a year.

104. If the consumption of Big Macs was divided evenly among all Americans, how many Big Macs would we each consume in a year?

In Exercises 105–106, use the Overproteined table and the fact that there are approximately 3.2×10^7 seconds in a year.

105. How many chickens are raised for food each second in the United States? Express the answer in scientific and decimal notations.

106. How many chickens are eaten per year in the United States? Express the answer in scientific notation.

The graph shows the cost, in billions of dollars, and the enrollment, in millions of people, for various federal social programs in 2005. Use the numbers shown to solve Exercises 107–109.

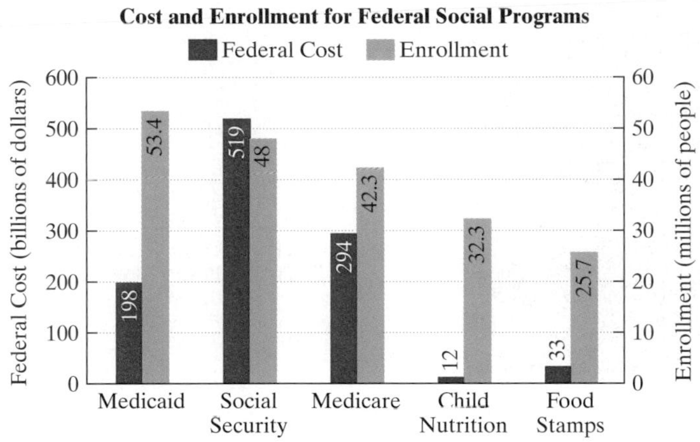

Source: Office of Management and Budget

107. a. What was the average per person benefit for Social Security? Express the answer in scientific notation and in decimal notation, rounded to the nearest dollar.

b. What was the average monthly per person benefit, rounded to the nearest dollar, for Social Security?

108. a. What was the average per person benefit for the food stamps program? Express the answer in scientific notation and in decimal notation, rounded to the nearest dollar.

b. What was the average monthly per person benefit, rounded to the nearest dollar, for the food stamps program?

109. Medicaid provides health insurance for the poor. Medicare provides health insurance for people 65 and older, as well as younger people who are disabled. Which program provides the greater per person benefit? By how much, rounded to the nearest dollar?

110. The area of Alaska is approximately 3.66×10^8 acres. The state was purchased in 1867 from Russia for \$7.2 million. What price per acre, to the nearest cent, did the United States pay Russia?

111. The mass of one oxygen molecule is 5.3×10^{-23} gram. Find the mass of 20,000 molecules of oxygen. Express the answer in scientific notation.

112. The mass of one hydrogen atom is 1.67×10^{-24} gram. Find the mass of 80,000 hydrogen atoms. Express the answer in scientific notation.

113. In Exercises 105–106, we used 3.2×10^7 as an approximation for the number of seconds in a year. Convert 365 days (one year) to hours, to minutes, and, finally, to seconds, to determine precisely how many seconds there are in a year. Express the answer in scientific notation.

• Writing in Mathematics

114. Explain the product rule for exponents. Use $2^3 \cdot 2^5$ in your explanation.

115. Explain the power rule for exponents. Use $(3^2)^4$ in your explanation.

116. Explain the quotient rule for exponents. Use $\frac{5^8}{5^2}$ in your explanation.

117. Explain the zero exponent rule and give an example.

118. Explain the negative exponent rule and give an example.

119. How do you know if a number is written in scientific notation?

120. Explain how to convert from scientific to decimal notation and give an example.

121. Explain how to convert from decimal to scientific notation and give an example.

122. Suppose you are looking at a number in scientific notation. Describe the size of the number you are looking at if the exponent on ten is **a.** positive, **b.** negative, **c.** zero.

123. Describe one advantage of expressing a number in scientific notation over decimal notation.

• Critical Thinking Exercises

124. Which one of the following is true?

a. $4^{-2} < 4^{-3}$

b. $5^{-2} > 2^{-5}$

c. $(-2)^4 = 2^{-4}$

d. $5^2 \cdot 5^{-2} > 2^5 \cdot 2^{-5}$

125. Which one of the following is true?

a. $534.7 = 5.347 \times 10^3$

b. $\frac{8 \times 10^{30}}{4 \times 10^{-5}} = 2 \times 10^{25}$

c. $(7 \times 10^5) + (2 \times 10^{-3}) = 9 \times 10^2$

d. $(4 \times 10^3) + (3 \times 10^2) = 43 \times 10^2$

126. Give an example of a number for which there is no advantage to using scientific notation instead of decimal notation. Explain why this is the case.

127. The mad Dr. Frankenstein has gathered enough bits and pieces (so to speak) for $2^{-1} + 2^{-2}$ of his creature-to-be. Write a fraction that represents the amount of his creature that must still be obtained.

• Technology Exercises

128. Use a calculator in a fraction mode to check your answers in Exercises 19–24.

129. Use a calculator to check any three of your answers in Exercises 31–46.

130. Use a calculator to check any three of your answers in Exercises 47–66.

131. Use a calculator with an EE or EXP key to check any four of your computations in Exercises 67–90. Display the result of the computation in scientific notation and in decimal notation.

• Group Exercises

132. Putting Numbers into Perspective. A large number can be put into perspective by comparing it with another number. For example, we put the $8.6 trillion national debt into perspective by comparing it to the number of U.S. citizens and computing the debt per person. For this project, each group member should consult an almanac, a newspaper, or the World Wide Web to find a number greater than one million. Explain to other members of the group the context in which the large number is used. Express the number in scientific notation. Then put the number into perspective by comparing it with another number.

133. Fermat's most notorious theorem baffled the greatest minds for more than three centuries. In 1994, after ten years of work, Princeton University's Andrew Wiles proved Fermat's Last Theorem. *People* magazine put him on its list of "the 25 most intriguing people of the year," the Gap asked him to model jeans, and Barbara Walters chased him for an interview. "Who's Barbara Walters?" asked the bookish Wiles, who had somehow gone through life without a television.

Using the 1993 PBS documentary "Solving Fermat: Andrew Wiles" or information about Andrew Wiles on the Internet, research and present a group seminar on what Wiles did to prove Fermat's Last Theorem, problems along the way, and how Wiles overcame them.

SECTION 5.7 • ARITHMETIC AND GEOMETRIC SEQUENCES

OBJECTIVES

1. Write terms of an arithmetic sequence.
2. Use the formula for the general term of an arithmetic sequence.
3. Write terms of a geometric sequence.
4. Use the formula for the general term of a geometric sequence.

Sequences

Many creations in nature involve intricate mathematical designs, including a variety of spirals. For example, the arrangement of the individual florets in the head of a sunflower forms spirals. In some species, there are 21 spirals in the clockwise direction and 34 in the counterclockwise direction. The precise numbers depend on the species of sunflower: 21 and 34, or 34 and 55, or 55 and 89, or even 89 and 144.

This observation becomes even more interesting when we consider a sequence of numbers investigated by Leonardo of Pisa, also known as Fibonacci, an Italian mathematician of the thirteenth century. The **Fibonacci sequence** of numbers is an infinite sequence that begins as follows:

$$1, 1, 2, 3, 5, 8, 13, 21, 34, 55, 89, 144, 233, \ldots.$$

The first two terms are 1. Every term thereafter is the sum of the two preceding terms. For example, the third term, 2, is the sum of the first and second terms: $1 + 1 = 2$. The fourth term, 3, is the sum of the second and third terms: $1 + 2 = 3$, and so on. Did you know that the number of spirals in a daisy or a sunflower, 21 and 34, are two Fibonacci numbers? The number of spirals in a pinecone, 8 and 13, and a pineapple, 8 and 13, are also Fibonacci numbers.

We can think of a **sequence** as a list of numbers that are related to each other by a rule. The numbers in a sequence are called its **terms**. The letter a with a subscript is used to represent the terms of a sequence. Thus, a_1 represents the first term of the sequence, a_2 represents the second term, a_3 the third term, and so on. This notation is shown for the first six terms of the Fibonacci sequence:

$$1, \quad 1, \quad 2, \quad 3, \quad 5, \quad 8.$$

$a_1 = 1$ $\quad a_2 = 1$ $\quad a_3 = 2$ $\quad a_4 = 3$ $\quad a_5 = 5$ $\quad a_6 = 8$

BLITZER BONUS

Fibonacci Numbers on the Piano Keyboard

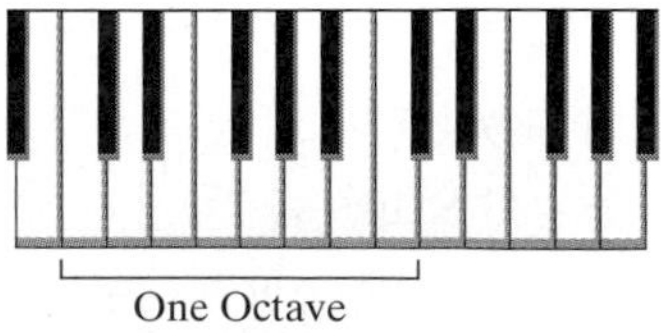

Numbers in the Fibonacci sequence can be found in an octave on the piano keyboard. The octave contains 2 black keys in one cluster, 3 black keys in another cluster, a total of 5 black keys, 8 white keys, and a total of 13 keys altogether. The numbers 2, 3, 5, 8, and 13 are the third through seventh terms of the Fibonacci sequence.

Arithmetic Sequences

The bar graph in Figure 5.8 shows annual salaries, rounded to the nearest thousand dollars, of U.S. senators from 2000 to 2005. The graph illustrates that each year salaries increased by \$4 thousand. The sequence of annual salaries

$$142, 146, 150, 154, 158, 162, \ldots$$

shows that each term after the first, 142, differs from the preceding term by a constant amount, namely 4. This sequence is an example of an *arithmetic sequence*.

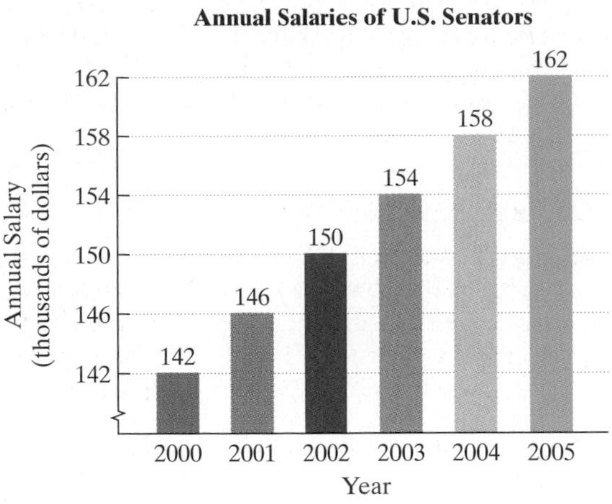

FIGURE 5.8
Source: U.S. Senate

> **DEFINITION OF AN ARITHMETIC SEQUENCE**
> An **arithmetic sequence** is a sequence in which each term after the first differs from the preceding term by a constant amount. The difference between consecutive terms is called the **common difference** of the sequence.

The common difference, d, is found by subtracting any term from the term that directly follows it. In the following examples, the common difference is found by subtracting the first term from the second term: $a_2 - a_1$.

Arithmetic Sequence	Common Difference
$142, 146, 150, 154, 158, \ldots$	$d = 146 - 142 = 4$
$-5, -2, 1, 4, 7, \ldots$	$d = -2 - (-5) = -2 + 5 = 3$
$8, 3, -2, -7, -12, \ldots$	$d = 3 - 8 = -5$

If the first term of an arithmetic sequence is a_1, each term after the first is obtained by adding d, the common difference, to the previous term.

1 Write terms of an arithmetic sequence.

EXAMPLE 1 WRITING THE TERMS OF AN ARITHMETIC SEQUENCE

Write the first six terms of the arithmetic sequence with first term 6 and common difference 4.

SOLUTION The first term is 6. The second term is $6 + 4$, or 10. The third term is $10 + 4$, or 14, and so on. The first six terms are

$$6, 10, 14, 18, 22, \text{ and } 26.$$

CHECK POINT 1 Write the first six terms of the arithmetic sequence with first term 100 and common difference 20.

EXAMPLE 2 WRITING THE TERMS OF AN ARITHMETIC SEQUENCE

Write the first six terms of the arithmetic sequence with $a_1 = 5$ and $d = -2$.

SOLUTION The first term, a_1, is 5. The common difference, d, is -2. To find the second term, we add -2 to 5, giving 3. For the next term, we add -2 to 3, and so on. The first six terms are

$$5, 3, 1, -1, -3, \text{ and } -5.$$

CHECK POINT 2 Write the first six terms of the arithmetic sequence with first term 8 and common difference −3.

2 Use the formula for the general term of an arithmetic sequence.

The General Term of an Arithmetic Sequence

Consider an arithmetic sequence whose first term is a_1 and whose common difference is d. We are looking for a formula for the general term, a_n. Let's begin by writing the first six terms. The first term is a_1. The second term is $a_1 + d$. The third term is $a_1 + d + d$, or $a_1 + 2d$. Thus, we start with a_1 and add d to each successive term. The first six terms are

$$a_1, \quad a_1 + d, \quad a_1 + 2d, \quad a_1 + 3d, \quad a_1 + 4d, \quad a_1 + 5d.$$

a_1, first term | a_2, second term | a_3, third term | a_4, fourth term | a_5, fifth term | a_6, sixth term

Applying inductive reasoning to the pattern of the terms results in the following formula for the general term, or the nth term, of an arithmetic sequence:

GENERAL TERM OF AN ARITHMETIC SEQUENCE

The nth term (the general term) of an arithmetic sequence with first term a_1 and common difference d is

$$a_n = a_1 + (n - 1)d.$$

EXAMPLE 3 USING THE FORMULA FOR THE GENERAL TERM OF AN ARITHMETIC SEQUENCE

Find the eighth term of the arithmetic sequence whose first term is 4 and whose common difference is −7.

SOLUTION To find the eighth term, a_8, we replace n in the formula with 8, a_1 with 4, and d with −7.

$$a_n = a_1 + (n - 1)d$$

$$a_8 = 4 + (8 - 1)(-7) = 4 + 7(-7) = 4 + (-49) = -45$$

The eighth term is −45. We can check this result by writing the first eight terms of the sequence:

$$4, -3, -10, -17, -24, -31, -38, -45.$$

CHECK POINT 3 Find the ninth term of the arithmetic sequence whose first term is 6 and whose common difference is −5.

In Chapter 1, we saw that the process of finding formulas to describe real-world phenomena is called mathematical modeling. Such formulas, together with the meaning assigned to the variables, are called mathematical models. Example 4 illustrates how the formula for the general term of an arithmetic sequence can be used to develop a mathematical model.

Changing Times in the U.S.

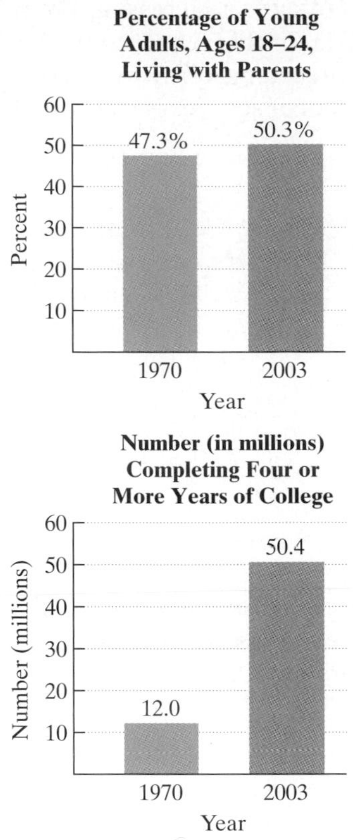

FIGURE 5.9
Source: U.S. Census Bureau

EXAMPLE 4 USING AN ARITHMETIC SEQUENCE TO MODEL CHANGING TIMES

The top graph in Figure 5.9 shows that in 1970, 47.3% of young adults, ages 18–24, lived at home with their parents. On average, this has increased by approximately 0.09% per year.

a. Write a formula for the nth term of the arithmetic sequence that models the percentage of young adults living at home with their parents n years after 1969.

b. According to the model in part (a), what percentage of young adults will be living at home with their parents in 2009?

SOLUTION

a. We can express the percentage of young adults living with their parents by the following arithmetic sequence:

$$47.3, \quad 47.39, \quad 47.48, \ldots.$$

a_1: 47.3% lived with parents in 1970, 1 year after 1969.

a_2: 47.39% lived with parents in 1971, 2 years after 1969.

a_3: 47.48% lived with parents in 1972, 3 years after 1969.

In this sequence, a_1, the first term, represents the percentage of young adults who lived at home in 1970. Each subsequent year this increased by 0.09%, so $d = 0.09$. We use the formula for the general term of an arithmetic sequence to write the nth term of the sequence that describes the percentage of young adults living at home with their parents n years after 1969.

$$a_n = a_1 + (n-1)d$$ This is the formula for the general term of an arithmetic sequence.

$$a_n = 47.3 + (n-1)0.09$$ $a_1 = 47.3$ and $d = 0.09$.

$$a_n = 47.3 + 0.09n - 0.09$$ Distribute 0.09 to each term in parentheses.

$$a_n = 0.09n + 47.21$$ Simplify: $47.3 - 0.09 = 47.21$.

Thus, the percentage of young adults living at home with their parents n years after 1969 can be described by $a_n = 0.09n + 47.21$.

b. Now we need to find the percentage who will be living with their parents in 2009. The year 2009 is 40 years after 1969: That is, $2009 - 1969 = 40$. We substitute 40 for n in $a_n = 0.09n + 47.21$.

$$a_{40} = 0.09(40) + 47.21 = 50.81$$

The 40th term of the sequence is 50.81. Therefore, the model indicates that 50.81% of young adults will be living at home with their parents by the year 2009.

CHECK POINT 4 The bottom graph in Figure 5.9 shows that in 1970, 12.0 million Americans had completed four or more years of college. On average, this has increased by approximately 1.16 million people per year.

a. Write a formula for the nth term of the arithmetic sequence that models the number of Americans, in millions, completing four or more years of college n years after 1969.

b. According to the model in part (a), how many Americans, to the nearest tenth of a million, will have completed four or more years of college in 2019?

Geometric Sequences

Figure 5.10 shows a sequence in which the number of squares is increasing. From left to right, the number of squares is 1, 5, 25, 125, and 625. In this sequence, each term after the first, 1, is obtained by multiplying the preceding term by a constant amount, namely 5. This sequence of increasing numbers of squares is an example of a *geometric sequence*.

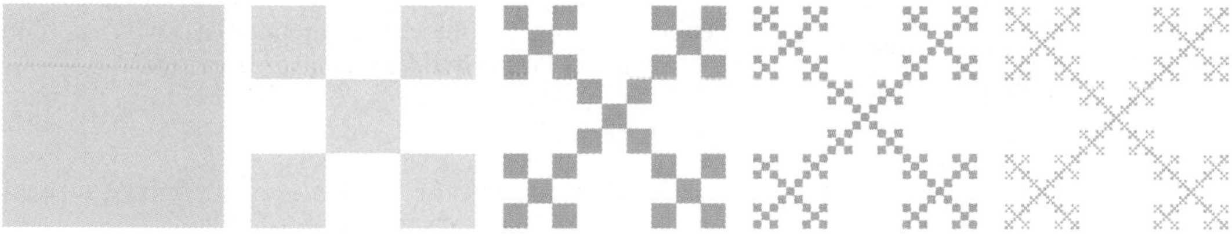

FIGURE 5.10 A geometric sequence of squares

> **DEFINITION OF A GEOMETRIC SEQUENCE**
> A **geometric sequence** is a sequence in which each term after the first is obtained by multiplying the preceding term by a fixed nonzero constant. The amount by which we multiply each time is called the **common ratio** of the sequence.

The common ratio, r, is found by dividing any term after the first term by the term that directly precedes it. In the examples below, the common ratio is found by dividing the second term by the first term: $\frac{a_2}{a_1}$.

Geometric sequence	Common ratio
$1, 5, 25, 125, 625, \ldots$	$r = \frac{5}{1} = 5$
$4, 8, 16, 32, 64, \ldots$	$r = \frac{8}{4} = 2$
$6, -12, 24, -48, 96, \ldots$	$r = \frac{-12}{6} = -2$
$9, -3, 1, -\frac{1}{3}, \frac{1}{9}, \ldots$	$r = \frac{-3}{9} = -\frac{1}{3}$

STUDY TIP

When the common ratio of a geometric sequence is negative, the signs of the terms alternate.

3 Write terms of a geometric sequence.

How do we write out the terms of a geometric sequence when the first term and the common ratio are known? We multiply the first term by the common ratio to get the second term, multiply the second term by the common ratio to get the third term, and so on.

EXAMPLE 5 WRITING THE TERMS OF A GEOMETRIC SEQUENCE

Write the first six terms of the geometric sequence with first term 6 and common ratio $\frac{1}{3}$.

SOLUTION The first term is 6. The second term is $6 \cdot \frac{1}{3}$, or 2. The third term is $2 \cdot \frac{1}{3}$, or $\frac{2}{3}$. The fourth term is $\frac{2}{3} \cdot \frac{1}{3}$, or $\frac{2}{9}$, and so on. The first six terms are

$$6, 2, \frac{2}{3}, \frac{2}{9}, \frac{2}{27}, \text{ and } \frac{2}{81}.$$

CHECK POINT 5 Write the first six terms of the geometric sequence with first term 12 and common ratio $-\frac{1}{2}$.

4 Use the formula for the general term of a geometric sequence.

The General Term of a Geometric Sequence

Consider a geometric sequence whose first term is a_1 and whose common ratio is r. We are looking for a formula for the general term, a_n. Let's begin by writing the first six terms. The first term is a_1. The second term is $a_1 r$. The third term is $a_1 r \cdot r$, or $a_1 r^2$. The fourth term is $a_1 r^2 \cdot r$, or $a_1 r^3$, and so on. Starting with a_1 and multiplying each successive term by r, the first six terms are

$$a_1, \quad a_1 r, \quad a_1 r^2, \quad a_1 r^3, \quad a_1 r^4, \quad a_1 r^5.$$

a_1, first term	a_2, second term	a_3, third term	a_4, fourth term	a_5, fifth term	a_6, sixth term

Applying inductive reasoning to the pattern of the terms results in the following formula for the general term, or the nth term, of a geometric sequence:

GENERAL TERM OF A GEOMETRIC SEQUENCE

The nth term (the general term) of a geometric sequence with first term a_1 and common ratio r is

$$a_n = a_1 r^{n-1}.$$

EXAMPLE 6 USING THE FORMULA FOR THE GENERAL TERM OF A GEOMETRIC SEQUENCE

Find the eighth term of the geometric sequence whose first term is -4 and whose common ratio is -2.

STUDY TIP

Be careful with the order of operations when evaluating

$$a_1 r^{n-1}.$$

First find r^{n-1}. Then multiply the result by a_1.

SOLUTION To find the eighth term, a_8, we replace n in the formula with 8, a_1 with -4, and r with -2.

$$a_n = a_1 r^{n-1}$$

$$a_8 = -4(-2)^{8-1} = -4(-2)^7 = -4(-128) = 512$$

The eighth term is 512. We can check this result by writing the first eight terms of the sequence:

$$-4, 8, -16, 32, -64, 128, -256, 512.$$

CHECK POINT 6 Find the seventh term of the geometric sequence whose first term is 5 and whose common ratio is -3.

EXAMPLE 7 GEOMETRIC POPULATION GROWTH

The table shows the population of the United States in 2000, with estimates given by the Census Bureau for 2001 through 2006.

Year	2000	2001	2002	2003	2004	2005	2006
Population (millions)	281.4	284.5	287.6	290.8	294.0	297.2	300.5

a. Show that the population is increasing geometrically.

b. Write the general term for the geometric sequence describing population growth for the United States n years after 1999.

c. Project the U.S. population, in millions, for the year 2009.

BLITZER BONUS

Geometric Population Growth

Economist Thomas Malthus (1766–1834) predicted that population growth would increase as a geometric sequence and food production would increase as an arithmetic sequence. He concluded that eventually population would exceed food production. If two sequences, one geometric and one arithmetic, are increasing, the geometric sequence will eventually overtake the arithmetic sequence, regardless of any head start that the arithmetic sequence might initially have.

SOLUTION

a. First, we use the sequence of population growth, 281.4, 284.5, 287.6, 290.8, and so on, to divide the population for each year by the population in the preceding year.

$$\frac{284.5}{281.4} \approx 1.011, \quad \frac{287.6}{284.5} \approx 1.011, \quad \frac{290.8}{287.6} \approx 1.011$$

Continuing in this manner, we will keep getting approximately 1.011. This means that the population is increasing geometrically with $r \approx 1.011$. In this situation, the common ratio is the growth rate, indicating that the population of the United States in any year shown in the sequence is approximately 1.011 times the population the year before.

b. The sequence of the U.S. population growth is

$$281.4, 284.5, 287.6, 290.8, 294.0, 297.2, 300.5, \ldots.$$

Because the population is increasing geometrically, we can find the general term of this sequence using

$$a_n = a_1 r^{n-1}.$$

In this sequence, $a_1 = 281.4$ and [from part (a)] $r \approx 1.011$. We substitute these values into the formula for the general term. This gives the general term for the geometric sequence describing the U.S. population n years after 1999.

$$a_n = 281.4(1.011)^{n-1}$$

c. We can use the formula for the general term, a_n, in part (b) to project the U.S. population for the year 2009. The year 2009 is 10 years after 1999—that is, $2009 - 1999 = 10$. Thus, $n = 10$. We substitute 10 for n in $a_n = 281.4(1.011)^{n-1}$.

$$a_{10} = 281.4(1.011)^{10-1} = 281.4(1.011)^9 \approx 310.5$$

The model projects that the United States will have a population of approximately 310.5 million in the year 2009.

CHECK POINT 7 Write the general term for the geometric sequence

$$3, 6, 12, 24, 48, \ldots.$$

Then use the formula for the general term to find the eighth term.

EXERCISE SET 5.7

• Practice Exercises

In Exercises 1–20, write the first six terms of the arithmetic sequence with the first term, a_1, and common difference, d.

1. $a_1 = 8, d = 2$
2. $a_1 = 5, d = 3$
3. $a_1 = 200, d = 20$
4. $a_1 = 300, d = 50$
5. $a_1 = -7, d = 4$
6. $a_1 = -8, d = 5$
7. $a_1 = -400, d = 300$
8. $a_1 = -500, d = 400$
9. $a_1 = 7, d = -3$
10. $a_1 = 9, d = -5$
11. $a_1 = 200, d = -60$
12. $a_1 = 300, d = -90$
13. $a_1 = \frac{5}{2}, d = \frac{1}{2}$
14. $a_1 = \frac{3}{4}, d = \frac{1}{4}$
15. $a_1 = \frac{3}{2}, d = \frac{1}{4}$
16. $a_1 = \frac{3}{2}, d = -\frac{1}{4}$
17. $a_1 = 4.25, d = 0.3$
18. $a_1 = 6.3, d = 0.25$
19. $a_1 = 4.5, d = -0.75$
20. $a_1 = 3.5, d = -1.75$

In Exercises 21–40, find the indicated term for the arithmetic sequence with first term, a_1, and common difference, d.

21. Find a_6, when $a_1 = 13, d = 4$.
22. Find a_{16}, when $a_1 = 9, d = 2$.
23. Find a_{50}, when $a_1 = 7, d = 5$.
24. Find a_{60}, when $a_1 = 8, d = 6$.
25. Find a_9, when $a_1 = -5, d = 9$.
26. Find a_{10}, when $a_1 = -8, d = 10$.
27. Find a_{200}, when $a_1 = -40, d = 5$.
28. Find a_{150}, when $a_1 = -60, d = 5$.
29. Find a_{10}, when $a_1 = -8, d = 10$.
30. Find a_{11}, when $a_1 = 10, d = -6$.
31. Find a_{60}, when $a_1 = 35, d = -3$.

32. Find a_{70}, when $a_1 = -32, d = 4$.

33. Find a_{12}, when $a_1 = 12, d = -5$.

34. Find a_{20}, when $a_1 = -20, d = -4$.

35. Find a_{90}, when $a_1 = -70, d = -2$.

36. Find a_{80}, when $a_1 = 106, d = -12$.

37. Find a_{12}, when $a_1 = 6, d = \frac{1}{2}$.

38. Find a_{14}, when $a_1 = 8, d = \frac{1}{4}$.

39. Find a_{50}, when $a_1 = 14, d = -0.25$.

40. Find a_{110}, when $a_1 = -12, d = -0.5$.

In Exercises 41–48, write a formula for the general term (the nth term) of each arithmetic sequence. Then use the formula for a_n to find a_{20}, the 20th term of the sequence.

41. $1, 5, 9, 13, \ldots$

42. $2, 7, 12, 17, \ldots$

43. $7, 3, -1, -5, \ldots$

44. $6, 1, -4, -9, \ldots$

45. $a_1 = 9, d = 2$

46. $a_1 = 6, d = 3$

47. $a_1 = -20, d = -4$

48. $a_1 = -70, d = -5$

In Exercises 49–70, write the first six terms of the geometric sequence with the first term, a_1, and common ratio, r.

49. $a_1 = 4, r = 2$

50. $a_1 = 2, r = 3$

51. $a_1 = 1000, r = 1$

52. $a_1 = 5000, r = 1$

53. $a_1 = 3, r = -2$

54. $a_1 = 2, r = -3$

55. $a_1 = 10, r = -4$

56. $a_1 = 20, r = -4$

57. $a_1 = 2000, r = -1$

58. $a_1 = 3000, r = -1$

59. $a_1 = -2, r = -3$

60. $a_1 = -4, r = -2$

61. $a_1 = -6, r = -5$

62. $a_1 = -8, r = -5$

63. $a_1 = \frac{1}{4}, r = 2$

64. $a_1 = \frac{1}{2}, r = 2$

65. $a_1 = \frac{1}{4}, r = \frac{1}{2}$

66. $a_1 = \frac{1}{5}, r = \frac{1}{2}$

67. $a_1 = -\frac{1}{16}, r = -4$

68. $a_1 = -\frac{1}{8}, r = -2$

69. $a_1 = 2, r = 0.1$

70. $a_1 = -1000, r = 0.1$

In Exercises 71–90, find the indicated term for the geometric sequence with first term, a_1, and common ratio, r.

71. Find a_7, when $a_1 = 4, r = 2$.

72. Find a_5, when $a_1 = 4, r = 3$.

73. Find a_{20}, when $a_1 = 2, r = 3$.

74. Find a_{20}, when $a_1 = 2, r = 2$.

75. Find a_{100}, when $a_1 = 50, r = 1$.

76. Find a_{200}, when $a_1 = 60, r = 1$.

77. Find a_7, when $a_1 = 5, r = -2$.

78. Find a_4, when $a_1 = 4, r = -3$.

79. Find a_{30}, when $a_1 = 2, r = -1$.

80. Find a_{40}, when $a_1 = 6, r = -1$.

81. Find a_6, when $a_1 = -2, r = -3$.

82. Find a_5, when $a_1 = -5, r = -2$.

83. Find a_8, when $a_1 = 6, r = \frac{1}{2}$.

84. Find a_8, when $a_1 = 12, r = \frac{1}{2}$.

85. Find a_6, when $a_1 = 18, r = -\frac{1}{3}$.

86. Find a_4, when $a_1 = 9, r = -\frac{1}{3}$.

87. Find a_{40}, when $a_1 = 1000, r = -\frac{1}{2}$.

88. Find a_{30}, when $a_1 = 8000, r = -\frac{1}{2}$.

89. Find a_8, when $a_1 = 1{,}000{,}000, r = 0.1$.

90. Find a_8, when $a_1 = 40{,}000, r = 0.1$.

In Exercises 91–98, write a formula for the general term (the nth term) of each geometric sequence. Then use the formula for a_n to find a_7, the seventh term of the sequence.

91. $3, 12, 48, 192, \ldots$

92. $3, 15, 75, 375, \ldots$

93. $18, 6, 2, \frac{2}{3}, \ldots$

94. $12, 6, 3, \frac{3}{2}, \ldots$

95. $1.5, -3, 6, -12, \ldots$

96. $5, -1, \frac{1}{5}, -\frac{1}{25}, \ldots$

97. $0.0004, -0.004, 0.04, -0.4, \ldots$

98. $0.0007, -0.007, 0.07, -0.7, \ldots$

Determine whether each sequence in Exercises 99–114 is arithmetic or geometric. Then find the next two terms.

99. $2, 6, 10, 14, \ldots$

100. $3, 8, 13, 18, \ldots$

101. $5, 15, 45, 135, \ldots$

102. $15, 30, 60, 120, \ldots$

103. $-7, -2, 3, 8, \ldots$

104. $-9, -5, -1, 3, \ldots$

105. $3, \frac{3}{2}, \frac{3}{4}, \frac{3}{8}, \ldots$

106. $6, 3, \frac{3}{2}, \frac{3}{4}, \ldots$

107. $\frac{1}{2}, 1, \frac{3}{2}, 2, \ldots$

108. $\frac{2}{3}, 1, \frac{4}{3}, \frac{5}{3}, \ldots$

109. $7, -7, 7, -7, \ldots$

110. $6, -6, 6, -6, \ldots$

111. $7, -7, -21, -35, \ldots$

112. $6, -6, -18, -30, \ldots$

113. $\sqrt{5}, 5, 5\sqrt{5}, 25, \ldots$

114. $\sqrt{3}, 3, 3\sqrt{3}, 9, \ldots$

• Practice Plus

The sum, S_n, of the first n terms of an arithmetic sequence is given by

$$S_n = \frac{n}{2}(a_1 + a_n),$$

in which a_1 is the first term and a_n is the nth term. The sum, S_n, of the first n terms of a geometric series is given by

$$S_n = \frac{a_1(1 - r^n)}{1 - r},$$

in which a_1 is the first term and r is the common ratio $(r \neq 1)$. In Exercises 115–122, determine whether each sequence is arithmetic or geometric. Then use the appropriate formula to find S_{10}, the sum of the first ten terms.

115. $4, 10, 16, 22, \ldots$

116. $7, 19, 31, 43, \ldots$

117. $2, 6, 18, 54, \ldots$

118. $3, 6, 12, 24, \ldots$

119. $3, -6, 12, -24, \ldots$

120. $4, -12, 36, -108, \ldots$

121. $-10, -6, -2, 2, \ldots$

122. $-15, -9, -3, 3, \ldots$

123. Use the appropriate formula shown above to find $1 + 2 + 3 + 4 + \cdots + 100$, the sum of the first 100 natural numbers.

124. Use the appropriate formula shown above to find $2 + 4 + 6 + 8 + \cdots + 200$, the sum of the first 100 positive even integers.

• Application Exercises

Use the formula for the nth term of an arithmetic sequence to solve Exercises 125–128.

The bar graphs show changes that have taken place in the United States from 1970 to 2002 or 2003. Exercises 125–126 involve developing arithmetic sequences that model the data.

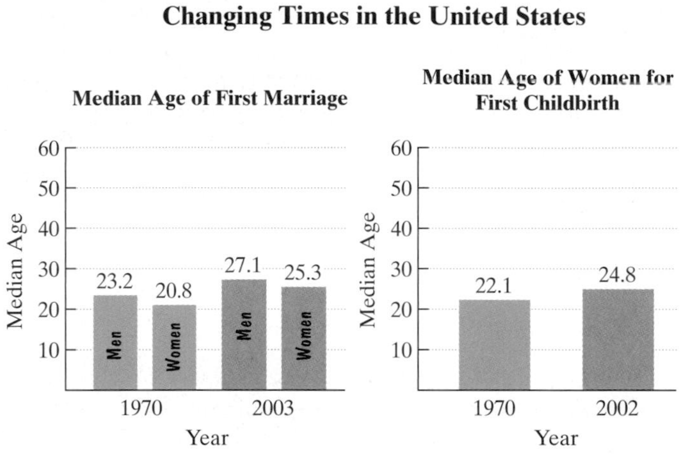

Source: U.S. Census Bureau

125. In 1970, the median age of first marriage for U.S. men was 23.2. On average, this age has increased by approximately 0.12 per year.

a. Write a formula for the nth term of the arithmetic sequence that describes the median age of first marriage for U.S. men n years after 1969.

b. According to the model in part (a), what will be the median age of first marriage for U.S. men in 2009?

126. In 1970, the median age of women for first childbirth was 22.1. On average, this age has increased by approximately 0.08 per year.

a. Write a formula for the nth term of the arithmetic sequence that describes the median age for first childbirth for U.S. women n years after 1969.

b. According to the model in part (a), what will be the median age for first childbirth for U.S. women in 2009?

127. Company A pays \$24,000 yearly with raises of \$1600 per year. Company B pays \$28,000 yearly with raises of \$1000 per year. Which company will pay more in year 10? How much more?

128. Company A pays \$23,000 yearly with raises of \$1200 per year. Company B pays \$26,000 yearly with raises of \$800 per year. Which company will pay more in year 10? How much more?

Use the formula for the nth term of a geometric sequence to solve Exercises 129–134.

In Exercises 129–130, suppose you save \$1 the first day of a month, \$2 the second day, \$4 the third day, and so on. That is, each day you save twice as much as you did the day before.

129. What will you put aside for savings on the fifteenth day of the month?

130. What will you put aside for savings on the thirtieth day of the month?

131. A professional baseball player signs a contract with a beginning salary of \$3,000,000 for the first year with an annual increase of 4% per year beginning in the second year. That is, beginning in year 2, the athlete's salary will be 1.04 times what it was in the previous year. What is the athlete's salary for year 7 of the contract? Round to the nearest dollar.

132. You are offered a job that pays \$30,000 for the first year with an annual increase of 5% per year beginning in the second year. That is, beginning in year 2, your salary will be 1.05 times what it was in the previous year. What can you expect to earn in your sixth year on the job? Round to the nearest dollar.

133. The population of California from 1990 through 1997 is shown in the following table.

Year	1990	1991	1992	1993
Population in millions	29.76	30.15	30.54	30.94

Year	1994	1995	1996	1997
Population in millions	31.34	31.75	32.16	32.58

a. Divide the population for each year by the population in the preceding year. Round to three decimal places and show that the population of California is increasing geometrically.

b. Write the general term of the geometric sequence describing population growth for California n years after 1989.

c. Estimate California's population, in millions, for the year 2000. According to the U.S. Census Bureau, California's population in 2000 was 33.87 million. How well does your geometric sequence describe the actual population?

134. The population of Texas from 1990 through 1997 is shown in the following table.

Year	1990	1991	1992	1993
Population in millions	16.99	17.35	17.71	18.08

Year	1994	1995	1996	1997
Population in millions	18.46	18.85	19.25	19.65

a. Divide the population for each year by the population in the preceding year. Round to three decimal places and show that the population of Texas is increasing geometrically.

b. Write the general term of the geometric sequence describing population growth for Texas n years after 1989.

c. Estimate Texas's population, in millions, for the year 2000. According to the U.S. Census Bureau, Texas's population in 2000 was 20.85 million. How well does your geometric sequence describe the actual population?

• Writing in Mathematics

135. What is a sequence? Give an example with your description.

136. What is an arithmetic sequence? Give an example with your description.

137. What is the common difference in an arithmetic sequence?

138. What is a geometric sequence? Give an example with your description.

139. What is the common ratio in a geometric sequence?

140. If you are given a sequence that is arithmetic or geometric, how can you determine which type of sequence it is?

141. For the first 30 days of a flu outbreak, the number of students on your campus who become ill is increasing. Which is worse: The number of students with the flu is increasing arithmetically or is increasing geometrically? Explain your answer.

• Critical Thinking Exercises

142. Which one of the following is true?

   a. The common difference for the arithmetic sequence given by $1, -1, -3, -5, \ldots$ is 2.

   b. The sequence $1, 4, 8, 13, 19, 26, \ldots$ is an arithmetic sequence.

   c. The nth term of an arithmetic sequence whose first term is a_1 and whose common difference is d is $a_n = a_1 + nd$.

   d. If the first term of an arithmetic sequence is 5 and the third term is -3, then the fourth term is -7.

143. Which one of the following is true?

   a. The sequence $2, 6, 24, 120, \ldots$ is an example of a geometric sequence.

   b. Adjacent terms in a geometric sequence have a common difference.

   c. A sequence that is not arithmetic must be geometric.

   d. If a sequence is geometric, we can write as many terms as we want by repeatedly multiplying by the common ratio.

144. A person is investigating two employment opportunities. They both have a beginning salary of $20,000 per year. Company A offers an increase of $1000 per year. Company B offers 5% more than during the preceding year. Which company will pay more in the sixth year?

• Group Exercise

145. Enough curiosities involving the Fibonacci sequence exist to warrant a flourishing Fibonacci Association. It publishes a quarterly journal. Do some research on the Fibonacci sequence by consulting the research department of your library or the Internet, and find one property that interests you. After doing this research, get together with your group to share these intriguing properties.

CHAPTER SUMMARY, REVIEW, AND TEST

• SUMMARY DEFINITIONS AND CONCEPTS — EXAMPLES

5.1 Number Theory: Prime and Composite Numbers

DEFINITIONS AND CONCEPTS	EXAMPLES
a. The set of natural numbers is $\{1, 2, 3, 4, 5, \ldots\}$. $b \mid a$ (b divides a: a is divisible by b) for natural numbers a and b if the operation of dividing a by b leaves a remainder of 0. Rules of divisibility are given in Table 5.1 on page 229.	Ex. 1, p. 230
b. A prime number is a natural number greater than 1 that has only itself and 1 as factors. A composite number is a natural number greater than 1 that is divisible by a number other than itself and 1. The Fundamental Theorem of Arithmetic: Every composite number can be expressed as a product of prime numbers in one and only one way (if the order of the factors is disregarded).	Ex. 2, p. 231
c. The greatest common divisor of two or more natural numbers is the largest number that is a divisor (or factor) of all the numbers. The procedure for finding the greatest common divisor is given in the box on page 232.	Ex. 3, p. 232; Ex. 4, p. 233
d. The least common multiple of two or more natural numbers is the smallest natural number that is divisible by all of the numbers. The procedure for finding the least common multiple is given in the box on page 234.	Ex. 5, p. 234; Ex. 6, p. 234

5.2 The Integers; Order of Operations

DEFINITIONS AND CONCEPTS	EXAMPLES
a. The set of whole numbers is $\{0, 1, 2, 3, 4, 5, \ldots\}$. The set of integers is $\{\ldots, -3, -2, -1, 0, 1, 2, 3, \ldots\}$. Integers are graphed on a number line by placing a dot at the correct location for each number.	Ex. 1, p. 238
b. $a < b$ (a is less than b) means a is to the left of b on a number line. $a > b$ (a is greater than b) means a is to the right of b on a number line.	Ex. 2, p. 239

c. $\lvert a \rvert$, the absolute value of a, is the distance of a from 0 on a number line. The absolute value of a positive number is the number itself. The absolute value of 0 is 0: $\lvert 0 \rvert = 0$. The absolute value of a negative number is the number without the negative sign. For example, $\lvert -8 \rvert = 8$.	Ex. 3, p. 240
d. Rules for performing operations with integers are given in the boxes on pages 241, 242, 244, and 245.	Ex. 4, p. 242; Ex. 5, p. 243; Ex. 6, p. 244
e. Order of Operations **1.** Perform all operations within grouping symbols. **2.** Evaluate all exponential expressions. **3.** Do all multiplications and divisions from left to right. **4.** Do all additions and subtractions from left to right.	Ex. 7, p. 246; Ex. 8, p. 247

5.3 The Rational Numbers

a. The set of rational numbers is the set of all numbers which can be expressed in the form $\frac{a}{b}$, where a and b are integers and b is not equal to 0.	
b. A rational number is reduced to its lowest terms, or simplified, by dividing both the numerator and the denominator by their greatest common divisor.	Ex. 1, p. 250
c. A mixed number consists of the sum of an integer and a rational number, expressed without the use of an addition sign. An improper fraction is a rational number whose numerator is greater than its denominator. Procedures for converting between these forms are given in the boxes on page 251.	Ex. 2, p. 251; Ex. 3, p. 252
d. Any rational number can be expressed as a decimal. The resulting decimal will either terminate (stop), or it will have a digit that repeats or a block of digits that repeat. The rational number $\frac{a}{b}$ is expressed as a decimal by dividing b into a.	Ex. 4, p. 252
e. To express a terminating decimal as a quotient of integers, the digits to the right of the decimal point are the numerator. The place-value of the last digit to the right of the decimal point is the denominator.	Ex. 5, p. 253
f. To express a repeating decimal as a quotient of integers, use the boxed procedure on page 254.	Ex. 6, p. 254; Ex. 7, p. 255
g. The product of two rational numbers is the product of their numerators divided by the product of their denominators.	Ex. 8, p. 255
h. Two numbers whose product is 1 are called reciprocals, or multiplicative inverses, of each other. The quotient of two rational numbers is the product of the first number and the reciprocal of the second number.	Ex. 9, p. 256
i. The sum or difference of two rational numbers with identical denominators is the sum or difference of their numerators over the common denominator.	Ex. 10, p. 257
j. Add or subtract rational numbers with unlike denominators by first expressing each rational number with the least common denominator and then following part (i) above.	Ex. 11, p. 257; Ex. 12, p. 258
k. Density of the Rational Numbers Given any two rational numbers, there is always a rational number between them. To find the rational number halfway between two rational numbers, add the rational numbers and divide their sum by 2.	Ex. 13, p. 259

5.4 The Irrational Numbers

a. The set of irrational numbers is the set of numbers whose decimal representations are neither terminating nor repeating. Examples of irrational numbers are $\sqrt{2} \approx 1.414$ and $\pi \approx 3.142$.	
b. Simplifying square roots: Use the product rule, $\sqrt{ab} = \sqrt{a} \cdot \sqrt{b}$, to remove from the square root any perfect squares that occur as factors.	Ex. 1, p. 265
c. Multiplying square roots: $\sqrt{a} \cdot \sqrt{b} = \sqrt{ab}$. The product of square roots is the square root of the product.	Ex. 2, p. 265

d. Dividing square roots: $\frac{\sqrt{a}}{\sqrt{b}} = \sqrt{\frac{a}{b}}$. The quotient of the square roots is the square root of the quotient.	Ex. 3, p. 266
e. Adding and subtracting square roots: If the radicals have the same radicand, add or subtract their coefficients. The answer is the sum or difference of the coefficients times the common square root. Addition or subtraction is sometimes possible by first simplifying the square roots.	Ex. 4, p. 266; Ex. 5, p. 267
f. Rationalizing denominators: Multiply the numerator and denominator by the smallest number that produces a perfect square radicand in the denominator.	Ex. 6, p. 268

5.5 Real Numbers and Their Properties

a. The set of real numbers is obtained by combining the rational numbers with the irrational numbers. The important subsets of the real numbers are summarized in Table 5.2 on page 272. A diagram representing the relationships among the subsets of the real numbers is given to the left of Table 5.2.	Ex. 1, p. 272
b. Properties of real numbers, including closure properties ($a + b$ and ab are real numbers), commutative properties ($a + b = b + a$; $ab = ba$), associative properties $[(a + b) + c = a + (b + c)$; $(ab)c = a(bc)]$, and the distributive property $[a(b + c) = ab + ac]$, are summarized in Table 5.3 on page 273.	Ex. 2, p. 274; Ex. 3, p. 274

5.6 Exponents and Scientific Notation

a. Properties of Exponents • Product rule: $b^m \cdot b^n = b^{m+n}$ • Power rule: $(b^m)^n = b^{m \cdot n}$ • Quotient rule: $\frac{b^m}{b^n} = b^{m-n}, b \neq 0$ • Zero exponent rule: $b^0 = 1, b \neq 0$ • Negative exponent rule: $b^{-m} = \frac{1}{b^m}, b \neq 0$	Table 5.4, p. 278; Ex. 1, p. 279; Ex. 2, p. 279
b. A positive number in scientific notation is expressed as $a \times 10^n$, where $1 \leq a < 10$ and n is an integer.	
c. Changing from Scientific to Decimal Notation: If n is positive, move the decimal point in a to the right n places. If n is negative, move the decimal point in a to the left $\lvert n \rvert$ places.	Ex. 3, p. 281
d. Changing from Decimal to Scientific Notation: Move the decimal point in the given number to obtain a, where $1 \leq a < 10$. The number of places the decimal point moves gives the absolute value of n in $a \times 10^n$; n is positive if the number is greater than 10 and negative if the number is less than 1.	Ex. 4, p. 281
e. The product and quotient rules for exponents are used to multiply and divide numbers in scientific notation.	Ex. 6, p. 283; Ex. 7, p. 283; Ex. 8, p. 284; Ex. 9, p. 285

5.7 Arithmetic and Geometric Sequences

a. In an arithmetic sequence, each term after the first differs from the preceding term by a constant, the common difference. Subtract any term from the term that directly follows to find the common difference.	Ex. 1, p. 289; Ex. 2, p. 289
b. The general term or the nth term of an arithmetic sequence is $a_n = a_1 + (n - 1)d$, where a_1 is the first term and d is the common difference.	Ex. 3, p. 290; Ex. 4, p. 291
c. In a geometric sequence, each term after the first is obtained by multiplying the preceding term by a nonzero constant, the common ratio. Divide any term after the first by the term that directly precedes it to find the common ratio.	Ex. 5, p. 292
d. The general term or the nth term of a geometric sequence is $a_n = a_1 r^{n-1}$, where a_1 is the first term and r is the common ratio.	Ex. 6, p. 293; Ex. 7, p. 293

REVIEW EXERCISES

5.1

In Exercises 1 and 2, determine whether the number is divisible by each of the following numbers: 2, 3, 4, 5, 6, 8, 9, 10, and 12. If you are using a calculator, explain the divisibility shown by your calculator using one of the rules of divisibility.

1. 238,632 **2.** 421,153,470

In Exercises 3–5, find the prime factorization of each composite number.

3. 705 **4.** 960 **5.** 6825

In Exercises 6–8, find the greatest common divisor and the least common multiple of the numbers.

6. 30 and 48 **7.** 36 and 150 **8.** 216 and 254

9. For an intramural league, you need to divide 24 men and 60 women into all-male and all-female teams so that each team has the same number of people. What is the largest number of people that can be placed on a team?

10. The media center at a college runs videotapes of two lectures continuously. One videotape runs for 42 minutes and a second runs for 56 minutes. Both videotapes begin at 9:00 A.M. When will the videos of the two lectures begin again at the same time?

5.2

In Exercises 11–12, insert either < or > in the shaded area between the integers to make the statement true.

11. $-93 \;\blacksquare\; 17$ **12.** $-2 \;\blacksquare\; -200$

In Exercise 13–15, find the absolute value.

13. $|-860|$ **14.** $|53|$ **15.** $|0|$

Perform the indicated operations in Exercises 16–28.

16. $8 + (-11)$ **17.** $-6 + (-5)$ **18.** $-7 - 8$

19. $-7 - (-8)$ **20.** $(-9)(-11)$ **21.** $5(-3)$

22. $\dfrac{-36}{-4}$ **23.** $\dfrac{20}{-5}$ **24.** $-40 \div 5 \cdot 2$

25. $-6 + (-2) \cdot 5$ **26.** $6 - 4(-3 + 2)$ **27.** $28 \div (2 - 4^2)$

28. $36 - 24 \div 4 \cdot 3 - 1$

29. For the year 2015, the Congressional Budget Office projects a budget deficit of −$57 billion. For the same year, the Brookings Institution forecasts a budget deficit of −$715 billion. What is the difference between the CBO projection and the Brookings projection?

5.3

In Exercises 30–32, reduce each rational number to its lowest terms.

30. $\frac{40}{75}$ **31.** $\frac{36}{150}$ **32.** $\frac{165}{180}$

In Exercises 33–34, convert each mixed number to an improper fraction.

33. $5\frac{9}{11}$ **34.** $-3\frac{2}{7}$

In Exercises 35–36, convert each improper fraction to a mixed number.

35. $\frac{27}{5}$ **36.** $-\frac{17}{9}$

In Exercises 37–40, express each rational number as a decimal.

37. $\frac{4}{5}$ **38.** $\frac{3}{7}$ **39.** $\frac{5}{8}$ **40.** $\frac{9}{16}$

In Exercises 41–44, express each terminating decimal as a quotient of integers in lowest terms.

41. 0.6 **42.** 0.68 **43.** 0.588 **44.** 0.0084

In Exercises 45–47, express each repeating decimal as a quotient of integers in lowest terms.

45. $0.\overline{5}$ **46.** $0.\overline{34}$ **47.** $0.\overline{113}$

In Exercises 48–56, perform the indicated operations. Where possible, reduce the answer to lowest terms.

48. $\frac{3}{5} \cdot \frac{7}{10}$ **49.** $\left(3\frac{1}{3}\right)\left(1\frac{3}{4}\right)$ **50.** $\frac{4}{5} \div \frac{3}{10}$

51. $-1\frac{2}{3} \div 6\frac{2}{3}$ **52.** $\frac{2}{9} + \frac{4}{9}$ **53.** $\frac{7}{9} + \frac{5}{12}$

54. $\frac{3}{4} - \frac{2}{15}$ **55.** $\frac{1}{3} + \frac{1}{2} \cdot \frac{4}{5}$ **56.** $\frac{3}{8}\left(\frac{1}{2} + \frac{1}{3}\right)$

In Exercises 57–58, find a rational number halfway between the two numbers in each pair.

57. $\frac{1}{7}$ and $\frac{1}{8}$ **58.** $\frac{3}{4}$ and $\frac{3}{5}$

59. A recipe for coq au vin is meant for six people and requires $4\frac{1}{2}$ pounds of chicken. If you want to serve 15 people, how much chicken is needed?

60. The gas tank of a car is filled to its capacity. The first day, $\frac{1}{4}$ of the tank's gas is used for travel. The second day, $\frac{1}{3}$ of the tank's original amount of gas is used for travel. What fraction of the tank is filled with gas at the end of the second day?

5.4

In Exercises 61–64, simplify the square root.

61. $\sqrt{28}$ **62.** $\sqrt{72}$ **63.** $\sqrt{150}$ **64.** $\sqrt{300}$

In Exercises 65–73, perform the indicated operation. Simplify the answer when possible.

65. $\sqrt{6} \cdot \sqrt{8}$ **66.** $\sqrt{10} \cdot \sqrt{5}$

67. $\dfrac{\sqrt{24}}{\sqrt{2}}$ **68.** $\dfrac{\sqrt{27}}{\sqrt{3}}$

69. $\sqrt{5} + 4\sqrt{5}$ **70.** $7\sqrt{11} - 13\sqrt{11}$

71. $\sqrt{50} + \sqrt{8}$ **72.** $\sqrt{3} - 6\sqrt{27}$

73. $2\sqrt{18} + 3\sqrt{8}$

In Exercises 74–75, rationalize the denominator.

74. $\dfrac{30}{\sqrt{5}}$ **75.** $\sqrt{\dfrac{2}{3}}$

76. Paleontologists use the mathematical model $W = 4\sqrt{2x}$ to estimate the walking speed of a dinosaur, W, in feet per second, where x is the length, in feet, of the dinosaur's leg. What is the walking speed of a dinosaur whose leg length is 6 feet? Express the answer in simplified radical form. Then use your calculator to estimate the walking speed to the nearest tenth of a foot per second.

5.5

77. Consider the set

$$\left\{-17, -\tfrac{9}{13}, 0, 0.75, \sqrt{2}, \pi, \sqrt{81}\right\}.$$

List all numbers from the set that are **a.** natural numbers, **b.** whole numbers, **c.** integers, **d.** rational numbers, **e.** irrational numbers, **f.** real numbers.

78. Give an example of an integer that is not a natural number.

79. Give an example of a rational number that is not an integer.

80. Give an example of a real number that is not a rational number.

In Exercises 81–86, state the name of the property illustrated.

81. $3 + 17 = 17 + 3$

82. $(6 \cdot 3) \cdot 9 = 6 \cdot (3 \cdot 9)$

83. $\sqrt{3}(\sqrt{5} + \sqrt{3}) = \sqrt{15} + 3$

84. $(6 \cdot 9) \cdot 2 = 2 \cdot (6 \cdot 9)$

85. $\sqrt{3}(\sqrt{5} + \sqrt{3}) = (\sqrt{5} + \sqrt{3})\sqrt{3}$

86. $(3 \cdot 7) + (4 \cdot 7) = (4 \cdot 7) + (3 \cdot 7)$

In Exercises 87–88, give on example to show that

87. The natural numbers are not closed with respect to division.

88. The whole numbers are not closed with respect to subtraction.

5.6

In Exercises 89–99, evaluate each expression.

89. $6 \cdot 6^2$ 90. $2^3 \cdot 2^3$ 91. $(2^2)^2$ 92. $(3^3)^2$

93. $\frac{5^6}{5^4}$ 94. 7^0 95. $(-7)^0$ 96. 6^{-3}

97. 2^{-4} 98. $\frac{7^4}{7^6}$ 99. $3^5 \cdot 3^{-2}$

In Exercises 100–103, express each number in decimal notation.

100. 4.6×10^2 101. 3.74×10^4

102. 2.55×10^{-3} 103. 7.45×10^{-5}

In Exercises 104–109, express each number in scientific notation.

104. 7520 105. 3,590,000 106. 0.00725

107. 0.000000409 108. 420×10^{11} 109. 0.97×10^{-4}

In Exercises 110–117, perform the indicated operation and express each answer in decimal notation.

110. $(3 \times 10^7)(1.3 \times 10^{-5})$ 111. $(5 \times 10^3)(2.3 \times 10^2)$

112. $\frac{6.9 \times 10^3}{3 \times 10^5}$ 113. $\frac{2.4 \times 10^{-4}}{6 \times 10^{-6}}$

In Exercises 114–117, perform the indicated operation by first expressing each number in scientific notation. Write the answer in scientific notation.

114. (60,000)(540,000) 115. (91,000)(0.0004)

116. $\frac{8{,}400{,}000}{4000}$ 117. $\frac{0.000003}{0.00000006}$

118. If you earned \$1 million per year ($\$10^6$), how long would it take to accumulate \$1 billion dollars ($\$10^9$)?

119. If the population of the United States is 3×10^8 and each person spends about \$150 per year going to the movies (or renting movies), express the total annual spending on movies in scientific notation.

120. The world's population is approximately 6.5×10^9 people. Current projections double this population in 40 years. Write the population 40 years from now in scientific notation.

5.7

In Exercises 121–123, write the first six terms of the arithmetic sequence with the first term, a_1, and common difference, d.

121. $a_1 = 7, d = 4$

122. $a_1 = -4, d = -5$

123. $a_1 = \frac{3}{2}, d = -\frac{1}{2}$

In Exercises 124–126, find the indicated term for the arithmetic sequence with first term, a_1, and common difference, d.

124. Find a_6, when $a_1 = 5, d = 3$.

125. Find a_{12}, when $a_1 = -8, d = -2$.

126. Find a_{14}, when $a_1 = 14, d = -4$.

In Exercises 127–128, write a formula for the general term (the nth term) of each arithmetic sequence. Then use the formula for a_n to find a_{20}, the 20th term of the sequence.

127. $-7, -3, 1, 5, \ldots$ 128. $a_1 = 200, d = -20$

In Exercises 129–131, write the first six terms of the geometric sequence with the first term, a_1, and common ratio, r.

129. $a_1 = 3, r = 2$ 130. $a_1 = \frac{1}{2}, r = \frac{1}{2}$ 131. $a_1 = 16, r = -\frac{1}{2}$

In Exercises 132–134, find the indicated term for the geometric sequence with first term, a_1, and common ratio, r.

132. Find a_4, when $a_1 = 2, r = 3$.

133. Find a_6, when $a_1 = 16, r = \frac{1}{2}$.

134. Find a_5, when $a_1 = -3, r = 2$.

In Exercises 135–136, write a formula for the general term (the nth term) of each geometric sequence. Then use the formula for a_n to find a_8, the eighth term of the sequence.

135. $1, 2, 4, 8, \ldots$ 136. $100, 10, 1, \frac{1}{10}, \ldots$

Determine whether each sequence in Exercises 137–140 is arithmetic or geometric. Then find the next two terms.

137. $4, 9, 14, 19, \ldots$ 138. $2, 6, 18, 54, \ldots$

139. $1, \frac{1}{4}, \frac{1}{16}, \frac{1}{64}, \ldots$ 140. $0, -7, -14, -21, \ldots$

141. The graph shows the percentage of in-home dinners in the United States having various items as a side dish from 1993 through 2004.

Percentage of U.S. In-Home Dinners Having Various Items as a Side Dish

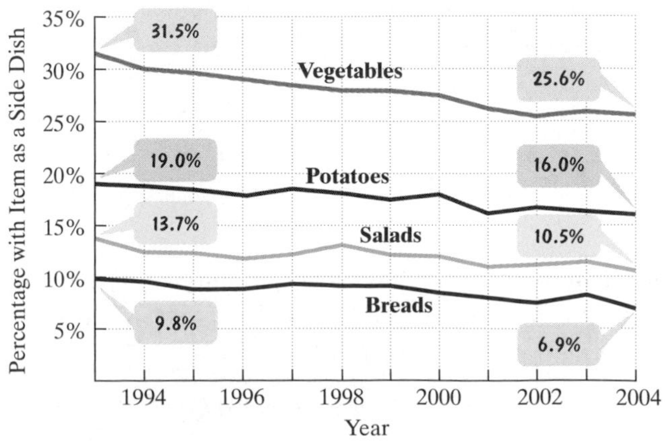

Source: The NPD Group

In 1993, 31.5% of home dinners had vegetables as a side dish. On average, this decreased by approximately 0.54% per year since then.

a. Write a formula for the nth term of the arithmetic sequence that describes the percentage of dinners that included vegetables n years after 1992.

b. Use the model to predict the percentage of dinners that will include vegetables by the year 2010.

c. Repeat parts (a) and (b) for the change in another one of the items shown in the graph at the bottom of the previous page from 1993 to 2004.

142. Projections for the U.S. population, ages 85 and older, are shown in the following table.

Year	2000	2010	2020	2030	2040	2050
Projected Population in millions	4.2	5.9	8.3	11.6	16.2	22.7

Actual 2000 population

Source: U.S. Census Bureau

a. Show that the U.S. population, ages 85 and older, is projected to increase geometrically.

b. Write the general term of the geometric sequence describing the U.S. population, ages 85 and older, in millions, n decades after 1990.

c. Use the model in part (b) to project the U.S. population, ages 85 and older, in 2080.

CHAPTER 5 TEST

1. Which of the numbers 2, 3, 4, 5, 6, 8, 9, 10, and 12 divide 391,248?

2. Find the prime factorization of 252.

3. Find the greatest common divisor and the least common multiple of 48 and 72.

Perform the indicated operations in Exercises 4–6.

4. $-6 - (5 - 12)$ **5.** $(-3)(-4) \div (7 - 10)$

6. $(6 - 8)^2(5 - 7)^3$

7. Express $\frac{7}{12}$ as a decimal.

8. Express $0.\overline{64}$ as a quotient of integers in lowest terms.

In Exercises 9–11, perform the indicated operations. Where possible, reduce the answer to its lowest terms.

9. $\left(-\frac{3}{7}\right) \div \left(-2\frac{1}{7}\right)$ **10.** $\frac{19}{24} - \frac{7}{40}$ **11.** $\frac{1}{2} - 8\left(\frac{1}{4} + 1\right)$

12. Find a rational number halfway between $\frac{1}{2}$ and $\frac{2}{3}$.

13. Multiply and simplify: $\sqrt{10} \cdot \sqrt{5}$.

14. Add: $\sqrt{50} + \sqrt{32}$.

15. Rationalize the denominator: $\dfrac{6}{\sqrt{2}}$.

16. List all the rational numbers in this set:

$$\left\{-7, -\tfrac{4}{5}, 0, 0.25, \sqrt{3}, \sqrt{4}, \tfrac{22}{7}, \pi\right\}.$$

In Exercises 17–18, state the name of the property illustrated.

17. $3(2 + 5) = 3(5 + 2)$

18. $6(7 + 4) = 6 \cdot 7 + 6 \cdot 4$

In Exercises 19–21, evaluate each expression.

19. $3^3 \cdot 3^2$ **20.** $\dfrac{4^6}{4^3}$ **21.** 8^{-2}

22. Multiply and express the answer in decimal notation.

$$(3 \times 10^8)(2.5 \times 10^{-5})$$

23. Divide by first expressing each number in scientific notation. Write the answer in scientific notation.

$$\frac{49{,}000}{0.007}$$

24. In 2006, the U.S. government collected 2.18×10^{12} dollars in taxes. At that time, the U.S. population was approximately 300 million, or 3×10^8. If the total tax collections were evenly divided among all Americans, how much would each citizen pay? Express the answer in decimal notation, rounded to the nearest dollar.

25. Write the first six terms of the arithmetic sequence with first term, a_1, and common difference, d.

$$a_1 = 1, d = -5$$

26. Find a_9, the ninth term of the arithmetic sequence with the first term, a_1, and common difference, d.

$$a_1 = -2, d = 3$$

27. Write the first six terms of the geometric sequence with first term, a_1, and common ratio, r.

$$a_1 = 16, r = \frac{1}{2}$$

28. Find a_7, the seventh term of the geometric sequence with the first term, a_1, and common ratio, r.

$$a_1 = 5, r = 2$$

CHAPTER 6

Algebra: Equations and Inequalities

America is a nation of immigrants. Since 1820, over 40 million people have immigrated to the United States from all over the world. They chose to come for various reasons, such as to live in freedom, to practice religion without persecution, to escape poverty or oppression, and to make better lives for themselves and their children. As a result, in 2003, 11.7% of the U.S. population was foreign-born. How can we use mathematical models to project when this percentage might grow to one in every five Americans, or even more?

In this chapter, you will learn to use formulas and mathematical models in new ways. With these skills, you will gain insights into a variety of issues, ranging from the growing diversity of the U.S. population to concerns about Social Security, and even the positive benefits that humor and laughter can have on our lives.

The foreign-born U.S. population model appears as Exercises 85–88 in Exercise Set 6.6. You will develop and use models for Social Security's income and outflow in Exercises 27–29 in the Chapter 6 Test. Humor opens Section 6.2, and the advantage of having a sense of humor becomes laughingly evident in the models in Example 6 on page 317.

SECTION 6.1 • ALGEBRAIC EXPRESSIONS AND FORMULAS

OBJECTIVES

1. Evaluate algebraic expressions.
2. Use mathematical models.
3. Understand the vocabulary of algebraic expressions.
4. Simplify algebraic expressions.

Algebraic Expressions

Feeling attractive with a suntan that gives you a "healthy glow"? Think again. Direct sunlight is known to promote skin cancer. Although sunscreens protect you from burning, dermatologists are concerned with the long-term damage that results from the sun even without sunburn.

Algebra uses letters, such as x and y, to represent numbers. If a letter is used to represent various numbers, it is called a **variable**. For example, we can let x represent the number of minutes that a person can stay in the sun without burning with no sunscreen. With a number 6 sunscreen, exposure time without burning is six times as long, or 6 times x. This can be written $6 \cdot x$, but it is usually expressed as $6x$. Placing a number and a letter next to one another indicates multiplication.

Notice that $6x$ combines the number 6 and the variable x using the operation of multiplication. A combination of variables and numbers using the operations of addition, subtraction, multiplication, or division, as well as powers or roots, is called an **algebraic expression**. Here are some examples of algebraic expressions:

$$x + 6, \quad x^2 - 6, \quad 6x, \quad \frac{x}{6}, \quad 3x + 5, \quad \sqrt{x} + 7.$$

1 Evaluate algebraic expressions.

Evaluating Algebraic Expressions

Evaluating an algebraic expression means finding the value of the expression for a given value of the variable. For example, we can evaluate $6x$ (from the sunscreen example) when $x = 15$. We substitute 15 for x. We obtain $6 \cdot 15$, or 90. This means that if you can stay in the sun for 15 minutes without burning when you don't put on any lotion, then with a number 6 lotion, you can "cook" for 90 minutes without burning.

Many algebraic expressions contain more than one operation. Evaluating an algebraic expression correctly involves carefully applying the order of operations agreement that we studied in Chapter 5.

THE ORDER OF OPERATIONS AGREEMENT

1. Perform operations within the innermost parentheses and work outward. If the algebraic expression involves a fraction, treat the numerator and the denominator as if they were each enclosed in parentheses.
2. Evaluate all exponential expressions.
3. Perform multiplications and divisions as they occur, working from left to right.
4. Perform additions and subtractions as they occur, working from left to right.

EXAMPLE 1 EVALUATING AN ALGEBRAIC EXPRESSION

Evaluate $7 + 5(x - 4)^3$ for $x = 6$.

SOLUTION

$$7 + 5(x - 4)^3 = 7 + 5(6 - 4)^3$$ Replace x with 6.

$$= 7 + 5(2)^3$$ First work inside parentheses: $6 - 4 = 2$.

$$= 7 + 5(8)$$ Evaluate the exponential expression: $2^3 = 2 \cdot 2 \cdot 2 = 8$.

$$= 7 + 40$$ Multiply: $5(8) = 40$.

$$= 47$$ Add.

CHECK POINT 1 Evaluate $8 + 6(x - 3)^2$ for $x = 13$.

EXAMPLE 2 EVALUATING AN ALGEBRAIC EXPRESSION

Evaluate $x^2 + 5x - 3$ for $x = -6$.

SOLUTION We substitute -6 for each of the two occurrences of x. Then we use the order of operations to evaluate the algebraic expression.

$$x^2 + 5x - 3$$ This is the given algebraic expression.

$$= (-6)^2 + 5(-6) - 3$$ Substitute -6 for each x.

$$= 36 + 5(-6) - 3$$ Evaluate the exponential expression: $(-6)^2 = (-6)(-6) = 36$.

$$= 36 + (-30) - 3$$ Multiply: $5(-6) = -30$.

$$= 6 - 3$$ Add and subtract from left to right. First add: $36 + (-30) = 6$.

$$= 3$$ Subtract.

CHECK POINT 2 Evaluate $x^2 + 4x - 7$ for $x = -5$.

STUDY TIP

Notice the difference between the following evaluations:

- x^2 for $x = -6$

  $x^2 = (-6)^2$

  $= (-6)(-6) = 36$

- $-x^2$ for $x = 6$

  $-x^2 = -6^2 = -6 \cdot 6 = -36$

  The negative is not inside parentheses and is not taken to the second power.

Work carefully when evaluating algebraic expressions with exponents and negatives.

EXAMPLE 3 EVALUATING AN ALGEBRAIC EXPRESSION

Evaluate $-2x^2 + 5xy - y^3$ for $x = 4$ and $y = -2$.

SOLUTION We substitute 4 for each x and -2 for each y. Then we use the order of operations to evaluate the algebraic expression.

$$-2x^2 + 5xy - y^3$$ This is the given algebraic expression.

$$= -2 \cdot 4^2 + 5 \cdot 4(-2) - (-2)^3$$ Substitute 4 for x and -2 for y.

$$= -2 \cdot 16 + 5(4)(-2) - (-8)$$ Evaluate the exponential expressions: $4^2 = 4 \cdot 4 = 16$ and $(-2)^3 = (-2)(-2)(-2) = -8$.

$$= -32 + (-40) - (-8)$$ Multiply: $-2 \cdot 16 = -32$ and $5(4)(-2) = 20(-2) = -40$.

$$= -72 - (-8)$$ Add and subtract from left to right. First add: $-32 + (-40) = -72$.

$$= -64$$ Subtract: $-72 - (-8) = -72 + 8 = -64$.

CHECK POINT 3 Evaluate $-3x^2 + 4xy - y^3$ for $x = 5$ and $y = -1$.

2 Use mathematical models.

Formulas and Mathematical Models

An **equation** is formed when an equal sign is placed between two algebraic expressions. One aim of algebra is to provide a compact, symbolic description of the world. These descriptions involve the use of *formulas*. A **formula** is an equation that uses letters to express a relationship between two or more variables. Here is an example of a formula:

$$C = \frac{5}{9}(F - 32).$$

Celsius temperature | is | $\frac{5}{9}$ of | the difference between Fahrenheit temperature and 32°.

These important definitions are repeated from earlier chapters in case your course did not cover this material.

The process of finding formulas to describe real-world phenomena is called **mathematical modeling**. Such formulas, together with the meaning assigned to the variables, are called **mathematical models**. We often say that these formulas model, or describe, the relationships among the variables.

EXAMPLE 4 MODELING THE AMOUNT SPENT ON ONLINE DATING

In 2003, 28.5 million U.S. adults browsed Internet personals and 17.4 million posted online personal ads. The bar graph in Figure 6.1 shows the amount spent in the United States, in millions of dollars, on online dating. Here are three mathematical models for the data shown in the graph. In each formula, D represents the amount spent on online dating, in millions of dollars, x years after 2002.

Shopping for a Date: Millions of Dollars Spent in the U.S. on Online Dating

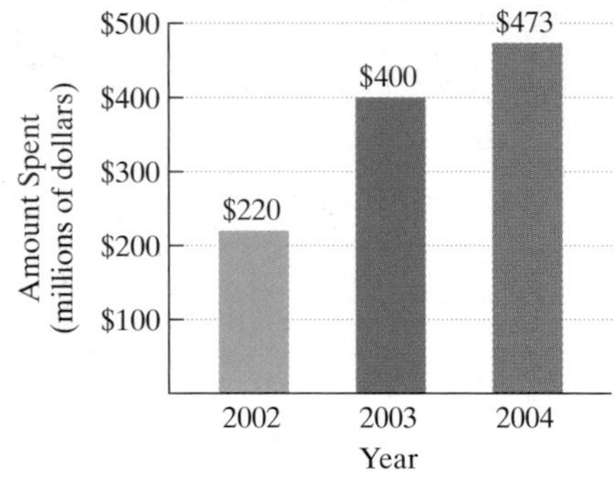

FIGURE 6.1
Source: Jupiter Research

Model 1 $D = 236(1.5)^x$

Model 2 $D = 127x + 239$

Model 3 $D = -54x^2 + 234x + 220$

Which model best describes the data for 2004?

SOLUTION Because 2004 is 2 years after 2002, we substitute 2 for x in each formula. Then we use the order of operations to find D, the amount spent, in millions of dollars, on online dating. The best model is the one that comes closest to giving the actual amount spent in 2004, namely $473 million.

Model 1

$$D = 236(1.5)^x$$
$$D = 236(1.5)^2$$
$$= 236(2.25)$$
$$= 531$$

Model 2

$$D = 127x + 239$$
$$D = 127(2) + 239$$
$$= 254 + 239$$
$$= 493$$

Model 3

$$D = -54x^2 + 234x + 220$$
$$D = -54 \cdot 2^2 + 234 \cdot 2 + 220$$
$$= -54 \cdot 4 + 234 \cdot 2 + 220$$
$$= -216 + 468 + 220$$
$$= 472$$

Figure 6.1 shows that $473 million was spent in 2004.

The formula for model 3 indicates that in 2004, $472 million was spent on online dating. The number given in Figure 6.1 is $473 million, so model 3 best describes the data for that year.

In Example 4, model 1 does not provide a very good approximation for the 2004 data. If a mathematical model gives an estimate that is a poor approximation or is extended to include values of the variable that do not make sense, we say that **model breakdown** has occurred.

CHECK POINT 4 Use the three models in Example 4 to determine which model best describes the data for 2003.

3 Understand the vocabulary of algebraic expressions.

The Vocabulary of Algebraic Expressions

We have seen that an algebraic expression combines numbers and variables. Here is another example of an algebraic expression:

$$7x - 9y - 3.$$

The **terms** of an algebraic expression are those parts that are separated by addition. For example, we can rewrite $7x - 9y - 3$ as

$$7x + (-9y) + (-3).$$

This expression contains three terms, namely $7x$, $-9y$, and -3.

The numerical part of a term is called its **coefficient**. In the term $7x$, the 7 is the coefficient. In the term $-9y$, the -9 is the coefficient.

Coefficients of 1 and -1 are not written. Thus, the coefficient of x, meaning $1x$, is 1. Similarly, the coefficient of $-y$, meaning $-1y$, is -1.

A term that consists of just a number is called a **numerical term** or a **constant**. The numerical term of $7x - 9y - 3$ is -3.

The parts of each term that are multiplied are called the **factors** of the term. The factors of the term $7x$ are 7 and x.

Like terms are terms that have the same variable factors. For example, $3x$ and $7x$ are like terms.

4 Simplify algebraic expressions.

Simplifying Algebraic Expressions

The properties of real numbers that we discussed in Chapter 5 can be applied to algebraic expressions.

PROPERTIES OF REAL NUMBERS

Property	Example
Commutative Property of Addition: $a + b = b + a$	$13x^2 + 7x = 7x + 13x^2$
Commutative Property of Multiplication: $ab = ba$	$x \cdot 6 = 6x$
Associative Property of Addition: $(a + b) + c = a + (b + c)$	$3 + (8 + x) = (3 + 8) + x = 11 + x$
Associative Property of Multiplication: $(ab)c = a(bc)$	$-2(3x) = (-2 \cdot 3)x = -6x$
Distributive Property: $a(b + c) = ab + ac$	$5(3x + 7) = 5 \cdot 3x + 5 \cdot 7 = 15x + 35$
$a(b - c) = ab - ac$	$4(2x - 5) = 4 \cdot 2x - 4 \cdot 5 = 8x - 20$

STUDY TIP

To combine like terms mentally, add or subtract the coefficients of the terms. Use this result as the coefficient of the terms' variable factor(s).

The distributive property in the form

$$ba + ca = (b + c)a$$

enables us to add or subtract like terms. For example,

$$3x + 7x = (3 + 7)x = 10x$$

$$7y^2 - y^2 = 7y^2 - 1y^2 = (7 - 1)y^2 = 6y^2.$$

This process is called **combining like terms.**

An algebraic expression is **simplified** when parentheses have been removed and like terms have been combined.

EXAMPLE 5 SIMPLIFYING AN ALGEBRAIC EXPRESSION

Simplify: $5(3x - 7) - 6x$.

SOLUTION

$5(3x - 7) - 6x$

$= 5 \cdot 3x - 5 \cdot 7 - 6x$ Use the distributive property to remove the parentheses.

$= 15x - 35 - 6x$ Multiply.

$= (15x - 6x) - 35$ Group like terms.

$= 9x - 35$ Combine like terms: $15x - 6x = (15 - 6)x = 9x$.

CHECK POINT 5 Simplify: $7(2x - 3) - 11x$.

EXAMPLE 6 SIMPLIFYING AN ALGEBRAIC EXPRESSION

Simplify: $6(2x^2 + 4x) + 10(4x^2 + 3x)$.

SOLUTION

$6(2x^2 + 4x) + 10(4x^2 + 3x)$

$= 6 \cdot 2x^2 + 6 \cdot 4x + 10 \cdot 4x^2 + 10 \cdot 3x$ Use the distributive property to remove the parentheses.

$= 12x^2 + 24x + 40x^2 + 30x$ Multiply.

$= (12x^2 + 40x^2) + (24x + 30x)$ Group like terms.

$= 52x^2 + 54x$ Combine like terms: $12x^2 + 40x^2 = (12 + 40)x^2 = 52x^2$ and $24x + 30x = (24 + 30)x = 54x$.

$52x^2$ and $54x$ are not like terms. They contain different variable factors, x^2 and x, and cannot be combined.

CHECK POINT 6 Simplify: $7(4x^2 + 3x) + 2(5x^2 + x)$.

It is not uncommon to see algebraic expressions with parentheses preceded by a negative sign or subtraction. An expression of the form $-(a + b)$ can be simplified as follows:

$$-(a + b) = -1(a + b) = (-1)a + (-1)b = -a + (-b) = -a - b.$$

Do you see a fast way to obtain the simplified expression on the right? **If a negative sign or a subtraction symbol appears outside parentheses, drop the parentheses and change the sign of every term within the parentheses.** For example,

$$-(3x^2 - 7x - 4) = -3x^2 + 7x + 4.$$

EXAMPLE 7 SIMPLIFYING AN ALGEBRAIC EXPRESSION

Simplify: $8x + 2[5 - (x - 3)]$.

SOLUTION

$8x + 2[5 - (x - 3)]$

$= 8x + 2[5 - x + 3]$ — Drop parentheses and change the sign of each term in parentheses: $-(x - 3) = -x + 3$.

$= 8x + 2[8 - x]$ — Simplify inside brackets: $5 + 3 = 8$.

$= 8x + 16 - 2x$ — Apply the distributive property: $2[8 - x] = 2 \cdot 8 - 2x = 16 - 2x$.

$= (8x - 2x) + 16$ — Group like terms.

$= 6x + 16$ — Combine like terms: $8x - 2x = (8 - 2)x = 6x$.

CHECK POINT 7 Simplify: $6x + 4[7 - (x - 2)]$.

EXERCISE SET 6.1

• Practice Exercises

In Exercises 1–30, evaluate the algebraic expression for the given value or values of the variables.

1. $5x + 7$; $x = 4$
2. $9x + 6$; $x = 5$
3. $-7x - 5$; $x = -4$
4. $-6x - 13$; $x = -3$
5. $x^2 + 4$; $x = 5$
6. $x^2 + 9$; $x = 3$
7. $x^2 - 6$; $x = -2$
8. $x^2 - 11$; $x = -3$
9. $x^2 + 4x$; $x = 10$
10. $x^2 + 6x$; $x = 9$
11. $8x^2 + 17$; $x = 5$
12. $7x^2 + 25$; $x = 3$
13. $x^2 - 5x$; $x = -11$
14. $x^2 - 8x$; $x = -5$
15. $x^2 + 5x - 6$; $x = 4$
16. $x^2 + 7x - 4$; $x = 6$
17. $4 + 5(x - 7)^3$; $x = 9$
18. $6 + 5(x - 6)^3$; $x = 8$
19. $x^2 - 3(x - y)$; $x = 2, y = 8$
20. $x^2 - 4(x - y)$; $x = 3, y = 8$
21. $2x^2 - 5x - 6$; $x = -3$
22. $3x^2 - 4x - 9$; $x = -5$
23. $-5x^2 - 4x - 11$; $x = -1$
24. $-6x^2 - 11x - 17$; $x = -2$
25. $3x^2 + 2xy + 5y^2$; $x = 2, y = 3$
26. $4x^2 + 3xy + 2y^2$; $x = 3, y = 2$
27. $-x^2 - 4xy + 3y^3$; $x = -1, y = -2$
28. $-x^2 - 3xy + 4y^3$; $x = -3, y = -1$
29. $\dfrac{2x + 3y}{x + 1}$; $x = -2, y = 4$
30. $\dfrac{2x + y}{xy - 2x}$; $x = -2, y = 4$

The formula

$$C = \frac{5}{9}(F - 32)$$

expresses the relationship between Fahrenheit temperature, F, and Celsius temperature, C. In Exercises 31–32, use the formula to convert the given Fahrenheit temperature to its equivalent temperature on the Celsius scale.

31. 50°F
32. 86°F

A football was kicked vertically upward from a height of 4 feet with an initial speed of 60 feet per second. The formula

$$h = 4 + 60t - 16t^2$$

describes the ball's height above the ground, h, in feet, t seconds after it was kicked. Use this formula to solve Exercises 33–34.

33. What was the ball's height 2 seconds after it was kicked?
34. What was the ball's height 3 seconds after it was kicked?

In Exercises 35–52, simplify each algebraic expression.

35. $7x + 10x$
36. $5x + 13x$
37. $5x^2 - 8x^2$
38. $7x^2 - 10x^2$
39. $3(x + 5)$
40. $4(x + 6)$
41. $4(2x - 3)$
42. $3(4x - 5)$
43. $5(3x + 4) - 4$
44. $2(5x + 4) - 3$
45. $5(3x - 2) + 12x$
46. $2(5x - 1) + 14x$
47. $7(3y - 5) + 2(4y + 3)$
48. $4(2y - 6) + 3(5y + 10)$
49. $5(3y - 2) - (7y + 2)$
50. $4(5y - 3) - (6y + 3)$
51. $7 - 4[3 - (4y - 5)]$
52. $6 - 5[8 - (2y - 4)]$

• Practice Plus

In Exercises 53–56, simplify each algebraic expression.

53. $18x^2 + 4 - [6(x^2 - 2) + 5]$
54. $14x^2 + 5 - [7(x^2 - 2) + 4]$
55. $2(3x^2 - 5) - [4(2x^2 - 1) + 3]$
56. $4(6x^2 - 3) - [2(5x^2 - 1) + 1]$

In Exercises 57–64, write each English phrase as an algebraic expression. Then simplify the expression. Let x represent the number.

57. A number decreased by the sum of the number and four

58. A number decreased by the difference between eight and the number

59. Six times the product of negative five and a number

60. Ten times the product of negative four and a number

61. The difference between the product of five and a number and twice the number

62. The difference between the product of six and a number and negative two times the number

63. The difference between eight times a number and six more than three times the number

64. Eight decreased by three times the sum of a number and six

• Application Exercises

The bar graph shows the number of billionaires in the United States from 2000 through 2004.

A Growing Club: U.S. Billionaires

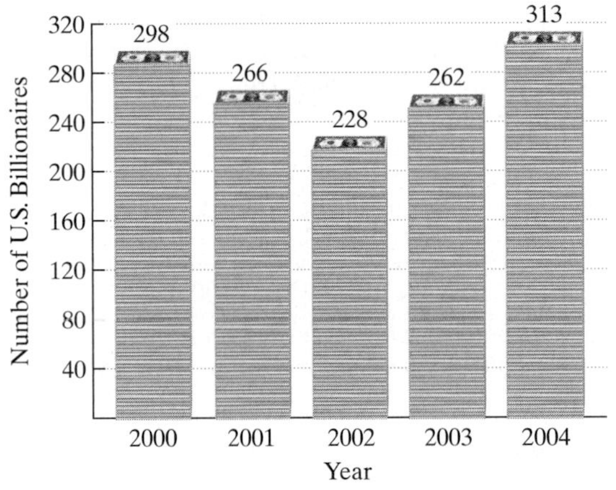

Source: *Forbes* magazine

The formula

$$N = 17x^2 - 65.4x + 302.2$$

models the number of billionaires, N, in the United States, x years after 2000. Use the formula to solve Exercises 65–68.

65. According to the formula, how many U.S. billionaires, to the nearest whole number, were there in 2004? How well does the formula model the actual data shown in the bar graph?

66. According to the formula, how many U.S. billionaires, to the nearest whole number, were there in 2003? How well does the formula model the actual data shown in the bar graph?

67. According to the formula, how many U.S. billionaires, to the nearest whole number, will there be in 2010?

68. According to the formula, how many U.S. billionaires, to the nearest whole number, will there be in 2008?

The bar graph shows the number of people in the United States, in millions, who do yoga.

Yoga Stretch: Number of U.S. Yoga Practitioners

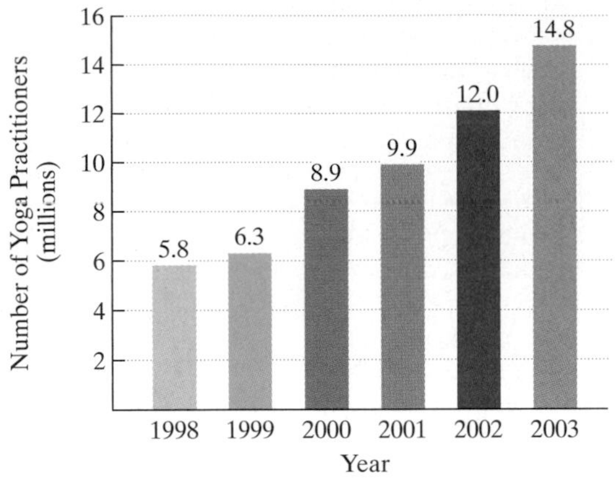

Source: *Yoga Journal*

Here are four mathematical models for the data shown in the graph. In each formula, N represents the number of U.S. yoga practitioners, in millions, x years after 1998.

Model 1 $N = 1.8x + 5.1$

Model 2 $N = 5.6(1.2)^x$

Model 3 $N = 0.17x^2 + 0.95x + 5.68$

Model 4 $N = 0.01x^3 + 0.09x^2 + 1.1x + 5.64$

Use these models to solve Exercises 69–72.

69. Which model best describes the data for 2000?

70. Which model best describes the data for 1998?

71. How well does model 3 describe the data for 2003?

72. How well does model 4 describe the data for 2002?

The line graph shows the cost of inflation. What cost $10,000 in 1975 would cost the amount shown by the graph in subsequent years.

The Cost of Inflation

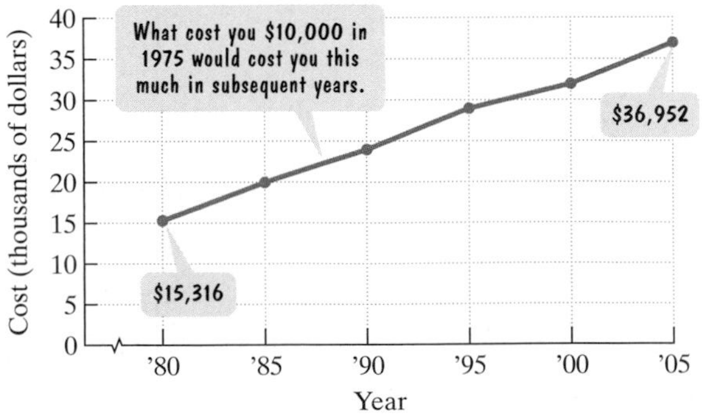

Source: Bureau of Labor Statistics

Here are two mathematical models for the data shown in the graph. In each formula, C represents the cost x years after 1980 of what cost $10,000 in 1975.

Model 1 $C = 865x + 15{,}316$

Model 2 $C = -2x^2 + 900x + 15{,}397$

Use these models to solve Exercises 73–75.

73. a. Use the graph to estimate the cost in 2000, to the nearest thousand dollars, of what cost \$10,000 in 1975.

b. Use model 1 to determine the cost in 2000. How well does this describe your estimate from part (a)?

c. Use model 2 to determine the cost in 2000. How well does this describe your estimate from part (a)?

74. a. Use the graph to estimate the cost in 1990, to the nearest thousand dollars, of what cost \$10,000 in 1975.

b. Use model 1 to determine the cost in 1990. How well does this describe your estimate from part (a)?

c. Use model 2 to determine the cost in 1990. How well does this describe your estimate from part (a)?

75. Which model is a better description for the cost in 2005 of what cost \$10,000 in 1975?

• Writing in Mathematics

76. What is an algebraic expression? Provide an example with your description.

77. What does it mean to evaluate an algebraic expression? Provide an example with your description.

78. What is a term? Provide an example with your description.

79. What are like terms? Provide an example with your description.

80. Explain how to add like terms. Give an example.

81. What does it mean to simplify an algebraic expression?

82. An algebra student incorrectly used the distributive property and wrote $3(5x + 7) = 15x + 7$. If you were that student's teacher, what would you say to help the student avoid this kind of error?

• Critical Thinking Exercises

83. Which one of the following is true?

a. The term x has no coefficient.

b. $5 + 3(x - 4) = 8(x - 4) = 8x - 32$

c. $-x - x = -x + (-x) = 0$

d. $x - 0.02(x + 200) = 0.98x - 4$

84. Which one of the following is true?

a. $3 + 7x = 10x$

b. $b \cdot b = 2b$

c. $(3y - 4) - (8y - 1) = -5y - 3$

d. $-4y + 4 = -4(y + 4)$

85. A business that manufactures small alarm clocks has weekly fixed costs of \$5000. The average cost per clock for the business to manufacture x clocks is described by

$$\frac{0.5x + 5000}{x}.$$

a Find the average cost when $x = 100$, 1000, and 10,000.

b. Like all other businesses, the alarm clock manufacturer must make a profit. To do this, each clock must be sold for at least 50¢ more than what it costs to manufacture. Due to competition from a larger company, the clocks can be sold for \$1.50 each and no more. Our small manufacturer can only produce 2000 clocks weekly. Does this business have much of a future? Explain.

SECTION 6.2 • LINEAR EQUATIONS IN ONE VARIABLE

OBJECTIVES

1. Solve linear equations.
2. Solve linear equations containing fractions.
3. Solve a formula for a variable.
4. Identify equations with no solution or infinitely many solutions.

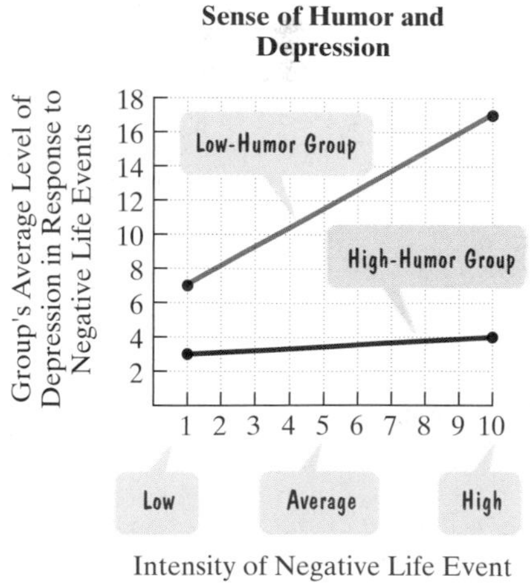

FIGURE 6.2
Source: Steven Davis and Joseph Palladino, *Psychology*, 3rd Edition. Prentice Hall, 2003.

The belief that humor and laughter can have positive benefits on our lives is not new. The graphs in Figure 6.2 indicate that persons with a low sense of humor have higher levels of depression in response to negative life events than those with a high sense of humor. These graphs can be modeled by the following formulas:

Low-Humor Group: $$D = \frac{10}{9}x + \frac{53}{9}$$

High-Humor Group: $$D = \frac{1}{9}x + \frac{26}{9}.$$

In each formula, x represents the intensity of a negative life event (from 1, low, to 10, high) and D is the level of depression in response to that event.

Suppose that the low-humor group averages a level of depression of 10 in response to a negative life event. We can determine the intensity of that event by substituting 10 for D in the low-humor model, $D = \frac{10}{9}x + \frac{53}{9}$:

$$10 = \frac{10}{9}x + \frac{53}{9}.$$

The two sides of an equation can be reversed. So, we can also express this equation as

$$\frac{10}{9}x + \frac{53}{9} = 10.$$

Notice that the highest exponent on the variable is 1. Such an equation is called a *linear equation in one variable*. In this section, we will study how to solve linear equations.

1 Solve linear equations.

Solving Linear Equations in One Variable

We begin with a general definition of a linear equation in one variable.

> **DEFINITION OF A LINEAR EQUATION**
>
> A **linear equation in one variable x** is an equation that can be written in the form
>
> $$ax + b = 0,$$
>
> where a and b are real numbers, and $a \neq 0$.

An example of a linear equation in one variable is

$$4x + 12 = 0.$$

Solving an equation in x involves determining all values of x that result in a true statement when substituted into the equation. Such values are **solutions**, or **roots**, of the equation. For example, substitute -3 for x in $4x + 12 = 0$. We obtain

$$4(-3) + 12 = 0, \quad \text{or} \quad -12 + 12 = 0.$$

This simplifies to the true statement $0 = 0$. Thus, -3 is a solution of the equation $4x + 12 = 0$. We also say that -3 **satisfies** the equation $4x + 12 = 0$, because when we substitute -3 for x, a true statement results. The set of all such solutions is called the equation's **solution set**. For example, the solution set of the equation $4x + 12 = 0$ is $\{-3\}$.

Two or more equations that have the same solution set are called **equivalent equations**. For example, the equations

$$4x + 12 = 0 \quad \text{and} \quad 4x = -12 \quad \text{and} \quad x = -3$$

are equivalent equations because the solution set for each is $\{-3\}$. To solve a linear equation in x, we transform the equation into an equivalent equation one or more times. Our final equivalent equation should be of the form

$$x = \text{a number}.$$

The solution set of this equation is the set consisting of the number.

To generate equivalent equations, we will use the following properties:

> **THE ADDITION AND MULTIPLICATION PROPERTIES OF EQUALITY**
>
> THE ADDITION PROPERTY OF EQUALITY
>
> The same real number or algebraic expression may be added to both sides of an equation without changing the equation's solution set.
>
> $a = b$ and $a + c = b + c$ are equivalent equations.
>
> THE MULTIPLICATION PROPERTY OF EQUALITY
>
> The same nonzero real number may multiply both sides of an equation without changing the equation's solution set.
>
> $a = b$ and $ac = bc$ are equivalent equations as long as $c \neq 0$.

Because subtraction is defined in terms of addition, the addition property also lets us subtract the same number from both sides of an equation without changing the equation's solution set. Similarly, because division is defined in terms of multiplication, the multiplication property of equality can be used to divide both sides of an equation by the same nonzero number to obtain an equivalent equation.

Table 6.1 illustrates how these properties are used to isolate x to obtain an equation of the form x = a number.

These equations are solved using the Addition Property of Equality.

These equations are solved using the Multiplication Property of Equality.

TABLE 6.1 USING PROPERTIES OF EQUALITY TO SOLVE EQUATIONS

Equation	How to Isolate x	Solving the Equation	The Equation's Solution Set
$x - 3 = 8$	Add 3 to both sides.	$x - 3 + 3 = 8 + 3$ $x = 11$	$\{11\}$
$x + 7 = -15$	Subtract 7 from both sides.	$x + 7 - 7 = -15 - 7$ $x = -22$	$\{-22\}$
$6x = 30$	Divide both sides by 6 (or multiply both sides by $\frac{1}{6}$).	$\frac{6x}{6} = \frac{30}{6}$ $x = 5$	$\{5\}$
$\frac{x}{5} = 9$	Multiply both sides by 5.	$5 \cdot \frac{x}{5} = 5 \cdot 9$ $x = 45$	$\{45\}$

EXAMPLE 1 USING PROPERTIES OF EQUALITY TO SOLVE AN EQUATION

Solve and check: $2x + 3 = 17$.

SOLUTION Our goal is to obtain an equivalent equation with x isolated on one side and a number on the other side.

$$2x + 3 = 17 \quad \text{This is the given equation.}$$

$$2x + 3 - 3 = 17 - 3 \quad \text{Subtract 3 from both sides.}$$

$$2x = 14 \quad \text{Simplify.}$$

$$\frac{2x}{2} = \frac{14}{2} \quad \text{Divide both sides by 2.}$$

$$x = 7 \quad \text{Simplify: } \frac{2x}{2} = 1x = x \text{ and } \frac{14}{2} = 7.$$

Now we check the proposed solution, 7, by replacing x with 7 in the original equation.

$$2x + 3 = 17 \quad \text{This is the original equation.}$$

$$2 \cdot 7 + 3 \stackrel{?}{=} 17 \quad \text{Substitute 7 for x. The question mark indicates that we do not yet know if the two sides are equal.}$$

$$14 + 3 \stackrel{?}{=} 17 \quad \text{Multiply: } 2 \cdot 7 = 14.$$

This statement is true.

$$17 = 17 \quad \text{Add: } 14 + 3 = 17.$$

Because the check results in a true statement, we conclude that the solution set of the given equation is $\{7\}$.

CHECK POINT 1 Solve and check: $4x + 5 = 29$.

Here is a step-by-step procedure for solving a linear equation in one variable. Not all of these steps are necessary to solve every equation.

SOLVING A LINEAR EQUATION

1. Simplify the algebraic expression on each side by removing grouping symbols and combining like terms.
2. Collect all the variable terms on one side and all the constants, or numerical terms, on the other side.
3. Isolate the variable and solve.
4. Check the proposed solution in the original equation.

EXAMPLE 2 SOLVING A LINEAR EQUATION

Solve and check: $2(x - 4) - 5x = -5$.

SOLUTION

Step 1. Simplify the algebraic expression on each side.

$$2(x - 4) - 5x = -5$$ This is the given equation.

$$2x - 8 - 5x = -5$$ Use the distributive property.

$$-3x - 8 = -5$$ Combine like terms: $2x - 5x = -3x$.

Step 2. Collect variable terms on one side and constants on the other side. The only variable term, $-3x$, is already on the left side. We will collect constants on the right side by adding 8 to both sides.

$$-3x - 8 + 8 = -5 + 8$$ Add 8 to both sides.

$$-3x = 3$$ Simplify.

Step 3. Isolate the variable and solve. We isolate the variable, x, by dividing both sides of $-3x = 3$ by -3.

$$\frac{-3x}{-3} = \frac{3}{-3}$$ Divide both sides by -3.

$$x = -1$$ Simplify: $\frac{-3x}{-3} = 1x = x$ and $\frac{3}{-3} = -1$.

Step 4. Check the proposed solution in the original equation. Substitute -1 for x in the original equation.

$$2(x - 4) - 5x = -5$$ This is the original equation.

$$2(-1 - 4) - 5(-1) \stackrel{?}{=} -5$$ Substitute -1 for x.

$$2(-5) - 5(-1) \stackrel{?}{=} -5$$ Simplify inside parentheses: $-1 - 4 = -1 + (-4) = -5$.

$$-10 - (-5) \stackrel{?}{=} -5$$ Multiply: $2(-5) = -10$ and $5(-1) = -5$.

$$-5 = -5$$ $-10 - (-5) = -10 + 5 = -5$

This statement is true.

Because the check results in a true statement, we conclude that the solution set of the given equation is $\{-1\}$.

CHECK POINT 2 Solve and check: $6(x - 3) - 10x = -10$.

STUDY TIP

We simplify algebraic expressions. We solve algebraic equations. Although basic rules of algebra are used in both procedures, notice the differences between the procedures:

Simplifying an Algebraic Expression

Simplify: $3(x - 7) - (5x - 11)$.

This is not an equation. There is no equal sign.

Solution
$$\begin{aligned} &3(x - 7) - (5x - 11) \\ &= 3x - 21 - 5x + 11 \\ &= (3x - 5x) + (-21 + 11) \\ &= -2x + (-10) \\ &= -2x - 10 \end{aligned}$$

Stop! Further simplification is not possible. Avoid the common error of setting $-2x - 10$ equal to 0.

Solving an Algebraic Equation

Solve: $3(x - 7) - (5x - 11) = 14$.

This is an equation. There is an equal sign.

Solution
$$\begin{aligned} 3(x - 7) - (5x - 11) &= 14 \\ 3x - 21 - 5x + 11 &= 14 \\ -2x - 10 &= 14 \\ -2x - 10 + 10 &= 14 + 10 \\ -2x &= 24 \\ \frac{-2x}{-2} &= \frac{24}{-2} \\ x &= -12 \end{aligned}$$

Add 10 to both sides.

Divide both sides by -2.

The solution set is $\{-12\}$.

EXAMPLE 3 SOLVING A LINEAR EQUATION

Solve and check: $5x - 12 = 8x + 24$.

SOLUTION

Step 1. Simplify the algebraic expression on each side. Neither side contains grouping symbols or like terms that can be combined. Therefore, we can skip this step.

Step 2. Collect variable terms on one side and constants on the other side. One way to do this is to collect variable terms on the left and constants on the right. This is accomplished by subtracting $8x$ from both sides and adding 12 to both sides.

$5x - 12 = 8x + 24$	This is the given equation.
$5x - 12 - 8x = 8x + 24 - 8x$	Subtract $8x$ from both sides.
$-3x - 12 = 24$	Simplify: $5x - 8x = -3x$.
$-3x - 12 + 12 = 24 + 12$	Add 12 to both sides and collect constants on the right side.
$-3x = 36$	Simplify.

Step 3. Isolate the variable and solve. We isolate the variable, x, by dividing both sides of $-3x = 36$ by -3.

$\frac{-3x}{-3} = \frac{36}{-3}$	Divide both sides by -3.
$x = -12$	Simplify.

Step 4. Check the proposed solution in the original equation. Substitute -12 for x in the original equation.

$5x - 12 = 8x + 24$	This is the original equation.
$5(-12) - 12 \stackrel{?}{=} 8(-12) + 24$	Substitute -12 for x.
$-60 - 12 \stackrel{?}{=} -96 + 24$	Multiply: $5(-12) = -60$ and $8(-12) = -96$.
$-72 = -72$	Add: $-60 + (-12) = -72$ and $-96 + 24 = -72$.

This statement is true.

Because the check results in a true statement, we conclude that the solution set of the given equation is $\{-12\}$.

STUDY TIP

You can solve

$$5x - 12 = 8x + 24$$

by collecting x-terms on the right and numbers on the left. To collect x-terms on the right, subtract $5x$ from both sides:

$$\begin{aligned} 5x - 12 - 5x &= 8x + 24 - 5x \\ -12 &= 3x + 24. \end{aligned}$$

To collect numbers on the left, subtract 24 from both sides:

$$\begin{aligned} -12 - 24 &= 3x + 24 - 24 \\ -36 &= 3x. \end{aligned}$$

Now isolate x by dividing both sides by 3:

$$\begin{aligned} \frac{-36}{3} &= \frac{3x}{3} \\ -12 &= x. \end{aligned}$$

This is the same solution that we obtained in Example 3.

CHECK POINT 3 Solve the equation: $2x + 9 = 8x - 3$.

EXAMPLE 4 SOLVING A LINEAR EQUATION

Solve and check: $2(x - 3) - 17 = 13 - 3(x + 2)$.

SOLUTION

Step 1. Simplify the algebraic expression on each side.

Do not begin with 13 − 3. Multiplication (the distributive property) is applied before subtraction.

$2(x - 3) - 17 = 13 - 3(x + 2)$	This is the given equation.
$2x - 6 - 17 = 13 - 3x - 6$	Use the distributive property.
$2x - 23 = -3x + 7$	Combine like terms.

Step 2. Collect variable terms on one side and constants on the other side. We will collect variable terms on the left by adding $3x$ to both sides. We will collect the numbers on the right by adding 23 to both sides.

$2x - 23 + 3x = -3x + 7 + 3x$	Add 3x to both sides.
$5x - 23 = 7$	Simplify: $2x + 3x = 5x$.
$5x - 23 + 23 = 7 + 23$	Add 23 to both sides.
$5x = 30$	Simplify.

Step 3. Isolate the variable and solve. We isolate the variable, x, by dividing both sides of $5x = 30$ by 5.

$\frac{5x}{5} = \frac{30}{5}$	Divide both sides by 5.
$x = 6$	Simplify.

Step 4. Check the proposed solution in the original equation. Substitute 6 for x in the original equation.

$2(x - 3) - 17 = 13 - 3(x + 2)$	This is the original equation.
$2(6 - 3) - 17 \stackrel{?}{=} 13 - 3(6 + 2)$	Substitute 6 for x.
$2(3) - 17 \stackrel{?}{=} 13 - 3(8)$	Simplify inside parentheses.
$6 - 17 \stackrel{?}{=} 13 - 24$	Multiply.
$-11 = -11$	Subtract.

The true statement $-11 = -11$ verifies that the solution set is $\{6\}$.

CHECK POINT 4 Solve and check: $4(2x + 1) = 29 + 3(2x - 5)$.

2 Solve linear equations containing fractions.

Linear Equations with Fractions

Equations are easier to solve when they do not contain fractions. How do we remove fractions from an equation? We begin by multiplying both sides of the equation by the least common denominator of the fractions in the equation. The least common denominator is the smallest number that all denominators will divide into. Multiplying every term on both sides of the equation by the least common denominator will eliminate the fractions in the equation. Example 5 shows how we "clear an equation of fractions."

EXAMPLE 5 SOLVING A LINEAR EQUATION INVOLVING FRACTIONS

Solve the equation: $\frac{3x}{2} = \frac{8x}{5} - \frac{39}{5}$.

SOLUTION The denominators are 2, 5, and 5. The smallest number that is divisible by 2, 5, and 5 is 10. We begin by multiplying both sides of the equation by 10, the least common denominator.

$$\frac{3x}{2} = \frac{8x}{5} - \frac{39}{5}$$ This is the given equation.

$$10 \cdot \frac{3x}{2} = 10\left(\frac{8x}{5} - \frac{39}{5}\right)$$ Multiply both sides by 10.

$$10 \cdot \frac{3x}{2} = 10 \cdot \frac{8x}{5} - 10 \cdot \frac{39}{5}$$ Use the distributive property. Be sure to multiply all terms by 10.

$$\overset{5}{\cancel{10}} \cdot \frac{3x}{\underset{1}{\cancel{2}}} = \overset{2}{\cancel{10}} \cdot \frac{8x}{\underset{1}{\cancel{5}}} - \overset{2}{\cancel{10}} \cdot \frac{39}{\underset{1}{\cancel{5}}}$$ Divide out common factors in the multiplications.

$$15x = 16x - 78$$ Complete the multiplications. The fractions are now cleared.

At this point, we have an equation similar to those we have previously solved. Collect the variable terms on one side and the constants on the other side.

$$15x - 16x = 16x - 16x - 78$$ Subtract 16x from both sides to get the variable terms on the left.

$$-x = -78$$ Simplify.

We're not finished. A negative sign should not precede x.

Isolate x by multiplying or dividing both sides of this equation by -1.

$$\frac{-x}{-1} = \frac{-78}{-1}$$ Divide both sides by -1.

$$x = 78$$ Simplify.

Check the proposed solution. Substitute 78 for x in the original equation. You should obtain $117 = 117$. This true statement verifies that the solution set is $\{78\}$.

CHECK POINT 5 Solve the equation: $\frac{x}{4} = \frac{2x}{3} + \frac{5}{6}$.

EXAMPLE 6 AN APPLICATION: RESPONDING TO NEGATIVE LIFE EVENTS

In the section opener, we used two formulas to model the level of depression, D, in response to the intensity of a negative life event, x, from 1, low, to 10, high:

Low-Humor Group $$D = \frac{10}{9}x + \frac{53}{9}$$

High-Humor Group $$D = \frac{1}{9}x + \frac{26}{9}.$$

If the high-humor group averages a level of depression of 3.5, or $\frac{7}{2}$, in response to a negative life event, what is the intensity of that event? How is the solution shown on the red line graph in Figure 6.2?

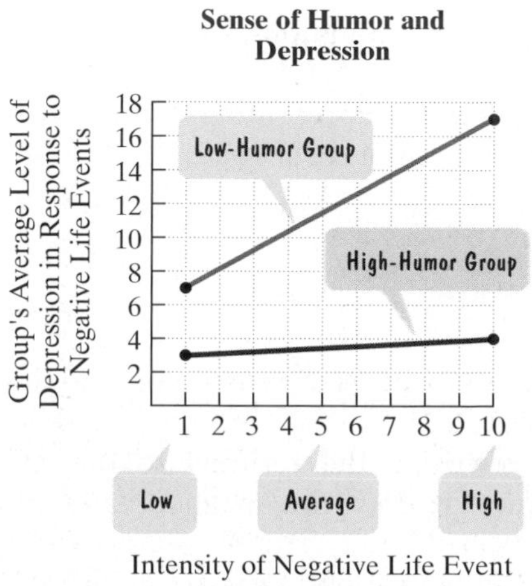

FIGURE 6.2 (repeated)

SOLUTION We are interested in the intensity of a negative life event with an average level of depression of $\frac{7}{2}$ for the high-humor group. We substitute $\frac{7}{2}$ for D in the high-humor model and solve for x, the intensity of the negative life event.

$$D = \frac{1}{9}x + \frac{26}{9}$$ This is the given formula for the high-humor group.

$$\frac{7}{2} = \frac{1}{9}x + \frac{26}{9}$$ Replace D with $\frac{7}{2}$.

$$18 \cdot \frac{7}{2} = 18\left(\frac{1}{9}x + \frac{26}{9}\right)$$ Multiply both sides by 18, the least common denominator.

$$18 \cdot \frac{7}{2} = 18 \cdot \frac{1}{9}x + 18 \cdot \frac{26}{9}$$ Use the distributive property.

$$\overset{9}{\cancel{18}} \cdot \frac{7}{\underset{1}{\cancel{2}}} = \overset{2}{\cancel{18}} \cdot \frac{1}{\underset{1}{\cancel{9}}}x + \overset{2}{\cancel{18}} \cdot \frac{26}{\underset{1}{\cancel{9}}}$$ Divide out common factors in the multiplications.

$$63 = 2x + 52$$ Complete the multiplications. The fractions are now cleared.

$$63 - 52 = 2x + 52 - 52$$ Subtract 52 from both sides to get constants on the left.

$$11 = 2x$$ Simplify.

$$\frac{11}{2} = \frac{2x}{2}$$ Divide both sides by 2.

$$\frac{11}{2} = x$$ Simplify.

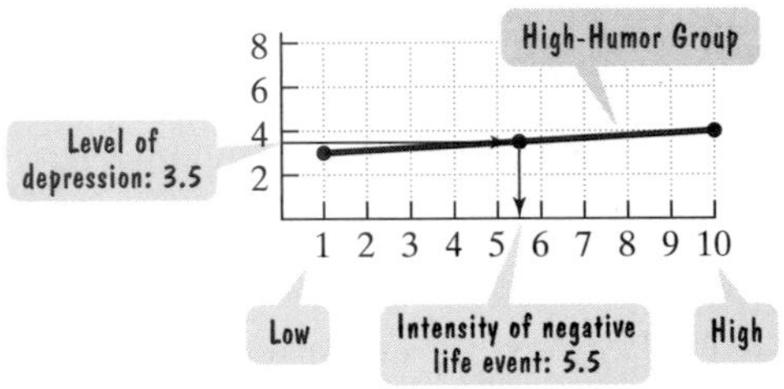

FIGURE 6.3

The formula indicates that if the high-humor group averages a level of depression of 3.5 in response to a negative life event, the intensity of that event is $\frac{11}{2}$, or 5.5. This is illustrated on the line graph for the high-humor group in Figure 6.3.

CHECK POINT 6 Use the model for the low-humor group given in Example 6 on the previous page to solve this problem. If the low-humor group averages a level of depression of 10 in response to a negative life event, what is the intensity of that event? How is the solution shown on the blue line graph in Figure 6.2?

3 Solve a formula for a variable.

Solving a Formula for One of Its Variables

We know that solving an equation is the process of finding the number (or numbers) that make the equation a true statement. All of the equations we have solved contained only one letter, x.

By contrast, formulas contain two or more letters, representing two or more variables. An example is the formula for the perimeter of a rectangle:

$$2l + 2w = P.$$

A rectangle's perimeter is the sum of twice its length and twice its width.

We say that this formula is solved for the variable P because P is alone on one side of the equation and the other side does not contain a P.

Solving a formula for a variable means rewriting the formula so that the variable is isolated on one side of the equation. It does not mean obtaining a numerical value for that variable.

To solve a formula for one of its variables, treat that variable as if it were the only variable in the equation. Think of the other variables as if they were numbers. Isolate all terms with the specified variable on one side of the equation and all terms without the specified variable on the other side. Then divide both sides by the same nonzero quantity to get the specified variable alone. The next example shows how to do this.

EXAMPLE 7 SOLVING A FORMULA FOR A VARIABLE

Solve the formula $2l + 2w = P$ for l.

SOLUTION First, isolate $2l$ on the left by subtracting $2w$ from both sides. Then solve for l by dividing both sides by 2.

We need to isolate l.

$2l + 2w = P$	This is the given formula.
$2l + 2w - 2w = P - 2w$	Isolate $2l$ by subtracting $2w$ from both sides.
$2l = P - 2w$	Simplify.
$\frac{2l}{2} = \frac{P - 2w}{2}$	Solve for l by dividing both sides by 2.
$l = \frac{P - 2w}{2}$	Simplify.

CHECK POINT 7 Solve the formula $2l + 2w = P$ for w.

EXAMPLE 8 SOLVING A FORMULA FOR A VARIABLE

The total price of an article purchased on a monthly deferred payment plan is described by the following formula:

$$T = D + pm.$$

In this formula, T is the total price, D is the down payment, p is the monthly payment, and m is the number of months one pays. Solve the formula for p.

SOLUTION First, isolate pm on the right by subtracting D from both sides. Then, isolate p from pm by dividing both sides of the formula by m.

We need to isolate p.

$T = D + pm$	This is the given formula. We want p alone.
$T - D = D - D + pm$	Isolate pm by subtracting D from both sides.
$T - D = pm$	Simplify.
$\frac{T - D}{m} = \frac{pm}{m}$	Now isolate p by dividing both sides by m.
$\frac{T - D}{m} = p$	Simplify: $\frac{pm}{m} = \frac{p\cancel{m}}{\cancel{m}} = \frac{p}{1} = p$.

CHECK POINT 8 Solve the formula $T = D + pm$ for m.

4 Identify equations with no solution or infinitely many solutions.

Linear Equations with No Solution or Infinitely Many Solutions

Thus far, each equation that we have solved has had a single solution. However, some equations are not true for even one real number. By contrast, other equations are true for all real numbers.

If you attempt to solve an equation with no solution, you will eliminate the variable and obtain a false statement, such as $2 = 5$. If you attempt to solve an equation that is true for every real number, you will eliminate the variable and obtain a true statement, such as $4 = 4$.

EXAMPLE 9 SOLVING A LINEAR EQUATION

Solve: $2x + 6 = 2(x + 4)$.

SOLUTION

$2x + 6 = 2(x + 4)$ This is the given equation.

$2x + 6 = 2x + 8$ Use the distributive property.

$2x + 6 - 2x = 2x + 8 - 2x$ Subtract 2x from both sides.

Keep reading. $6 = 8$ is not the solution.

$6 = 8$ Simplify.

The original equation, $2x + 6 = 2(x + 4)$, is equivalent to the statement $6 = 8$, which is false for every value of x. The equation has no solution. The solution set is $\emptyset$, the empty set.

CHECK POINT 9 Solve: $3x + 7 = 3(x + 1)$.

EXAMPLE 10 SOLVING A LINEAR EQUATION

Solve: $4x + 6 = 6(x + 1) - 2x$.

SOLUTION

$4x + 6 = 6(x + 1) - 2x$ This is the given equation.

$4x + 6 = 6x + 6 - 2x$ Apply the distributive property on the right side.

$4x + 6 = 4x + 6$ Combine like terms on the right side: $6x - 2x = 4x$.

Can you see that the equation $4x + 6 = 4x + 6$ is true for every value of x? Let's continue solving the equation by subtracting $4x$ from both sides.

$$4x - 4x + 6 = 4x - 4x + 6$$

Keep reading. $6 = 6$ is not the solution.

$$6 = 6$$

The original equation is equivalent to the statement $6 = 6$, which is true for every value of x. Thus, the solution set consists of the set of all real numbers, expressed in set-builder notation as $\{x | x \text{ is a real number}\}$. Try substituting any real number of your choice for x in the original equation. You will obtain a true statement.

STUDY TIP

Because of the fundamental role that sets play in mathematics, it's a good idea to use set notation to express an equation's solution set. If a linear equation has no solution, its solution set is $\emptyset$, the empty set. If a linear equation with variable x has infinitely many solutions, its solution set is $\{x | x \text{ is a real number}\}$.

CHECK POINT 10 Solve: $7x + 9 = 9(x + 1) - 2x$.

EXERCISE SET 6.2

• Practice Exercises

In Exercises 1–42, solve each equation. Be sure to check your proposed solution by substituting it for the variable in the given equation.

1. $x - 7 = 3$

2. $x - 3 = -17$

3. $x + 5 = -12$

4. $x + 12 = -14$

5. $\frac{x}{3} = 4$

6. $\frac{x}{5} = 3$

7. $5x = 45$

8. $6x = 18$

9. $8x = -24$

10. $5x = -25$

11. $-8x = 2$

12. $-6x = 3$

13. $5x + 3 = 18$

14. $3x + 8 = 50$

15. $6x - 3 = 63$

16. $5x - 8 = 72$

17. $4x - 14 = -82$

18. $9x - 14 = -77$

19. $14 - 5x = -41$

20. $25 - 6x = -83$

21. $9(5x - 2) = 45$

22. $10(3x + 2) = 70$

23. $5x - (2x - 10) = 35$

24. $11x - (6x - 5) = 40$

25. $3x + 5 = 2x + 13$

26. $2x - 7 = 6 + x$

27. $8x - 2 = 7x - 5$

28. $13x + 14 = -5 + 12x$

29. $7x + 4 = x + 16$

30. $8x + 1 = x + 43$

31. $8y - 3 = 11y + 9$

32. $5y - 2 = 9y + 2$

33. $2(4 - 3x) = 2(2x + 5)$

34. $3(5 - x) = 4(2x + 1)$

35. $8(y + 2) = 2(3y + 4)$

36. $3(3y - 1) = 4(3 + 3y)$

37. $3(x + 1) = 7(x - 2) - 3$

38. $5x - 4(x + 9) = 2x - 3$

39. $5(2x - 8) - 2 = 5(x - 3) + 3$

40. $7(3x - 2) + 5 = 6(2x - 1) + 24$

41. $5(x - 2) - 2(2x + 1) = 2 + 5x$

42. $2(5x + 4) + 3(2x + 11) = 4x - 19$

Solve and check each equation in Exercises 43–50. Begin your work by rewriting each equation without fractions.

43. $\frac{x}{3} + \frac{x}{2} = \frac{5}{6}$

44. $\frac{x}{4} - 1 = \frac{x}{5}$

45. $\frac{x}{2} = 20 - \frac{x}{3}$

46. $\frac{x}{5} - \frac{1}{2} = \frac{x}{6}$

47. $\frac{3y}{4} - 3 = \frac{y}{2} + 2$

48. $y + \frac{1}{2} = 1 - \frac{y}{3}$

49. $\frac{3x}{5} - x = \frac{x}{10} - \frac{5}{2}$

50. $2x - \frac{2x}{7} = \frac{x}{2} + \frac{17}{2}$

In Exercises 51–68, solve each formula for the specified variable. Do you recognize the formula? If so, what does it describe?

51. $A = LW$ for L

52. $D = RT$ for R

53. $A = \frac{1}{2}bh$ for b

54. $V = \frac{1}{3}Bh$ for B

55. $I = Prt$ for P

56. $C = 2\pi r$ for r

57. $E = mc^2$ for m

58. $V = \pi r^2 h$ for h

59. $y = mx + b$ for m

60. $P = C + MC$ for M

61. $A = \frac{1}{2}(a + b)$ for a

62. $A = \frac{1}{2}(a + b)$ for b

63. $S = P + Prt$ for r

64. $S = P + Prt$ for t

65. $Ax + By = C$ for x

66. $Ax + By = C$ for y

67. $a_n = a_1 + (n - 1)d$ for n

68. $a_n = a_1 + (n - 1)d$ for d

In Exercises 69–84, solve each equation. Use set notation to express solution sets for equations with no solution or equations that are true for all real numbers.

69. $3x - 7 = 3(x + 1)$

70. $2(x - 5) = 2x + 10$

71. $2(x + 4) = 4x + 5 - 2x + 3$

72. $3(x - 1) = 8x + 6 - 5x - 9$

73. $7 + 2(3x - 5) = 8 - 3(2x + 1)$

74. $2 + 3(2x - 7) = 9 - 4(3x + 1)$

75. $4x + 1 - 5x = 5 - (x + 4)$

76. $5x - 5 = 3x - 7 + 2(x + 1)$

77. $4(x + 2) + 1 = 7x - 3(x - 2)$

78. $5x - 3(x + 1) = 2(x + 3) - 5$

79. $3 - x = 2x + 3$

80. $5 - x = 4x + 5$

81. $\frac{x}{3} + 2 = \frac{x}{3}$

82. $\frac{x}{4} + 3 = \frac{x}{4}$

83. $\frac{x}{2} - \frac{x}{4} + 4 = x + 4$

84. $\frac{x}{2} + \frac{2x}{3} + 3 = x + 3$

• Practice Plus

85. Evaluate $x^2 - x$ for the value of x satisfying $4(x - 2) + 2 = 4x - 2(2 - x)$.

86. Evaluate $x^2 - x$ for the value of x satisfying $2(x - 6) = 3x + 2(2x - 1)$.

87. Evaluate $x^2 - (xy - y)$ for x satisfying $\frac{x}{5} - 2 = \frac{x}{3}$ and y satisfying $-2y - 10 = 5y + 18$.

88. Evaluate $x^2 - (xy - y)$ for x satisfying $\frac{3x}{2} + \frac{3x}{4} = \frac{x}{4} - 4$ and y satisfying $5 - y = 7(y + 4) + 1$.

In Exercises 89–96, solve each equation.

89. $[(3 + 6)^2 \div 3] \cdot 4 = -54x$

90. $2^3 - [4(5 - 3)^3] = -8x$

91. $5 - 12x = 8 - 7x - [6 \div 3(2 + 5^3) + 5x]$

92. $2(5x + 58) = 10x + 4(21 \div 3.5 - 11)$

93. $0.7x + 0.4(20) = 0.5(x + 20)$

94. $0.5(x + 2) = 0.1 + 3(0.1x + 0.3)$

95. $4x + 13 - \{2x - [4(x - 3) - 5]\} = 2(x - 6)$

96. $-2\{7 - [4 - 2(1 - x) + 3]\} = 10 - [4x - 2(x - 3)]$

• Application Exercises

The bar graph shows the average amount of time, in hours, that each American aged 12 or older spent playing video games from 2001 through 2006.

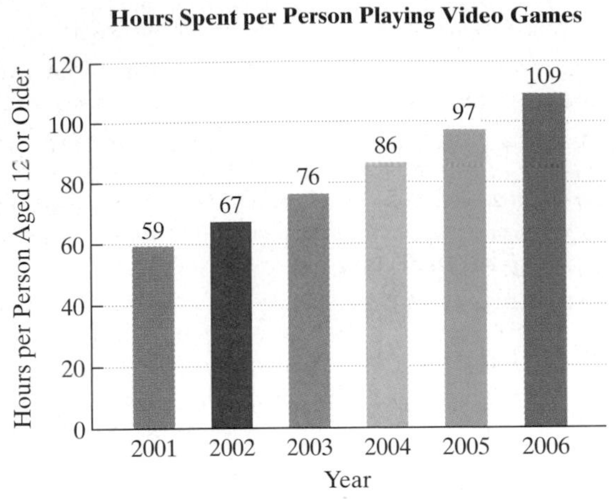

Source: U.S. Census Bureau

The data can be modeled by

$$H = 10x + 59,$$

where H is the annual hours spent playing video games per person x years after 2001. Use this formula to solve Exercises 97–98.

97. If trends continue, in which year will Americans average 179 hours per person playing video games?

98. If trends continue, in which year will Americans average 199 hours per person playing video games?

The formula

$$\frac{n}{2} + 80 = 2T$$

models the relationship between temperature, T, in degrees Fahrenheit, and the number of cricket chirps per minute, n, for the snow tree cricket. Use this mathematical model to solve Exercises 99–100.

99. Find the number of chirps per minute at a temperature of 70°F.

100. Find the number of chirps per minute at a temperature of 80°F.

The formula

$$p = 15 + \frac{5d}{11}$$

describes the pressure of sea water, p, in pounds per square foot, at a depth of d feet below the surface. Use the formula to solve Exercises 101–102.

101. The record depth for breath-held diving, by Francisco Ferreras (Cuba) off Grand Bahama Island, on November 14, 1993, involved pressure of 201 pounds per square foot. To what depth did Ferreras descend on this ill-advised venture? (He was underwater for 2 minutes and 9 seconds!)

102. At what depth is the pressure 20 pounds per square foot?

The line graphs show the average writing test scores for U.S. high school seniors. The graphs reflect general trends in which boys continue to fall behind girls in reading and writing proficiency, with fewer boys than girls going to college.

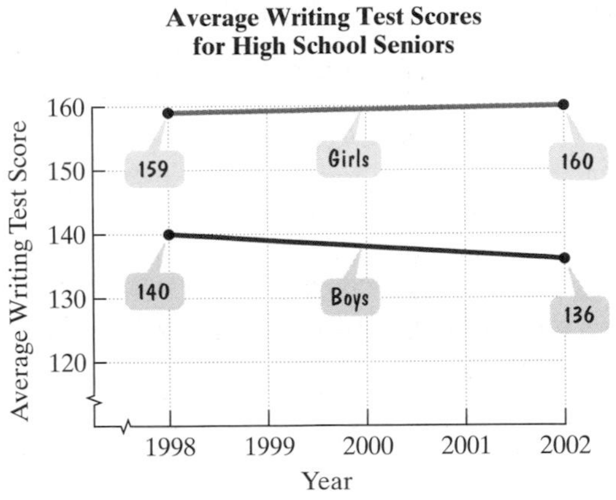

Source: *Newsweek*, January 30, 2006

The data can be modeled by the following formulas:

Girls $W = \frac{1}{4}x + 159$ Boys $W = -x + 140.$

In each formula, W is the average writing test score x years after 1998. Use the formulas to solve Exercises 103–108.

103. If current trends continue, when will the average test score for boys be 127?

104. If current trends continue, when will the average test score for boys be 126?

105. If current trends continue, when will the average test score for girls be 163?

106. If current trends continue, when will the average test score for girls be 164?

107. If current trends continue, when will the average test score for girls be 49 points higher than for boys?

108. If current trends continue, when will the average test score for girls be 54 points higher than for boys?

• Writing in Mathematics

109. What is the solution set of an equation?

110. State the addition property of equality and give an example.

111. State the multiplication property of equality and give an example.

112. How do you know if a linear equation has one solution, no solution, or infinitely many solutions?

113. What is the difference between solving an equation such as $2(x - 4) + 5x = 34$ and simplifying an algebraic expression such as $2(x - 4) + 5x$? If there is a difference, which topic should be taught first? Why?

114. Suppose that you solve $\frac{x}{5} - \frac{x}{2} = 1$ by multiplying both sides by 20, rather than the least common denominator of 5 and 2 (namely, 10). Describe what happens. If you get the correct solution, why do you think we clear the equation of fractions by multiplying by the *least* common denominator?

115. Suppose you are an algebra teacher grading the following solution on an examination:

$$\text{Solve: } -3(x - 6) = 2 - x.$$
$$\text{Solution: } -3x - 18 = 2 - x$$
$$-2x - 18 = 2$$
$$-2x = -16$$
$$x = 8.$$

You should note that 8 checks, and the solution set is $\{8\}$. The student who worked the problem therefore wants full credit. Can you find any errors in the solution? If full credit is 10 points, how many points should you give the student? Justify your position.

116. Although the formulas in Example 6 on page 317 are correct, some people object to representing the variables with numbers, such as a 1-to-10 scale for the intensity of a negative life event. What might be their objection to quantifying the variables in this situation?

• Critical Thinking Exercises

117. Which one of the following is true?

a. If $3x + 7 = 0$, then $x = \frac{7}{3}$.

b. Solving $A = LW$ for W gives $W = \frac{L}{A}$.

c. The equation $6x = 0$ has exactly one solution.

d. The final step in solving $x - b = 6x - c$ for x is $x = 6x - c + b$.

118. Write three equations whose solution set is $\{5\}$.

119. If x represents a number, write an English sentence about the number that results in an equation with no solution.

120. A woman's height, h, is related to the length of the femur, f (the bone from the knee to the hip socket), by the formula $f = 0.432h - 10.44$. Both h and f are measured in inches. A partial skeleton is found of a woman in which the femur is 16 inches long. Police find the skeleton in an area where a woman slightly over 5 feet tall has been missing for over a year. Can the partial skeleton be that of the missing woman? Explain.

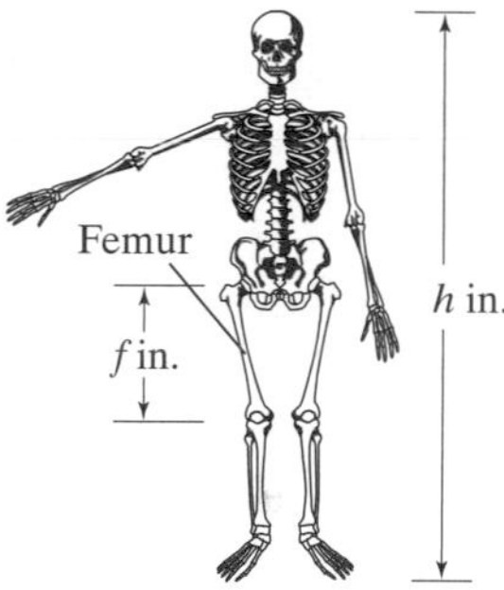

SECTION 6.3 • APPLICATIONS OF LINEAR EQUATIONS

OBJECTIVE

1. Use linear equations to solve problems.

The human race is undeniably becoming a faster race. Since the beginning of the past century, track-and-field records have fallen in everything from sprints to miles to marathons. The performance arc is clearly rising, but no one knows how much higher it can climb. At some point, even the best-trained body simply has to up and quit. The question is, just where is that point, and is it possible for athletes, trainers, and genetic engineers to push it higher? In this section, you will learn a problem-solving strategy that uses linear equations to determine if anyone will ever run a 3-minute mile.

1 Use linear equations to solve problems.

Problem Solving with Linear Equations

We have seen that a model is a mathematical representation of a real-world situation. In this section, we will be solving problems that are presented in English. This means that we must obtain models by translating from the ordinary language of English into the language of algebraic equations. To translate, however, we must understand the English prose and be familiar with the forms of algebraic language. Here are some general steps we will follow in solving word problems:

STRATEGY FOR SOLVING WORD PROBLEMS

Step 1. Read the problem carefully at least twice. Attempt to state the problem in your own words and state what the problem is looking for. Let x (or any variable) represent one of the quantities in the problem.

Step 2. If necessary, write expressions for any other unknown quantities in the problem in terms of x.

Step 3. Write an equation in x that models the verbal conditions of the problem.

Step 4. Solve the equation and answer the problem's question.

Step 5. Check the solution *in the original wording* of the problem, not in the equation obtained from the words.

The most difficult step in this process is step 3 because it involves translating verbal conditions into an algebraic equation. Translations of some commonly used English phrases are listed in Table 6.2. We choose to use x to represent the variable, but we can use any letter.

STUDY TIP

Cover the right column in Table 6.2 with a sheet of paper and attempt to formulate the algebraic expression in the column on your own. Then slide the paper down and check your answer. Work through the entire table in this manner.

TABLE 6.2 ALGEBRAIC TRANSLATIONS OF ENGLISH PHRASES

English Phrase	Algebraic Expression
Addition	
The sum of a number and 7	$x + 7$
Five more than a number; a number plus 5	$x + 5$
A number increased by 6; 6 added to a number	$x + 6$
Subtraction	
A number minus 4	$x - 4$
A number decreased by 5	$x - 5$
A number subtracted from 8	$8 - x$
The difference between a number and 6	$x - 6$
The difference between 6 and a number	$6 - x$
Seven less than a number	$x - 7$
Seven minus a number	$7 - x$
Nine fewer than a number	$x - 9$
Multiplication	
Five times a number	$5x$
The product of 3 and a number	$3x$
Two-thirds of a number (used with fractions)	$\frac{2}{3}x$
Seventy-five percent of a number (used with decimals)	$0.75x$
Thirteen multiplied by a number	$13x$
A number multiplied by 13	$13x$
Twice a number	$2x$
Division	
A number divided by 3	$\frac{x}{3}$
The quotient of 7 and a number	$\frac{7}{x}$
The quotient of a number and 7	$\frac{x}{7}$
The reciprocal of a number	$\frac{1}{x}$
More than one operation	
The sum of twice a number and 7	$2x + 7$
Twice the sum of a number and 7	$2(x + 7)$
Three times the sum of 1 and twice a number	$3(1 + 2x)$
Nine subtracted from 8 times a number	$8x - 9$
Twenty-five percent of the sum of 3 times a number and 14	$0.25(3x + 14)$
Seven times a number, increased by 24	$7x + 24$
Seven times the sum of a number and 24	$7(x + 24)$

STUDY TIP

Here are three similar English phrases that have very different translations:

7 minus 10: $7 - 10$

7 less than 10: $10 - 7$

7 is less than 10: $7 < 10$.

Think carefully about what is expressed in English before you translate into the language of algebra.

EXAMPLE 1 SOLVING A WORD PROBLEM

Nine subtracted from eight times a number is 39. Find the number.

SOLUTION

Step 1. Let x represent one of the quantities. Because we are asked to find a number, let

$$x = \text{the number.}$$

Step 2. Represent other quantities in terms of x. There are no other unknown quantities to find, so we can skip this step.

Step 3. Write an equation in x that models the conditions.

Nine subtracted from | eight times a number | is | 39.

$$8x - 9 = 39$$

Step 4. Solve the equation and answer the question.

$$8x - 9 = 39$$ This is the equation that models the problem's conditions.

$$8x - 9 + 9 = 39 + 9$$ Add 9 to both sides.

$$8x = 48$$ Simplify.

$$\frac{8x}{8} = \frac{48}{8}$$ Divide both sides by 8.

$$x = 6$$ Simplify.

The number is 6.

Step 5. Check the proposed solution in the original wording of the problem. "Nine subtracted from eight times a number is 39." The proposed number is 6. Eight times 6 is $8 \cdot 6$, or 48. Nine subtracted from 48 is $48 - 9$, or 39. The proposed solution checks in the problem's wording, verifying that the number is 6.

CHECK POINT 1 Four subtracted from six times a number is 68. Find the number.

EXAMPLE 2 WILL ANYONE EVER RUN A THREE-MINUTE MILE?

One yardstick for measuring how steadily—if slowly—athletic performance has improved is the mile run. In 1923, the record for the mile was a comparatively sleepy 4 minutes, 10.4 seconds. In 1954, Roger Bannister of Britain cracked the 4-minute mark, coming in at 3 minutes, 59.4 seconds. In the half-century since, about 0.3 second per year has been shaved off Bannister's record. If this trend continues, by which year will someone run a 3-minute mile?

Mile Records

1886	4:12.3	1958	3:54.5
1923	4:10.4	1966	3:51.3
1933	4:07.6	1979	3:48.9
1945	4:01.3	1985	3:46.3
1954	3:59.4	1999	3:43.1

Source: U.S.A. Track and Field

SOLUTION In solving this problem, we will express time for the mile run in seconds. Our interest is in a time of 3 minutes, or 180 seconds.

Step 1. Let x represent one of the quantities. Here is the critical information in the problem:

- In 1954, the record was 3 minutes, 59.4 seconds, or 239.4 seconds.
- The record has decreased by 0.3 second per year since then.

We are interested in when the record will be 180 seconds. Let

x = the number of years after 1954 when someone will run a 3-minute mile.

BLITZER BONUS

A Poky Species

For a species that prides itself on its athletic prowess, human beings are a pretty poky group. Lions can sprint at up to 50 miles per hour; cheetahs move even faster, flooring it to a sizzling 70 miles per hour. But most humans—with our willowy spines and awkward, upright gait—would have trouble cracking 20 miles per hour with a tail wind, a flat track, and a good pair of running shoes.

Step 2. Represent other quantities in terms of x. There are no other unknown quantities to find, so we can skip this step.

Step 3. Write an equation in x that models the conditions.

The 1954 record time	decreased by	0.3 second per year for x years	equals	the 3-minute, or 180-second, mile.
239.4	$-$	$0.3x$	$=$	180

Step 4. Solve the equation and answer the question.

$$239.4 - 0.3x = 180$$ This is the equation that models the problem's conditions.

$$239.4 - 239.4 - 0.3x = 180 - 239.4$$ Subtract 239.4 from both sides.

$$-0.3x = -59.4$$ Simplify.

$$\frac{-0.3x}{-0.3} = \frac{-59.4}{-0.3}$$ Divide both sides by -0.3.

$$x = 198$$ Simplify.

Using current trends, 198 years (gasp!) after 1954, or in 2152, someone will run a 3-minute mile.

Step 5. Check the proposed solution in the original wording of the problem. The problem states that the record time should be 180 seconds. Do we obtain 180 seconds if we decrease the 1954 record time, 239.4 seconds, by 0.3 second per year for 198 years, our proposed solution?

$$239.4 - 0.3(198) = 239.4 - 59.4 = 180$$

This verifies that, using current trends, the 3-minute mile will be run 198 years after 1954.

CHECK POINT 2 Got organic milk? Although organic milk accounts for only 1.2% of the market, consumption is increasing. In 2004, Americans purchased 40.7 million gallons of organic milk, increasing at a rate of 5.6 million gallons per year. If this trend continues, when will Americans purchase 79.9 million gallons of organic milk? (*Source:* National Dairy Council)

EXAMPLE 3 WALK IT OFF

Experts concerned with fitness and health suggest that we should walk 10,000 steps per day, about 5 miles. Depending on stride length, each mile ranges between 2000 and 2500 steps. The graph in Figure 6.4 shows the number of steps it takes to burn off various foods. (The data are based on a body weight of 150 to 165 pounds.)

The number of steps needed to burn off a cheeseburger exceeds the number needed to burn off a 12-ounce soda by 4140. The number needed to burn off a doughnut exceeds the number needed to burn off a 12-ounce soda by 2300. If you chow down a cheeseburger, doughnut, and 12-ounce soda, a 16,790-step walk is needed to burn off the calories (and perhaps alleviate the guilt). Determine the number of steps it takes to burn off a cheeseburger, a doughnut, and a 12-ounce soda.

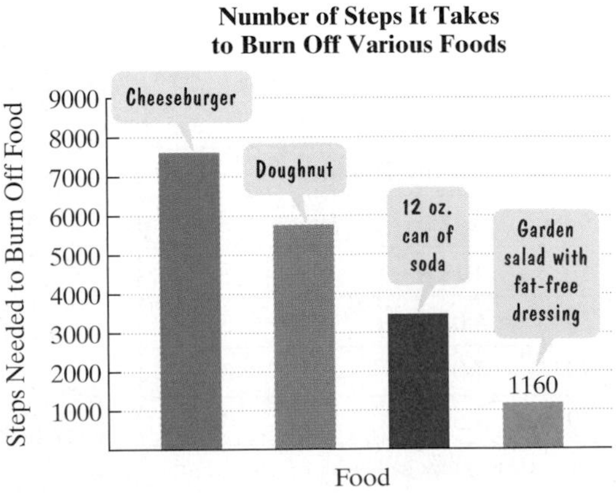

FIGURE 6.4

Source: The Step Diet Book

SOLUTION

Step 1. Let x represent one of the quantities. We know something about the number of steps needed to burn off a cheeseburger and a doughnut: The numbers exceed that of a 12-ounce soda by 4140 and 2300, respectively. We will let

$x =$ the number of steps needed to burn off a 12-ounce soda.

Step 2. Represent other quantities in terms of x. Because the number of steps needed to burn off a cheeseburger exceeds the number needed to burn off a 12-ounce soda by 4140, let

$x + 4140 =$ the number of steps needed to burn off a cheeseburger.

Because the number of steps needed to burn off a doughnut exceeds the number needed to burn off a 12-ounce soda by 2300, let

$x + 2300 =$ the number of steps needed to burn off a doughnut.

Step 3. Write an equation in x that models the conditions. A 16,790-step walk is needed to burn off a "meal" consisting of a cheeseburger, a doughnut, and a 12-ounce soda.

Steps needed to burn off cheeseburger	plus	steps needed to burn off doughnut	plus	steps needed to burn off soda	equals	16,790.
$(x + 4140)$	$+$	$(x + 2300)$	$+$	x	$=$	16,790

Step 4. Solve the equation and answer the question.

$$(x + 4140) + (x + 2300) + x = 16{,}790$$ This is the equation that models the problem's conditions.

$$3x + 6440 = 16{,}790$$ Remove parentheses, regroup, and combine like terms.

$$3x = 10{,}350$$ Subtract 6440 from both sides.

$$x = 3450$$ Divide both sides by 3.

Thus,

the number of steps needed to burn off a 12-ounce soda $= x = 3450$.

the number of steps needed to burn off a cheeseburger
$= x + 4140 = 3450 + 4140 = 7590$.

the number of steps needed to burn off a doughnut
$= x + 2300 = 3450 + 2300 = 5750$.

It takes 7590 steps to burn off a cheeseburger, 5750 steps to burn off a doughnut, and 3450 steps to burn off a 12-ounce soda.

Step 5. Check the proposed solution in the original wording of the problem. The problem states that a 16,790-step walk is needed to burn off the calories in the three foods combined. By adding 7590, 5750, and 3450, the numbers that we found for each of the foods, we obtain

$$7590 + 5750 + 3450 = 16{,}790,$$

as specified by the problem's conditions.

STUDY TIP

Modeling with the word *exceeds* can be a bit tricky. It's helpful to identify the smaller quantity. Then add to this quantity to represent the larger quantity. For example, suppose that Tim's height exceeds Tom's height by a inches. Tom is the shorter person. If Tom's height is represented by x, then Tim's height is represented by $x + a$.

CHECK POINT 3 Basketball, bicycle riding, and football are the three sports and recreational activities in the United States with the greatest number of medically treated injuries. In 2004, the number of injuries from basketball exceeded those from football by 0.6 million. The number of injuries from bicycling exceeded those from football by 0.3 million. Combined, basketball, bicycling, and football accounted for 3.9 million injuries. Determine the number of medically treated injuries from each of these recreational activities in 2004.

(*Source:* U.S. Consumer Product Safety Commission)

STUDY TIP

There is great value in reasoning through a word problem. This value comes from the problem-solving skills that are attained and is often more important than the specific problem or its solution.

EXAMPLE 4 SELECTING A LONG-DISTANCE CARRIER

You are choosing between two long-distance telephone plans. Plan A has a monthly fee of \$20 with a charge of \$0.05 per minute for all long-distance calls. Plan B has a monthly fee of \$5 with a charge of \$0.10 per minute for all long-distance calls. For how many minutes of long-distance calls will the costs for the two plans be the same?

SOLUTION

Step 1. Let x represent one of the quantities. Let

x = the number of minutes of long-distance calls for which the two plans cost the same.

Step 2. Represent other unknown quantities in terms of x. There are no other unknown quantities, so we can skip this step.

Step 3. Write an equation in x that models the conditions. The monthly cost for plan A is the monthly fee, \$20, plus the per minute charge, \$0.05, times the number of minutes of long-distance calls, x. The monthly cost for plan B is the monthly fee, \$5, plus the per-minute charge, \$0.10, times the number of minutes of long-distance calls, x.

The monthly cost for plan A | must equal | the monthly cost for plan B.

$$20 + 0.05x \quad = \quad 5 + 0.10x$$

Step 4. Solve the equation and answer the question.

$$20 + 0.05x = 5 + 0.10x$$ This is the equation that models the problem's conditions.

$$20 = 5 + 0.05x$$ Subtract 0.05x from both sides.

$$15 = 0.05x$$ Subtract 5 from both sides.

$$\frac{15}{0.05} = \frac{0.05x}{0.05}$$ Divide both sides by 0.05.

$$300 = x$$ Simplify.

Because x represents the number of minutes of long-distance calls for which the two plans cost the same, the costs will be the same with 300 minutes of long-distance calls.

Step 5. Check the proposed solution in the original wording of the problem. The problem states that the costs for the two plans should be the same. Let's see if they are with 300 minutes of long-distance calls.

$$\text{Cost for plan A} = \$20 + \$0.05(300) = \$20 + \$15 = \$35$$

Monthly fee | Per-minute charge

$$\text{Cost for plan B} = \$5 + \$0.10(300) = \$5 + \$30 = \$35$$

With 300 minutes, or 5 hours, of long-distance calls, both plans cost \$35 for the month. Thus, the proposed solution, 300 minutes, satisfies the problem's conditions.

CHECK POINT 4 You are choosing between two long-distance telephone plans. Plan A has a monthly fee of \$15 with a charge of \$0.08 per minute for all long-distance calls. Plan B has a monthly fee of \$3 with a charge of \$0.12 per minute for all long-distance calls. For how many minutes of long-distance calls will the costs for the two plans be the same?

EXERCISE SET 6.3

• Practice and Application Exercises

In Exercises 1–24, use the five-step strategy to solve each problem.

1. When five times a number is decreased by 4, the result is 26. What is the number?

2. When two times a number is decreased by 3, the result is 11. What is the number?

3. One number exceeds another by 26. The sum of the numbers is 64. What are the numbers?

4. One number exceeds another by 24. The sum of the numbers is 58. What are the numbers?

According to one mathematical model, the average life expectancy for American men born in 1900 was 55 years. Life expectancy has increased by about 0.2 year for each birth year after 1900. Use this information to solve Exercises 5–6.

5. If this trend continues, for which birth year will the average life expectancy be 85 years?

6. If this trend continues, for which birth year will the average life expectancy be 91 years?

The graph shows the number of Americans without health insurance from 2000 through 2003.

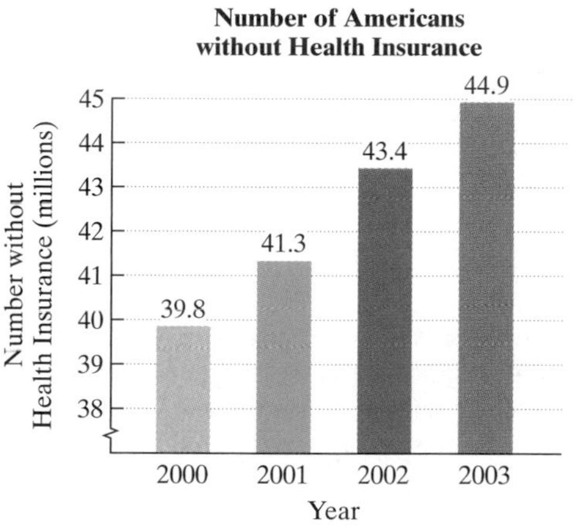

Source: U.S. Census Bureau

In 2000, there were 39.8 million Americans without health insurance. This number has increased at an average rate of 1.7 million people per year. Use this description to solve Exercises 7–8.

7. Determine when the number of Americans without health insurance will exceed the number in 2003 by 8.5 million.

8. Determine when the number of Americans without health insurance will exceed the number in 2003 by 10.2 million.

9. In 2000, the population of Greece was 10,600,000, with projections of a population decrease of 28,000 people per year. In the same year, the population of Belgium was 10,200,000, with projections of a population decrease of 12,000 people per year. (*Source*: United Nations) According to these projections, when will the two countries have the same population? What will be the population at that time?

10. In 2007, there were 13,300 students at college A, with a projected enrollment increase of 1000 students per year. In the same year, there were 26,800 students at college B, with a projected enrollment decline of 500 students per year. According to these projections, when will the colleges have the same enrollment? What will be the enrollment in each college at that time?

11. Each day, the number of births in the world exceeds the number of deaths by 229 thousand. The combined number of births and deaths is 521 thousand. Determine the number of births and the number of deaths per day.

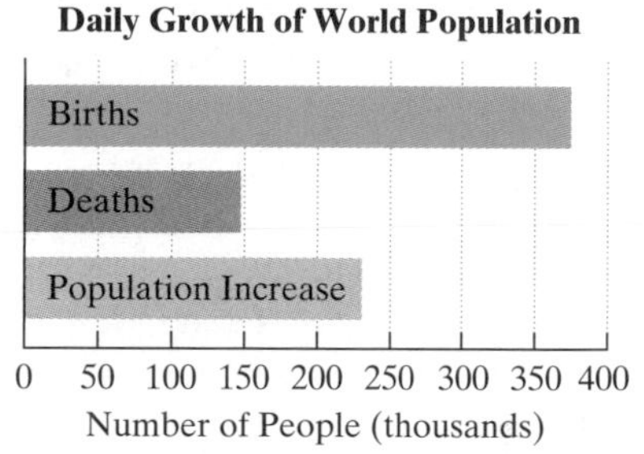

Source: "Population Update" 2000

12. The number of pages in the U.S. tax code exceeds the number of pages in the King James Bible by 18,528. The combined number of pages in the U.S. tax code and the King James Bible is 21,472. Determine the number of pages in each. (*Sources*: Amazon.com and Internal Revenue Service)

13. The bar graph shows the breakdown of the 7485 hate crimes reported in the United States in 2004. The number of hate crimes based on race exceeded three times the number based on sexual orientation by 127. Find the number of hate crimes reported in the United States in 2004 based on race and based on sexual orientation.

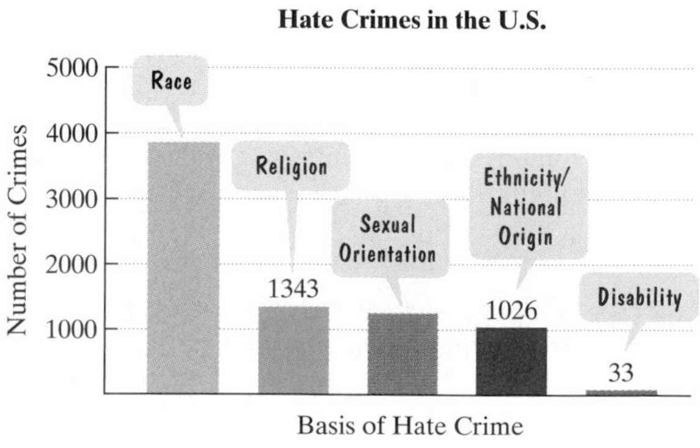

Source: FBI.

14. The bar graph on the next page shows the percentage of global energy used by the countries consuming the most energy. The percentage of global energy used by China exceeds Russia by 6% and the percentage of global energy used by the United States exceeds Russia by 16.4%.

Combined, the United States, China, and Russia consume 40.4% of the world's energy. Determine the percentage of global energy used by each country.

Countries Using the Most Energy

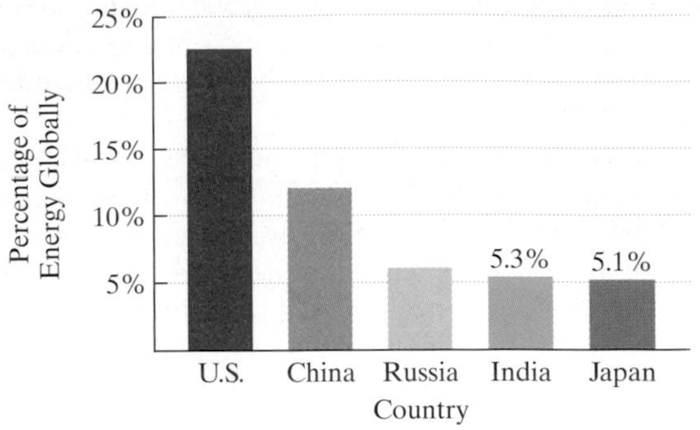

Source: World Bank Group

15. You are choosing between two health club plans. Plan A offers membership for a fee of \$40 plus a monthly fee of \$25. Plan B offers membership for a fee of \$15 plus a monthly fee of \$30. After how many months will the total cost for each plan be the same? What will be the total cost for each plan?

16. Video Store A charges \$9 to rent a video game for one week. Although only members can rent from the store, membership is free. Video Store B charges only \$4 to rent a video game for one week. Only members can rent from the store and membership is \$50 per year. After how many video-game rentals will the total amount spent at each store be the same? What will be the total amount spent at each store?

17. The bus fare in a city is \$1.25. People who use the bus have the option of purchasing a monthly coupon book for \$15.00. With the coupon book, the fare is reduced to \$0.75. Determine the number of times in a month the bus must be used so that the total monthly cost without the coupon book is the same as the total monthly cost with the coupon book.

18. A coupon book for a bridge costs \$30 per month. The toll for the bridge is normally \$5.00, but it is reduced to \$3.50 for people who have purchased the coupon book. Determine the number of times in a month the bridge must be crossed so that the total monthly cost without the coupon book is the same as the total monthly cost with the coupon book.

19. You are choosing between two plans at a discount warehouse. Plan A offers an annual membership fee of \$100 and you pay 80% of the manufacturer's recommended list price. Plan B offers an annual membership fee of \$40 and you pay 90% of the manufacturer's recommended list price. How many dollars of merchandise would you have to purchase in a year to pay the same amount under both plans? What will be the cost for each plan?

20. You are choosing between two plans at a discount warehouse. Plan A offers an annual membership fee of \$300 and you pay 70% of the manufacturer's recommended list price. Plan B offers an annual membership fee of \$40 and you pay 90% of the manufacturer's recommended list price. How many dollars of merchandise would you have to purchase in a year to pay the same amount under both plans? What will be the cost for each plan?

21. An automobile repair shop charged a customer \$448, listing \$63 for parts and the remainder for labor. If the cost of labor is \$35 per hour, how many hours of labor did it take to repair the car?

22. A repair bill on a sailboat came to \$1603, including \$532 for parts and the remainder for labor. If the cost of labor is \$63 per hour, how many hours of labor did it take to repair the sailboat?

23. A job pays an annual salary of \$33,150, which includes a holiday bonus of \$750. If paychecks are issued twice a month, what is the gross amount for each paycheck?

24. A bookcase is to be constructed as shown in the figure. The length is to be 3 times the height. If 60 feet of lumber is available for the entire unit, find the length and height of the bookcase.

• Writing in Mathematics

25. In your own words, describe a step-by-step approach for solving algebraic word problems.

26. Many students find solving linear equations much easier than solving algebraic word problems. Discuss some of the reasons why this is the case.

27. Did you have difficulties solving some of the problems that were assigned in this exercise set? Discuss what you did if this happened to you. Did your course of action enhance your ability to solve algebraic word problems?

28. The mile records in Example 2 on page 325 are a yardstick for measuring how athletes are getting better and better. Do you think that there is a limit to human performance? Explain your answer. If so, when might we reach it?

• Critical Thinking Exercises

29. An HMO pamphlet contains the following recommended weight for women: "Give yourself 100 pounds for the first 5 feet plus 5 pounds for every inch over 5 feet tall." Using this description, which height corresponds to an ideal weight of 135 pounds?

30. The rate for a particular international long distance telephone call is \$0.55 for the first minute and \$0.40 for each additional minute. Determine the length of a call that cost \$6.95.

31. In a film, the actor Charles Coburn plays an elderly "uncle" character criticized for marrying a woman when he is 3 times her age. He wittily replies, "Ah, but in 20 years time I shall only be twice her age." How old are the "uncle" and the woman?

32. Suppose that we agree to pay you 8¢ for every problem in this chapter that you solve correctly and fine you 5¢ for every problem done incorrectly. If at the end of 26 problems we do not owe each other any money, how many problems did you solve correctly?

33. It was wartime when the Ricardos found out Mrs. Ricardo was pregnant. Ricky Ricardo was drafted and made out a will, deciding that \$14,000 in a savings account was to be divided between his wife and his child-to-be. Rather strangely, and certainly with gender bias, Ricky stipulated that if the child were a boy, he would get twice the amount of the mother's portion. If it were a girl, the mother would get twice the amount the girl was to receive. We'll never know what Ricky was thinking of, for (as fate would have it) he did not return from war. Mrs. Ricardo gave birth to twins—a boy and a girl. How was the money divided?

34. A thief steals a number of rare plants from a nursery. On the way out, the thief meets three security guards, one after another. To each security guard, the thief is forced to give one-half the plants that he still has, plus 2 more. Finally, the thief leaves the nursery with 1 lone palm. How many plants were originally stolen?

• Group Exercise

35. One of the best ways to learn how to *solve* a word problem in algebra is to *design* word problems of your own. Creating a word problem makes you very aware of precisely how much information is needed to solve the problem. You must also focus on the best way to present information to a reader and on how much information to give. As you write your problem, you gain skills that will help you solve problems created by others.

The group should design five different word problems that can be solved using algebraic equations. All of the problems should be on different topics. For example, the group should not have more than one problem on finding a number. The group should turn in both the problems and their algebraic solutions.

SECTION 6.4 • RATIO, PROPORTION, AND VARIATION

OBJECTIVES

1. Solve proportions.
2. Solve problems using proportions.
3. Solve direct variation problems.
4. Solve inverse variation problems.

The possibility of seeing a blue whale, the largest mammal ever to grace the Earth, increases the excitement of gazing out over the ocean's swell of waves. Blue whales were hunted to near extinction in the last half of the nineteenth and the first half of the twentieth centuries. Using a method for estimating wildlife populations that we discuss in this section, by the mid-1960s it was determined that the world population of blue whales was less than 1000. This led the International Whaling Commission to ban the killing of blue whales to prevent their extinction. A dramatic increase in blue whale sightings indicates an ongoing increase in their population and the success of the killing ban.

1 Solve proportions.

Proportions

A **ratio** compares quantities by division. For example, a group contains 60 women and 30 men. The ratio of women to men is $\frac{60}{30}$. We can express this ratio as a fraction reduced to lowest terms:

$$\frac{60}{30} = \frac{2 \cdot \cancel{30}}{1 \cdot \cancel{30}} = \frac{2}{1}.$$

This ratio can be expressed as 2:1, or 2 to 1.

A **proportion** is a statement that says that two ratios are equal. If the ratios are $\frac{a}{b}$ and $\frac{c}{d}$, then the proportion is

$$\frac{a}{b} = \frac{c}{d}.$$

We can clear this equation of fractions by multiplying both sides by bd, the least common denominator:

$$\frac{a}{b} = \frac{c}{d}$$ This is the given proportion.

$$bd \cdot \frac{a}{b} = bd \cdot \frac{c}{d}$$ Multiply both sides by $bd(b \neq 0$ and $d \neq 0)$. Then simplify. On the left, $\frac{\not{b}d}{1} \cdot \frac{a}{\not{b}} = da = ad$. On the right, $\frac{b\not{d}}{1} \cdot \frac{c}{\not{d}} = bc$.

$$ad = bc$$

We see that the following principle is true for any proportion:

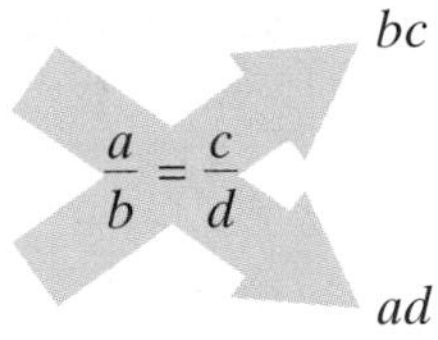

The cross-products principle: $ad = bc$

THE CROSS-PRODUCTS PRINCIPLE FOR PROPORTIONS

If $\frac{a}{b} = \frac{c}{d}$, then $ad = bc$. $(b \neq 0$ and $d \neq 0.)$

The cross products ad and bc are equal.

For example, if $\frac{2}{3} = \frac{6}{9}$, we see that $2 \cdot 9 = 3 \cdot 6$, or $18 = 18$.

If three of the numbers in a proportion are known, the value of the missing quantity can be found by using the cross-products principle. This idea is illustrated in Example 1.

EXAMPLE 1 SOLVING PROPORTIONS

Solve each proportion for x:

a. $\frac{63}{x} = \frac{7}{5}$ **b.** $\frac{20}{x-10} = \frac{30}{x}$.

SOLUTION

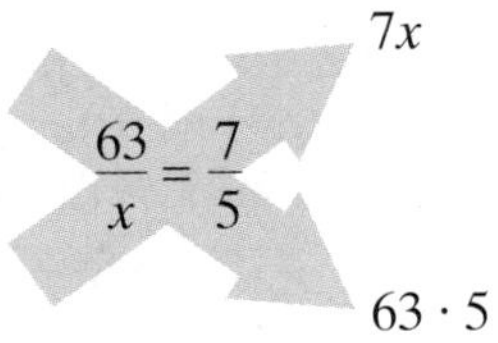

Cross products

a. $\frac{63}{x} = \frac{7}{5}$ This is the given proportion.

$63 \cdot 5 = 7x$ Apply the cross-products principle.

$315 = 7x$ Simplify.

$\frac{315}{7} = \frac{7x}{7}$ Divide both sides by 7.

$45 = x$ Simplify.

The solution set is $\{45\}$.

Check

$\frac{63}{45} \stackrel{?}{=} \frac{7}{5}$ Substitute 45 for x in $\frac{63}{x} = \frac{7}{5}$.

$\frac{7 \cdot \not{9}}{5 \cdot \not{9}} \stackrel{?}{=} \frac{7}{5}$ Reduce $\frac{63}{45}$ to lowest terms.

$\frac{7}{5} = \frac{7}{5}$ This true statement verifies that the solution set is $\{45\}$.

b. $\frac{20}{x-10} = \frac{30}{x}$ This is the given proportion.

$20x = 30(x - 10)$ Apply the cross-products principle.

$20x = 30x - 30 \cdot 10$ Use the distributive property.

$20x = 30x - 300$ Simplify.

$$20x - 30x = 30x - 300 - 30x \quad \text{Subtract } 30x \text{ from both sides.}$$
$$-10x = -300 \quad \text{Simplify.}$$
$$\frac{-10x}{-10} = \frac{-300}{-10} \quad \text{Divide both sides by } -10.$$
$$x = 30 \quad \text{Simplify.}$$

Check

$$\frac{20}{30-10} \stackrel{?}{=} \frac{30}{30} \quad \text{Substitute 30 for x in } \frac{20}{x-10} = \frac{30}{x}.$$
$$\frac{20}{20} \stackrel{?}{=} \frac{30}{30} \quad \text{Subtract: } 30 - 10 = 20.$$
$$1 = 1 \quad \text{This true statement verifies that the solution is 30.}$$

The solution set is $\{30\}$.

CHECK POINT 1 Solve each proportion for x:

a. $\frac{10}{x} = \frac{2}{3}$ **b.** $\frac{11}{910 - x} = \frac{2}{x}$.

2 Solve problems using proportions.

Applications of Proportions

We now turn to practical application problems that can be solved using proportions. Here is a procedure for solving these problems:

SOLVING APPLIED PROBLEMS USING PROPORTIONS

1. Read the problem and represent the unknown quantity by x (or any letter).
2. Set up a proportion by listing the given ratio on one side and the ratio with the unknown quantity on the other side. Each respective quantity should occupy the same corresponding position on each side of the proportion.
3. Drop units and apply the cross-products principle.
4. Solve for x and answer the question.

EXAMPLE 2 APPLYING PROPORTIONS: CALCULATING TAXES

The property tax on a house whose assessed value is \$65,000 is \$825. Determine the property tax on a house with an assessed value of \$180,000, assuming the same tax rate.

SOLUTION

Step 1. Represent the unknown by x. Let x = the tax on a \$180,000 house.

Step 2. Set up a proportion. We will set up a proportion comparing taxes to assessed value.

$$\frac{\text{Tax on \$65,000 house}}{\text{Assessed value (\$65,000)}} \quad \text{equals} \quad \frac{\text{Tax on \$180,000 house}}{\text{Assessed value (\$180,000)}}$$

Given ratio $\frac{\$825}{\$65,000} = \frac{\$x}{\$180,000}$ ← Unknown ← Given quantity

STUDY TIP

Here are three other correct proportions you can use in step 2:

- $\frac{\$65,000 \text{ value}}{\$825 \text{ tax}} = \frac{\$180,000 \text{ value}}{\$x \text{ tax}}$
- $\frac{\$65,000 \text{ value}}{\$180,000 \text{ value}} = \frac{\$825 \text{ tax}}{\$x \text{ tax}}$
- $\frac{\$180,000 \text{ value}}{\$65,000 \text{ value}} = \frac{\$x \text{ tax}}{\$825 \text{ tax}}$.

Each proportion gives the same cross product obtained in step 3.

Step 3. Drop the units and apply the cross-products principle. We drop the dollar signs and begin to solve for x.

$$\frac{825}{65{,}000} = \frac{x}{180{,}000}$$ This is the proportion that models the problem's conditions.

$$65{,}000x = (825)(180{,}000)$$ Apply the cross-products principle.

$$65{,}000x = 148{,}500{,}000$$ Multiply.

Step 4. Solve for x and answer the question.

$$\frac{65{,}000x}{65{,}000} = \frac{148{,}500{,}000}{65{,}000}$$ Divide both sides by 65,000.

$$x \approx 2284.62$$ Round the value of x to the nearest cent.

The property tax on the \$180,000 house is approximately \$2284.62.

CHECK POINT 2 The property tax on a house with an assessed value of \$45,000 is \$600. Determine the property tax on a house with an assessed value of \$112,500, assuming the same tax rate.

Sampling in Nature

The method that was used to estimate the blue whale population described in the section opener is called the **capture-recapture method**. Because it is impossible to count each individual animal within a population, wildlife biologists randomly catch and tag a given number of animals. Sometime later they recapture a second sample of animals and count the number of recaptured tagged animals. The total size of the wildlife population is then estimated using the following proportion:

$$\frac{\text{Original number of tagged animals}}{\text{Total number of animals in the population}} = \frac{\text{Number of recaptured tagged animals}}{\text{Number of animals in second sample}}.$$

Initially unknown (x) → Total number of animals in the population; Known ratio → right side.

Although this is called the capture-recapture method, it is not necessary to recapture animals in order to observe whether or not they are tagged. This could be done from a distance, with binoculars for instance.

EXAMPLE 3 APPLYING PROPORTIONS: ESTIMATING WILDLIFE POPULATION

Wildlife biologists catch, tag, and then release 135 deer back into a wildlife refuge. Two weeks later they observe a sample of 140 deer, 30 of which are tagged. Assuming the ratio of tagged deer in the sample holds for all deer in the refuge, approximately how many deer are in the refuge?

SOLUTION

Step 1. Represent the unknown by x. Let x = the total number of deer in the refuge.

Step 2. Set up a proportion.

Unknown → $\frac{\text{Original number of tagged deer}}{\text{Total number of deer}}$ equals $\frac{\text{Number of tagged deer in the observed sample}}{\text{Total number of deer in the observed sample}}$ ← Known ratio

$$\frac{135}{x} = \frac{30}{140}$$

Steps 3 and 4. Apply the cross-products principle, solve, and answer the question.

$$\frac{135}{x} = \frac{30}{140}$$ This is the proportion that models the problem's conditions.

$$(135)(140) = 30x$$ Apply the cross-products principle.

$$18{,}900 = 30x$$ Multiply.

$$\frac{18{,}900}{30} = \frac{30x}{30}$$ Divide both sides by 30.

$$630 = x$$ Simplify.

There are approximately 630 deer in the refuge.

CHECK POINT 3 Wildlife biologists catch, tag, and then release 120 deer back into the wildlife refuge. Two weeks later they observe a sample of 150 deer, 25 of which are tagged. Assuming the ratio of tagged deer in the sample holds for all deer in the refuge, approximately how many deer are in the refuge?

3 Solve direct variation problems.

Direct Variation

In Example 2, we saw that as the assessed value on a house goes up, so do the taxes. When the assessed value is doubled, the taxes are doubled; when the assessed value is tripled, the taxes are tripled. Because of this, the tax on a house is said to **vary directly** as its assessed value. Direct variation situations can be solved using a proportion.

EXAMPLE 4 SOLVING A DIRECT VARIATION PROBLEM

An alligator's tail length varies directly as its body length. An alligator with a body length of 4 feet has a tail length of 3.6 feet. What is the tail length of an alligator whose body length is 6 feet?

SOLUTION

Step 1. Represent the unknown by x. Let x = the tail length of an alligator whose body length is 6 feet.

Step 2. Set up a proportion. We will set up a proportion comparing body length to tail length.

$$\frac{4 \text{ ft}}{3.6 \text{ ft}} = \frac{6 \text{ ft}}{x \text{ ft}}$$

Body length / Tail length (over each ratio)

Given ratio: body length is 4 ft and tail length is 3.6 ft.

Ratio with unknown: Body length is 6 ft and we're seeking tail length.

Steps 3 and 4. Apply the cross-products principle, solve, and answer the question.

$$\frac{4}{3.6} = \frac{6}{x}$$ This is the proportion that models the problem's conditions.

$$4x = (3.6)(6)$$ Apply the cross-products principle.

$$4x = 21.6$$ Multiply.

$$\frac{4x}{4} = \frac{21.6}{4}$$ Divide both sides by 4.

$$x = 5.4$$ Simplify.

An alligator whose body length is 6 feet has a tail length measuring 5.4 feet.

CHECK POINT 4 The number of gallons of water used when taking a shower varies directly as the time, in minutes, in the shower. A shower lasting 5 minutes uses 30 gallons of water. How much water is used in a shower lasting 11 minutes?

EXAMPLE 5 SOLVING A DIRECT VARIATION PROBLEM

The distance that the sky divers shown in the photograph fall varies directly as the square of the time in which they fall. The sky divers fall 64 feet in 2 seconds. How far will they fall in 5 seconds?

SOLUTION

Step 1. Represent the unknown by *x*. Let x = the distance the sky divers fall in 5 seconds.

Step 2. Set up a proportion. We will set up a proportion comparing the distance that the sky divers fall to the square of the time in which they fall.

$\frac{\text{Distance they fall in 2 seconds}}{\text{Square of the time they fall}}$ equals $\frac{\text{Distance they fall in 5 seconds}}{\text{Square of the time they fall}}$

Given ratio $\left\{ \frac{64 \text{ feet}}{2^2 \text{ seconds}} \right.$ $=$ $\frac{x}{5^2 \text{ seconds}}$ ← Unknown (x); ← Given quantity (5^2 seconds)

Steps 3 and 4. Apply the cross-products principle, solve, and answer the question.

$$\frac{64}{2^2} = \frac{x}{5^2}$$ This is the proportion that models the problem's conditions.

$$\frac{64}{4} = \frac{x}{25}$$ Square 2 and 5: $2^2 = 2 \cdot 2 = 4$ and $5^2 = 5 \cdot 5 = 25$.

$$4x = (64)(25)$$ Apply the cross-products principle.

$$4x = 1600$$ Multiply.

$$\frac{4x}{4} = \frac{1600}{4}$$ Divide both sides by 4.

$$x = 400$$ Simplify.

The sky divers will fall 400 feet in 5 seconds.

CHECK POINT 5 The distance required to stop a car varies directly as the square of its speed. If 200 feet are required to stop a car traveling 60 miles per hour, how many feet are required to stop a car traveling 100 miles per hour? Round to the nearest foot.

4 Solve inverse variation problems.

Inverse Variation

So far, we have created models for situations in which an increase in one quantity is accompanied by an increase in a second quantity. However, there are other situations in which one quantity increases as the other decreases, or vice versa. For example, if you drive to campus, consider the rate at which you drive and the time it takes you to get there. As your driving rate increases, the time it takes you to get to campus decreases. This is an example of *inverse variation*. When two quantities **vary inversely**, as one quantity increases, the other decreases, and vice versa.

The distance from Atlanta, Georgia, to Orlando, Florida, is 450 miles. If you average 45 miles per hour, the time for the drive is 10 hours. If you average 75 miles per hour, the time for the drive is 6 hours. The following proportion represents this situation in which time varies inversely as driving rate:

$$\frac{\text{time at the slower rate}}{\text{the faster rate}} = \frac{\text{time at the faster rate}}{\text{the slower rate}}$$

$$\frac{10 \text{ hours}}{75 \text{ miles per hour}} = \frac{6 \text{ hours}}{45 \text{ miles per hour}}.$$

The cross products are equal:

$$\frac{10\ \cancel{\text{hours}}}{1} \cdot \frac{45 \text{ miles}}{\cancel{\text{hour}}} = 10 \cdot 45 \text{ miles} = 450 \text{ miles}$$

$$\frac{75 \text{ miles}}{\cancel{\text{hour}}} \cdot \frac{6\ \cancel{\text{hours}}}{1} = 75 \cdot 6 \text{ miles} = 450 \text{ miles}.$$

Because the product of rate and time is distance, each cross product gives the distance from Atlanta to Orlando.

There is something unusual about the placement of quantities in a proportion in an inverse variation situation:

These quantities correspond to each other. 6 hours is the travel time at 75 miles per hour.

$$\frac{10 \text{ hours}}{75 \text{ miles per hour}} = \frac{6 \text{ hours}}{45 \text{ miles per hour}}$$

These quantities correspond to each other. 10 hours is the travel time at 45 miles per hour.

In an inverse variation situation, corresponding values are not placed in the same ratio. *Placing corresponding values in opposite ratios* allows one quantity to increase while the other decreases, or vice versa.

STUDY TIP

When you apply the cross-products principle in an inverse variation proportion, you multiply corresponding quantities.

SETTING UP A PROPORTION WHEN y VARIES INVERSELY AS x

$$\frac{\text{The first value for } y}{\text{The value for } x \text{ corresponding to the second value for } y} = \frac{\text{The second value for } y}{\text{The value for } x \text{ corresponding to the first value for } y}$$

FIGURE 6.5

EXAMPLE 6 SOLVING AN INVERSE VARIATION PROBLEM

Figure 6.5 shows that a bicyclist tips the cycle when making a turn. The angle B, formed by the vertical direction and the bicycle, is called the banking angle. The banking angle varies inversely as the cycle's turning radius. When the turning radius is 4 feet, the banking angle is 28°. What is the banking angle when the turning radius is 3.5 feet?

SOLUTION

Step 1. Represent the unknown by x. Let

x = the banking angle when the turning radius is 3.5 feet.

Step 2. Set up a proportion. We will set up a proportion comparing the banking angle to the turning radius. Because this is an inverse variation situation, we place corresponding values in opposite ratios.

A banking angle of 28° corresponds to a turning radius of 4 ft.

We must find the banking angle, x°, corresponding to a turning radius of 3.5 ft.

$$\frac{28°}{3.5 \text{ ft}} = \frac{x°}{4 \text{ ft}}$$

banking angle / turning radius   banking angle / turning radius

Steps 3 and 4. Apply the cross-products principle, solve, and answer the question.

$$\frac{28}{3.5} = \frac{x}{4}$$ This is the proportion that models the problem's conditions.

$$3.5x = 28 \cdot 4$$ Apply the cross-products principle.

$$3.5x = 112$$ Multiply.

$$\frac{3.5x}{3.5} = \frac{112}{3.5}$$ Divide both sides by 3.5.

$$x = 32$$ Simplify.

When the turning radius is 3.5 feet, the banking angle is 32°.

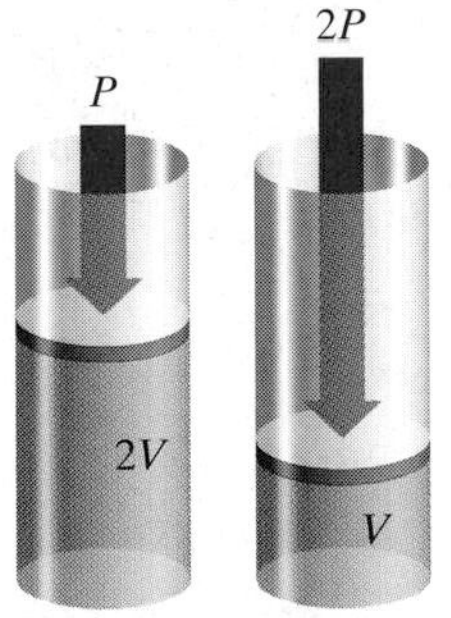

Doubling the pressure halves the volume.

CHECK POINT 6 When you use a spray can and press the value at the top, you decrease the pressure of the gas in the can. This decrease of pressure causes the volume of the gas in the can to increase. Because the gas needs more room than is provided in the can, it expands in spray form through the small hole near the valve. In general, if the temperature is constant, the pressure of a gas in a container varies inversely as the volume of the container. The pressure of a gas sample in a container whose volume is 8 cubic inches is 12 pounds per square inch. If the sample expands to a volume of 22 cubic inches, what is the new pressure of the gas?

EXERCISE SET 6.4

• Practice Exercises

In Exercises 1–12, solve each proportion.

1. $\frac{24}{x} = \frac{12}{7}$
2. $\frac{56}{x} = \frac{8}{7}$
3. $\frac{x}{6} = \frac{18}{4}$
4. $\frac{x}{32} = \frac{3}{24}$
5. $\frac{x}{3} = -\frac{3}{4}$
6. $\frac{x}{2} = -\frac{1}{5}$
7. $\frac{-3}{8} = \frac{x}{40}$
8. $\frac{-3}{8} = \frac{6}{x}$
9. $\frac{x-2}{5} = \frac{3}{10}$
10. $\frac{x+4}{8} = \frac{3}{16}$
11. $\frac{y+10}{10} = \frac{y-2}{4}$
12. $\frac{2}{y-5} = \frac{3}{y+6}$

In Exercises 13–16, use a proportion to solve each variation problem.

13. y varies directly as x. $y = 65$ when $x = 5$. Find y when $x = 12$.

14. y varies directly as x. $y = 45$ when $x = 5$. Find y when $x = 13$.

15. y varies inversely as x. $y = 12$ when $x = 5$. Find y when $x = 2$.

16. y varies inversely as x. $y = 6$ when $x = 3$. Find y when $x = 9$.

• Practice Plus

In Exercises 17–22, solve each proportion for x.

17. $\frac{x}{a} = \frac{b}{c}$

18. $\frac{a}{x} = \frac{b}{c}$

19. $\frac{a + b}{c} = \frac{x}{d}$

20. $\frac{a - b}{c} = \frac{x}{d}$

21. $\frac{x + a}{a} = \frac{b + c}{c}$

22. $\frac{ax - b}{b} = \frac{c - d}{d}$

• Application Exercises

Use a proportion to solve Exercises 23–28.

23. The tax on a property with an assessed value of \$65,000 is \$725. Find the tax on a property with an assessed value of \$100,000.

24. The maintenance bill for a shopping center containing 180,000 square feet is \$45,000. What is the bill for a store in the center that is 4800 square feet?

25. St. Paul Island in Alaska has 12 fur seal rookeries (breeding places). In 1961, to estimate the fur seal pup population in the Gorbath rookery, 4963 fur seal pups were tagged in early August. In late August, a sample of 900 pups was observed and 218 of these were found to have been previously tagged. Estimate the total number of fur seal pups in this rookery.

26. To estimate the number of bass in a lake, wildlife biologists tagged 50 bass and released them in the lake. Later they netted 108 bass and found that 27 of them were tagged. Approximately how many bass are in the lake?

27. The ratio of monthly child support to a father's yearly income is 1:40. How much should a father earning \$38,000 annually pay in monthly child support?

28. Many areas of Northern California depend on the snowpack of the Sierra Nevada mountain range for their water supply. Meteorologists have determined that 250 cubic centimeters of snow will melt to 28 cubic centimeters of water. How much water does 1200 cubic centimeters of melting snow produce?

Exercises 29–42 involve direct and inverse variation. Use a proportion to solve each exercise.

29. An object's weight on the moon varies directly as its weight on Earth. Neil Armstrong, the first person to step on the moon on July 20, 1969, weighed 360 pounds on Earth (with all of his equipment on) and 60 pounds on the moon. What is the moon weight of a person who weighs 186 pounds on Earth?

30. The height that a ball bounces varies directly as the height from which it was dropped. A tennis ball dropped from 12 inches bounces 8.4 inches. From what height was the tennis ball dropped if it bounces 56 inches?

31. Height varies directly as foot length. A person whose foot length is 10 inches is 67 inches tall. In 1951, photos of large footprints were published. Some believed that these footprints were made by the "Abominable Snowman." Each footprint was 23 inches long. If indeed they belonged to the Abominable Snowman, how tall is the critter?

32. A person's hair length varies directly as the number of years it has been growing. After 2 years, a person's hair length is 8 inches. The longest moustache on record was grown by Kalyan Sain of India. Sain grew his moustache for 17 years. How long was it?

33. If all men had identical body types, their weights would vary directly as the cube of their heights. Shown is Robert Wadlow, who reached a record height of 8 feet 11 inches (107 inches) before his death at age 22. If a man who is 5 feet 10 inches tall (70 inches) with the same body type as Mr. Wadlow weighs 170 pounds, what was Robert Wadlow's weight shortly before his death?

34. The Mach number is a measurement of speed named after the man who suggested it, Ernst Mach (1838–1916). The speed of an aircraft varies directly as its Mach number. Shown here are two aircraft. Use the figures for the Concorde to determine the Blackbird's speed.

Concorde
Mach 2.03
Speed = 1502.2 miles per hour

SR-71 Blackbird
Mach 3.3
Speed = ?

35. On a dry asphalt road, a car's stopping distance varies directly as the square of its speed. A car traveling at 45 miles per hour can stop in 67.5 feet. What is the stopping distance for a car traveling at 60 miles per hour?

36. The distance that an object falls varies directly as the square of the time it has been falling. An object falls 144 feet in 3 seconds. Find how far it will fall in 7 seconds.

37. The water temperature of the Pacific Ocean varies inversely as the water's depth. At a depth of 1000 meters, the water temperature is 4.4° Celsius. What is the water temperature at a depth of 5000 meters?

38. The time that it takes you to get to campus varies inversely as your driving rate. Averaging 20 miles per hour in terrible traffic, it takes you 1.5 hours to get to campus. How long would the trip take averaging 60 miles per hour?

39. The volume of a gas in a container at a constant temperature varies inversely as the pressure. If the volume is 32 cubic centimeters at a pressure of 8 pounds, find the pressure when the volume is 40 cubic centimeters.

40. The current in a circuit varies inversely as the resistance. The current is 20 amperes when the resistance is 5 ohms. Find the current for a resistance of 16 ohms.

41. The loudness of a stereo speaker, measured in decibels, varies inversely as the square of your distance from the speaker. When you are 8 feet from the speaker, the loudness is 28 decibels. What is the loudness when you are 4 feet from the speaker?

42. Radiation machines, used to treat tumors, produce an intensity of radiation that varies inversely as the square of the distance from the machine. At 3 meters, the radiation intensity is 62.5 milliroentgens per hour. What is the intensity at a distance of 2.5 meters?

• Writing in Mathematics

43. What is a ratio? Give an example with your description.

44. What is a proportion? Give an example with your description.

45. Explain how to solve a proportion. Illustrate your explanation with an example.

46. Explain the meaning of this statement: A company's monthly sales vary directly as its advertising budget.

47. Explain the meaning of this statement: A company's monthly sales vary inversely as the price of its product.

48. Explain the difference between setting up proportions for direct and inverse variation problems.

• Critical Thinking Exercises

49. The front sprocket on a bicycle has 60 teeth and the rear sprocket has 20 teeth. For mountain biking, an owner needs a 5:1 front: rear ratio. If only one of the sprockets is to be replaced, describe the two ways in which this can be done.

50. My friend is 44 years old. My dog Phideaux is 7 years old. If Phideaux were human, he would be 56. Phideaux thinks my friend is another dog, which makes me wonder: If my friend were a dog, how old would my friend be?

51. In a hurricane, the wind pressure varies directly as the square of the wind velocity. If wind pressure is a measure of a hurricane's destructive capacity, what happens to this destructive power when the wind velocity doubles?

52. The illumination from a light source varies inversely as the square of the distance from the light source. If you raise a lamp from 15 inches to 30 inches over your desk, what happens to the illumination?

SECTION 6.5 • LINEAR INEQUALITIES IN ONE VARIABLE

OBJECTIVES

1. Graph subsets of real numbers on a number line.
2. Solve linear inequalities.
3. Solve applied problems using linear inequalities.

Rent-a-Heap, a car rental company, charges $125 per week plus $0.20 per mile to rent one of their cars. Suppose you are limited by how much money you can spend for the week: You can spend at most $335. If we let x represent the number of miles you drive the heap in a week, we can write an inequality that models the given conditions:

The weekly charge of $125	plus	the charge of $0.20 per mile for x miles	must be less than or equal to	$335.
125	+	$0.20x$	$\leq$	335.

Notice that the highest exponent on the variable is 1. Such an inequality is called a *linear inequality in one variable*. The symbol between the two sides of an inequality can be $\leq$ (is less than or equal to), $<$ (is less than), $\geq$ (is greater than or equal to), or $>$ (is greater than).

69. $6x^2 + 6x + 1 = 0$

70. $3x^2 = 5x - 1$

71. $4x^2 = 12x - 9$

72. $9x^2 + 6x + 1 = 0$

Practice Plus

In Exercises 73–80, solve each equation by the method of your choice.

73. $\frac{3x^2}{4} - \frac{5x}{2} - 2 = 0$

74. $\frac{x^2}{3} - \frac{x}{2} - \frac{3}{2} = 0$

75. $(x - 1)(3x + 2) = -7(x - 1)$

76. $x(x + 1) = 4 - (x + 2)(x + 2)$

77. $(2x - 6)(x + 2) = 5(x - 1) - 12$

78. $7x(x - 2) = 3 - 2(x + 4)$

79. $2x^2 - 9x - 3 = 9 - 9x$

80. $3x^2 - 6x - 3 = 12 - 6x$

81. When the sum of 6 and twice a positive number is subtracted from the square of the number, 0 results. Find the number.

82. When the sum of 1 and twice a negative number is subtracted from twice the square of the number, 0 results. Find the number.

Application Exercises

The formula

$$N = \frac{t^2 - t}{2}$$

describes the number of football games, N, that must be played in a league with t teams if each team is to play every other team once. Use this information to solve Exercises 83–84.

83. If a league has 36 games scheduled, how many teams belong to the league, assuming that each team plays every other team once?

84. If a league has 45 games scheduled, how many teams belong to the league, assuming that each team plays every other team once?

The bar graph shows the percentage of foreign-born Americans from 1930 through 2003. The percentage, P, of the U.S. population that was foreign-born x years after 1930 can be modeled by the formula

$$P = 0.005x^2 - 0.37x + 11.8.$$

Use the formula to solve Exercises 85–88.

Percentage of U.S. Population That Was Foreign-Born, 1930-2003

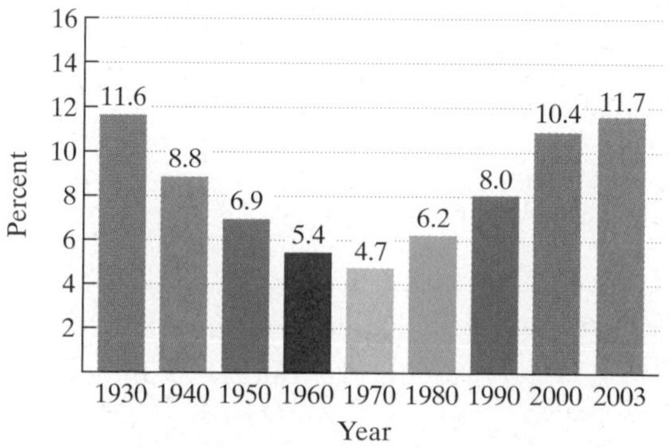

Source: U.S. Census Bureau

85. How well does the formula model the data for 2000?

86. How well does the formula model the data for 1940?

87. In which future year does the model project that 16% of the U.S. population will be foreign-born?

88. In which future year does the model project that 19% of the U.S. population will be foreign-born?

A driver's age has something to do with his or her chance of getting into a fatal car crash. The bar graph shows the number of fatal vehicle crashes per 100 million miles driven for drivers of various age groups. For example, 25-year-old drivers are involved in 4.1 fatal crashes per 100 million miles driven. Thus, when a group of 25-year-old Americans has driven a total of 100 million miles, approximately 4 have been in accidents in which someone died.

Age of U.S. Drivers and Fatal Crashes

Source: Insurance Institute for Highway Safety

The number of fatal vehicle crashes per 100 million miles, N, for drivers of age x can be modeled by the formula

$$N = 0.013x^2 - 1.19x + 28.24.$$

Use the formula to solve Exercises 89–90. Use a calculator and round answers to the nearest year.

89. What age groups are expected to be involved in 3 fatal crashes per 100 million miles driven? How well does the formula model the trend in the actual data shown in the bar graph?

90. What age groups are expected to be involved in 10 fatal crashes per 100 million miles driven? How well does the formula model the trend in the actual data shown in the bar graph?

• Writing in Mathematics

91. Explain how to multiply two binomials using the FOIL method. Give an example with your explanation.

92. Explain how to factor $x^2 - 5x + 6$.

93. Explain how to solve a quadratic equation by factoring. Use the equation $x^2 + 6x + 8 = 0$ in your explanation.

94. Explain how to solve a quadratic equation using the quadratic formula. Use the equation $x^2 + 6x + 8 = 0$ in your explanation.

95. Describe the trend shown by the data for the percentage of foreign-born Americans in the graph for Exercises 85–88. Do you believe that this trend is likely to continue or might something occur that would make it impossible to extend the model into the future? Explain your answer.

• Critical Thinking Exercises

96. The radicand of the quadratic formula, $b^2 - 4ac$, can be used to determine whether $ax^2 + bx + c = 0$ has solutions that are rational, irrational, or not real numbers. Explain how this works. Is it possible to determine the kinds of answers that one will obtain to a quadratic equation without actually solving the equation? Explain.

In Exercises 97–98, find all positive integers b so that the trinomial can be factored.

97. $x^2 + bx + 15$

98. $x^2 + 4x + b$

99. Factor: $x^{2n} + 20x^n + 99$.

100. Solve: $x^2 + 2\sqrt{3}x - 9 = 0$.

CHAPTER SUMMARY, REVIEW, AND TEST

• SUMMARY DEFINITIONS AND CONCEPTS

DEFINITIONS AND CONCEPTS	EXAMPLES
6.1 Algebraic Expressions and Formulas	
a. An algebraic expression combines variables and numbers using addition, subtraction, multiplication, division, powers, or roots.	
b. Evaluating an algebraic expression means finding its value for a given value of the variable or for given values of the variables. Once these values are substituted, follow the order of operations agreement in the box on page 304.	Ex. 1, p. 305; Ex. 2, p. 305; Ex. 3, p. 305
c. An equation is a statement that two expressions are equal. Formulas are equations that express relationships among two or more variables. Mathematical modeling is the process of finding formulas to describe real-world phenomena. Such formulas, together with the meaning assigned to the variables, are called mathematical models. The formulas are said to model, or describe, the relationships among the variables.	Ex. 4, p. 306
d. Terms of an algebraic expression are separated by addition. Like terms have the same variables with the same exponents on the variables. To add or subtract like terms, add or subtract the coefficients and copy the common variable	
e. An algebraic expression is simplified when parentheses have been removed (using the distributive property) and like terms have been combined.	Ex. 5, p. 308; Ex. 6, p. 308; Ex. 7, p. 308
6.2 Linear Equations in One Variable	
a. A linear equation in one variable can be written in the form $ax + b = 0$, where a and b are real numbers, and $a \neq 0$.	
b. Solving a linear equation is the process of finding the set of numbers that make the equation a true statement. These numbers are the solutions. The set of all such solutions is the solution set.	
c. Equivalent equations have the same solution set. Properties for generating equivalent equations are given in the box on page 312.	Ex. 1, p. 313
d. A step-by-step procedure for solving a linear equation is given in the box on page 314.	Ex. 2, p. 314; Ex. 3, p. 315; Ex. 4, p. 316
e. If an equation contains fractions, begin by multiplying both sides of the equation by the least common denominator of the fractions in the equation, thereby clearing fractions.	Ex. 5, p. 317; Ex. 6, p. 317
f. Solving a formula for a variable means rewriting the formula so that the variable is isolated on one side of the equation.	Ex. 7, p. 319; Ex. 8, p. 319
g. If a false statement (such as $-6 = 7$) is obtained in solving a linear equation, the equation has no solution. The solution set is $\varnothing$, the empty set.	Ex. 9, p. 320
h. If a true statement (such as $-6 = -6$) is obtained in solving a linear equation, the equation has infinitely many solutions. The solution set is the set of all real numbers, written $\{x \mid x \text{ is a real number}\}$.	Ex. 10, p. 320

6.3 Applications of Linear Equations

a. Algebraic translations of English phrases are given in Table 6.2 on page 324.

b. A step-by-step strategy for solving word problems using linear equations is given in the box on page 324.
Ex. 1, p. 325; Ex. 2, p. 325; Ex. 3, p. 326; Ex. 4, p. 328

6.4 Ratio, Proportion, and Variation

a. The ratio of a to b is written $\frac{a}{b}$, or $a:b$.

b. A proportion is a statement in the form $\frac{a}{b} = \frac{c}{d}$.

c. The cross-products principle states that if $\frac{a}{b} = \frac{c}{d}$, then $ad = bc$.
Ex. 1, p. 332

d. A step-by-step procedure for solving applied problems using proportions is given in the box on page 333.
Ex. 2, p. 333; Ex. 3, p. 334

e. If two quantities vary directly, as one increases, so does the other. As one decreases, so does the other. Proportions can be used to solve direct variation problems.
Ex. 4, p. 335; Ex. 5, p. 336

f. If two quantities vary inversely, as one increases, the other decreases. As one decreases, the other increases. Proportions, as explained in the box on page 337, can be used to solve inverse variation problems.
Ex. 6, p. 338

6.5 Linear Inequalities in One Variable

A procedure for solving a linear inequality is given in the box on page 342. Remember to reverse the direction of the inequality symbol when multiplying or dividing both sides of an inequality by a negative number.
Ex. 2, p. 343; Ex. 3, p. 343; Ex. 4, p. 344; Ex. 5, p. 344; Ex. 6, p. 345

6.6 Quadratic Equations

a. A quadratic equation can be written in the form $ax^2 + bx + c = 0, a \neq 0$.

b. Some quadratic equations can be solved using factoring and the zero-product principle. A step-by-step procedure is given in the box on page 355.
Ex. 8, p. 355; Ex. 9, p. 356

c. All quadratic equations in the form $ax^2 + bx + c = 0$ can be solved using the quadratic formula:

$$x = \frac{-b \pm \sqrt{b^2 - 4ac}}{2a}.$$

Ex. 10, p. 357; Ex. 11, p. 358; Ex. 12, p. 359

REVIEW EXERCISES

6.1

In Exercises 1–3, evaluate the algebraic expression for the given value of the variable.

1. $6x + 9; x = 4$

2. $7x^2 + 4x - 5; x = -2$

3. $6 + 2(x - 8)^3; x = 5$

4. The bar graph on the right shows the number of music CD sales, in millions, in the United States from 1998 through 2002. The data can be modeled by the formula

$$N = -26x^2 + 143x + 740,$$

where N represents the number of music CD sales, in millions, x years after 1997. According to the formula, how many millions of CDs were sold in 2002? How well does the formula describe sales for that year shown by the graph?

Music CD Sales in the United States

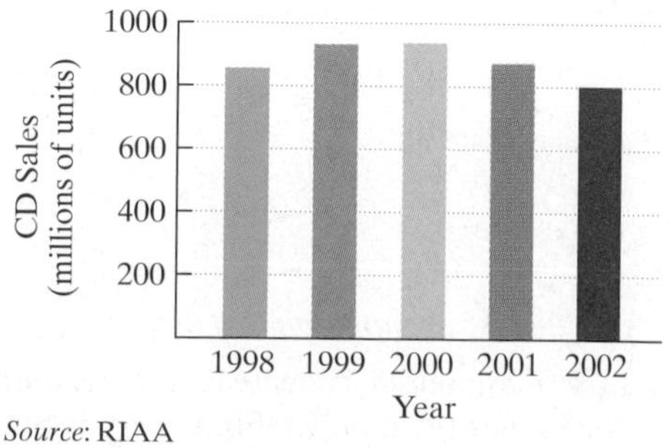

Source: RIAA

In Exercises 5–7, simplify each algebraic expression.

5. $5(2x - 3) + 7x$

6. $3(4y - 5) - (7y - 2)$

7. $2(x^2 + 5x) + 3(4x^2 - 3x)$

6.2

In Exercises 8–14, solve each equation.

8. $4x + 9 = 33$

9. $5x - 3 = x + 5$

10. $3(x + 4) = 5x - 12$

11. $2(x - 2) + 3(x + 5) = 2x - 2$

12. $\frac{2x}{3} = \frac{x}{6} + 1$

13. $7x + 5 = 5(x + 3) + 2x$

14. $7x + 13 = 2(2x - 5) + 3x + 23$

In Exercises 15–18, solve each formula for the specified variable.

15. $Ax - By = C$ for x

16. $A = \frac{1}{2}bh$ for h

17. $A = \frac{B + C}{2}$ for B

18. $vt + gt^2 = s$ for g

19. The bar graph shows the average prescription-drug price in the United States from 2000 through 2004. The data can be modeled by the formula

$$P = 4.6x + 45.8,$$

where P is the average price of a prescription drug, in dollars, x years after 2000. In which year does this model project that the average prescription-drug price will be \$101?

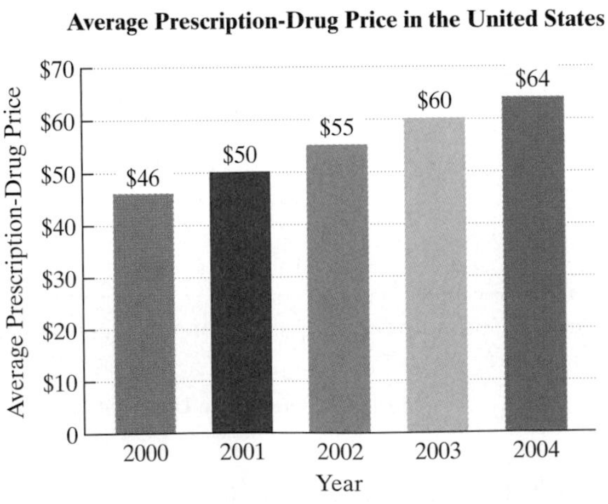

Source: U.S. Census Bureau

6.3

In Exercises 20–24, use an equation to solve each problem.

20. When 7 times a number is decreased by 1, the result is 9 more than 5 times the number. Find the number.

21. The fast-food chains may be touting their "new and improved" salads, but how do they measure up in terms of calories?

Source: Newsweek

Combined, the three salads contain 1705 calories. Determine the number of calories in each salad.

22. The bar graph shows the number of endangered plant species in the United States from 1998 through 2003. In 1998, there were 567 endangered species. For the period shown, the number of endangered plants increased at an average rate of 6.4 species per year. If this trend continues, in which year will there be 663 endangered plant species in the United States?

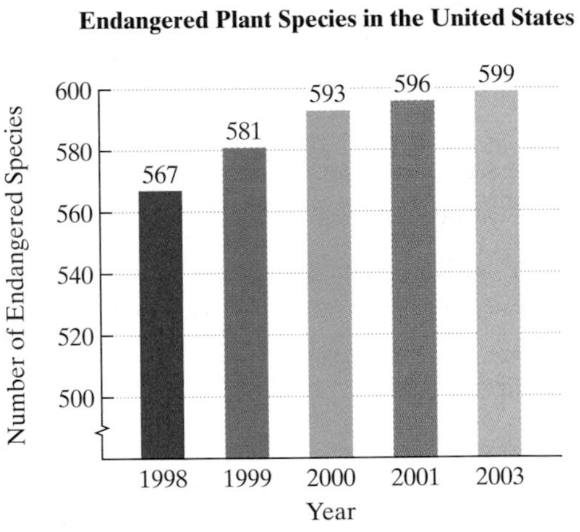

Source: U.S. Fish and Wildlife Service

23. You are choosing between two long-distance telephone plans. One plan has a monthly fee of \$15 with a charge of \$0.05 per minute. The other plan has a monthly fee of \$5 with a charge of \$0.07 per minute. For how many minutes of long-distance calls will the costs for the two plans be the same?

24. In 2004, the world's largest oil consumers were the United States and China. Oil consumption in the United States exceeded three times that of China by 1 million barrels per day. If the two countries combined consumed 27 million barrels of oil per day, determine the oil consumption, in millions of barrels per day, for each country.

(*Source*: Energy Information Administration)

6.4

In Exercises 25–28, solve each proportion.

25. $\frac{3}{x} = \frac{15}{25}$

26. $\frac{-7}{5} = \frac{91}{x}$

27. $\frac{x + 2}{3} = \frac{4}{5}$

28. $\frac{5}{x + 7} = \frac{3}{x + 3}$

Use a proportion to solve Exercises 29–30.

29. If a school board determines that there should be 3 teachers for every 50 students, how many teachers are needed for an enrollment of 5400 students?

30. To determine the number of trout in a lake, a conservationist catches 112 trout, tags them, and returns them to the lake. Later, 82 trout are caught, and 32 of them are found to be tagged. How many trout are in the lake?

Exercises 31–33 involve direct and inverse variation. Use a proportion to solve each exercise.

31. An electric bill varies directly as the amount of electricity used. The bill for 1400 kilowatts of electricity is \$98. What is the bill for 2200 kilowatts of electricity?

32. The distance that a body falls from rest varies directly as the square of the time of the fall. If skydivers fall 144 feet in 3 seconds, how far will they fall in 10 seconds?

33. The time it takes to drive a certain distance varies inversely as the rate of travel. If it takes 4 hours at 50 miles per hour to drive the distance, how long will it take at 40 miles per hour?

6.5

In Exercises 34–40, solve each inequality and graph the solution set on a number line.

34. $2x - 5 < 3$

35. $\frac{x}{2} > -4$

36. $3 - 5x \leq 18$

37. $4x + 6 < 5x$

38. $6x - 10 \geq 2(x + 3)$

39. $4x + 3(2x - 7) \leq x - 3$

40. $-1 < 4x + 2 \leq 6$

41. To pass a course, a student must have an average on three examinations of at least 60. If a student scores 42 and 74 on the first two tests, what must be earned on the third test to pass the course?

6.6

Use FOIL to find the products in Exercises 42–43.

42. $(x + 9)(x - 5)$

43. $(4x - 7)(3x + 2)$

Factor the trinomials in Exercises 44–49, or state that the trinomial is prime.

44. $x^2 - x - 12$

45. $x^2 - 8x + 15$

46. $x^2 + 2x + 3$

47. $3x^2 - 17x + 10$

48. $6x^2 - 11x - 10$

49. $3x^2 - 6x - 5$

Solve the quadratic equations in Exercises 50–53 by factoring.

50. $x^2 + 5x - 14 = 0$

51. $x^2 - 4x = 32$

52. $2x^2 + 15x - 8 = 0$

53. $3x^2 = -21x - 30$

Solve the quadratic equations in Exercises 54–57 using the quadratic formula.

54. $x^2 - 4x + 3 = 0$

55. $x^2 - 5x = 4$

56. $2x^2 + 5x - 3 = 0$

57. $3x^2 - 6x = 5$

58. In 1945, 35.4% of taxes collected by the U.S. Treasury came from corporate income taxes. Since then, corporations have worked hard to convince lawmakers that they shouldn't pay taxes. The bar graph shows the percentage of federal taxes from corporate income taxes for selected years from 1985 through 2003. The data can be modeled by the formula

$$P = -0.035x^2 + 0.65x + 7.6,$$

where P represents the percentage of federal taxes from corporations x years after 1985. If these trends continue, by which year (to the nearest year) will corporations pay no taxes?

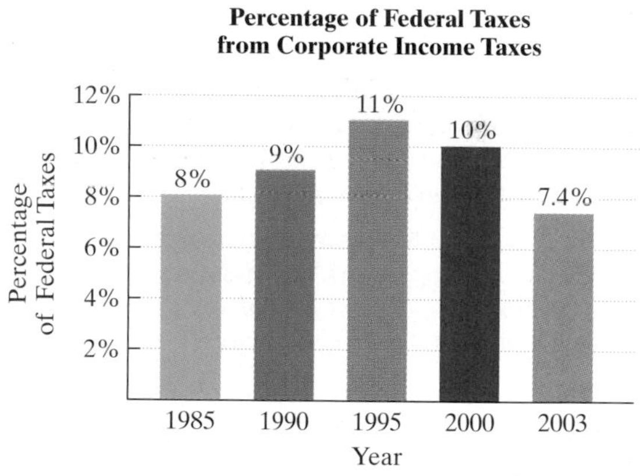

Source: White House Office of Management and Budget

CHAPTER 6 TEST

1. Evaluate $x^3 - 4(x - 1)^2$ when $x = -2$.

2. Simplify: $5(3x - 2) - (x - 6)$.

3. The formula

$$F = 24t^2 - 260t + 816$$

models the number of police officers in the United States, F, convicted of felonies t years after 1990. How many convictions of police officers were there in 2000? (*Source:* FBI)

In Exercises 4–7, solve each equation.

4. $12x + 4 = 7x - 21$

5. $3(2x - 4) = 9 - 3(x + 1)$

6. $3(x - 4) + x = 2(6 + 2x)$

7. $\frac{x}{5} - 2 = \frac{x}{3}$

8. Solve for y: $By - Ax = A$.

9. The formula $D = 0.12x + 5.44$ models the number of children in the United States with physical disabilities, D, in millions, x years after 2000. According to this model, in which year will there be 6.4 million children in the United States with physical disabilities?

In Exercises 10–13, use an equation to solve each problem.

10. The product of 5 and a number, decreased by 9, is 310. What is the number?

11. In New York City, a fitness trainer earns \$22,870 more per year than a preschool teacher. The yearly average salaries for fitness trainers and preschool teachers combined are \$79,030. Determine the average yearly salary of a fitness trainer and a preschool teacher in New York City.

(*Source: Time*, April 14, 2003)

12. You bought a new car for \$13,805. Its value is decreasing by \$1820 per year. After how many years will its value be \$4705?

13. Photo Shop A charges \$1.60 to develop a roll of film plus \$0.11 for each print. Photo Shop B charges \$1.20 to develop a roll of film plus \$0.13 per print. For how many prints will the amount spent at each photo shop be the same? What will be that amount?

In Exercises 14–15, solve each proportion.

14. $\frac{5}{8} = \frac{x}{12}$ **15.** $\frac{x+5}{8} = \frac{x+2}{5}$

16. Park rangers catch, tag, and release 200 tule elk back into a wildlife refuge. Two weeks later they observe a sample of 150 elk, of which 5 are tagged. Assuming that the ratio of tagged elk in the sample holds for all elk in the refuge, how many elk are there in the park?

17. The pressure of water on an object below the surface varies directly as its distance below the surface. If a submarine experiences a pressure of 25 pounds per square inch 60 feet below the surface, how much pressure will it experience 330 feet below the surface?

18. The time required to accomplish a task varies inversely as the number of people working on the task. It takes 6 hours for 20 people to put a new roof on a porch. How long would it take 30 people to do the job?

In Exercises 19–21, solve each inequality and graph the solution set on a number line.

19. $6 - 9x \geq 33$

20. $4x - 2 > 2(x + 6)$

21. $-3 \leq 2x + 1 < 6$

22. A student has grades on three examinations of 76, 80, and 72. What must the student earn on a fourth examination in order to have an average of at least 80?

23. Use FOIL to find this product: $(2x - 5)(3x + 4)$.

24. Factor: $2x^2 - 9x + 10$.

25. Solve by factoring: $x^2 + 5x = 36$.

26. Solve using the quadratic formula: $2x^2 + 4x = -1$.

Without changes, the graphs show projections for the amount being paid in Social Security benefits and the amount going into the system. All data are expressed in billions of dollars.

Social Insecurity: Projected Income and Outflow of the Social Security System

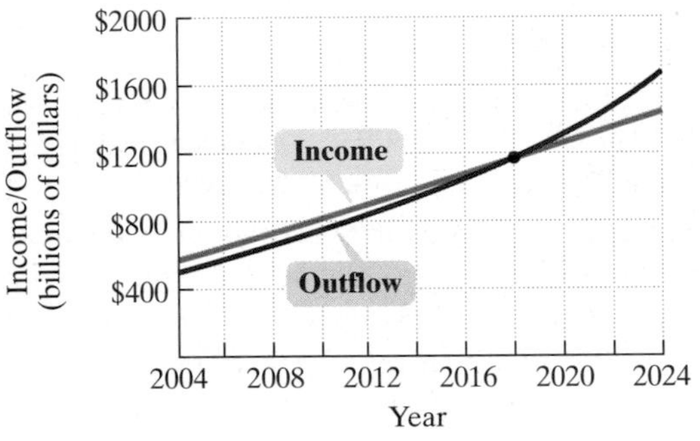

Source: 2004 Social Security Trustees Report

Exercises 27–29 are based on the data shown by the graphs.

27. In 2004, the system's income was \$575 billion, projected to increase at an average rate of \$43 billion per year. In which year will the system's income be \$1177 billion?

28. The data for the system's outflow can be modeled by the formula

$$B = 0.07x^2 + 47.4x + 500,$$

where B represents the amount paid in benefits, in billions of dollars, x years after 2004. According to this model, when will the amount paid in benefits be \$1177 billion? Round to the nearest year.

29. How well do your answers to Exercises 27 and 28 model the data shown by the graphs?

CHAPTER 7

Algebra: Graphs, Functions, and Linear Systems

The most casual cruise on the Internet shows how people disagree when it comes to making predictions about the effects of the world's growing population. Some argue that there is a recent slowdown in the growth rate, economies remain robust, and famines in North Korea and Ethiopia are aberrations rather than signs of the future. Others say that the 6.5 billion people on Earth is twice as many as can be supported in middle-class comfort, and the world is running out of arable land and fresh water. How can we approach this debate mathematically?

Various models for the world's population growth appear in Example 2 of Section 7.6. on page 422.

SECTION 7.1 • GRAPHING AND FUNCTIONS

OBJECTIVES

1. Plot points in the rectangular coordinate system.
2. Graph equations in the rectangular coordinate system.
3. Use $f(x)$ notation.
4. Graph functions.
5. Use the vertical line test.
6. Obtain information about a function from its graph.

The beginning of the seventeenth century was a time of innovative ideas and enormous intellectual progress in Europe. English theatergoers enjoyed a succession of exciting new plays by Shakespeare. William Harvey proposed the radical notion that the heart was a pump for blood rather than the center of emotion. Galileo, with his new-fangled invention called the telescope, supported the theory of Polish astronomer Copernicus that the sun, not the Earth, was the center of the solar system. Monteverdi was writing the world's first grand operas. French mathematicians Pascal and Fermat invented a new field of mathematics called probability theory.

Into this arena of intellectual electricity stepped French aristocrat René Descartes (1596–1650). Descartes (pronounced "day cart"), propelled by the creativity surrounding him, developed a new branch of mathematics that brought together algebra and geometry in a unified way—a way that visualized numbers as points on a graph, equations as geometric figures, and geometric figures as equations. This new branch of mathematics, called *analytic geometry*, established Descartes as one of the founders of modern thought and among the most original mathematicians and philosophers of any age. We begin this section by looking at Descartes's deceptively simple idea, called the **rectangular coordinate system** or (in his honor) the **Cartesian coordinate system**.

1 Plot points in the rectangular coordinate system.

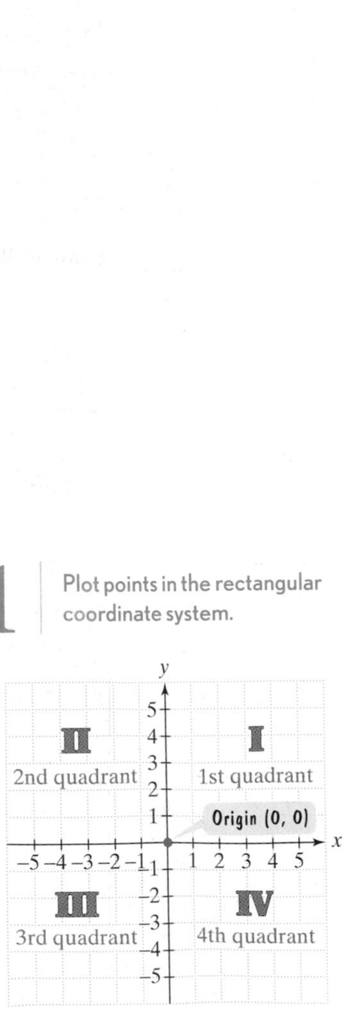

FIGURE 7.1 The rectangular coordinate system

Points and Ordered Pairs

Descartes used two number lines that intersect at right angles at their zero points, as shown in Figure 7.1. The horizontal number line is the ***x*-axis**. The vertical number line is the ***y*-axis**. The point of intersection of these axes is their zero points, called the **origin**. Positive numbers are shown to the right and above the origin. Negative numbers are shown to the left and below the origin. The axes divide the plane into four quarters, called **quadrants**. The points located on the axes are not in any quadrant.

Each point in the rectangular coordinate system corresponds to an **ordered pair** of real numbers, (x, y). Examples of such pairs are $(-5, 3)$ and $(3, -5)$. The first number in each pair, called the ***x*-coordinate**, denotes the distance and direction from the origin along the x-axis. The second number in each pair, called the ***y*-coordinate**, denotes vertical distance and direction along a line parallel to the y-axis or along the y-axis itself.

Figure 7.2 shows how we **plot**, or locate, the points corresponding to the ordered pairs $(-5, 3)$ and $(3, -5)$. We plot $(-5, 3)$ by going 5 units from 0 to the left along the x-axis. Then we go 3 units up parallel to the y-axis. We plot $(3, -5)$ by going 3 units from 0 to the right along the x-axis and 5 units down parallel to the y-axis. The phrase "the points corresponding to the ordered pairs $(-5, 3)$ and $(3, -5)$" is often abbreviated as "the points $(-5, 3)$ and $(3, -5)$."

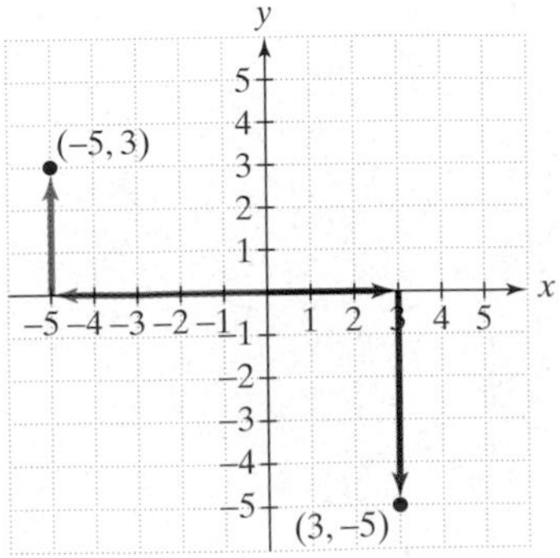

FIGURE 7.2 Plotting $(-5, 3)$ and $(3, -5)$

STUDY TIP

The phrase *ordered pair* is used because order is important. The order in which coordinates appear makes a difference in a point's location. This is illustrated in Figure 7.2.

EXAMPLE 1 PLOTTING POINTS IN THE RECTANGULAR COORDINATE SYSTEM

Plot the points: $A(-3, 5)$, $B(2, -4)$, $C(5, 0)$, $D(-5, -3)$, $E(0, 4)$, and $F(0, 0)$.

SOLUTION See Figure 7.3. We move from the origin and plot the points in the following way:

$A(-3, 5)$: 3 units left, 5 units up

$B(2, -4)$: 2 units right, 4 units down

$C(5, 0)$: 5 units right, 0 units up or down

$D(-5, -3)$: 5 units left, 3 units down

$E(0, 4)$: 0 units right or left, 4 units up

$F(0, 0)$: 0 units right or left, 0 units up or down

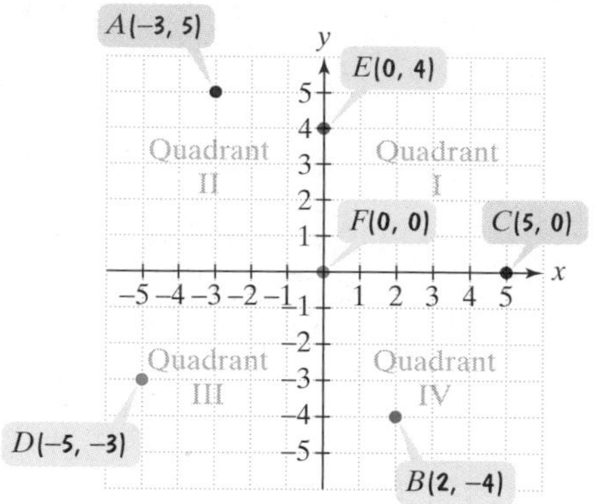

FIGURE 7.3 Plotting points

CHECK POINT 1 Plot the points: $A(-2, 4)$, $B(4, -2)$, $C(-3, 0)$, and $D(0, -3)$.

2 Graph equations in the rectangular coordinate system.

Graphs of Equations

A relationship between two quantities can sometimes be expressed as an **equation in two variables**, such as

$$y = 4 - x^2.$$

A **solution of an equation in two variables**, x and y, is an ordered pair of real numbers with the following property: When the x-coordinate is substituted for x and the y-coordinate is substituted for y in the equation, we obtain a true statement. For example, consider the equation $y = 4 - x^2$ and the ordered pair $(3, -5)$. When 3 is substituted for x and -5 is substituted for y, we obtain the statement $-5 = 4 - 3^2$, or $-5 = 4 - 9$, or $-5 = -5$. Because this statement is true, the ordered pair $(3, -5)$ is a solution of the equation $y = 4 - x^2$. We also say that $(3, -5)$ **satisfies** the equation.

We can generate as many ordered-pair solutions as desired to $y = 4 - x^2$ by substituting numbers for x and then finding the corresponding values for y. For example, suppose we let $x = 3$:

Start with x. Compute y. Form the ordered pair (x, y).

x	$y = 4 - x^2$	Ordered Pair (x, y)
3	$y = 4 - 3^2 = 4 - 9 = -5$	$(3, -5)$

Let $x = 3$. $(3, -5)$ is a solution of $y = 4 - x^2$.

The **graph of an equation in two variables** is the set of all points whose coordinates satisfy the equation. One method for graphing such equations is the **point-plotting method**. First, we find several ordered pairs that are solutions of the equation. Next, we plot these ordered pairs as points in the rectangular coordinate system. Finally, we connect the points with a smooth curve or line. This often gives us a picture of all ordered pairs that satisfy the equation.

EXAMPLE 2 GRAPHING AN EQUATION USING THE POINT-PLOTTING METHOD

Graph $y = 4 - x^2$. Select integers for x, starting with -3 and ending with $3 (-3 \leq x \leq 3)$.

SOLUTION For each value of x, we find the corresponding value for y.

Start with x. Compute y. Form the ordered pair (x, y).

We selected integers from -3 to 3, inclusive, to include three negative numbers, 0, and three positive numbers. We also wanted to keep the resulting computations for y relatively simple.

x	$y = 4 - x^2$	Ordered Pair (x, y)
-3	$y = 4 - (-3)^2 = 4 - 9 = -5$	$(-3, -5)$
-2	$y = 4 - (-2)^2 = 4 - 4 = 0$	$(-2, 0)$
-1	$y = 4 - (-1)^2 = 4 - 1 = 3$	$(-1, 3)$
0	$y = 4 - 0^2 = 4 - 0 = 4$	$(0, 4)$
1	$y = 4 - 1^2 = 4 - 1 = 3$	$(1, 3)$
2	$y = 4 - 2^2 = 4 - 4 = 0$	$(2, 0)$
3	$y = 4 - 3^2 = 4 - 9 = -5$	$(3, -5)$

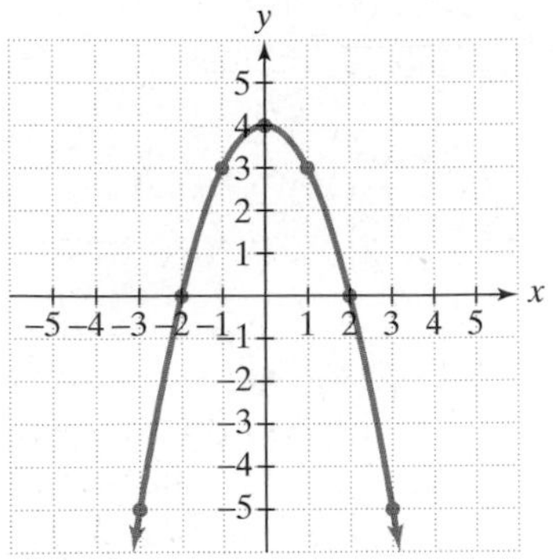

FIGURE 7.4 The graph of $y = 4 - x^2$

Now we plot the seven points and join them with a smooth curve, as shown in Figure 7.4. The graph of $y = 4 - x^2$ is a curve where the part of the graph to the right of the y-axis is a reflection of the part to the left of it and vice versa. The arrows on the left and the right of the curve indicate that it extends indefinitely in both directions.

CHECK POINT 2 Graph $y = x^2 - 1$. Select integers for x, $-3 \leq x \leq 3$.

Part of the beauty of the rectangular coordinate system is that it allows us to "see" formulas and visualize the solution to a problem. This idea is demonstrated in Example 3.

EXAMPLE 3 AN APPLICATION USING GRAPHS OF EQUATIONS

The toll to a bridge costs \$2.50. Commuters who use the bridge frequently have the option of purchasing a monthly coupon book for \$21.00. With the coupon book, the toll is reduced to \$1.00. The monthly cost, y, of using the bridge x times can be described by the following formulas:

Without the coupon book:

$y = 2.5x$ — The monthly cost, y, is \$2.50 times the number of times, x, that the bridge is used.

With the coupon book:

$y = 21 + 1 \cdot x$ — The monthly cost, y, is \$21 for the book plus \$1 times
$y = 21 + x.$ — the number of times, x, that the bridge is used.

a. Let $x = 0, 2, 4, 10, 12, 14,$ and 16. Make a table of values for each equation showing seven solutions for the equation.

b. Graph the equations in the same rectangular coordinate system.

c. What are the coordinates of the intersection point for the two graphs? Interpret the coordinates in practical terms.

SOLUTION

a. Tables of values showing seven solutions for each equation follow.

WITHOUT THE COUPON BOOK

x	$y = 2.5x$	(x, y)
0	$y = 2.5(0) = 0$	$(0, 0)$
2	$y = 2.5(2) = 5$	$(2, 5)$
4	$y = 2.5(4) = 10$	$(4, 10)$
10	$y = 2.5(10) = 25$	$(10, 25)$
12	$y = 2.5(12) = 30$	$(12, 30)$
14	$y = 2.5(14) = 35$	$(14, 35)$
16	$y = 2.5(16) = 40$	$(16, 40)$

WITH THE COUPON BOOK

x	$y = 21 + x$	(x, y)
0	$y = 21 + 0 = 21$	$(0, 21)$
2	$y = 21 + 2 = 23$	$(2, 23)$
4	$y = 21 + 4 = 25$	$(4, 25)$
10	$y = 21 + 10 = 31$	$(10, 31)$
12	$y = 21 + 12 = 33$	$(12, 33)$
14	$y = 21 + 14 = 35$	$(14, 35)$
16	$y = 21 + 16 = 37$	$(16, 37)$

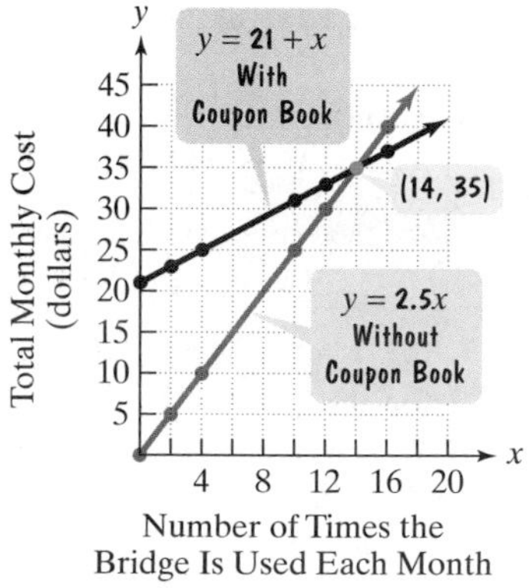

FIGURE 7.5 Options for a toll

b. Now we are ready to graph the two equations. Because the x- and y-coordinates are nonnegative, it is only necessary to use the origin, the positive portions of the x- and y-axes, and the first quadrant of the rectangular coordinate system. The x-coordinates begin at 0 and end at 16. We will let each tick-mark on the x-axis represent two units. However, the y-coordinates begin at 0 and get as large as 40 in the formula that describes the monthly cost without the coupon book. So that our y-axis does not get too long, we will let each tick mark on the y-axis represent five units. Using this setup and the two tables of values, we construct the graphs of $y = 2.5x$ and $y = 21 + x$, shown in Figure 7.5.

c. The graphs intersect at $(14, 35)$. This means that if the bridge is used 14 times in a month, the total monthly cost without the coupon book is the same as the total monthly cost with the coupon book, namely \$35.

In Figure 7.5, look at the two graphs to the right of the intersection point $(14, 35)$. The red graph of $y = 21 + x$ lies below the blue graph of $y = 2.5x$. This means that if the bridge is used more than 14 times in a month ($x > 14$), the (red) monthly cost, y, with the coupon book is less than the (blue) monthly cost, y, without the coupon book.

CHECK POINT 3 The toll to a bridge costs \$2.00. If you use the bridge x times in a month, the monthly cost, y, is $y = 2x$. With a \$10 coupon book, the toll is reduced to \$1.00. The monthly cost, y, of using the bridge x times in a month with the coupon book is $y = 10 + x$.

a. Let $x = 0, 2, 4, 6, 8, 10$, and 12. Make tables of values showing seven solutions of $y = 2x$ and seven solutions of $y = 10 + x$.

b. Graph the equations in the same rectangular coordinate system.

c. What are the coordinates of the intersection point for the two graphs? Interpret the coordinates in practical terms.

3 Use $f(x)$ notation.

Functions

Reconsider one of the equations from Example 3, $y = 2.5x$. Recall that this equation describes the monthly cost, y, of using the bridge x times, with a toll cost of \$2.50 each time the bridge is used. The monthly cost, y, depends on the number of times the bridge is used, x. For each value of x, there is one and only one value of y. If an equation in two variables (x and y) yields precisely one value of y for each value of x, we say that y is a **function** of x.

The notation $y = f(x)$ indicates that the variable y is a function of x. The notation $f(x)$ is read "f of x."

For example, the formula for the cost of the bridge

$$y = 2.5x$$

can be expressed in function notation as

$$f(x) = 2.5x.$$

We read this as "f of x is equal to $2.5x$." If, say, x equals 10 (meaning that the bridge is used 10 times), we can find the corresponding value of y (monthly cost) using the equation $f(x) = 2.5x$.

$$f(x) = 2.5x$$

$$f(10) = 2.5(10) \quad \text{To find } f(10)\text{, read "}f\text{ of 10," replace } x \text{ with 10.}$$

$$= 25$$

Because $f(10) = 25$ (f of 10 equals 25), this means that if the bridge is used 10 times in a month, the total monthly cost is $25.

Table 7.1 compares our previous notation with the new notation of functions.

STUDY TIP

The notation $f(x)$ does not mean "f times x." The notation describes the "output" for the function f when the "input" is x. Think of $f(x)$ as another name for y.

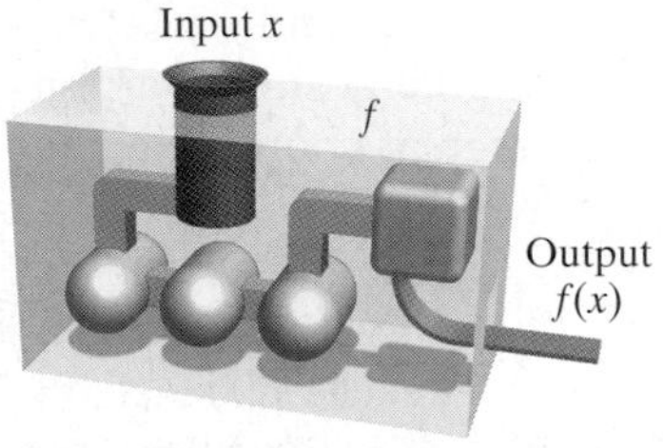

TABLE 7.1 FUNCTION NOTATION

"y Equals" Notation	"$f(x)$ Equals" Notation
$y = 2.5x$	$f(x) = 2.5x$
If $x = 10$, $y = 2.5(10) = 25$.	$f(10) = 2.5(10) = 25$ f of 10 equals 25.

EXAMPLE 4 USING FUNCTION NOTATION

The wage gap is used to compare the status of women's earnings relative to men's. The wage gap is expressed as a percent and is calculated by dividing the median, or middlemost, annual earnings for women by the median annual earnings for men. The line graph in Figure 7.6 shows the wage gap for selected years from 1960 through 2003.

a. Use the graph to estimate, to the nearest percent, women's earnings as a percentage of men's in 2003.

b. The function

$$f(x) = 0.012x^2 - 0.16x + 60$$

models median women's earnings as a percentage of men's earnings, $f(x)$, x years after 1960. Use this function to find women's earnings as a percentage of men's in 2003. Round to the nearest tenth of a percent.

FIGURE 7.6
Source: U.S. Women's Bureau

SOLUTION

a. The data for 2003 is obtained using the point on the far right of the line graph in Figure 7.6. This point extends slightly above the tick mark representing 75 on the vertical axis. Thus, 76 is a reasonable estimate. We conclude that in 2003, women's earnings were approximately 76% of men's.

b. The given function models the wage gap x years after 1960. Because 2003 is 43 years after 1960 ($2003 - 1960 = 43$), we need to find $f(43)$. We can find $f(43)$, f of 43, by replacing each occurrence of x with 43. The arithmetic gets somewhat "messy," so it is probably a good idea to use a calculator.

TECHNOLOGY

On most calculators, here is how to find
$0.012(43)^2 - 0.16(43) + 60$.

MANY SCIENTIFIC CALCULATORS

.012 [×] 43 [x^2] [−]

.16 [×] 43 [+] 60 [=]

MANY GRAPHING CALCULATORS

.012 [×] 43 [∧] 2 [−]

.16 [×] 43 [+] 60 [ENTER]

$f(x) = 0.012x^2 - 0.16x + 60$	This is the given function.
$f(43) = 0.012(43)^2 - 0.16(43) + 60$	Replace each x with 43.
$= 0.012(1849) - 0.16(43) + 60$	Use the order of operations, evaluating the exponential expression.
$= 22.188 - 6.88 + 60$	Perform the multiplications.
$= 75.308$	Subtract and add as indicated.
≈ 75.3	As directed, we've rounded to the nearest tenth.

We see that $f(43) \approx 75.3$—that is, f of 43 is approximately 75.3. The model indicates that 43 years after 1960, in 2003, women's earnings were approximately 75.3% of men's.

In 2003, median annual earnings for U.S. women and men were \$30,724 and \$40,688, respectively. Women's earnings as a percentage of men's were

$$\frac{30{,}724}{40{,}688} \approx 0.755 = 75.5\%.$$

The actual wage gap was 75.5%. The values that we obtained from the function and the graph in Example 4, 75.3% and 76%, respectively, are quite close to this percent.

CHECK POINT 4

a. Use the graph in Figure 7.6 to estimate, to the nearest percent, women's earnings as a percentage of men's in 2000.

b. Use the function in Example 4(b) to find women's earnings as a percentage of men's in 2000.

4 Graph functions.

Graphing Functions

The **graph of a function** is the graph of its ordered pairs. In our next example, we will graph two functions. It would be awkward to call both of them f. We will call one function f and the other g. These are the letters most frequently used to name functions.

EXAMPLE 5 GRAPHING FUNCTIONS

Graph the functions $f(x) = 2x$ and $g(x) = 2x + 4$ in the same rectangular coordinate system. Select integers for x, $-2 \le x \le 2$.

SOLUTION For each function, we use the suggested values for x to create a table of some of the coordinates. These tables are shown below. Now, we plot the five points in each table and connect them, as shown in Figure 7.7. The graph of each function is a straight line. Do you see a relationship between the two graphs? The graph of g is the graph of f shifted vertically up 4 units.

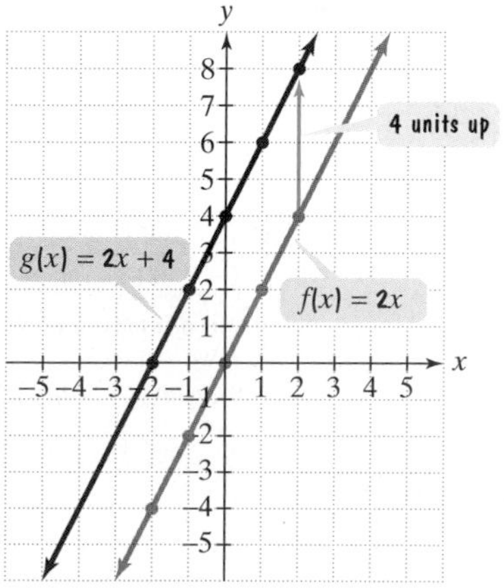

FIGURE 7.7

x	$f(x) = 2x$	(x, y) or $(x, f(x))$
−2	$f(-2) = 2(-2) = -4$	$(-2, -4)$
−1	$f(-1) = 2(-1) = -2$	$(-1, -2)$
0	$f(0) = 2 \cdot 0 = 0$	$(0, 0)$
1	$f(1) = 2 \cdot 1 = 2$	$(1, 2)$
2	$f(2) = 2 \cdot 2 = 4$	$(2, 4)$

Choose x. Compute $f(x)$ by evaluating f at x. Form the ordered pair.

x	$g(x) = 2x + 4$	(x, y) or $(x, g(x))$
−2	$g(-2) = 2(-2) + 4 = 0$	$(-2, 0)$
−1	$g(-1) = 2(-1) + 4 = 2$	$(-1, 2)$
0	$g(0) = 2 \cdot 0 + 4 = 4$	$(0, 4)$
1	$g(1) = 2 \cdot 1 + 4 = 6$	$(1, 6)$
2	$g(2) = 2 \cdot 2 + 4 = 8$	$(2, 8)$

Choose x. Compute $g(x)$ by evaluating g at x. Form the ordered pair.

CHECK POINT 5

Graph the functions $f(x) = 2x$ and $g(x) = 2x - 3$ in the same rectangular coordinate system. Select integers for x, $-2 \le x \le 2$. How is the graph of g related to the graph of f?

5 Use the vertical line test.

TECHNOLOGY

A graphing calculator is a powerful tool that quickly generates the graph of an equation in two variables. Here is the graph of $y = 4 - x^2$ that we drew by hand in Figure 7.4 on page 370.

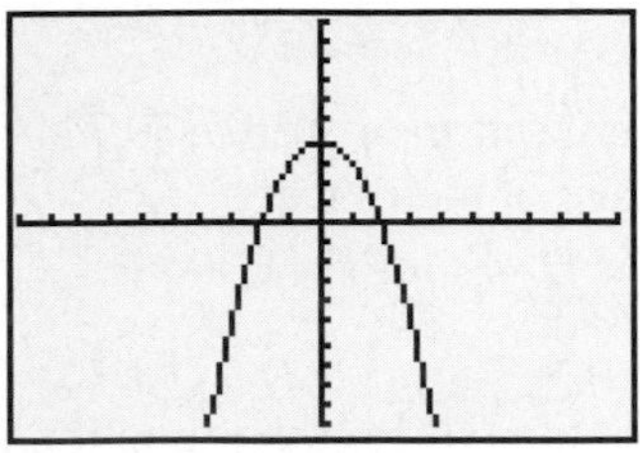

What differences do you notice between this graph and the graph we drew by hand? This graph seems a bit "jittery." Arrows do not appear on the left and right ends of the graph. Furthermore, numbers are not given along the axes. For the graph shown above, the x-axis extends from -10 to 10 and the y-axis also extends from -10 to 10. The distance represented by each consecutive tick mark is one unit. We say that the **viewing window** is $[-10, 10, 1]$ by $[-10, 10, 1]$.

To graph an equation in x and y using a graphing calculator, enter the equation and specify the size of the viewing window. The size of the viewing window sets minimum and maximum values for both the x- and y-axes. Enter these values, as well as the values between consecutive tick marks, on the respective axes. The $[-10, 10, 1]$ by $[-10, 10, 1]$ viewing rectangle used above is called the **standard viewing window**.

The Vertical Line Test

Not every graph in the rectangular coordinate system is the graph of a function. The definition of a function specifies that no value of x can be paired with two or more different values of y. Consequently, if a graph contains two or more different points with the same first coordinate, the graph cannot represent a function. This is illustrated in Figure 7.8. Observe that points sharing a common first coordinate are vertically above or below each other.

This observation is the basis of a useful test for determining whether a graph defines y as a function of x. The test is called the **vertical line test**.

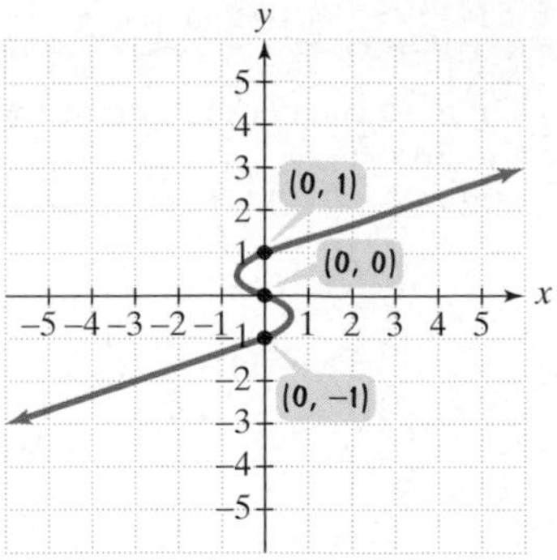

FIGURE 7.8 y is not a function of x because 0 is paired with three values of y, namely, 1, 0, and -1.

> **THE VERTICAL LINE TEST FOR FUNCTIONS**
> If any vertical line intersects a graph in more than one point, the graph does not define y as a function of x.

EXAMPLE 6 USING THE VERTICAL LINE TEST

Use the vertical line test to identify graphs in which y is a function of x.

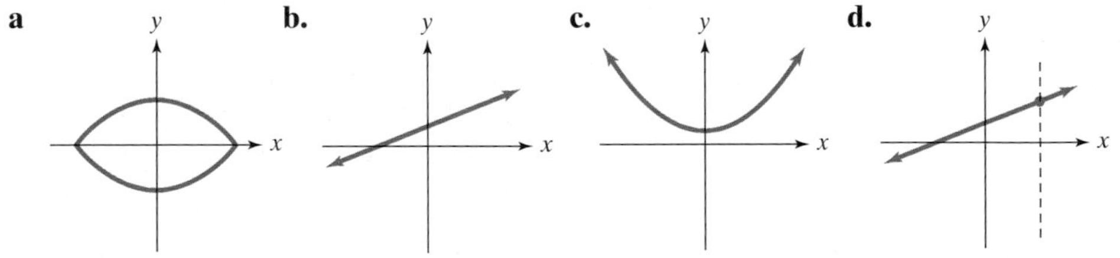

SOLUTION y is a function of x for the graphs in (b) and (c).

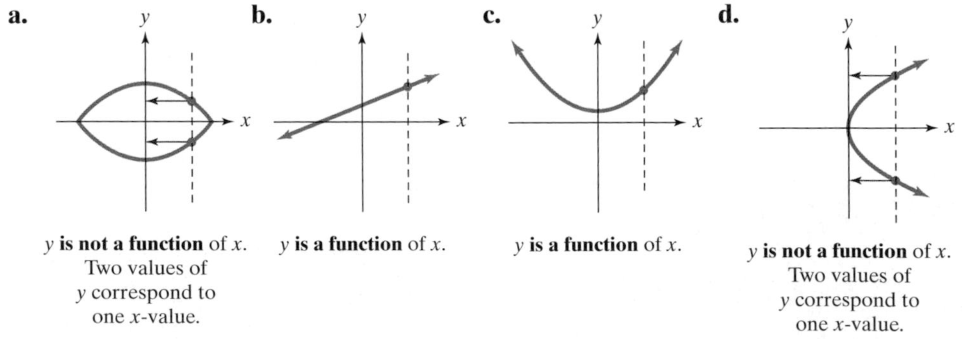

CHECK POINT 6 Use the vertical line test to identify graphs in which y is a function of x.

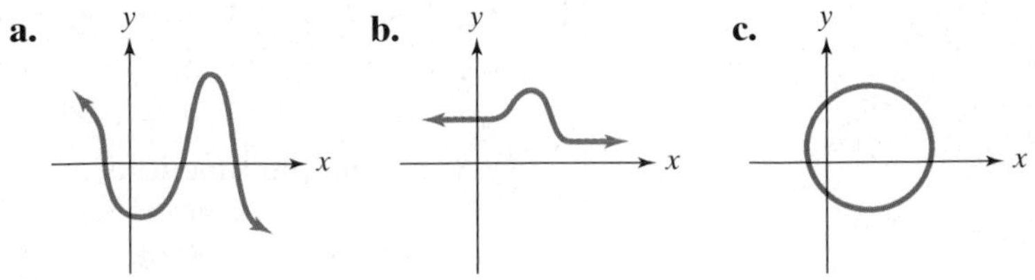

6 Obtain information about a function from its graph.

Obtaining Information from Graphs

Example 7 illustrates how to obtain information about a function from its graph.

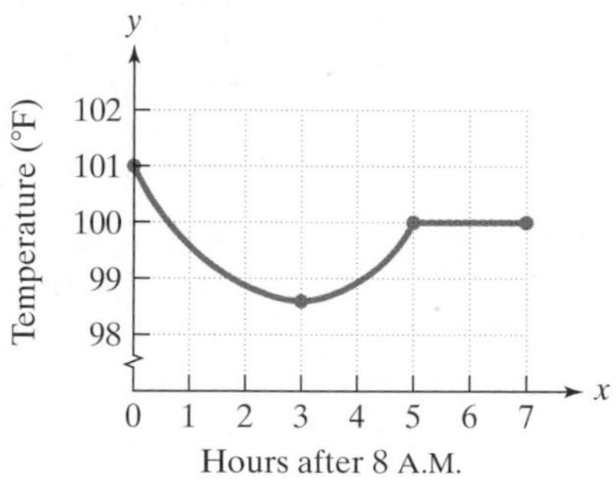

FIGURE 7.9 Body temperature from 8 A.M. through 3 P.M.

EXAMPLE 7 ANALYZING THE GRAPH OF A FUNCTION

Too late for that flu shot now! It's only 8 A.M. and you're feeling lousy. Fascinated by the way that algebra models the world (your author is projecting a bit here), you construct a graph showing your body temperature from 8 A.M. through 3 P.M. You decide to let x represent the number of hours after 8 A.M. and y represent your body temperature at time x. The graph is shown in Figure 7.9. The symbol ⇞ on the y-axis shows that there is a break in values between 0 and 98. Thus, the first tick mark on the y-axis represents a temperature of 98°F.

a. What is your temperature at 8 A.M.?

b. During which period of time is your temperature decreasing?

c. Estimate your minimum temperature during the time period shown. How many hours after 8 A.M. does this occur? At what time does this occur?

d. During which period of time is your temperature increasing?

e. Part of the graph is shown as a horizontal line segment. What does this mean about your temperature and when does this occur?

f. Explain why the graph defines y as a function of x.

SOLUTION

a. Because x is the number of hours after 8 A.M., your temperature at 8 A.M. corresponds to $x = 0$. Locate 0 on the horizontal axis and look at the point on the graph above 0. The first figure on the right shows that your temperature at 8 A.M. is 101°F.

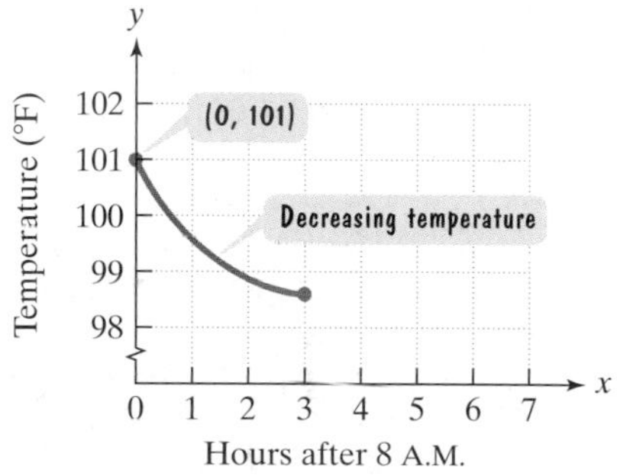

b. Your temperature is decreasing when the graph falls from left to right. This occurs between $x = 0$ and $x = 3$, also shown in the first figure on the right. Because x represents the number of hours after 8 A.M., your temperature is decreasing between 8 A.M. and 11 A.M.

c. Your minimum temperature can be found by locating the lowest point on the graph. This point lies above 3 on the horizontal axis, shown in the second figure on the right. The y-coordinate of this point falls more than midway between 98 and 99, at approximately 98.6. The lowest point on the graph, (3, 98.6), shows that your minimum temperature, 98.6°F, occurs 3 hours after 8 A.M., at 11 A.M.

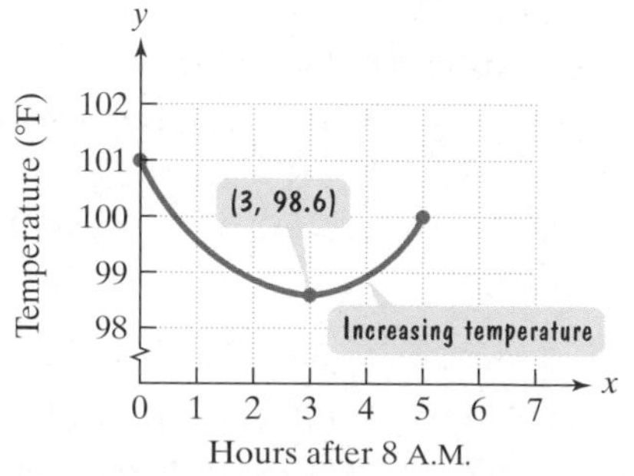

d. Your temperature is increasing when the graph rises from left to right. This occurs between $x = 3$ and $x = 5$, shown in the second figure. Because x represents the number of hours after 8 A.M., your temperature is increasing between 11 A.M. and 1 P.M.

e. The horizontal line segment shown in the figure on the right indicates that your temperature is neither increasing nor decreasing. Your temperature remains the same, 100°F, between $x = 5$ and $x = 7$. Thus, your temperature is at a constant 100°F between 1 P.M. and 3 P.M.

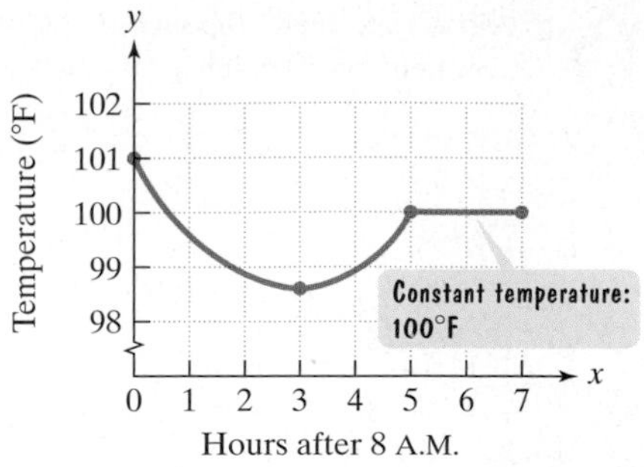

f. The complete graph of your body temperature from 8 A.M. through 3 P.M. is shown above in part (e). No vertical line can be drawn that intersects this blue graph more than once. By the vertical line test, the graph defines y as a function of x. In practical terms, this means that your body temperature is a function of time. Each hour (or fraction of an hour) after 8 A.M., represented by x, yields precisely one body temperature, represented by y.

CHECK POINT 7 When a person receives a drug injected into a muscle, the concentration of the drug in the body, measured in milligrams per 100 milliliters, depends on the time elapsed after the injection, measured in hours. The figure shows the graph of drug concentration over time, where x represents hours after the injection and y represents the drug concentration at time x.

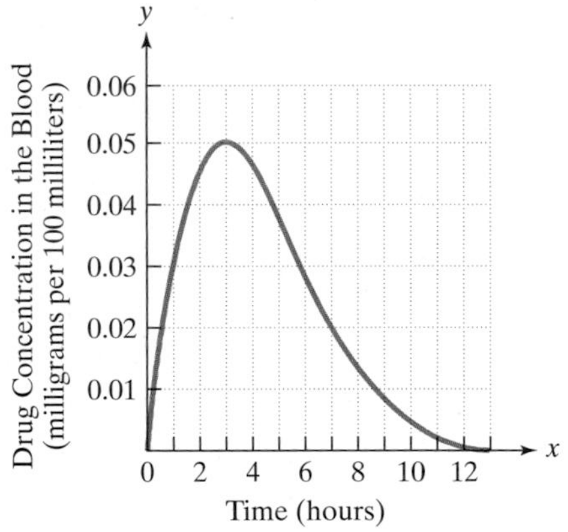

a. During which period of time is the drug concentration increasing?

b. During which period of time is the drug concentration decreasing?

c. What is the drug's maximum concentration and when does this occur?

d. What happens by the end of 13 hours?

e. Explain why the graph defines y as a function of x.

EXERCISE SET 7.1

• Practice Exercises

In Exercises 1–20, plot the given point in a rectangular coordinate system.

1. $(1, 4)$ **2.** $(2, 5)$

3. $(-2, 3)$ **4.** $(-1, 4)$

5. $(-3, -5)$ **6.** $(-4, -2)$

7. $(4, -1)$ **8.** $(3, -2)$

9. $(-4, 0)$ **10.** $(-5, 0)$

11. $(0, -3)$ **12.** $(0, -4)$

13. $(0, 0)$ **14.** $\left(-3, -1\frac{1}{2}\right)$

15. $\left(-2, -3\frac{1}{2}\right)$ **16.** $(-5, -2.5)$

17. $(3.5, 4.5)$ **18.** $(2.5, 3.5)$

19. $(1.25, -3.25)$ **20.** $(2.25, -4.25)$

Graph each equation in Exercises 21–32. Select integers for x, $-3 \le x \le 3$.

21. $y = x^2 - 2$ **22.** $y = x^2 + 2$

23. $y = x - 2$ **24.** $y = x + 2$

25. $y = 2x + 1$ **26.** $y = 2x - 4$

27. $y = -\frac{1}{2}x$ **28.** $y = -\frac{1}{2}x + 2$

29. $y = x^3$ **30.** $y = x^3 - 1$

31. $y = |x| + 1$ **32.** $y = |x| - 1$

In Exercises 33–42, find f of each given value of x.

33. $f(x) = x - 4$ **a.** $f(8)$ **b.** $f(1)$

34. $f(x) = x - 6$ **a.** $f(9)$ **b.** $f(2)$

35. $f(x) = 3x - 2$ **a.** $f(7)$ **b.** $f(0)$

36. $f(x) = 4x - 3$ **a.** $f(7)$ **b.** $f(0)$

37. $f(x) = x^2 + 1$ **a.** $f(2)$ **b.** $f(-2)$

38. $f(x) = x^2 + 4$ **a.** $f(3)$ **b.** $f(-3)$

39. $f(x) = 3x^2 + 5$ **a.** $f(4)$ **b.** $f(-1)$

40. $f(x) = 2x^2 - 4$ **a.** $f(5)$ **b.** $f(-1)$

41. $f(x) = 2x^2 + 3x - 1$ **a.** $f(3)$ **b.** $f(-4)$

42. $f(x) = 3x^2 + 4x - 2$ **a.** $f(2)$ **b.** $f(-1)$

In Exercises 43–50, evaluate $f(x)$ for the given values of x. Then use the ordered pairs $(x, f(x))$ from your table to graph the function.

43. $f(x) = x^2 - 1$

x	$f(x) = x^2 - 1$
−2	
−1	
0	
1	
2	

44. $f(x) = x^2 + 1$

x	$f(x) = x^2 + 1$
−2	
−1	
0	
1	
2	

45. $f(x) = x - 1$

x	$f(x) = x - 1$
−2	
−1	
0	
1	
2	

46. $f(x) = x + 1$

x	$f(x) = x + 1$
−2	
−1	
0	
1	
2	

47. $f(x) = (x - 2)^2$

x	$f(x) = (x - 2)^2$
0	
1	
2	
3	
4	

48. $f(x) = (x + 1)^2$

x	$f(x) = (x + 1)^2$
−3	
−2	
−1	
0	
1	

49. $f(x) = x^3 + 1$

x	$f(x) = x^3 + 1$
−3	
−2	
−1	
0	
1	

50. $f(x) = (x + 1)^3$

x	$f(x) = (x + 1)^3$
−3	
−2	
−1	
0	
1	

For Exercises 51–58, use the vertical line test to identify graphs in which y is a function of x.

51.

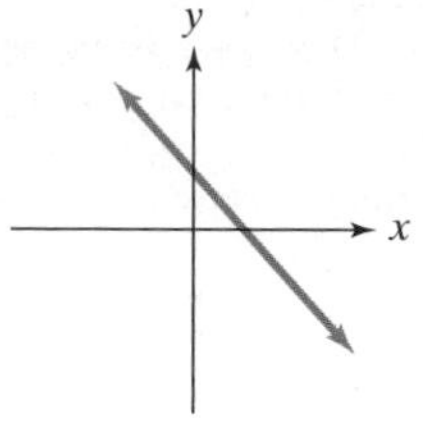

52.

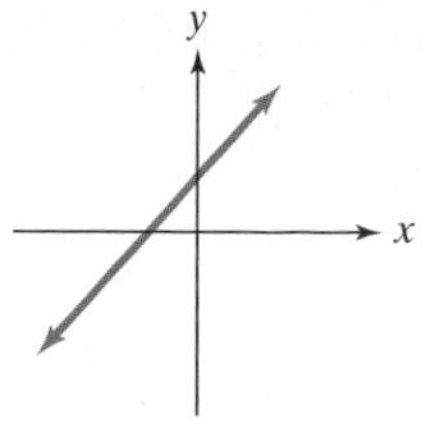

53.

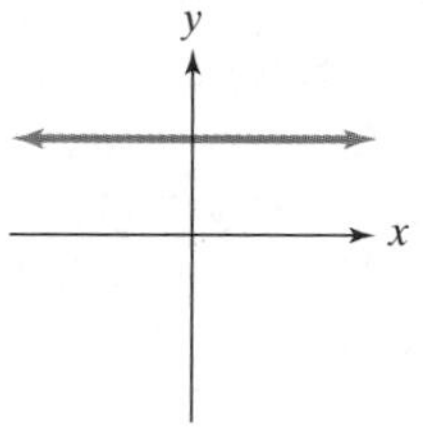

54.

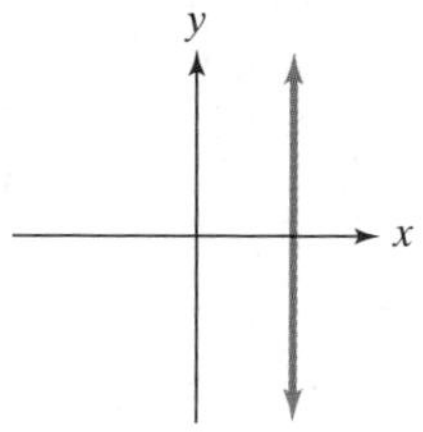

55.

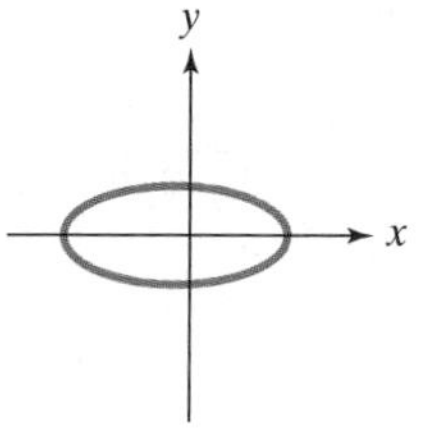

56.

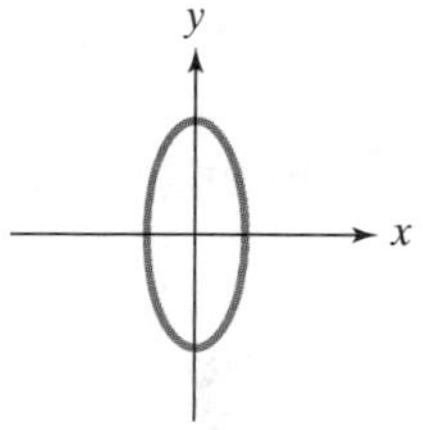

57.

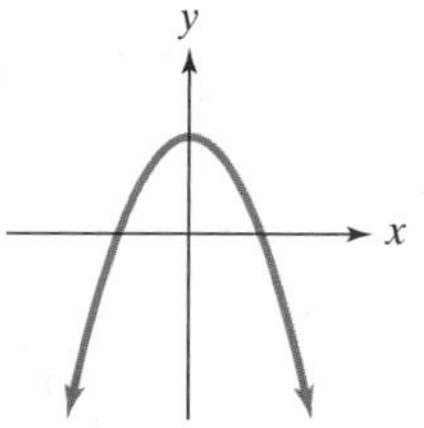

58.

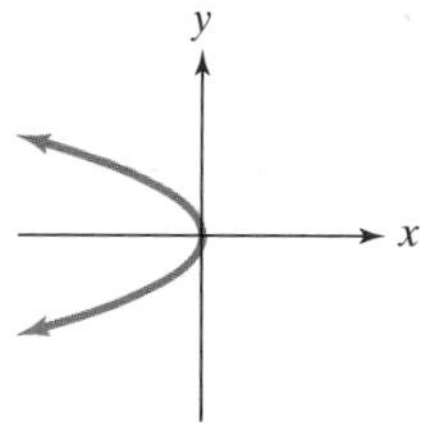

• Practice Plus

In Exercises 59–60, let $f(x) = x^2 - x + 4$ and $g(x) = 3x - 5$.

59. Find $g(1)$ and $f(g(1))$.

60. Find $g(-1)$ and $f(g(-1))$.

In Exercises 61–62, let f and g be defined by the following table:

x	$f(x)$	$g(x)$
−2	6	0
−1	3	4
0	−1	1
1	−4	−3
2	0	−6

61. Find $\sqrt{f(-1) - f(0)} - [g(2)]^2 + f(-2) \div g(2) \cdot g(-1)$.

62. Find $|f(1) - f(0)| - [g(1)]^2 + g(1) \div f(-1) \cdot g(2)$.

In Exercises 63–66, write each English sentence as an equation in two variables. Then graph the equation.

63. The y-value is four more than twice the x-value.

64. The y-value is the difference between four and twice the x-value.

65. The y-value is three decreased by the square of the x-value.

66. The y-value is two more than the square of the x-value.

• Application Exercises

Afghanistan accounts for 76% of the world's illegal opium production. Opium-poppy cultivation nets big money in a country where most people earn less than $1 per day. (Source: Newsweek) The line graph shows opium-poppy cultivation, in thousands of acres, in Afghanistan from 1990 through 2004. Use the graph to solve Exercises 67–74.

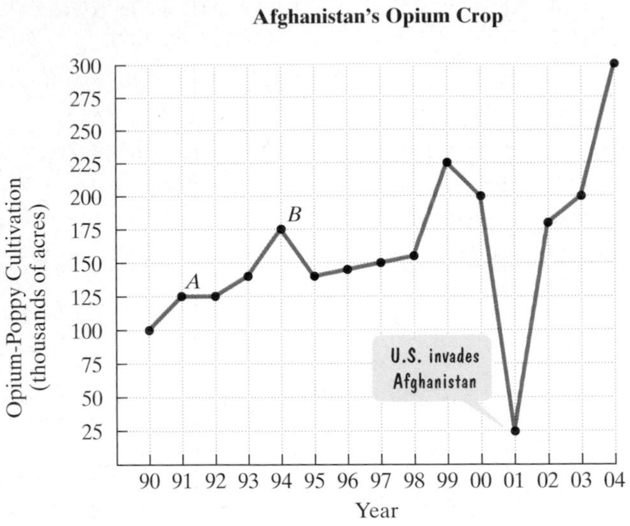

Source: U.N. Office on Drugs and Crime

67. What are the coordinates of point A? What does this mean in terms of the information given by the graph?

68. What are the coordinates of point B? What does this mean in terms of the information given by the graph?

69. In which year(s) were 200 thousand acres used for opium-poppy cultivation?

70. In which year were 150 thousand acres used for opium-poppy cultivation?

71. For the period shown, when did opium cultivation reach a minimum? How many thousands of acres were used to cultivate the illegal crop that year?

72. For the period shown, when did opium cultivation reach a maximum? How many thousands of acres were used to cultivate the illegal crop that year?

73. Between which two years did opium cultivation not change?

74. Between which two years did opium cultivation increase at the greatest rate? What is a reasonable estimate of the increase, in thousands of acres, used to cultivate the illegal crop during this period?

The male minority? The bar graph shows the number of bachelor's degrees, in thousands, awarded to men and women in the United States for selected years, with projections for 2010. The trend indicated by the graphs is among the hottest topics of debate among college-admissions officers. Some private liberal arts colleges have quietly begun special efforts to recruit men—including admissions preferences for them.

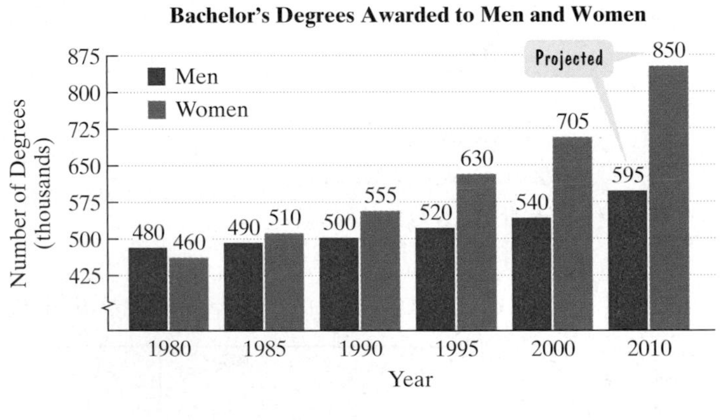

Source: Department of Education

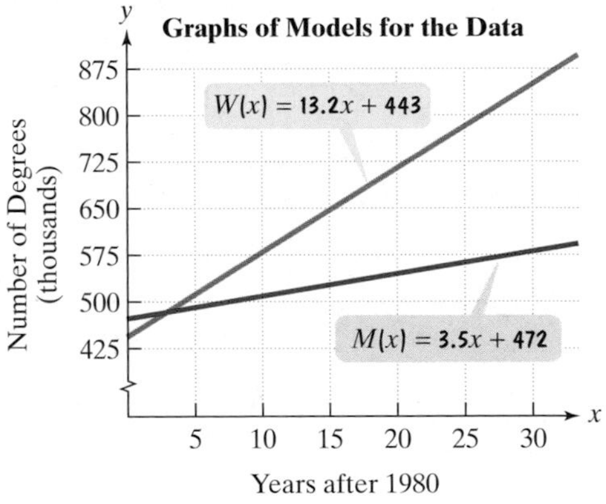

The function

$$M(x) = 3.5x + 472$$

models the number of bachelor's degrees, in thousands, awarded to men x years after 1980. The function

$$W(x) = 13.2x + 443$$

models the number of bachelor's degrees, in thousands, awarded to women x years after 1980. The graphs of functions M and W are shown to the right of the actual data. Use this information to solve Exercises 75–78.

75. a. Find and interpret $W(20)$. Identify this information as a point on the graph of the function for women.

b. How well does $W(20)$ model the actual data shown by the bar graph?

76. a. Find and interpret $M(20)$. Identify this information as a point on the graph of the function for men.

b. How well does $M(20)$ model the actual data shown by the bar graph?

77. a. Use the two functions to find and interpret $W(10) - M(10)$. Identify this information as an appropriate distance between the graphs of the functions for women and men.

b. How well does $W(10) - M(10)$ model the actual data shown by the bar graph?

78. a. Use the two functions to find and interpret $W(5) - M(5)$. Identify this information as an appropriate distance between the graphs of the functions for women and men.

b. How well does $W(5) - M(5)$ model the actual data shown by the bar graph?

The function

$$f(x) = 339x^3 - 2085x^2 + 2814x + 8123$$

models the number of hate-crime incidents reported by law enforcement agencies in the United States, $f(x)$, x years after 2000. The graph of f is shown in the figure. Use this information to solve Exercises 79–82.

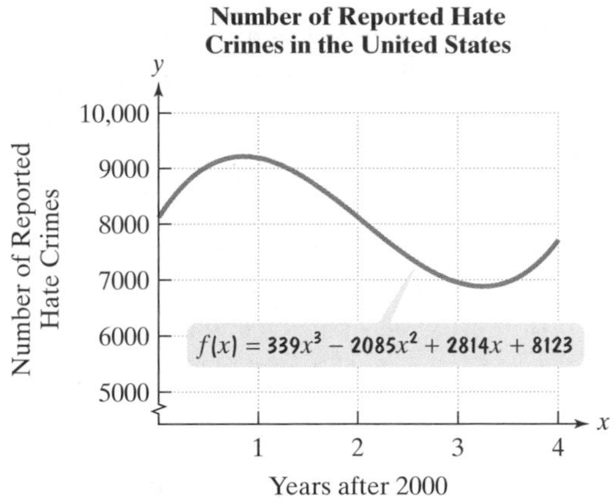

Source: Department of Justice

79. **a.** For the period shown, in which year did the number of hate crimes reach a maximum? Use the graph to find a reasonable estimate of the number of hate crimes for that year.

b. Use the function to find the number of hate crimes for the year in part (a).

80. **a.** For the period shown, in which year did the number of hate crimes reach a minimum? Use the graph to find a reasonable estimate of the number of hate crimes for that year.

b. Use the function to find the number of hate crimes for the year in part (a).

81. Use the function to find $f(2)$. Identify this information on the graph of f.

82. Use the function to find $f(4)$. Identify this information on the graph of f.

• Writing in Mathematics

83. What is the rectangular coordinate system?

84. Explain how to plot a point in the rectangular coordinate system. Give an example with your explanation.

85. Explain why $(5, -2)$ and $(-2, 5)$ do not represent the same ordered pair.

86. Explain how to graph an equation in the rectangular coordinate system.

87. What is a function?

88. Explain how the vertical line test is used to determine whether a graph represents a function.

• Critical Thinking Exercises

In Exercises 89–92, use the graphs of f and g to find each number.

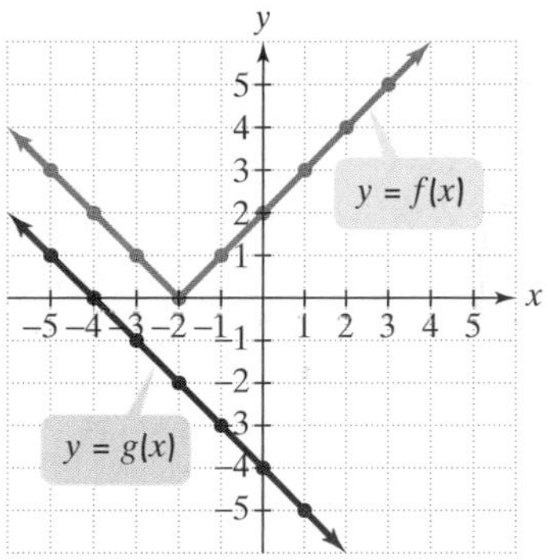

89. $f(-1) + g(-1)$

90. $f(1) + g(1)$

91. $f(g(-1))$

92. $f(g(1))$

• Technology Exercise

93. Use a graphing calculator to verify the graphs that you drew by hand in Exercises 43–50.

SECTION 7.2 • LINEAR FUNCTIONS AND THEIR GRAPHS

OBJECTIVES

1. Use intercepts to graph a linear equation.
2. Calculate slope.
3. Use the slope and y-intercept to graph a line.
4. Graph horizontal or vertical lines.
5. Interpret slope as rate of change.
6. Use slope and y-intercept to model data.

A best guess at the look of our nation in the next decades indicates that the number of men and women living alone will increase each year. Figure 7.10 shows that in 2003, approximately 12.5 million men and 16.9 million women lived alone, an increase over the numbers displayed for 1990.

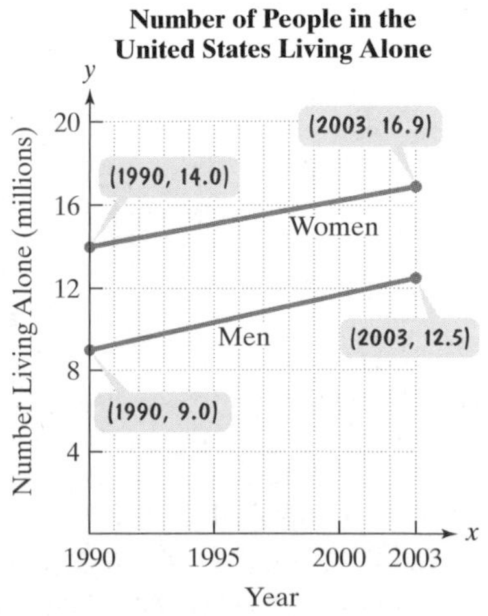

FIGURE 7.10
Source: U.S. Census Bureau

The data for the men can be modeled by

$$y = 0.27x + 9,$$

where y represents the number of men living alone, in millions, x years after 1990. Using function notation, we can rewrite the equation as

$$f(x) = 0.27x + 9.$$

A function such as this, whose graph is a straight line, is called a **linear function**. In this section, we will study linear functions and their graphs.

1 Use intercepts to graph a linear equation.

Graphing Using Intercepts

There is another way that we can write the equation

$$y = 0.27x + 9.$$

We will collect the x- and y-terms on the left side. This is done by subtracting $0.27x$ from both sides:

$$-0.27x + y = 9.$$

All equations of the form $Ax + By = C$ are straight lines when graphed, as long as A and B are not both zero. Such equations are called **linear equations in two variables**. We can quickly obtain the graph for equations in this form by finding the points where the graph crosses the x-axis and the y-axis. The x-coordinate of the point where the graph crosses the x-axis is called the ***x*-intercept**. The y-coordinate of the point where the graph crosses the y-axis is called the ***y*-intercept**.

LOCATING INTERCEPTS

To locate the x-intercept, set $y = 0$ and solve the equation for x.

To locate the y-intercept, set $x = 0$ and solve the equation for y.

An equation of the form $Ax + By = C$ can be graphed by finding the x- and y-intercepts, plotting the intercepts, and drawing a straight line through these points. When graphing using intercepts, it is a good idea to use a third point, a checkpoint, before drawing the line. A checkpoint can be obtained by selecting a value for x, other than 0, and finding the corresponding value for y. The checkpoint should lie on the same line as the x- and y-intercepts. If it does not, recheck your work and find the error.

EXAMPLE 1 USING INTERCEPTS TO GRAPH A LINEAR EQUATION

Graph: $3x + 2y = 6$.

SOLUTION

Find the *x*-intercept by letting $y = 0$ and solving for x.	Find the *y*-intercept by letting $x = 0$ and solving for y.
$3x + 2y = 6$	$3x + 2y = 6$
$3x + 2 \cdot 0 = 6$	$3 \cdot 0 + 2y = 6$
$3x = 6$	$2y = 6$
$x = 2$	$y = 3$

The x-intercept is 2, so the line passes through the point $(2, 0)$. The y-intercept is 3, so the line passes through the point $(0, 3)$.

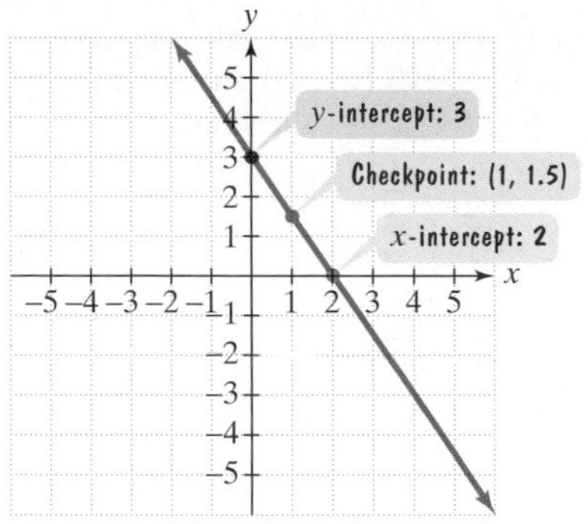

FIGURE 7.11 The graph of $3x + 2y = 6$

For our checkpoint, we will let $x = 1$ and find the corresponding value for y.

$3x + 2y = 6$	This is the given equation.
$3 \cdot 1 + 2y = 6$	Substitute 1 for x.
$3 + 2y = 6$	Simplify.
$2y = 3$	Subtract 3 from both sides.
$y = \frac{3}{2}$	Divide both sides by 2.

The checkpoint is the ordered pair $\left(1, \frac{3}{2}\right)$, or $(1, 1.5)$.

The three points in Figure 7.11 lie along the same line. Drawing a line through the three points results in the graph of $3x + 2y = 6$.

CHECK POINT 1 Graph: $2x + 3y = 6$.

2 Calculate slope.

Slope

Mathematicians have developed a useful measure of the steepness of a line, called the *slope* of the line. Slope compares the vertical change (the **rise**) to the horizontal change (the **run**) when moving from one fixed point to another along the line. To calculate the slope of a line, we use a ratio that compares the change in y (the rise) to the change in x (the run).

DEFINITION OF SLOPE

The **slope** of the line through the distinct points (x_1, y_1) and (x_2, y_2) is

$$\frac{\text{Change in } y}{\text{Change in } x} = \frac{\text{Rise}}{\text{Run}} = \frac{y_2 - y_1}{x_2 - x_1},$$

where $x_2 - x_1 \neq 0$.

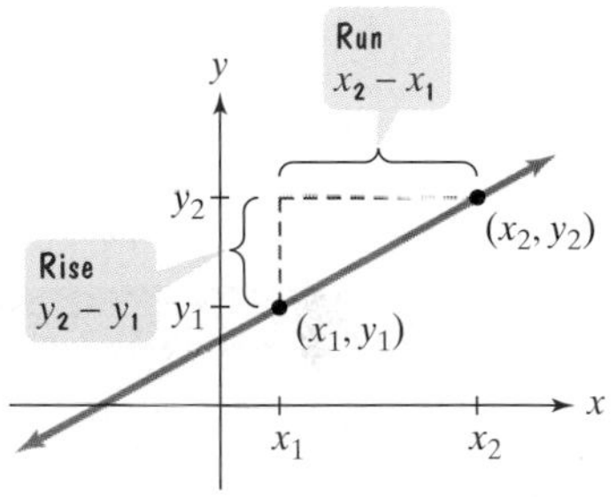

It is common notation to let the letter m represent the slope of a line. The letter m is used because it is the first letter of the French verb *monter*, meaning to rise, or to ascend.

EXAMPLE 2 USING THE DEFINITION OF SLOPE

Find the slope of the line passing through each pair of points:

a. $(-3, -1)$ and $(-2, 4)$ **b.** $(-3, 4)$ and $(2, -2)$.

SOLUTION

a. Let $(x_1, y_1) = (-3, -1)$ and $(x_2, y_2) = (-2, 4)$. We obtain the slope as follows:

$$m = \frac{\text{Change in } y}{\text{Change in } x} = \frac{y_2 - y_1}{x_2 - x_1} = \frac{4 - (-1)}{-2 - (-3)} = \frac{5}{1} = 5.$$

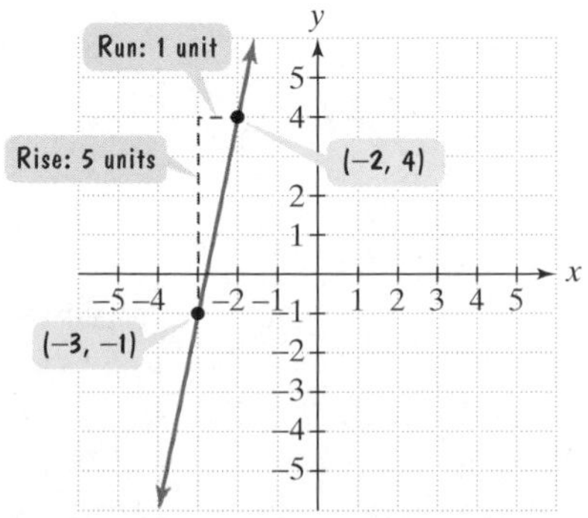

FIGURE 7.12 Visualizing a slope of 5

The situation is illustrated in Figure 7.12. The slope of the line is 5, indicating that there is a vertical change, a rise, of 5 units for each horizontal change, a run, of 1 unit. The slope is positive and the line rises from left to right.

STUDY TIP

When computing slope, it makes no difference which point you call (x_1, y_1) and which point you call (x_2, y_2). If we let $(x_1, y_1) = (-2, 4)$ and $(x_2, y_2) = (-3, -1)$, the slope is still 5:

$$m = \frac{\text{Change in } y}{\text{Change in } x} = \frac{y_2 - y_1}{x_2 - x_1} = \frac{-1 - 4}{-3 - (-2)} = \frac{-5}{-1} = 5.$$

However, you should not subtract in one order in the numerator $(y_2 - y_1)$ and then in a different order in the denominator $(x_1 - x_2)$. The slope is *not* -5:

$$\frac{-1 - 4}{-2 - (-3)} = \frac{-5}{1} = -5. \quad \text{Incorrect}$$

b. We can let $(x_1, y_1) = (-3, 4)$ and $(x_2, y_2) = (2, -2)$. The slope of the line shown in Figure 7.13 is computed as follows:

$$m = \frac{\text{Change in } y}{\text{Change in } x} = \frac{y_2 - y_1}{x_2 - x_1} = \frac{-2 - 4}{2 - (-3)} = \frac{-6}{5} = -\frac{6}{5}.$$

The slope of the line is $-\frac{6}{5}$. For every vertical change of -6 units (6 units down), there is a corresponding horizontal change of 5 units. The slope is negative and the line falls from left to right.

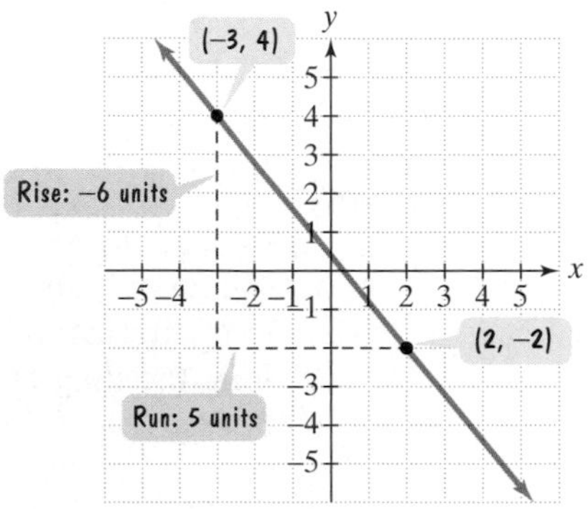

FIGURE 7.13 Visualizing a slope of $-\frac{6}{5}$

CHECK POINT 2 Find the slope of the line passing through each pair of points:

a. $(-3, 4)$ and $(-4, -2)$

b. $(4, -2)$ and $(-1, 5)$.

Example 2 illustrates that a line with a positive slope is rising from left to right and a line with a negative slope is falling from left to right. By contrast, a horizontal line neither rises nor falls and has a slope of zero. A vertical line has no horizontal change, so $x_2 - x_1 = 0$ in the formula for slope. Because we cannot divide by zero, the slope of a vertical line is undefined. This discussion is summarized in Table 7.2.

TABLE 7.2 POSSIBILITIES FOR A LINE'S SLOPE

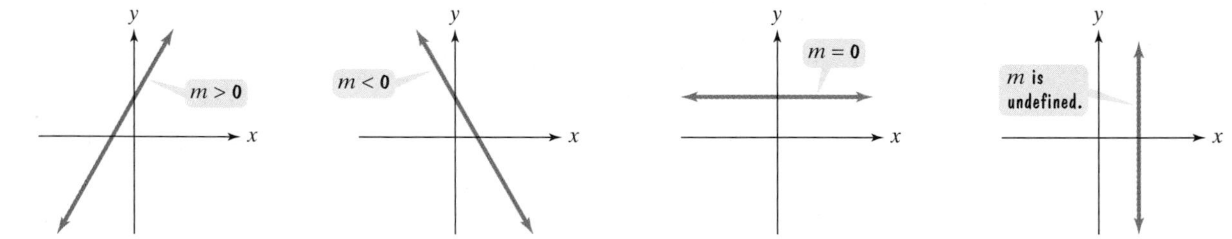

Line rises from left to right.	Line falls from left to right.	Line is horizontal.	Line is vertical.

3 Use the slope and y-intercept to graph a line.

The Slope-Intercept Form of the Equation of a Line

We can use the definition of slope to write the equation of any nonvertical line with slope m and y-intercept b. Because the y-intercept is b, the point $(0, b)$ lies on the line. Now, let (x, y) represent any other point on the line, shown in Figure 7.14. Keep in mind that the point (x, y) is arbitrary and is not in one fixed position. By contrast, the point $(0, b)$ is fixed.

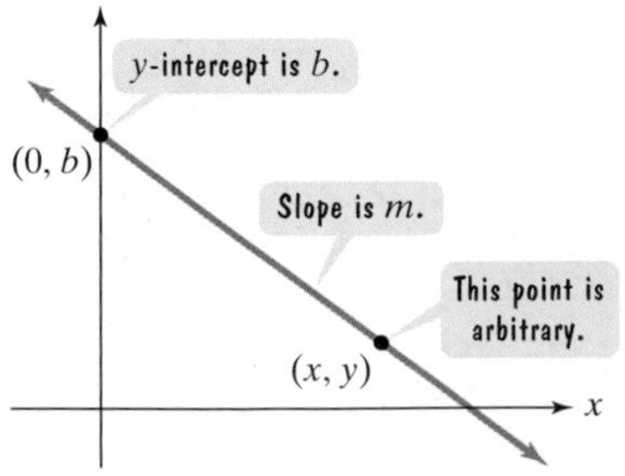

FIGURE 7.14 A line with slope m and y-intercept b

Regardless of where the point (x, y) is located, the steepness of the line in Figure 7.14

remains the same. Thus, the ratio for slope stays a constant m. This means that for all points along the line

$$m = \frac{\text{Change in } y}{\text{Change in } x} = \frac{y - b}{x - 0} = \frac{y - b}{x}.$$

We can clear the fraction by multiplying both sides by x, the least common denominator.

$m = \frac{y - b}{x}$	This is the slope of the line in Figure 7.14.
$mx = \frac{y - b}{x} \cdot x$	Multiply both sides by x.
$mx = y - b$	Simplify: $\frac{y - b}{\cancel{x}} \cdot \cancel{x} = y - b$.
$mx + b = y - b + b$	Add b to both sides and solve for y.
$mx + b = y$	Simplify.

Now, if we reverse the two sides, we obtain the *slope-intercept form* of the equation of a line.

SLOPE-INTERCEPT FORM OF THE EQUATION OF A LINE

The **slope-intercept form of the equation** of a nonvertical line with slope m and y-intercept b is

$$y = mx + b.$$

The slope-intercept form of a line's equation, $y = mx + b$, can be expressed in function notation by replacing y with $f(x)$:

$$f(x) = mx + b.$$

We have seen that functions in this form are called **linear functions**. Thus, in the equation of a linear function, the x-coefficient is the line's slope and the constant term is the y-intercept. Here are two examples:

$$y = 2x - 4 \qquad\qquad f(x) = \frac{1}{2}x + 2.$$

The slope is 2. The y-intercept is -4. The slope is $\frac{1}{2}$. The y-intercept is 2.

If a linear function's equation is in slope-intercept form, we can use the y-intercept and the slope to obtain its graph.

GRAPHING $y = mx + b$ USING THE SLOPE AND y-INTERCEPT

1. Plot the point containing the y-intercept on the y-axis. This is the point $(0, b)$.
2. Obtain a second point using the slope, m. Write m as a fraction, and use rise over run, starting at the point containing the y-intercept, to plot this point.
3. Use a straightedge to draw a line through the two points. Draw arrowheads at the ends of the line to show that the line continues indefinitely in both directions.

EXAMPLE 3 GRAPHING BY USING THE SLOPE AND y-INTERCEPT

Graph the linear function $y = \frac{2}{3}x + 2$ by using the slope and y-intercept.

SOLUTION The equation of the linear function is in the form $y = mx + b$. We can find the slope, m, by identifying the coefficient of x. We can find the y-intercept, b, by identifying the constant term.

$$y = \frac{2}{3}x + 2$$

The slope is $\frac{2}{3}$. The y-intercept is 2.

Now that we have identified the slope and the y-intercept, we use the three-step procedure to graph the equation.

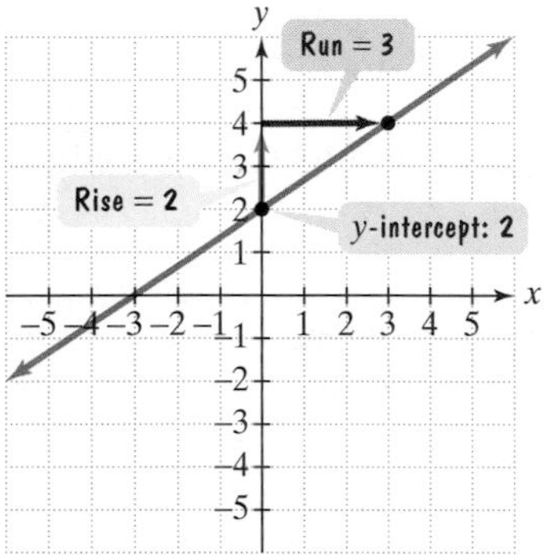

FIGURE 7.15 The graph of $y = \frac{2}{3}x + 2$

Step 1. Plot the point containing the y-intercept on the y-axis. The y-intercept is 2. We plot $(0, 2)$, shown in Figure 7.15.

Step 2. Obtain a second point using the slope, m. Write m as a fraction, and use rise over run, starting at the point containing the y-intercept, to plot this point. The slope, $\frac{2}{3}$, is already written as a fraction:

$$m = \frac{2}{3} = \frac{\text{Rise}}{\text{Run}}.$$

We plot the second point on the line by starting at $(0, 2)$, the first point. Based on the slope, we move 2 units *up* (the rise) and 3 units to the *right* (the run). This puts us at a second point on the line, $(3, 4)$, shown in Figure 7.15.

Step 3. Use a straightedge to draw a line through the two points. The graph of $y = \frac{2}{3}x + 2$ is shown in Figure 7.15.

CHECK POINT 3 Graph the linear function $y = \frac{3}{5}x + 1$ by using the slope and y-intercept.

Earlier in this section, we considered linear functions of the form $Ax + By = C$. We used x- and y-intercepts, as well as checkpoints, to graph these functions. It is also possible to obtain the graphs by using the slope and y-intercept. To do this, begin by solving $Ax + By = C$ for y. This will put the equation in slope-intercept form. Then use the three-step procedure to graph the equation. This is illustrated in Example 4.

EXAMPLE 4 GRAPHING BY USING THE SLOPE AND y-INTERCEPT

Graph the linear function $2x + 5y = 0$ by using the slope and y-intercept.

SOLUTION We put the equation in slope-intercept form by solving for y.

$2x + 5y = 0$	This is the given equation.
$2x - 2x + 5y = -2x + 0$	Subtract $2x$ from both sides.
$5y = -2x + 0$	Simplify.
$\frac{5y}{5} = \frac{-2x + 0}{5}$	Divide both sides by 5.
$y = \frac{-2x}{5} + \frac{0}{5}$	Divide each term in the numerator by 5.
$y = -\frac{2}{5}x + 0$	Simplify. Equivalently, $f(x) = -\frac{2}{5}x + 0$.

Now that the equation is in slope-intercept form, we can use the slope and y-intercept to obtain its graph. Examine the slope-intercept form:

$$y = -\frac{2}{5}x + 0.$$

slope: $-\frac{2}{5}$ | y-intercept: 0

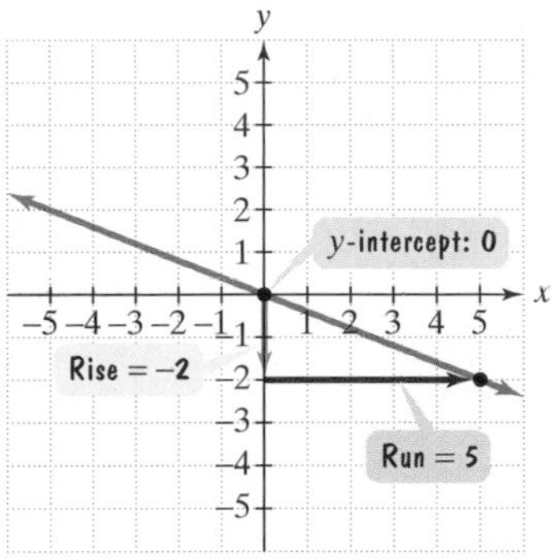

FIGURE 7.16 The graph of $2x + 5y = 0$, or $y = -\frac{2}{5}x$

Note that the slope is $-\frac{2}{5}$ and the y-intercept is 0. Use the y-intercept to plot $(0, 0)$ on the y-axis. Then locate a second point by using the slope.

$$m = -\frac{2}{5} = \frac{-2}{5} = \frac{\text{Rise}}{\text{Run}}$$

Because the rise is -2 and the run is 5, move *down* 2 units and to the *right* 5 units, starting at the point $(0, 0)$. This puts us at a second point on the line, $(5, -2)$. The graph of $2x + 5y = 0$ is the line drawn through these points, shown in Figure 7.16.

If you try graphing $2x + 5y = 0$ by using intercepts, you will find that the x-intercept is 0 and the y-intercept is 0. This means that the graph passes through the origin. A second point must be found to graph the line. In Example 4, the line's slope gave us the second point.

CHECK POINT 4 Graph the linear function $3x + 4y = 0$ by using the slope and y-intercept.

4 Graph horizontal or vertical lines.

Equations of Horizontal and Vertical Lines

Some things change very little. For example, from 1997 through 2005, the federal minimum wage remained constant at \$5.15 per hour, indicated by the brown bars in Figure 7.17. These bars show the minimum wage before it was adjusted for inflation. Also shown in the figure is a blue horizontal line segment that passes through the tops of the nine brown bars.

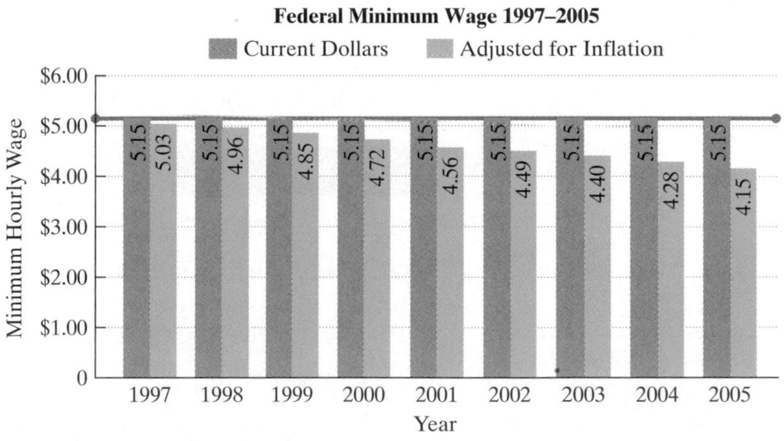

FIGURE 7.17
Source: Department of Labor

We can use $y = mx + b$, the slope-intercept form of a line's equation, to obtain an equation that models the federal minimum wage, y, in current dollars, in year x, where x is between 1997 and 2005, inclusive. The horizontal blue line segment in Figure 7.17 provides the values for m and b:

$$y = mx + b.$$

Because the line segment is horizontal, $m = 0$. | The y-intercept is shown as \$5.15, so $b = 5.15$.

Thus, an equation that models the federal minimum wage between 1997 and 2005, inclusive, is

$$y = 0x + 5.15, \quad \text{or } y = 5.15.$$

The federal minimum wage remained constant at \$5.15 per hour. Using function notation, we can write

$$f(x) = 5.15.$$

For all year inputs, x, from 1997 through 2005, inclusive,

the output is a constant 5.15.

In general, if a line is horizontal, its slope is zero: $m = 0$. Thus, the equation $y = mx + b$ becomes $y = b$, where b is the y-intercept. All horizontal lines have equations of the form $y = b$.

EXAMPLE 5 GRAPHING A HORIZONTAL LINE

Graph $y = -4$ in the rectangular coordinate system.

SOLUTION All ordered pairs that are solutions of $y = -4$ have a value of y that is always -4. Any value can be used for x. In the table on the right, we have selected three of the possible values for x: -2, 0, and 3. The table shows that three ordered pairs that are solutions of $y = -4$ are $(-2, -4)$, $(0, -4)$, and $(3, -4)$. Drawing a line that passes through the three points gives the horizontal line shown in Figure 7.18.

x	$y = -4$	(x, y)
-2	-4	$(-2, -4)$
0	-4	$(0, -4)$
3	-4	$(3, -4)$

For all choices of x,

y is a constant -4.

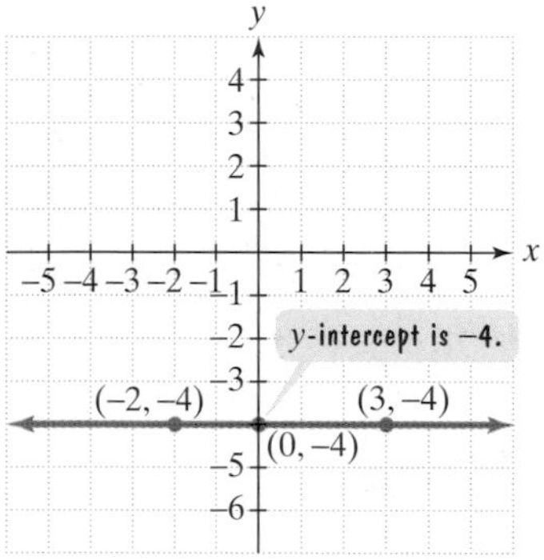

FIGURE 7.18 The graph of $y = -4$ or $f(x) = -4$

CHECK POINT 5 Graph $y = 3$ in the rectangular coordinate system.

Next, let's see what we can discover about the graph of an equation of the form $x = a$ by looking at an example.

EXAMPLE 6 GRAPHING A VERTICAL LINE

Graph $x = 2$ in the rectangular coordinate system.

SOLUTION All ordered pairs that are solutions of $x = 2$ have a value of x that is always 2. Any value can be used for y. In the table on the right, we have selected three of the possible values for y: -2, 0, and 3. The table shows that three ordered pairs that are solutions of $x = 2$ are $(2, -2)$, $(2, 0)$, and $(2, 3)$. Drawing a line that passes through the three points gives the vertical line shown in Figure 7.19.

For all choices of y,

$x = 2$	y	(x, y)
2	-2	$(2, -2)$
2	0	$(2, 0)$
2	3	$(2, 3)$

x is always 2.

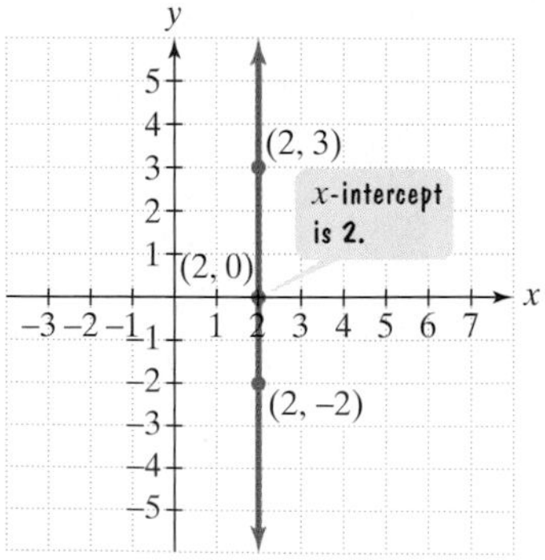

FIGURE 7.19 The graph of $x = 2$

Does a vertical line represent the graph of a linear function? No. Look at the graph of $x = 2$ in Figure 7.19. A vertical line drawn through $(2, 0)$ intersects the graph infinitely many times. This shows that infinitely many outputs are associated with the input 2. **No vertical line is a linear function.** All other lines are graphs of functions.

HORIZONTAL AND VERTICAL LINES

The graph of $y = b$ or $f(x) = b$ is a horizontal line. The y-intercept is b.

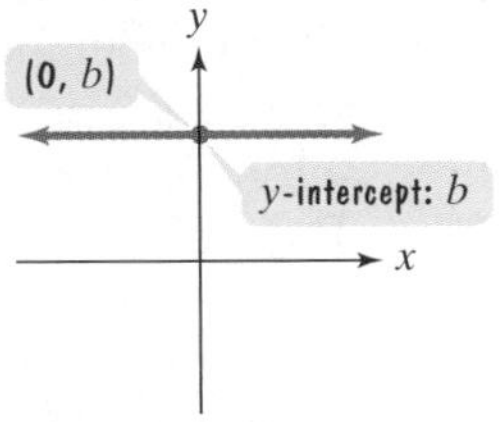

The graph of $x = a$ is a vertical line. The x-intercept is a.

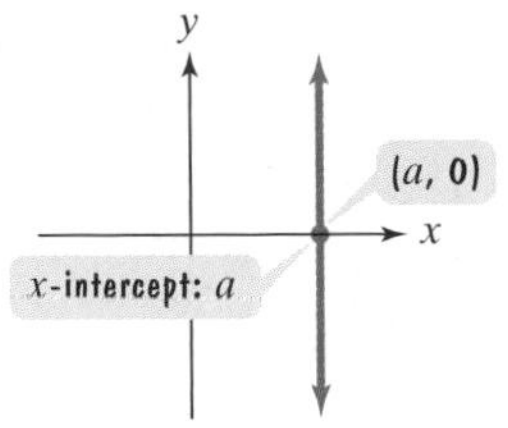

CHECK POINT 6 Graph $x = -2$ in the rectangular coordinate system.

5 Interpret slope as rate of change.

Slope as Rate of Change

Slope is defined as the ratio of a change in y to a corresponding change in x. Our next example shows how slope can be interpreted as a **rate of change** in an applied situation.

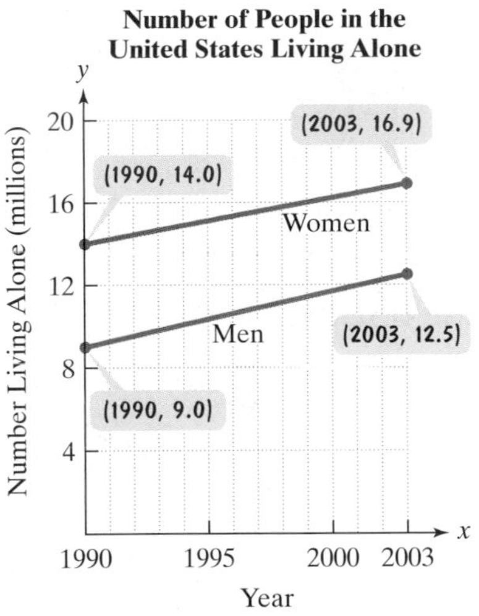

FIGURE 7.10 (repeated)

EXAMPLE 7 SLOPE AS A RATE OF CHANGE

Shown, again, in Figure 7.10, are the line graphs for the number of U.S. men and women living alone from 1990 through 2003. Find the slope of the line segment for the women. Describe what the slope represents.

SOLUTION We let x represent a year and y the number of women living alone in that year. The two points shown on the line segment for women have the following coordinates:

$$(1990, 14.0) \quad \text{and} \quad (2003, 16.9).$$

In 1990, 14 million U.S. women lived alone.

In 2003, 16.9 million U.S. women lived alone.

Now we compute the slope.

$$m = \frac{\text{Change in } y}{\text{Change in } x} = \frac{16.9 - 14.0}{2003 - 1990}$$

$$= \frac{2.9}{13} \approx 0.22$$

The unit in the numerator is million women.

The unit in the denominator is year.

The slope indicates that for the period from 1990 through 2003, the number of U.S. women living alone increased by approximately 0.22 million each year. The rate of change is approximately 0.22 million women per year.

CHECK POINT 7 Use the graph in Figure 7.10 to find the slope of the line segment for the men. Express the slope correct to two decimal places and describe what it represents.

6 Use slope and y-intercept to model data.

Modeling Data with the Slope-Intercept Form of the Equation of a Line

Linear functions are useful for modeling data that fall on or near a line. For example, Figure 7.20 shows the number, in millions, of cars and SUVs sold by America's big three automakers from 1990 through 2003. Example 8 and Check Point 8 illustrate how we can use the equation $y = mx + b$ to develop models for the data. The red modifications below the x-axis show additions to the original display so that we can obtain these models.

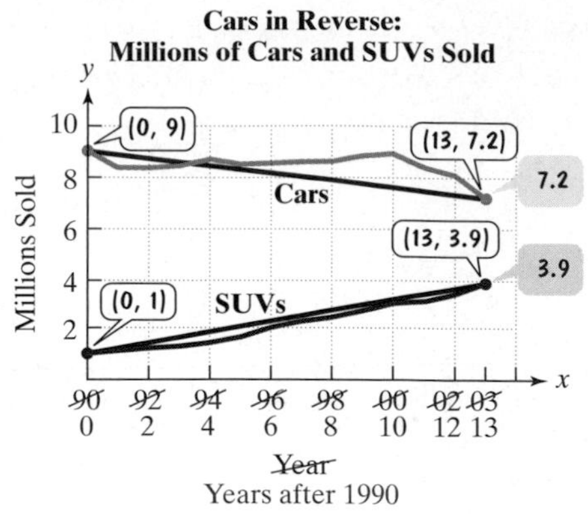

FIGURE 7.20 Obtaining models from data

EXAMPLE 8 MODELING WITH THE SLOPE-INTERCEPT EQUATION

Find a function in the form $C(x) = mx + b$ that models car sales, $C(x)$, in millions, x years after 1990.

SOLUTION We will use the line segment passing through the points $(0, 9)$ and $(13, 7.2)$ to obtain a model. We need values for m, the slope, and b, the y-intercept.

$$C(x) = mx + b$$

$$m = \frac{\text{Change in } y}{\text{Change in } x} = \frac{7.2 - 9}{13 - 0} \approx -0.14$$

The point $(0, 9)$ lies on the line segment, so the y-intercept is 9: $b = 9$.

Car sales, $C(x)$, in millions, x years after 1990 can be modeled by the linear function

$$C(x) = -0.14x + 9.$$

The slope, approximately -0.14, indicates a decrease in sales of about 0.14 million cars per year from 1990 through 2003.

CHECK POINT 8 Use Figure 7.20 to find a function in the form $S(x) = mx + b$ that models SUV sales, $S(x)$, in millions, x years after 1990.

EXERCISE SET 7.2

• Practice Exercises

In Exercises 1–8, use the x- and y-intercepts to graph each linear equation.

1. $x - y = 3$
2. $x + y = 4$
3. $3x - 4y = 12$
4. $2x - 5y = 10$
5. $2x + y = 6$
6. $x + 3y = 6$
7. $5x = 3y - 15$
8. $3x = 2y + 6$

In Exercises 9–20, calculate the slope of the line passing through the given points. If the slope is undefined, so state. Then indicate whether the line rises, falls, is horizontal, or is vertical.

9. $(2, 6)$ and $(3, 5)$
10. $(4, 2)$ and $(3, 4)$
11. $(-2, 1)$ and $(2, 2)$
12. $(-1, 3)$ and $(2, 4)$
13. $(-2, 4)$ and $(-1, -1)$
14. $(6, -4)$ and $(4, -2)$
15. $(5, 3)$ and $(5, -2)$
16. $(3, -4)$ and $(3, 5)$
17. $(2, 0)$ and $(0, 8)$
18. $(3, 0)$ and $(0, -9)$
19. $(5, 1)$ and $(-2, 1)$
20. $(-2, 3)$ and $(1, 3)$

In Exercises 21–32, graph each linear function using the slope and y-intercept.

21. $y = 2x + 3$
22. $y = 2x + 1$
23. $y = -2x + 4$
24. $y = -2x + 3$
25. $y = \frac{1}{2}x + 3$
26. $y = \frac{1}{2}x + 2$
27. $f(x) = \frac{2}{3}x - 4$
28. $f(x) = \frac{3}{4}x - 5$
29. $y = -\frac{3}{4}x + 4$
30. $y = -\frac{2}{3}x + 5$
31. $f(x) = -\frac{5}{3}x$
32. $f(x) = -\frac{4}{3}x$

In Exercises 33–40,

a. *Put the equation in slope-intercept form by solving for y.*

b. *Identify the slope and the y-intercept.*

c. *Use the slope and y-intercept to graph the line.*

33. $3x + y = 0$ **34.** $2x + y = 0$

35. $3y = 4x$ **36.** $4y = 5x$

37. $2x + y = 3$ **38.** $3x + y = 4$

39. $7x + 2y = 14$ **40.** $5x + 3y = 15$

In Exercises 41–48, graph each horizontal or vertical line.

41. $y = 4$ **42.** $y = 2$

43. $y = -2$ **44.** $y = -3$

45. $x = 2$ **46.** $x = 4$

47. $x + 1 = 0$ **48.** $x + 5 = 0$

• Practice Plus

In Exercises 49–52, find the slope of the line passing through each pair of points or state that the slope is undefined. Assume that all variables represent positive real numbers. Then indicate whether the line through the points rises, falls, is horizontal, or is vertical.

49. $(0, a)$ and $(b, 0)$

50. $(-a, 0)$ and $(0, -b)$

51. (a, b) and $(a, b + c)$

52. $(a - b, c)$ and $(a, a + c)$

In Exercises 53–54, give the slope and y-intercept of each line whose equation is given. Assume that $B \neq 0$.

53. $Ax + By = C$

54. $Ax = By - C$

In Exercises 55–56, find the value of y if the line through the two given points is to have the indicated slope.

55. $(3, y)$ and $(1, 4)$, $m = -3$

56. $(-2, y)$ and $(4, -4)$, $m = \frac{1}{3}$

Use the figure to make the lists in Exercises 57–58.

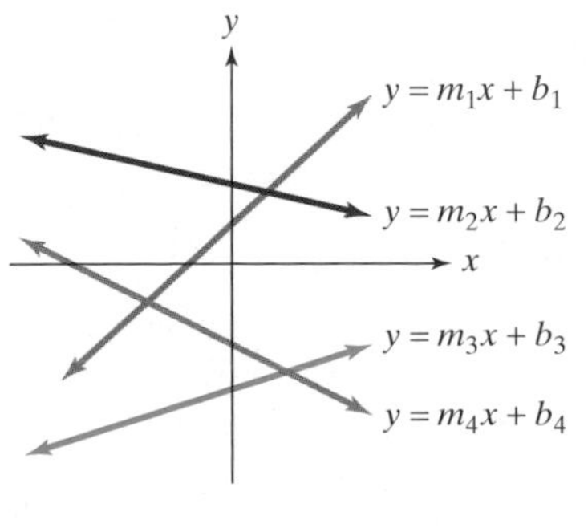

57. List the slopes m_1, m_2, m_3, and m_4 in order of decreasing size.

58. List the y-intercepts b_1, b_2, b_3, and b_4 in order of decreasing size.

• Application Exercises

59. The graph shows the nationwide average for unleaded regular gas from 2000 through 2005.

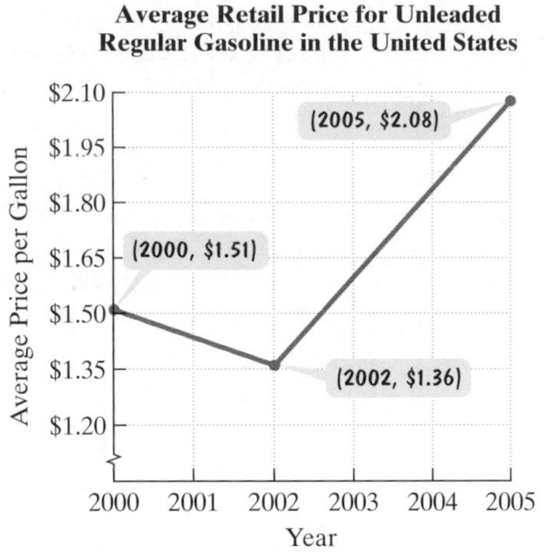

Source: Energy Information Administration

a. Find the slope of the line through (2000, 1.51) and (2002, 1.36). What does this represent in terms of the rate of change in the average price for a gallon of gas from 2000 through 2002?

b. Find the slope of the line through (2002, 1.36) and (2005, 2.08). What does this represent in terms of the rate of change in the average price for a gallon of gas from 2002 through 2005?

60. The graph shows the percentage of sales of recorded music in the United States for rock and rap/hip hop.

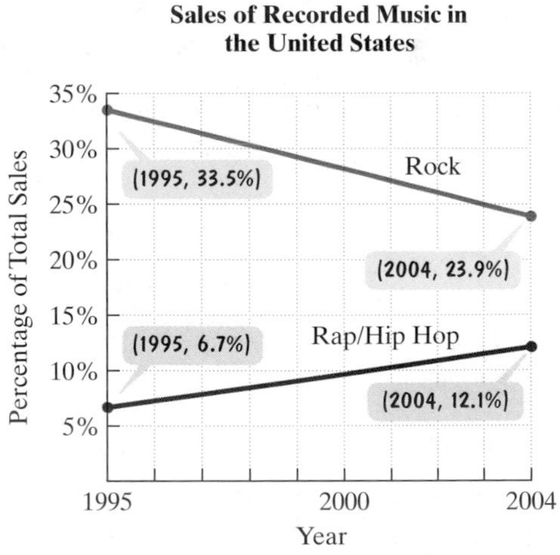

Source: RIAA

a. Find the slope of the line through (1995, 33.5) and (2004, 23.9). Round to one decimal place. What does this represent in terms of the rate of change in the percentage of total sales of rock for the period shown?

b. Find the slope of the line through (1995, 6.7) and (2004, 12.1). What does this represent in terms of the rate of change in the percentage of total sales of rap/hip hop for the period shown?

61. The five points shown below represent the number of global HIV/AIDS cases, in millions, from 1999 through 2003. Also shown is the graph of a linear function that passes through or near the points.

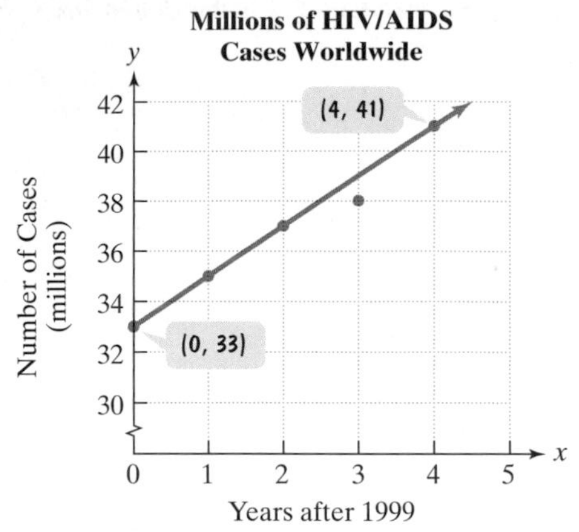

Source: UNAIDS

a. According to the graph, what is the y-intercept? Describe what this represents in this situation.

b. Use the coordinates of the two points shown to compute the slope. What does this mean about the number of HIV/AIDS cases worldwide?

c. Use the y-intercept from part (a) and the slope from part (b) to write a linear function that models the number of HIV/AIDS cases worldwide, y, in millions, x years after 1999.

d. Use the linear function from part (c) to predict the number of HIV/AIDS cases worldwide, in millions, in 2010.

62. The five points shown below represent retail prescription drug sales in the United States, in billions of dollars, from 2000 through 2004. Also shown is the graph of a linear function that passes through or near the points.

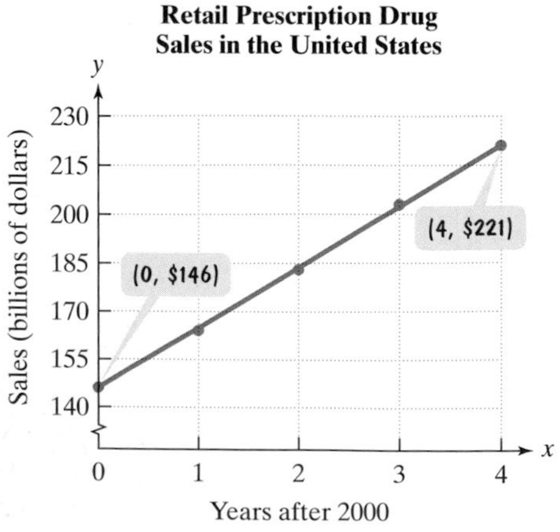

Source: U.S. Census Bureau

a. According to the graph, what is the y-intercept? Describe what this represents in this situation.

b. Use the coordinates of the two points shown to compute the slope. What does this mean about retail prescription drug sales in the United States?

c. Use the y-intercept from part (a) and the slope from part (b) to write a linear function that models prescription drug sales in the United States, y, in billions of dollars, x years after 2000.

d. Use the linear function from part (c) to predict prescription drug sales, in billions of dollars, in 2010.

• Writing in Mathematics

63. Describe how to find the x-intercept of a linear equation.

64. Describe how to find the y-intercept of a linear equation.

65. What is the slope of a line?

66. Describe how to calculate the slope of a line passing through two points.

67. Describe how to graph a line using the slope and y-intercept. Provide an original example with your description.

68. What does it mean if the slope of a line is 0?

69. What does it mean if the slope of a line is undefined?

70. What is the least number of points needed to graph a line? How many should actually be used? Explain.

71. Explain why the y-values can be any number for the equation $x = 5$. How is this shown in the graph of the equation?

• Critical Thinking Exercises

72. Which one of the following is true?

a. The equation $y = mx + b$ shows that no line can have a y-intercept that is numerically equal to its slope.

b. Every line in the rectangular coordinate system has an equation that can be expressed in slope-intercept form.

c. The line $3x + 2y = 5$ has slope $-\frac{3}{2}$.

d. The line $2y = 3x + 7$ has a y-intercept of 7.

73. The relationship between Celsius temperature, C, and Fahrenheit temperature, F, can be described by a linear equation in the form $F = mC + b$. The graph of this equation contains the point (0, 32): Water freezes at 0°C or at 32°F. The line also contains the point (100, 212): Water boils at 100°C or at 212°F. Write the linear equation expressing Fahrenheit temperature in terms of Celsius temperature.

• Technology Exercises

74. Use a graphing utility to verify any three of your hand-drawn graphs in Exercises 21–32.

75. Use a graphing utility to verify any three of your hand-drawn graphs in Exercises 33–40. Solve the equation for y before entering it.

CHAPTER 8

Consumer Mathematics and Financial Management

"I realize, of course, that it's no shame to be poor, but it's no great honor either. So what would have been so terrible if I had a small fortune?"

–TEVYE, A POOR DAIRYMAN, IN THE MUSICAL *FIDDLER ON THE ROOF*

We all want a wonderful life with fulfilling work, good health, and loving relationships. And let's be honest: Financial security, or even a small fortune, wouldn't hurt! Achieving this goal depends on understanding basic ideas about savings, loans, and investments. A solid understanding of the topics in this chapter can pay, literally, by making your financial goals a reality.

A number of examples illustrate how to attain fortunes ranging from over a half-million dollars to $4 million through regular savings. See Example 3 in Section 8.4 and Exercises 35–36 in Exercise Set 8.4.

SECTION 8.1 • PERCENT, SALES TAX, AND INCOME TAX

OBJECTIVES

1. Express a fraction as a percent.
2. Express a decimal as a percent.
3. Express a percent as a decimal.
4. Solve applied problems involving sales tax and discounts.
5. Compute income tax.
6. Determine percent increase or decrease.
7. Investigate some of the ways percent can be abused.

"And if elected, it is my solemn pledge to cut your taxes by 10% for each of my first three years in office, for a total cut of 30%."

Did you know that one of the most common ways that you are given numerical information is with percents? This section will provide you with the tools to make sense of the politician's promise, as we present the uses, and abuses, of percent.

Basics of Percent

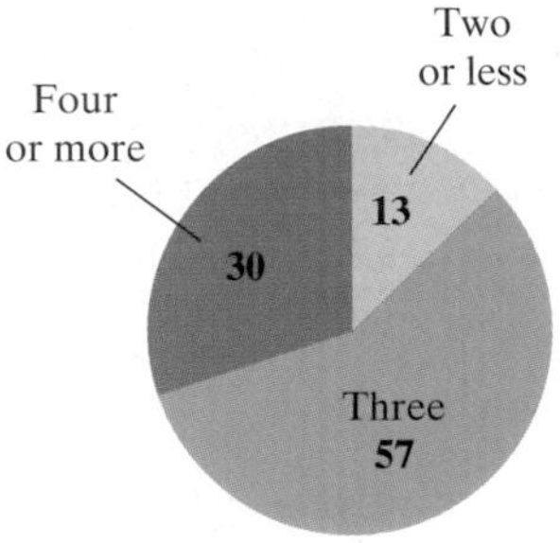

Source: U.S. Census Bureau and HUD

FIGURE 8.1 Number of bedrooms in privately owned single-family U.S. houses per 100 houses

Percents are the result of expressing numbers as a part of 100. The word *percent* means *per hundred*. For example, the circle graph in Figure 8.1 shows that 57 out of every 100 single-family homes have three bedrooms. Thus, $\frac{57}{100} = 57\%$, indicating that 57% of the houses have three bedrooms. The percent sign, %, is used to indicate the number of parts out of one hundred parts.

A fraction can be expressed as a percent using the following procedure:

EXPRESSING A FRACTION AS A PERCENT

1. Divide the numerator by the denominator.
2. Multiply the quotient by 100. This is done by moving the decimal point in the quotient two places to the right.
3. Add a percent sign.

1 Express a fraction as a percent.

EXAMPLE 1 EXPRESSING A FRACTION AS A PERCENT

Express $\frac{5}{8}$ as a percent.

SOLUTION

Step 1. Divide the numerator by the denominator.

$$5 \div 8 = 0.625$$

Step 2. Multiply the quotient by 100.

$$0.625 \times 100 = 62.5$$

Step 3. Add a percent sign.

$$62.5\%$$

Thus, $\frac{5}{8} = 62.5\%$.

CHECK POINT 1 Express $\frac{1}{8}$ as a percent.

2 Express a decimal as a percent.

STUDY TIP

Dictionaries indicate that the word *percentage* has the same meaning as the word *percent*. Use the word that sounds best in the circumstance.

Our work in Example 1 shows that $0.625 = 62.5\%$. This illustrates the procedure for expressing a decimal number as a percent.

EXPRESSING A DECIMAL NUMBER AS A PERCENT

1. Move the decimal point two places to the right.
2. Attach a percent sign.

EXAMPLE 2 EXPRESSING A DECIMAL AS A PERCENT

Express 0.47 as a percent.

SOLUTION

Move decimal point two places right.

$$0.47\ \%$$

Add a percent sign.

Thus, $0.47 = 47\%$.

CHECK POINT 2 Express 0.023 as a percent.

3 Express a percent as a decimal.

We reverse the procedure of Example 2 to express a percent as a decimal number.

EXPRESSING A PERCENT AS A DECIMAL NUMBER

1. Move the decimal point two places to the left.
2. Remove the percent sign.

EXAMPLE 3 EXPRESSING PERCENTS AS DECIMALS

Express each percent as a decimal:

a. 19% **b.** 180%.

SOLUTION Use the two steps in the box.

a.

$$19\% = 19.\% = 0.19\not\%$$

The percent sign is removed.

The decimal point starts at the far right.

The decimal point is moved two places to the left.

Thus, $19\% = 0.19$.

b. $180\% = 1.80\not\% = 1.80$ or 1.8.

CHECK POINT 3 Express each percent as a decimal:

a. 67% **b.** 250%.

If a fraction is part of a percent, as in $\frac{1}{4}\%$, begin by expressing the fraction as a decimal, retaining the percent sign. Then, use the two steps in the box to express the percent as a decimal number. For example,

$$\frac{1}{4}\% = 0.25\% = 00.25\not\% = 0.0025.$$

4 Solve applied problems involving sales tax and discounts.

Percent, Sales Tax, and Discounts

Many applications involving percent are based on the following formula:

A is P percent of B.

$$A = P \cdot B.$$

Note that the word *of* implies multiplication.

We can use this formula to determine the **sales tax** collected by states, counties, and cities on sales of items to customers. The sales tax is a percent of the cost of an item.

$$\text{Sales tax amount} = \text{tax rate} \times \text{item's cost}$$

EXAMPLE 4 PERCENT AND SALES TAX

Suppose that the local sales tax rate is 7.5% and you purchase a bicycle for \$394.

a. How much tax is paid?

b. What is the bicycle's total cost?

SOLUTION

a. $\text{Sales tax amount} = \text{tax rate} \times \text{item's cost}$

$= 7.5\% \times \$394 = 0.075 \times \$394 = \$29.55$

7.5% of the item's cost, or 7.5% of \$394

The tax paid is \$29.55.

b. The bicycle's total cost is the purchase price, \$394, plus the sales tax, \$29.55.

$$\text{Total cost} = \$394.00 + \$29.55 = \$423.55$$

The bicycle's total cost is \$423.55.

CHECK POINT 4 Suppose that the local sales tax rate is 6% and you purchase a computer for \$1260.

a. How much tax is paid?

b. What is the computer's total cost?

None of us is thrilled about sales tax, but we do like buying things that are *on sale*. Businesses reduce prices, or **discount**, to attract customers and to reduce inventory. The discount rate is a percent of the original price.

$$\text{Discount amount} = \text{discount rate} \times \text{original price}$$

EXAMPLE 5 PERCENT AND SALES PRICE

A computer with an original price of \$1460 is on sale at 15% off.

a. What is the discount amount?

b. What is the computer's sale price?

SOLUTION

a. $\text{Discount amount} = \text{discount rate} \times \text{original price}$

$= 15\% \times \$1460 = 0.15 \times \$1460 = \$219$

15% of the original price, or 15% of \$1460

The discount amount is \$219.

TECHNOLOGY

A calculator is useful, and sometimes essential, in this chapter. The keystroke sequence that gives the sale price in Example 5 is

1460 [−] .15 [×] 1460.

Press [=] on a scientific calculator or [ENTER] on a graphing calculator to display the answer, 1241.

b. The computer's sale price is the original price, \$1460, minus the discount amount, \$219.

$$\text{Sale price} = \$1460 - \$219 = \$1241$$

The computer's sale price is \$1241.

CHECK POINT 5 A CD player with an original price of \$380 is on sale at 35% off.

a. What is the discount amount?

b. What is the CD player's sale price?

5 Compute income tax.

Percent and Income Tax

We have seen how tax rates determine the amount of sales tax on an item. They also determine the amount that we must each pay in income tax.

CALCULATING INCOME TAX

1. Determine your adjusted gross income:

$$\text{Adjusted gross income} = \text{Gross income} - \text{Adjustments}.$$

Gross income: All income for the year, including wages, tips, earnings from investments, and unemployment compensation

Adjustments: Includes payments to tax-deferred savings plans

2. Determine your taxable income:

$$\text{Taxable income} = \text{Adjusted gross income} - (\text{Exemptions} + \text{Deductions}).$$

Exemptions: A fixed amount for yourself (\$3200 in 2005) and the same amount for each dependent

Deductions: Choose the greater of a standard deduction or an itemized deduction, which includes interest on home mortgages, state income taxes, property taxes, charitable contributions, and medical expenses exceeding 7.5% of adjusted gross income.

3. Determine the income tax:

$$\text{Income tax} = \text{Tax computation} - \text{Tax credits}.$$

Tax computation: Use your taxable income and tax rates for your filing status (single, married, etc.) to determine this amount.

Tax credits: May include up to \$1000 per child, the cost of child care so a parent can work, and adoption credits for qualified expenses.

Tax Rate	Single
10%	up to \$7300
15%	\$7301 to \$29,700

A portion of Table 8.1. (The complete table appears on the next page.)

Table 8.1 on the next page shows 2005 tax rates, standard deductions, and exemptions for the four **filing status** categories described in the voice balloons. The tax rates in the left column, called **marginal tax rates**, are assigned to various income ranges, called **margins**. For example, suppose you are single and your taxable income is \$25,000. The singles column of the table shows that you must pay 10% tax on the first \$7300, which is

$$10\% \text{ of } \$7300 = 0.10 \times \$7300 = \$730.$$

You must also pay 15% tax on the remaining \$17,700 (\$25,000 − \$7300 = \$17,700), which is

$$15\% \text{ of } \$17,700 = 0.15 \times \$17,700 = \$2655.$$

Your total tax is \$730 + \$2655 = \$3385. In this scenario, your *marginal rate* is 15% and you are in the 15% *tax bracket*.

TABLE 8.1 2005 MARGINAL TAX RATES, STANDARD DEDUCTIONS, AND EXEMPTIONS

Tax Rate	Single (Unmarried, divorced, or legally separated)	Married Filing Separately (Married and each partner files a separate tax return)	Married Filing Jointly (Married and both partners file a single tax return)	Head of Household (Unmarried and paying more than half the cost of supporting a child or parent)
10%	up to $7300	up to $7300	up to $14,600	up to $10,450
15%	$7301 to $29,700	$7301 to $29,700	$14,601 to $59,400	$10,451 to $39,800
25%	$29,701 to $71,950	$29,701 to $59,975	$59,401 to $119,950	$39,801 to $102,800
28%	$71,951 to $150,150	$59,976 to $91,400	$119,951 to $182,800	$102,801 to $166,450
33%	$150,151 to $326,450	$91,401 to $163,225	$182,801 to $326,450	$166,451 to $326,450
35%	more than $326,450	more than $163,225	more than $326,450	more than $326,450
Standard Deduction	$5000	$5000	$10,000	$7300
Exemptions (per person)	$3200	$3200	$3200	$3200

SINGLE WOMAN WITH NO DEPENDENTS

Gross income: $52,000

Adjustments: $4000 paid to a tax-deferred IRA (Individual Retirement Account)

Deductions:

- $7500: mortgage interest
- $2200: property taxes
- $2400: charitable contributions
- $1500: medical expenses not covered by insurance

Tax credit: $500

EXAMPLE 6 COMPUTING INCOME TAX

Calculate the income tax owed by a single woman with no dependents whose gross income, adjustments, deductions, and credits are given in the margin. Use the 2005 marginal tax rates in Table 8.1.

SOLUTION

Step 1. Determine the adjusted gross income.

Adjusted gross income = Gross income − Adjustments
= $52,000 − $4000
= $48,000

Step 2. Determine the taxable income.

Taxable income = Adjusted gross income − (Exemptions + Deductions)
= $48,000 − ($3200 + Deductions)

The singles column in Table 8.1 shows a personal exemption of $3200.

The singles column in Table 8.1 shows a $5000 standard deduction. A greater deduction can be obtained by itemizing.

Itemized Deductions

$7500 : mortgage interest
$2200 : property taxes
$2400 : charitable contributions
~~$1500 : medical expenses~~
$12,100 : total of deductible expenditures

Can only deduct amount in excess of 7.5% of gross income: 0.075 × $52,000 = $3900

We substitute $12,100 for deductions in the formula for taxable income.

Taxable income = Adjusted gross income − (Exemptions + Deductions)
= $48,000 − ($3200 + $12,100)
= $48,000 − $15,300
= $32,700

Step 3. Determine the income tax.

$$\text{Income Tax} = \text{Tax computation} - \text{Tax credits}$$
$$= \text{Tax computation} - \$500$$

Tax Rate	Single
10%	up to $7300
15%	$7301 to $29,700
25%	$29,701 to $71,950

A portion of Table 8.1 (repeated)

We perform the tax computation using the singles rates in Table 8.1. Our taxpayer is in the 25% tax bracket because her taxable income, $32,700, is in the $29,701 to $71,950 income range. This means that she owes 10% on the first $7300 of her taxable income, 15% on her taxable income between $7301 and $29,700, inclusive, and 25% on her taxable income above $29,700.

10% marginal rate on first $7300 of taxable income

15% marginal rate on taxable income between $7301 and $29,700

25% marginal rate on taxable income above $29,700

$$\begin{aligned}\text{Tax computation} &= 0.10 \times \$7300 + 0.15 \times (\$29{,}700 - \$7300) + 0.25 \times (\$32{,}700 - \$29{,}700)\\ &= 0.10 \times \$7300 + 0.15 \times \$22{,}400 + 0.25 \times \$3000\\ &= \$730 + \$3360 + \$750\\ &= \$4840\end{aligned}$$

STUDY TIP

A tax credit is not the same thing as a tax deduction. The *tax credit* of $500 in Example 6 *reduces the income tax owed by the full dollar-for-dollar amount*, namely, $500. The *tax deduction* of $12,100 *reduces the taxable income* by $12,100, thereby saving only a percentage of $12,100 in taxes.

We substitute $4840 for the tax computation in the formula for income tax.

$$\begin{aligned}\text{Income tax} &= \text{Tax computation} - \text{Tax credits}\\ &= \$4840 - \$500\\ &= \$4340\end{aligned}$$

The income tax owed is $4340.

CHECK POINT 6 Use the 2005 marginal tax rates in Table 8.1 to calculate the tax owed by a single man with no dependents whose gross income, adjustments, deductions, and credits are given as follows:

Gross income: $40,000
Adjustments: $1000
Deductions: $3000: charitable contributions
$1500: theft loss
$300: cost of tax preparation
Tax credit: none.

6 Determine percent increase or decrease.

Percent and Change

Percents are used for comparing changes, such as increases or decreases in sales, population, prices, and production. If a quantity changes, its **percent increase** or its **percent decrease** can be found as follows:

FINDING PERCENT INCREASE OR PERCENT DECREASE

1. Find the fraction for the percent increase or the percent decrease:

$$\frac{\text{amount of increase}}{\text{original amount}} \quad \text{or} \quad \frac{\text{amount of decrease}}{\text{original amount}}.$$

2. Find the percent increase or the percent decrease by expressing the fraction in step 1 as a percent.

EXAMPLE 7 FINDING PERCENT INCREASE AND DECREASE

In 2000, world population was approximately 6 billion. Figure 8.2 shows world population projections through the year 2150. The data are from the United Nations Family Planning Program and are based on optimistic or pessimistic expectations for successful control of human population growth.

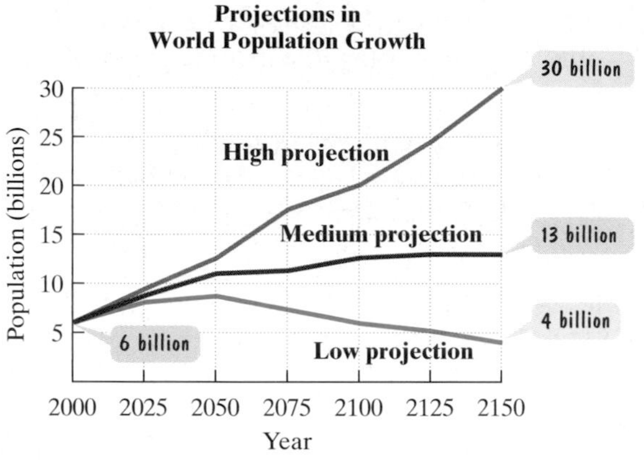

FIGURE 8.2
Source: United Nations

a. Find the percent increase in world population from 2000 to 2150 using the high projection data.

b. Find the percent decrease in world population from 2000 to 2150 using the low projection data.

SOLUTION

a. Use the data shown on the blue, high-projection, graph.

$$\text{Percent increase} = \frac{\text{amount of increase}}{\text{original amount}}$$

$$= \frac{30 - 6}{6} = \frac{24}{6} = 4 = 400\%$$

The projected percent increase in world population is 400%.

b. Use the data shown on the green, low-projection, graph.

$$\text{Percent decrease} = \frac{\text{amount of decrease}}{\text{original amount}}$$

$$= \frac{6 - 4}{6} = \frac{2}{6} = \frac{1}{3} = 0.33\frac{1}{3} = 33\frac{1}{3}\%$$

The projected percent decrease in world population is $33\frac{1}{3}\%$.

In Example 7, we expressed the percent decrease as $33\frac{1}{3}\%$ because of the familiar conversion $\frac{1}{3} = 0.33\frac{1}{3}$. However, in many situations, rounding is needed. We suggest that you round to the nearest tenth of a percent. Carry the division in the fraction for percent increase or decrease to four places after the decimal point. Then round the decimal to three places, or to the nearest thousandth. Expressing this rounded decimal as a percent gives percent increase or decrease to the nearest tenth of a percent.

CHECK POINT 7

a. If 6 is increased to 10, find the percent increase.

b. If 10 is decreased to 6, find the percent decrease.

EXAMPLE 8 FINDING PERCENT DECREASE

A jacket regularly sells for \$135.00. The sale price is \$60.75. Find the percent decrease of the sale price from the regular price.

SOLUTION

$$\text{Percent decrease} = \frac{\text{amount of decrease}}{\text{original amount}}$$

$$= \frac{135.00 - 60.75}{135} = \frac{74.25}{135} = 0.55 = 55\%$$

The percent decrease of the sale price from the regular price is 55%. This means that the sale price of the jacket is 55% lower than the regular price.

CHECK POINT 8 A television regularly sells for \$940. The sale price is \$611. Find the percent decrease of the sale price from the regular price.

7 Investigate some of the ways percent can be abused.

Abuses of Percent

In our next examples, we look at a few of the many ways that percent can be used incorrectly. Confusion often arises when percent increase (or decrease) refers to a changing quantity that is itself a percent.

EXAMPLE 9 PERCENTS OF PERCENTS

John Tesh, while he was still coanchoring *Entertainment Tonight*, reported that the PBS series *The Civil War* had an audience of 13% versus the usual 4% PBS audience, "an increase of more than 300%." Did Tesh report the percent increase correctly?

SOLUTION We begin by finding the percent increase.

$$\text{Percent increase} = \frac{\text{amount of increase}}{\text{original amount}}$$

$$= \frac{13\% - 4\%}{4\%} = \frac{9\cancel{\%}}{4\cancel{\%}} = \frac{9}{4} = 2.25 = 225\%$$

The percent increase for PBS was 225%. This is not more than 300%, so Tesh did not report the percent increase correctly.

CHECK POINT 9 An episode of a television series had an audience of 12% versus its usual 10%. What was the percent increase for this episode?

EXAMPLE 10 PROMISES OF A POLITICIAN

A politician states, "If you elect me to office, I promise to cut your taxes for each of my first three years in office by 10% each year, for a total reduction of 30%." Evaluate the accuracy of the politician's statement.

SOLUTION To make things simple, let's assume that a taxpayer paid \$100 in taxes in the year previous to the politician's election. A 10% reduction during year 1 is 10% of \$100.

$$10\% \text{ of previous year tax} = 10\% \text{ of } \$100 = 0.10 \times \$100 = \$10$$

BLITZER BONUS

Percents and Tax Rates

In 1944 and 1945, the highest marginal tax rate in the United States was a staggering 94%. (Does a 94% tax bracket qualify as an abuse of percent?) The tax rate on the highest-income Americans remained at approximately 90% throughout the 1950s, decreased to 70% in the 1960s and 1970s, and to 50% in the early 1980s before reaching a post–World War II low of 28% in 1998. (*Source*: IRS) In 2006, Denmark had the world's highest tax rate, starting at 43.7% and climbing to 62.9% for its wealthiest taxpayers.

With a 10% reduction the first year, the taxpayer will pay only \$100 − \$10, or \$90, in taxes during the politician's first year in office.

The following table shows how we calculate the new, reduced tax for each of the first three years in office:

Year	Tax Paid the Year Before	10% Reduction	Taxes Paid This Year
1	\$100	0.10 × \$100 = \$10	\$100 − \$10 = \$90
2	\$ 90	0.10 × \$90 = \$9	\$90 − \$9 = \$81
3	\$ 81	0.10 × \$81 = \$8.10	\$81 − \$8.10 = \$72.90

Now, we determine the percent decrease in taxes over the three years.

$$\text{Percent decrease} = \frac{\text{amount of decrease}}{\text{original amount}}$$

$$= \frac{\$100 - \$72.90}{\$100} = \frac{\$27.10}{\$100} = \frac{27.1}{100} = 0.271 = 27.1\%$$

The taxes decline by 27.1%, not by 30%. The politician is ill-informed in saying that three consecutive 10% cuts add up to a total tax cut of 30%. In our calculation, which serves as a counterexample to the promise, the total tax cut is only 27.1%.

CHECK POINT 10 Suppose you paid \$1200 in taxes. During year 1, taxes decrease by 20%. During year 2, taxes increase by 20%.

a. What do you pay in taxes for year 2?

b. How do your taxes for year 2 compare with what you originally paid, namely \$1200? If the taxes are not the same, find the percent increase or decrease.

EXERCISE SET 8.1

• Practice Exercises

In Exercises 1–10, express each fraction as a percent.

1. $\frac{2}{5}$ **2.** $\frac{3}{5}$ **3.** $\frac{1}{4}$ **4.** $\frac{3}{4}$
5. $\frac{3}{8}$ **6.** $\frac{7}{8}$ **7.** $\frac{1}{40}$ **8.** $\frac{3}{40}$
9. $\frac{9}{80}$ **10.** $\frac{13}{80}$

In Exercises 11–20, express each decimal as a percent.

11. 0.59 **12.** 0.96 **13.** 0.3844 **14.** 0.003
15. 2.87 **16.** 9.83 **17.** 14.87 **18.** 19.63
19. 100 **20.** 95

In Exercises 21–34, express each percent as a decimal.

21. 72% **22.** 38% **23.** 43.6% **24.** 6.25%
25. 130% **26.** 260% **27.** 2% **28.** 6%
29. $\frac{1}{2}\%$ **30.** $\frac{3}{4}\%$ **31.** $\frac{5}{8}\%$ **32.** $\frac{1}{8}\%$
33. $62\frac{1}{2}\%$ **34.** $87\frac{1}{2}\%$

Use the percent formula, A = PB: A is P percent of B, to solve Exercises 35–38.

35. What is 3% of 200? **36.** What is 8% of 300?
37. What is 18% of 40? **38.** What is 16% of 90?

• Practice Plus

There are three basic types of percent problems that can be solved using the percent formula A = PB.

Question	Given	Percent Formula
What is *P* percent of *B*?	*P* and *B*	Solve for *A*.
A is *P* percent of what?	*A* and *P*	Solve for *B*.
A is what percent of *B*?	*A* and *B*	Solve for *P*.

Exercises 35–38 involved using the formula to answer the first question. In Exercises 39–46, use the percent formula to answer the second or third question.

39. 3 is 60% of what?

40. 8 is 40% of what?

41. 24% of what number is 40.8?

42. 32% of what number is 51.2?

43. 3 is what percent of 15?

44. 18 is what percent of 90?

45. What percent of 2.5 is 0.3?

46. What percent of 7.5 is 0.6?

• Application Exercises

47. Suppose that the local sales tax rate is 6% and you purchase a car for $16,800.

a. How much tax is paid?

b. What is the car's total cost?

48. Suppose that the local sales tax rate is 7% and you purchase a graphing calculator for $96.

a. How much tax is paid?

b. What is the calculator's total cost?

49. An exercise machine with an original price of $860 is on sale at 12% off.

a. What is the discount amount?

b. What is the exercise machine's sale price?

50. A dictionary that normally sells for $16.50 is on sale at 40% off.

a. What is the discount amount?

b. What is the dictionary's sale price?

In Exercises 51–54, use the 2005 marginal tax rates in Table 8.1 on page 448 to calculate the income tax owed by each person.

51. Single male, no dependents

Gross income: $75,000

Adjustments: $4000

Deductions:

$28,000 mortgage interest

$4200 property taxes

$3000 charitable contributions

Tax credit: none

52. Single female, no dependents

Gross income: $70,000

Adjustments: $2000

Deductions:

$10,000 mortgage interest

$2500 property taxes

$1200 charitable contributions

Tax credit: none

53. Unmarried head of household with two dependent children

Gross income: $50,000

Adjustments: none

Deductions:

$4500 state taxes

$2000 theft loss

Tax credit: $2000

54. Unmarried head of household with one dependent child

Gross income: $40,000

Adjustments: $1500

Deductions:

$3600 state taxes
$800 charitable contributions

Tax credit: $2500

In addition to income tax, we are required to pay the federal government FICA (Federal Insurance Contribution Act) taxes that are used for Social Security and Medicare benefits. For people who are not self-employed, the 2005 FICA tax rates were as follows:

- *7.65% on the first $90,000 from wages and tips*
- *1.45% on income in excess of $90,000.*

The individual's employer must also pay matching amounts of FICA taxes. People who are self-employed pay double the rates shown above. Taxpayers are not permitted to subtract adjustments, exemptions, or deductions when determining FICA taxes. Use this information to solve Exercises 55–60.

55. If you are not self-employed and earn $100,000, what are your FICA taxes?

56. If you are not self-employed and earn $120,000, what are your FICA taxes?

57. If you are self-employed and earn $140,000, what are your FICA taxes?

58. If you are self-employed and earn $160,000, what are your FICA taxes?

59. In 2005, to help pay for college, you worked part-time at a local restaurant, earning $20,000 in wages and tips.

a. Calculate your FICA taxes.

b. Use Table 8.1 on page 448 to calculate your income tax. Assume you are single with no dependents, have no adjustments or tax credit, and you take the standard deduction.

c. Including both FICA and income tax, what percent of your gross income are your federal taxes? Round to the nearest tenth of a percent.

60. In 2005, to help pay for college, you worked part-time at a local restaurant, earning $18,000 in wages and tips.

a. Calculate your FICA taxes.

b. Use Table 8.1 on page 448 to calculate your income tax. Assume you are single with no dependents, have no adjustments or tax credit, and take the standard deduction.

c. Including both FICA and income tax, what percent of your gross income are your federal taxes? Round to the nearest tenth of a percent.

The table shows the fastest-growing U.S. jobs, by number of 2004 employees and expected employees in 2014.

Fastest-Growing U.S. Jobs

Occupation	Number of jobs (thousands) 2004	2014
Home Health Aides	624	974
Medical Assistants	387	589
Physician Assistants	62	93
Computer Software Engineers	460	682
Physical Therapist Assistants	59	85
Dental Hygienists	158	226

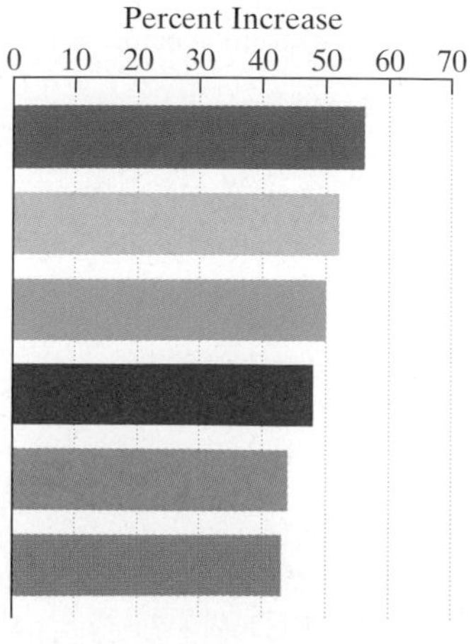

Source: Bureau of Labor Statistics

In Exercises 61–64, use the number of jobs given at the bottom of the previous page to find the percent increase, to the nearest tenth of a percent, in the number of employees in the given occuptation from 2004 to 2014.

61. home health aides

62. medical assistants

63. physician assistants

64. computer software engineers

65. A sofa regularly sells for $840. The sale price is $714. Find the percent decrease of the sale price from the regular price.

66. A FAX machine regularly sells for $380. The sale price is $266. Find the percent decrease of the sale price from the regular price.

67. Suppose that you have $10,000 in a rather risky investment recommended by your financial advisor. During the first year, your investment decreases by 30% of its original value. During the second year, your investment increases by 40% of its first-year value. Your advisor tells you that there must have been a 10% overall increase of your original $10,000 investment. Is your financial advisor using percentages properly? If not, what is your actual percent gain or loss of your original $10,000 investment?

68. The price of a color printer is reduced by 30% of its original price. When it still does not sell, its price is reduced by 20% of the reduced price. The salesperson informs you that there has been a total reduction of 50%. Is the salesperson using percentages properly? If not, what is the actual percent reduction from the original price?

• Writing in Mathematics

69. What is a percent?

70. Describe how to express a decimal number as a percent and give an example.

71. Describe how to express a percent as a decimal number and give an example.

72. Explain how to use the sales tax rate to determine an item's total cost.

73. A common complaint about income tax is "I can't afford to work more because it will put me in a higher tax bracket." Is it possible that being in a higher bracket means you actually lose money? Explain your answer.

74. Because of the mortgage interest tax deduction, is it possible to save money buying a house rather than renting, even though rent payments are lower than mortgage payments? Explain your answer.

75. Describe how to find percent increase and give an example.

• Critical Thinking Exercises

76. Which one of the following is true?

a. If your weight increases by 5% this year and 5% next year, the increase in weight over two years is 10%.

b. A grade point average that increases by 10% this semester and decreases by 10% next semester will be unchanged after two semesters.

c. If $\frac{1}{10}$ of a person's salary is spent for clothing, $\frac{1}{3}$ for food, and $\frac{1}{5}$ for rent, the percent of the salary that is left is $36\frac{2}{3}\%$.

d. If the amount that a person spends on rent increases from 20% to 30% of that person's income, the percent increase is 10%.

77. A condominium is taxed based on its $78,500 value. The tax rate is $3.40 for every $100 of value. If the tax is paid before March 1, 3% of the normal tax is given as a discount. How much tax is paid if the condominium owner takes advantage of the discount?

78. In January, each of 60 people purchased a $200 washing machine. In February, 10% fewer customers purchased the same washing machine that had increased in price by 20%. What was the change in sales from January to February?

• Group Exercise

79. Group members should research and present a report on the Alternative Minimum Tax (AMT). How do the AMT calculations differ from the income tax calculations that we discussed in this section? What are some of the hot political issues surrounding the AMT? On whom will it have the greatest financial impact?

SECTION 8.2 • SIMPLE INTEREST

OBJECTIVES

1. Calculate simple interest.
2. Use the future value formula.
3. Use the simple interest formula on discounted loans.

In 1626, Peter Minuit convinced the Wappinger Indians to sell him Manhattan Island for $24. If the native Americans had put the $24 into a bank account at a 5% interest rate compounded monthly, by the year 2006 there would be well over $4 billion in the account!

Although you may not yet understand terms such as *interest rate* and *compounded monthly*, one thing seems clear: Money in certain savings accounts grows in remarkable ways. You, too, can take advantage of such accounts with astonishing results. In the next two sections, we will show you how.

1 Calculate simple interest.

Simple Interest

Interest is the dollar amount that we get paid for lending money or pay for borrowing money. When we deposit money in a savings institution, the institution pays us interest for its use. When we borrow money, interest is the price we pay for the privilege of using the money until we repay it.

The amount of money that we deposit or borrow is called the **principal**. For example, if you deposit \$2000 in a savings account, then \$2000 is the principal. The amount of interest depends on the principal, the interest **rate**, which is given as a percent and varies from bank to bank, and the length of time for which the money is deposited. In this section, the rate is assumed to be per year.

Simple interest involves interest calculated only on the principal. The following formula is used to find simple interest:

CALCULATING SIMPLE INTEREST

$$\text{Interest} = \text{principal} \times \text{rate} \times \text{time}$$
$$I = Prt$$

The rate, r, is expressed as a decimal when calculating simple interest.

EXAMPLE 1 CALCULATING SIMPLE INTEREST FOR A YEAR

You deposit \$2000 in a savings account at Hometown Bank, which has a rate of 6%. Find the interest at the end of the first year.

SOLUTION To find the interest at the end of the first year, we use the simple interest formula.

$$I = Prt = (2000)(0.06)(1) = 120$$

Principal, or amount deposited, is \$2000. Rate is 6% = 0.06. Time is 1 year.

At the end of the first year, the interest is \$120. You can withdraw the \$120 interest and you still have \$2000 in the savings account.

CHECK POINT 1 You deposit \$3000 in a savings account at Yourtown Bank, which has a rate of 5%. Find the interest at the end of the first year.

EXAMPLE 2 CALCULATING SIMPLE INTEREST FOR MORE THAN A YEAR

A student took out a simple interest loan for \$1800 for two years at a rate of 8% to purchase a used car. What is the interest on the loan?

SOLUTION To find the interest on the loan, we use the simple interest formula.

$$I = Prt = (1800)(0.08)(2) = 288$$

Principal, or amount borrowed, is \$1800. Rate is 8% = 0.08. Time is 2 years.

The interest on the loan is \$288.

CHECK POINT 2 A student took out a simple interest loan for \$2400 for two years at a rate of 7%. What is the interest on the loan?

Future Value: Principal Plus Interest

2 Use the future value formula.

When a loan is repaid, the interest is added to the original principal to find the total amount due. In Example 2, at the end of two years, the student will have to repay

$$\text{principal} + \text{interest} = \$1800 + \$288 = \$2088.$$

In general, if a principal P is borrowed at a simple interest rate r, then after t years the amount due, A, can be determined as follows:

$$A = P + I = P + Prt = P(1 + rt).$$

The amount due, A, is called the **future value** of the loan. The principal borrowed now, P, is also known as the loan's **present value**.

CALCULATING FUTURE VALUE FOR SIMPLE INTEREST

The future value, A, of P dollars at simple interest rate r (as a decimal) for t years is given by

$$A = P(1 + rt).$$

STUDY TIP

Throughout this chapter, keep in mind that all given rates are assumed to be *per year*, unless otherwise stated.

EXAMPLE 3 CALCULATING FUTURE VALUE

A loan of \$1060 has been made at 6.5% for three months. Find the loan's future value.

SOLUTION The amount borrowed, or principal, P, is \$1060. The rate, r, is 6.5%, or 0.065. The time, t, is given as 3 months. We need to express the time in years because the rate is understood to be 6.5% per year. Because 3 months is $\frac{3}{12}$ of a year, $t = \frac{3}{12} = \frac{1}{4} = 0.25$.

The loan's future value, or the total amount due after three months, is

$$A = P(1 + rt) = 1060[1 + (0.065)(0.25)] \approx \$1077.23.$$

Rounded to the nearest cent, the loan's future value is \$1077.23.

CHECK POINT 3 A loan of \$2040 has been made at 7.5% for four months. Find the loan's future value.

Simple interest is used for many short-term loans, including automobile and consumer loans. Imagine that a short-term loan is taken for 125 days. The time of the loan is $\frac{125}{365}$ because there are 365 days in a year. However, the **Banker's rule** allows financial institutions to use 360 in the denominator of such a fraction, claiming that this simplifies the interest calculation. The time, t, for a 125-day short-term loan is

$$\frac{125 \cancel{\text{ days}}}{360 \cancel{\text{ days}}} = \frac{125}{360}.$$

Consumer groups question whether a year should be simplified to 360 days. Why? Compare the values for time, t, for a 125-day short-term loan using denominators of 360 and 365.

$$\frac{125}{360} \approx 0.347 \qquad \frac{125}{365} \approx 0.342$$

The denominator of 360 benefits the bank by resulting in a greater period of time for the loan, and consequently more interest.

The formula for future value, $A = P(1 + rt)$, has four variables. If we are given values for any three of these variables, we can solve for the fourth.

EXAMPLE 4 DETERMINING A SIMPLE INTEREST RATE

You borrow $2500 from a friend and promise to pay back $2655 in six months. What simple interest rate will you pay?

SOLUTION We use the formula for future value, $A = P(1 + rt)$. You borrow \$2500: $P = 2500$. You will pay back \$2655, so this is the future value: $A = 2655$. You will do this in six months, which must be expressed in years: $t = \frac{6}{12} = \frac{1}{2} = 0.5$. To determine the simple interest rate you will pay, we solve the future value formula for r.

$A = P(1 + rt)$	This is the formula for future value.
$2655 = 2500[1 + r(0.5)]$	Substitute the given values.
$2655 = 2500 + 1250r$	Use the distributive property.
$155 = 1250r$	Subtract 2500 from both sides.
$\frac{155}{1250} = \frac{1250r}{1250}$	Divide both sides by 1250.
$r = 0.124 = 12.4\%$	Express $\frac{155}{1250}$ as a percent.

You will pay a simple interest rate of 12.4%.

CHECK POINT 4 You borrow $5000 from a friend and promise to pay back $6800 in two years. What simple interest rate will you pay?

EXAMPLE 5 DETERMINING A PRESENT VALUE

You plan to save $2000 for a trip to Europe in two years. You decide to purchase a certificate of deposit (CD) from your bank that pays a simple interest rate of 4%. How much must you put in this CD now in order to have the $2000 in two years?

SOLUTION We use the formula for future value, $A = P(1 + rt)$. We are interested in finding the principal, P, or the present value.

$A = P(1 + rt)$	This is the formula for future value.
$2000 = P[1 + (0.04)(2)]$	A(future value) = \$2000, r(interest rate) = 0.04, and t = 2 (you want \$2000 in two years).
$2000 = 1.08P$	Simplify: $1 + (0.04)(2) = 1.08$.
$\frac{2000}{1.08} = \frac{1.08P}{1.08}$	Divide both sides by 1.08.
$P \approx 1851.852$	Simplify.

To make sure you will have enough money for the vacation, let's round this principal *up* to $1851.86. Thus, you should put $1851.86 in the CD now to have $2000 in two years.

CHECK POINT 5 How much should you put in an investment paying a simple interest rate of 8% if you need $4000 in six months?

3 Use the simple interest formula on discounted loans.

Discounted Loans

Some lenders collect the interest from the amount of the loan at the time that the loan is made. This type of loan is called a **discounted loan**. The interest that is deducted from the loan is the **discount**.

EXAMPLE 6 A DISCOUNTED LOAN

You borrow \$10,000 on a 10% discounted loan for a period of 8 months.

a. What is the loan's discount?

b. Determine the net amount of money you receive.

c. What is the loan's actual interest rate?

SOLUTION

a. Because the loan's discount is the deducted interest, we use the simple interest formula.

$$I = Prt = (10{,}000)(0.10)\left(\tfrac{2}{3}\right) \approx 666.67$$

Principal is \$10,000. Rate is 10% = 0.10. Time is 8 months $= \frac{8}{12} = \frac{2}{3}$ year.

The loan's discount is \$666.67.

b. The net amount that you receive is the amount of the loan, \$10,000, minus the discount, \$666.67:

$$10{,}000 - 666.67 = 9333.33.$$

Thus, you receive \$9333.33.

c. We can calculate the loan's actual interest rate, rather than the stated 10%, by using the simple interest formula.

$I = Prt$ — This is the simple interest formula.

$666.67 = (9333.33)r\left(\frac{2}{3}\right)$ — I(interest) = \$666.67, P (principal, or the net amount received) = \$9333.33, and $t = \frac{2}{3}$ year.

$666.67 = 6222.22r$ — Simplify: $9333.33\left(\frac{2}{3}\right) = 6222.22$.

$r = \frac{666.67}{6222.22} \approx 0.107 = 10.7\%$ — Solve for r and express r to the nearest tenth of a percent.

The actual rate of interest on the 10% discounted loan is approximately 10.7%.

CHECK POINT 6 You borrow \$5000 on a 12% discounted loan for a period of two years. Determine: **a.** the loan's discount; **b.** the net amount you receive; **c.** the actual interest rate.

EXERCISE SET 8.2

• Practice Exercises

In Exercises 1–8, the principal P is borrowed at simple interest rate r for a period of time t. Find the simple interest owed for the use of the money. Assume 360 days in a year and round answers to the nearest cent.

1. $P = \$4000, r = 6\%, t = 1$ year

2. $P = \$7000, r = 5\%, t = 1$ year

3. $P = \$180, r = 3\%, t = 2$ years

4. $P = \$260, r = 4\%, t = 3$ years

5. $P = \$5000, r = 8.5\%, t = 9$ months

6. $P = \$18{,}000, r = 7.5\%, t = 18$ months

7. $P = \$15{,}500, r = 11\%, t = 90$ days

8. $P = \$12{,}600, r = 9\%, t = 60$ days

In Exercises 9–14, the principal P is borrowed at simple interest rate r for a period of time t. Find the loan's future value, A, or the total amount due at time t. Round answers to the nearest cent.

9. $P = \$3000, r = 7\%, t = 2$ years

10. $P = \$2000, r = 6\%, t = 3$ years

11. $P = \$26{,}000$, $r = 9.5\%$, $t = 5$ years

12. $P = \$24{,}000$, $r = 8.5\%$, $t = 6$ years

13. $P = \$9000$, $r = 6.5\%$, $t = 8$ months

14. $P = \$6000$, $r = 4.5\%$, $t = 9$ months

In Exercises 15–20, the principal P is borrowed and the loan's future value, A, at time t is given. Determine the loan's simple interest rate, r, to the nearest tenth of a percent.

15. $P = \$2000$, $A = \$2150$, $t = 1$ year

16. $P = \$3000$, $A = \$3180$, $t = 1$ year

17. $P = \$5000$, $A = \$5900$, $t = 2$ years

18. $P = \$10{,}000$, $A = \$14{,}060$, $t = 2$ years

19. $P = \$2300$, $A = \$2840$, $t = 9$ months

20. $P = \$1700$, $A = \$1820$, $t = 6$ months

In Exercises 21–26, determine the present value, P, you must invest to have the future value, A, at simple interest rate r after time t. Round answers up to the nearest cent.

21. $A = \$6000$, $r = 8\%$, $t = 2$ years

22. $A = \$8500$, $r = 7\%$, $t = 3$ years

23. $A = \$14{,}000$, $r = 9.5\%$, $t = 6$ years

24. $A = \$16{,}000$, $r = 11.5\%$, $t = 5$ years

25. $A = \$5000$, $r = 14.5\%$, $t = 9$ months

26. $A = \$2000$, $r = 12.6\%$, $t = 8$ months

Exercises 27–30 involve discounted loans. In each exercise, determine

a. *the loan's discount.*

b. *the net amount of money you receive.*

c. *the loan's actual interest rate, to the nearest tenth of a percent.*

27. You borrow \$2000 on a 7% discounted loan for a period of 8 months.

28. You borrow \$3000 on an 8% discounted loan for a period of 9 months.

29. You borrow \$12,000 on a 6.5% discounted loan for a period of two years.

30. You borrow \$20,000 on an 8.5% discounted loan for a period of three years.

• Practice Plus

31. Solve for r: $A = P(1 + rt)$.

32. Solve for t: $A = P(1 + rt)$.

33. Solve for P: $A = P(1 + rt)$.

34. Solve for P: $A = P\left(1 + \frac{r}{n}\right)^{nt}$. (We will be using this formula in the next section.)

• Application Exercises

35. In order to start a small business, a student takes out a simple interest loan for \$4000 for 9 months at a rate of 8.25%.

    a. How much interest must the student pay?

    b. Find the future value of the loan.

36. In order to pay for baseball uniforms, a school takes out a simple interest loan for \$20,000 for 7 months at a rate of 12%.

    a. How much interest must the school pay?

    b. Find the future value of the loan.

37. You borrow \$1400 from a friend and promise to pay back \$2000 in two years. What simple interest rate, to the nearest tenth of a percent, will you pay?

38. Treasury bills (T-bills) can be purchased from the U.S. Treasury Department. You buy a T-bill for \$981.60 that pays \$1000 in 13 weeks. What simple interest rate, to the nearest tenth of a percent, does this T-bill earn?

39. A bank offers a CD that pays a simple interest rate of 6.5%. How much must you put in this CD now in order to have \$3000 for a home-entertainment center in two years? Round *up* to the nearest cent.

40. A bank offers a CD that pays a simple interest rate of 5.5%. How much must you put in this CD now in order to have \$8000 for a kitchen remodeling project in two years? Round *up* to the nearest cent.

• Writing in Mathematics

41. Explain how to calculate simple interest.

42. What is the future value of a loan and how is it determined?

43. What is a discounted loan? How is the net amount of money received from such a loan determined?

• Critical Thinking Exercises

44. Use the future value formula to show that the time required for an amount of money P to double in value to $2P$ is given by

$$t = \frac{1}{r}.$$

45. You deposit \$5000 in an account that earns 5.5% simple interest.

    a. Express the future value in the account as a linear function of time, t.

    b. Determine the slope of the function in part (a) and describe what this means. Use the phrase "rate of change" in your description.

SECTION 8.3 • COMPOUND INTEREST

OBJECTIVES

1. Use compound interest formulas.
2. Calculate present value.
3. Understand and compute effective annual yield.

So, how did the present value of Manhattan in 1626—that is, the \$24 paid to the native Americans—attain a future value of over \$4 billion in 2006, 380 years later, at a mere 5% interest rate? After all, the future value on \$24 for 380 years at 5% simple interest is

$$A = P(1 + rt)$$
$$= 24[1 + (0.05)(380)] = 480,$$

or a paltry \$480, compared to over \$4 billion. To understand this dramatic difference in future value, we turn to the concept of *compound interest*.

1 Use compound interest formulas.

Compound Interest

Compound interest is interest computed on the original principal as well as on any accumulated interest. Many savings accounts pay compound interest. For example, suppose you deposit \$1000 in a savings account at a rate of 5%. Table 8.2 shows how the investment grows if the interest earned is automatically added on to the principal.

TABLE 8.2 CALCULATING THE AMOUNT IN AN ACCOUNT SUBJECT TO COMPOUND INTEREST

Use $A = P(1 + rt)$ with $r = 0.05$ and $t = 1$, or $A = P(1 + 0.05)$.

Year	Starting Balance	Amount in the Account at Year's End
1	\$1000	$A = \$1000(1 + 0.05) = \$1050$
2	\$1050 or $\$1000(1 + 0.05)$	$A = \$1050(1 + 0.05) = \$1102.50$ or $A = \$1000(1 + 0.05)(1 + 0.05) = \$1000(1 + 0.05)^2$
3	\$1102.50 or $\$1000(1 + 0.05)^2$	$A = \$1102.50(1 + 0.05) \approx \$1157.63$ or $A = \$1000(1 + 0.05)^2(1 + 0.05) = \$1000(1 + 0.05)^3$

Using inductive reasoning, the amount, A, in the account after t years is the original principal, \$1000, times $(1 + 0.05)^t$: $A = 1000(1 + 0.05)^t$.

If the original principal is P and the interest rate is r, we can use this same approach to determine the amount, A, in an account subject to compound interest.

CALCULATING THE AMOUNT IN AN ACCOUNT FOR COMPOUND INTEREST PAID ONCE A YEAR

If you deposit P dollars at rate r, in decimal form, subject to compound interest, then the amount, A, of money in the account after t years is given by

$$A = P(1 + r)^t.$$

The amount A is called the account's **future value** and the principal P is called its **present value**.

EXAMPLE 1 USING THE COMPOUND INTEREST FORMULA

You deposit \$2000 in a savings account at Hometown Bank, which has a rate of 6%.

a. Find the amount, A, of money in the account after 3 years subject to compound interest.

b. Find the interest.

SOLUTION

a. The amount deposited, or principal, P, is \$2000. The rate, r, is 6%, or 0.06. The time of the deposit, t, is three years. The amount in the account after three years is

$$A = P(1 + r)^t = 2000(1 + 0.06)^3 = 2000(1.06)^3 \approx 2382.03.$$

Rounded to the nearest cent, the amount in the savings account after three years is \$2382.03.

b. Because the amount in the account is \$2382.03 and the original principal is \$2000, the interest is \$2382.03 − \$2000, or \$382.03.

TECHNOLOGY

Here are the calculator keystrokes to compute $2000(1.06)^3$:

MANY SCIENTIFIC CALCULATORS

2000 [×] 1.06 [y^x] 3 [=]

MANY GRAPHING CALCULATORS

2000 [×] 1.06 [∧] 3 [ENTER] .

CHECK POINT 1 You deposit \$1000 in a savings account at a bank that has a rate of 4%.

a. Find the amount, A, of money in the account after 5 years subject to compound interest. Round to the nearest cent.

b. Find the interest.

Compound Interest Paid More Than Once a Year

The period of time between two interest payments is called the **compounding period**. When compound interest is paid once per year, the compounding period is one year. We say that the interest is **compounded annually**.

Most savings institutions have plans in which interest is paid more than once per year. If compound interest is paid twice per year, the compounding period is six months. We say that the interest is **compounded semiannually**. When compound interest is paid four times per year, the compounding period is three months and the interest is said to be **compounded quarterly**. Some plans allow for monthly compounding or daily compounding.

In general, when compound interest is paid n times per year, we say that there are ***n* compounding periods per year**. The following formula is used to calculate the amount in an account subject to compound interest with n compounding periods per year:

CALCULATING THE AMOUNT IN AN ACCOUNT FOR COMPOUND INTEREST PAID n TIMES A YEAR

If you deposit P dollars at rate r, in decimal form, subject to compound interest paid n times per year, then the amount, A, of money in the account after t years is given by

$$A = P\left(1 + \frac{r}{n}\right)^{nt}.$$

A is the account's **future value** and the principal P is its **present value**.

EXAMPLE 2 USING THE COMPOUND INTEREST FORMULA

You deposit \$7500 in a savings account that has a rate of 6%. The interest is compounded monthly.

a. How much money will you have after five years?

b. Find the interest after five years.

TECHNOLOGY

Here are the calculator keystrokes to compute

$$7500\left(1 + \frac{0.06}{12}\right)^{12\cdot 5}:$$

MANY SCIENTIFIC CALCULATORS

7500 [×] [(] 1 [+] .06 [÷] 12 [)] [y^x] [(] 12 [×] 5 [)] [=]

MANY GRAPHING CALCULATORS

7500 [(] 1 [+] .06 [÷] 12 [)] [∧] [(] 12 [×] 5 [)] [ENTER].

SOLUTION

a. The amount deposited, or principal, P, is \$7500. The rate, r, is 6%, or 0.06. Because interest is compounded monthly, there are 12 compounding periods per year, so $n = 12$. The time of the deposit, t, is five years. The amount in the account after five years is

$$A = P\left(1 + \frac{r}{n}\right)^{nt} = 7500\left(1 + \frac{0.06}{12}\right)^{12\cdot 5} = 7500(1.005)^{60} \approx 10{,}116.38.$$

Rounded to the nearest cent, you will have \$10,116.38 after five years.

b. Because the amount in the account is \$10,116.38 and the original principal is \$7500, the interest after five years is \$10,116.38 − \$7500, or \$2616.38.

CHECK POINT 2 You deposit \$4200 in a savings account that has a rate of 4%. The interest is compounded quarterly.

a. How much money will you have after ten years? Round to the nearest cent.

b. Find the interest after ten years.

Continuous Compounding

Some banks use **continuous compounding**, where the compounding periods increase infinitely (compounding interest every trillionth of a second, every quadrillionth of a second, etc.). As n, the number of compounding periods in a year, increases without bound, the expression $\left(1 + \frac{1}{n}\right)^n$ approaches the irrational number e: $e \approx 2.71828$. This is illustrated in Table 8.3. As a result, the formula for the balance in an account with n compoundings per year, $A = P\left(1 + \frac{r}{n}\right)^{nt}$, becomes $A = Pe^{rt}$ with continuous compounding. Although continuous compounding sounds terrific, it yields only a fraction of a percent more interest over a year than daily compounding.

TABLE 8.3 AS n TAKES ON INCREASINGLY LARGE VALUES, THE EXPRESSION $\left(1 + \frac{1}{n}\right)^n$ APPROACHES THE IRRATIONAL NUMBER e.

n	$\left(1 + \frac{1}{n}\right)^n$
1	2
2	2.25
5	2.48832
10	2.59374246
100	2.704813829
1000	2.716923932
10,000	2.718145927
100,000	2.718268237
1,000,000	2.718280469
1,000,000,000	2.718281827

FORMULAS FOR COMPOUND INTEREST

After t years, the balance, A, in an account with principal P and annual interest rate r (in decimal form) is given by the following formulas:

1. For n compoundings per year: $A = P\left(1 + \frac{r}{n}\right)^{nt}$

2. For continuous compounding: $A = Pe^{rt}$.

TECHNOLOGY

You can compute e to a power using the [e^x] key on your calculator. Use the key to enter e^1 and verify that e is approximately equal to 2.71828.

Scientific Calculators	Graphing Calculators
1 [e^x]	[e^x] 1 [ENTER]

EXAMPLE 3 CHOOSING BETWEEN INVESTMENTS

You decide to invest \$8000 for 6 years and you have a choice between two accounts. The first pays 7% per year, compounded monthly. The second pays 6.85% per year, compounded continuously. Which is the better investment?

SOLUTION The better investment is the one with the greater balance in the account after 6 years. Let's begin with the account with monthly compounding. We use the compound interest formula with $P = 8000$, $r = 7\% = 0.07$, $n = 12$ (monthly compounding means 12 compoundings per year), and $t = 6$.

$$A = P\left(1 + \frac{r}{n}\right)^{nt} = 8000\left(1 + \frac{0.07}{12}\right)^{12 \cdot 6} \approx 12{,}160.84$$

The balance in this account after 6 years would be \$12,160.84.

For the second investment option, we use the formula for continuous compounding with $P = 8000$, $r = 6.85\% = 0.0685$, and $t = 6$.

$$A = Pe^{rt} = 8000e^{0.0685(6)} \approx 12{,}066.60$$

The balance in this account after 6 years would be \$12,066.60, slightly less than the previous amount. Thus, the better investment is the 7% monthly compounding option.

TECHNOLOGY

Here are the calculator keystrokes to compute

$8000e^{0.0685(6)}$:

MANY SCIENTIFIC CALCULATORS

8000 [×] [(] .0685 [×] 6 [)] [e^x] [=]

MANY GRAPHING CALCULATORS

8000 [e^x] [(] .0685 [×] 6 [)] [ENTER]

CHECK POINT 3 A sum of \$10,000 is invested at an annual rate of 8%. Find the balance in the account after 5 years subject to **a.** quarterly compounding and **b.** continuous compounding.

2 Calculate present value.

Planning for the Future with Compound Interest

Just as we did in Section 8.2, we can determine P, the principal or present value, that should be deposited now in order to have a certain amount, A, in the future. If an account earns compound interest, the amount of money that should be invested today to obtain a future value of A dollars can be determined by solving the compound interest formula for P:

CALCULATING PRESENT VALUE

If A dollars are to be accumulated in t years in an account that pays rate r compounded n times per year, then the present value, P, that needs to be invested now is given by

$$P = \frac{A}{\left(1 + \frac{r}{n}\right)^{nt}}.$$

EXAMPLE 4 CALCULATING PRESENT VALUE

How much money should be deposited in an account today that earns 8% compounded monthly so that it will accumulate to \$20,000 in five years?

SOLUTION The amount we need today, or the present value, is determined by the present value formula. Because the interest is compounded monthly, $n = 12$. Furthermore, A (the future value) = \$20,000, r (the rate) = 8% = 0.08, and t (time in years) = 5.

$$P = \frac{A}{\left(1 + \frac{r}{n}\right)^{nt}} = \frac{20{,}000}{\left(1 + \frac{0.08}{12}\right)^{12 \cdot 5}} \approx 13{,}424.21$$

Approximately \$13,424.21 should be invested today in order to accumulate to \$20,000 in five years.

TECHNOLOGY

Here are the keystrokes for Example 4:

MANY SCIENTIFIC CALCULATORS

20000 [÷] [(] 1 [+] .08 [÷] 12 [)]

[y^x] [(] 12 [×] 5 [)] [=]

MANY GRAPHING CALCULATORS

20000 [÷] [(] 1 [+] .08 [÷] 12 [)]

[∧] [(] 12 [×] 5 [)] [ENTER].

CHECK POINT 4 How much money should be deposited in an account today that earns 6% compounded weekly so that it will accumulate to \$10,000 in eight years?

3 Understand and compute effective annual yield.

Effective Annual Yield

As we've seen before, a common problem in financial planning is selecting the best investment from two or more investments. For example, is an investment that pays 8.25% interest compounded quarterly better than one that pays 8.3% interest compounded semiannually? Another way to answer the question is to compare their *effective rates*, also called their *effective annual yields*.

EFFECTIVE ANNUAL YIELD

The **effective annual yield**, or the **effective rate**, is the simple interest rate that produces the same amount of money in an account at the end of one year as when the account is subjected to compound interest at a stated rate.

BLITZER BONUS

Doubling Your Money: The Rule of 72

Here's a shortcut for estimating the number of years it will take for your investment to double: Divide 72 by the effective annual yield without the percent sign. For example, if the effective annual yield is 6%, your money will double in approximately

$$\frac{72}{6}$$

years, or in 12 years.

EXAMPLE 5 UNDERSTANDING EFFECTIVE ANNUAL YIELD

You deposit \$4000 in an account that pays 8% interest compounded monthly.

a. Find the future value after one year.

b. Use the future value formula for simple interest to determine the effective annual yield.

SOLUTION

a. We use the compound interest formula to find the account's future value after one year.

$$A = P\left(1+\frac{r}{n}\right)^{nt} = 4000\left(1+\frac{0.08}{12}\right)^{12\cdot 1} \approx \$4332.00$$

Principal is \$4000. Stated rate is 8% = 0.08. Monthly compounding: $n = 12$ Time is one year: $t = 1$.

Rounded to the nearest cent, the future value after one year is \$4332.00.

b. The effective annual yield, or effective rate, **is a simple interest rate**. We use the future value formula for simple interest to determine the simple interest rate that produces a future value of \$4332 for a \$4000 deposit after one year.

$A = P(1 + rt)$ This is the future value formula for simple interest.

$4332 = 4000(1 + r\cdot 1)$ Substitute the given values.

$4332 = 4000 + 4000r$ Use the distributive property.

$332 = 4000r$ Subtract 4000 from both sides.

$\frac{332}{4000} = \frac{4000r}{4000}$ Divide both sides by 4000.

$r = \frac{332}{4000} = 0.083 = 8.3\%$ Express r as a percent.

The effective annual yield, or effective rate, is 8.3%. This means that money invested at 8.3% simple interest earns the same amount in one year as money invested at 8% interest compounded monthly.

In Example 5, the stated 8% rate is called the **nominal rate**. The 8.3% rate is the effective rate and is a simple interest rate.

CHECK POINT 5 You deposit \$6000 in an account that pays 10% interest compounded monthly.

a. Find the future value after one year.

b. Determine the effective annual yield.

BLITZER BONUS

High-Yield Savings

Online banks can afford to pay the best rates on savings accounts by avoiding the expense of managing a brick-and-mortar bank. To search for the best deals, go to BankRate.com for bank accounts and iMoneyNet.com for money-market funds.

Generalizing the procedure of Example 5 and Check Point 5 gives a formula for effective annual yield:

CALCULATING EFFECTIVE ANNUAL YIELD

Suppose that an investment has a nominal interest rate, r, in decimal form, and pays compound interest n times per year. The investment's effective annual yield, Y, is given by

$$Y = \left(1 + \frac{r}{n}\right)^n - 1.$$

TECHNOLOGY

Here are the keystrokes for Example 6:

MANY SCIENTIFIC CALCULATORS

(1 + .05 ÷ 360) y^x 360

− 1 =

MANY GRAPHING CALCULATORS

(1 + .05 ÷ 360) ∧ 360

− 1 ENTER .

Given the nominal rate and the number of compounding periods per year, some graphing calculators display the effective annual yield. The screen shows the calculation of the effective rate in Example 6 on the TI-83 Plus.

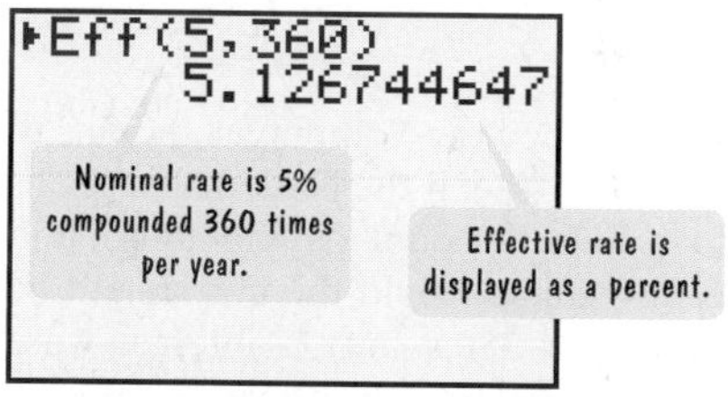

EXAMPLE 6 CALCULATING EFFECTIVE ANNUAL YIELD

A passbook savings account has a nominal rate of 5%. The interest is compounded daily. Find the account's effective annual yield. (Assume 360 days in a year.)

SOLUTION The rate, r, is 5%, or 0.05. Because interest is compounded daily and we assume 360 days in a year, $n = 360$. The account's effective annual yield is

$$Y = \left(1 + \frac{r}{n}\right)^n - 1 = \left(1 + \frac{0.05}{360}\right)^{360} - 1 \approx 0.0513 = 5.13\%.$$

The effective annual yield is 5.13%. Thus, money invested at 5.13% simple interest earns the same amount of interest in one year as money invested at 5% interest, the nominal rate, compounded daily.

CHECK POINT 6 What is the effective annual yield of an account paying 8% compounded quarterly?

The effective annual yield is often included in the information about investments or loans. Because it's the true interest rate you're earning or paying, it's the number you should pay attention to. **If you are selecting the best investment from two or more investments, the best choice is the account with the greatest effective annual yield.** However, there are differences in the types of accounts that you need to take into consideration. Some pay interest from the day of deposit to the day of withdrawal. Other accounts start paying interest the first day of the month that follows the day of deposit. Some savings institutions stop paying interest if the balance in the account falls below a certain amount.

When borrowing money, the effective rate or effective annual yield is usually called the **annual percentage rate**. If all other factors are equal and you are borrowing money, select the option with the least annual percentage rate. In the section on installment buying, we will discuss annual percentage rates in more detail.

EXERCISE SET 8.3

• Practice Exercises

In Exercises 1–12, the principal represents an amount of money deposited in a savings account subject to compound interest at the given rate.

a. *Use the formula* $A = P(1 + r)^t$ *for one compounding period per year or* $A = P\left(1 + \frac{r}{n}\right)^{nt}$ *for n compounding periods per year to find how much money there will be in the account after the given number of years. (Assume 360 days in a year.)*

b. *Find the interest earned.*

Round answers to the nearest cent.

Principal	Rate	Compounded	Time
1. \$10,000	4%	annually	2 years
2. \$8000	6%	annually	3 years
3. \$3000	5%	semiannually	4 years
4. \$4000	4%	semiannually	5 years
5. \$9500	6%	quarterly	5 years
6. \$2500	8%	quarterly	6 years
7. \$4500	4.5%	monthly	3 years
8. \$2500	6.5%	monthly	4 years
9. \$1500	8.5%	daily	2.5 years
10. \$1200	8.5%	daily	3.5 years
11. \$20,000	4.5%	daily	20 years
12. \$25,000	5.5%	daily	20 years

Use the compound interest formulas $A = P\left(1 + \frac{r}{n}\right)^{nt}$ *and* $A = Pe^{rt}$ *to solve Exercises 13–16. Round answers to the nearest cent.*

13. Find the accumulated value of an investment of \$10,000 for 5 years at an interest rate of 5.5% if the money is **a.** compounded semiannually; **b.** compounded quarterly; **c.** compounded monthly; **d.** compounded continuously.

14. Find the accumulated value of an investment of \$5000 for 10 years at an interest rate of 6.5% if the money is **a.** compounded semiannually; **b.** compounded quarterly; **c.** compounded monthly; **d.** compounded continuously.

15. Suppose that you have \$12,000 to invest. Which investment yields the greater return over 3 years: 7% compounded monthly or 6.85% compounded continuously?

16. Suppose that you have \$6000 to invest. Which investment yields the greater return over 4 years: 8.25% compounded quarterly or 8.3% compounded semiannually?

Solve Exercises 17–20 using the present value formula:

$$P = \frac{A}{\left(1 + \frac{r}{n}\right)^{nt}}.$$

Round answers up to the nearest cent.

17. How much money should be deposited today in an account that earns 6% compounded semiannually so that it will accumulate to \$10,000 in three years?

18. How much money should be deposited today in an account that earns 7% compounded semiannually so that it will accumulate to \$12,000 in four years?

19. How much money should be deposited today in an account that earns 9.5% compounded monthly so that it will accumulate to \$10,000 in three years?

20. How much money should be deposited today in an account that earns 10.5% compounded monthly so that it will accumulate to \$22,000 in four years?

21. You deposit \$10,000 in an account that pays 4.5% interest compounded quarterly.

a. Find the future value after one year.

b. Use the future value formula for simple interest to determine the effective annual yield.

22. You deposit \$12,000 in an account that pays 6.5% interest compounded quarterly.

a. Find the future value after one year.

b. Use the future value formula for simple interest to determine the effective annual yield.

Solve Exercises 23–28 using the effective annual yield formula:

$$Y = \left(1 + \frac{r}{n}\right)^{n} - 1.$$

A passbook savings account has a rate of 6%. Find the effective annual yield, rounded to the nearest tenth of a percent, if the interest is compounded

23. semiannually.

24. quarterly.

25. monthly.

26. daily. (Assume 360 days in a year.)

27. 1000 times per year.

28. 100,000 times per year.

In Exercises 29–32, determine the effective annual yield, to the nearest tenth of a percent, for each investment. Then select the better investment. Assume 360 days in a year.

29. 8% compounded monthly; 8.25% compounded annually

30. 5% compounded monthly; 5.25% compounded quarterly

31. 5.5% compounded semiannually; 5.4% compounded daily

32. 7% compounded annually; 6.85% compounded daily

• Practice Plus

In Exercises 33–38, assume that you place money in an account subject to interest compounded annually. Use the formula $A = P(1 + r)^t$*, a calculator, and trial and error to answer each question. Give answers to the nearest tenth of a year.*

33. How long will it take for the investment to triple at an interest rate of 5%?

34. How long will it take for the investment to triple at an interest rate of 10%?

35. How long will it take for the investment to increase by 50% at an interest rate of 10%?

36. How long will it take for the investment to increase by 50% at an interest rate of 5%?

37. How long will it take for the investment to increase by 90% at an interest rate of 8%?

38. How long will it take for the investment to increase by 90% at an interest rate of 12%?

• Application Exercises

39. In 1626, Peter Minuit convinced the Wappinger Indians to sell him Manhattan Island for \$24. If the Native Americans had put the \$24 into a bank account paying compound interest at a 5% rate, how much would the investment be worth in the year 2006 ($t = 380$ years) if interest were compounded **a.** monthly? **b.** 360 times per year?

40. In 1777, Jacob DeHaven loaned George Washington's army \$450,000 in gold and supplies. Due to a disagreement over the method of repayment (gold versus Continental money), DeHaven was never repaid, dying penniless. In 1989, his descendants sued the U.S. government over the 212-year-old debt. If the DeHavens used an interest rate of 6% and daily compounding (the rate offered by the Continental Congress in 1777), how much money did the DeHaven family demand in their suit? (*Hint:* Use the compound interest formula with $n = 360$ and $t = 212$ years.)

41. At the time of her grandson's birth, a grandmother deposits \$10,000 in an account that pays 9% compounded monthly. What will be the value of the account at the child's twenty-first birthday, assuming that no other deposits or withdrawals are made during this period?

42. Parents wish to have \$80,000 available for a child's education. If the child is now 5 years old, how much money must be set aside at 6% compounded semiannually to meet their financial goal when the child is 18?

43. A 30-year-old worker plans to retire at age 65. He believes that \$500,000 is needed to retire comfortably. How much should be deposited now at 9% compounded monthly to meet the \$500,000 retirement goal?

44. In 2001, First Internet Bank of Indiana offered a money market account paying 4.5% interest compounded monthly. NetBank offered a money market account paying 4.4% interest compounded daily. (*Source:* www.bankrate.com) Which account is the better investment?

• Writing in Mathematics

45. Describe the difference between simple and compound interest.

46. Give two examples that illustrate the difference between a compound interest problem involving future value and a compound interest problem involving present value.

47. What is effective annual yield?

48. Explain how to select the best investment from two or more investments.

49. Shown are figures in an actual advertisement for Great Western Bank. Explain the meaning of the given percents, as well as the statement below these percents.

9.21%	8.85%
Yield	*Rate*

Interest compounded monthly

• Critical Thinking Exercises

50. A depositor opens a new savings account with $6000 at 5% compounded semiannually. At the beginning of year 3, an additional $4000 is deposited. At the end of six years, what is the balance in the account?

51. A depositor opens a money market account with $5000 at 8% compounded monthly. After two years, $1500 is withdrawn from the account to buy a new computer. A year later, $2000 is put in the account. What will be the ending balance if the money is kept in the account for another three years?

52. Use the future value formulas for simple and compound interest in one year to derive the formula for effective annual yield.

• Group Exercise

53. This activity is a group research project intended for four or five people. Present your research in a seminar on the history of interest and banking. The seminar should last about 30 minutes. Address the following questions:

When was interest first charged on loans? How was lending money for a fee opposed historically? What is usury? What connection did banking and interest rates play in the historic European rivalries between Christians and Jews? When and where were some of the highest interest rates charged? What were the rates? Where does the word *interest* come from? What is the origin of the word *shylock*? What is the difference between usury and interest in modern times? What is the history of a national bank in the United States?

SECTION 8.4 • ANNUITIES, STOCKS, AND BONDS

OBJECTIVES

1. Determine the value of an annuity.
2. Determine regular annuity payments needed to achieve a financial goal.
3. Understand stocks and bonds as investments.
4. Read stock tables.

"Good Times Are Predicted in 1929"

—THE WASHINGTON POST, JAN. 1, 1929

"In a few months, I expect to see the stock market much higher than today."

—ESTEEMED ECONOMIST IRVING FISHER: OCT. 14, 1929

Date on which the stock market crashed and began the Depression: Oct. 29, 1929

According to the *Forbes Billionaires List*, in 2005 the two richest Americans were Bill Gates (net worth: $46.5 billion) and Warren Buffett (net worth: $44 billion). In May 1965, Buffett's new company, Berkshire Hathaway, was selling one share of stock for $18. By the end of 2004, the price of a share had increased to $86,300. If you purchased one share, your **return**, or percent increase, would be

$$\frac{\text{amount of increase}}{\text{original amount}} = \frac{\$86{,}300 - \$18}{\$18} \approx 4793.44 = 479{,}344\%.$$

What does a return of nearly 480,000% mean? If you invested $250 in Warren Buffett's company in May 1965, your shares would have been worth over $1.1 million by December 2004. (*Source*: *Pensions and Investments*)

Of course, investments that potentially offer outrageous returns come with great risk of losing part or all of the principal. The bottom line: Is there a safe way to save regularly and have an investment worth one million dollars or more? In this section, we consider such savings plans, some of which come with special tax treatment, as well as riskier investments in stocks and bonds.

1 Determine the value of an annuity.

Annuities

The compound interest formula

$$A = P(1 + r)^t$$

gives the future value, A, after t years, when a fixed amount of money, P, the principal, is deposited in an account that pays an annual interest rate r (in decimal form) compounded once a year. However, money is often invested in small amounts at periodic intervals. For example, to save for retirement, you might decide to place $1000 into an Individual Retirement Account (IRA) at the end of each year until you retire. An **annuity** is a sequence of equal payments made at equal time periods. An IRA is an example of an annuity.

The **value of an annuity** is the sum of all deposits plus all interest paid. Our first example illustrates how to find this value.

EXAMPLE 1 DETERMINING THE VALUE OF AN ANNUITY

You deposit $1000 into a savings plan at the end of each year for three years. The interest rate is 8% per year compounded annually.

a. Find the value of the annuity after three years.

b. Find the interest.

SOLUTION

a. The value of the annuity after three years is the sum of all deposits made plus all interest paid over three years.

This is the $1000 deposit at year's end.

Value at end of year 1 = $1000

This is the first-year deposit with interest earned for a year. This is the $1000 deposit at year's end.

Value at end of year 2 = $1000(1 + 0.08) + $1000

= $1080 + $1000 = $2080

Use $A = P(1 + r)^t$ with $r = 0.08$ and $t = 1$, or $A = P(1 + 0.08)$.

This is the second-year balance, $2080, with interest earned for a year. This is the $1000 deposit at year's end.

Value at end of year 3 = $2080(1 + 0.08) + $1000

= $2246.40 + $1000 = $3246.40

The value of the annuity at the end of three years is $3246.40.

b. You made three payments of $1000 each, depositing a total of 3 × $1000, or $3000. Because the value of the annuity is $3246.40, the interest is $3246.40 − $3000, or $246.40.

CHECK POINT 1 You deposit \$2000 into a savings plan at the end of each year for three years. The interest rate is 10% per year compounded annually.

a. Find the value of the annuity after three years.

b. Find the interest.

Suppose that you deposit P dollars into an account at the end of each year. The account pays an annual interest rate, r, compounded annually. At the end of the first year, the account contains P dollars. At the end of the second year, P dollars is deposited again. At the time of this deposit, the first deposit has received interest earned during the second year. Thus, the value of the annuity after two years is

$$P + P(1 + r).$$

- P: Deposit of P dollars at end of second year
- $P(1 + r)$: First-year deposit of P dollars with interest earned for a year

The value of the annuity after three years is

$$P + P(1 + r) + P(1 + r)^2.$$

- P: Deposit of P dollars at end of third year
- $P(1 + r)$: Second-year deposit of P dollars with interest earned for a year
- $P(1 + r)^2$: First-year deposit of P dollars with interest earned over two years

The value of the annuity after t years is

$$P + P(1 + r) + P(1 + r)^2 + P(1 + r)^3 + \cdots + P(1 + r)^{t-1}.$$

- P: Deposit of P dollars at end of year t
- $P(1 + r)^{t-1}$: First-year deposit of P dollars with interest earned over $t - 1$ years

Each term in this sum is obtained by multiplying the preceding term by $(1 + r)$. Thus, the terms form a geometric sequence. Using a formula for the sum of the terms of a geometric sequence, we can obtain the following formula that gives the value of this annuity:

VALUE OF AN ANNUITY: INTEREST COMPOUNDED ONCE A YEAR

If P is the deposit made at the end of each year for an annuity that pays an annual interest rate r (in decimal form) compounded once a year, the value, A, of the annuity after t years is

$$A = \frac{P[(1 + r)^t - 1]}{r}.$$

EXAMPLE 2 DETERMINING THE VALUE OF AN ANNUITY

To save for retirement, you decide to deposit \$1000 into an IRA at the end of each year for the next 30 years. If you can count on an interest rate of 10% per year compounded annually,

a. How much will you have from the IRA after 30 years?

b. Find the interest.

SOLUTION

a. The amount that you will have from the IRA is its value after 30 years.

$$A = \frac{P[(1+r)^t - 1]}{r}$$ Use the formula for the value of an annuity.

$$A = \frac{1000[(1+0.10)^{30} - 1]}{0.10}$$ The annuity involves year-end deposits of \$1000: $P = 1000$. The interest rate is 10%: $r = 0.10$. The number of years is 30: $t = 30$.

$$= \frac{1000[(1.10)^{30} - 1]}{0.10}$$ Using parentheses keys on a graphing calculator, this calculation can be done in a single step.

$$\approx \frac{1000(17.4494 - 1)}{0.10}$$ Use a calculator to find $(1.10)^{30}$: 1.1 [y^x] 30 [=].

$$= \frac{1000(16.4494)}{0.10}$$

$$= 164{,}494$$

After 30 years, you will have approximately \$164,494 from the IRA.

b. You made 30 payments of \$1000 each, depositing a total of 30 × \$1000, or \$30,000. Because the value of the annuity is approximately \$164,494, the interest is approximately

\$164,494 − \$30,000, or \$134,494.

The interest is nearly $4\frac{1}{2}$ times the amount of your payments, illustrating the power of compounding.

CHECK POINT 2 You deposit \$3000 into an IRA at the end of each year for the next 40 years. If you can count on an interest rate of 8% per year compounded annually,

a. How much will you have from the IRA after 40 years?

b. Find the interest.

We can adjust the formula for the value of an annuity if equal payments are made at the end of each of n yearly compounding periods.

STUDY TIP

Annuities can be categorized by when payments are made. The formula in the box describes **ordinary annuities**, where payments are made at the end of each period. The formula assumes the same number of yearly payments and yearly compounding periods. An annuity plan in which the payments are made at the beginning of each period is called an **annuity due**.

VALUE OF AN ANNUITY: INTEREST COMPOUNDED n TIMES PER YEAR

If P is the deposit made at the end of each compounding period for an annuity that pays an annual interest rate r (in decimal form) compounded n times per year, the value, A, of the annuity after t years is

$$A = \frac{P\left[\left(1+\frac{r}{n}\right)^{nt} - 1\right]}{\frac{r}{n}}.$$

EXAMPLE 3 DETERMINING THE VALUE OF AN ANNUITY

At age 25, to save for retirement, you decide to deposit \$200 at the end of each month into an IRA that pays 7.5% compounded monthly.

a. How much will you have from the IRA when you retire at age 65?

b. Find the interest.

SOLUTION

a. Because you are 25, the amount that you will have from the IRA when you retire at 65 is its value after 40 years.

$$A = \frac{P\left[\left(1+\frac{r}{n}\right)^{nt}-1\right]}{\frac{r}{n}}$$

Use the formula for the value of an annuity.

$$A = \frac{200\left[\left(1+\frac{0.075}{12}\right)^{12\cdot 40}-1\right]}{\frac{0.075}{12}}$$

The annuity involves month-end deposits of \$200: $P = 200$. The interest rate is 7.5%: $r = 0.075$. The interest is compounded monthly: $n = 12$. The number of years is 40: $t = 40$.

$$= \frac{200[(1+0.00625)^{480}-1]}{0.00625}$$

Using parentheses keys, this can be performed in a single step on a graphing calculator.

$$= \frac{200[(1.00625)^{480}-1]}{0.00625}$$

$$\approx \frac{200(19.8989-1)}{0.00625}$$

Use a calculator to find $(1.00625)^{480}$: 1.00625 $\boxed{y^x}$ 480 $\boxed{=}$.

$$\approx 604{,}765$$

After 40 years, you will have approximately \$604,765 when retiring at age 65.

b. Interest = Value of the IRA − Total deposits
≈ \$604,765 − \$200 · 12 · 40

\$200 per month × 12 months per year × 40 years

= \$604,765 − \$96,000 = \$508,765

The interest is approximately \$508,765, more than five times the amount of your contributions to the IRA.

CHECK POINT 3 At age 30, to save for retirement, you decide to deposit \$100 at the end of each month into an IRA that pays 9.5% compounded monthly.

a. How much will you have from the IRA when you retire at age 65?

b. Find the interest.

BLITZER BONUS

Stashing Cash and Making Taxes Less Taxing

As you prepare for your future career, retirement probably seems very far away. Making regular deposits into an IRA may not be fun, but there is a special incentive from Uncle Sam that makes it far more appealing. Traditional IRAs are **tax-deferred savings plans**. This means that you do not pay taxes on deposits and interest until you begin withdrawals, typically at retirement. Before then, yearly deposits count as adjustments to gross income and are not part of your taxable income. Not only do you get a tax break now, but you ultimately earn more. This is because you do not pay taxes on interest from year to year, allowing earnings to accumulate until you start withdrawals. With a tax code that encourages long-term savings, opening an IRA early in your career is a smart way to gain more control over how you will spend a large part of your life.

2 Determine regular annuity payments needed to achieve a financial goal.

Planning for the Future with an Annuity

By solving the annuity formula for P, we can determine the amount of money that should be deposited at the end of each compounding period so that an annuity has a future value of A dollars. The following formula gives the regular payments, P, needed to reach a financial goal, A:

REGULAR PAYMENTS NEEDED TO ACHIEVE A FINANCIAL GOAL

The deposit, P, that must be made at the end of each compounding period into an annuity that pays an annual interest rate r (in decimal form) compounded n times per year in order to achieve a value of A dollars after t years is

$$P = \frac{A\left(\frac{r}{n}\right)}{\left[\left(1+\frac{r}{n}\right)^{nt}-1\right]}.$$

EXAMPLE 4 ACHIEVING A FINANCIAL GOAL

You would like to have \$20,000 to use as a down payment for a home in five years by making regular, end-of-month deposits in an annuity that pays 8% compounded monthly.

a. How much should you deposit each month?

b. How much of the \$20,000 down payment comes from deposits and how much comes from interest?

SOLUTION

a. $$P = \frac{A\left(\frac{r}{n}\right)}{\left[\left(1+\frac{r}{n}\right)^{nt} - 1\right]}$$

Use the formula for regular payments, P, needed to achieve a financial goal, A.

$$P = \frac{20{,}000\left(\frac{0.08}{12}\right)}{\left[\left(1+\frac{0.08}{12}\right)^{12\cdot 5} - 1\right]}$$

Your goal is to accumulate \$20,000 ($A = 20{,}000$) over five years ($t = 5$). The interest rate is 8% ($r = 0.08$) compounded monthly ($n = 12$).

$$\approx 273$$

Use a calculator and round up to the nearest dollar to be certain you do not fall short of your goal.

You should deposit \$273 each month to be certain of having \$20,000 for a down payment on a home.

b. Total deposits $= \$273 \cdot 12 \cdot 5 = \$16{,}380$

\$273 per month × 12 months per year × 5 years

Interest $= \$20{,}000 - \$16{,}380 = \$3620$

We see that \$16,380 of the \$20,000 comes from your deposits and the remainder, \$3620, comes from interest.

STUDY TIP

In Example 4 of Section 8.3, we saw that a lump-sum deposit of approximately \$13,424 at 8% compounded monthly would accumulate to \$20,000 in five years. In Example 4 on the right, we see that total deposits of \$16,380 are required to reach the same goal. With the same interest rate, compounding period, and time period, a lump-sum deposit will generate more interest than an annuity. If you don't have a large sum of money to open an account, an annuity is a realistic, although more expensive, option to a lump-sum deposit for achieving the same financial goal.

CHECK POINT 4 Parents of a baby girl are in a financial position to begin saving for her college education. They plan to have \$100,000 in a college fund in 18 years by making regular, end-of-month deposits in an annuity that pays 9% compounded monthly.

a. How much should they deposit each month? Round up to the nearest dollar.

b. How much of the \$100,000 college fund comes from deposits and how much comes from interest?

3 Understand stocks and bonds as investments.

Investments

When you deposit money into a bank account, you are making a **cash investment**. Bank accounts up to \$100,000 are insured by the federal government, so there is no risk of losing the principal you've invested. The account's interest rate guarantees a certain percent increase in your investment, called its **return**. For example, if you deposit \$7500 in a savings account that has a rate of 4% compounded annually, the annual return is 4%. There are other kinds of investments that are riskier, meaning that it is possible to lose all or part of your principal. These investments include **stocks** and **bonds**.

BLITZER BONUS

Risk

The Chinese define *risk* as a combination of danger and opportunity. Investments in which all or part of the principal is in danger frequently offer the opportunity of a greater return. Table 8.4 includes five types of investments, listed from no risk to high risk, and their average annual returns from 1926 through 2004. Although stocks offer the prospects of greater returns, large-company shareholders lost money for 22 of the 79 years shown in the table.

TABLE 8.4 INVESTMENTS FROM NO RISK TO HIGH RISK AND THEIR RETURNS: 1926-2004

Investment Type	Average Annual Return
U.S. Treasury Bills (Federally insured and risk free)	3.8%
Long-Term Government Bonds	5.8%
Long-Term Corporate Bonds	6.2%
Large-Company Stocks	12.4%
Small-Company Stocks	17.5%

Source: *Summary Statistics of Annual Total Returns: 1926 to 2004 Yearbook*, Ibbotson Associates, Chicago

Stocks

Investors purchase **stock**, shares of ownership in a company. The shares indicate the percent of ownership. For example, if a company has issued a total of one million shares and an investor owns 20,000 of these shares, that investor owns

$$\frac{20{,}000 \text{ \sout{shares}}}{1{,}000{,}000 \text{ \sout{shares}}} = 0.02$$

or 2% of the company. Any investor who owns some percentage of the company is called a **shareholder**.

Buying or selling stock is referred to as **trading**. Shares of stock need both a seller and a buyer to be traded. Stocks are traded on a **stock exchange**. The price of a share of stock is determined by the law of supply and demand. If a company is prospering, investors will be willing to pay a good price for its stock, and so the stock price goes up. If the company does not do well, investors may decide to sell, and the stock price goes down. Stock prices indicate the performance of the companies they represent, as well as the state of the national and global economies.

There are two ways to make money by investing in stock:

- You sell the shares for more money than what you paid for them, in which case you have a **capital gain** on the sale of stock. (There can also be a capital loss by selling for less than what you paid, or if the company goes bankrupt.)
- While you own the stock, the company distributes all or part of its profits to shareholders as **dividends**. Each share is paid the same dividend, so the amount you receive depends on the number of shares owned. (Some companies reinvest all profits and do not distribute dividends.)

When more and more average Americans began investing and making money in stocks in the 1990s, the federal government cut the capital-gains tax rate in 1997. Long-term capital gains (profits on items held for more than a year before being sold) and dividends are taxed at lower rates than wages and interest earnings.

Bonds

People who buy stock become part owners in a company. In order to raise money and not dilute the ownership of current stockholders, companies sell **bonds**. People who buy a bond are **lending money** to the company from which they buy the bond. Bonds are a commitment from a company to pay the price an investor pays for the bond at the time it was purchased, called the **face value**, along with interest payments at a given rate.

There are many reasons for issuing bonds. A company might need to raise money for research on a drug that has the potential for curing AIDS, so it issues bonds. The U.S. Treasury Department issues 30-year bonds at a fixed 7% annual rate to borrow money to cover possible federal deficits. Local governments often issue bonds to borrow money to build schools, parks, and libraries.

Bonds are traded like stock, and their price is a function of supply and demand. If a company goes bankrupt, bondholders are the first to claim the company's assets. They make their claims before the stockholders, even though (unlike stockholders) they do not own a share of the company. Buying and selling bonds is frequently done through online investing.

Generally speaking, investing in bonds is less risky than investing in stocks, although the return is lower. A listing of all the investments that a person holds is called a **financial portfolio**. Most financial advisors recommend a portfolio with a mixture of low-risk and high-risk investments, called a **diversified portfolio**.

4 Read stock tables.

Reading Stock Tables

Daily newspapers and online services give current stock prices and other information about stocks. We will use Citigroup stock to learn how to read these daily stock tables. Look at the following newspaper listing of Citigroup stock.

52-Week High	Low	Stock	SYM	Div	Yld %	PE	Vol 100s	Hi	Lo	Close	Net Chg
77	28.50	Citigroup	C	.84	1.1	29	64981	76	74.44	74.56	−0.94

The headings indicate the meanings of the numbers across the row.

52-Week High
77

The heading **52-Week High** refers to the *highest price* at which Citigroup stock traded during the past 52 weeks. The highest price was $77.00 per share. This means that during the past 52 weeks an investor was willing to pay $77.00 for a share of stock. Notice that 77 represents a quantity in dollars, although the stock table does not show the dollar sign.

52-Week Low
28.50

The heading **52-Week Low** refers to the *lowest price* that Citigroup stock reached during the past 52 weeks. This price is $28.50.

Stock	SYM
Citigroup	C

The heading **Stock** is the *company name*, Citigroup. The heading **SYM** is the *symbol* the company uses for trading. Citigroup uses the symbol C.

Div
.84

The heading **Div** refers to *dividends* paid per share to stockholders last year. Citigroup paid a dividend of $0.84 per share. Once again, the dollar symbol does not appear in the table. Thus, if you owned 100 shares, you received a dividend of $0.84 × 100, or $84.00.

Yld %
1.1

The heading **Yld %** stands for *percent yield*. In this case, the percent yield is 1.1%. (The stock table does not show the percent sign.) This means that the dividends alone give investors an annual return of 1.1%. This is much lower than interest rates offered by most banks. However, this percent does not take into account the fact that Citigroup stock prices might rise. If an investor sells shares for more than what they were paid for, the gain will probably make Citigroup stock a much better investment than a bank account.

In order to understand the meaning of the heading PE, we need to understand some of the other numbers in the table. We will return to this column.

Vol 100s
64981

The heading **Vol 100s** stands for *sales volume in hundreds*. This is the number of shares traded yesterday, in hundreds. The number in the table is 64,981. This means that yesterday, a total of 64,981 × 100, or 6,498,100 shares of Citigroup were traded.

Hi
76

The heading **Hi** stands for the *highest price* at which Citigroup stock traded *yesterday*. This number is 76. Yesterday, Citigroup's highest trading price was $76 a share.

Lo
74.44

The heading **Lo** stands for the *lowest price* at which Citigroup stock traded *yesterday*. This number is 74.44. Yesterday, Citigroup's lowest trading price was $74.44 a share.

Close
74.56

The heading **Close** stands for the *price* at which shares traded *when the stock exchange closed yesterday*. This number is 74.56. Thus, the the price at which shares of Citigroup traded when the stock exchange closed yesterday was $74.56 per share. This is called yesterday's **closing price**.

Net Chg
−0.94

The heading **Net Chg** stands for *net change*. This is the change in price from the market close two days ago to yesterday's market close. This number is −0.94. Thus, the price of a share of Citigroup stock went down by $0.94. For some stock listings, the notation . . . appears under Net Chg. This means that there was *no change in price* for a share of stock from the market close two days ago to yesterday's market close.

PE
29

Now, we are ready to return to the heading **PE**, standing for the *price-to-earnings ratio*.

$$\text{PE ratio} = \frac{\text{Yesterday's closing price per share}}{\text{Annual earnings per share}}$$

This can be expressed as

$$\text{Annual earnings per share} = \frac{\text{Yesterday's closing price per share}}{\text{PE ratio}}.$$

Close
74.56

PE
29

The PE ratio for Citigroup is given to be 29. Yesterday's closing price per share was 74.56. We can substitute these numbers into the formula to find annual earnings per share:

$$\text{Annual earnings per share} = \frac{74.56}{29} \approx 2.57.$$

The annual earnings per share for Citigroup are $2.57. The PE ratio, 29, tells us that yesterday's closing price per share, $74.56, is 29 times greater than the earnings per share, $2.57.

EXAMPLE 5 READING STOCK TABLES

52-Week High	Low	Stock	SYM	Div	Yld %	PE	Vol 100s	Hi	Lo	Close	Net Chg
42.38	22.50	Disney	DIS	.21	.6	43	115900	32.50	31.25	32.50	...

Use the stock table for Disney to answer the following questions.

a. What were the high and low prices for the past 52 weeks?

b. If you owned 3000 shares of Disney stock last year, what dividend did you receive?

c. What is the annual return for dividends alone? How does this compare to a bank account offering a 3.5% interest rate?

d. How many shares of Disney were traded yesterday?

e. What were the high and low prices for Disney shares yesterday?

f. What was the price at which Disney shares traded when the stock exchange closed yesterday?

g. What does ... in the net change column mean?

h. Compute Disney's annual earnings per share using

$$\text{Annual earnings per share} = \frac{\text{Yesterday's closing price per share}}{\text{PE ratio}}.$$

SOLUTION

a. We find the high price for the past 52 weeks by looking under the heading **High**. The price is listed in dollars, given as 42.38. Thus, the high price for a share of stock for the past 52 weeks was $42.38. We find the low price for the past 52 weeks by looking under the heading **Low**. This price is also listed in dollars, given as 22.50. Thus, the low price for a share of Disney stock for the past 52 weeks was $22.50.

b. We find the dividend paid for a share of Disney stock last year by looking under the heading **Div**. The price is listed in dollars, given as .21. Thus, Disney paid a dividend of $0.21 per share to stockholders last year. If you owned 3000 shares, you received a dividend of $0.21 × 3000, or $630.

c. We find the annual return for dividends alone by looking under the heading **Yld %**, standing for percent yield. The number in the table, .6, is a percent. This means that the dividends alone give Disney investors an annual return of 0.6%. This is much lower than a bank account paying a 3.5% interest rate. However, if Disney shares increase in value, the gain might make Disney stock a better investment than the bank account.

52-Week High	Low	Stock	SYM	Div	Yld %	PE	Vol 100s	Hi	Lo	Close	Net Chg
42.38	22.50	Disney	DIS	.21	.6	43	115900	32.50	31.25	32.50	...

Disney stock table (repeated)

d. We find the number of shares of Disney traded yesterday by looking under the heading **Vol 100s**, standing for sales volume in hundreds. The number in the table is 115900. This means that yesterday, a total of 115,900 × 100, or 11,590,000 shares, were traded.

e. We find the high and low prices for Disney shares yesterday by looking under the headings **Hi** and **Lo**. Both prices are listed in dollars, given as 32.50 and 31.25. Thus, the high and low prices for Disney shares yesterday were \$32.50 and \$31.25, respectively.

f. We find the price at which Disney shares traded when the stock exchange closed yesterday by looking under the heading **Close**. The price is listed in dollars, given as 32.50. Thus, when the stock exchange closed yesterday, the price of a share of Disney stock was \$32.50.

g. The ... under **Net Chg** means that there was no change in price in Disney stock from the market close two days ago to yesterday's market close. In part (f), we found that the price of a share of Disney stock at yesterday's close was \$32.50, so the price at the market close two days ago was also \$32.50.

h. We are now ready to use

$$\text{Annual earnings per share} = \frac{\text{Yesterday's closing price per share}}{\text{PE ratio}}$$

to compute Disney's annual earnings per share. We found that yesterday's closing price per share was \$32.50. We find the PE ratio under the heading **PE**. The given number is 43. Thus,

$$\text{Annual earnings per share} = \frac{\$32.50}{43} \approx \$0.76.$$

The annual earnings per share for Disney are \$0.76. The PE ratio, 43, tells us that yesterday's closing price per share, \$32.50, is 43 times greater than the earnings per share, approximately \$0.76.

CHECK POINT 5 Use the stock table for Coca Cola to solve parts (a) through (h) in Example 5.

52-Week High	Low	Stock	Div	Yld %	PE	Vol 100s	Hi	Lo	Close	Net Chg
63.38	42.37	CocaCl	.72	1.5	37	72032	49.94	48.33	49.50	+0.03

Ways to Invest in Annuities, Stocks, and Bonds

Investments in annuities, stocks, and bonds can be bought directly, which means making these investments on your own. You can open an IRA at a bank, purchase stock through stockbrokers, who charge a commission for their services, or buy bonds from the government.

It is not an easy job to determine which stocks and bonds to buy or sell, or when to do so. Even IRAs can be funded by mixing stocks and bonds. Many small investors have decided that they do not have the time to stay informed about the progress of corporations, even with the help of online industry research. Instead, they invest in a **mutual fund**. A mutual fund is a group of stocks and/or bonds managed by a professional investor. When you purchase shares in a mutual fund, you give your money to the **fund manager**. Your money is combined with the money of other investors in the mutual fund. The fund manager invests this pool of money, buying and selling shares of stocks and bonds to obtain the maximum possible returns.

Investors in mutual funds own a small portion of many different companies, which may protect them against the poor performance of a single company. When comparing mutual funds, consider both the fees charged for investing and how well the fund manager is doing with the fund's money. Newspapers publish ratings from 1 (worst) to 5 (best) of mutual fund performance based on whether the manager is doing a good job with its investors' money. Two numbers are given. The first number compares the performance of the mutual fund to a large group of similar funds. The second number compares the performance to funds that are nearly identical. The best rating a fund manager can receive is 5/5; the worst is 1/1.

EXERCISE SET 8.4

• Practice Exercises

In Exercises 1–10,

a. *Use the formula*

$$A = \frac{P[(1+r)^t - 1]}{r} \quad \text{or} \quad A = \frac{P\left[\left(1+\frac{r}{n}\right)^{nt} - 1\right]}{\frac{r}{n}}$$

to find the value of each annuity. Round to the nearest dollar.

b. *Find the interest.*

Periodic Deposit	Rate	Time
1. \$2000 at the end of each year	5% compounded annually	20 years
2. \$3000 at the end of each year	4% compounded annually	20 years
3. \$4000 at the end of each year	6.5% compounded annually	40 years
4. \$4000 at the end of each year	5.5% compounded annually	40 years
5. \$50 at the end of each month	6% compounded monthly	30 years
6. \$60 at the end of each month	5% compounded monthly	30 years
7. \$100 at the end of every six months	4.5% compounded semiannually	25 years
8. \$150 at the end of every six months	6.5% compounded semiannually	25 years
9. \$1000 at the end of every three months	6.25% compounded quarterly	6 years
10. \$1200 at the end of every three months	3.25% compounded quarterly	6 years

In Exercises 11–18,

a. *Use the formula*

$$P = \frac{A\left(\frac{r}{n}\right)}{\left[\left(1+\frac{r}{n}\right)^{nt} - 1\right]}$$

to determine the periodic deposit. Round up to the nearest dollar.

b. *How much of the financial goal comes from deposits and how much comes from interest?*

Periodic Deposit	Rate	Time	Financial Goal
11. \$? at the end of each year	6% compounded annually	18 years	\$140,000
12. \$? at the end of each year	5% compounded annually	18 years	\$150,000
13. \$? at the end of each month	4.5% compounded monthly	10 years	\$200,000
14. \$? at the end of each month	7.5% compounded monthly	10 years	\$250,000
15. \$? at the end of each month	7.25% compounded monthly	40 years	\$1,000,000
16. \$? at the end of each month	8.25% compounded monthly	40 years	\$1,500,000
17. \$? at the end of every three months	3.5% compounded quarterly	5 years	\$20,000
18. \$? at the end of every three months	4.5% compounded quarterly	5 years	\$25,000

Exercises 19 and 20 refer to the stock tables for Goodyear (the tire company) and JC Penney (the department store) given below. In each exercise, use the stock table to answer the following questions. Where necessary, round dollar amounts to the nearest cent.

a. *What were the high and low prices for a share for the past 52 weeks?*

b. *If you owned 700 shares of this stock last year, what dividend did you receive?*

c. *What is the annual return for the dividends alone? How does this compare to a bank offering a 3% interest rate?*

d. *How many shares of this company's stock were traded yesterday?*

e. *What were the high and low prices for a share yesterday?*

f. *What was the price at which a share traded when the stock exchange closed yesterday?*

g. *What was the change in price for a share of stock from the market close two days ago to yesterday's market close?*

h. *Compute the company's annual earnings per share using*

$$\text{Annual earnings per share} = \frac{\text{Yesterday's closing price per share}}{\text{PE ratio}}.$$

19.

52-Week High	Low	Stock	SYM	Div	Yld %	PE	Vol 100s	Hi	Lo	Close	Net Chg
73.25	45.44	Goodyear	GT	1.20	2.2	17	5915	56.38	54.38	55.50	+1.25

20.

52-Week High	Low	Stock	SYM	Div	Yld %	PE	Vol 100s	Hi	Lo	Close	Net Chg
78.34	35.38	Penney JC	JCP	2.18	4.7	22	7473	48.19	46.63	46.88	−1.31

• Practice Plus

In Exercises 21–22, round all answers to the nearest dollar.

21. Here are two ways of investing $30,000 for 20 years.

-

Lump-Sum Deposit	Rate	Time
$30,000	5% compounded annually	20 years

-

Periodic Deposit	Rate	Time
$1500 at the end of each year	5% compounded annually	20 years

a. After 20 years, how much more will you have from the lump-sum investment than from the annuity?

b. After 20 years, how much more interest will be earned from the lump-sum investment than from the annuity?

22. Here are two ways of investing $40,000 for 25 years.

-

Lump-Sum Deposit	Rate	Time
$40,000	6.5% compounded annually	25 years

-

Periodic Deposit	Rate	Time
$1600 at the end of each year	6.5% compounded annually	25 years

a. After 25 years, how much more will you have from the lump-sum investment than from the annuity?

b. After 25 years, how much more interest will be earned from the lump-sum investment than from the annuity?

In Exercises 23–24,

a. *Determine the deposit at the end of each month. Round up to the nearest dollar.*

b. *Assume that the annuity in part (a) is a tax-deferred IRA belonging to a man whose gross income in 2005 was $50,000. Use Table 8.1 on page 448 to calculate his 2005 taxes first with and then without the IRA. Assume the man is single with no dependents, has no tax credits, and takes the standard deduction.*

c. *What percent of his gross income are the man's federal taxes with and without the IRA? Round to the nearest tenth of a percent.*

	Periodic Deposit	Rate	Time	Financial Goal
23.	$? at the end of each month	8% compounded monthly	40 years	$1,000,000
24.	$? at the end of each month	7% compounded monthly	40 years	$650,000

25. Solve for P:

$$A = \frac{P[(1 + r)^t - 1]}{r}.$$

What does the resulting formula describe?

26. Solve for P:

$$A = \frac{P\left[\left(1 + \frac{r}{n}\right)^{nt} - 1\right]}{\frac{r}{n}}.$$

What does the resulting formula describe?

Application Exercises

In Exercises 27–32, use the formula

$$A = \frac{P[(1+r)^t - 1]}{r} \quad \text{or} \quad A = \frac{P\left[\left(1+\frac{r}{n}\right)^{nt} - 1\right]}{\frac{r}{n}}.$$

Round to the nearest dollar.

27. To save money for a sabbatical to earn a master's degree, you deposit \$2000 at the end of each year in an annuity that pays 7.5% compounded annually.

a. How much will you have saved at the end of five years?

b. Find the interest.

28. To save money for a sabbatical to earn a master's degree, you deposit \$2500 at the end of each year in an annuity that pays 6.25% compounded annually.

a. How much will you have saved at the end of five years?

b. Find the interest.

29. At age 25, to save for retirement, you decide to deposit \$50 at the end of each month in an IRA that pays 5.5% compounded monthly.

a. How much will you have from the IRA when you retire at age 65?

b. Find the interest.

30. At age 25, to save for retirement, you decide to deposit \$75 at the end of each month in an IRA that pays 6.5% compounded monthly.

a. How much will you have from the IRA when you retire at age 65?

b. Find the interest.

31. To offer scholarship funds to children of employees, a company invests \$10,000 at the end of every three months in an annuity that pays 10.5% compounded quarterly.

a. How much will the company have in scholarship funds at the end of ten years?

b. Find the interest.

32. To offer scholarship funds to children of employees, a company invests \$15,000 at the end of every three months in an annuity that pays 9% compounded quarterly.

a. How much will the company have in scholarship funds at the end of ten years?

b. Find the interest.

In Exercises 33–36, use the formula

$$P = \frac{A\left(\frac{r}{n}\right)}{\left[\left(1+\frac{r}{n}\right)^{nt} - 1\right]}.$$

Round up to the nearest dollar.

33. You would like to have \$3500 in four years for a special vacation following graduation by making deposits at the end of every six months in an annuity that pays 5% compounded semiannually.

a. How much should you deposit at the end of every six months?

b. How much of the \$3500 comes from deposits and how much comes from interest?

34. You would like to have \$4000 in four years for a special vacation following graduation by making deposits at the end of every six months in an annuity that pays 7% compounded semiannually.

a. How much should you deposit at the end of every six months?

b. How much of the \$4000 comes from deposits and how much comes from interest?

35. How much should you deposit at the end of each month into an IRA that pays 8.5% compounded monthly to have \$4 million when you retire in 45 years? How much of the \$4 million comes from interest?

36. How much should you deposit at the end of each month into an IRA that pays 6.5% compounded monthly to have \$2 million when you retire in 45 years? How much of the \$2 million comes from interest?

• Writing in Mathematics

37. What is an annuity?

38. What is meant by the value of an annuity?

39. Write a problem involving the formula for regular payments needed to achieve a financial goal. The problem should be similar to Example 4 on page 472. However, the problem should be unique to your situation. Include something for which you would like to save, how much you need to save, and how long it will take to achieve your goal. Then solve the problem.

40. What is stock?

41. Describe how to find the percent ownership that a shareholder has in a company.

42. Describe the two ways that investors make money with stock.

43. What is a bond? Describe the difference between a stock and a bond.

44. Using a recent newspaper, copy the stock table for a company of your choice. Then explain the meaning of the numbers in the columns.

45. If an investor sees that the dividends for a stock have a lower annual rate than those for a no-risk bank account, should the stock be sold and the money placed in the bank account? Explain your answer.

Use the following investments to answer Exercises 46–49.

Investment 1: 1000 shares of IBM stock
Investment 2: A 5-year bond with a 22% interest rate issued by a small company that is testing and planning to sell delicious, nearly zero-calorie desserts
Investment 3: A 30-year U.S. treasury bond at a fixed 7% annual rate

46. Which of these investments has the greatest risk? Explain why.

47. Which of these investments has the least risk? Explain why.

48. Which of these investments has the possibility of the greatest return? Explain why.

49. If you could be given one of these investments as a gift, which one would you choose? Explain why.

• Critical Thinking Exercise

50. How much should you deposit at the end of each month in an IRA that pays 8% compounded monthly to earn $60,000 per year from interest alone, while leaving the principal untouched, when you retire in 30 years?

• Group Exercises

51. Each group should have a newspaper with current stock quotations. Choose nine stocks that group members think would make good investments. Imagine that you invest $1000 in each of these nine investments. Check the value of your stock each day over the next five weeks and then sell the nine stocks after five weeks. What is the group's profit or loss over the five-week period? Compare this figure with the profit or loss of other groups in your class for this activity.

52. This activity is a group research project intended for four or five people. Use the research to present a seminar on investments. The seminar is intended to last about 30 minutes and should result in an interesting and informative presentation to the entire class. The seminar should include investment considerations, how to read the bond section of the newspaper, how to read the mutual fund section, and higher-risk investments.

53. Group members have inherited $1 million. However, the group cannot spend any of the money for ten years. As a group, determine how to invest this money in order to maximize the money you will make over ten years. The money can be invested in as many ways as the group decides. Explain each investment decision. What are the risks involved in each investment plan?

SECTION 8.5 • INSTALLMENT BUYING

OBJECTIVES

1. Determine the amount financed, the installment price, and the finance charge for a fixed loan.
2. Determine the APR.
3. Compute unearned interest and the payoff amount for a loan paid off early.
4. Find the interest, the balance due, and the minimum monthly payment for credit card loans.
5. Calculate interest on credit cards using three methods.

Do you buy products with a credit card? Although your card lets you use a product while paying for it, the costs associated with such cards, including their high interest rates, fees, and penalties, stack the odds in favor of your getting hurt by them. In 2004, the average credit-card debt per U.S. household was $9312. If you use a credit card, you are engaging in **installment buying**, in which you repay a loan for the cost of a product on a monthly basis. A loan that you pay off with weekly or monthly payments, or payments in some other time period, is called an **installment loan**. The advantage of an installment loan is that the consumer gets to use a product immediately. In this section, we will see that the disadvantage is that it can add a substantial amount to the cost of a purchase. When it comes to installment buying, consumer beware!

1 Determine the amount financed, the installment price, and the finance charge for a fixed loan.

Fixed Installment Loans

You decide to purchase a used pick-up truck that costs $9345. You can finance the truck by paying $300 at the time of purchase, called the **down payment**, and $194.38 per month for 60 months. A loan like this that has a schedule for paying a fixed amount each period is called a **fixed installment loan**. We begin with three terms associated with such loans.

THE VOCABULARY OF FIXED INSTALLMENT LOANS

The **amount financed** is what the consumer borrows:

$$\text{Amount financed} = \text{Cash price} - \text{Down payment.}$$

The **total installment price** is the sum of all monthly payments plus the down payment:

$$\text{Total installment price} = \text{Total of all monthly payments} + \text{Down payment.}$$

The **finance charge** is the interest on the installment loan:

$$\text{Finance charge} = \text{Total installment price} - \text{Cash price.}$$

EXAMPLE 1 BUYING A PICK-UP TRUCK USING A FIXED INSTALLMENT LOAN

The cost of a used pick-up truck is $9345. We can finance the truck by paying $300 down and $194.38 per month for 60 months.

a. Determine the amount financed.

b. Determine the total installment price.

c. Determine the finance charge.

SOLUTION

a.
$$\begin{aligned}\text{Amount financed} &= \text{Cash price} - \text{Down payment}\\ &= \$9345 - \$300\\ &= \$9045\end{aligned}$$

The amount financed is $9045.

b. The total installment price is obtained by adding the total of all monthly payments and the down payment. Because we are paying $194.38 per month for 60 months, the total of all monthly payments is

$$\frac{\$194.38}{\cancel{\text{month}}} \times 60\ \cancel{\text{months}} = \$194.38 \times 60.$$

$$\begin{aligned}\text{Total installment price} &= \text{Total of all monthly payments} + \text{Down payment}\\ &= \$194.38 \times 60 + \$300\\ &= \$11{,}662.80 + \$300\\ &= \$11{,}962.80\end{aligned}$$

The total installment price is $11,962.80.

c.
$$\begin{aligned}\text{Finance charge} &= \text{Total installment price} - \text{Cash price}\\ &= \$11{,}962.80 - \$9345\\ &= \$2617.80\end{aligned}$$

The finance charge for the loan is $2617.80.

CHECK POINT 1 The cost of a new car is $14,000. You can finance the car by paying $280 down and $315 per month for 60 months.

a. Determine the amount financed.

b. Determine the total installment price.

c. Determine the finance charge.

You will be using these figures in Check Points 2, 3, and 4, so keep track of your answers.

2 Determine the APR.

In Example 1, the finance charge for the loan, $2617.80, is the **interest** paid to finance the truck. What interest rate are we paying when we pay $2617.80 interest over 60 months? The interest rate per year is called the **annual percentage rate**, abbreviated **APR**. In 1969, the Federal Reserve Board established the **Truth-in-Lending Act**. It requires lending institutions to inform borrowers in writing of a loan's APR. **When comparing two or more loans with different terms, the loan with the lowest APR is the one that charges the least interest**. For many people, an important factor in deciding on a fixed installment loan is the cash down payment that is required. If you do not have a lot of cash at the time of purchase, you might select a loan with a smaller down payment even though it has a not-so-desirable APR.

The APR for a fixed installment loan can be determined using a table similar to the abbreviated version shown in Table 8.5. Here are the steps involved in using an APR table. These steps are illustrated in Example 2.

STUDY TIP

Do not confuse effective annual yield with annual percentage rate. Effective annual yield applies to *interest earned* on invested money. By contrast, annual percentage rate applies to *interest owed* on loans.

STEPS IN USING AN APR TABLE

1. Compute the finance charge per $100 financed:
$$\frac{\text{Finance charge}}{\text{Amount financed}} \times \$100.$$
2. Look in the row corresponding to the number of payments to be made and find the entry closest to the value in step 1.
3. Find the APR at the top of the column in which the entry from step 2 is found. (This is the APR rounded to the nearest $\frac{1}{2}$%.)

TABLE 8.5 ANNUAL PERCENTAGE RATE (APR) FOR MONTHLY PAYMENT LOANS

Number of Monthly Payments	Annual Percentage Rate (APR)												
	10.0%	10.5%	11.0%	11.5%	12.0%	12.5%	13.0%	13.5%	14.0%	14.5%	15.0%	15.5%	16.0%
	(Finance charge per $100 of amount financed)												
6	$2.94	$3.08	$3.23	$3.38	$3.53	$3.68	$3.83	$3.97	$4.12	$4.27	$4.42	$4.57	$4.72
12	5.50	5.78	6.06	6.34	6.62	6.90	7.18	7.46	7.74	8.03	8.31	8.59	8.88
18	8.10	8.52	8.93	9.35	9.77	10.19	10.61	11.03	11.45	11.87	12.29	12.72	13.14
24	10.75	11.30	11.86	12.42	12.98	13.54	14.10	14.66	15.23	15.80	16.37	16.94	17.51
30	13.43	14.13	14.83	15.54	16.24	16.95	17.66	18.38	19.10	19.81	20.54	21.26	21.99
36	16.16	17.01	17.86	18.71	19.57	20.43	21.30	22.17	23.04	23.92	24.80	25.68	26.57
48	21.74	22.90	24.06	25.23	26.40	27.58	28.77	29.97	31.17	32.37	33.59	34.81	36.03
60	27.48	28.96	30.45	31.96	33.47	34.99	36.52	38.06	39.61	41.17	42.74	44.32	45.91

EXAMPLE 2 DETERMINING THE APR

In Example 1, we found that the amount financed for the truck was $9045 and the finance charge was $2617.80. The borrower financed the truck with 60 monthly payments. Use Table 8.5 to determine the APR.

SOLUTION

Step 1. Find the finance charge per $100 of the amount financed.

$$\text{Finance charge per \$100 financed} = \frac{\text{Finance charge}}{\text{Amount financed}} \times \$100$$
$$= \frac{\$2617.80}{\$9045.00} \times \$100$$
$$\approx \$28.94$$

This means that the borrower pays $28.94 interest for each $100 being financed.

STUDY TIP

Use Table 8.5 for this example as follows.

$$\begin{array}{cc} & 10.5\% \\ \downarrow & \uparrow \\ 60 \rightarrow & \textcircled{28.96} \end{array}$$

Step 2. Look in the row corresponding to the number of payments to be made (60) and find the entry closest to the value in step 1 ($28.94). Table 8.5 presents three types of information: the number of monthly payments, the APR, and the finance charge per $100 financed. There are 60 monthly payments, so look for 60 in the left column. Then move across to the right until you find the amount closest to the finance charge per $100 financed, namely $28.94. This amount, $28.96, is circled in the table.

Step 3. Find the APR at the top of the column in which the entry from step 2 is found. Take a second look at the circled entry, $28.96. At the top of this column is 10.5%. Thus, the APR for the fixed installment truck loan is approximately 10.5%.

CHECK POINT 2 Use Table 8.5 to determine the APR for the car loan described in Check Point 1.

3 Compute unearned interest and the payoff amount for a loan paid off early.

A fixed installment loan can be paid off early so that a borrower need not pay the entire finance charge. The amount by which the finance charge is reduced is called the **unearned interest**. The interest saved by paying off the loan early can be calculated by one of two methods, the **actuarial method** or the **rule of 78**. The actuarial method uses the APR table and the rule of 78 does not. The Truth-in-Lending Act requires that the method for calculating the reduction of the finance charge be disclosed at the time the loan is signed.

Here are two formulas for computing unearned interest:

STUDY TIP

Keep in mind that a loan's finance charge is the same thing as the loan's interest.

METHODS FOR COMPUTING UNEARNED INTEREST

Unearned interest is the amount by which a loan's finance charge is reduced when the loan is paid off early.

Actuarial Method

$$u = \frac{kRV}{100 + V}$$

u = unearned interest

k = remaining number of scheduled payments (excluding current payment)

R = regular monthly payment

V = finance charge per $100 (from the APR table) for a loan with the same APR and k monthly payments

Rule of 78

$$u = \frac{k(k+1)}{n(n+1)} \times F$$

u = unearned interest

k = remaining number of scheduled payments (excluding current payment)

n = original number of payments

F = original finance charge

Pick-up truck
cost: $9345
Financing: $300 + $194.38 per month for 60 months
Amount financed: $9045
Total installment price: $11,962.80
Finance charge (interest): $2617.80
Finance charge per $100 financed: $28.94
APR: 10.5%

The total amount due on the day that a loan is paid off early is called the **payoff amount**. Unearned interest is subtracted in computing the payoff amount. Examples 3 and 4 illustrate how the payoff amount is computed using the actuarial method in Example 3 and the rule of 78 in Example 4. Both examples refer back to the pick-up truck in Example 1. Shown in the margin is a summary of given and computed amounts for the truck.

EXAMPLE 3 EARLY PAYOFF: THE ACTUARIAL METHOD

You got a big bonus at work—and a raise. Instead of making the thirty-sixth payment on your truck, you decide to pay the remaining balance and terminate the loan.

a. Use the actuarial method to determine how much interest will be saved (the unearned interest, u) by repaying the loan early.

b. Find the payoff amount.

Pick-up truck
cost: \$9345
Financing: \$300 + \$194.38 per month for 60 months
Amount financed: \$9045
Total installment price: \$11,962.80
Finance charge (interest): \$2617.80
Finance charge per \$100 financed: \$28.94
APR: 10.5%

Given and computed amounts for the truck (repeated)

SOLUTION

a. We will use the formula $u = \frac{kRV}{100 + V}$ to find u, the unearned interest. We need values for k, R, and V. The current payment is payment number 36. There are 60 payments total. We subtract the number of the current payment from the total number of payments to find the number of remaining payments, k: $k = 60 - 36 = 24$. The value of R, the regular monthly payment, is given: $R = \$194.38$. To find the value for the finance charge per \$100, V, use the APR table (Table 8.5 on page 482). In the Number of Monthly Payments Column, find the number of remaining payments, 24, and then look to the right until you reach the column headed by 10.5%, the APR. This row and column intersect at 11.30. Thus, $V = 11.30$. This is the finance charge per \$100 for a loan with the same APR and k ($k = 24$) monthly payments. We substitute these values into the actuarial method formula.

$$u = \frac{kRV}{100 + V} = \frac{24 \times 194.38 \times 11.30}{100 + 11.30} \approx 473.64$$

Approximately \$473.64 will be saved in interest by terminating the loan early using the actuarial method.

b. The payoff amount, the amount due on the day of the loan's termination, is determined as follows:

Payoff amount	=	payment number 36	plus	total of remaining payments after payment 36	minus	interest saved (unearned interest).
	=	\$194.38	+	24 × \$194.38	−	\$473.64
	=	\$4385.86.				

The payment needed to terminate the loan at the end of 36 months is \$4385.86.

CHECK POINT 3 Instead of making the twenty-fourth payment on the car loan described in Check Points 1 and 2, you decide to pay the remaining balance and terminate the loan.

a. Use the actuarial method to determine how much interest will be saved (the unearned interest, u) by repaying the loan early.

b. Find the payoff amount.

EXAMPLE 4 EARLY PAYOFF: THE RULE OF 78

The loan in Example 3 is paid off at the time of the thirty-sixth monthly payment. Use the rule of 78 to find

a. the unearned interest.

b. the payoff amount.

SOLUTION

a. We will use the formula

$$u = \frac{k(k+1)}{n(n+1)} \times F$$

to find u, the unearned interest. We need values for k, n, and F. From Example 3, k, the number of remaining payments, is 24: $k = 24$. The original number of payments, n, is 60: $n = 60$. The summary of figures for the pick-up truck shown in the margin lists the finance charge: $F = \$2617.80$. We substitute these values into the rule of 78 formula.

$$u = \frac{k(k+1)}{n(n+1)} \times F = \frac{24(24+1)}{60(60+1)} \times \$2617.80 \approx \$429.15$$

By the rule of 78, the borrower will save \$429.15 in interest.

b. Next, we determine the payoff amount.

$$\text{Payoff amount} = \text{payment number 36} \text{ plus } \text{total of remaining payments after payment 36} \text{ minus } \text{interest saved (unearned interest)}.$$

$$= \$194.38 + 24 \times \$194.38 - \$429.15$$

$$= \$4430.35$$

The payoff amount is \$4430.35.

In Example 3, we found that \$473.64 is saved in interest using the actuarial method, while in Example 4, we found that \$429.15 is saved in interest using the rule of 78. These examples illustrate that the actuarial method is more beneficial to the borrower than the rule of 78 because it results in greater savings in interest at the loan's termination. For loans of 61 months or longer, only the actuarial method is allowed. Also, some states have shorter loan periods that do not allow the rule of 78.

CHECK POINT 4 The loan in Check Point 3 is paid off at the time of the twenty-fourth monthly payment. Use the rule of 78 to find

a. the unearned interest.

b. the payoff amount.

4 Find the interest, the balance due, and the minimum monthly payment for credit card loans.

Open-End Installment Loans

Using a credit card is an example of an open-end installment loan, commonly called **revolving credit**. Open-end loans differ from fixed installment loans in that there is no schedule for paying a fixed amount each period. Credit card loans require users to make only a minimum monthly payment that depends on the unpaid balance and the interest rate. Credit cards have high interest rates compared to other kinds of loans. The interest on credit cards is computed using the simple interest formula $I = Prt$. However, r represents the *monthly* interest rate and t is time in months rather than in years. A typical interest rate is 1.57% monthly. This is equivalent to a yearly rate of $12 \times 1.57\%$, or 18.84%. With such a high APR, credit card balances should be paid off as quickly as possible.

Most credit card customers are billed every month. A typical billing period is May 1 through May 31, but it can also run from, say, May 5 through June 4. Customers receive a statement, called an **itemized billing**, that contains the unpaid balance on the first day of the billing period, the total balance owed on the last day of the billing period, a list of purchases and cash advances made during the billing period, the date of the last day of the billing period, the payment due date, and the minimum payment required.

Customers who make a purchase during the billing period and pay the entire amount of the purchase by the payment due date are not charged interest. By contrast, customers who make cash advances using their credit cards must pay interest from the day the money is advanced until the day it is repaid.

One method for calculating interest on credit cards is the **unpaid balance method**. Interest is calculated on the unpaid balance on the first day of the billing period less payments and credits.

BLITZER BONUS

A Bad Idea: Charging Your Education

A survey by the Smith College Women and Financial Independence program found that 23% of college students were using credit cards to pay for tuition and fees. Because credit cards are probably the most expensive source of money for students in college in terms of interest rates and fees, the study concluded that many students did not know there were better ways to borrow. Some alternatives from financial professionals:

- **Federal Stafford Loans** In 2006, freshmen could borrow up to $2625 and the APR was 6.5%.
- **Parent Loans for Undergraduate Student Loans** Parents can borrow any amount not covered by the student's financial aid and have up to ten years to repay the loan. In 2006, the APR was 8%.

Students who use credit cards to pay for tuition risk graduating with high-interest debt that could take decades to repay. In 2006, 25% of students who paid tuition with a credit card had debt exceeding $5000 versus 11% of students who used their cards for other purposes.

Source: Sandra Block, "Your Money," *USA Today*

EXAMPLE 5 BALANCE DUE ON A CREDIT CARD

A particular VISA card calculates interest using the unpaid balance method. The monthly interest rate is 1.3% on the unpaid balance on the first day of the billing period less payments and credits. Here are some of the details in the May 1–May 31 itemized billing:

May 1 Unpaid Balance: $1350

Payment Received May 8: $250

Purchases Charged to the VISA Account: Airline tickets: $375, Books: $57, Meals: $65

Last Day of the Billing Period: May 31

Payment Due Date: June 9

a. Find the interest due on the payment due date.

b. Find the total balance owed on the last day of the billing period.

c. This credit card requires a $10 minimum monthly payment if the total balance owed on the last day of the billing period is less than $360. Otherwise, the minimum monthly payment is $\frac{1}{36}$ of the balance owed on the last day of the billing period, rounded to the nearest whole dollar. What is the minimum monthly payment due by June 9?

SOLUTION

a. The monthly interest rate is 1.3% on the unpaid balance on the first day of the billing period, $1350, less payments and credits, $250. The interest due is computed using $I = Prt$.

$$I = Prt = (\$1350 - \$250) \times 0.013 \times 1 = \$1100 \times 0.013 \times 1 = \$14.30$$

Time, t, is measured in months, and $t = 1$ month.

The interest due on the payment due date is $14.30.

b. The total balance owed on the last day of the billing period is determined as follows:

Balance owed = unpaid balance on the first day of the billing period minus payments plus interest plus charges for three items during billing period.

$$= \$1100 + \$14.30 + \$375 + \$57 + \$65$$

$$= \$1611.30.$$

The total balance owed on the last day of the billing period is $1611.30.

c. Because the balance owed on the last day of the billing period, $1611.30, exceeds $360, the customer must pay a minimum of $\frac{1}{36}$ of the balance owed.

$$\text{Minimum monthly payment} = \frac{\text{balance owed}}{36} = \frac{\$1611.30}{36} \approx \$45$$

Rounded to the nearest whole dollar, the minimum monthly payment due by June 9 is $45.

CHECK POINT 5 A credit card calculates interest using the unpaid balance method. The monthly interest rate is 1.6% on the unpaid balance on the first day of the billing period less payments and credits. Here are some of the details in the May 1–May 31 itemized billing:

May 1 Unpaid Balance: \$4720
Payment Received May 8: \$1000
Purchases Charged to the Account: Computer: \$1025, Meals: \$45
Last Day of the Billing Period: May 31
Payment Due Date: June 9
Answer parts (a) through (c) in Example 5 using this information.

5 Calculate interest on credit cards using three methods.

Methods for calculating interest on credit cards vary and the interest can differ on credit cards that show the same APR. The three methods for calculating interest are summarized in the following box:

METHODS FOR CALCULATING INTEREST ON CREDIT CARDS

For all three methods, $I = Prt$, where r is the monthly rate and t is one month.

Unpaid balance method:

The principal, P, is the balance on the first day of the billing period less payments and credits.

Previous balance method:

The principal, P, is the unpaid balance on the first day of the billing period.

Average daily balance method:

The principal, P, is the **average daily balance**. This is determined by adding the unpaid balances for each day in the billing period and dividing by the number of days in the billing period.

BLITZER BONUS

Credit Cards and College

When College Students with Credit Cards Obtained a Card

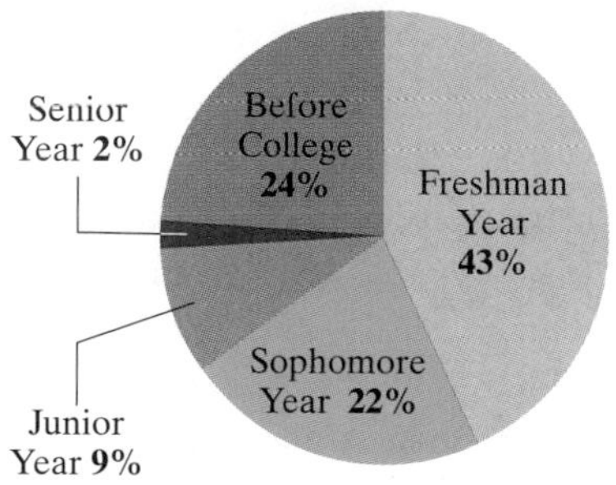

Source: Nellie Mae

EXAMPLE 6 COMPARING METHODS FOR CALCULATING INTEREST

A credit card has a monthly rate of 1.75%. (The APR is 21%.) In the January 1–January 31 itemized billing, the January 1 unpaid balance is \$2500. A payment of \$1000 was received on January 8. There are no purchases or cash advances in this billing period. The payment due date is February 9. Find the interest due on this date using each of the three methods for calculating credit card interest.

SOLUTION Because the monthly rate is 1.75%, for all three methods $I = Prt = P \times 0.0175 \times 1$ month. The principal, P, is different for each method.

a. The Unpaid Balance Method
The principal, P, is the unpaid balance on the first day of the billing period, \$2500, less payments and credits, \$1000. The interest is

$$I = Prt = (\$2500 - \$1000) \times 0.0175 \times 1 = \$1500 \times 0.0175 \times 1 = \$26.25.$$

The interest due on the payment due date is \$26.25.

b. The Previous Balance Method
The principal, P, is the unpaid balance on the first day of the billing period, \$2500. The interest is

$$I = Prt = \$2500 \times 0.0175 \times 1 = \$43.75.$$

The interest due on the payment due date is \$43.75.

c. The Average Daily Balance Method
The principal, P, is the average daily balance. Add the unpaid balances for each day in the billing period and divide by the number of days in the billing period, 31. The unpaid balance on the first day of the billing period is \$2500 and a \$1000 payment is recorded on January 8. The sum of the balances owed for each day of

the billing period is \$2500 added for each of the first 7 days, expressed as $\$2500 \times 7$, plus \$1500 added for each of the remaining 24 days, expressed as $\$1500 \times 24$.

Average daily balance

$$= \frac{\text{Sum of the unpaid balances for each day in the billing period}}{\text{Number of days in the billing period}}$$

$$= \frac{\$2500(7) + \$1500(24)}{31} \approx \$1725.81$$

The average daily balance serves as the principal. The interest is

$$I = Prt = \$1725.81 \times 0.0175 \times 1 \approx \$30.20.$$

The interest due on the payment due date is \$30.20.

Most credit cards use the average daily balance method to determine interest due. Calculating the average daily balance by hand can be quite tedious when there are numerous transactions during a billing period. Credit card customers who are charged interest by the average daily balance method will find the average daily balance provided on monthly statements.

CHECK POINT 6 A credit card has a monthly rate of 1.8%. In the January 1–January 31 itemized billing, the January 1 unpaid balance is \$6800. A payment of \$500 was received on January 8. There are no purchases or cash advances in this billing period. The payment due date is February 9. Find the interest due on this date using each of the three methods for calculating credit card interest.

BLITZER BONUS

Comparing Credit Cards

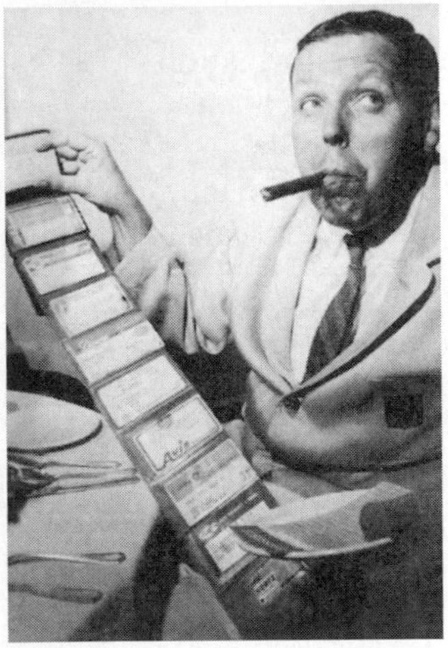

With features such as miles toward air travel, insurance on rental cars, and special introductory rates, shopping for a credit card can be a daunting task. You can search the Internet for the most current information regarding annual fees and interest rates. Compare credit cards at Web sites such as Bankrate.com and CardWeb.com. Also check *Consumer Reports*' site, www.consumerreports.org, for the "ten most consumer-friendly credit cards."

EXERCISE SET 8.5

• Practice and Application Exercises

1. The cost of a sports utility vehicle is \$27,000. We can finance this by paying \$5000 down and \$410 per month for 60 months. Determine **a.** the amount financed; **b.** the total installment price; **c.** the finance charge.
2. The cost of a computer is \$2450. We can finance this by paying \$550 down and \$94.50 per month for 24 months. Determine **a.** the amount financed; **b.** the total installment price; **c.** the finance charge.
3. The cost of a washer-dryer is \$1100. We can finance this by paying \$100 down and \$110 per month for 12 months. Determine **a.** the amount financed; **b.** the total installment price; **c.** the finance charge.
4. The cost of a used car is \$5675. We can finance this by paying \$1223 down and \$125 per month for 48 months. Determine **a.** the amount financed; **b.** the total installment price; **c.** the finance charge.
5. You plan to pay for a computer in 12 equal monthly payments. The finance charge per \$100 financed is \$6.90. Use Table 8.5 on page 482 to find the APR for this loan.
6. You plan to pay for a refrigerator in 18 equal monthly payments. The finance charge per \$100 financed is \$12.72. Use Table 8.5 on page 482 to find the APR for this loan.
7. The finance charge per \$100 financed for a computer that is paid off in 24 equal monthly payments is \$15.80. Use Table 8.5 on page 482 to find the APR for this loan.
8. The finance charge per \$100 financed for a refrigerator that is paid off in 12 monthly payments is \$8.59. Use Table 8.5 on page 482 to find the APR for this loan.
9. A used car is financed for \$4450 over 48 months. If the total finance charge is \$1279, find the APR for this loan.
10. A desk is financed for \$1200 over 30 months. If the total finance charge is \$264, find the APR for this loan.
11. The cash price for furniture for all rooms of a three-bedroom house is \$17,500. The furniture can be financed by paying \$500 down and \$360.55 per month for 60 months.
    a. Determine the amount financed.
    b. Determine the total installment price.
    c. Determine the finance charge.
    d. What is the APR for this loan?

12. The cost of a Blazer is $18,000, which can be financed by paying $600 down and $385 per month for 60 months.
   a. Determine the amount financed.
   b. Determine the total installment price.
   c. Determine the finance charge.
   d. What is the APR for this loan?

13. In Exercise 11, instead of making the twenty-fourth payment, the borrower decides to pay the remaining balance and terminate the loan for the furniture.
   a. Use the actuarial method to determine how much interest will be saved by repaying the loan early.
   b. By the actuarial method, what is the total amount due on the day of the loan's termination?
   c. Use the rule of 78 to determine how much interest will be saved by repaying the loan early.
   d. By the rule of 78, what is the total amount due on the day of the loan's termination?

14. In Exercise 12, instead of making the twenty-fourth payment, the borrower decides to pay the remaining balance and terminate the loan for the Blazer.
   a. Use the actuarial method to determine how much interest will be saved by repaying the loan early.
   b. By the actuarial method, what is the total amount due on the day of the loan's termination?
   c. Use the rule of 78 to determine how much interest will be saved by repaying the loan early.
   d. By the rule of 78, what is the total amount due on the day of the loan's termination?

15. A particular VISA card calculates interest using the unpaid balance method. The monthly interest rate is 1.3% on the unpaid balance on the first day of the billing period less payments and credits. Here are some of the details in the May 1–May 31 itemized billing:

   May 1 Unpaid Balance: $950
   Payment Received May 8: $100
   Purchases Charged to the VISA Account: clothing, $85 and car repair, $67
   Last Day of the Billing Period: May 31
   Payment Due Date: June 9

   a. Find the interest due on the payment due date.
   b. Find the total balance owed on the last day of the billing period.
   c. This credit card requires a $10 minimum monthly payment if the total balance owed on the last day of the billing period is less than $360. Otherwise, the minimum monthly payment is $\frac{1}{36}$ of the balance owed on the last day of the billing period, rounded to the nearest whole dollar. What is the minimum monthly payment due by June 9?

16. A particular credit card calculates interest using the unpaid balance method. The monthly interest rate is 1.75% on the unpaid balance on the first day of the billing period less payments and credits. Here are some of the details in the September 1–September 30 itemized billing:

   September 1 Unpaid Balance: $425
   Payment Received September 6: $75
   Purchases Charged to the Account: groceries, $45 and clothing, $77
   Last Day of the Billing Period: September 30
   Payment Due Date: October 9

   a. Find the interest due on the payment due date.
   b. Find the total balance owed on the last day of the billing period.
   c. Terms for this credit card are shown in the following table. What is the minimum monthly payment due by October 9?

New Balance	Minimum Payment
$0.01 to $10.00	No payment due
10.01 to 200.00	$10.00
200.01 to 250.00	15.00
250.01 to 300.00	20.00
300.01 to 350.00	25.00
350.01 to 400.00	30.00
400.01 to 450.00	35.00
450.01 to 500.00	40.00
Over $500.00	$\frac{1}{10}$ of new balance

17. A credit card has a monthly rate of 1.5% and uses the average daily balance method for calculating interest. Here are some of the details in the April 1–April 30 itemized billing:

   April 1 Unpaid Balance: $445.59
   Payment Received April 5: $110
   Purchases Charged to the Account: $278.06
   Average Daily Balance: $330.90
   Last Day of the Billing Period: April 30
   Payment Due Date: May 9

   a. Find the interest due on the payment due date.
   b. Find the total balance owed on the last day of the billing period.
   c. Terms for this credit card are given in Exercise 16. What is the minimum monthly payment due by May 9?

18. A credit card has a monthly rate of 1.8% and uses the average daily balance method for calculating interest. Here are some of the details in the December 1–December 31 itemized billing:

   December 1 Unpaid Balance: $220
   Payment Received December 7: $60
   Purchases Charged to the Account: $90
   Average Daily Balance: $205.60
   Last Day of the Billing Period: December 31
   Payment Due Date: January 9

   a. Find the interest due on the payment due date.
   b. Find the total balance owed on the last day of the billing period.
   c. Terms for this credit card are given in Exercise 16. What is the minimum monthly payment due on January 9?

19. A credit card has a monthly rate of 1.5%. In the September 1–September 30 itemized billing, the September 1 unpaid balance is $3000. A payment of $2500 was received on September 6. There are no purchases or cash advances in this billing period. The payment due date is October 9. Find the interest due on this date using
   a. the unpaid balance method.
   b. the previous balance method.
   c. the average daily balance method.

20. A credit card has a monthly rate of 2.2%. In the October 1–October 31 itemized billing, the October 1 unpaid balance is \$2000. A payment of \$400 was received on October 6. There are no purchases or cash advances in this billing period. The payment due date is November 9. Find the interest due on this date using

a. the unpaid balance method.

b. the previous balance method.

c. the average daily balance method.

• Writing in Mathematics

21. Describe the difference between a fixed installment loan and an open-end installment loan.

22. For a fixed installment loan, what is the total installment price?

23. For a fixed installment loan, how is the total finance charge determined?

24. What is the APR?

25. What are the two methods for computing unearned interest when a loan is paid off early? Describe how the payoff amount is determined regardless of which method is used in the computation.

26. Name and describe each of the three methods for calculating interest on credit cards.

27. For a credit card billing period, describe how the average daily balance is determined. Why is this computation somewhat tedious when done by hand?

28. Which method for calculating interest on credit cards is most beneficial to the borrower and which is least benefical? Explain why this is so.

29. A Sears Revolving Charge Card has a monthly rate of 1.75%. The interest is a minimum of 50¢ if the average daily balance is \$28.50 or less. Explain how this policy is beneficial to Sears.

• Critical Thinking Exercise

30. Which one of the following is true?

a. The finance charge on a fixed installment loan is the cash price minus the total installment price.

b. It is to a borrower's advantage to have unearned interest computed by the rule of 78 rather than by the actuarial method.

c. It is not necessary to know the number of days in a credit card billing period to determine the average daily balance.

d. If a credit card has a 2.2% monthly interest rate, the annual rate exceeds 25%.

Use estimation and not calculation to select the most reasonable value in Exercises 31–32.

31. If you purchase a \$1400 item, put \$200 down, and pay the balance in 30 monthly installments, what is a reasonable estimate of the monthly payment?

a. \$35 b. \$47 c. \$70 d. \$100

32. A reasonable estimate of the monthly interest on an average daily balance of \$359.58 at a 1.3% monthly rate is

a. \$50 b. \$10 c. \$5 d. \$2

33. A bank bills its credit card holders on the first of each month for each itemized billing. The card provides a 20-day period in which to pay the bill before charging interest. If the card holder wants to buy an expensive gift for a September 30 wedding but can't pay for it until November 5, explain how this can be done without adding an interest charge.

34. A \$1500 computer can be purchased using a credit card that charges a monthly rate of 1.5% using the unpaid balance method. The borrower is considering one of the following options:

Option A: Make a credit card payment of \$300 at the end of each month for five months and pay off the balance at the end of the sixth month.

Option B: Make a credit card payment of \$300 plus the month's interest at the end of each month for five months.

How much is saved in interest using option B?

• Technology Exercises

35. Set up a spreadsheet with one column each for the balance, number of days at that balance, payments, charges, and the product of each balance and the number of days at that balance. The balance on John and Jane Doe's credit card on July 5, their billing date, was \$375.80. For the period ending August 4, they had the following transactions:

July 13, Payment: \$150.00
July 15, Charge: Computer Store, \$74.35
July 23, Charge: Clothing, \$123.50
July 29, Charge: Restaurant, \$42.50

a. Use the summation capabilities of the spreadsheet to determine the number of days in the billing period and the average daily balance.

b. Find the finance charge (the interest) that is owed on August 4. Assume the monthly rate is 1.3%.

c. Find the balance that is owed on August 4.

36. Set up a spreadsheet with one column each for the balance, number of days at that balance, payments, charges, and the product of each balance and the number of days at that balance. The balance on the Does' credit card on May 12, their billing date, was \$378.50. For the period ending June 11, they had the following transactions:

May 13, Charge: Toys, \$129.79

May 15, Payment: \$50.00

May 18, Charge: Clothing, \$135.85

May 29, Charge: Housewares, \$37.63

a. Use the summation capabilities of the spreadsheet to determine the number of days in the billing period and the average daily balance.

b. Find the finance charge (the interest) that is owed on June 11. Assume the monthly rate is 0.75%.

c. Find the balance that is owed on June 11.

SECTION 8.6 • AMORTIZATION AND THE COST OF HOME OWNERSHIP

OBJECTIVES

1. Understand mortgage options.
2. Compute the monthly payment and interest costs for a mortgage.
3. Prepare a partial loan amortization schedule.
4. Compute payments and interest for other kinds of installment loans.

In 2006, the median U.S. home price jumped to $206,000, up a stunning 15% in a year and 55% over five years. (*Source*: National Association of Realtors) Americans now brag about having bought their home in the 1990s the way they used to boast about having bought Microsoft stock in the 1980s. The deeper implication of this real estate boom is the notion that a house is no longer just a home: Real estate has become as much about nest feathering as it is about nesting. And when love and money collide, things can get a little crazy. In this section, we focus on the cost of home ownership and the mathematics underlying America's raucous house party.

1 Understand mortgage options.

Mortgages

A **mortgage** is a long-term loan (perhaps up to 30, 40, or even 50 years) for the purpose of buying a home, and for which the property is pledged as security for payment. If payments are not made on the loan, the lender gets to take possession of the property. The **down payment** is the portion of the sale price of the home that the buyer initially pays to the seller. The minimum required down payment is computed as a percentage of the sale price. For example, suppose you decide to buy a $220,000 home that requires you to pay the seller 10% of the sale price. You must pay 10% of $220,000, which is 0.10 × $220,000, or $22,000, to the seller. Thus, $22,000 is the down payment. The **amount of the mortgage** is the difference between the sale price and the down payment. For your $220,000 home, the amount of the mortgage is $220,000 − $22,000, or $198,000.

There are many types of lenders and types of mortgages to choose from. Many banks, savings associations, mortgage companies, and credit unions provide mortgage loans. Some companies, called **mortgage brokers**, offer to find you a mortgage lender willing to make you a loan. Computer loan origination systems, or CLOs, are computer terminals sometimes available in real estate offices to help buyers sort through the various types of loans offered by different lenders.

Monthly payments for a mortgage depend on the amount of the mortgage, or the principal, the interest rate, and the time of the mortgage. Mortgages can have a fixed interest rate or a variable interest rate. **Fixed-rate mortgages** have the same monthly payment during the entire time of the loan. **Variable-rate mortgages**, also known as **adjustable-rate mortgages** (ARMs), have payment amounts that change from time to time depending on changes in the interest rate. ARMS are less predictable than fixed-rate mortgages. They start out at lower rates than fixed-rate mortgages. Caps limit how high rates can go over the term of the loan.

There are many other mortgage options. One option involves a short-term loan in which only the interest is paid, followed by a final payment (called a "balloon payment") for the entire loan amount. This kind of mortgage might appeal to a

> **BLITZER BONUS**
>
> **An Easy Way to Find the Cheapest Mortgage**
>
> When people learn all the major costs of getting a mortgage, they often feel like they're drowning in an ocean of rates, points, and formulas. Assume you'll be in your new home for five years, the average length of time most people stay. An easy way to shop for the best mortgage is to ask six different lenders for the total *dollar costs* of
>
> 1. up-front fees (such as appraisal and credit reports)
> 2. closing costs, including points
> 3. interest for the first five years.
>
> Then add up the total cost of these three items at each lender and compare the various deals. Don't let lenders get away with saying, "Then, of course, there are certain other fees and charges." You want them all now—period.

buyer who plans to sell the house in a short period of time. Some buyers are eligible for a mortgage insured through the Federal Housing Administration (FHA) or guaranteed by the Department of Veteran Affairs or similar programs operated by cities or states. These programs require a smaller down payment than standard loans.

2 Compute the monthly payment and interest costs for a mortgage.

Computation Involved with Buying a Home

Although monthly payments for a mortgage depend on the amount of the mortgage, the time of the loan, and the interest rate, the rate is not the only cost of a mortgage. Most lending institutions require the buyer to pay one or more **points** at the time of closing—that is, the time at which the mortgage begins. A point is a one-time charge that equals 1% of the loan amount. For example, two points means that the buyer must pay 2% of the loan amount at closing. Often, a buyer can pay fewer points in exchange for a higher interest rate or more points for a lower rate. A document, called the **Truth-in-Lending Disclosure Statement**, shows the buyer the APR for the mortgage. The APR takes into account the interest rate and points.

A monthly mortgage payment is used to repay the principal plus interest. In addition, lending institutions can require that part of the monthly payment be deposited into an **escrow account**, an account used by the lender to pay real estate taxes and insurance. Interest is paid to the buyer on the amount in an escrow account.

We can use formulas for compound interest and the value of an annuity to determine the amount of mortgage payments for fixed-rate mortgages. Suppose that you borrow P dollars at interest rate r over t years.

The lender expects A dollars at the end of t years.

$$A = P\left(1 + \frac{r}{n}\right)^{nt}$$

You save the A dollars in an annuity by paying PMT dollars n times per year.

$$A = \frac{PMT\left[\left(1 + \frac{r}{n}\right)^{nt} - 1\right]}{\frac{r}{n}}$$

To find your regular payment amount, PMT, we set the amount the lender expects to receive equal to the amount you will save in the annuity:

$$P\left(1 + \frac{r}{n}\right)^{nt} = \frac{PMT\left[\left(1 + \frac{r}{n}\right)^{nt} - 1\right]}{\frac{r}{n}}.$$

Solving this equation for PMT, we obtain a formula for the loan payment for any installment loan, including payments on fixed-rate mortgages.

STUDY TIP

Because the formula in the box assumes the same number of yearly payments and yearly compounding periods, the actual payments may differ slightly from those calculated using the formula.

LOAN PAYMENT FORMULA FOR INSTALLMENT LOANS

The regular payment amount, PMT, required to repay a loan of P dollars paid n times per year over t years at an annual rate r is given by

$$PMT = \frac{P\left(\frac{r}{n}\right)}{1 - \left(1 + \frac{r}{n}\right)^{-nt}}.$$

EXAMPLE 1 COMPUTING THE MONTHLY PAYMENT AND INTEREST COSTS FOR A MORTGAGE

The price of a home is $195,000. The bank requires a 10% down payment and two points at the time of closing. The cost of the home is financed with a 30-year fixed-rate mortgage at 7.5%.

a. Find the required down payment.

b. Find the amount of the mortgage.

c. How much must be paid for the two points at closing?

d. Find the monthly payment (excluding escrowed taxes and insurance).

e. Find the total interest paid over 30 years.

SOLUTION

a. The required down payment is 10% of $195,000 or

$$0.10 \times \$195{,}000 = \$19{,}500.$$

b. The amount of the mortgage is the difference between the price of the home and the down payment.

$$\text{Amount of the mortgage} = \text{sale price} - \text{down payment}$$

$$= \$195{,}000 - \$19{,}500$$

$$= \$175{,}500$$

c. To find the cost of two points on a mortgage of $175,500, find 2% of $175,500.

$$0.02 \times \$175{,}500 = \$3510$$

The down payment ($19,500) is paid to the seller and the cost of two points ($3510) is paid to the lending institution.

d. We are interested in finding the monthly payment for a $175,500 mortgage at 7.5% for 30 years. We use the loan payment formula for installment loans.

P, the mortgage amount, is $175,500. Fixed rate, *r*, is 7.5%. 12 payments per year. The mortgage time, *t*, is 30 years.

$$PMT = \frac{P\left(\frac{r}{n}\right)}{1 - \left(1 + \frac{r}{n}\right)^{-nt}} = \frac{175{,}500\left(\frac{0.075}{12}\right)}{1 - \left(1 + \frac{0.075}{12}\right)^{-12(30)}}$$

$$= \frac{1096.875}{1 - (1.00625)^{-360}} \approx 1227$$

The monthly mortgage payment for principal and interest is approximately $1227.00. (Keep in mind that this payment does not include escrowed taxes and insurance.)

e. The total cost of interest over 30 years is equal to the difference between the total of all monthly payments and the amount of the mortgage. The total of all monthly payments is equal to the amount of the monthly payment multiplied by the number of payments. We found the amount of each monthly payment in (d): $1227. The number of payments is equal to the number of months in a year, 12, multiplied by the number of years in the mortgage, 30: $12 \times 30 = 360$. Thus, the total of all montlhly payments $= \$1227 \times 360$.
Now we can calculate the interest over 30 years.

$$\text{Total interest paid} = \text{total of all monthly payments} \text{ minus } \text{amount of the mortgage.}$$

$$= \$1227 \times 360 - \$175{,}500$$

$$= \$441{,}720 - \$175{,}500 = \$266{,}220$$

The total interest paid over 30 years is approximately $266,220.

BLITZER BONUS

The Point Is, Don't Ignore Points

WHAT A FIXED-RATE $100,000 MORTGAGE AT 7% REALLY COSTS

Points	APR 30 years	APR 15 years
1	7.10%	7.16%
2	7.20%	7.33%
3	7.30%	7.49%
4	7.41%	7.66%
5	7.52%	7.83%

CHECK POINT 1 In Example 1, the \$175,500 mortgage was financed with a 30-year fixed rate at 7.5%. The total interest paid over 30 years was approximately \$266,220.

a. Use the loan payment formula for installment loans to find the monthly payment if the time of the mortgage is reduced to 15 years. Round to the nearest dollar.

b. Find the total interest paid over 15 years.

c. How much interest is saved by reducing the mortgage from 30 to 15 years?

3 Prepare a partial loan amortization schedule.

Loan Amortization Schedules

When a loan is paid off through a series of regular payments, it is said to be **amortized**, which literally means "killed off." In working Check Point 1(c), were you surprised that nearly \$150,000 was saved when the mortgage was amortized over 15 years rather than over 30 years? What adds to the interest cost is the long period over which the loan is financed. **Although each payment is the same, with each successive payment the interest portion decreases and the principal portion increases.** The interest is computed using the simple interest formula $I = Prt$. The principal, P, is equal to the balance of the loan, which changes each month. The rate, r, is the annual interest rate of the mortgage loan. Because a payment is made each month, the time, t, is

$$\frac{1 \text{ month}}{12 \text{ months}} = \frac{1 \cancel{\text{month}}}{12 \cancel{\text{months}}}$$

or $\frac{1}{12}$ of a year.

A document showing important information about the status of the mortgage is called a **loan amortization schedule**. Typically, this document includes the number of the most recent payment and those of any previous monthly payments, the interest for each monthly payment, the principal payment for each monthly payment, and the balance of the loan.

EXAMPLE 2 PREPARING A LOAN AMORTIZATION SCHEDULE

Prepare a loan amortization schedule for the first two months of the mortgage loan shown in the following table:

LOAN AMORTIZATION SCHEDULE

Annual % rate: 9.5% Amount of Mortgage: \$130,000 Number of Monthly Payments: 180		Monthly payment: \$1357.50 Term: Years 15, Months 0	
Payment Number	**Interest Payment**	**Principal Payment**	**Balance of Loan**
1			
2			

SOLUTION We begin with payment number 1.

$$\text{Interest for the month} = Prt = \$130{,}000 \times 0.095 \times \frac{1}{12} \approx \$1029.17$$

$$\text{Principal payment} = \text{Monthly payment} - \text{Interest payment}$$
$$= \$1357.50 - \$1029.17 = \$328.33$$

$$\text{Balance of loan} = \text{Principal balance} - \text{Principal payment}$$
$$= \$130{,}000 - \$328.33 = \$129{,}671.67$$

Now, starting with a loan balance of \$129,671.67, we repeat these computations for the second month.

$$\text{Interest for the month} = Prt = \$129{,}671.67 \times 0.095 \times \frac{1}{12} = \$1026.57$$

$$\begin{aligned}\text{Principal payment} &= \text{Monthly payment} - \text{Interest payment}\\ &= \$1357.50 - \$1026.57 = \$330.93\\ \text{Balance of loan} &= \text{Principal balance} - \text{Principal payment}\\ &= \$129{,}671.67 - \$330.93 = \$129{,}340.74\end{aligned}$$

The results of these computations are included in Table 8.6, a partial loan amortization schedule. By using the simple interest formula month-to-month on the loan's balance, a complete loan amortization schedule for all 180 payments can be calculated.

TABLE 8.6 LOAN AMORTIZATION SCHEDULE

Annual % rate: 9.5%
Amount of Mortgage: \$130,000 | **Monthly payment: \$1357.50**
Number of Monthly Payments: 180 | **Term: Years 15, Months 0**

Payment Number	Interest Payment	Principal Payment	Balance of Loan
1	\$1029.17	\$328.33	\$129,671.67
2	1026.57	330.93	129,340.74
3	1023.96	333.54	129,007.22
4	1021.32	336.18	128,671.04
30	944.82	412.68	118,931.35
31	941.55	415.95	118,515.52
125	484.62	872.88	60,340.84
126	477.71	879.79	59,461.05
179	21.26	1336.24	1347.74
180	9.76	1347.74	

Many lenders supply a loan amortization schedule like the one in Example 2. Such a schedule shows how the buyer pays slightly less in interest and more in principal for each payment over the entire life of the loan.

CHECK POINT 2 Prepare a loan amortization schedule for the first two months of the mortgage loan shown in the following table:

Annual % rate: 7.0%
Amount of Mortgage: \$200,000 | **Monthly payment: \$1550.00**
Number of Monthly Payments: 240 | **Term: Years 20, Months 0**

Payment Number	Interest Payment	Principal Payment	Balance of Loan
1			
2			

BLITZER BONUS

Bittersweet Interest

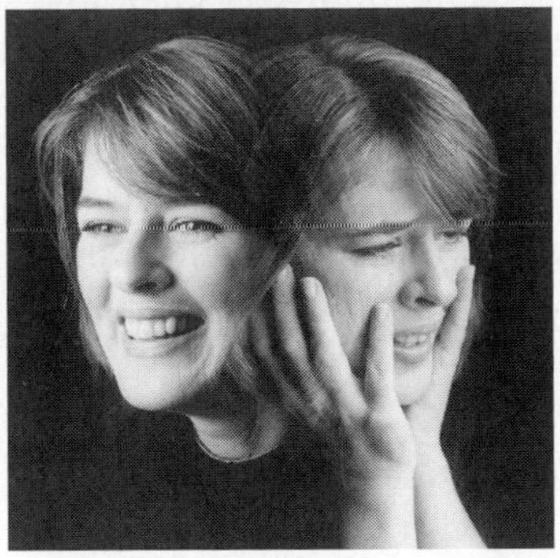

Early mortgage payments illustrate that it can be discouraging to realize how much goes toward interest and how little goes toward paying off the principal. Although you get socked with tons of interest in the early years of a loan, the one bright side to the staggering cost of a mortgage is the **mortgage interest tax deduction**. To make the cost of owning a home more affordable, the tax code permits deducting all the mortgage interest (but not the principal) that you pay per year on the loan. Table 8.7 illustrates how this tax loophole reduces the cost of the mortgage.

TABLE 8.7 TAX DEDUCTIONS FOR A \$100,000 MORTGAGE AT 7% FOR A TAXPAYER IN THE 28% TAX BRACKET

Year	Interest	Tax Savings	Net Cost of Mortgage
1	\$6968	\$1951	\$5017
2	\$6895	\$1931	\$4964
3	\$6816	\$1908	\$4908
4	\$6732	\$1885	\$4847
5	\$6641	\$1859	\$4782

4 Compute payments and interest for other kinds of installment loans.

Monthly Payments and Interest Costs for Other Kinds of Installment Loans

The loan payment formula can be used to determine how much your regular payments will be on installment loans other than mortgages, including car loans and student loans. The portions of each payment going toward the principal and toward the interest will vary as the loan balance declines. Near the beginning of the loan term, the portion going toward the interest will be relatively high and the portion going toward the principal will be relatively low. As the loan term continues, the principal portion will gradually increase and the interest portion will gradually decrease.

BLITZER BONUS

Checking Out Financing Options

It's a good idea to get preapproved for a car loan through a bank or credit union before going to the dealer. You can then compare the loan offered by the dealer to your preapproved loan. Furthermore, with more money in hand, you'll have more negotiating power.

EXAMPLE 3 COMPARING CAR LOANS

You decide to take a \$20,000 loan for a new car. You can select one of the following loans, each requiring regular monthly payments:

Installment Loan A: 3-year loan at 7%

Installment Loan B: 5-year loan at 9%.

a. Find the monthly payments and the total interest for Loan A.

b. Find the monthly payments and the total interest for Loan B.

c. Compare the monthly payments and total interest for the two loans.

SOLUTION For each loan, we use the loan payment formula to compute the monthly payments.

a. We first determine monthly payments and total interest for Loan A.

P, the loan amount, is \$20,000. Rate, r, is 7%. 12 payments per year. The loan is for 3 years.

$$PMT = \frac{P\left(\frac{r}{n}\right)}{1-\left(1+\frac{r}{n}\right)^{-nt}} = \frac{20{,}000\left(\frac{0.07}{12}\right)}{1-\left(1+\frac{0.07}{12}\right)^{-12(3)}} \approx 618$$

The monthly payments are approximately \$618.

Now we calculate the interest over 3 years, or 36 months.

Total interest over 3 years = Total of all monthly payments minus amount of the loan.

$$= \$618 \times 36 - \$20{,}000$$

$$= \$2248$$

The total interest paid over 3 years is approximately \$2248.

b. Next, we determine monthly payments and total interest for Loan B.

P, the loan amount, is \$20,000. Rate, r, is 9%. 12 payments per year. The loan is for 5 years.

$$PMT = \frac{P\left(\frac{r}{n}\right)}{1-\left(1+\frac{r}{n}\right)^{-nt}} = \frac{20{,}000\left(\frac{0.09}{12}\right)}{1-\left(1+\frac{0.09}{12}\right)^{-12(5)}} \approx 415$$

The monthly payments are approximately \$415.

Now we calculate the interest over 5 years, or 60 months.

Total interest over 5 years	=	Total of all monthly payments	minus	amount of the loan.
	=	\$415 × 60	−	\$20,000
	=	\$4900		

The total interest paid over 5 years is approximately \$4900.

c. Table 8.8 compares the monthly payments and total interest for the two loans.

TABLE 8.8 COMPARING CAR LOANS

\$20,000 loan	Monthly Payment	Total Interest
3-year loan at 7%	\$618	\$2248
5-year loan at 9%	\$415	\$4900

Monthly payments are less with the longer-term loan.

Interest is more with the longer-term loan.

BLITZER BONUS

The Dark Side of Student Loans

Exercises 17 and 18 in the Exercise Set that follows apply the loan payment formula to determine regular payments and interest on student loans. Sallie Mae, the private company that makes, holds, and buys the most student loans, has been criticized as being a moneymaker for its executives rather than an agency designed to help students without the means to finance a college education. Initially a government agency, Sallie Mae has been profiting mightily since it was privatized in 1997. It had the second-highest return on revenue in 2005 among *Fortune* 500 companies. Getting money to pay for college may be tough, but paying it back can break you. Visit the Web site of Student Loan Justice, where borrowers tell how their lives have been ruined by the burden of debts and harsh treatment by lenders.

Sources: *60 Minutes*, May 14, 2006, and *Consumer Reports Money Adviser*, March 2006

CHECK POINT 3 You decide to take a \$15,000 loan for a new car. You can select one of the following loans, each requiring regular monthly payments:

Installment Loan A: 4-year loan at 8%

Installment Loan B: 6-year loan at 10%

a. Find the monthly payments and the total interest for Loan A.

b. Find the monthly payments and the total interest for Loan B.

c. Compare the monthly payments and total interest for the two loans.

EXERCISE SET 8.6

• Practice and Application Exercises

In all exercises, use

$$PMT = \frac{P\left(\frac{r}{n}\right)}{1 - \left(1 + \frac{r}{n}\right)^{-nt}}$$

to determine the regular payment amount, rounded to the nearest dollar.

Exercises 1–8 involve home mortgages.

1. The price of a home is \$220,000. The bank requires a 20% down payment and three points at the time of closing. The cost of the home is financed with a 30-year fixed-rate mortgage at 7%.
   - **a.** Find the required down payment.
   - **b.** Find the amount of the mortgage.
   - **c.** How much must be paid for the three points at closing?
   - **d.** Find the monthly payment (excluding escrowed taxes and insurance).
   - **e.** Find the total cost of interest over 30 years.
2. The price of a condominium is \$180,000. The bank requires a 5% down payment and one point at the time of closing. The cost of the condominium is financed with a 30-year fixed-rate mortgage at 8%.
   - **a.** Find the required down payment.
   - **b.** Find the amount of the mortgage.
   - **c.** How much must be paid for the one point at closing?
   - **d.** Find the monthly payment (excluding escrowed taxes and insurance).
   - **e.** Find the total cost of interest over 30 years.
3. The price of a small cabin is \$100,000. The bank requires a 5% down payment. The buyer is offered two mortgage options: 20-year fixed at 8% or 30-year fixed at 8%. Calculate the amount of interest paid for each option. How much does the buyer save in interest with the 20-year option?
4. The price of a home is \$160,000. The bank requires a 15% down payment. The buyer is offered two mortgage options: 15-year fixed at 8% or 30-year fixed at 8%. Calculate the amount of interest paid for each option. How much does the buyer save in interest with the 15-year option?
5. In terms of paying less in interest, which is more economical for a \$150,000 mortgage: a 30-year fixed-rate at 8% or a 20-year fixed-rate at 7.5%? How much is saved in interest?

6. In terms of paying less in interest, which is more economical for a $90,000 mortgage: a 30-year fixed-rate at 8% or a 15-year fixed-rate at 7.5%? How much is saved in interest?

In Exercises 7–8, which mortgage loan has the greater total cost (closing costs + the amount paid for points + total cost of interest)? By how much?

7. A $120,000 mortgage with two loan options:

Mortgage A: 30-year fixed at 7% with closing costs of $2000 and one point

Mortgage B: 30-year fixed at 6.5% with closing costs of $1500 and four points

8. A $250,000 mortgage with two loan options:

Mortgage A: 30-year fixed at 7.25% with closing costs of $2000 and one point

Mortgage B: 30-year fixed at 6.25% with closing costs of costs of $350 and four points

Exercises 9–18 involve installment loans other than mortgages.

9. Your credit card has a balance of $4200 and an annual interest rate of 18%. You decide to pay off the balance over two years. If there are no further purchases charged to the card,

a. How much must you pay each month?

b. How much total interest will you pay?

10. Your credit card has a balance of $3600 and an annual interest rate of 16.5%. You decide to pay off the balance over two years. If there are no further purchases charged to the card,

a. How much must you pay each month?

b. How much total interest will you pay?

11. To pay off the $4200 credit-card balance in Exercise 9, you can get a bank loan at 10.5% with a term of three years.

a. How much will you pay each month? How does this compare with your credit-card payment in Exercise 9?

b. How much total interest will you pay? How does this compare with your total credit-card interest in Exercise 9?

12. To pay off the $3600 credit-card balance in Exercise 10, you can get a bank loan at 9.5% with a term of three years.

a. How much will you pay each month? How does this compare with your credit-card payment in Exercise 10?

b. How much total interest will you pay? How does this compare with your total credit-card interest in Exercise 10?

13. Rework Exercise 9 if you decide to pay off the balance over one year, rather than two. How much more must you pay each month and how much less will you pay in total interest?

14. Rework Exercise 10 if you decide to pay off the balance over one year rather than two. How much more must you pay each month and how much less will you pay in total interest?

15. You borrow $10,000 for four years at 8% toward the purchase of a car.

a. Find the monthly payments and the total interest for the loan.

b. Prepare a loan amortization schedule for the first three months of the car loan. Round entries to the nearest cent.

Payment Number	Interest	Principal	Loan Balance
1			
2			
3			

16. You borrow $30,000 for four years at 8% toward the purchase of a car.

a. Find the monthly payments and the total interest for the loan.

b. Prepare a loan amortization schedule for the first three months of the car loan. Use the table in Exercise 15(b) and round entries to the nearest cent.

17. A student graduates from college with a loan of $40,000. The interest rate is 8.5% and the loan term is 20 years.

a. Find the monthly payments and the total interest for the loan.

b. Prepare a loan amortization schedule for the first three months of the student loan. Use the table in Exercise 15(b) and round entries to the nearest cent.

c. If the interest rate remains at 8.5% and the loan term is reduced to ten years, how much more must the student pay each month and how much less will be paid in total interest?

18. A student graduates from college with a loan of $50,000. The interest rate is 7.5% and the loan term is 20 years.

a. Find the monthly payments and the total interest for the loan.

b. Prepare a loan amortization schedule for the first three months of the student loan. Use the table in Exercise 15(b) and round entries to the nearest cent.

c. If the interest rate remains at 7.5% and the loan term is reduced to ten years, how much more must the student pay each month and how much less will be paid in total interest?

• Writing in Mathematics

19. What is a mortgage?

20. What is a down payment?

21. How is the amount of a mortgage determined?

22. Describe why a buyer would select a 30-year fixed-rate mortgage instead of a 15-year fixed-rate mortgage if interest rates are $\frac{1}{4}$% to $\frac{1}{2}$% lower on a 15-year mortgage.

23. Describe one advantage and one disadvantage of an adjustable-rate mortgage over a fixed-rate mortgage.

24. What is a loan amortization schedule?

25. Describe what happens to the portions of payments going to principal and interest over the life of an installment loan.

26. Describe one advantage and one disadvantage of home ownership over renting.

• Critical Thinking Exercises

27. Use the discussion that precedes the box on page 492 to prove the loan payment formula shown in the box. Work with the equation in which the amount the lender expects to receive is equal to the amount saved in the annuity. Multiply both sides of this equation by $\frac{r}{n}$ and then solve for PMT by dividing both sides by the appropriate expression. Finally, divide the numerator and the denominator of the resulting formula for PMT by $\left(1+\frac{r}{n}\right)^{nt}$ to obtain the form of the loan payment formula shown in the box.

28. The unpaid balance of an installment loan is equal to the present value of the remaining payments. The unpaid balance, P, is given by

$$P = PMT\frac{1-\left(1+\frac{r}{n}\right)^{-nt}}{\frac{r}{n}},$$

where PMT is the regular payment amount, r is the annual interest rate, n is the number of payments per year, and t is the number of years remaining in the mortgage.

a. Use the loan payment formula to derive the unpaid balance formula.

b. The price of a home is \$180,000. The bank requires a 10% down payment. After the down payment, the balance is financed with a 30-year fixed-rate mortgage at 6.3%. Determine the unpaid balance after ten years.

• Group Exercise

29. Group members should go to the Internet and select a car that they might like to buy. Price the car and its options. Then find two loans with the best rates, but with different terms. For each loan, calculate the monthly payments and total interest. Select one of the loans and prepare a partial or complete amortization schedule.

CHAPTER SUMMARY, REVIEW, AND TEST

• SUMMARY DEFINITIONS AND CONCEPTS — EXAMPLES

8.1 Percent, Sales Tax, and Income Tax

a. Percent means per hundred. Thus, $97\% = \frac{97}{100}$.

b. To express a fraction as a percent, divide the numerator by the denominator, move the decimal point in the quotient two places to the right, and add a percent sign. — Ex. 1, p. 444

c. To express a decimal number as a percent, move the decimal point two places to the right and add a percent sign. — Ex. 2, p. 445

d. To express a percent as a decimal number, move the decimal point two places to the left and remove the percent sign. — Ex. 3, p. 445

e. The percent formula, $A = PB$, means A is P percent of B.

f. Sales tax amount = tax rate × item's cost — Ex. 4, p. 446

g. Discount amount = discount rate × original price — Ex. 5, p. 446

h. Calculating Income Tax — Ex. 6, p. 448

1. Determine adjusted gross income:

Adjusted gross income = Gross income − Adjustments.

2. Determine taxable income:

Taxable income = Adjusted gross income − (Exemptions + Deductions).

3. Determine the income tax:

Income tax = Tax computation − Tax credits.

See details in the box on page 447.

i. The fraction for percent increase (or decrease) is

$$\frac{\text{amount of increase (or decrease)}}{\text{original amount}}.$$

Find the percent increase (or decrease) by expressing this fraction as a percent.

Ex. 7, p. 450; Ex. 8, p. 451; Ex. 9, p. 451; Ex. 10, p. 451

8.2 Simple Interest

a. Interest is the price we are paid for lending money or pay for borrowing money. The amount deposited or borrowed is the principal. The charge for interest, given as a percent, is the rate, assumed to be per year.

b. Simple interest involves interest calculated only on the principal and is computed using $I = Prt$.

Ex. 1, p. 455; Ex. 2, p. 455

c. The future value, A, of P dollars at simple interest rate r for t years is $A = P(1 + rt)$.

Ex. 3, p. 456; Ex. 4, p. 457; Ex. 5, p. 457

d. Discounted loans deduct the interest, called the discount, from the loan amount at the time the loan is made.

Ex. 6, p. 458

8.3 Compound Interest

a. Compound interest involves interest computed on the original principal as well as on any accumulated interest. The amount in an account for one compounding period per year is $A = P(1 + r)^t$. For n compoundings per year, the amount is $A = P\left(1 + \frac{r}{n}\right)^{nt}$. For continuous compounding, the amount is $A = Pe^{rt}$, where $e \approx 2.72$.

Ex. 1, p. 461; Ex. 2, p. 461; Ex. 3, p. 462

b. Calculating Present Value
If A dollars are to be accumulated in t years in an account that pays rate r compounded n times per year, then the present value, P, that needs to be invested now is given by

$$P = \frac{A}{\left(1 + \frac{r}{n}\right)^{nt}}.$$

Ex. 4, p. 463

c. Effective Annual Yield
Effective annual yield is defined in the box on page 464. The effective annual yield, Y, for an account that pays rate r compounded n times per year is given by

$$Y = \left(1 + \frac{r}{n}\right)^n - 1.$$

Ex. 5, p. 464; Ex. 6, p. 465

8.4 Annuities, Stocks, and Bonds

a. An annuity is a sequence of equal payments made at equal time periods. The value of an annuity is the sum of all deposits plus all interest paid.

Ex. 1, p. 468

b. The value of an annuity after t years is

$$A = \frac{P[(1 + r)^t - 1]}{r} \quad \text{or} \quad A = \frac{P\left[\left(1 + \frac{r}{n}\right)^{nt} - 1\right]}{\frac{r}{n}},$$

depending on whether interest is compounded once a year or n times per year. See the box on page 469 and the box on page 470.

Ex. 2, p. 469; Ex. 3, p. 470

c. The formula

$$P = \frac{A\left(\frac{r}{n}\right)}{\left[\left(1 + \frac{r}{n}\right)^{nt} - 1\right]}$$

gives the deposit, P, into an annuity at the end of each compounding period needed to achieve a value of A dollars after t years. See the box on page 471. Ex. 4, p. 472

d. The return on an investment is the percent increase in the investment.

e. Investors purchase stock, shares of ownership in a company. The shares indicate the percent of ownership. Trading refers to buying and selling stock. Investors make money by selling a stock for more money than they paid for it. They can also make money while they own stock if a company distributes all or part of its profits as dividends. Each share of stock is paid the same dividend.

f. Investors purchase a bond, lending money to the company from which they purchase the bond. The company commits itself to pay the price an investor pays for the bond at the time it was purchased, called its face value, along with interest payments at a given rate.

g. Reading stock tables is explained on pages 474–475. Ex. 5, p. 475

8.5 Installment Buying

a. A fixed installment loan is paid off with a series of equal periodic payments. An open-end installment loan is paid off with variable monthly payments. Credit card loans are open-end installment loans.

b. The terms of fixed installment loans—the amount financed, the total installment price, and the finance charge—are explained in the box on page 481. Ex. 1, p. 481

c. The interest rate per year on a loan is called the annual percentage rate (APR). The box on page 482 shows how to find the APR for a fixed installment loan. Ex. 2, p. 482

d. Unearned interest is the amount by which the original finance charge is reduced when a fixed installment loan is paid off early. The two methods for computing unearned interest—the actuarial method and the rule of 78—are explained in the box on page 483. Ex. 3, p. 483; Ex. 4, p. 484

e. Open-end installment loans, such as credit cards, calculate interest using the simple interest formula $I = Prt$. The methods for determining the interest, the unpaid balance method, the previous balance method, and the average daily balance method, are described in the box on page 487. Ex. 5, p. 486; Ex. 6, p. 487

8.6 Amortization and the Cost of Home Ownership

a. A mortgage is a long-term loan for the purpose of buying a home, and for which the property is pledged as security for payment. The term of the mortgage is the number of years until final payoff. The down payment is the portion of the sale price of the home that the buyer initially pays. The amount of the mortgage is the difference between the sale price and the down payment.

b. Fixed-rate mortgages have the same monthly payment during the entire time of the loan. Variable-rate mortgages, or adjustable-rate mortgages, have payment amounts that change from time to time depending on changes in the interest rate.

c. A point is a one-time charge that equals 1% of the amount of a mortgage loan.

d. Loan Payment Formula for Installment Loans Ex. 1, p. 492; Ex. 3, p. 496

$$PMT = \frac{P\left(\frac{r}{n}\right)}{1 - \left(1 + \frac{r}{n}\right)^{-nt}}$$

PMT is the regular payment amount required to repay a loan of P dollars paid n times per year over t years at an annual interest rate r.

e. Amortizing a loan is the process of making regular payments on the principal and interest until the loan is paid off. A document containing the payment number, payment toward the interest, payment toward the principal, and balance of the loan is called a loan amortization schedule. Such a schedule shows how the buyer pays slightly less in interest and more in principal for each payment over the entire life of the loan. Ex. 2, p. 494

REVIEW EXERCISES

8.1

In Exercises 1–3, express each fraction as a percent.

1. $\frac{4}{5}$ **2.** $\frac{1}{8}$ **3.** $\frac{3}{4}$

In Exercises 4–6, express each decimal as a percent.

4. 0.72 **5.** 0.0035 **6.** 4.756

In Exercises 7–12, express each percent as a decimal.

7. 65% **8.** 99.7% **9.** 150%

10. 3% **11.** 0.65% **12.** $\frac{1}{4}$%

13. What is 8% of 120?

14. Suppose that the local sales tax rate is 6% and you purchase a backpack for $24.

a. How much tax is paid?

b. What is the backpack's total cost?

15. A television with an original price of $850 is on sale at 35% off.

a. What is the discount amount?

b. What is the television's sale price?

16. Use the 2005 marginal tax rates in Table 8.1 on page 448 to calculate the income tax owed by the following person:

- Single, no dependents
- Gross income: $40,000
- $2500 paid to a tax-deferred IRA
- $6500 mortgage interest
- $1800 property taxes
- No tax credits

17. A college that had 40 students for each lecture course increased the number to 45 students. What is the percent increase in the number of students in a lecture course?

18. A dictionary regularly sells for $56.00. The sale price is $36.40. Find the percent decrease of the sale price from the regular price.

19. Consider the following statement:

My portfolio fell 10% last year, but then it rose 10% this year, so at least I recouped my losses.

Is this statement true? In particular, suppose you invested $10,000 in the stock market last year. How much money would be left in your portfolio with a 10% fall and then a 10% rise? If there is a loss, what is the percent decrease, to the nearest tenth of a percent, in your portfolio?

8.2

In Exercises 20–23, find the simple interest. (Assume 360 days in a year.)

Principal	Rate	Time
20. $6000	3%	1 year
21. $8400	5%	6 years
22. $20,000	8%	9 months
23. $36,000	15%	60 days

24. In order to pay for tuition and books, a student borrows $3500 for four months at 10.5% interest.

a. How much interest must the student pay?

b. Find the future value of the loan.

In Exercises 25–29, use the formula for future value at simple interest, $A = P(1 + rt)$, to find the missing quantity. Round dollar amounts to the nearest cent and rates to the nearest tenth of a percent.

25. $A = ?, P = \$12{,}000, r = 8.2\%, t = 9$ months

26. $A = \$5750, P = \$5000, r = ?, t = 2$ years

27. $A = \$16{,}000, P = ?, r = 6.5\%, t = 3$ years

28. You plan to buy a $12,000 sailboat in four years. How much should you invest now, at 7.3% simple interest, to have enough for the boat in four years? (Round up to the nearest cent.)

29. You borrow $1500 from a friend and promise to pay back $1800 in six months. What simple interest rate will you pay?

30. You borrow $1800 on a 7% discounted loan for a period of 9 months.

a. What is the loan's discount?

b. Determine the net amount of money you will receive.

c. What is the loan's actual interest rate, to the nearest tenth of a percent?

8.3

In Exercises 31–33, the principal represents an amount of money deposited in a savings account that provides the lender compound interest at the given rate.

a. *Use the formula $A = P(1 + r)^t$ for one compounding period per year or $A = P\left(1 + \frac{r}{n}\right)^{nt}$ for n compounding periods per year to find how much money, to the nearest cent, there will be in the account after the given number of years.*

b. *Find the interest earned.*

Principal	Rate	Compoundings per Year	Time
31. $7000	3%	1	5 years
32. $30,000	2.5%	4	10 years
33. $2500	4%	12	20 years

34. Use $A = P\left(1 + \frac{r}{n}\right)^{nt}$ and $A = Pe^{rt}$ to solve this exercise. Suppose that you have $14,000 to invest. Which investment yields the greater return over 10 years: 7% compounded monthly or 6.85% compounded continuously? How much more (to the nearest dollar) is yielded by the better investment?

Solve Exercises 35–36 using the present value formula

$$P = \frac{A}{\left(1 + \frac{r}{n}\right)^{nt}}.$$

Round answers to the nearest cent.

35. How much money should parents deposit today in an account that earns 10% compounded monthly so that it will accumulate to $100,000 in 18 years for their child's college education?

36. How much money should be deposited today in an account that earns 5% compounded quarterly so that it will accumulate to $75,000 in 35 years for retirement?

37. You deposit $2000 in an account that pays 6% interest compounded quarterly.

a. Find the future value, to the nearest cent, after one year.

b. Use the future value formula for simple interest to determine the effective annual yield. Round to the nearest tenth of a percent.

Use the effective annual yield formula

$$Y = \left(1 + \frac{r}{n}\right)^n - 1$$

to solve Exercises 38–39.

38. What is the effective annual yield, to the nearest hundredth of a percent, of an account paying 5.5% compounded quarterly? What does your answer mean?

39. Which investment is the better choice: 6.25% compounded monthly or 6.3% compounded annually?

8.4

In Exercises 40–41, use the formula

$$A = \frac{P[(1 + r)^t - 1]}{r} \quad \text{or} \quad A = \frac{P\left[\left(1 + \frac{r}{n}\right)^{nt} - 1\right]}{\frac{r}{n}}$$

to find the value of each annuity. Round to the nearest dollar.

40. You spend $10 per week on lottery tickets, averaging $520 per year. Instead of buying tickets, if you deposited the $520 at the end of each year in an annuity paying 6% compounded annually,

a. How much would you have after 20 years?

b. Find the interest.

41. To save for retirement, you decide to deposit $100 at the end of each month in an IRA that pays 5.5% compounded monthly.

a. How much will you have from the IRA after 30 years?

b. Find the interest.

42. You would like to have $25,000 to use as a down payment for a home in five years by making regular deposits at the end of every three months in an annuity that pays 7.25% compounded quarterly.

a. Use the formula

$$P = \frac{A\left(\frac{r}{n}\right)}{\left[\left(1 + \frac{r}{n}\right)^{nt} - 1\right]}$$

to determine the amount of each deposit. Round up to the nearest dollar.

b. How much of the $25,000 comes from deposits and how much comes from interest?

Exercises 43–50, refer to the stock table for Harley Davidson (the motorcycle company). Where necessary, round dollar amounts to the nearest cent.

52-Week High	Low	Stock	SYM	Div	Yld %	PE
64.06	26.13	Harley Dav	HDI	.16	.3	41

Vol 100s	Hi	Lo	Close	Net Chg
5458	61.25	59.25	61	+1.75

43. What were the high and low prices for a share for the past 52 weeks?

44. If you owned 900 shares of this stock last year, what dividend did you receive?

45. What is the annual return for the dividends alone?

46. How many shares of this company's stock were traded yesterday?

47. What were the high and low prices for a share yesterday?

48. What was the price at which a share traded when the stock exchange closed yesterday?

49. What was the change in price for a share of stock from the market close two days ago to yesterday's market close?

50. Compute the company's annual earnings per share using

$$\text{Annual earnings per share} = \frac{\text{Yesterday's closing price per share}}{\text{PE ratio}}.$$

51. Explain the difference between investing in a stock and investing in a bond.

8.5

52. The cost of a new car is $16,500. You can finance the purchase by paying $500 down and $350 per month for 60 months.

a. Determine the amount financed.

b. Determine the total installment price.

c. Determine the finance charge.

d. Use Table 8.5 on page 482 to find the APR for this loan.

53. Use the actuarial method formula

$$u = \frac{kRV}{100 + V}$$

to solve this problem. In Exercise 52, instead of making the forty-eighth payment, the borrower decides to pay the remaining balance and terminate the loan for the car.

a. How much interest is saved by repaying the loan early?

b. What is the total amount due on the day of the loan's termination?

54. Use the rule of 78 formula

$$u = \frac{k(k + 1)}{n(n + 1)} \times F$$

to solve this problem. In Exercise 52, instead of making the forty-eighth payment, the borrower decides to pay the remaining balance and terminate the loan for the car.

a. How much interest is saved by repaying the loan early?

b. What is the total amount due on the day of the loan's termination?

55. Describe the difference between the answers in Exercises 53 and 54. Which method saves the borrower more money?

56. The terms of a particular credit card are based on the unpaid balance method. The monthly interest rate is 1.5% on the unpaid balance on the first day of the billing period less payments and credits. Here are some of the details in the June 1–June 30 itemized billing:

June 1 Unpaid Balance: $1300

Payment Received June 4: $200

Purchases Charged to the Account: airline ticket, $380; car repair, $120; groceries, $140

Last Day of the Billing Period: June 30

Due Date: July 9

a. Find the interest due on the payment due date.

b. Find the total balance owed on the last day of the billing period.

c. Terms for the credit card require a $10 minimum monthly payment if the balance due is less than $360. Otherwise, the minimum monthly payment is $\frac{1}{36}$ of the balance due, rounded to the nearest whole dollar. What is the minimum monthly payment due by July 9?

57. A credit card has a monthly rate of 1.8%. In the March 1–March 31 itemized billing, the March 1 unpaid balance is $3600. A payment of $2000 was received on March 6. There are no purchases or cash advances in this billing period. The payment due date is April 9. Find the interest due on this date using

a. the unpaid balance method.

b. the previous balance method.

c. the average daily balance method.

8.6

In Exercises 58–62, use

$$PMT = \frac{P\left(\frac{r}{n}\right)}{1 - \left(1 + \frac{r}{n}\right)^{-nt}}$$

to determine the regular payment amount, rounded to the nearest dollar.

58. The price of a home is $240,000. The bank requires a 20% down payment and two points at the time of closing. The cost of the home is financed with a 30-year fixed-rate mortgage at 7%.

a. Find the required down payment.

b. Find the amount of the mortgage.

c. How much must be paid for the two points at closing?

d. Find the monthly payment (excluding escrowed taxes and insurance).

e. Find the total cost of interest over 30 years.

59. In terms of paying less in interest, which is more economical for a $70,000 mortgage: a 30-year fixed-rate at 8.5% or a 20-year fixed-rate at 8%? How much is saved in interest? Discuss one advantage and one disadvantage for each mortgage option.

60. You need a loan of $100,000 to buy a home. Here are your options:

Option A: 30-year fixed-rate at 8.5% with no closing costs and no points

Option B: 30-year fixed-rate at 7.5% with closing costs of $1300 and three points.

a. Determine your monthly payments for each option and discuss how you would decide between the two options.

b. Which mortgage loan has the greater total cost (closing costs + the amount paid for points + total cost of interest)? By how much?

61. You decide to take a $15,000 loan for a new car. You can select one of the following loans, each requiring regular monthly payments:

Loan A: 3-year loan at 7.2%

Loan B: 5-year loan at 8.1%.

a. Find the monthly payments and the total interest for Loan A.

b. Find the monthly payments and the total interest for Loan B.

c. Compare the monthly payments and interest for the longer-term loan to the monthly payments and interest for the shorter-term loan.

62. The bar graph shows credit-card debt per U.S. household from 1995 through 2004.

Credit-Card Debt Per U.S. Household

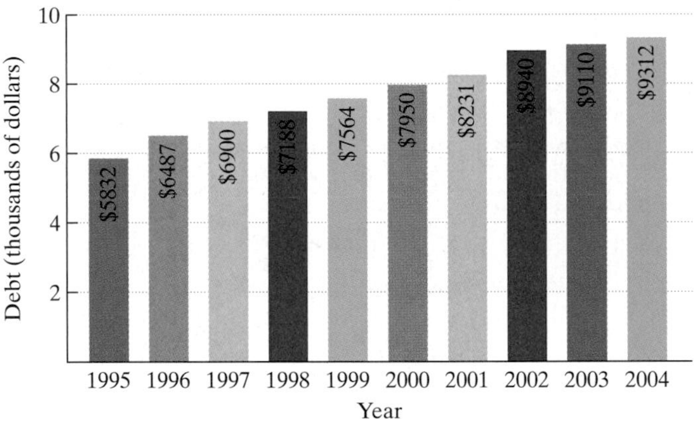

Source: CardWeb.com

In 2004, the average credit-card debt was $9312. Suppose your card has this balance and an annual interest rate of 18%. You decide to pay off the balance over two years. If there are no further purchases charged to the card,

a. How much must you pay each month?

b. How much total interest will you pay?

c. Prepare an amortization schedule for the first three months of payments. Round entries to the nearest cent.

Payment Number	Interest	Principal	Balance
1			
2			
3			

SUMMARY OF FINANCIAL MANAGEMENT FORMULAS

Simple Interest

$$I = Prt$$

$$A = P(1 + rt)$$

Compound Interest

$$A = P(1 + r)^t$$

$$A = P\left(1 + \frac{r}{n}\right)^{nt}$$

$$P = \frac{A}{\left(1 + \frac{r}{n}\right)^{nt}}$$

$$Y = \left(1 + \frac{r}{n}\right)^{n} - 1$$

Annuities

$$A = \frac{P[(1 + r)^t - 1]}{r}$$

$$A = \frac{P\left[\left(1 + \frac{r}{n}\right)^{nt} - 1\right]}{\frac{r}{n}}$$

$$P = \frac{A\left(\frac{r}{n}\right)}{\left[\left(1 + \frac{r}{n}\right)^{nt} - 1\right]}$$

Amortization

$$PMT = \frac{P\left(\frac{r}{n}\right)}{1 - \left(1 + \frac{r}{n}\right)^{-nt}}$$

CHAPTER 8 TEST

The box summarizes the financial management formulas you have worked with throughout the chapter. Where applicable, use the appropriate formula to solve an exercise in this test. Unless otherwise stated, round dollar amounts to the nearest cent and rates to the nearest tenth of a percent.

1. A CD player with an original price of $120 is on sale at 15% off.

a. What is the amount of the discount?

b. What is the sale price of the CD player?

2. Use the 2005 marginal tax rates in Table 8.1 on page 448 to calculate the income tax owed by the following person:

- Single, no dependents
- Gross income: $36,500
- $2000 paid to a tax-deferred IRA
- $4700 mortgage interest
- $1300 property taxes
- No tax credits

3. You purchased shares of stock for $2000 and sold them for $3500. Find the percent increase, or your return, on this investment.

4. You borrow $2400 for three months at 12% simple interest. Find the amount of interest paid and the future value of the loan.

5. You borrow $2000 from a friend and promise to pay back $3000 in two years. What simple interest rate will you pay?

6. In six months, you want to have $7000 worth of remodeling done to your home. How much should you invest now, at 9% simple interest, to have enough money for the project? (Round up to the nearest cent.)

7. Find the effective annual yield, to the nearest hundredth of a percent, of an account paying 4.5% compounded quarterly. What does your answer mean?

8. To save money to use as a down payment for a home in five years, you deposit $6000 in an account that pays 6.5% compounded monthly.

a. How much, to the nearest dollar, will you have as a down payment after five years?

b. Find the interest.

9. Instead of making the lump-sum deposit of $6000 described in Exercise 8, you decide to deposit $100 at the end of each month in an annuity that pays 6.5% compounded monthly.

a. How much, to the nearest dollar, will you have as a down payment after five years?

b. Find the interest.

c. Why is less interest earned from this annuity than from the lump-sum deposit in Exercise 8? With less interest earned, why would one select the annuity rather than the lump-sum deposit?

10. You would like to have $3000 in four years for a special vacation by making a lump-sum investment in an account that pays 9.5% compounded semiannually. How much should you deposit now? Round up to the nearest dollar.

11. How much should you deposit at the end of each month in an IRA that pays 6.25% compounded monthly to have \$1,500,000 when you retire in 40 years? How much of the \$1.5 million comes from interest?

Use the stock table for AT&T to solve Exercises 12–14.

52-Week High	Low	Stock	SYM	Div	Yld %	PE
26.50	24.25	AT & T	PNS	2.03	7.9	18

Vol 100s	Hi	Lo	Close	Net Chg
961	25.75	25.50	25.75	+0.13

12. What were the high and low prices for a share yesterday?
13. If you owned 1000 shares of this stock last year, what dividend did you receive?
14. Suppose that you bought 600 shares of AT&T, paying the price per share at which a share traded when the stock exchange closed yesterday. If the broker charges 2.5% of the price paid for all 600 shares, find the broker's commission.

In Exercises 15–20, the cost of a new car is \$16,000, which can be financed by paying \$3000 down and \$300 per month for 60 months.

15. Determine the amount financed.
16. Determine the total installment price.
17. Determine the finance charge.
18. Use Table 8.5 on page 482 to find the APR for this loan.
19. Use the rule of 78 formula

$$u = \frac{k(k+1)}{n(n+1)} \times F$$

to solve this problem. Instead of making the thirty-sixth payment, the borrower decides to pay the remaining balance and terminate the loan for the car. How much interest is saved by repaying the loan early?

20. Use the answer from Exercise 19 to find the total amount due on the day of the loan's termination.

Use the information at the top of the next column to solve Exercises 21–23. The terms of a particular credit card are based on the unpaid balance method. The monthly interest rate is 2% on the unpaid balance on the first day of the billing period less payments and credits. Here are some of the details in the November 1–November 30 itemized billing:

November 1 Unpaid Balance: \$880
Payment Received November 5: \$100
Purchases Charged to the Account: clothing, \$350; gasoline, \$70; groceries, \$120
Last Day of the Billing Period: November 30
Due Date: December 8

21. Find the interest due on the payment due date.
22. Find the total balance owed on the last day of the billing period.
23. Terms for the credit card require a \$10 minimum monthly payment if the balance due is less than \$360. Otherwise, the minimum monthly payment is $\frac{1}{36}$ of the balance due, rounded to the nearest whole dollar. What is the minimum monthly payment due by December 8?
24. A credit card has a monthly rate of 1.6%. In the September 1–September 30 itemized billing, the September 1 unpaid balance is \$2400. A payment of \$1500 was received on September 4. There are no purchases or cash advances in this billing period. The payment due date is October 10. Find the interest due on this date using the average daily balance method.

Use this information to solve Exercises 25–29. The price of a home is \$120,000. The bank requires a 10% down payment and two points at the time of closing. The cost of the home is financed with a 30-year fixed-rate mortgage at 8.5%.

25. Find the required down payment. Round to the nearest dollar.
26. Find the amount of the mortgage.
27. How much must be paid for the two points at closing?
28. Find the monthly payment (excluding escrowed taxes and insurance).
29. Find the total cost of interest over 30 years.
30. A student graduates from college with a loan of \$20,000. The interest rate is 6.8% and the loan term is ten years.
    a. Find the monthly payments, rounded to the nearest dollar, and the total interest for the loan.
    b. Prepare a loan amortization schedule for the first two months of the student loan. Round entries to the nearest cent.

Payment Number	Interest	Principal	Balance
1			
2			

CHAPTER 9

Measurement

You are feeling crowded in. Perhaps it would be a good time to move to a state with more elbow room. But which state? You can look up the population of each state, but that does not take into account the amount of land the population occupies. How is this land measured and how can you use this measure to select a place where wildlife outnumber humans?

In this chapter, we explore ways of measuring things in our English system, as well as in the metric system. We return to finding a state with lots of room to spread out in Example 2 of Section 9.2. Knowing how units of measure are used to describe your world can help you make decisions on issues ranging from where to live to alcohol consumption (see the Blitzer Bonus on page 528).

SECTION 9.1 • MEASURING LENGTH; THE METRIC SYSTEM

OBJECTIVES

1. Use dimensional analysis to change units of measurement.
2. Understand and use metric prefixes.
3. Convert units within the metric system.
4. Use dimensional analysis to change to and from the metric system.

Linear units of measure were originally based on parts of the body. The Egyptians used the palm (equal to four fingers), the span (a handspan), and the cubit (length of forearm).

Have you seen either of the *Jurassic Park* films? The popularity of these movies reflects our fascination with dinosaurs and their incredible size. From end to end, the largest dinosaur from the Jurassic period, which lasted from 208 to 146 million years ago, was about 88 feet. To **measure** an object such as a dinosaur is to assign a number to its size. The number representing its measure from end to end is called its **length**. Measurements are used to describe properties of length, area, volume, weight, and temperature. Over the centuries, people have developed systems of measurement that are now accepted in most of the world.

Length

Every measurement consists of two parts: a number and a unit of measure. For example, if the length of a dinosaur is 88 feet, the number is 88 and the unit of measure is the foot. Many different units are commonly used in measuring length. The foot is from a system of measurement called the **English system**, which is generally used in the United States. In this system of measurement, length is expressed in such units as inches, feet, yards, and miles.

The result obtained from measuring length is called a **linear measurement** and is stated in **linear units**.

LINEAR UNITS OF MEASURE: THE ENGLISH SYSTEM

12 inches (in.) = 1 foot (ft)

3 feet = 1 yard (yd)

36 inches = 1 yard

5280 feet = 1 mile (mi)

Because many of us are familiar with the measures in the box, we find it simple to change from one measure to another, say from feet to inches. We know that there are 12 inches in a foot. To convert from 5 feet to a measure in inches, we multiply by 12. Thus, 5 feet $= 5 \times 12$ inches $= 60$ inches.

1 Use dimensional analysis to change units of measurement.

Another procedure to convert from one unit of measurement to another is called **dimensional analysis**. Dimensional analysis uses **unit fractions**. A unit fraction has two properties: The numerator and denominator contain different units and the value of the unit fraction is 1. Here are some examples of unit fractions:

$$\frac{12 \text{ in.}}{1 \text{ ft}}; \quad \frac{1 \text{ ft}}{12 \text{ in.}}; \quad \frac{3 \text{ ft}}{1 \text{ yd}}; \quad \frac{1 \text{ yd}}{3 \text{ ft}}; \quad \frac{5280 \text{ ft}}{1 \text{ mi}}; \quad \frac{1 \text{ mi}}{5280 \text{ ft}}.$$

In each unit fraction, the numerator and denominator are equal, making the value of the fraction 1.

Let's see how to convert 5 feet to inches using a unit fraction.

$$5 \text{ ft} = ? \text{ in.}$$

We need to eliminate feet and introduce inches. The unit we need to introduce, inches, must appear in the numerator of the fraction. The unit we need to eliminate, feet, must appear in the denominator. Therefore, we choose the unit fraction with inches in the numerator and feet in the denominator. The units divide out as follows:

$$5 \text{ ft} = \frac{5 \cancel{\text{ft}}}{1} \cdot \frac{12 \text{ in.}}{1 \cancel{\text{ft}}} = 5 \cdot 12 \text{ in.} = 60 \text{ in.}$$

unit fraction

DIMENSIONAL ANALYSIS

To convert a measurement to a different unit, multiply by a unit fraction (or by unit fractions). The given unit of measurement should appear in the denominator of the unit fraction so that this unit cancels upon multiplication. The unit of measurement that needs to be introduced should appear in the numerator of the fraction so that this unit will be retained upon multiplication.

EXAMPLE 1 USING DIMENSIONAL ANALYSIS TO CHANGE UNITS OF MEASUREMENT

Convert:

a. 40 inches to feet

b. 13,200 feet to miles

c. 9 inches to yards.

SOLUTION

STUDY TIP

The abbreviations for units of measurement are written without the period, such as ft for feet, except for the abbreviation for inch (in.).

a. Because we want to convert 40 inches to feet, feet should appear in the numerator and inches in the denominator. We use the unit fraction

$$\frac{1 \text{ ft}}{12 \text{ in.}}$$

and proceed as follows:

$$40 \text{ in.} = \frac{40 \cancel{\text{in.}}}{1} \cdot \frac{1 \text{ ft}}{12 \cancel{\text{in.}}} = \frac{40}{12} \text{ft} = 3\tfrac{1}{3} \text{ft or } 3.\overline{3} \text{ ft.}$$

This period ends the sentence and is not part of the abbreviated unit.

b. To convert 13,200 feet to miles, miles should appear in the numerator and feet in the denominator. We use the unit fraction

$$\frac{1 \text{ mi}}{5280 \text{ ft}}$$

and proceed as follows:

$$13{,}200 \text{ ft} = \frac{13{,}200 \cancel{\text{ft}}}{1} \cdot \frac{1 \text{ mi}}{5280 \cancel{\text{ft}}} = \frac{13{,}200}{5280} \text{mi} = 2.5 \text{ mi.}$$

c. To convert 9 inches to yards, yards should appear in the numerator and inches in the denominator. We use the unit fraction

$$\frac{1 \text{ yd}}{36 \text{ in.}}$$

and proceed as follows:

$$9 \text{ in.} = \frac{9 \cancel{\text{in.}}}{1} \cdot \frac{1 \text{ yd}}{36 \cancel{\text{in.}}} = \frac{9}{36} \text{yd} = \frac{1}{4} \text{yd or } 0.25 \text{ yd.}$$

CHECK POINT 1 Convert:

a. 78 inches to feet
b. 17,160 feet to miles
c. 3 inches to yards.

2 Understand and use metric prefixes.

Length and the Metric System

Although the English system of measurement is most commonly used in the United States, most industrialized countries use the metric system of measurement. One of the advantages of the metric system is that units are based on powers of ten, making it much easier than the English system to change from one unit of measure to another.

The basic unit for linear measure in the metric system is the meter (m). A meter is slightly longer than a yard, approximately 39.37 inches. Prefixes are used to denote a multiple or part of a meter. Table 9.1 summarizes the more commonly used metric prefixes and their meanings.

kilodollar

hectodollar

dekadollar

dollar

decidollar

centidollar

TABLE 9.1 COMMONLY USED METRIC PREFIXES

Prefix	Symbol	Meaning
kilo	k	1000 × base unit
hecto	h	100 × base unit
deka	da	10 × base unit
deci	d	$\frac{1}{10}$ of base unit
centi	c	$\frac{1}{100}$ of base unit
milli	m	$\frac{1}{1000}$ of base unit

STUDY TIP

Prefixes containing an "i" (deci, centi, milli) are all fractional parts of one unit.

The prefixes kilo, centi, and milli are used more frequently than hecto, deka, and deci. Table 9.2 applies all six prefixes to the meter. The first part of the symbol indicates the prefix and the second part (m) indicates meter.

TABLE 9.2 COMMONLY USED UNITS OF LINEAR MEASURE IN THE METRIC SYSTEM

Symbol	Unit	Meaning
km	kilometer	1000 meters
hm	hectometer	100 meters
dam	dekameter	10 meters
m	meter	1 meter
dm	decimeter	0.1 meter
cm	centimeter	0.01 meter
mm	millimeter	0.001 meter

Kilometer is pronounced kil'-oh-met-er with the accent on the FIRST syllable. If pronounced correctly, kilometers should sound something like "kill all meters."

In the metric system, the kilometer is used to measure distances comparable to those measured in miles in the English system. One kilometer is approximately 0.6 mile, and one mile is approximately 1.6 kilometers.

Metric units of centimeters and millimeters are used to measure what the English system measures in inches. Figure 9.1 shows that a centimeter is less than half an inch; there are 2.54 centimeters in an inch. The smaller markings on the bottom scale are millimeters. A millimeter is approximately the thickness of a dime. The length of a bee or a fly may be measured in millimeters.

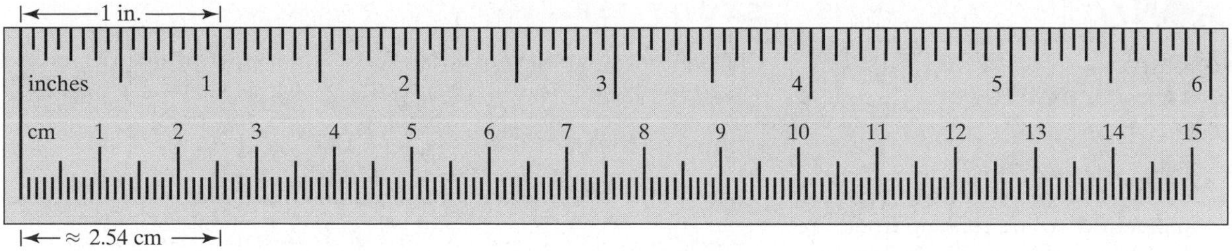

FIGURE 9.1

Those of us born in the United States have a good sense of what a length in the English system tells us about an object. An 88-foot dinosaur is huge, about 15 times the length of a 6-foot man. But what sense can we make of knowing that a whale is 25 meters long? The following lengths and the given approximations can help give you a feel for metric units of linear measure.

(1 meter ≈ 39 inches 1 kilometer ≈ 0.62 mile)

Item	Approximate Length
Width of lead in pencil	2 mm or 0.08 in.
Width of an adult's thumb	2 cm or 0.8 in.
Height of adult male	1.8 m or 6 ft
Typical room height	2.5 m or 8.3 ft
Length of medium-size car	5 m or 16.7 ft
Height of Empire State Building	381 m or 1270 ft
Average depth of ocean	4 km or 2.5 mi
Length of Manhattan Island	18 km or 11.25 mi
Distance from New York City to San Francisco	4800 km or 3000 mi
Radius of Earth	6378 km or 3986 mi
Distance from Earth to the moon	384,401 km or 240,251 mi

3 Convert units within the metric system.

Although dimensional analysis can be used to convert from one unit to another within the metric system, there is an easier, faster way to accomplish this conversion. The procedure is based on the observation that successively smaller units involve division by 10 and successively larger units involve multiplication by 10.

CHANGING UNITS WITHIN THE METRIC SYSTEM

Use the following chart to find equivalent measures of length:

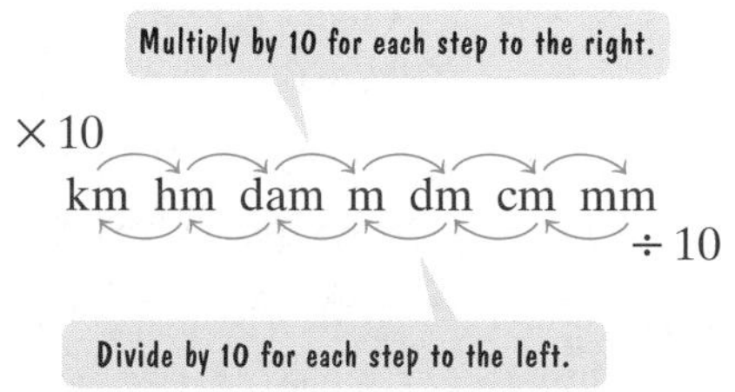

1. To change from a larger unit to a smaller unit (moving to the right in the diagram), multiply by 10 for each step to the right. Thus, move the decimal point in the given quantity one place to the right for each smaller unit until the desired unit is reached.
2. To change from a smaller unit to a larger unit (moving to the left in the diagram), divide by 10 for each step to the left. Thus, move the decimal point in the given quantity one place to the left for each larger unit until the desired unit is reached.

BLITZER BONUS

The First Meter

The French first defined the meter in 1791, calculating its length as a romantic one ten-millionth of a line running from the Equator through Paris to the North Pole. Today's meter, officially accepted in 1983, is equal to the length of the path traveled by light in a vacuum during the time interval of 1/299,794,458 of a second.

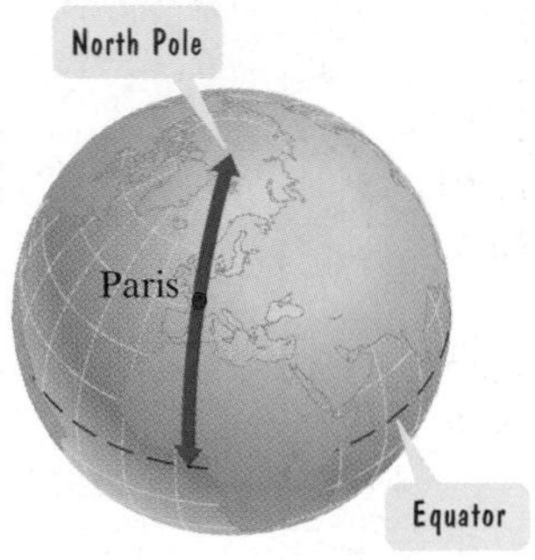

1 meter = 1/10,000,000 of the distance from the North Pole to the Equator on the meridian through Paris.

STUDY TIP

The following question provides a way to remember the metric units for length from largest to smallest.

Kitty, how does my dog catch mice?

km hm dam m dm cm mm

EXAMPLE 2 CHANGING UNITS WITHIN THE METRIC SYSTEM

a. Convert 504.7 meters to kilometers.

b. Convert 27 meters to centimeters.

c. Convert 704 mm to hm.

d. Convert 9.71 dam to dm.

SOLUTION

a. To convert from meters to kilometers, we start at meters and move three steps to the left to obtain kilometers:

km hm dam m dm cm mm.

Hence, we move the decimal point three places to the left:

504.7 m = 0.5047 km.

Thus, 504.7 meters converts to 0.5047 kilometer. Changing from a smaller unit of measurement (meter) to a larger unit of measurement (kilometer) results in an answer with a smaller number of units.

b. To convert from meters to centimeters, we start at meters and move two steps to the right to obtain centimeters:

km hm dam m dm cm mm.

Hence, we move the decimal point two places to the right:

27 m = 2700 cm.

Thus, 27 meters converts to 2700 centimeters. Changing from a larger unit of measurement (meter) to a smaller unit of measurement (centimeter) results in an answer with a larger number of units.

c. To convert from mm (millimeters) to hm (hectometers), we start at mm and move five steps to the left to obtain hm:

km hm dam m dm cm mm.

Hence, we move the decimal point five places to the left:

704 mm = 0.00704 hm.

d. To convert from dam (dekameters) to dm (decimeters), we start at dam and move two places to the right to obtain dm:

km hm dam m dm cm mm.

Hence, we move the decimal point two places to the right:

$$9.71 \text{ dam} = 971 \text{ dm}.$$

In Example 2(b), we showed that 27 meters converts to 2700 centimeters. This is the average length of the California blue whale, the longest of the great whales. Blue whales can have lengths that exceed 30 meters, making them over 100 feet long.

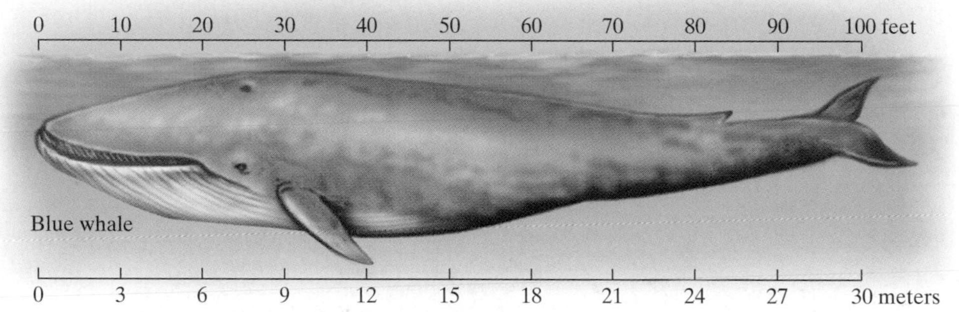

CHECK POINT 2

a. Convert 8000 meters to kilometers.

b. Convert 53 meters to millimeters.

c. Convert 604 cm to hm.

d. Convert 6.72 dam to cm.

BLITZER BONUS

Viruses and Metric Prefixes

Viruses are measured in attometers. An attometer is one quintillionth of a meter, or 10^{-18} meter, symbolized am. If a virus measures 1 am, you can place 10^{15} of them across a penciled 1 millimeter dot. If you were to enlarge each of these viruses to the size of the dot, they would stretch far into space, almost reaching Saturn.

Here is a list of all twenty metric prefixes. When applied to the meter, they range from the yottameter (10^{24} meters) to the yoctometer (10^{-24} meters).

LARGER THAN THE BASIC UNIT

Prefix	Symbol	Power of Ten	English Name
yotta-	Y	+24	septillion
zetta-	Z	+21	sextillion
exa-	E	+18	quintillion
peta-	P	+15	quadrillion
tera-	T	+12	trillion
giga-	G	+9	billion
mega-	M	+6	million
kilo-	k	+3	thousand
hecto-	h	+2	hundred
deca-	da	+1	ten

SMALLER THAN THE BASIC UNIT

Prefix	Symbol	Power of Ten	English Name
deci-	d	−1	tenth
centi-	c	−2	hundredth
milli-	m	−3	thousandth
micro-	μ	−6	millionth
nano-	n	−9	billionth
pico-	p	−12	trillionth
femto-	f	−15	quadrillionth
atto-	a	−18	quintillionth
zepto-	z	−21	sextillionth
yocto-	y	−24	septillionth

4 Use dimensional analysis to change to and from the metric system.

Although dimensional analysis is not necessary when changing units within the metric system, it is a useful tool when converting to and from the metric system. Some approximate conversions are given in Table 9.3.

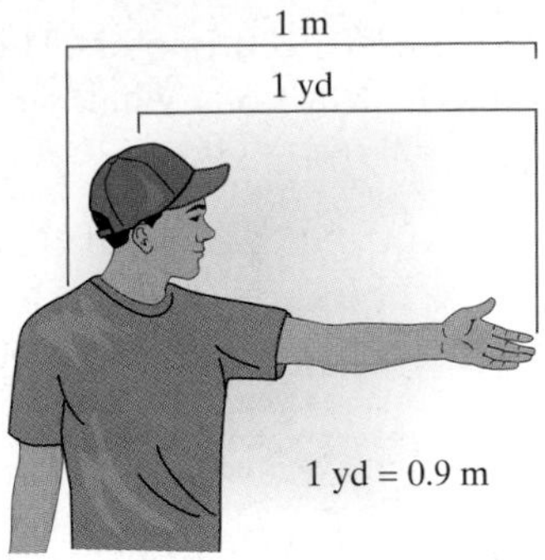

TABLE 9.3 APPROXIMATE ENGLISH AND METRIC EQUIVALENTS

1 inch (in.) = 2.54 centimeters (cm)
1 foot (ft) = 30.48 centimeters (cm)
1 yard (yd) = 0.9 meter (m)
1 mile (mi) = 1.6 kilometers (km)

These conversions are exact.

These conversions are approximate.

EXAMPLE 3 USING DIMENSIONAL ANALYSIS TO CHANGE TO AND FROM THE METRIC SYSTEM

a. Convert 8 inches to centimeters.

b. Convert 125 miles to kilometers.

c. Convert 26,800 millimeters to inches.

SOLUTION

a. To convert 8 inches to centimeters, we use a unit fraction with centimeters in the numerator and inches in the denominator:

$$\frac{2.54 \text{ cm}}{1 \text{ in.}}. \qquad \text{Table 9.3 shows that 1 in.} = 2.54 \text{ cm.}$$

We proceed as follows.

$$8 \text{ in.} = \frac{8 \cancel{\text{in.}}}{1} \cdot \frac{2.54 \text{ cm}}{1 \cancel{\text{in.}}} = 8(2.54) \text{ cm} = 20.32 \text{ cm}$$

b. To convert 125 miles to kilometers, we use a unit fraction with kilometers in the numerator and miles in the denominator:

$$\frac{1.6 \text{ km}}{1 \text{ mi}}. \qquad \text{Table 9.3 shows that 1 mi} = 1.6 \text{ km.}$$

Thus,

$$125 \text{ mi} = \frac{125 \cancel{\text{mi}}}{1} \cdot \frac{1.6 \text{ km}}{1 \cancel{\text{mi}}} = 125(1.6) \text{ km} = 200 \text{ km.}$$

STUDY TIP

Keep in mind that the conversions shown here are *approximate*. More accurately,

$$1 \text{ mi} \approx 1.61 \text{ km.}$$

Thus,

$$125 \text{ mi} \approx 125(1.61) \text{ km} \approx 201.25 \text{ km.}$$

c. To convert 26,800 millimeters to inches, we observe that Table 9.3 has only a conversion factor between inches and centimeters. We begin by changing millimeters to centimeters:

$$26{,}800 \text{ mm} = 2680.0 \text{ cm}$$

Now we need to convert 2680 centimeters to inches. We use a unit fraction with inches in the numerator and centimeters in the denominator:

$$\frac{1 \text{ in.}}{2.54 \text{ cm}}.$$

Thus,

$$26{,}800\text{ mm} = 2680\text{ cm} = \frac{2680\ \cancel{\text{cm}}}{1}\cdot\frac{1\text{ in.}}{2.54\ \cancel{\text{cm}}} = \frac{2680}{2.54}\text{in.} \approx 1055\text{ in.}$$

This measure is equivalent to about 88 feet, the length of the largest dinosaur from the Jurassic period. The diplodocus, a plant eater, was 26.8 meters, approximately 88 feet, long.

CHECK POINT 3

a. Convert 8 feet to centimeters.

b. Convert 20 meters to yards.

c. Convert 30 meters to inches.

So far, we have used dimensional analysis to change units of length. Dimensional analysis may also be used to convert other kinds of measures, such as speed.

EXAMPLE 4 USING DIMENSIONAL ANALYSIS

a. The speed limit on many highways in the United States is 55 miles per hour (mi/hr). How many kilometers per hour (km/hr) is this?

b. If a high-speed train in Japan is capable of traveling at 200 kilometers per hour, how many miles per hour is this?

SOLUTION

a. To change miles per hour to kilometers per hour, we need to concentrate on changing miles to kilometers, so we need a unit fraction with kilometers in the numerator and miles in the denominator:

$$\frac{1.6\text{ km}}{1\text{ mi}}.$$

Thus,

$$\frac{55\text{ mi}}{\text{hr}} = \frac{55\ \cancel{\text{mi}}}{\text{hr}}\cdot\frac{1.6\text{ km}}{1\ \cancel{\text{mi}}} = 55(1.6)\frac{\text{km}}{\text{hr}} = 88\text{ km/hr}.$$

This shows that 55 miles per hour is equivalent to 88 kilometers per hour.

b. To change 200 kilometers per hour to miles per hour, we must convert kilometers to miles. We need a unit fraction with miles in the numerator and kilometers in the denominator:

$$\frac{1\text{ mi}}{1.6\text{ km}}.$$

Thus,

$$\frac{200\text{ km}}{\text{hr}} = \frac{200\ \cancel{\text{km}}}{\text{hr}}\cdot\frac{1\text{ mi}}{1.6\ \cancel{\text{km}}} = \frac{200}{1.6}\frac{\text{mi}}{\text{hr}} = 125\text{ mi/hr}.$$

A train capable of traveling at 200 kilometers per hour can therefore travel at 125 miles per hour.

CHECK POINT 4 A road in Europe has a speed limit of 60 kilometers per hour. How many miles per hour is this?

BLITZER BONUS

The Mars Climate Orbiter

If you think that using dimensional analysis to change to and from the metric system is no big deal, consider this: The Mars Climate Orbiter, launched on December 11, 1998, was lost when it crashed into Mars about a year later due to failure to properly convert English units into metric units. The price tag: \$125 million!

EXERCISE SET 9.1

• Practice Exercises

In Exercises 1–16, use dimensional analysis to convert the quantity to the indicated unit. If necessary, round the answer to two decimal places.

1. 30 in. to ft
2. 100 in. to ft
3. 30 ft to in.
4. 100 ft to in.
5. 6 in. to yd
6. 21 in. to yd
7. 6 yd to in.
8. 21 yd to in.
9. 6 yd to ft
10. 12 yd to ft
11. 6 ft to yd
12. 12 ft to yd
13. 23,760 ft to mi
14. 19,800 ft to mi
15. 0.75 mi to ft
16. 0.25 mi to ft

In Exercises 17–26, use the diagram in the box on page 511 to convert the given measurement to the unit indicated.

17. 5 m to cm
18. 8 dam to m
19. 16.3 hm to m
20. 0.37 hm to m
21. 317.8 cm to hm
22. 8.64 hm to cm
23. 0.023 mm to m
24. 0.00037 km to cm
25. 2196 mm to dm
26. 71 dm to km

In Exercises 27–44, use the following English and metric equivalents, along with dimensional analysis, to convert the given measurement to the unit indicated.

Approximate English and Metric Equivalents

1 in. = 2.54 cm
1 ft = 30.48 cm
1 yd = 0.9 m
1 mi = 1.6 km

27. 14 in. to cm
28. 26 in. to cm
29. 14 cm to in.
30. 26 cm to in.
31. 265 mi to km
32. 776 mi to km
33. 265 km to mi
34. 776 km to mi
35. 12 m to yd
36. 20 m to yd
37. 14 dm to in.
38. 1.2 dam to in.
39. 160 in. to dam
40. 180 in. to hm
41. 5 ft to m
42. 8 ft to m
43. 5 m to ft
44. 8 m to ft

Use 1 mi = 1.6 km *to solve Exercises 45–48.*

45. Express 96 kilometers per hour in miles per hour.
46. Express 104 kilometers per hour in miles per hour.
47. Express 45 miles per hour in kilometers per hour.
48. Express 50 miles per hour in kilometers per hour.

• Practice Plus

In Exercises 49–52, use the unit fractions

$$\frac{36 \text{ in.}}{1 \text{ yd}} \text{ and } \frac{2.54 \text{ cm}}{1 \text{ in.}}.$$

49. Convert 5 yd to cm.
50. Convert 8 yd to cm.
51. Convert 762 cm to yd.
52. Convert 1016 cm to yd.

In Exercises 53–54, use the unit fractions

$$\frac{5280 \text{ ft}}{1 \text{ mi}}, \frac{12 \text{ in.}}{1 \text{ ft}}, \text{ and } \frac{2.54 \text{ cm}}{1 \text{ in.}}.$$

53. Convert 30 mi to km.
54. Convert 50 mi to km.
55. Use unit fractions to express 120 miles per hour in feet per second.
56. Use unit fractions to express 100 miles per hour in feet per second.

• Application Exercises

In Exercises 57–66, selecting from millimeter, meter, and kilometer, determine the best unit of measure to express the given length.

57. A person's height
58. The length of a football field
59. The length of a bee
60. The distance from New York City to Washington, D.C.
61. The distance around a one-acre lot
62. The length of a car
63. The width of a book
64. The altitude of an airplane
65. The diameter of a screw
66. The width of a human foot

In Exercises 67–74, select the best estimate for the measure of the given item.

67. The length of a pen
a. 30 cm **b.** 19 cm **c.** 19 mm

68. The length of this page
a. 2.5 mm **b.** 25 mm **c.** 250 mm

69. The height of a skyscraper
a. 325 m **b.** 32.5 km **c.** 325 km **d.** 3250 km

70. The length of a pair of pants
a. 700 cm **b.** 70 cm **c.** 7 cm

71. The height of a room
a. 4 mm **b.** 4 cm **c.** 4 m **d.** 4 dm

72. The length of a rowboat
a. 4 cm **b.** 4 dm **c.** 4 m **d.** 4 dam

73. The width of an electric cord
a. 4 mm **b.** 4 cm **c.** 4 dm **d.** 4 m

74. The dimensions of a piece of typing paper
a. 22 mm by 28 mm **b.** 22 cm by 28 cm
c. 22 dm by 28 dm **d.** 22 m by 28 m

75. A baseball diamond measures 27 meters along each side. If a batter scored two home runs in a game, how many kilometers did the batter run?
76. If you jog six times around a track that is 700 meters long, how many kilometers have you covered?
77. The distance from the Earth to the sun is about 93 million miles. What is this distance in kilometers?
78. The distance from New York City to Los Angeles is 4690 kilometers. What is the distance in miles?

• Writing in Mathematics

79. Describe the two parts of a measurement.
80. Describe how to use dimensional analysis to convert 20 inches to feet.
81. Describe advantages of the metric system over the English system.
82. Explain how to change units within the metric system.
83. You jog 500 meters in a given period of time. The next day, you jog 500 yards over the same time period. On which day was your speed faster? Explain your answer.
84. What kind of difficulties might arise if the United States immediately eliminated all units of measure in the English system and replaced the system by the metric system?
85. The United States is the only Westernized country that does not use the metric system as its primary system of measurement. What reasons might be given for continuing to use the English system?

• Critical Thinking Exercises

In Exercises 86–90, convert to an appropriate metric unit so that the numerical expression in the given measure does not contain any zeros.

86. 6000 cm **87.** 900 m **88.** 7000 dm

89. 11,000 mm **90.** 0.0002 km

SECTION 9.2 • MEASURING AREA AND VOLUME

OBJECTIVES

1. Use square units to measure area.
2. Use dimensional analysis to change units for area.
3. Use cubic units to measure volume.
4. Use English and metric units to measure capacity.

Are you feeling a bit crowded in? Although there are more people on the East coast of the United States than there are bears, there are places in the Northwest where bears outnumber humans. The most densely populated state is New Jersey, averaging 1134.5 people per square mile. The least densely populated state is Alaska, averaging 1.1 persons per square mile.

A square mile is one way of measuring the **area** of a state. A state's area is the region within its boundaries. Its **population density** is its population divided by its area. In this section, we discuss methods for measuring both area and volume.

1 Use square units to measure area.

Measuring Area

In order to measure a region that is enclosed by boundaries, we begin by selecting a **square unit**. A square unit is a square, each of whose sides is one unit in length, illustrated in Figure 9.2. The region in Figure 9.2 is said to have an area of **one square unit**. The side of the square can be 1 inch, 1 centimeter, 1 meter, 1 foot, or 1 of any linear unit of measure. The corresponding units of area are the square inch (in.^{2}), the square centimeter (cm^2), the square meter (m^2), the square foot (ft^2), and so on. Figure 9.3 illustrates 1 square inch and 1 square centimeter, drawn to actual size.

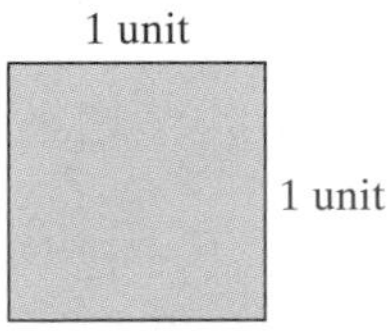

FIGURE 9.2 One square unit

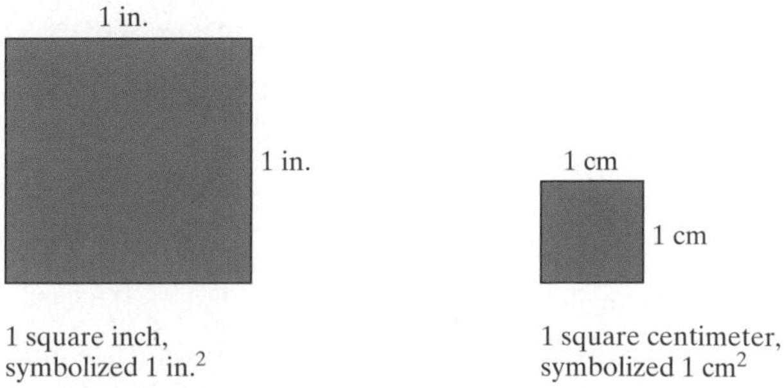

FIGURE 9.3 Common units of measurement for area, drawn to actual size

EXAMPLE 1 MEASURING AREA

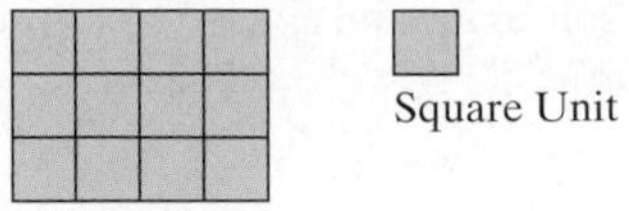

FIGURE 9.4

What is the area of the region shown in Figure 9.4?

SOLUTION We can determine the area of the region by counting the number of square units contained within the region. There are 12 such units. Therefore, the area of the region is 12 square units.

CHECK POINT 1 What is the area of the region represented by the first two rows in Figure 9.4?

Although there are 12 inches in one foot and 3 feet in one yard, these numerical relationships are not the same for square units.

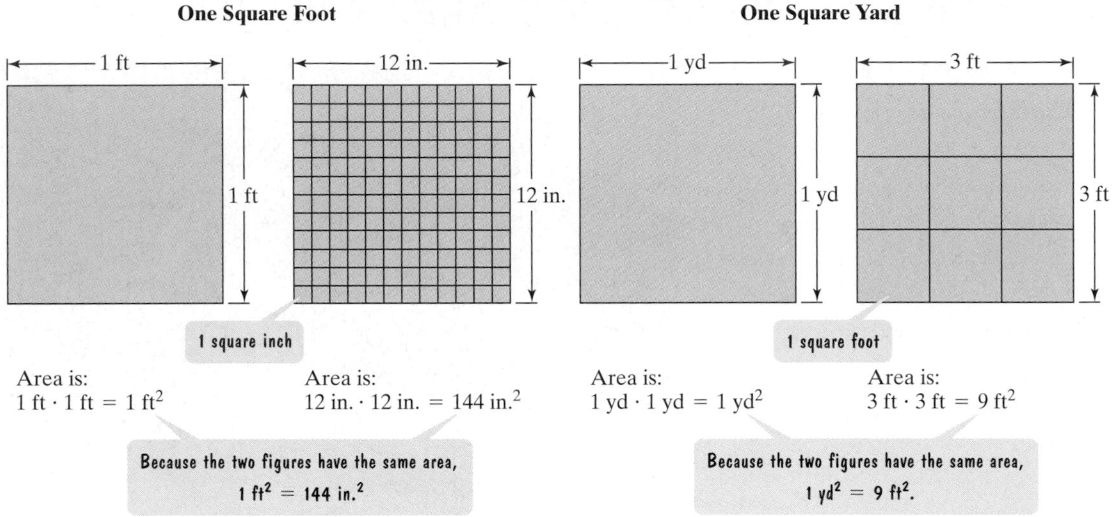

STUDY TIP

A small plot of land is usually measured in square feet, rather than a small fraction of an acre. Curiously, square yards are rarely used. However, square yards are commonly used for carpet and flooring measures.

SQUARE UNITS OF MEASURE: THE ENGLISH SYSTEM

1 square foot (ft^2) = 144 square inches ($in.^2$)
1 square yard (yd^2) = 9 square feet (ft^2)
1 acre (a) = 43,560 ft^2 or 4840 yd^2
1 square mile (mi^2) = 640 acres

EXAMPLE 2 USING SQUARE UNITS TO COMPUTE POPULATION DENSITY

After Alaska, Wyoming is the least densely populated state. The population of Wyoming is 506,529 and its area is 97,814 square miles. What is Wyoming's population density?

SOLUTION We compute the population density by dividing Wyoming's population by its area.

$$\text{population density} = \frac{\text{population}}{\text{area}} = \frac{506{,}529 \text{ people}}{97{,}814 \text{ square miles}}$$

Using a calculator and rounding to the nearest tenth, we obtain a population density of 5.2 people per square mile. This means that there is an average of only 5.2 people for each square mile of area.

CHECK POINT 2 The population of California is 35,893,799 and its area is 163,696 square miles. What is California's population density?

2 Use dimensional analysis to change units for area.

One theory is that using square units to measure area has its origin in the weaving of fabric.

In Section 9.1, we saw that in most other countries, the system of measurement that is used is the metric system. In the metric system, the square centimeter is used instead of the square inch. The square meter replaces the square foot and the square yard.

The English system uses the acre and the square mile to measure large land areas. The metric system uses the hectare (symbolized ha and pronounced "hectair"). A hectare is about the area of two football fields placed side by side, approximately 2.5 acres. One square mile of land consists of approximately 260 hectares. Just as the hectare replaces the acre, the square kilometer is used instead of the square mile. One square kilometer is approximately 0.38 square mile.

Some basic approximate conversions for units of area are given in Table 9.4.

TABLE 9.4 ENGLISH AND METRIC EQUIVALENTS FOR AREA

1 square inch (in.^{2})	= 6.5 square centimeters (cm^2)
1 square foot (ft^2)	= 0.09 square meter (m^2)
1 square yard (yd^2)	= 0.8 square meter (m^2)
1 square mile (mi^2)	= 2.6 square kilometers (km^2)
1 acre	= 0.4 hectare (ha)

EXAMPLE 3 USING DIMENSIONAL ANALYSIS ON UNITS OF AREA

A property in Italy is advertised at $545,000 for 6.8 hectares.

a. Find the area of the property in acres.

b. What is the price per acre?

SOLUTION

a. Using Table 9.4, we see that 1 acre = 0.4 hectare. To convert 6.8 hectares to acres, we use a unit fraction with acres in the numerator and hectares in the denominator.

$$6.8 \text{ ha} = \frac{6.8 \cancel{\text{ha}}}{1} \cdot \frac{1 \text{ acre}}{0.4 \cancel{\text{ha}}} = \frac{6.8}{0.4} \text{ acres} = 17 \text{ acres}$$

The area of the property is 17 acres.

b. The price per acre is the total price, $545,000, divided by the number of acres, 17.

$$\text{price per acre} = \frac{\$545{,}000}{17 \text{ acres}} \approx \$32{,}059/\text{acre}$$

The price is approximately $32,059 per acre.

CHECK POINT 3 A property in Northern California is on the market at $415,000 for 1.8 acres.

a. Find the area of the property in hectares.

b. What is the price per hectare?

3 Use cubic units to measure volume.

Measuring Volume

A shoe box and a basketball are examples of three-dimensional figures. **Volume** refers to the amount of space occupied by such figures. In order to measure this space, we begin by selecting a *cubic unit*. Two such cubic units are shown in Figure 9.5.

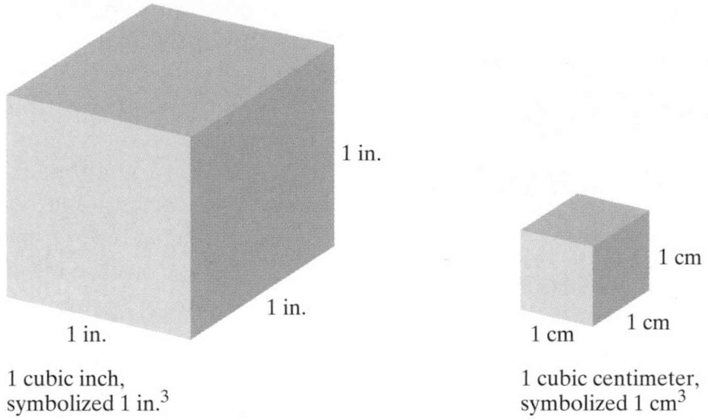

FIGURE 9.5 Common units of measurement for volume

The edges of a cube all have the same length. Other cubic units used to measure volume include 1 cubic foot (1 ft^3) and 1 cubic meter (1 m^3). One way to measure the volume of a solid is to calculate the number of cubic units contained in its interior.

EXAMPLE 4 MEASURING VOLUME

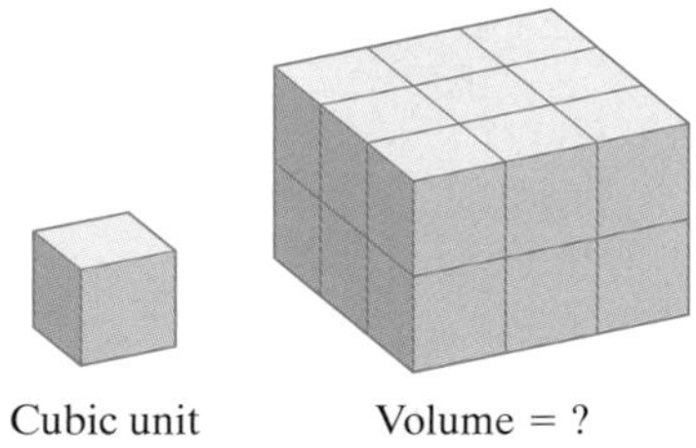

FIGURE 9.6

What is the volume of the solid shown in Figure 9.6?

SOLUTION We can determine the volume of the solid by counting the number of cubic units contained within the region. Because we have drawn a solid three-dimensional figure on a flat two-dimensional page, some of the small cubic units in the back, right are hidden. The figures below show how the cubic units are used to fill the inside of the solid.

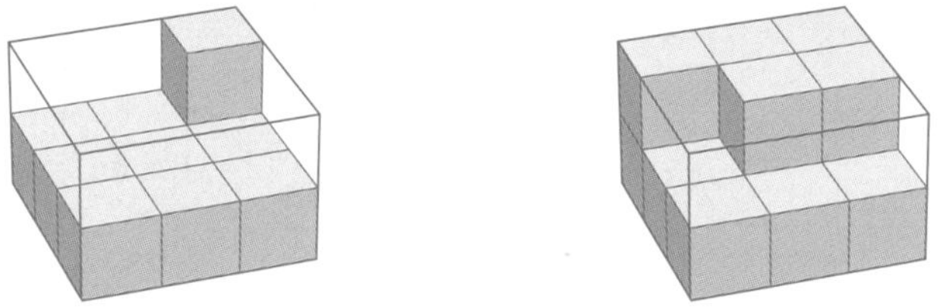

Do these figures help you to see that there are 18 cubic units inside the solid? The volume of the solid is 18 cubic units.

CHECK POINT 4 What is the volume of the region represented by the bottom row of blocks in Figure 9.6?

We have seen that there are 3 feet in a yard, but 9 square feet in a square yard. Neither of these relationships holds for cubic units. Figure 9.7 illustrates that there are 27 cubic feet in a cubic yard. Furthermore, there are 1728 cubic inches in a cubic foot.

STUDY TIP

If you have difficulty seeing the detail in Figure 9.7, cubing numbers is helpful:

$$3\text{ ft} = 1\text{ yd}$$
$$(3\text{ ft})^3 = (1\text{ yd})^3$$
$$3\cdot3\cdot3\text{ ft}^3 = 1\cdot1\cdot1\text{ yd}^3.$$

Conclusion: $27\text{ ft}^3 = 1\text{ yd}^3$

$$12\text{ in.} = 1\text{ ft}$$
$$(12\text{ in.})^3 = (1\text{ ft})^3$$
$$12\cdot12\cdot12\text{ in.}^3 = 1\cdot1\cdot1\text{ ft}^3$$

Conclusion: $1728\text{ in.}^3 = 1\text{ ft}^3$

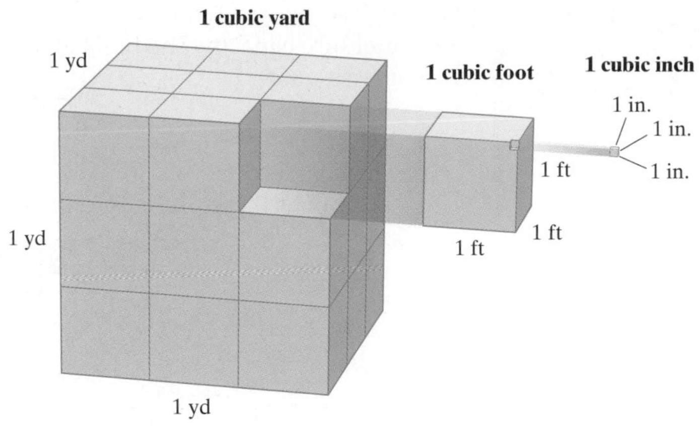

FIGURE 9.7 $27\text{ ft}^3 = 1\text{ yd}^3$ and $1728\text{ in.}^3 = 1\text{ ft}^3$

4 Use English and metric units to measure capacity.

The measure of volume also includes the amount of fluid that a three-dimensional object can hold. This is often called the object's **capacity.** For example, we often refer to the capacity, in gallons, of a gas tank. A cubic yard has a capacity of about 200 gallons and a cubic foot has a capacity of about 7.48 gallons.

Table 9.5 contains information about standard units of capacity in the English system.

TABLE 9.5 ENGLISH UNITS FOR CAPACITY

2 pints (pt)	= 1 quart (qt)
4 quarts	= 1 gallon (gal)
1 gallon	= 128 ounces (oz)
1 cup (c)	= 8 ounces
Volume in Cubic Units	**Capacity**
1 cubic yard	about 200 gallons
1 cubic foot	about 7.48 gallons
231 cubic inches	about 1 gallon

EXAMPLE 5 VOLUME AND CAPACITY IN THE ENGLISH SYSTEM

A swimming pool has a volume of 22,500 cubic feet. How many gallons of water does the pool hold?

SOLUTION We use the fact that 1 cubic foot has a capacity of about 7.48 gallons to set up our unit fraction:

$$\frac{7.48\text{ gal}}{1\text{ ft}^3}.$$

We use this unit fraction to find the capacity of the 22,500 cubic feet.

$$22{,}500\text{ ft}^3 = \frac{22{,}500\text{ }\cancel{\text{ft}^3}}{1}\cdot\frac{7.48\text{ gal}}{1\text{ }\cancel{\text{ft}^3}} = 22{,}500(7.48)\text{ gal} = 168{,}300\text{ gal}$$

The pool holds approximately 168,300 gallons of water.

CHECK POINT 5 A pool has a volume of 10,000 cubic feet. How many gallons of water does the pool hold?

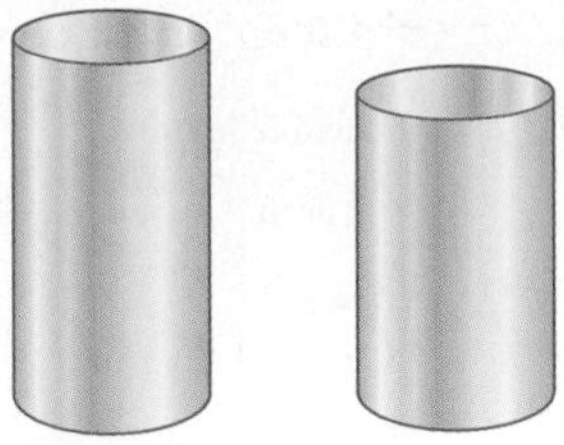

As we have come to expect, things are simpler when the metric system is used to measure capacity. The basic unit is the **liter,** symbolized by L. A liter is slightly larger than a quart.

$$1 \text{ liter} \approx 1.0567 \text{ quarts}$$

The standard metric prefixes are used to denote a multiple or part of a liter. Table 9.6 applies these prefixes to the liter.

TABLE 9.6 UNITS OF CAPACITY IN THE METRIC SYSTEM

Symbol	Unit	Meaning
kL	kiloliter	1000 liters
hL	hectoliter	100 liters
daL	dekaliter	10 liters
L	liter	1 liter ≈ 1.06 quarts
dL	deciliter	0.1 liter
cL	centiliter	0.01 liter
mL	milliliter	0.001 liter

The following list should help give you a feel for capacity in the metric system.

Item	Capacity
Average cup of coffee	250 mL
12-ounce can of soda	355 mL
One quart of fruit juice	0.95 L
One gallon of milk	3.78 L
Average gas capacity of a car (about 18.5 gallons)	70 L

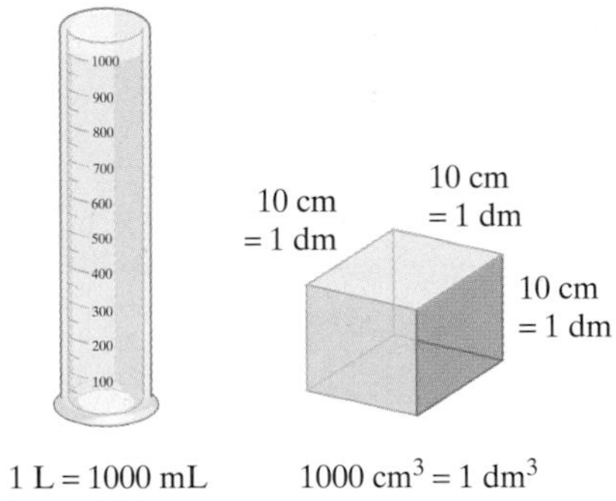

FIGURE 9.8

Figure 9.8 shows a 1-liter container filled with water. The water in the liter container will fit exactly into the box shown to its right. The volume of this box is 1000 cubic centimeters, or equivalently, 1 cubic decimeter. Thus,

$$1000 \text{ cm}^3 = 1 \text{ dm}^3 = 1 \text{ L}.$$

Table 9.7 expands on this relationship between volume and capacity in the metric system.

TABLE 9.7 VOLUME AND CAPACITY IN THE METRIC SYSTEM

Volume in Cubic Units		Capacity
1 cm^3	=	1 mL
1 dm^3 = 1000 cm^3	=	1 L
1 m^3	=	1 kL

BLITZER BONUS

Measuring Dosages of Medicine

Table 9.7 indicates that

$$1 \text{ cm}^3 = 1 \text{ mL}.$$

Dosages of medicine are measured using cubic centimeters, or milliliters as they are also called. (In the United States, cc, rather than cm^3, denotes cubic centimeters.) When taking medication by mouth, such as cough syrup, there is an easy conversion between the English and metric systems:

$$1 \text{ teaspoon} = 5 \text{ cc}.$$

EXAMPLE 6 VOLUME AND CAPACITY IN THE METRIC SYSTEM

An aquarium has a volume of 36,000 cubic centimeters. How many liters of water does the aquarium hold?

SOLUTION We use the fact that 1000 cubic centimeters corresponds to a capacity of 1 liter to set up our unit fraction:

$$\frac{1 \text{ L}}{1000 \text{ cm}^3}.$$

We use this unit fraction to find the capacity of the 36,000 cubic centimeters.

$$36{,}000 \text{ cm}^3 = \frac{36{,}000 \cancel{\text{cm}^3}}{1} \cdot \frac{1 \text{ L}}{1000 \cancel{\text{cm}^3}} = \frac{36{,}000}{1000} \text{L} = 36 \text{ L}$$

The aquarium holds 36 liters of water.

CHECK POINT 6 A fish pond has a volume of 220,000 cubic centimeters. How many liters of water does the pond hold?

EXERCISE SET 9.2

Practice Exercises

In Exercises 1–4, use the given figure to find its area in square units.

1. 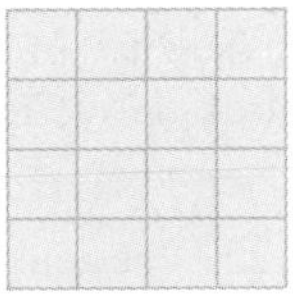

2. 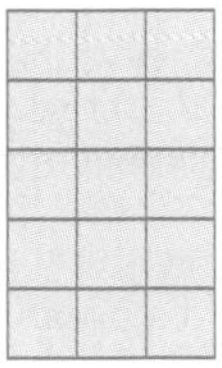

3. 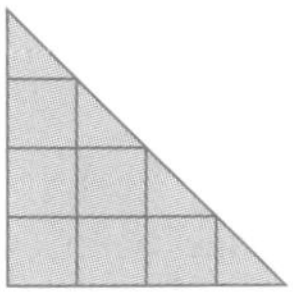

4. 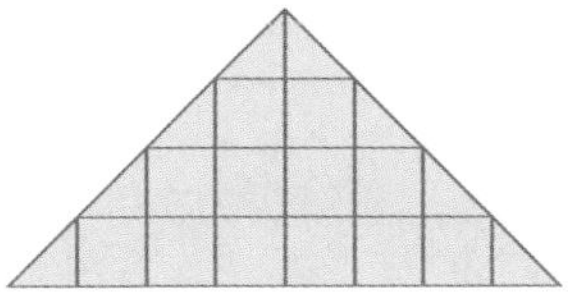

In Exercises 5–12, use Table 9.4 on page 519, along with dimensional analysis, to convert the given square unit to the square unit indicated. Where necessary, round answers to two decimal places.

5. 14 cm^2 to in.^2

6. 20 m^2 to ft^2

7. 30 m^2 to yd^2

8. 14 mi^2 to km^2

9. 10.2 ha to acres

10. 20.6 ha to acres

11. 14 in.^2 to cm^2

12. 20 in.^2 to cm^2

In Exercises 13–14, use the given figure to find its volume in cubic units.

13. 

14. 

In Exercises 15–22, use Table 9.5 on page 521, along with dimensional analysis, to convert the given unit to the unit indicated. Where necessary, round answers to two decimal places.

15. 10,000 ft^3 to gal

16. 25,000 ft^3 to gal

17. 8 yd^3 to gal

18. 35 yd^3 to gal

19. 2079 in.^3 to gal

20. 6237 in.^3 to gal

21. 2700 gal to yd^3

22. 1496 gal to ft^3

In Exercises 23–32, use Table 9.7 on page 522, along with dimensional analysis, to convert the given unit to the unit indicated.

23. 45,000 cm^3 to L

24. 75,000 cm^3 to L

25. 17 cm^3 to mL

26. 19 cm^3 to mL

27. 1.5 L to cm^3

28. 4.5 L to cm^3

29. 150 mL to cm^3

30. 250 mL to cm^3

31. 12 kL to dm^3

32. 16 kL to dm^3

• Practice Plus

The bar graph shows the resident population and the land area of the United States for selected years from 1800 through 2000. Use the information shown by the graph to solve Exercises 33–36.

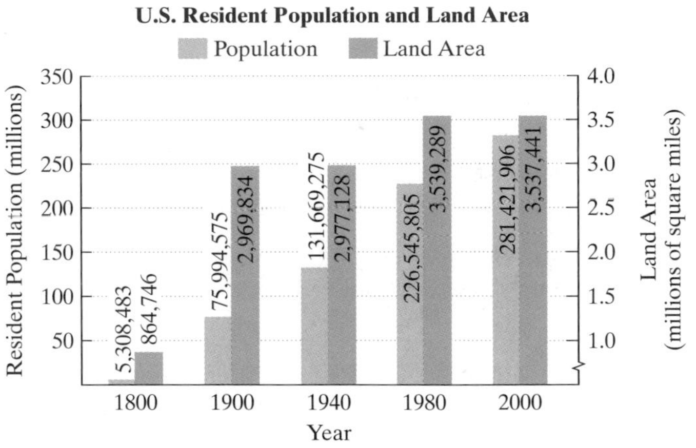

Source: U.S. Bureau of the Census

33. a. Find the population density of the United States, to the nearest tenth, in 1900 and in 2000.

b. Find the percent increase in population density, to the nearest tenth of a percent, from 1900 to 2000.

34. a. Find the population density of the United States, to the nearest tenth, in 1800 and in 2000.

b. Find the percent increase in population density, to the nearest tenth of a percent, from 1800 to 2000.

35. Find the population density of the United States, to the nearest tenth, expressed in people per square kilometer, in 1940.

36. Find the population density of the United States, to the nearest tenth, expressed in people per square kilometer, in 1980.

• Application Exercises

37. A property that measures 8 hectares is for sale.

a. How large is the property in acres?

b. If the property is selling for \$250,000, what is the price per acre?

38. A property that measures 100 hectares is for sale.

a. How large is the property in acres?

b. If the property is selling for \$350,000, what is the price per acre?

In Exercises 39–42, selecting from square centimeters, square meters, or square kilometers, determine the best unit of measure to express the area of the object described.

39. The top of a desk

40. A dollar bill

41. A national park

42. The wall of a room

In Exercises 43–46, select the best estimate for the measure of the area of the object described.

43. The area of the floor of a room

a. 25 cm^2 **b.** 25 m^2 **c.** 25 km^2

44. The area of a television screen

a. 2050 mm^2 **b.** 2050 cm^2 **c.** 2050 dm^2

45. The area of the face of a small coin

a. 6 mm^2 **b.** 6 cm^2 **c.** 6 dm^2

46. The area of a parcel of land in a large metropolitan area on which a house can be built

a. 900 cm^2 **b.** 900 m^2 **c.** 900 ha

47. A swimming pool has a volume of 45,000 cubic feet. How many gallons of water does the pool hold?

48. A swimming pool has a volume of 66,000 cubic feet. How many gallons of water does the pool hold?

49. A container of grapefruit juice has a volume of 4000 cubic centimeters. How many liters of juice does the container hold?

50. An aquarium has a volume of 17,500 cubic centimeters. How many liters of water does the aquarium hold?

• Writing in Mathematics

51. Describe how area is measured. Explain why linear units cannot be used.

52. New Mexico has a population density of 15 people per square mile. Describe what this means. Use an almanac or the Internet to compare this population density to that of the state in which you are now living.

53. Describe the difference between the following problems: How much fencing is needed to enclose a garden? How much fertilizer is needed for the garden?

54. Describe how volume is measured. Explain why linear or square units cannot be used.

55. For a swimming pool, what is the difference between the following units of measure: cubic feet and gallons? For each unit, write a sentence about the pool that makes the use of the unit appropriate.

56. If there are 10 decimeters in a meter, explain why there are not 10 cubic decimeters in a cubic meter.

• Critical Thinking Exercises

57. Singapore has the highest population density of any country: 46,690 people per 1000 hectares. How many people are there per square mile?

58. Nebraska has a population density of 22.3 people per square mile and a population of 1,747,214. What is the area of Nebraska?

59. A high population density is a condition common to extremely poor and extremely rich locales. Explain why this is so.

60. Although Alaska is the least densely populated state, over 90% of its land is protected federal property that is off-limits to settlement. A resident of Anchorage, Alaska, might feel hemmed in. In terms of "elbow room," what other important factor must be considered when calculating a state's population density?

61. Does an adult's body contain approximately 6.5 liters, kiloliters, or milliliters of blood? Explain your answer.

62. Is the volume of a coin approximately 1 cubic centimeter, 1 cubic millimeter, or 1 cubic decimeter? Explain your answer.

• Group Exercise

63. If you could select any place in the world, where would you like to live? Look up the population and area of your ideal place, and compute its population density. Group members should share places to live and population densities. What trend, if any, does the group observe?

SECTION 9.3 • MEASURING WEIGHT AND TEMPERATURE

OBJECTIVES

1. Apply metric prefixes to units of weight.
2. Convert units of weight within the metric system.
3. Use relationships between volume and weight within the metric system.
4. Use dimensional analysis to change units of weight to and from the metric system.
5. Understand temperature scales.

You are watching CNN International on cable television. The temperature in Honolulu, Hawaii, is reported as 30°C. Are Honolulu's tourists running around in winter jackets? In this section, we will make sense of Celsius temperature readings, as we discuss methods for measuring temperature and weight.

Measuring Weight

You step on the scale at the doctor's office to check your weight, discovering that you are 150 pounds. Compare this to your weight on the moon: 25 pounds. Why the difference? **Weight** is the measure of the gravitational pull on an object. The gravitational pull on the moon is only about one-sixth the gravitational pull on Earth. Although your weight varies depending on the force of gravity, your mass is exactly the same in all locations. **Mass** is a measure of the quantity of matter in an object, determined by its molecular structure. On Earth, as your weight increases, so does your mass. In this section, we will treat weight and mass as equivalent and refer strictly to weight.

UNITS OF WEIGHT: THE ENGLISH SYSTEM

16 ounces (oz) = 1 pound (lb)

2000 pounds (lb) = 1 ton (T)

1 Apply metric prefixes to units of weight.

The basic metric unit of weight is the **gram** (g), used for very small objects such as a coin, a candy bar, or a teaspoon of salt. A nickel has a weight of about 5 grams.

As with meters, prefixes are used to denote a multiple or part of a gram. Table 9.8 applies the common metric prefixes to the gram. The first part of the symbol indicates the prefix and the second part (g) indicates gram.

TABLE 9.8 COMMONLY USED UNITS OF WEIGHT IN THE METRIC SYSTEM

Symbol	Unit	Meaning
kg	kilogram	1000 grams
hg	hectogram	100 grams
dag	dekagram	10 grams
g	gram	1 gram
dg	decigram	0.1 gram
cg	centigram	0.01 gram
mg	milligram	0.001 gram

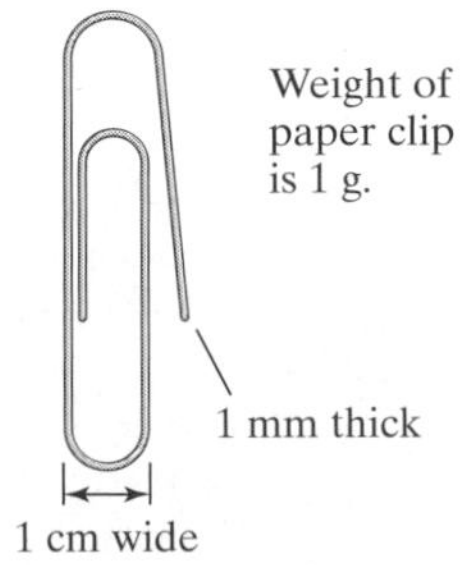

In the metric system, the kilogram is the comparable unit to the pound in the English system. **A weight of 1 kilogram is approximately 2.2 pounds.** Thus, an average man has a weight of about 75 kilograms. Objects that we measure in pounds are measured in kilograms in most countries.

A milligram, equivalent to 0.001 gram, is an extremely small unit of weight and is used extensively in the pharmaceutical industry. If you look at the label on a bottle of tablets, you will see that the amounts of different substances in each tablet are expressed in milligrams.

The weight of a very heavy object is expressed in terms of the metric tonne (t), which is equivalent to 1000 kilograms, or about 2200 pounds. This is 10 percent more than the English ton (T) of 2000 pounds.

We change units of weight within the metric system exactly the same way that we changed units of length.

2 Convert units of weight within the metric system.

CHANGING UNITS OF WEIGHT WITHIN THE METRIC SYSTEM

Use the following diagram to find equivalent measures of weight:

Multiply by 10 for each step to the right.

kg hg dag g dg cg mg.

Divide by 10 for each step to the left.

EXAMPLE 1 CHANGING UNITS WITHIN THE METRIC SYSTEM

a. Convert 8.7 dg to mg.

b. Convert 950 mg to g.

SOLUTION

a. To convert from dg (decigrams) to mg (milligrams), we start at dg and move two steps to the right:

kg hg dag g dg cg mg.

Hence, we move the decimal point two places to the right:

$$8.7 \text{ dg} = 870 \text{ mg}.$$

b. To convert from mg (milligrams) to g (grams), we start at mg and move three steps to the left:

kg hg dag g dg cg mg.

Hence, we move the decimal point three places to the left:

$$950 \text{ mg} = 0.950 \text{ g}.$$

CHECK POINT 1

a. Convert 4.2 dg to mg.

b. Convert 620 cg to g.

3 Use relationships between volume and weight within the metric system.

We have seen a convenient relationship in the metric system between volume and capacity:

$$1000 \text{ cm}^3 = 1 \text{ dm}^3 = 1 \text{ L}.$$

This relationship can be extended to include weight based on the following:

One kilogram of water has a volume of 1 liter.

Thus,

$$1000 \text{ cm}^3 = 1 \text{ dm}^3 = 1 \text{ L} = 1 \text{ kg}.$$

Table 9.9 shows the relationships between volume and weight of water in the metric system.

TABLE 9.9 VOLUME AND WEIGHT OF WATER IN THE METRIC SYSTEM

Volume		Capacity	Weight
1 cm^3	=	1 mL	= 1 g
1 dm^3 = 1000 cm^3	=	1 L	= 1 kg
1 m^3	=	1 kL	= 1000 kg = 1 t

EXAMPLE 2 VOLUME AND WEIGHT IN THE METRIC SYSTEM

An aquarium holds 0.25 m^3 of water. How much does the water weigh?

SOLUTION We use the fact that 1 m^3 of water = 1000 kg of water to set up our unit fraction:

$$\frac{1000 \text{ kg}}{1 \text{ m}^3}.$$

Thus,

$$0.25 \text{ m}^3 = \frac{0.25 \cancel{\text{m}^3}}{1} \cdot \frac{1000 \text{ kg}}{1 \cancel{\text{m}^3}} = 250 \text{ kg}.$$

The water weighs 250 kilograms.

CHECK POINT 2 An aquarium holds 0.145 m^3 of water. How much does the water weigh?

4 Use dimensional analysis to change units of weight to and from the metric system.

A problem like Example 2 involves more awkward computation in the English system. For example, if you know the aquarium's volume in cubic feet, you must also know that 1 cubic foot of water weighs about 62.5 pounds to determine the water's weight.

Dimensional analysis is a useful tool when converting units of weight between the English and metric systems. Some basic conversions are given in Table 9.10.

BLITZER BONUS

The SI System

The metric system is officially called the Système International d'Unités, abbreviated the SI system. Yemen, Brunei, and the United States are the only countries in the world not using the SI system.

In 1975, the United States prepared to adopt the SI system with the Metric Conversion Act. However, due to concerns in grassroots America, Congress made the conversion voluntary, effectively chasing it off. But it's not as bleak as you think; from metric tools to milligram measures of medication, we have been edging, inching, even centimetering toward the metric system.

TABLE 9.10 WEIGHT: ENGLISH AND METRIC EQUIVALENTS

1 ounce (oz)	= 28 grams (g)
1 pound (lb)	= 0.45 kilogram (kg)
1 ton (T)	= 0.9 tonne (t)

EXAMPLE 3 USING DIMENSIONAL ANALYSIS

a. Convert 160 pounds to kilograms.

b. Convert 300 grams to ounces.

SOLUTION

a. To convert 160 pounds to kilograms, we use a unit fraction with kilograms in the numerator and pounds in the denominator:

$$\frac{0.45 \text{ kg}}{1 \text{ lb}}.$$

Table 9.10 shows that 1 lb = 0.45 kg.

Thus,

$$160 \text{ lb} = \frac{160 \cancel{\text{lb}}}{1} \cdot \frac{0.45 \text{ kg}}{1 \cancel{\text{lb}}} = 160(0.45) \text{ kg} = 72 \text{ kg}.$$

b. To convert 300 grams to ounces, we use a unit fraction with ounces in the numerator and grams in the denominator:

$$\frac{1\text{ oz}}{28\text{ g}}.$$ Table 9.10 shows that 1 oz = 28 g.

Thus,

$$300\text{ g} = \frac{300\text{ g}}{1}\cdot\frac{1\text{ oz}}{28\text{ g}} = \frac{300}{28}\text{oz} \approx 10.7\text{ oz}.$$

CHECK POINT 3

a. A man weighs 186 pounds. Convert his weight to kilograms.

b. For each kilogram of weight, 1.2 milligrams of a drug is to be given. What dosage should a 186-pound man be given?

BLITZER BONUS

Using the Metric System to Measure Blood Alcohol Concentration

Blood alcohol concentration (BAC) is measured in grams of alcohol per 100 milliliters of blood. To put this measurement into perspective, a 175-pound man has approximately 5 liters (5000 milliliters) of blood and a 12-ounce can of 6%-alcohol-by-volume beer contains about 15 grams of alcohol. Based on the time it takes for alcohol to be absorbed into the bloodstream, as well as its elimination at a rate of 10–15 grams per hour, Figure 9.9 shows the effect on BAC of a number of drinks on individuals within weight classes. It is illegal to drive with a BAC at 0.08 g/100 mL, or 0.8 gram of alcohol per 100 milliliters of blood, or greater.

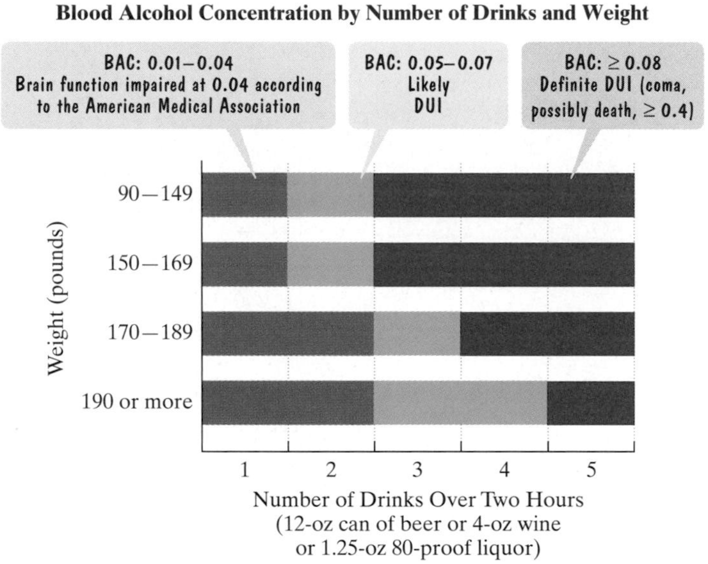

FIGURE 9.9
Source: Patrick McSharry, *Everyday Numbers*, Random House, 2002

5 Understand temperature scales.

Measuring Temperature

You'll be leaving the cold of winter for a vacation to Hawaii. CNN International reports a temperature in Hawaii of 30°C. Should you pack a winter coat?

The idea of changing from Celsius readings—or is it Centigrade?—to familiar Fahrenheit readings can be disorienting. Reporting a temperature of 30°C doesn't have the same impact as the Fahrenheit equivalent of 86 degrees (don't pack the coat). Why these annoying temperature scales?

The **Fahrenheit temperature scale**, the one we are accustomed to, was established in 1714 by the German physicist Gabriel Daniel Fahrenheit. He took a mixture of salt and ice, then thought to be the coldest possible temperature, and called it 0 degrees. He called the temperature of the human body 96 degrees, dividing the space between 0 and 96 into 96 parts. Fahrenheit was wrong about body temperature. It was later found to be 98.6 degrees. On his scale, water froze (without salt) at 32 degrees and boiled at 212 degrees. The symbol ° was used to replace the word *degree*.

Twenty years later, the Swedish scientist Anders Celsius introduced another temperature scale. He set the freezing point of water at 0° and its boiling point at 100°, dividing the space into 100 parts. Degrees were called centigrade until 1948, when the name was officially changed to honor its inventor. However, *centigrade* is still commonly used in the United States.

FIGURE 9.10 The Celsius scale is on the left and the Fahrenheit scale is on the right.

STUDY TIP

The formula used to convert from Celsius to Fahrenheit can be expressed without the use of fractions:

$$F = 1.8C + 32.$$

Some students find this form of the formula easier to memorize.

Figure 9.10 shows a thermometer that measures temperatures in both degrees Celsius (°C is the scale on the left) and degrees Fahrenheit (°F is the scale on the right). The thermometer should help orient you if you need to know what a temperature in °C means. For example, if it is 40°C, find the horizontal line representing this temperature on the left. Now read across to the °F scale on the right. The reading is above 100°, indicating heat wave conditions.

The following formulas can be used to convert from one temperature scale to the other:

FROM CELSIUS TO FAHRENHEIT

$$F = \frac{9}{5}C + 32$$

FROM FAHRENHEIT TO CELSIUS

$$C = \frac{5}{9}(F - 32)$$

EXAMPLE 4 CONVERTING FROM CELSIUS TO FAHRENHEIT

The bills from your European vacation have you feeling a bit feverish, so you decide to take your temperature. The thermometer reads 37°C. Should you panic?

SOLUTION Use the formula

$$F = \frac{9}{5}C + 32$$

to convert 37°C from °C to °F. Substitute 37 for C in the formula and find the value of F.

$$F = \frac{9}{5}(37) + 32 = 66.6 + 32 = 98.6$$

No need to panic! Your temperature is 98.6°F, which is perfectly normal.

CHECK POINT 4 Convert 50°C from °C to °F.

EXAMPLE 5 CONVERTING FROM FAHRENHEIT TO CELSIUS

The temperature on a warm spring day is 77°F. Find the equivalent temperature on the Celsius scale.

SOLUTION Use the formula

$$C = \frac{5}{9}(F - 32)$$

to convert 77°F from °F to °C. Substitute 77 for F in the formula and find the value of C.

$$C = \frac{5}{9}(77 - 32) = \frac{5}{9}(45) = 25$$

Thus, 77°F is equivalent to 25°C.

CHECK POINT 5 Convert 59°F from °F to °C.

Lake Baikal, Siberia, is one of the coldest places on Earth, reaching −76°F (−60°C) in winter. The lowest temperature possible is absolute zero. Scientists have cooled atoms to a few millionths of a degree above absolute zero.

Because temperature is a measure of heat, scientists do not find negative temperatures meaningful in their work. In 1948, the British physicist Lord Kelvin introduced a third temperature scale. He put 0 degrees at absolute zero, the coldest possible temperature, at which there is no heat and molecules stop moving. Figure 9.11 illustrates the three temperature scales.

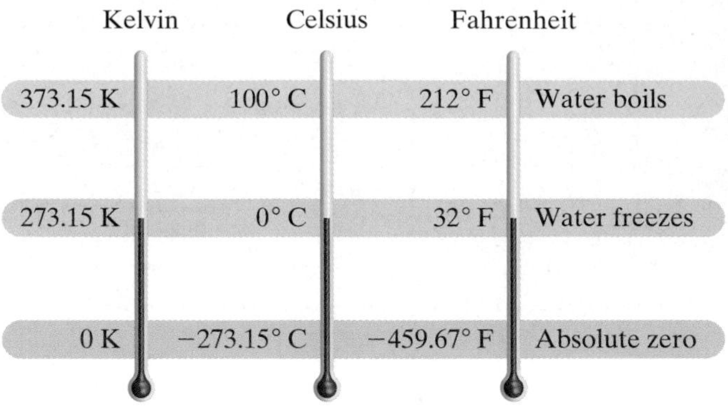

FIGURE 9.11 The three temperature scales

Figure 9.11 shows that water freezes at 273.15 K (read "K" or "Kelvins," not "degrees Kelvin") and boils at 373.15 K. The Kelvin scale is the same as the Celsius scale, except in its starting (zero) point. This makes it easy to go back and forth from Celsius to Kelvin.

FROM CELSIUS TO KELVIN

$$K = C + 273.15$$

FROM KELVIN TO CELSIUS

$$C = K - 273.15$$

Kelvin's scale was embraced by the scientific community. Today, it is the final authority, as scientists define Celsius and Fahrenheit in terms of Kelvins.

BLITZER BONUS

Running a 5 K Race?

A 5 K race means a race at 5 Kelvins. This is a race so cold that no one would be able to move because all the participants would be frozen solid! The proper symbol for a race five kilometers long is a 5 km race.

EXERCISE SET 9.3

• Practice Exercises

In Exercises 1–10, convert the given unit of weight to the unit indicated.

1. 7.4 dg to mg
2. 6.9 dg to mg
3. 870 mg to g
4. 640 mg to g
5. 8 g to cg
6. 7 g to cg
7. 18.6 kg to g
8. 0.37 kg to g
9. 0.018 mg to g
10. 0.029 mg to g

In Exercises 11–18, use Table 9.9 on page 527 to convert the given measurement of water to the unit indicated.

11. 0.05 m^3 to kg
12. 0.02 m^3 to kg
13. 4.2 kg to cm^3
14. 5.8 kg to cm^3
15. 1100 m^3 to t
16. 1500 t to m^3
17. 0.04 kL to g
18. 0.03 kL to g

In Exercises 19–30, use the following equivalents, along with dimensional analysis, to convert the given unit to the unit indicated. When necessary, round answers to two decimal places.

16 oz = 1 lb
2000 lb = 1 T
1 oz = 28 g
1 lb = 0.45 kg
1 T = 0.9 t

19. 36 oz to lb
20. 26 oz to lb
21. 36 oz to g
22. 26 oz to g

23. 540 lb to kg
24. 220 lb to kg
25. 80 lb to g
26. 150 lb to g
27. 540 kg to lb
28. 220 kg to lb
29. 200 t to T
30. 100 t to T

In Exercises 31–38, convert the given Celsius temperature to its equivalent temperature on the Fahrenheit scale. Where appropriate, round to the nearest tenth of a degree.

31. 10°C
32. 20°C
33. 35°C
34. 45°C
35. 57°C
36. 98°C
37. −5°C
38. −10°C

In Exercises 39–50, convert the given Fahrenheit temperature to its equivalent temperature on the Celsius scale. Where appropriate, round to the nearest tenth of a degree.

39. 68°F
40. 86°F
41. 41°F
42. 50°F
43. 72°F
44. 90°F
45. 23°F
46. 14°F
47. 350°F
48. 475°F
49. −22°F
50. −31°F

• Practice Plus

51. The nine points shown below represent Celsius temperatures and their equivalent Fahrenheit temperatures. Also shown is a line that passes through the points.

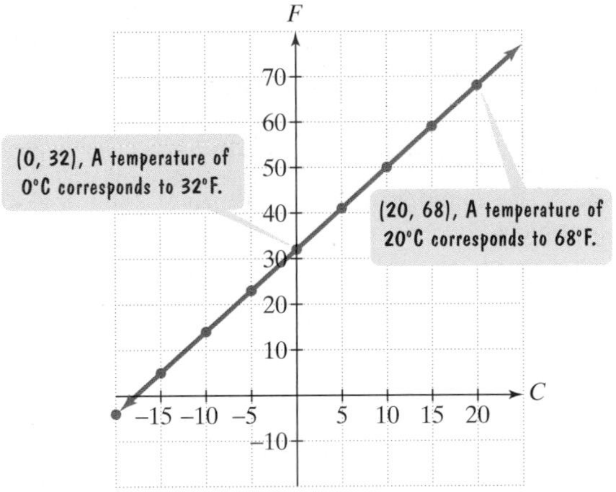

a. Use the coordinates of the two points identified by the voice balloons to compute the line's slope. Express the answer as a fraction reduced to lowest terms. What does this mean about the change in Fahrenheit temperature for each degree change in Celsius temperature?

b. Use the slope-intercept form of the equation of a line, $y = mx + b$, the slope from part (a), and the y-intercept shown by the graph to derive the formula used to convert from Celsius to Fahrenheit.

52. Solve the formula used to convert from Celsius to Fahrenheit for C and derive the other temperature conversion formula.

In Exercises 53–58, determine whether each compound statement is true or false.

53. −40°C = −40°F and 20°C is a reasonable classroom temperature.

54. −85°C = −121°F and 180°C is a reasonable oven temperature for roasting a turkey.

55. This textbook weights approximately 2 mg or the temperature of freezing rain is 0 K.

56. This textbook weighs approximately 6 mg or a good temperature for skiing is 20°C.

57. $(-85°C = -121°F \wedge -103°F = -75°C) \rightarrow$ normal body temperature is 40°C.

58. Normal body temperature is $40°C \rightarrow (-85°C = -121°F \wedge -103°F = -75°C)$.

• Application Exercises

In Exercises 59–65, selecting from milligram, gram, kilogram, and tonne, determine the best unit of measure to express the given item's weight.

59. A bee
60. This book
61. A tablespoon of salt
62. A Boeing 747
63. A stacked washer-dryer
64. A pen
65. An adult male

In Exercises 66–72, select the best estimate for the weight of the given item.

66. A newborn infant's weight
a. 3000 kg **b.** 300 kg **c.** 30 kg **d.** 3 kg

67. The weight of a nickel
a. 5 kg **b.** 5 g **c.** 5 mg

68. A person's weight
a. 60 kg **b.** 60 g **c.** 60 dag

69. The weight of a box of cereal
a. 0.5 kg **b.** 0.5 g **c.** 0.5 t

70. The weight of a glass of water
a. 400 dg **b.** 400 g **c.** 400 dag **d.** 400 hg

71. The weight of a regular-size car
a. 1500 dag **b.** 1500 hg **c.** 1500 kg **d.** 15,000 kg

72. The weight of a bicycle
a. 140 kg **b.** 140 hg **c.** 140 dag **d.** 140 g

73. Six items purchased at a grocery store weigh 14 kilograms. One of the items is detergent weighing 720 grams. What is the total weight, in kilograms, of the other five items?

74. If a nickel weighs 5 grams, how many nickels are there in 4 kilograms of nickels?

75. If the cost to mail a letter is 39 cents for mail weighing up to one ounce and 24 cents for each additional ounce or fraction of an ounce, find the cost of mailing a letter that weighs 85 grams.

76. Using the information given below the pictured finback whale, estimate the weight, in tons and kilograms, of the killer whale.

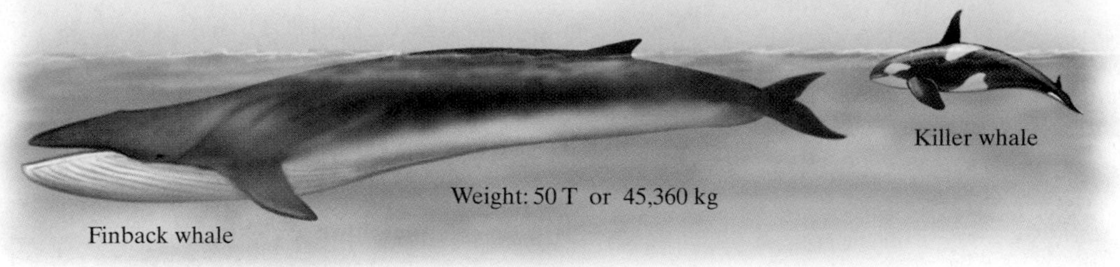

77. Which is more economical: purchasing the economy size of a detergent at 3 kilograms for \$3.15 or purchasing the regular size at 720 grams for 60¢?

Exercises 78–79 ask you to determine drug dosage by a patient's weight. Use the fact that 1 lb = 0.45 kg.

78. For each kilogram of a person's weight, 20 milligrams of a drug is to be given. What dosage should be given to a person who weighs 200 pounds?

79. For each kilogram of a person's weight, 2.5 milligrams of a drug is to be given. What dosage should be given to a child who weighs 80 pounds?

The label on a bottle of Emetrol ("for food or drink indiscretions") reads

> *Each 5 mL teaspoonful contains glucose, 1.87 g; levulose, 1.87 g; and phosphoric acid, 21.5 mg.*

Use this information to solve Exercises 80–81.

80. a. Find the amount of glucose in the recommended dosage of two teaspoons.

b. If the bottle contains 4 ounces, find the quantity of glucose in the bottle. (1 oz = 30 mL)

81. a. Find the amount of phosphoric acid in the recommended dosage of two teaspoons.

b. If the bottle contains 4 ounces, find the quantity of phosphoric acid in the bottle. (1 oz = 30 mL)

In Exercises 82–85, select the best estimate of the Celsius temperature of

82. A very hot day.

a. 85°C **b.** 65°C **c.** 35°C **d.** 20°C

83. A warm winter day in Washington, D.C.

a. 10°C **b.** 30°C **c.** 50°C **d.** 70°C

84. A setting for a home thermostat.

a. 20°C **b.** 40°C **c.** 60°C **d.** 80°C

85. The oven temperature for cooking a roast.

a. 80°C **b.** 100°C **c.** 175°C **d.** 350°C

86. Key West, Florida, has the highest average yearly temperature of any city in the United States: 25.7°C. What is this temperature, in °F, to the nearest tenth of a degree?

87. Plateau Station, Antarctica, has the lowest average yearly temperature of any place on Earth: −7°C. What is this temperature, in °F, to the nearest tenth of a degree?

• Writing in Mathematics

88. Describe the difference between weight and mass.

89. Explain how to use dimensional analysis to convert 200 pounds to kilograms.

90. Why do you think that countries using the metric system prefer the Celsius scale over the Fahrenheit scale?

91. Describe in words how to convert from Celsius to Fahrenheit.

92. Describe in words how to convert from Fahrenheit to Celsius.

93. If you decide to travel outside the United States, which one of the two temperature conversion formulas should you take? Explain your answer.

• Critical Thinking Exercises

94. Which one of the following is true?

a. A 4-pound object weighs more than a 2000-gram object.

b. A 100-milligram object weighs more than a 2-ounce object.

c. A 50-gram object weighs more than a 2-ounce object.

d. A 10-pound object weighs more than a 4-kilogram object.

95. Which one of the following is true?

a. Flour selling at 3¢ per gram is a better buy than flour selling at 55¢ per pound.

b. The measures

32,600 g, 32.1 kg, 4 lb, 36 oz

are arranged in order, from greatest to least weight.

c. If you are taking aspirin to relieve cold symptoms, a reasonable dose is 2 kilograms four times a day.

d. A large dog weighs about 350 kilograms.

• Group Exercise

96. Present a group report on the current status of the metric system in the United States. At present, does it appear that the United States will convert to the metric system? Who supports the conversion and who opposes it? Summarize each side's position. Give examples of how our current system of weights and measures is an economic liability. What are the current obstacles to metric conversion?

CHAPTER SUMMARY, REVIEW, AND TEST

SUMMARY — DEFINITIONS AND CONCEPTS — EXAMPLES

9.1 Measuring Length; The Metric System

a. The result obtained from measuring length is called a linear measurement, stated in linear units.

b. Linear Units: The English System

12 in. = 1 ft, 3 ft = 1 yd, 36 in. = 1 yd, 5280 ft = 1 mi

c. Dimensional Analysis
Multiply the given measurement by a unit fraction with the unit of measurement that needs to be introduced in the numerator and the unit of measurement that needs to be eliminated in the denominator. Ex. 1, p. 509

d. Linear Units: The Metric System
The basic unit is the meter (m), approximately 39 inches.

1 km = 1000 m, 1 hm = 100 m, 1 dam = 10 m,

1 dm = 0.1 m, 1 cm = 0.01 m, 1 mm = 0.001 m

e. Changing Linear Units within the Metric System Ex. 2, p. 512

× 10

km hm dam m dm cm mm

÷ 10

f. English and metric equivalents for length are given in Table 9.3 on page 514. Ex. 3, p. 514; Ex. 4, p. 515

9.2 Measuring Area and Volume

a. The area measure of a plane region is the number of square units contained in the given region. Ex. 1, p. 518

b. English and metric equivalents for area are given in Table 9.4 on page 519. Ex. 3, p. 519

c. The volume measure of a three-dimensional figure is the number of cubic units contained in its interior. Ex. 4, p. 520

d. Capacity refers to the amount of fluid that a three-dimensional object can hold. English units for capacity include pints, quarts, and gallons: 2 pt = 1 qt; 4 qt = 1 gal; one cubic yard has a capacity of about 200 gallons. See Table 9.5 on page 521. Ex. 5, p. 521

e. The basic unit for capacity in the metric system is the liter (L). One liter is about 1.06 quarts. Prefixes for the liter are the same as throughout the metric system.

f. Table 9.7 on page 522 shows relationships between volume and capacity in the metric system. Ex. 6, p. 522

$$1 \text{ dm}^3 = 1000 \text{ cm}^3 = 1 \text{ L}$$

9.3 Measuring Weight and Temperature

a. Weight: The English System

16 oz = 1 lb, 2000 lb = 1 T

b. Units of Weight: The Metric System
The basic unit is the gram (g).

$$1000 \text{ grams } (1 \text{ kg}) \approx 2.2 \text{ lb},$$
$$1 \text{ kg} = 1000 \text{ g}, 1 \text{ hg} = 100 \text{ g}, 1 \text{ dag} = 10 \text{ g},$$
$$1 \text{ dg} = 0.1 \text{ g}, 1 \text{ cg} = 0.01 \text{ g}, 1 \text{ mg} = 0.001 \text{ g}$$

c. Changing Units of Weight within the Metric System Ex. 1, p. 526

× 10

kg hg dag g dg cg mg

÷ 10

d. One kilogram of water has a volume of 1 liter. Table 9.9 on page 527 shows relationships between volume and weight of water in the metric system. Ex. 2, p. 527

e. English and metric equivalents for weight are given in Table 9.10 on page 527. Ex. 3, p. 527

f. Temperature Scales: Celsius to Fahrenheit: $F = \frac{9}{5}C + 32$ Ex. 4, p. 529

g. Temperature Scales: Fahrenheit to Celsius: $C = \frac{5}{9}(F - 32)$ Ex. 5, p. 529

REVIEW EXERCISES

9.1

In Exercises 1–4, use dimensional analysis to convert the quantity to the indicated unit.

1. 69 in. to ft

2. 9 in. to yd

3. 21 ft to yd

4. 13,200 ft to mi

In Exercises 5–10, convert the given linear measurement to the metric unit indicated.

5. 22.8 m to cm

6. 7 dam to m

7. 19.2 hm to m

8. 144 cm to hm

9. 0.5 mm to m

10. 18 cm to mm

In Exercises 11–16, use the given English and metric equivalents, along with dimensional analysis, to convert the given measurement to the unit indicated. Where necessary, round answers to two decimal places.

1 in. = 2.54 cm
1 ft = 30.48 cm
1 yd = 0.9 m
1 mi = 1.6 km

11. 23 in. to cm

12. 19 cm to in.

13. 330 mi to km

14. 600 km to mi

15. 14 m to yd

16. 12 m to ft

17. Express 45 kilometers per hour in miles per hour.

18. Express 60 miles per hour in kilometers per hour.

19. Arrange from smallest to largest: 0.024 km, 2400 m, 24,000 cm.

20. If you jog six times around a track that is 800 meters long, how many kilometers have you covered?

9.2

21. Use the given figure to find its area in square units.

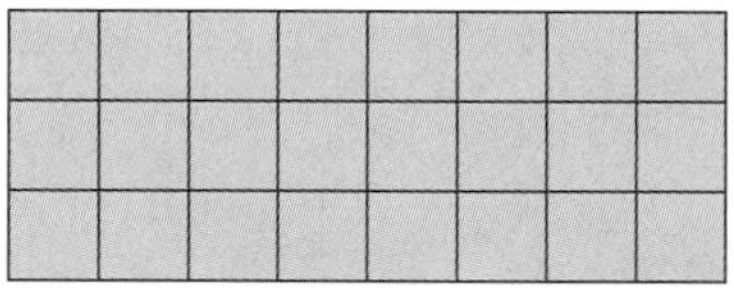

22. In April 2006, the United States, with an area of 3,537,441 square miles, had a population of 298,923,319. Find the population density, to the nearest tenth, at that time. Describe what this means.

23. Given 1 acre = 0.4 hectare, use dimensional analysis to find the size of a property in acres measured at 7.2 hectares.

24. Using $1 \text{ ft}^2 = 0.09 \text{ m}^2$, convert 30 m^2 to ft^2.

25. Using $1 \text{ mi}^2 = 2.6 \text{ km}^2$, convert 12 mi^2 to km^2.

26. Which one of the following is a reasonable measure for the area of a flower garden in a person's yard?

a. 100 m^2 **b.** 0.4 ha **c.** 0.01 km^2

27. Use the given figure to find its volume in cubic units.

28. A swimming pool has a volume of 33,600 cubic feet. Given that 1 cubic foot has a capacity of about 7.48 gallons, how many gallons of water does the pool hold?

29. An aquarium has a volume of 76,000 cubic centimeters. How many liters of water does the aquarium hold?

30. The capacity of a one-quart container of juice is approximately

a. 0.1 kL **b.** 0.5 L **c.** 1 L **d.** 1 mL

31. There are 3 feet in a yard. Explain why there are not 3 square feet in a square yard. If helpful, illustrate your explanation with a diagram.

32. Explain why the area of Texas could not be measured in cubic miles.

9.3

In Exercises 33–36, convert the given unit of weight to the unit indicated.

33. 12.4 dg to mg **34.** 12 g to cg

35. 0.012 mg to g **36.** 450 mg to kg

In Exercises 37–38, use Table 9.9 on page 527 to convert the given measurement of water to the unit or units indicated.

37. 50 kg to cm^3 **38.** 4 kL to dm^3 to g

39. Using 1 lb = 0.45 kg, convert 210 pounds to kilograms.

40. Using 1 oz = 28 g, convert 392 grams to ounces.

41. If you are interested in your weight in the metric system, would it be best to report it in milligrams, grams, or kilograms? Explain why the unit you selected would be most appropriate. Explain why each of the other two units is not the best choice for reporting your weight.

42. Given 16 oz = 1 lb, use dimensional analysis to convert 36 ounces to pounds.

In Exercises 43–44, select the best estimate for the weight of the given item.

43. A dollar bill:

a. 1 g **b.** 10 g **c.** 1 kg **d.** 4 kg

44. A hamburger:

a. 3 kg **b.** 1 kg **c.** 200 g **d.** 5 g

In Exercises 45–49, convert the given Celsius temperature to its equivalent temperature on the Fahrenheit scale.

45. 15°C **46.** 100°C **47.** 5°C

48. 0°C **49.** −25°C

In Exercises 50–55, convert the given Fahrenheit temperature to its equivalent temperature on the Celsius scale.

50. 59°F **51.** 41°F **52.** 212°F

53. 98.6°F **54.** 0°F **55.** 14°F

56. Is a decrease of 15° Celsius more or less than a decrease of 15° Fahrenheit? Explain your answer.

CHAPTER 9 TEST

1. Change 807 mm to hm.

2. Given 1 inch = 2.54 centimeters, use dimensional analysis to change 635 centimeters to inches.

3. If you jog eight times around a track that is 600 meters long, how many kilometers have you covered?

In Exercises 4–6, write the most reasonable metric unit for length in each blank. Select from mm, cm, m, and km.

4. A human thumb is 20_____ wide.

5. The height of the table is 45_____.

6. The towns are 60_____ apart.

7. If 1 mile = 1.6 kilometers, express 80 miles per hour in kilometers per hour.

8. How many times greater is a square yard than a square foot?

9. Spain has a population of 39,133,966 and an area of 194,896 square miles. Find Spain's population density to the nearest tenth. Describe what this means.

10. Given 1 acre = 0.4 hectare, use dimensional analysis to find the area of a property measured at 18 hectares.

11. The area of a dollar bill is approximately

a. 10 cm^2 **b.** 100 cm^2 **c.** 1000 cm^2 **d.** 1 m^2

12. There are 10 decimeters in a meter. Explain why there are not 10 cubic decimeters in a cubic meter. How many times greater is a cubic meter than a cubic decimeter?

13. A swimming pool has a volume of 10,000 cubic feet. Given that 1 cubic foot has a capacity of about 7.48 gallons, how many gallons of water does the pool hold?

14. The capacity of a pail used to wash floors is approximately

a. 3 L **b.** 12 L **c.** 80 L **d.** 2 kL

15. Change 137 g to kg.

16. Using 1 lb = 0.45 kg, convert 90 pounds to kilograms.

In Exercises 17–18, write the most reasonable metric unit for weight in each blank. Select from mg, g, and kg.

17. My suitcase weighs 20_____.

18. I took a 350_____ aspirin.

19. Convert 30°C to Fahrenheit.

20. Convert 176°F to Celsius.

21. Comfortable room temperature is approximately

a. 70°C **b.** 50°C **c.** 30°C **d.** 20°C

CHAPTER 10

Geometry

Geometry is the study of the space you live in and the shapes that surround you. You're even made of it! The human lung consists of nearly 300 spherical air sacs, geometrically designed to provide the greatest surface area within the limited volume of our bodies. Viewed in this way, geometry becomes an intimate experience.

For thousands of years, people have studied geometry in some form to obtain a better understanding of the world in which they live. A study of the shape of your world will provide you with many practical applications and perhaps help to increase your appreciation of its beauty.

SECTION 10.1 • POINTS, LINES, PLANES, AND ANGLES

OBJECTIVES

1. Understand points, lines, and planes as the basis of geometry.
2. Solve problems involving angle measures.
3. Solve problems involving angles formed by parallel lines and transversals.

The San Francisco Museum of Modern Art was constructed in 1995 to illustrate how art and architecture can enrich one another. The exterior involves geometric shapes, symmetry, and unusual facades. Although there are no windows, natural light streams in through a truncated cylindrical skylight that crowns the building. The architect worked with a scale model of the museum at the site and observed how light hit it during different times of the day. These observations were used to cut the cylindrical skylight at an angle that maximizes sunlight entering the interior.

Angles play a critical role in creating modern architecture. They are also fundamental in the study of geometry. The word "geometry" means "earth measure." Because it involves the mathematics of shapes, geometry connects mathematics to art and architecture. It also has many practical applications. You can use geometry at home when you buy a carpet, build a fence, tile a floor, or determine whether a piece of furniture will fit through your doorway. In this chapter, we look at the shapes that surround us and their applications.

1 Understand points, lines, and planes as the basis of geometry.

Points, Lines, and Planes

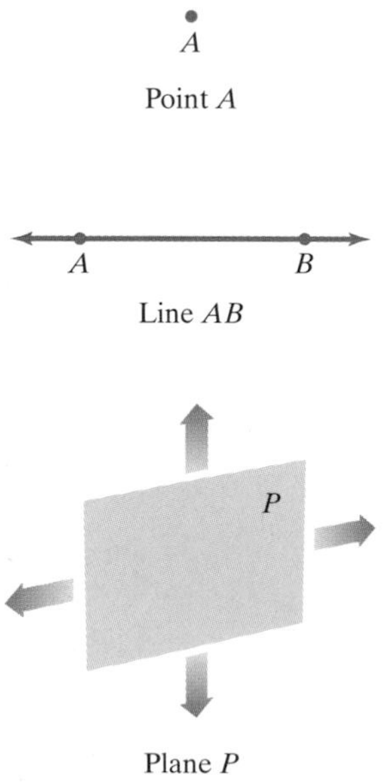

FIGURE 10.1 Representing a point, a line, and a plane

Points, lines, and planes make up the basis of all geometry. Stars in the night sky look like points of light. Long stretches of overhead power lines that appear to extend endlessly look like lines. The top of a flat table resembles part of a plane. However, stars, power lines, and table tops only approximate points, lines, and planes. Points, lines, and planes do not exist in the physical world. Representations of these forms are shown in Figure 10.1. A **point**, represented as a small dot, has no length, width, or thickness. No object in the real world has zero size. A **line**, connecting two points along the shortest possible path, has no thickness and extends infinitely in both directions. However, no familiar everyday object is infinite in length. A **plane** is a flat surface with no thickness and no boundaries. This page resembles a plane, although it does not extend indefinitely and it does have thickness.

A line may be named using any two of its points. In Figure 10.2(a), shown at the top of the next page, line AB can be symbolized $\overleftrightarrow{AB}$ or $\overleftrightarrow{BA}$. Any point on the line divides the line into three parts—the point and two **half-lines**. Figure 10.2(b) illustrates half-line AB, symbolized $\overset{\circ\!\!\longrightarrow}{AB}$. The open circle above the A in the symbol and below the A in the diagram indicates that point A is not included in the half-line. A **ray** is a half-line with its endpoint included. Figure 10.2(c) illustrates ray AB, symbolized $\overrightarrow{AB}$. The closed dot below the A in the diagram shows that point A is included in the ray. A portion of a line joining two points and including the endpoints is called a **line segment**. Figure 10.2(d) illustrates line segment AB, symbolized $\overline{AB}$ or $\overline{BA}$.

(a) Line AB $\overleftrightarrow{AB}$ or $\overleftrightarrow{BA}$ (b) Half line AB $\overset{\circ\!\rightarrow}{AB}$ (c) Ray AB $\overrightarrow{AB}$ (d) Line Segment AB $\overline{AB}$ or $\overline{BA}$

FIGURE 10.2 Lines, half-lines, rays, and line segments

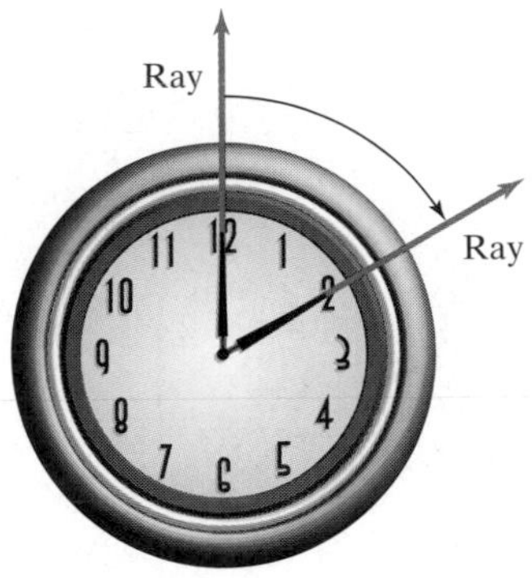

FIGURE 10.3 Clock with hands forming an angle

Angles

An **angle**, symbolized $\measuredangle$, is formed by the union of two rays that have a common endpoint. One ray is called the **initial side** and the other the **terminal side**.

A rotating ray is often a useful way to think about angles. The ray in Figure 10.3 rotates from 12 to 2. The ray pointing to 12 is the initial side and the ray pointing to 2 is the terminal side. The common endpoint of an angle's initial side and terminal side is the **vertex** of the angle.

Figure 10.4 shows an angle. The common endpoint of the two rays, B, is the vertex. The two rays that form the angle, $\overrightarrow{BA}$ and $\overrightarrow{BC}$, are the sides. The four ways of naming the angle are shown to the right of Figure 10.4.

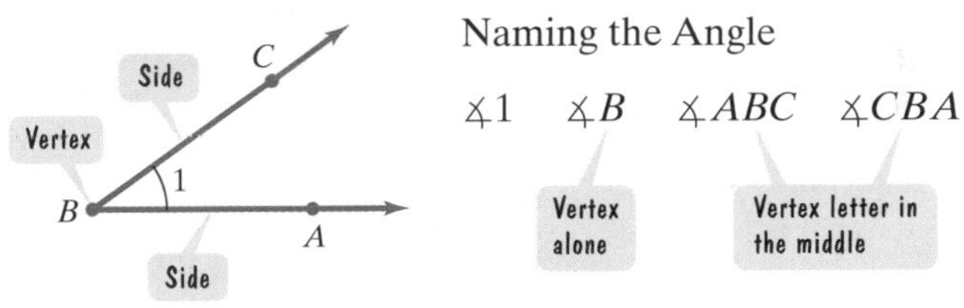

FIGURE 10.4 An angle: two rays with a common endpoint

2 Solve problems involving angle measures.

Measuring Angles Using Degrees

Angles are measured by determining the amount of rotation from the initial side to the terminal side. One way to measure angles is in **degrees**, symbolized by a small, raised circle °. Think of the hour hand of a clock. From 12 noon to 12 midnight, the hour hand moves around in a complete circle. By definition, the ray has rotated through 360 degrees, or 360°. Using 360° as the amount of rotation of a ray back onto itself, **a degree, 1°, is $\frac{1}{360}$ of a complete rotation**.

A complete 360° rotation

EXAMPLE 1 USING DEGREE MEASURE

The hand of a clock moves from 12 to 2 o'clock, shown in Figure 10.3. Through how many degrees does it move?

SOLUTION We know that one complete rotation is 360°. Moving from 12 to 2 o'clock is $\frac{2}{12}$, or $\frac{1}{6}$, of a complete revolution. Thus, the hour hand moves

$$\frac{1}{6} \times 360° = \frac{360°}{6} = 60°$$

in going from 12 to 2 o'clock.

CHECK POINT 1 The hand of a clock moves from 12 to 1 o'clock. Through how many degrees does it move?

Figure 10.5 shows angles classified by their degree measurement. An **acute angle** measures less than 90° [see Figure 10.5(a)]. A **right angle**, one-quarter of a complete rotation, measures 90° [Figure 10.5(b)]. Examine the right angle—do you see a small square at the vertex? This symbol is used to indicate a right angle. An **obtuse angle** measures more than 90°, but less than 180° [Figure 10.5(c)]. Finally, a **straight angle**, one-half a complete rotation, measures 180° [Figure 10.5(d)]. The two rays in a straight angle form a straight line.

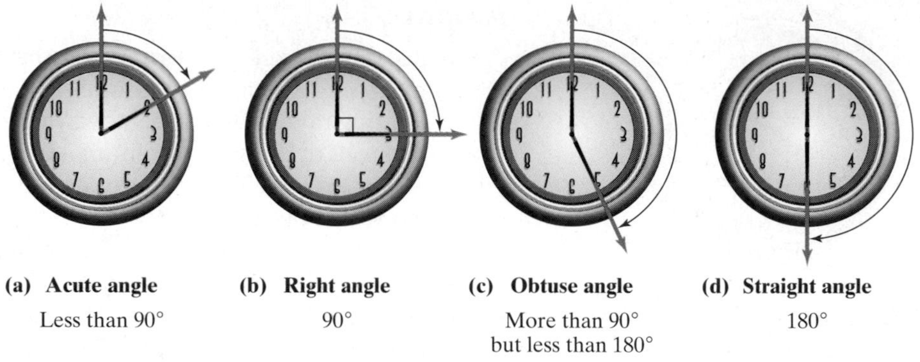

FIGURE 10.5 Classifying angles by their degree measurements

Figure 10.6 illustrates a **protractor**, used for finding the degree measure of an angle. As shown in the figure, we measure an angle by placing the center point of the protractor on the vertex of the angle and the straight side of the protractor along one side of the angle. The measure of $\measuredangle ABC$ is then read as 50°. Observe that the measure is not 130° because the angle is obviously less than 90°. We indicate the angle's measure by writing $m\measuredangle ABC = 50°$, read "the measure of angle ABC is 50°."

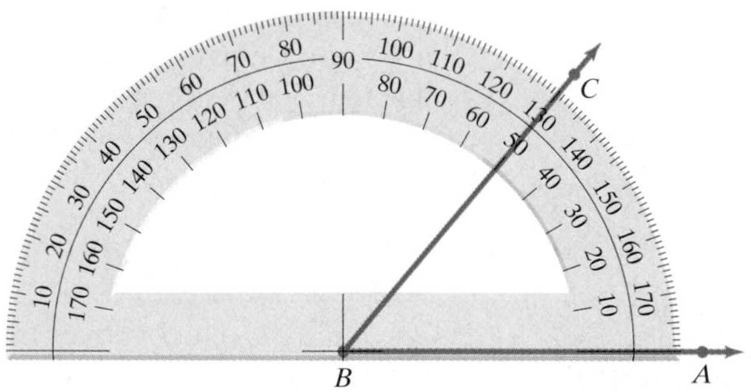

FIGURE 10.6 Using a protractor to measure an angle: $m\measuredangle ABC = 50°$

Two angles whose measures have a sum of 90° are called **complementary angles**. For example, angles measuring 70° and 20° are complementary angles because $70° + 20° = 90°$. For angles such as those measuring 70° and 20°, each angle is the **complement** of the other: The 70° angle is the complement of the 20° angle and the 20° angle is the complement of the 70° angle. **The measure of the complement can be found by subtracting the angle's measure from 90°.** For example, we can find the complement of a 25° angle by subtracting 25° from 90°: $90° - 25° = 65°$. Thus, an angle measuring 65° is the complement of one measuring 25°.

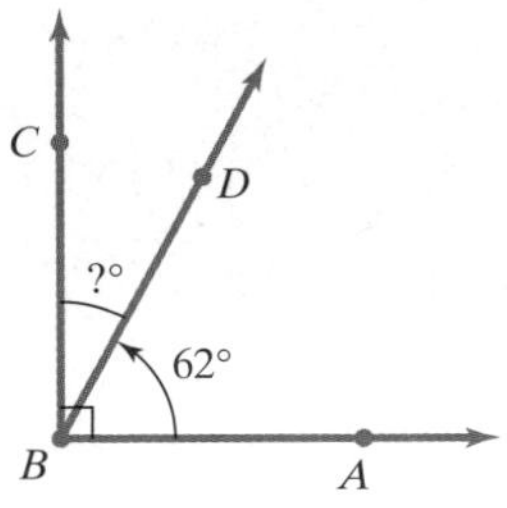

FIGURE 10.7

EXAMPLE 2 ANGLE MEASURES AND COMPLEMENTS

Use Figure 10.7 to find $m\measuredangle DBC$.

SOLUTION The measure of $\measuredangle DBC$ is not yet known. It is shown as ?° in Figure 10.7. The acute angles $\measuredangle ABD$, which measures 62°, and $\measuredangle DBC$ form a right angle, indicated by the square at the vertex. This means that the measures of the acute angles add up to 90°. Thus, $\measuredangle DBC$ is the complement of the angle measuring 62°. The measure of $\measuredangle DBC$ is found by subtracting 62° from 90°:

$$m\measuredangle DBC = 90° - 62° = 28°.$$

The measure of $\measuredangle DBC$ can also be found using an algebraic approach.

$m\measuredangle ABD + m\measuredangle DBC = 90°$	The sum of the measures of complementary angles is 90°.
$62° + m\measuredangle DBC = 90°$	We are given $m\measuredangle ABD = 62°$.
$m\measuredangle DBC = 90° - 62° = 28°$	Subtract 62° from both sides of the equation.

CHECK POINT 2 In Figure 10.7, let $m\measuredangle DBC = 19°$. Find $m\measuredangle DBA$.

Two angles whose measures have a sum of 180° are called **supplementary angles**. For example, angles measuring 110° and 70° are supplementary angles because $110° + 70° = 180°$. For angles such as those measuring 110° and 70°, each angle is the **supplement** of the other: the 110° angle is the supplement of the 70° angle, and the 70° angle is the supplement of the 110° angle. **The measure of the supplement can be found by subtracting the angle's measure from 180°.** For example, we can find the supplement of a 25° angle by subtracting 25° from 180°: $180° - 25° = 155°$. Thus, an angle measuring 155° is the supplement of one measuring 25°.

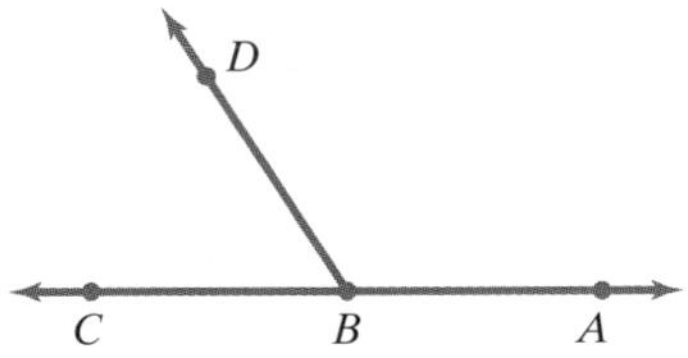

FIGURE 10.8

EXAMPLE 3 ANGLE MEASURES AND SUPPLEMENTS

Figure 10.8 shows that $\measuredangle ABD$ and $\measuredangle DBC$ are supplementary angles. If $m\measuredangle ABD$ is 66° greater than $m\measuredangle DBC$, find the measure of each angle.

SOLUTION Let $m\measuredangle DBC = x$. Because $m\measuredangle ABD$ is 66° greater than $m\measuredangle DBC$, then $m\measuredangle ABD = x + 66°$. We are given that these angles are supplementary.

$m\measuredangle DBC + m\measuredangle ABD = 180°$	The sum of the measures of supplementary angles is 180°.
$x + (x + 66°) = 180°$	Substitute the variable expressions for the measures.
$2x + 66° = 180°$	Combine like terms: $x + x = 2x$.
$2x = 114°$	Subtract 66° from both sides.
$x = 57°$	Divide both sides by 2.

Thus, $m\measuredangle DBC = 57°$ and $m\measuredangle ABD = 57° + 66° = 123°$.

CHECK POINT 3 In Figure 10.8, if $m\measuredangle ABD$ is 88° greater than $m\measuredangle DBC$, find the measure of each angle.

FIGURE 10.9

Figure 10.9 illustrates a highway sign that warns of a railroad crossing. When two lines intersect, the opposite angles formed are called **vertical angles**.

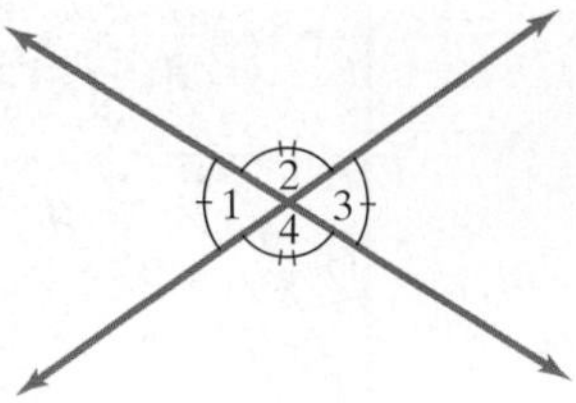

FIGURE 10.10

In Figure 10.10, there are two pairs of vertical angles. Angles 1 and 3 are vertical angles. Angles 2 and 4 are also vertical angles.

We can use Figure 10.10 to show that vertical angles have the same measure. Let's concentrate on angles 1 and 3, each denoted by one tick mark. Can you see that each of these angles is supplementary to angle 2?

$$m\measuredangle 1 + m\measuredangle 2 = 180^\circ$$

The sum of the measures of supplementary angles is 180°.

$$m\measuredangle 2 + m\measuredangle 3 = 180^\circ$$

$$m\measuredangle 1 + m\measuredangle 2 = m\measuredangle 2 + m\measuredangle 3$$

Substitute $m\measuredangle 2 + m\measuredangle 3$ for 180° in the first equation.

$$m\measuredangle 1 = m\measuredangle 3$$

Subtract $m\measuredangle 2$ from both sides.

Using a similar approach, we can show that $m\measuredangle 2 = m\measuredangle 4$, each denoted by two tick marks in Figure 10.10.

> Vertical angles have the same measure.

EXAMPLE 4 USING VERTICAL ANGLES

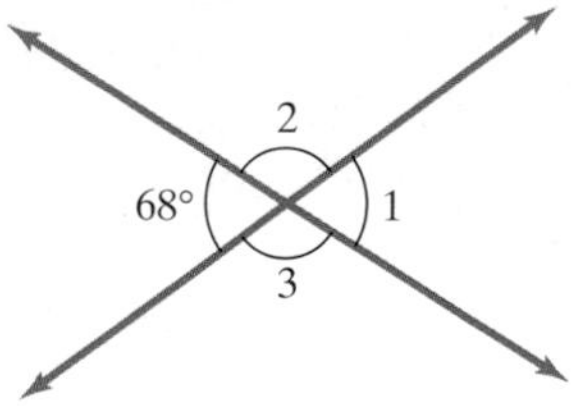

FIGURE 10.11

Figure 10.11 shows that the angle on the left measures 68°. Find the measures of the other three angles.

SOLUTION Angle 1 and the angle measuring 68° are vertical angles. Because vertical angles have the same measure,

$$m\measuredangle 1 = 68^\circ.$$

Angle 2 and the angle measuring 68° form a straight angle and are supplementary. Because their measures add up to 180°,

$$m\measuredangle 2 = 180^\circ - 68^\circ = 112^\circ.$$

Angle 2 and angle 3 are also vertical angles, so they have the same measure. Because the measure of angle 2 is 112°,

$$m\measuredangle 3 = 112^\circ.$$

CHECK POINT 4 In Figure 10.11, assume that the angle on the left measures 57°. Find the measures of the other three angles.

Parallel Lines

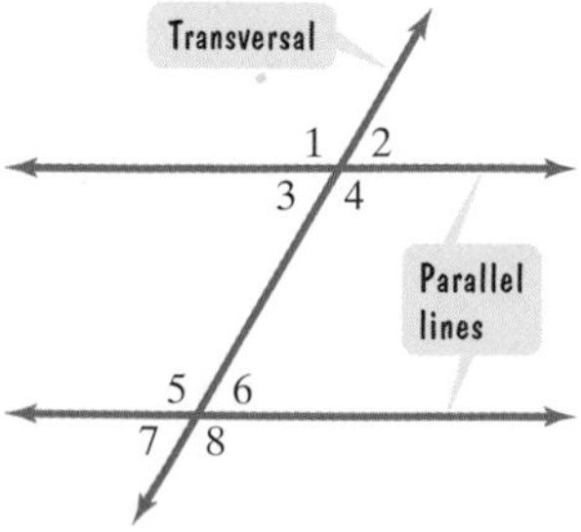

FIGURE 10.12

Parallel lines are lines that lie in the same plane and have no points in common. If two different lines in the same plane are not parallel, they have a single point in common and are called **intersecting lines**. If the lines intersect at an angle of 90°, they are called **perpendicular lines**.

If we intersect a pair of parallel lines with a third line, called a **transversal**, eight angles are formed, as shown in Figure 10.12. Certain pairs of these angles have special names, as well as special properties. These names and properties are summarized in Table 10.1.

TABLE 10.1 NAMES OF ANGLE PAIRS FORMED BY A TRANSVERSAL INTERSECTING PARALLEL LINES

Name	Description	Sketch	Angle Pairs Described	Property
Alternate interior angles	Interior angles that do not have a common vertex on alternate sides of the transversal	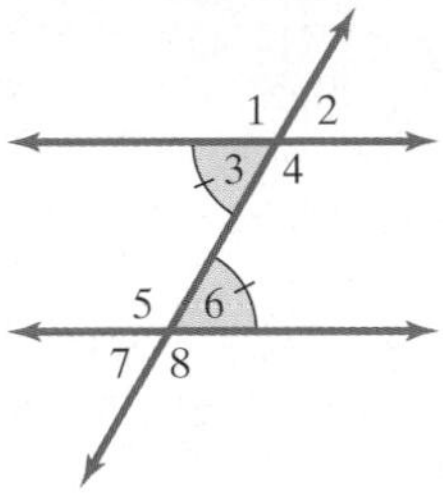	$\measuredangle 3$ and $\measuredangle 6$ $\measuredangle 4$ and $\measuredangle 5$	Alternate interior angles have the same measure. $m\measuredangle 3 = m\measuredangle 6$ $m\measuredangle 4 = m\measuredangle 5$
Alternate exterior angles	Exterior angles that do not have a common vertex on alternate sides of the transversal	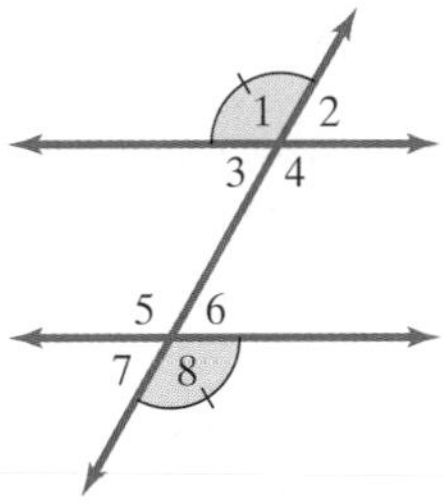	$\measuredangle 1$ and $\measuredangle 8$ $\measuredangle 2$ and $\measuredangle 7$	Alternate exterior angles have the same measure. $m\measuredangle 1 = m\measuredangle 8$ $m\measuredangle 2 = m\measuredangle 7$
Corresponding angles	One interior and one exterior angle on the same side of the transversal	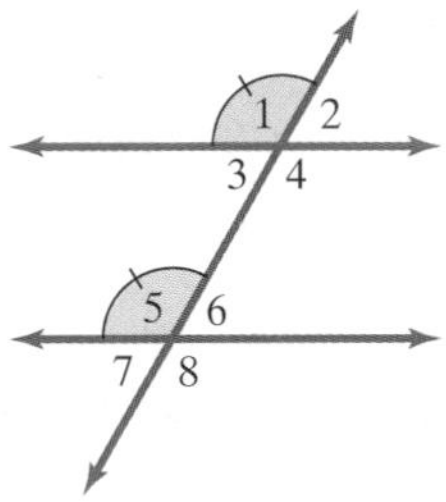	$\measuredangle 1$ and $\measuredangle 5$ $\measuredangle 2$ and $\measuredangle 6$ $\measuredangle 3$ and $\measuredangle 7$ $\measuredangle 4$ and $\measuredangle 8$	Corresponding angles have the same measure. $m\measuredangle 1 = m\measuredangle 5$ $m\measuredangle 2 = m\measuredangle 6$ $m\measuredangle 3 = m\measuredangle 7$ $m\measuredangle 4 = m\measuredangle 8$

3 Solve problems involving angles formed by parallel lines and transversals.

When two parallel lines are intersected by a transversal, the following relationships are true:

PARALLEL LINES AND ANGLE PAIRS

If parallel lines are intersected by a transversal,

- alternate interior angles have the same measure,
- alternate exterior angles have the same measure, and
- corresponding angles have the same measure.

Conversely, if two lines are intersected by a third line and an alternate interior angle pair or an alternate exterior angle pair or a pair of corresponding angles have the same measure, then the two lines are parallel.

EXAMPLE 5 FINDING ANGLE MEASURES WHEN PARALLEL LINES ARE INTERSECTED BY A TRANSVERSAL

In Figure 10.13, two parallel lines are intersected by a transversal. One of the angles ($\measuredangle 8$) has a measure of 35°. Find the measure of each of the other seven angles.

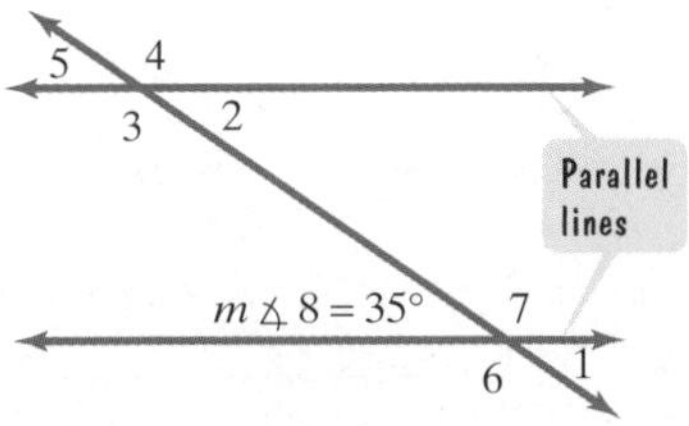

FIGURE 10.13

SOLUTION Look carefully at Figure 10.13 and fill in the angle measures as you read each line in this solution.

$m\measuredangle 1 = 35°$ — $\measuredangle 8$ and $\measuredangle 1$ are vertical angles and vertical angles have the same measure.

$m\measuredangle 6 = 180° - 35° = 145°$ — $\measuredangle 8$ and $\measuredangle 6$ are supplementary.

$m\measuredangle 7 = 145°$ — $\measuredangle 6$ and $\measuredangle 7$ are vertical angles, so they have the same measure.

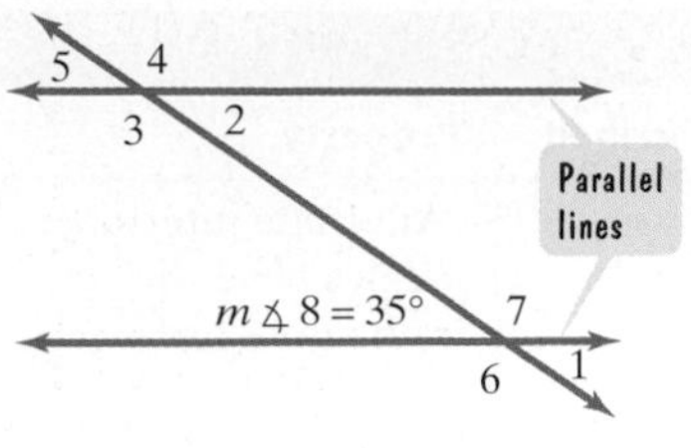

FIGURE 10.13 (repeated)

$m\measuredangle 2 = 35°$ — ∡8 and ∡2 are alternate interior angles, so they have the same measure.

$m\measuredangle 3 = 145°$ — ∡7 and ∡3 are alternate interior angles. Thus, they have the same measure.

$m\measuredangle 5 = 35°$ — ∡8 and ∡5 are corresponding angles. Thus, they have the same measure.

$m\measuredangle 4 = 180° - 35° = 145°$ — ∡4 and ∡5 are supplementary.

STUDY TIP

There is more than one way to solve Example 5. For example, once you know that $m\measuredangle 2 = 35°$, $m\measuredangle 5$ is also 35° because ∡2 and ∡5 are vertical angles.

CHECK POINT 5 In Figure 10.13, assume that $m\measuredangle 8 = 29°$. Find the measure of each of the other seven angles.

EXERCISE SET 10.1

• Practice Exercises

1. The hour hand of a clock moves from 12 to 5 o'clock. Through how many degrees does it move?
2. The hour hand of a clock moves from 12 to 4 o'clock. Through how many degrees does it move?
3. The hour hand of a clock moves from 1 to 4 o'clock. Through how many degrees does it move?
4. The hour hand of a clock moves from 1 to 7 o'clock. Through how many degrees does it move?

In Exercises 5–10, use the protractor to find the measure of each angle. Then classify the angle as acute, right, straight, or obtuse.

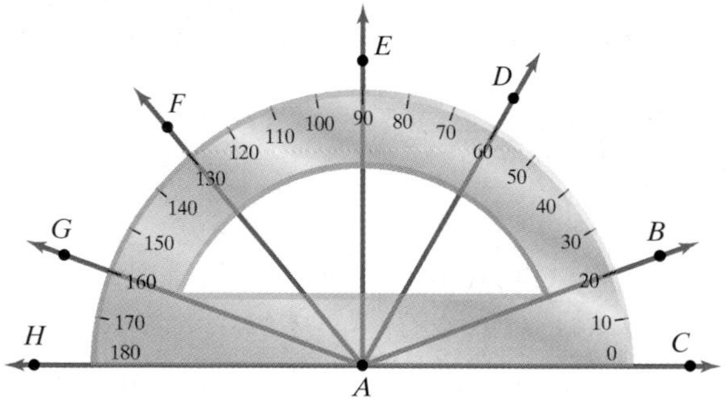

5. ∡CAB 6. ∡CAF 7. ∡HAB
8. ∡HAF 9. ∡CAH 10. ∡HAE

In Exercises 11–14, find the measure of the angle in which ?° appears.

11.

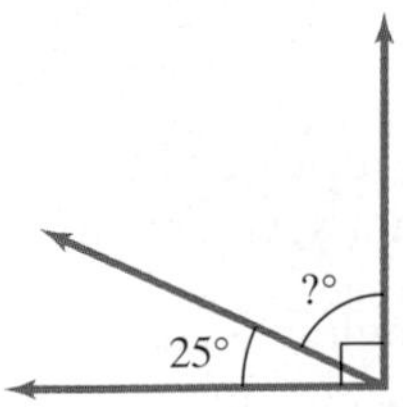

12.

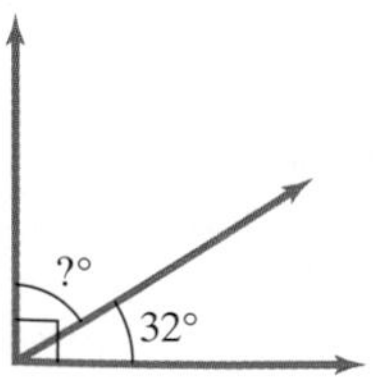

13.

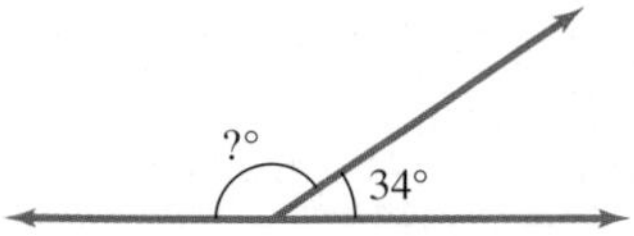

14.

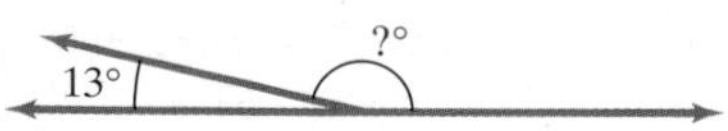

In Exercises 15–20, find the measure of the complement and the supplement of each angle.

15. 48° **16.** 52° **17.** 89° **18.** 1° **19.** 37.4° **20.** $15\frac{1}{3}°$

In Exercises 21–24, use an algebraic equation to find the measures of the two angles described. Begin by letting x represent the degree measure of the angle's complement or its supplement.

21. The measure of the angle is 12° greater than its complement.
22. The measure of the angle is 56° greater than its complement.
23. The measure of the angle is three times greater than its supplement.
24. The measure of the angle is 81° more than twice that of its supplement.

In Exercises 25–28, find the measures of angles 1, 2, and 3.

25.

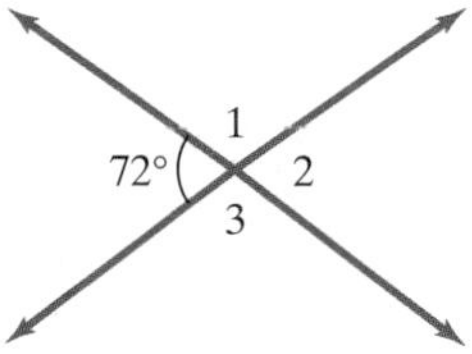

26.

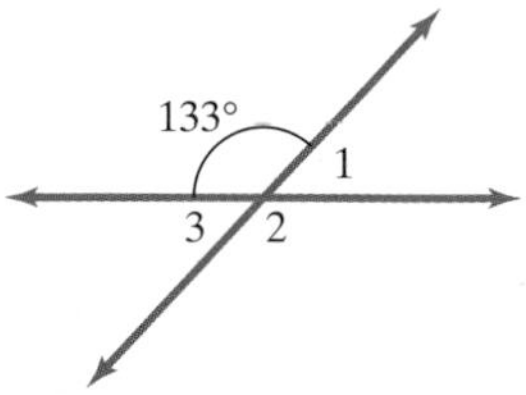

27.

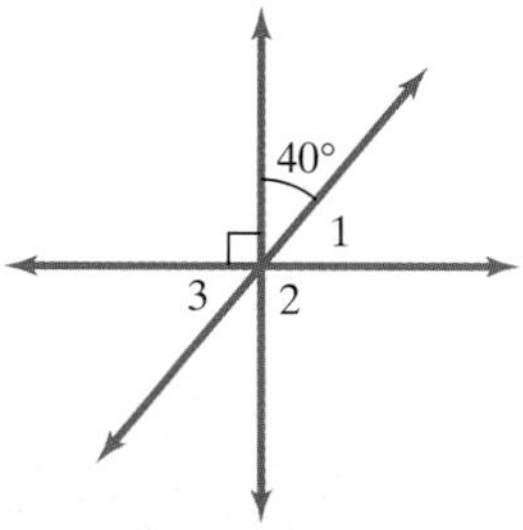

28.

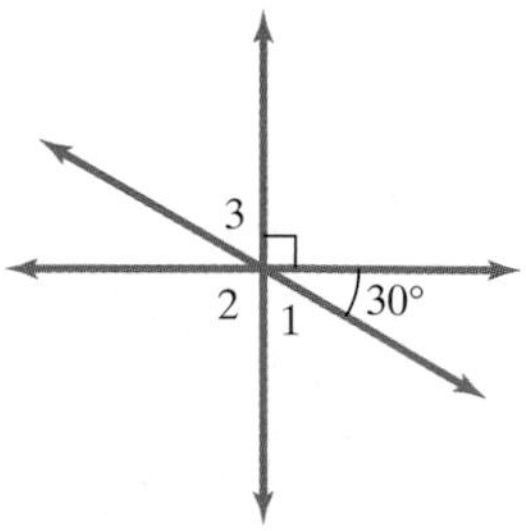

The figures for Exercises 29–30 show two parallel lines intersected by a transversal. One of the angle measures is given. Find the measure of each of the other seven angles.

29.

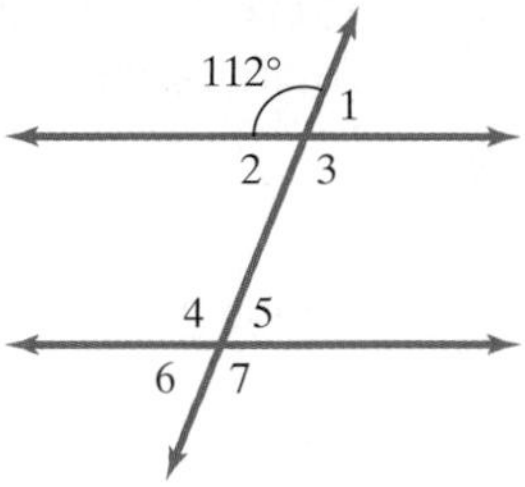

30.

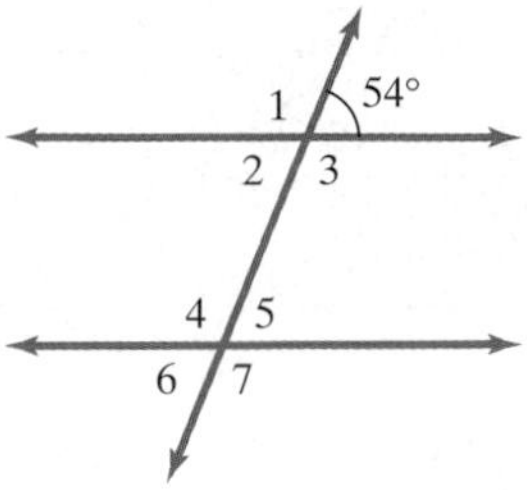

The figures for Exercises 31–32 show two parallel lines intersected by more than one transversal. Two of the angle measures are given. Find the measures of angles 1, 2, and 3.

31.

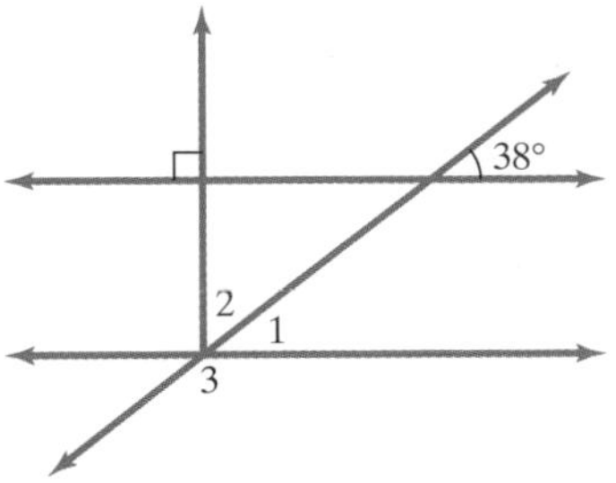

32.

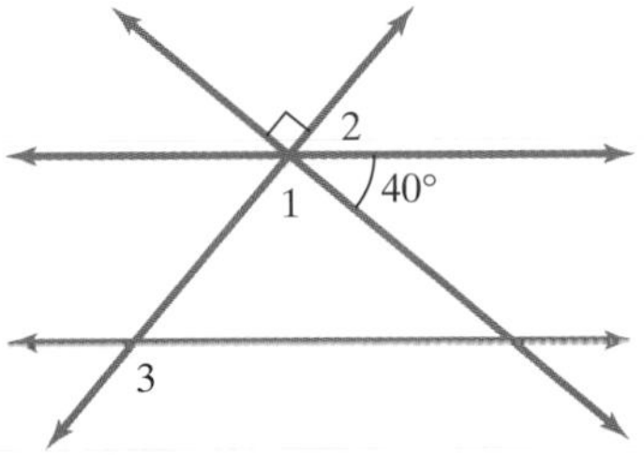

• Practice Plus

In Exercises 33–36, use an algebraic equation to find the measure of each angle that is represented in terms of x.

33.

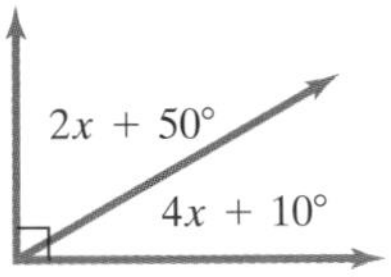

34.

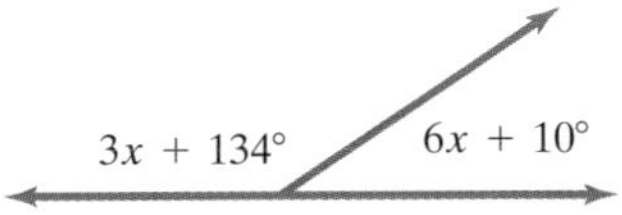

35.

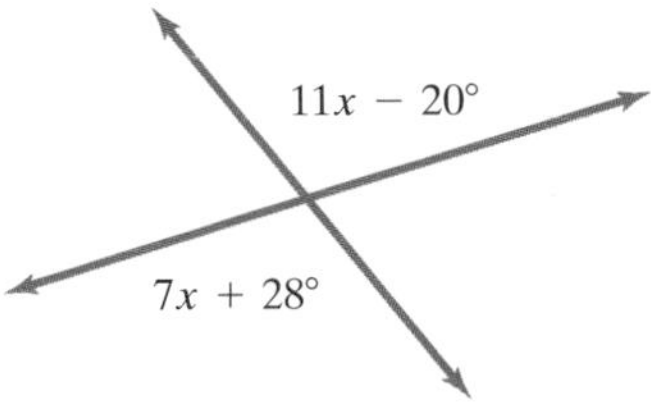

36.

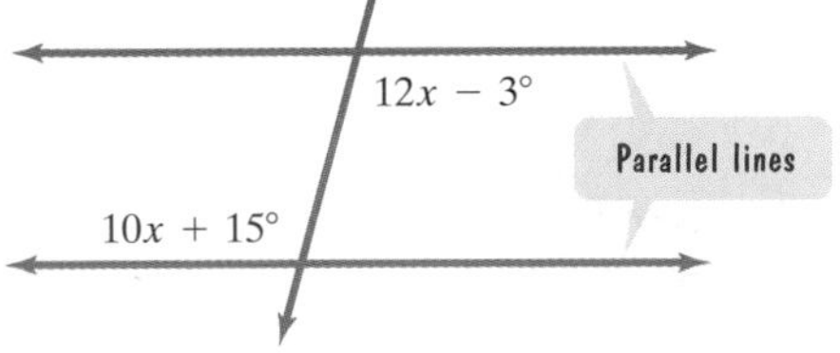

Because geometric figures consist of sets of points, we can apply set operations to obtain the union, ∪, or the intersection, ∩, of such figures. The union of two geometric figures is the set of points that belong to either of the figures or to both figures. The intersection of two geometric figures is the set of points common to both figures. In Exercises 37–44, use the line shown to find each set of points.

37. $\overline{AC} \cap \overline{BD}$ **38.** $\overline{AB} \cap \overline{BC}$ **39.** $\overline{AC} \cup \overline{BD}$

40. $\overline{AB} \cup \overline{BC}$ **41.** $\overrightarrow{BA} \cup \overrightarrow{BC}$ **42.** $\overrightarrow{CB} \cup \overrightarrow{CD}$

43. $\overrightarrow{AD} \cap \overrightarrow{DB}$ **44.** $\overrightarrow{AC} \cap \overrightarrow{CB}$

• Application Exercises

45. The picture shows the top of an umbrella in which all the angles formed by the spokes have the same measure. Find the measure of each angle.

46. Use the definition of parallel lines to explain the joke in this B.C. cartoon.

Reproduced by permission of John L. Hart FLP and Creators Syndicate, Inc.

47. The picture shows a window with parallel framing in which snow has collected in the corners. What property of parallel lines is illustrated by where the snow has collected?

• Writing in Mathematics

48. Describe the differences among lines, half-lines, rays, and line segments.

49. What is an angle and what determines its size?

50. Describe each type of angle: acute, right, obtuse, and straight.

51. What are complementary angles? Describe how to find the measure of an angle's complement.

52. What are supplementary angles? Describe how to find the measure of an angle's supplement.

53. Describe the difference between perpendicular and parallel lines.

54. If two parallel lines are intersected by a transversal, describe the location of the alternate interior angles, the alternate exterior angles, and the corresponding angles.

55. Describe everyday objects that approximate points, lines, and planes.

56. If a transversal is perpendicular to one of two parallel lines, must it be perpendicular to the other parallel line as well? Explain your answer.

• Critical Thinking Exercises

57. Use the figure shown at the top of the next column to select a pair of complementary angles from the following choices:

a. ∡1 and ∡4 **b.** ∡3 and ∡6

c. ∡2 and ∡5 **d.** ∡1 and ∡5.

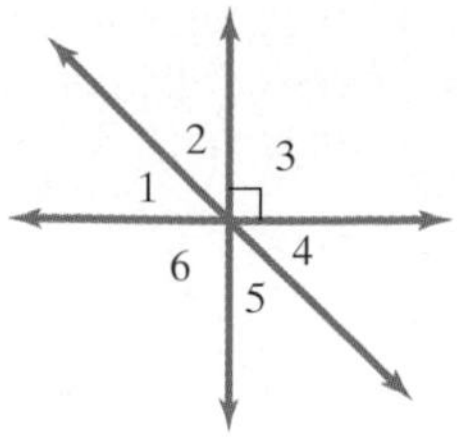

58. If $m\measuredangle AGB = m\measuredangle BGC$, and $m\measuredangle CGD = m\measuredangle DGE$, find $m\measuredangle BGD$.

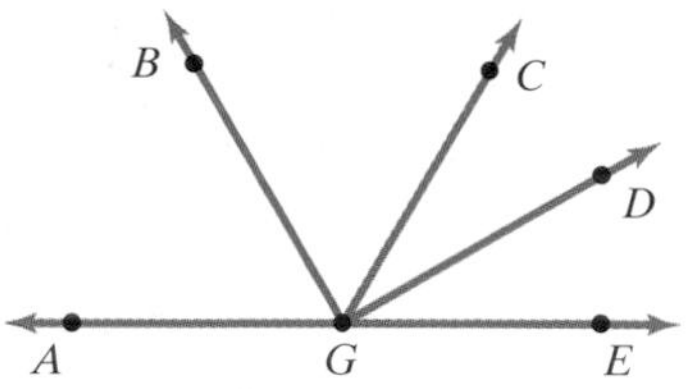

SECTION 10.2 • TRIANGLES

OBJECTIVES

1. Solve problems involving angle relationships in triangles.
2. Solve problems involving similar triangles.
3. Solve problems using the Pythagorean Theorem.

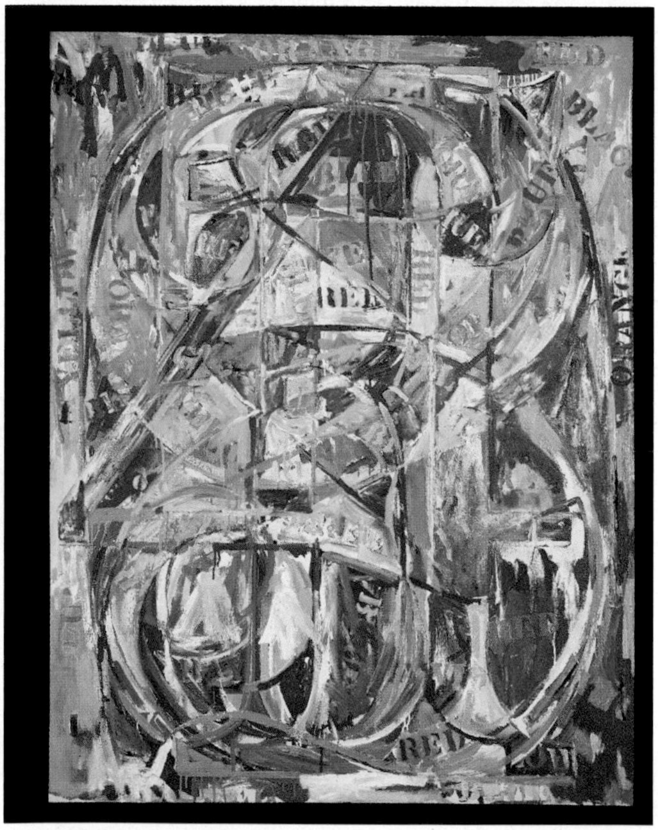

Jasper Johns "*0 Through 9*," 1961. Oil on canvas, 137 × 105 cm.
The Saatchi Collection, courtesy of the Leo Castelli Gallery. (c) Jasper Johns/ Licensed by VAGA, New York, NY

In Chapter 1, we defined *deductive reasoning* as the process of proving a specific conclusion from one or more general statements. A conclusion that is proved to be true through deductive reasoning is called a **theorem**. The Greek mathematician Euclid, who lived more than 2000 years ago, used deductive reasoning. In his 13-volume book, the *Elements*, Euclid proved over 465 theorems about geometric figures. Euclid's work established deductive reasoning as a fundamental tool of mathematics.

A **triangle** is a geometric figure that has three sides, all of which lie on a flat surface or plane. If you start at any point along the triangle and trace along the entire figure exactly once, you will end at the same point at which you started. Because the beginning point and ending point are the same, the triangle is called a **closed** geometric figure. Euclid used parallel lines to prove one of the most important properties of triangles: The sum of the measures of the three angles of any triangle is 180°. Here is how he did it. He began with the following general statement:

EUCLID'S ASSUMPTION ABOUT PARALLEL LINES

Given a line and a point not on the line, one and only one line can be drawn through the given point parallel to the given line.

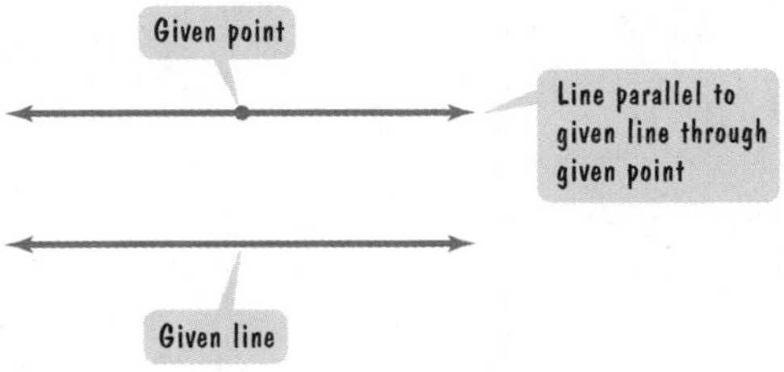

In Figure 10.14, triangle ABC represents any triangle. Using the general assumption given above, we draw a line through point B parallel to line AC.

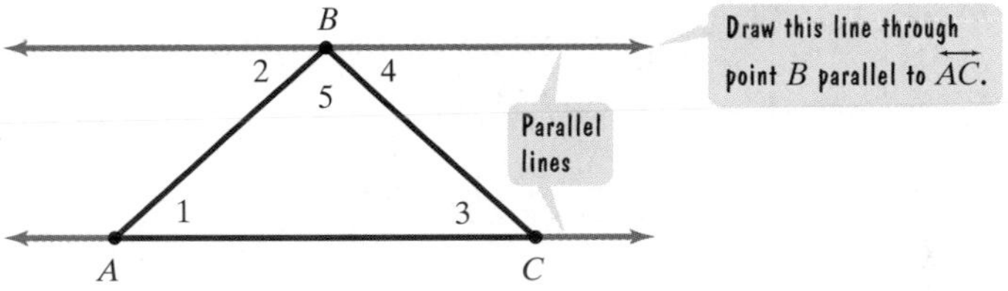

FIGURE 10.14

Because the lines are parallel, alternate interior angles have the same measure.

$$m\measuredangle 1 = m\measuredangle 2 \quad \text{and} \quad m\measuredangle 3 = m\measuredangle 4$$

Also observe that angles 2, 5, and 4 form a straight angle.

$$m\measuredangle 2 + m\measuredangle 5 + m\measuredangle 4 = 180°$$

Because $m\measuredangle 1 = m\measuredangle 2$, replace $m\measuredangle 2$ with $m\measuredangle 1$.

Because $m\measuredangle 3 = m\measuredangle 4$, replace $m\measuredangle 4$ with $m\measuredangle 3$.

$$m\measuredangle 1 + m\measuredangle 5 + m\measuredangle 3 = 180°$$

Because $\measuredangle 1$, $\measuredangle 5$, and $\measuredangle 3$ are the three angles of the triangle, this last equation shows that the measures of the triangle's three angles have a 180° sum.

THE ANGLES OF A TRIANGLE

The sum of the measures of the three angles of any triangle is 180°.

1 Solve problems involving angle relationships in triangles.

EXAMPLE 1 USING ANGLE RELATIONSHIPS IN TRIANGLES

Find the measure of angle A for triangle ABC in Figure 10.15.

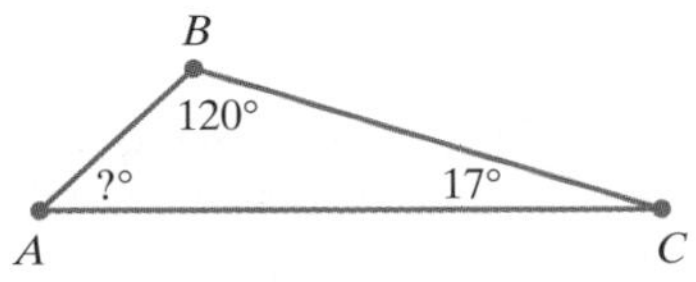

FIGURE 10.15

SOLUTION Because $m\measuredangle A + m\measuredangle B + m\measuredangle C = 180°$, we obtain

$m\measuredangle A + 120° + 17° = 180°.$ The sum of the measures of a triangle's three angles is 180°.

$m\measuredangle A + 137° = 180°$ Simplify: $120° + 17° = 137°$.

$m\measuredangle A = 180° - 137°$ Find the measure of A by subtracting 137° from both sides of the equation.

$m\measuredangle A = 43°$ Simplify.

CHECK POINT 1 In Figure 10.15, suppose that $m\measuredangle B = 116°$ and $m\measuredangle C = 15°$. Find $m\measuredangle A$.

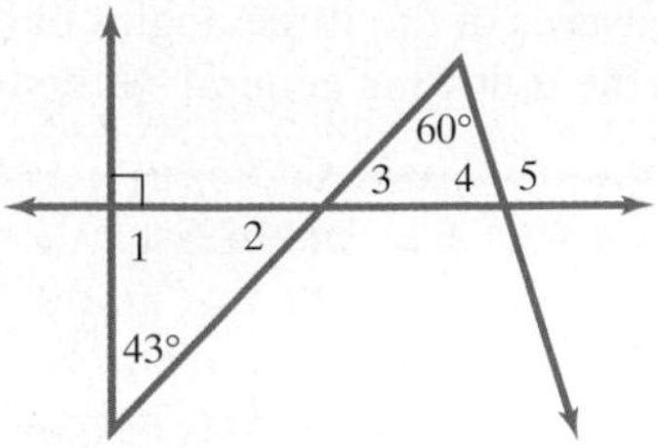

FIGURE 10.16

EXAMPLE 2 USING ANGLE RELATIONSHIPS IN TRIANGLES

Find the measures of angles 1 through 5 in Figure 10.16.

SOLUTION Because $\measuredangle 1$ is supplementary to the right angle, $m\measuredangle 1 = 90°$.

$m\measuredangle 2$ can be found using the fact that the sum of the measures of the angles of a triangle is 180°.

$m\measuredangle 1 + m\measuredangle 2 + 43° = 180°$	The sum of the measures of a triangle's three angles is 180°.
$90° + m\measuredangle 2 + 43° = 180°$	We previously found that $m\measuredangle 1 = 90°$.
$m\measuredangle 2 + 133° = 180°$	Simplify: $90° + 43° = 133°$.
$m\measuredangle 2 = 180° - 133°$	Subtract 133° from both sides.
$m\measuredangle 2 = 47°$	Simplify.

$m\measuredangle 3$ can be found using the fact that vertical angles have equal measures. $m\measuredangle 3 = m\measuredangle 2$. Thus, $m\measuredangle 3 = 47°$.

$m\measuredangle 4$ can be found using the fact that the sum of the measures of the angles of a triangle is 180°. Refer to the triangle at the top of Figure 10.16.

$m\measuredangle 3 + m\measuredangle 4 + 60° = 180°$	The sum of the measures of a triangle's three angles is 180°.
$47° + m\measuredangle 4 + 60° = 180°$	We previously found that $m\measuredangle 3 = 47°$.
$m\measuredangle 4 + 107° = 180°$	Simplify: $47° + 60° = 107°$.
$m\measuredangle 4 = 180° - 107°$	Subtract 107° from both sides.
$m\measuredangle 4 = 73°$	Simplify.

Finally, we can find $m\measuredangle 5$ by observing that angles 4 and 5 form a straight angle.

$m\measuredangle 4 + m\measuredangle 5 = 180°$	A straight angle measures 180°.
$73° + m\measuredangle 5 = 180°$	We previously found that $m\measuredangle 4 = 73°$.
$m\measuredangle 5 = 180° - 73°$	Subtract 73° from both sides.
$m\measuredangle 5 = 107°$	Simplify.

CHECK POINT 2 In Figure 10.16, suppose that the angle shown to measure 43° measures, instead, 36°. Further suppose that the angle shown to measure 60° measures, instead, 58°. Under these new conditions, find the measures of angles 1 through 5 in the figure.

Triangles can be described using characteristics of their angles or their sides.

TRIANGLES AND THEIR CHARACTERISTICS

Classification by Angles

Acute Triangle
All angles are acute.

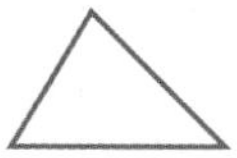

Right Triangle
One angle measures 90°.

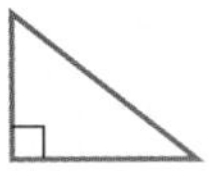

Obtuse Triangle
One angle is obtuse.

Classification by Sides

Isosceles Triangle
Two sides have equal length. (Angles opposite these sides have the same measure.)

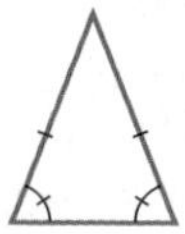

Equilateral Triangle
All sides have equal length. (Each angle measures 60°.)

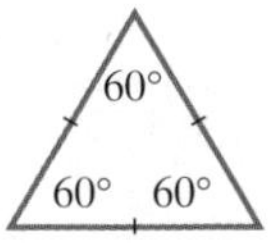

Scalene Triangle
No two sides are equal in length.

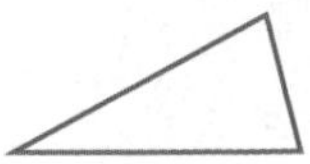

2 Solve problems involving similar triangles.

Similar Triangles

Shown in the margin is an international road sign. This sign is shaped just like the actual sign, although its size is smaller. Figures that have the same shape, but not the same size, are used in **scale drawings**. A scale drawing always pictures the exact shape of the object that the drawing represents. Architects, engineers, landscape gardeners, and interior decorators use scale drawings in planning their work.

Pedestrian crossing

Figures that have the same shape, but not necessarily the same size, are called **similar figures**. In Figure 10.17, triangles ABC and DEF are similar. Angles A and D measure the same number of degrees and are called **corresponding angles**. Angles C and F are corresponding angles, as are angles B and E. Angles with the same number of tick marks in Figure 10.17 are the corresponding angles.

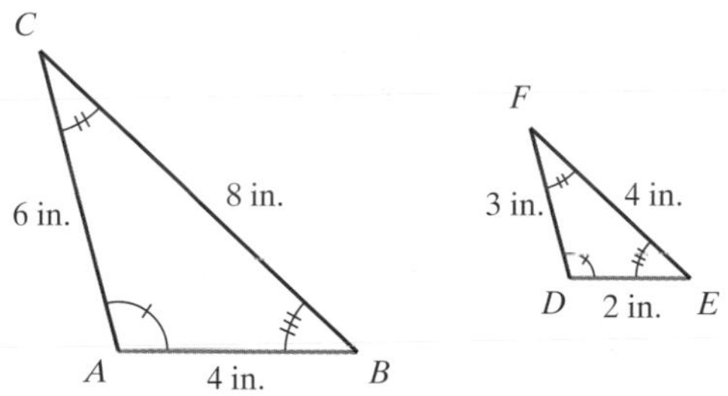

FIGURE 10.17

The sides opposite the corresponding angles are called **corresponding sides**. Thus, $\overline{CB}$ and $\overline{FE}$ are corresponding sides. $\overline{AB}$ and $\overline{DE}$ are also corresponding sides, as are $\overline{AC}$ and $\overline{DF}$. Corresponding angles measure the same number of degrees, but corresponding sides may or may not be the same length. For the triangles in Figure 10.17, each side in the smaller triangle is half the length of the corresponding side in the larger triangle.

The triangles in Figure 10.17 illustrate what it means to be **similar triangles**. **Corresponding angles have the same measure and the ratios of the lengths of the corresponding sides are equal.**

$$\frac{\text{length of } \overline{AC}}{\text{length of } \overline{DF}} = \frac{6 \cancel{\text{in.}}}{3 \cancel{\text{in.}}} = \frac{2}{1}; \quad \frac{\text{length of } \overline{CB}}{\text{length of } \overline{FE}} = \frac{8 \cancel{\text{in.}}}{4 \cancel{\text{in.}}} = \frac{2}{1}; \quad \frac{\text{length of } \overline{AB}}{\text{length of } \overline{DE}} = \frac{4 \cancel{\text{in.}}}{2 \cancel{\text{in.}}} = \frac{2}{1}$$

In similar triangles, the lengths of the corresponding sides are proportional. Thus,

AC represents the length of $\overline{AC}$, DF the length of $\overline{DF}$, and so on.

$$\frac{AC}{DF} = \frac{CB}{FE} = \frac{AB}{DE}.$$

If we know that two triangles are similar, we can set up a proportion to solve for the length of an unknown side.

BLITZER BONUS

Triangles in Construction Work

The triangle is used in most types of construction work, including bridges, radio towers, airplane wings, and pitched roofs. Its use in construction gives an object the quality of firmness, or stiffness, resulting in rigid, strong structures.

EXAMPLE 3 USING SIMILAR TRIANGLES

Triangles I and II in Figure 10.18 are similar. Find the missing length, x.

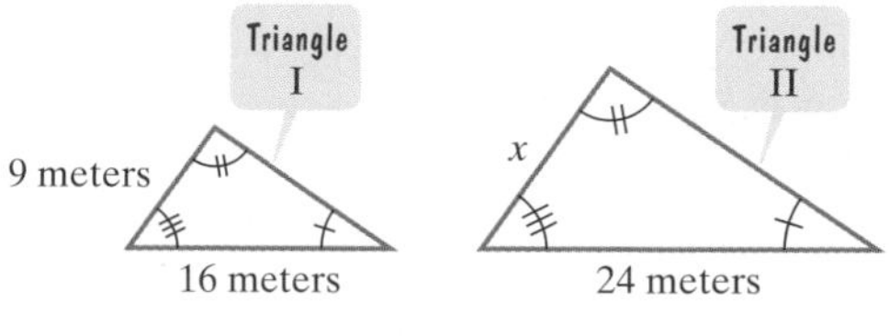

FIGURE 10.18

SOLUTION Because the triangles are similar, their corresponding sides are proportional.

Left side of △I

Corresponding side on left of △II

$$\frac{9}{x} = \frac{16}{24}$$

Bottom side of △I

Corresponding side on bottom of △II

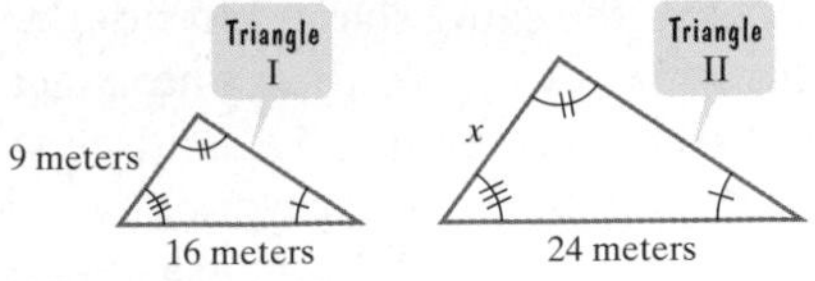

FIGURE 10.18 (repeated)

We solve $\frac{9}{x} = \frac{16}{24}$ for x by applying the cross-products principle for proportions that we discussed in Section 6.4: If $\frac{a}{b} = \frac{c}{d}$, then $ad = bc$.

$$16x = 9 \cdot 24 \quad \text{Apply the cross-products principle.}$$
$$16x = 216 \quad \text{Multiply: } 9 \cdot 24 = 216.$$
$$\frac{16x}{16} = \frac{216}{16} \quad \text{Divide both sides by 16.}$$
$$x = 13.5 \quad \text{Simplify.}$$

The missing length, x, is 13.5 meters.

CHECK POINT 3 The similar triangles in the figure have the same orientation, positioned so that corresponding parts are in the same relative position. Find the missing length, x.

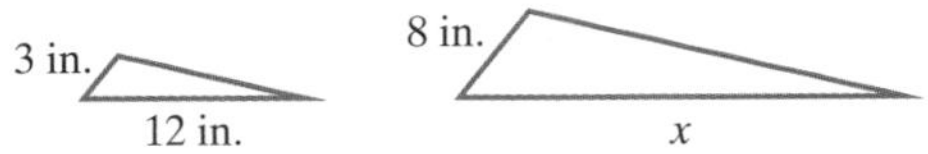

How can we quickly determine if two triangles are similar? **If the measures of two angles of one triangle are equal to those of two angles of a second triangle, then the two triangles are similar.** If the triangles are similar, then their corresponding sides are proportional.

EXAMPLE 4 PROBLEM SOLVING USING SIMILAR TRIANGLES

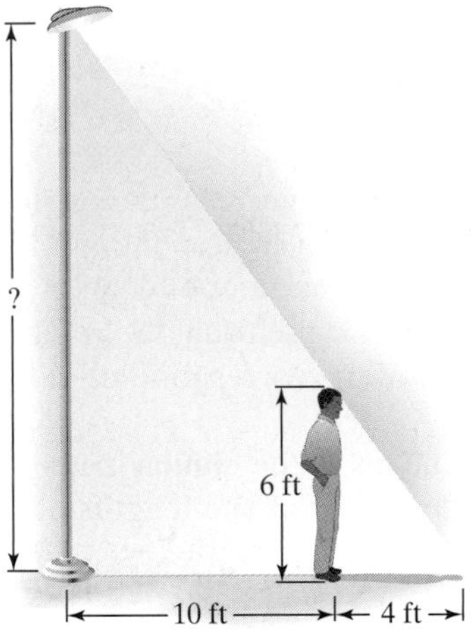

FIGURE 10.19

A man who is 6 feet tall is standing 10 feet from the base of a lamppost (see Figure 10.19). The man's shadow has a length of 4 feet. How tall is the lamppost?

SOLUTION The drawing in Figure 10.20 makes the similarity of the triangles easier to see. The large triangle with the lamppost on the left and the small triangle with the man on the left both contain 90° angles. They also share an angle. Thus, two angles of the large triangle are equal in measure to two angles of the small triangle. This means that the triangles are similar and their corresponding sides are proportional. We begin by letting x represent the height of the lamppost, in feet. Because corresponding sides of the two similar triangles are proportional,

$$\frac{x}{6} = \frac{14}{4}.$$

(Left side of big △: x; Corresponding side on left of small △: 6; Bottom side of big △: 14; Corresponding side on bottom of small △: 4)

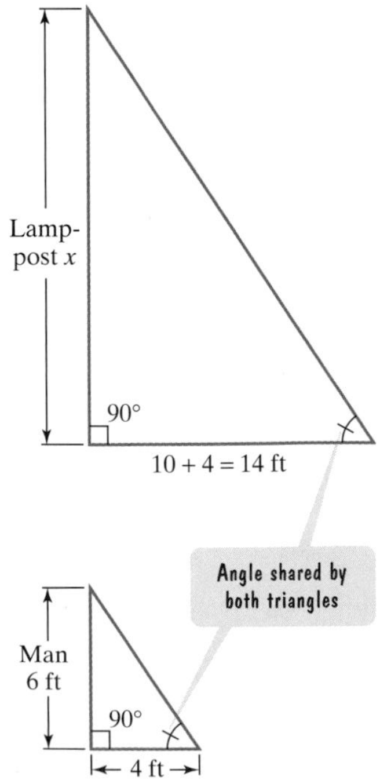

FIGURE 10.20

We solve for x by applying the cross-products principle.

$$4x = 6 \cdot 14 \quad \text{Apply the cross-products principle.}$$
$$4x = 84 \quad \text{Multiply: } 6 \cdot 14 = 84.$$
$$\frac{4x}{4} = \frac{84}{4} \quad \text{Divide both sides by 4.}$$
$$x = 21 \quad \text{Simplify.}$$

The lamppost is 21 feet tall.

CHECK POINT 4 Find the height of the lookout tower shown at the top of the next page using the figure that lines up the top of the tower with the top of a stick that is 2 yards long.

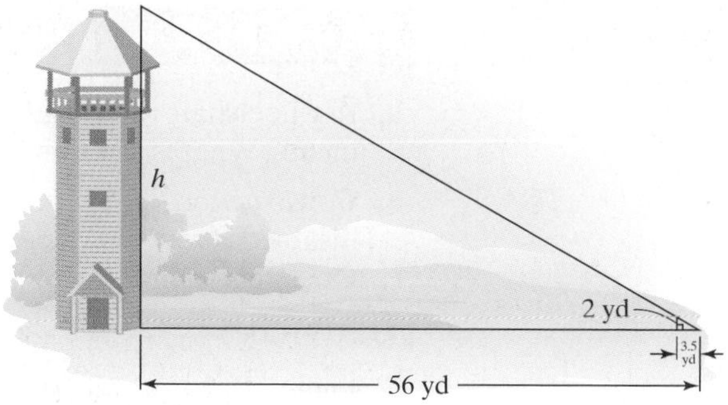

3 Solve problems using the Pythagorean Theorem.

The Pythagorean Theorem

The ancient Greek philosopher and mathematician Pythagoras (approximately 582–500 B.C.) founded a school whose motto was "All is number." Pythagoras is best remembered for his work with the **right triangle**, a triangle with one angle measuring 90°. The side opposite the 90° angle is called the **hypotenuse**. The other sides are called **legs**. Pythagoras found that if he constructed squares on each of the legs, as well as a larger square on the hypotenuse, the sum of the areas of the smaller squares is equal to the area of the larger square. This is illustrated in Figure 10.21.

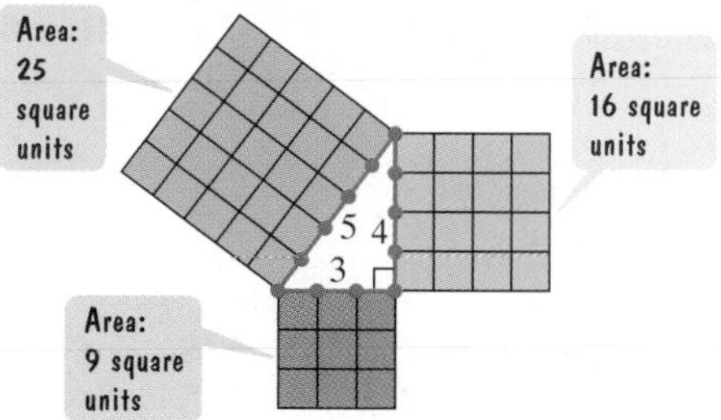

FIGURE 10.21 The area of the large square equals the sum of the areas of the smaller squares.

This relationship is usually stated in terms of the lengths of the three sides of a right triangle and is called the **Pythagorean Theorem.**

THE PYTHAGOREAN THEOREM

The sum of the squares of the lengths of the legs of a right triangle equals the square of the length of the hypotenuse.

If the legs have lengths a and b and the hypotenuse has length c, then

$$a^2 + b^2 = c^2.$$

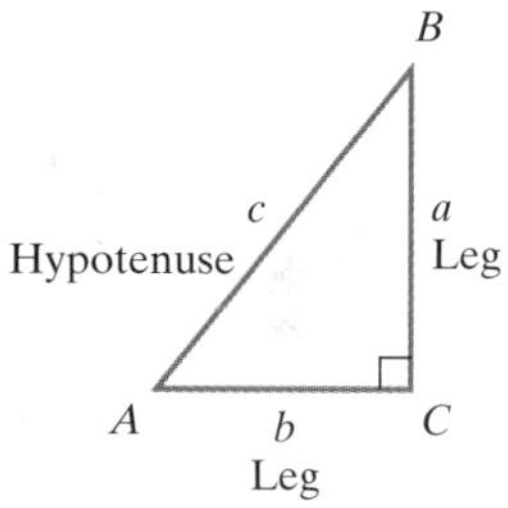

BLITZER BONUS

The Universality of Mathematics

Is mathematics discovered or invented? The "Pythagorean" Theorem, credited to Pythagoras, was known in China, from land surveying, and in Egypt, from pyramid building, centuries before Pythagoras was born. The same mathematics is often discovered/invented by independent researchers separated by time, place, and culture.

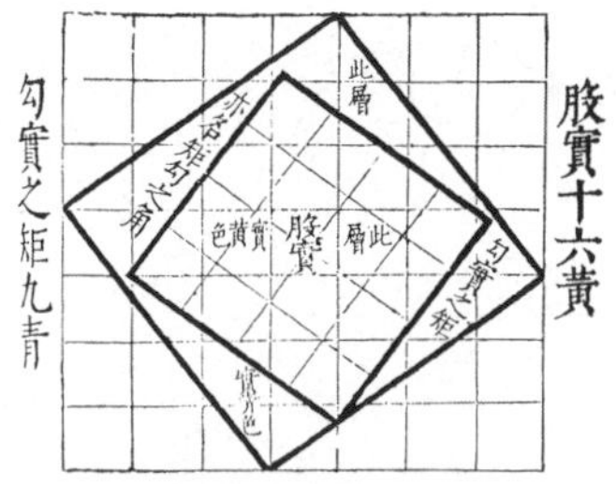

This diagram of the Pythagorean Theorem is from a Chinese manuscript dated as early as 1200 B.C.

EXAMPLE 5 USING THE PYTHAGOREAN THEOREM

Find the length of the hypotenuse c in the right triangle shown in Figure 10.22.

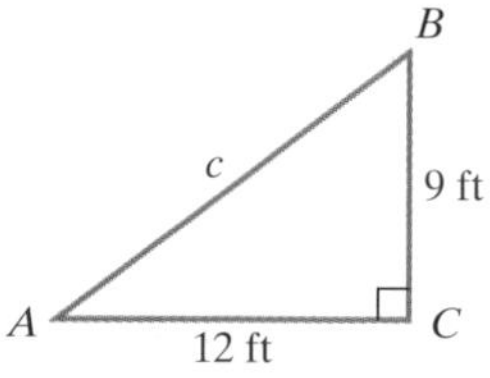

FIGURE 10.22

SOLUTION Let $a = 9$ and $b = 12$. Substituting these values into $c^2 = a^2 + b^2$ enables us to solve for c.

$c^2 = a^2 + b^2$ Use the symbolic statement of the Pythagorean Theorem.

$c^2 = 9^2 + 12^2$ Let $a = 9$ and $b = 12$.

$c^2 = 81 + 144$ $9^2 = 9 \cdot 9 = 81$ and $12^2 = 12 \cdot 12 = 144$.

$c^2 = 225$ Add.

$c = \sqrt{225} = 15$ Solve for c by taking the positive square root of 225.

The length of the hypotenuse is 15 feet.

CHECK POINT 5 Find the length of the hypotenuse in a right triangle whose legs have lengths 7 feet and 24 feet.

EXAMPLE 6 USING THE PYTHAGOREAN THEOREM

a. A wheelchair ramp with a length of 122 inches has a horizontal distance of 120 inches. What is the ramp's vertical distance?

b. Construction laws are very specific when it comes to access ramps for the disabled. Every vertical rise of 1 inch requires a horizontal run of 12 inches. Does this ramp satisfy the requirement?

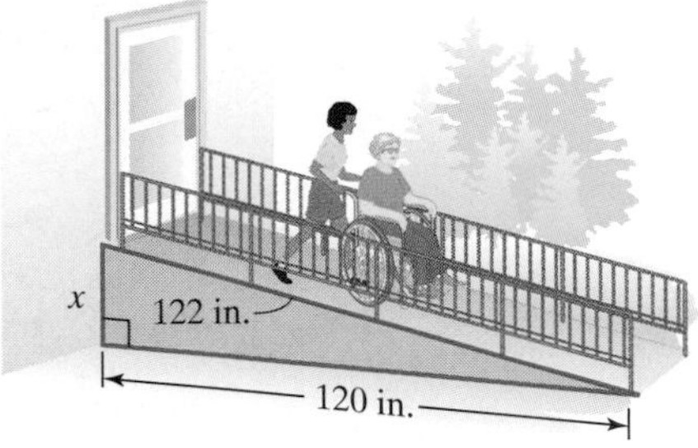

FIGURE 10.23

SOLUTION

a. Figure 10.23 shows the right triangle that is formed by the ramp, the wall, and the ground. We can find x, the ramp's vertical distance, using the Pythagorean Theorem.

(leg)^2	plus	(leg)^2	equals	(hypotenuse)^2
x^2	$+$	120^2	$=$	122^2

$x^2 + 120^2 = 122^2$ This is the equation resulting from the Pythagorean Theorem.

$x^2 + 14{,}400 = 14{,}884$ Square 120 and 122.

$x^2 = 484$ Isolate x^2 by subtracting 14,400 from both sides.

$x = \sqrt{484} = 22$ Solve for x by taking the positive square root of 484.

The ramp's vertical distance is 22 inches.

b. Every vertical rise of 1 inch requires a horizontal run of 12 inches. Because the ramp has a vertical distance of 22 inches, it requires a horizontal distance of 22(12) inches, or 264 inches. The horizontal distance is only 120 inches, so this ramp does not satisfy construction laws for access ramps for the disabled.

CHECK POINT 6 A radio tower is supported by two wires that are each 130 yards long and attached to the ground 50 yards from the base of the tower. How tall is the tower?

EXERCISE SET 10.2

• Practice Exercises

In Exercises 1–4, find the measure of angle A for the triangle shown.

1.

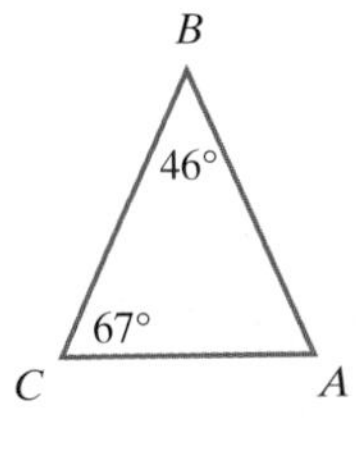

2.

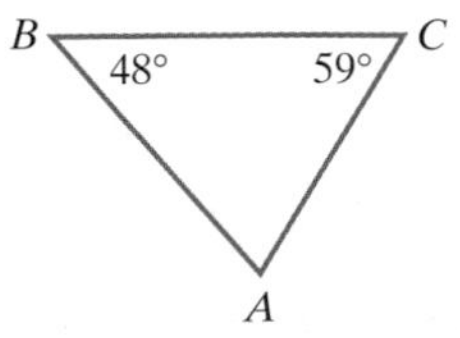

3.

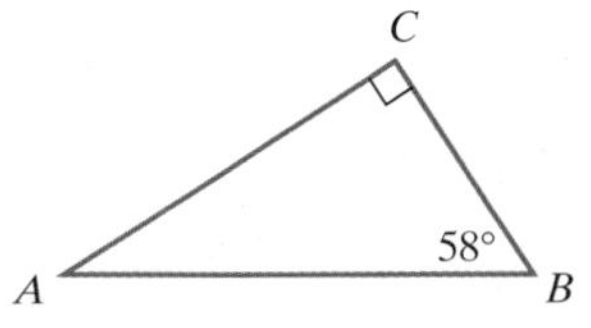

4.

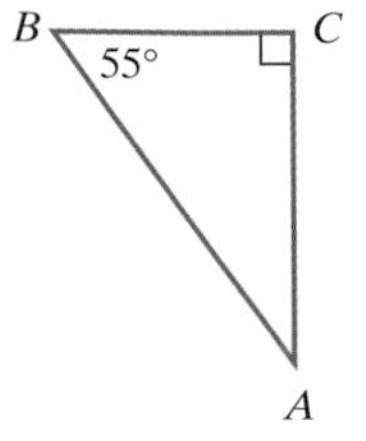

In Exercises 5–6, find the measures of angles 1 through 5 in the figure shown.

5.

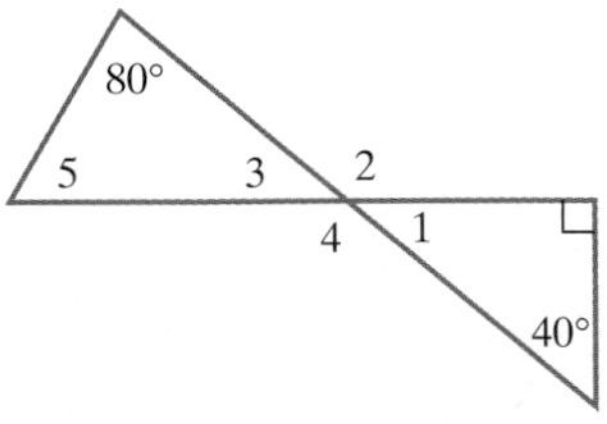

6.

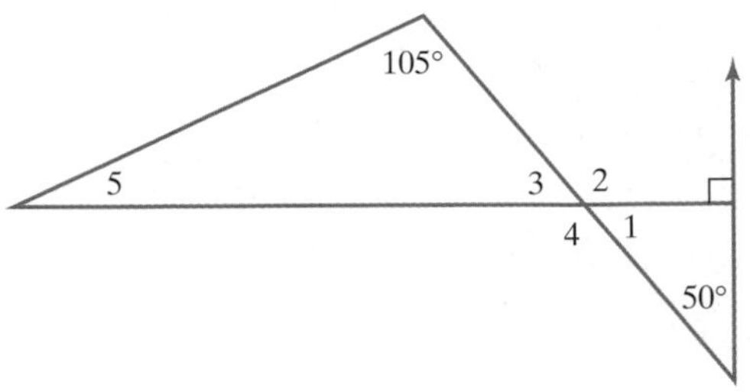

We have seen that isosceles triangles have two sides of equal length. The angles opposite these sides have the same measure. In Exercises 7–8, use this information to help find the measure of each numbered angle.

7.

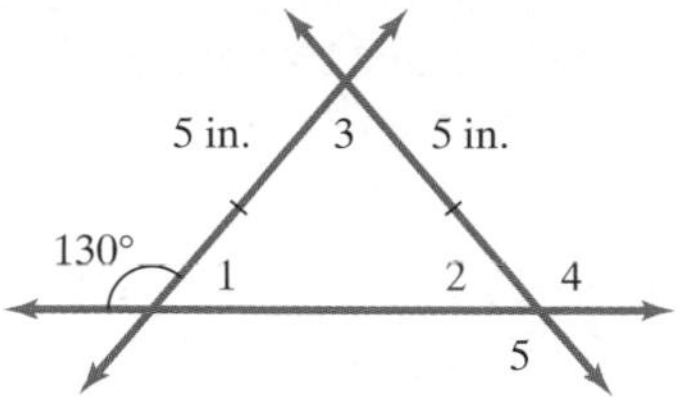

8.

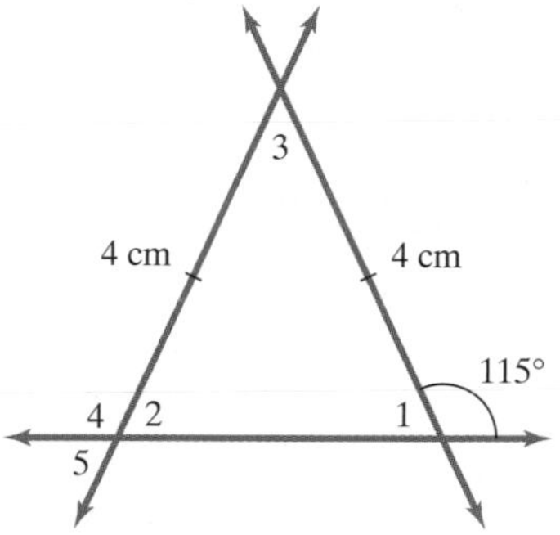

In Exercises 9–10, lines l and m are parallel. Find the measure of each numbered angle.

9.

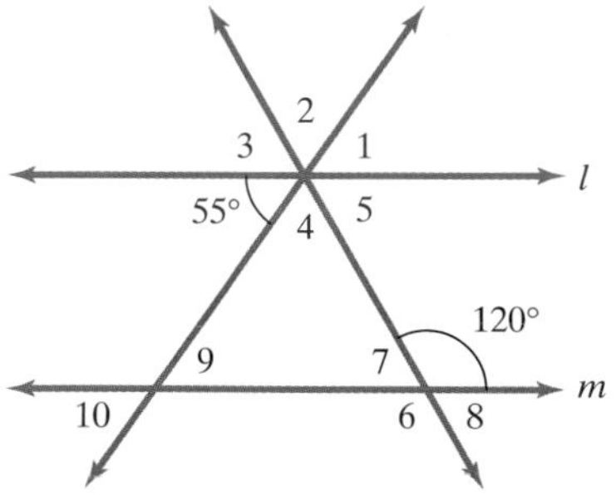

10.

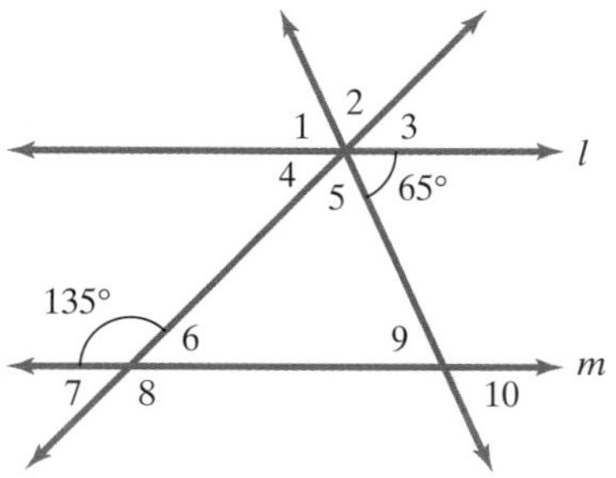

In Exercises 11–16, use similar triangles and the fact that corresponding sides are proportional to find the missing length, x.

11.

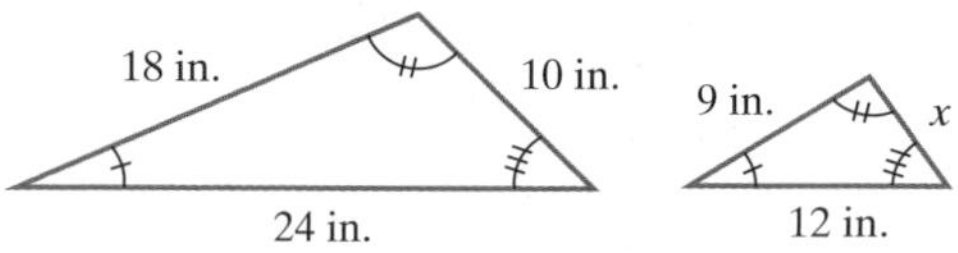

12.

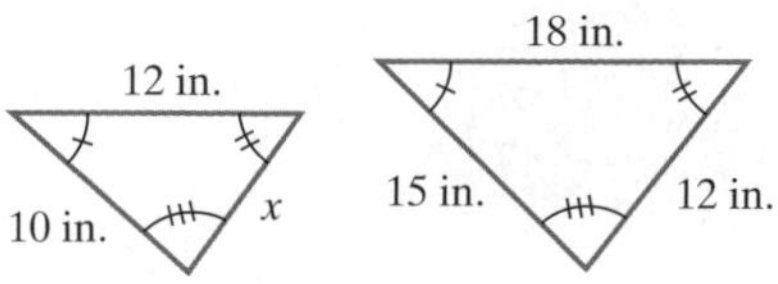

13.

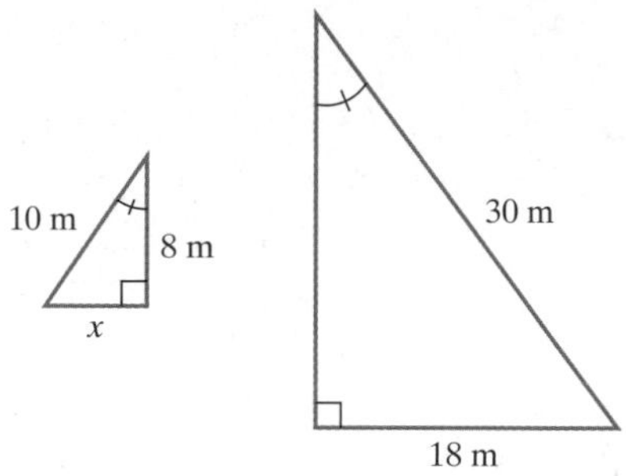

14.

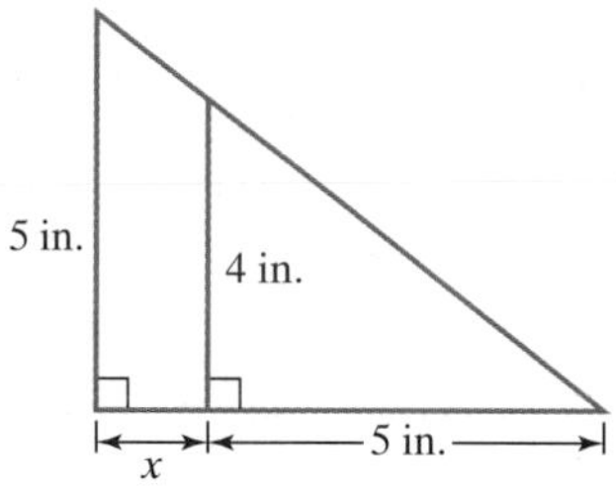

15.

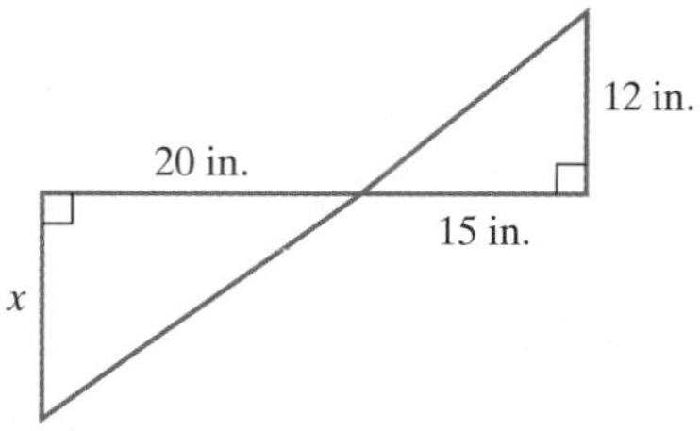

16.

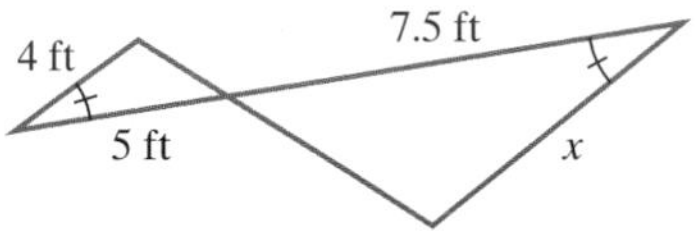

In Exercises 17–19, $\triangle ABC$ and $\triangle ADE$ are similar. Find the length of the indicated side.

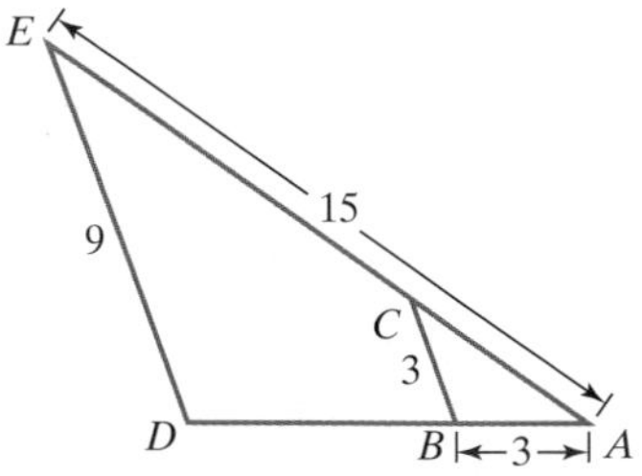

17. $\overline{CA}$ **18.** $\overline{DB}$ **19.** $\overline{DA}$

20. In the diagram for Exercises 17–19, suppose that you are not told that $\triangle ABC$ and $\triangle ADE$ are similar. Instead, you are given that $\overleftrightarrow{ED}$ and $\overleftrightarrow{CB}$ are parallel. Under these conditions, explain why the triangles must be similar.

In Exercises 21–26, use the Pythagorean Theorem to find the missing length in each right triangle. Use your calculator to find square roots, rounding, if necessary, to the nearest tenth.

21.

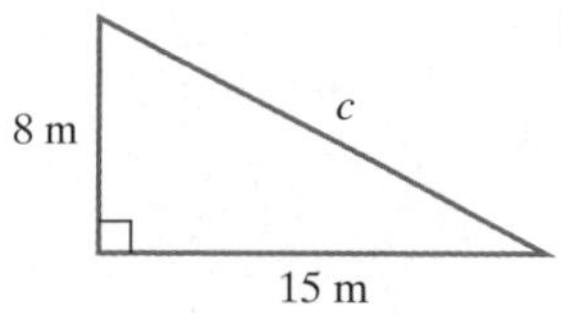

22.

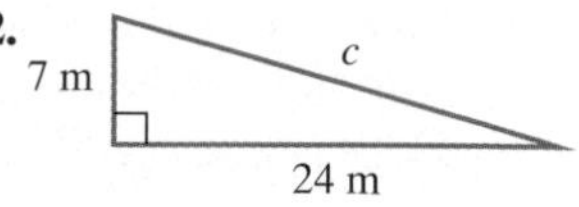

23.

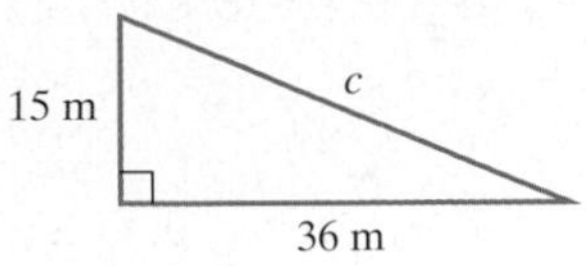

24.

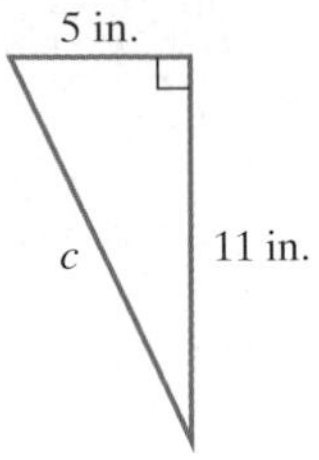

25.

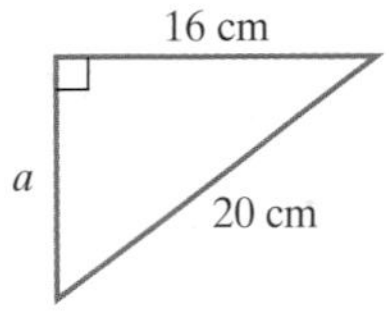

26.

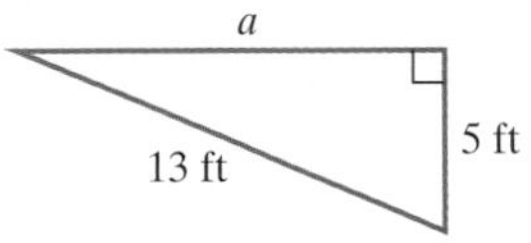

• Practice Plus

Use algebraic equations to solve Exercises 27–30.

27. Two angles of a triangle have the same measure and the third angle is 30° greater than the measure of the other two. Find the measure of each angle.

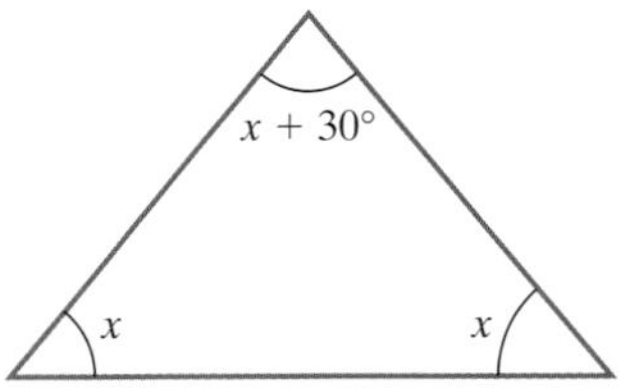

28. One angle of a triangle is three times as large as another. The measure of the third angle is 40° more than that of the smallest angle. Find the measure of each angle.

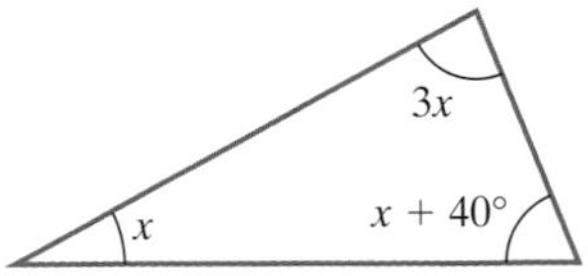

29. One angle of a triangle is twice as large as another. The measure of the third angle is 20° more than that of the smallest angle. Find the measure of each angle.

30. One angle of a triangle is three times as large as another. The measure of the third angle is 30° greater than that of the smallest angle. Find the measure of each angle.

31. The Pythagorean Theorem tells us that if a triangle is a right triangle, then $a^2 + b^2 = c^2$. State the converse of the Pythagorean Theorem.

In Exercises 32–34, use the fact that the converse of the Pythagorean Theorem is a true statement to determine if each triangle with sides of the given lengths is a right triangle.

32. 10 cm, 24 cm, 26 cm

33. 4 m, 8 m, 9 m

34. $\sqrt{2}$ ft, $\sqrt{7}$ ft, 3 ft

• Application Exercises

Use similar triangles to solve Exercises 35–36.

35. A person who is 5 feet tall is standing 80 feet from the base of a tree, and the tree casts an 86-foot shadow. The person's shadow is 6 feet in length. What is the tree's height?

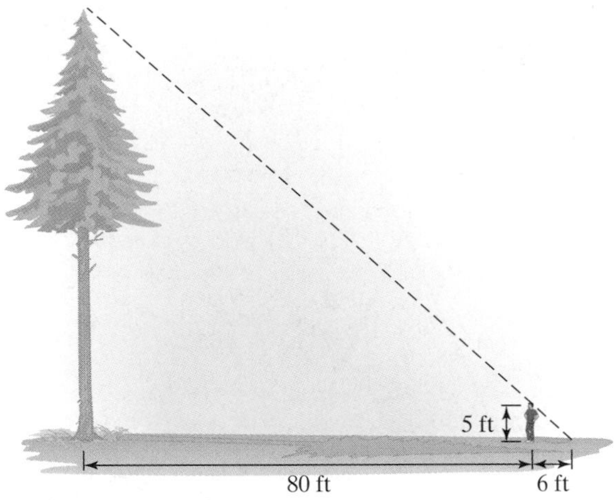

36. A tree casts a shadow 12 feet long. At the same time, a vertical rod 8 feet high casts a shadow that is 6 feet long. How tall is the tree?

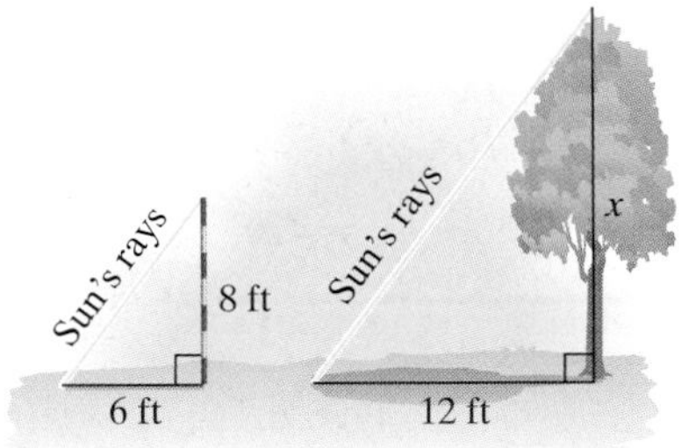

Use the Pythagorean Theorem to solve Exercises 37–45. Use your calculator to find square roots, rounding, if necessary, to the nearest tenth.

37. The doorway into a room is 4 feet wide and 8 feet high. What is the length of the longest rectangular panel that can be taken through this doorway diagonally?

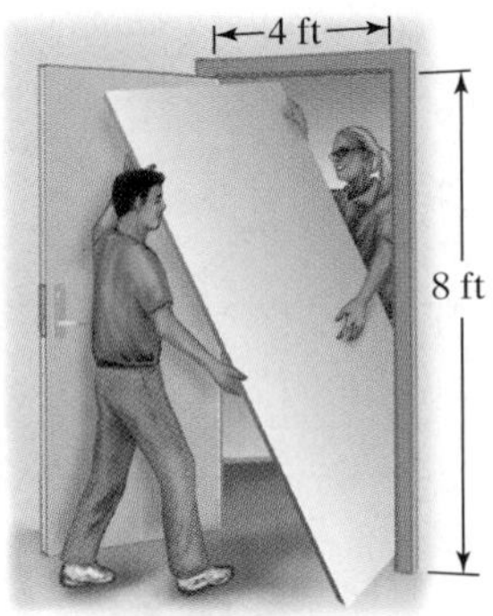

38. A baseball diamond is actually a square with 90-foot sides. What is the distance from home plate to second base?

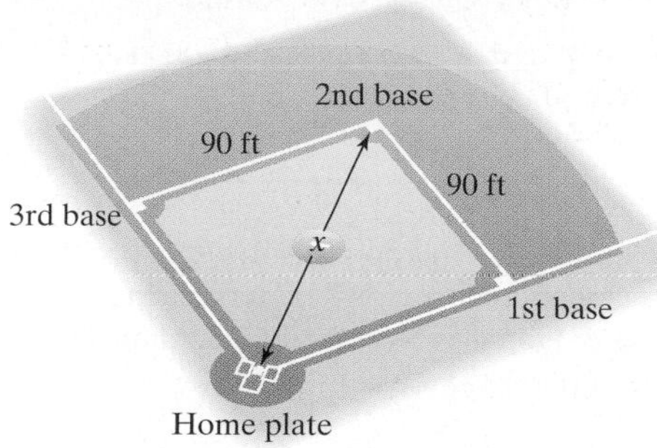

39. A 20-foot ladder is 15 feet from the house. How far up the house does the ladder reach?

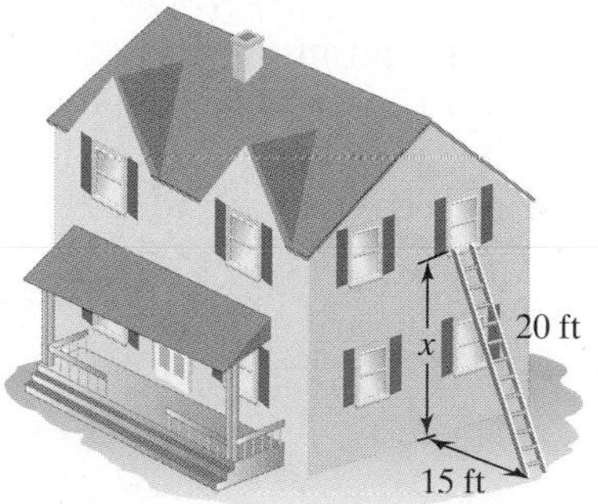

40. A supporting wire is to be attached to the top of a 50-foot antenna. If the wire must be anchored 50 feet from the base of the antenna, what length of wire is required?

41. A supporting wire is to be attached to the top of a 70-foot antenna. If the wire must be anchored 70 feet from the base of the antenna, what length of wire is required?

42. A rectangular park is 6 miles long and 3 miles wide. How long is a pedestrian route that runs diagonally across the park?

43. A rectangular park is 4 miles long and 2 miles wide. How long is a pedestrian route that runs diagonally across the park?

44. If construction costs are $150,000 per kilometer, find the cost of building the new road in the figure shown.

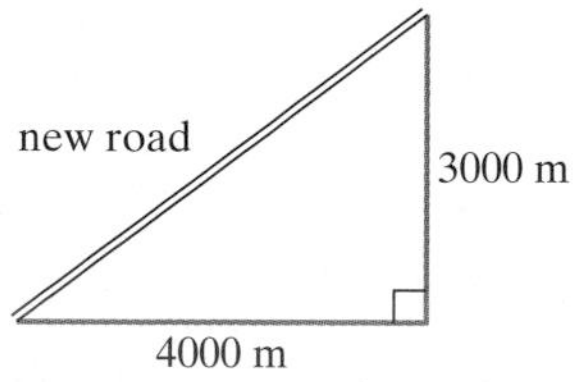

45. Picky, Picky, Picky This problem appeared on Arizona's high school exit exam:

Alex is building a ramp for a bike competition. He has two rectangular boards. One board is six meters and the other is five meters long. If the ramp has to form a right triangle, what should its height be?

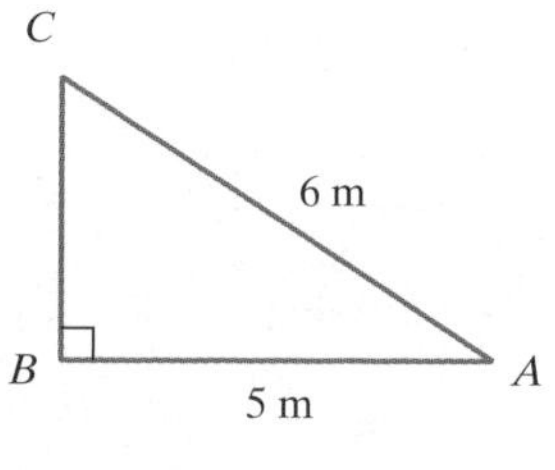

Students were asked to select the correct answer from the following options:

3 meters; 4 meters; 3.3 meters; 7.8 meters.

a. Among the available choices, which option best expresses the ramp's height? How many feet, to the nearest tenth of a foot, is this? Does a bike competition that requires riders to jump off these heights seem realistic? (ouch!)

b. Express the ramp's height to the nearest hundredth of a meter. By how many centimeters does this differ from the "correct" answer on the test? How many inches, to the nearest half inch, is this? Is it likely that a carpenter with a tape measure would make this error?

c. According to the problem, Alex has boards that measure 5 meters and 6 meters. A 6-meter board? How many feet, to the nearest tenth of a foot, is this? When was the last time you found a board of this length at Home Depot? (*Source*: *The New York Times*, April 24, 2005)

• Writing in Mathematics

46. If the measures of two angles of a triangle are known, explain how to find the measure of the third angle.

47. Can a triangle contain two right angles? Explain your answer.

48. What general assumption did Euclid make about a point and a line in order to prove that the sum of the measures of the angles of a triangle is 180°?

49. What are similar triangles?

50. If the ratio of the corresponding sides of two similar triangles is 1 to 1 $\left(\frac{1}{1}\right)$, what must be true about the triangles?

51. What are corresponding angles in similar triangles?

52. Describe how to identify the corresponding sides in similar triangles.

53. In your own words, state the Pythagorean Theorem.

54. In the 1939 movie *The Wizard of Oz*, upon being presented with a Th.D. (Doctor of Thinkology), the Scarecrow proudly exclaims, "The sum of the square roots of any two sides of an isosceles triangle is equal to the square root of the remaining side." Did the Scarecrow get the Pythagorean Theorem right? In particular, describe four errors in the Scarecrow's statement.

• Critical Thinking Exercises

55. Find the measure of angle R.

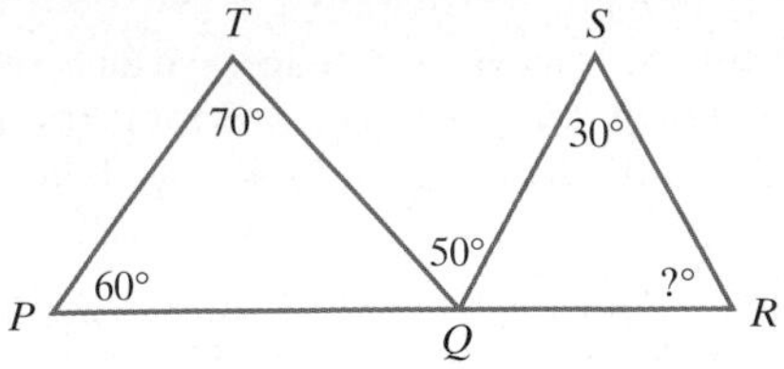

56. What is the length of $\overline{AB}$ in the accompanying figure?

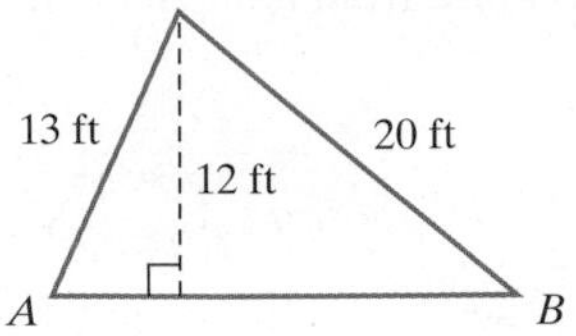

57. Use a quadratic equation to solve this problem. The width of a rectangular carpet is 7 meters shorter than the length, and the diagonal is 1 meter longer than the length. What are the carpet's dimensions?

SECTION 10.3 • POLYGONS, PERIMETER, AND TESSELLATIONS

OBJECTIVES

1. Name certain polygons according to the number of sides.
2. Recognize the characteristics of certain quadrilaterals.
3. Solve problems involving a polygon's perimeter.
4. Find the sum of the measures of a polygon's angles.
5. Understand tessellations and their angle requirements.

You have just purchased a beautiful plot of land in the country, shown in Figure 10.24. In order to have more privacy, you decide to put fencing along each of its four sides. The cost of this project depends on the distance around the four outside edges of the plot, called its **perimeter**, as well as the cost for each foot of fencing.

FIGURE 10.24

Your plot of land is a geometric figure: It has four straight sides that are line segments. The plot is on level ground, so that the four sides all lie on a flat surface, or plane. The plot is an example of a *polygon*. Any closed shape in the plane formed by three or more line segments is a **polygon**.

1 | Name certain polygons according to the number of sides.

A polygon is named according to the number of sides it has. We know that a three-sided polygon is called a **triangle**. A four-sided polygon is called a **quadrilateral**.

A polygon whose sides are all the same length and whose angles all have the same measure is called a **regular polygon**. Table 10.2 provides the names of six polygons. Also shown are illustrations of regular polygons.

TABLE 10.2 ILLUSTRATIONS OF REGULAR POLYGONS

Name	Picture
Triangle 3 sides	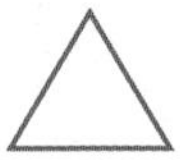
Quadrilateral 4 sides	
Pentagon 5 sides	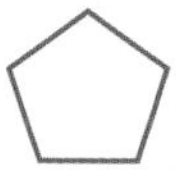

Name	Picture
Hexagon 6 sides	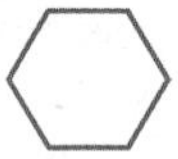
Heptagon 7 sides	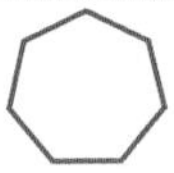
Octagon 8 sides	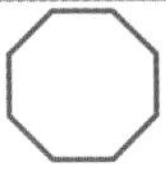

2 Recognize the characteristics of certain quadrilaterals.

Quadrilaterals

The plot of land in Figure 10.24 is a four-sided polygon, or a quadrilateral. However, when you first looked at the figure, perhaps you thought of the plot as a rectangular field. A **rectangle** is a special kind of quadrilateral in which both pairs of opposite sides are parallel, have the same measure, and whose angles are right angles. Table 10.3 presents some special quadrilaterals and their characteristics.

BLITZER BONUS

Bees and Regular Hexagons

Bees use honeycombs to store honey and house larvae. They construct honey storage cells from wax. Each cell has the shape of a regular hexagon. The cells fit together perfectly, preventing dirt or predators from entering. Squares or equilateral triangles would fit equally well, but regular hexagons provide the largest storage space for the amount of wax used.

TABLE 10.3 TYPES OF QUADRILATERALS

Name	Characteristics	Representation
Parallelogram	Quadrilateral in which both pairs of opposite sides are parallel and have the same measure. Opposite angles have the same measure.	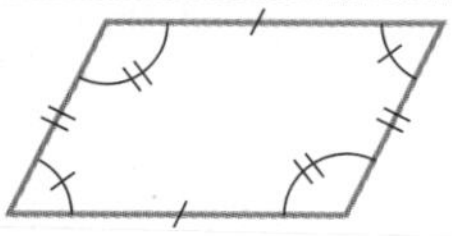
Rhombus	Parallelogram with all sides having equal length.	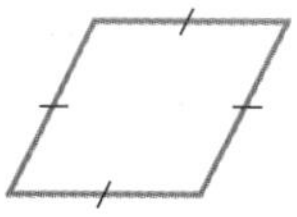
Rectangle	Parallelogram with four right angles. Because a rectangle is a parallelogram, opposite sides are parallel and have the same measure.	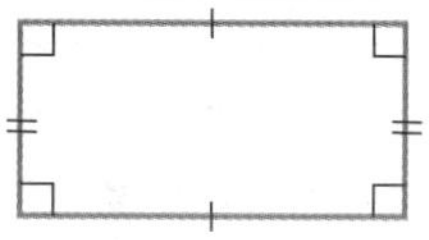
Square	A rectangle with all sides having equal length. Each angle measures 90°, and the square is a regular quadrilateral.	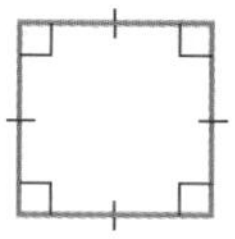
Trapezoid	A quadrilateral with exactly one pair of parallel sides.	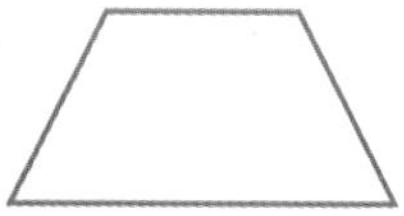

Perimeter

The **perimeter**, P, of a polygon is the sum of the lengths of its sides. Perimeter is measured in linear units, such as inches, feet, yards, meters, or kilometers.

Example 1 involves the perimeter of a rectangle. Because perimeter is the sum of the lengths of the sides, the perimeter of the rectangle shown in Figure 10.25 is $l + w + l + w$. This can be expressed as

$$P = 2l + 2w.$$

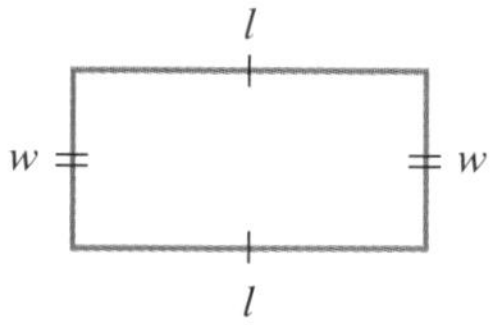

FIGURE 10.25 A rectangle with length l and width w

3 Solve problems involving a polygon's perimeter.

EXAMPLE 1 AN APPLICATION OF PERIMETER

The rectangular field we discussed at the beginning of this section (see Figure 10.24 on page 556) has a length of 42 yards and a width of 28 yards. If fencing costs \$5.25 per foot, find the cost to enclose the field with fencing.

SOLUTION We begin by finding the perimeter of the rectangle in yards. Using 3 ft = 1 yd and dimensional analysis, we express the perimeter in feet. Finally, we multiply the perimeter, in feet, by \$5.25 because the fencing costs \$5.25 per foot.

The length, l, is 42 yards and the width, w, is 28 yards. The perimeter of the rectangle is determined using the formula $P = 2l + 2w$.

$$P = 2l + 2w = 2 \cdot 42 \text{ yd} + 2 \cdot 28 \text{ yd} = 84 \text{ yd} + 56 \text{ yd} = 140 \text{ yd}$$

Because 3 ft = 1 yd, we use the unit fraction $\frac{3\text{ ft}}{1\text{ yd}}$ to convert from yards to feet.

$$140\text{ yd} = \frac{140\ \cancel{\text{yd}}}{1} \cdot \frac{3\text{ ft}}{1\ \cancel{\text{yd}}} = 140 \cdot 3\text{ ft} = 420\text{ ft}$$

The perimeter of the rectangle is 420 feet. Now we are ready to find the cost of the fencing. We multiply 420 feet by \$5.25, the cost per foot.

$$\text{Cost} = \frac{420\ \cancel{\text{feet}}}{1} \cdot \frac{\$5.25}{\cancel{\text{foot}}} = 420(\$5.25) = \$2205$$

The cost to enclose the rectangle with fencing is \$2205.

CHECK POINT 1 A rectangular field has a length of 50 yards and a width of 30 yards. If fencing costs \$6.50 per foot, find the cost to enclose the rectangle with fencing.

The Sum of the Measures of a Polygon's Angles

We know that the sum of the measures of the three angles of any triangle is 180°. We can use inductive reasoning to find the sum of the measures of the angles of any polygon. Start by drawing line segments from a single point where two sides meet so that nonoverlapping triangles are formed. This is done in Figure 10.26.

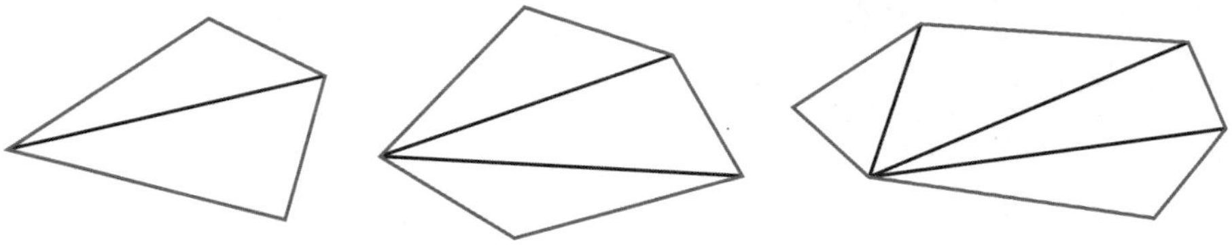

4 sides
2 triangles
Angle sum: 2(180°) = 360°

5 sides
3 triangles
Angle sum: 3(180°) = 540°

6 sides
4 triangles
Angle sum: 4(180°) = 720°

FIGURE 10.26

In each case, the number of triangles is two less than the number of sides of the polygon. Thus, for an n-sided polygon, there are $n - 2$ triangles. Because each triangle has an angle-measure sum of 180°, the sum of the measures for the angles in the $n - 2$ triangles is $(n - 2)180°$. Thus, the sum of the measures of the angles of an n-sided polygon is $(n - 2)180°$.

4 Find the sum of the measures of a polygon's angles.

THE ANGLES OF A POLYGON

The sum of the measures of the angles of a polygon with n sides is

$$(n - 2)180°.$$

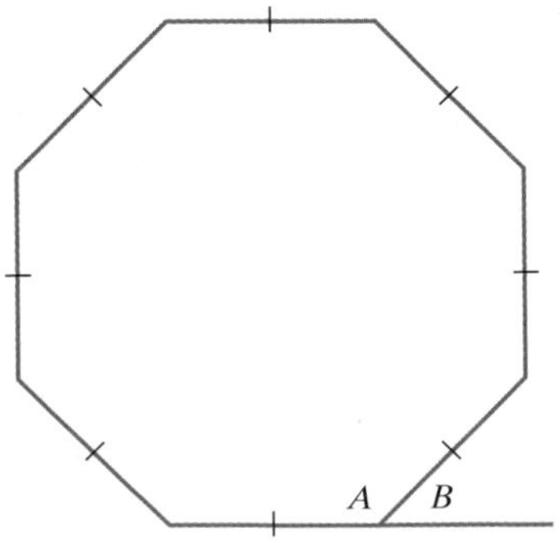

FIGURE 10.27 A regular octagon

EXAMPLE 2 USING THE FORMULA FOR THE ANGLES OF A POLYGON

a. Find the sum of the measures of the angles of an octagon.

b. Figure 10.27 shows a regular octagon. Find the measure of angle A.

c. Find the measure of exterior angle B.

SOLUTION

a. An octagon has eight sides. Using the formula $(n - 2)180°$ with $n = 8$, we can find the sum of the measures of its eight angles.

The sum of the measures of an octagon's angles

$$= (n - 2)180°$$
$$= (8 - 2)180°$$
$$= 6 \cdot 180°$$
$$= 1080°.$$

b. Examine the regular octagon in Figure 10.27. Note that all eight sides have the same length. Likewise, all eight angles have the same degree measure. Angle A is one of these eight angles. We find its measure by taking the sum of the measures of all eight angles, 1080°, and dividing by 8.

$$m\measuredangle A = \frac{1080°}{8} = 135°$$

c. Because $\measuredangle B$ is the supplement of $\measuredangle A$,

$$m\measuredangle B = 180° - 135° = 45°.$$

CHECK POINT 2

a. Find the sum of the measures of the angles of a 12-sided polygon.

b. Find the measure of an angle of a regular 12-sided polygon.

5 Understand tessellations and their angle requirements.

Tessellations

A relationship between geometry and the visual arts is found in an art form called *tessellations*. A **tessellation**, or **tiling**, is a pattern consisting of the repeated use of the same geometric figures to completely cover a plane, leaving no gaps and no overlaps. Figure 10.28 shows eight tessellations, each consisting of the repeated use of two or more regular polygons.

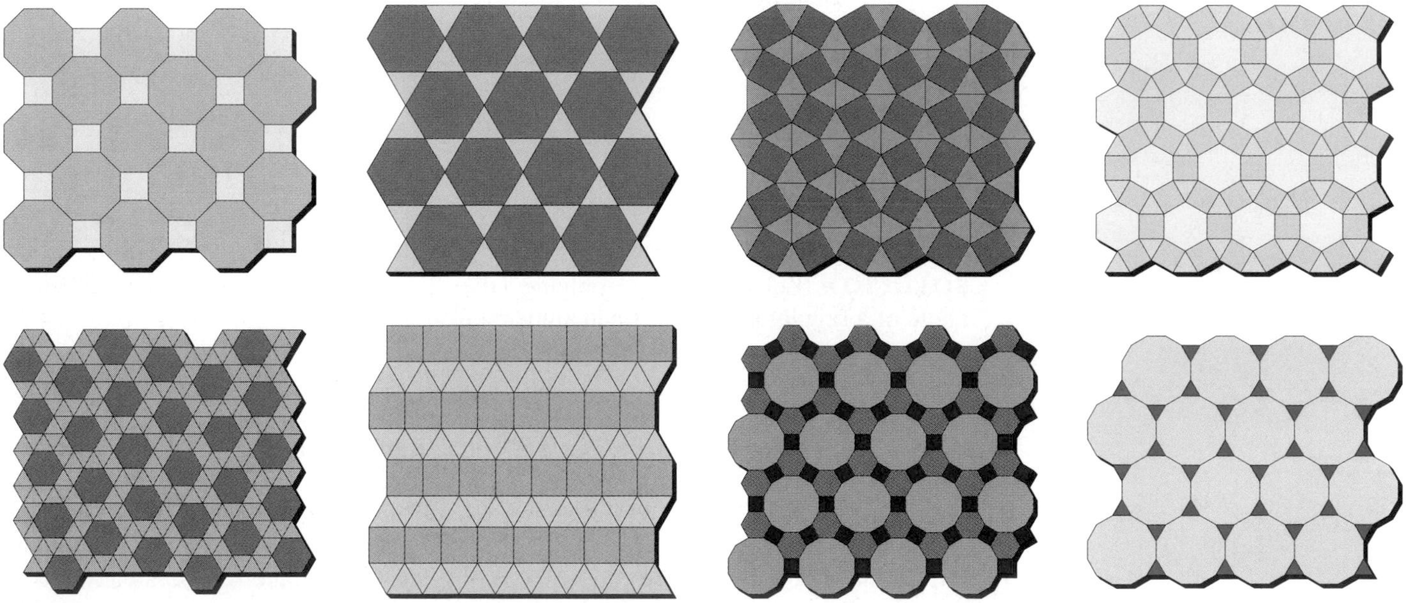

FIGURE 10.28 Eight tessellations formed by two or more regular polygons

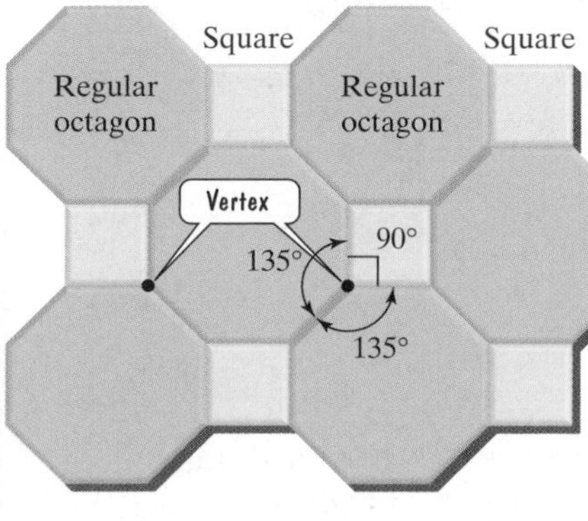

FIGURE 10.29

In each tessellation in Figure 10.28, the same types of regular polygons surround every vertex (intersection point). Furthermore, **the sum of the measures of the angles that come together at each vertex is 360°, a requirement for the formation of a tessellation.** This is illustrated in the enlarged version of the tessellation in Figure 10.29. If you select any vertex and count the sides of the polygons that touch it, you'll see that vertices are surrounded by two regular octagons and a square. Can you see why the sum of the angle measures at every vertex is 360°?

$$135° + 135° + 90° = 360°$$

In Example 2, we found that each angle of a regular octagon measures 135°.

Each angle of a square measures 90°.

The most restrictive condition in creating tessellations is that just *one type of regular polygon* may be used. With this restriction, there are only three possible tessellations, made from equilateral triangles or squares or regular hexagons, as shown in Figure 10.30.

FIGURE 10.30 The three tessellations formed using one regular polygon

Each tessellation is possible because the angle sum at every vertex is 360°:

Six equilateral triangles at each vertex: $60° + 60° + 60° + 60° + 60° + 60° = 360°$

Four squares at each vertex: $90° + 90° + 90° + 90° = 360°$

Three regular hexagons at each vertex: $120° + 120° + 120° = 360°.$

Each angle measures $\frac{(n-2)180°}{n} = \frac{(6-2)180°}{6} = 120°.$

EXAMPLE 3 ANGLE REQUIREMENTS OF TESSELLATIONS

Explain why a tessellation cannot be created using only regular pentagons.

SOLUTION Let's begin by applying $(n - 2)180°$ to find the measure of each angle of a regular pentagon. Each angle measures

$$\frac{(5-2)180°}{5} = \frac{3(180°)}{5} = 108°.$$

A requirement for the formation of a tessellation is that the measures of the angles that come together at each vertex is 360°. With each angle of a regular pentagon measuring 108°, Figure 10.31 shows that three regular pentagons fill in $3 \cdot 108° = 324°$ and leave a $360° - 324°$, or a 36°, gap. Because the 360° angle requirement cannot be met, no tessellation by regular pentagons is possible.

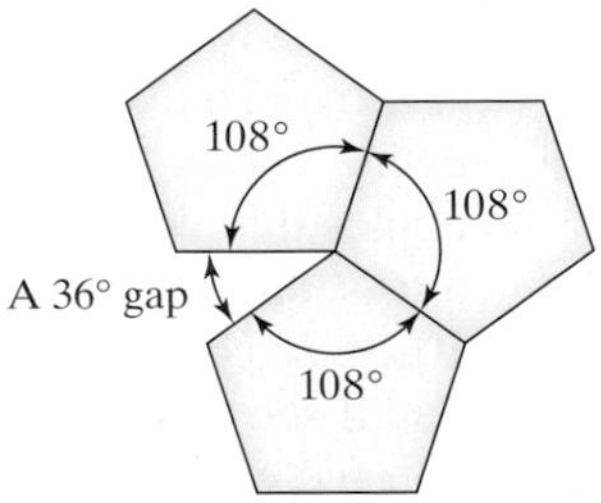

FIGURE 10.31

CHECK POINT 3 Explain why a tessellation cannot be created using only regular octagons.

"Drawings showing how a surface can be regularly filled with similar-shaped figures which are contiguous to one another, without leaving any open spaces, are my richest source of inspiration."

—M. C. ESCHER

Tessellations that are not restricted to the repeated use of regular polygons are endless in number. They are prominent in Islamic art, Italian mosaics, quilts, and ceramics. The Dutch artist M. C. Escher (1898–1972) created a dazzling array of prints, drawings, and paintings using tessellations composed of stylized interlocking animals. Escher's art reflects the mathematics that underlies all things, while creating surreal manipulations of space and perspective that make gentle fun of consensus reality.

M.C. Escher, *Symmetry Drawing, E85 (Lizard, Fish, Bat)*, drawn at Baarn, April, 1952, ink, pencil, watercolor.

EXERCISE SET 10.3

• Practice Exercises

In Exercises 1–4, use the number of sides to name the polygon.

1.

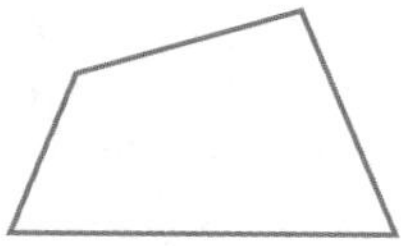

2.

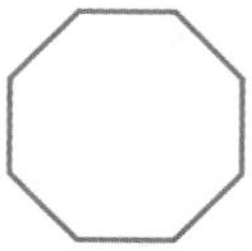

3.

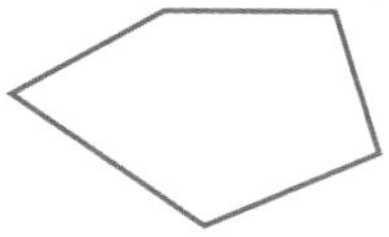

4.

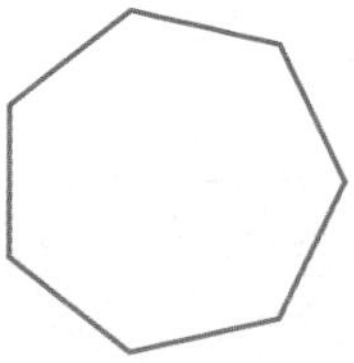

Use these quadrilaterals to solve Exercises 5–10.

a.

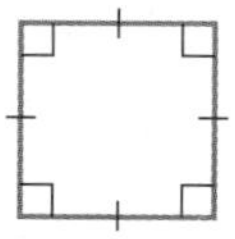

b.

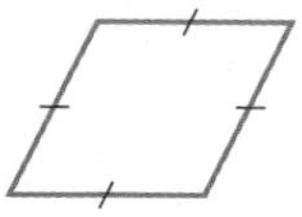

c.

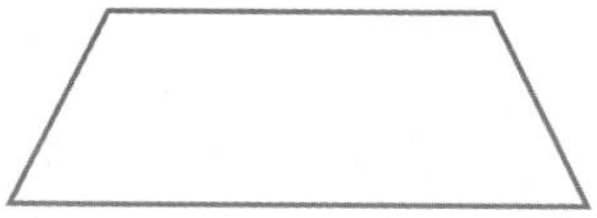

d.

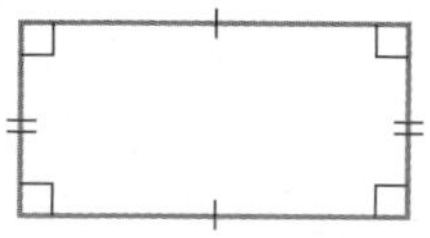

e.

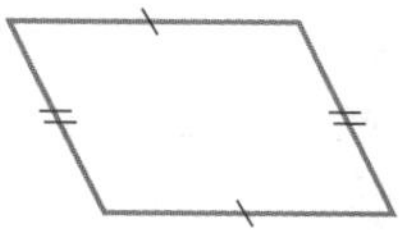

5. Which of these quadrilaterals have opposite sides that are parallel? Name these quadrilaterals.

6. Which of these quadrilaterals have sides of equal length that meet at a vertex? Name these quadrilaterals.

7. Which of these quadrilaterals have right angles? Name these quadrilaterals.

8. Which of these quadrilaterals do not have four sides of equal length? Name these quadrilaterals.

9. Which of these quadrilaterals is not a parallelogram? Name this quadrilateral.

10. Which of these quadrilaterals is/are a regular polygon? Name this/these quadrilateral(s).

In Exercises 11–20, find the perimeter of the figure named and shown. Express the perimeter using the same unit of measure that appears on the given side or sides.

11. Rectangle

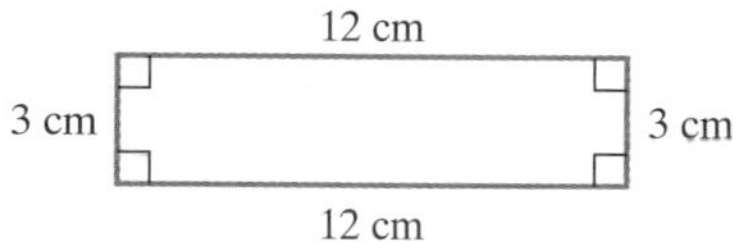

12. Parallelogram

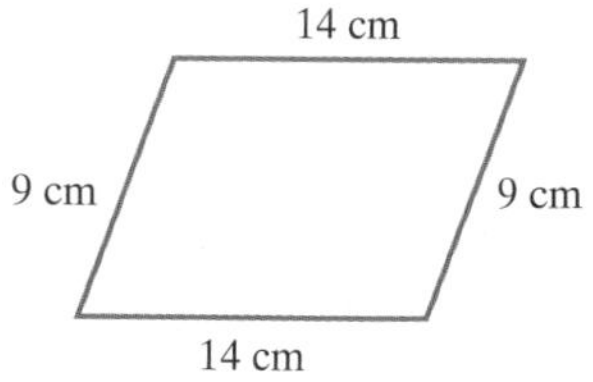

13. Rectangle

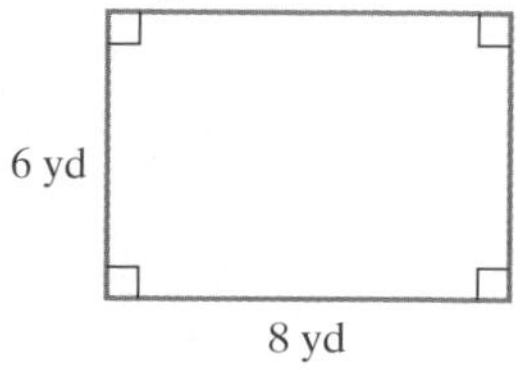

14. Rectangle

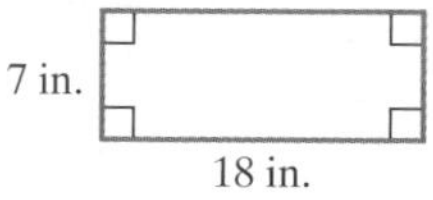

15. Square

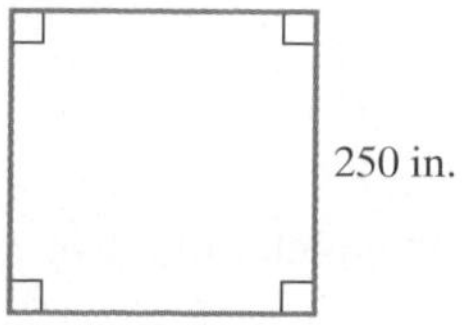

16. Square

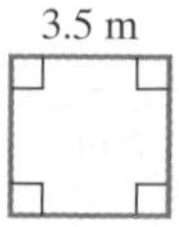

17. Triangle

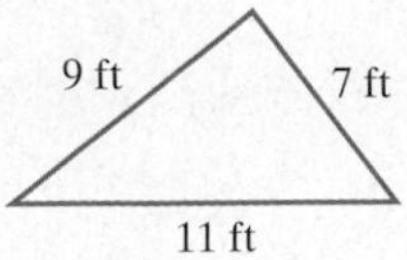

18. Triangle

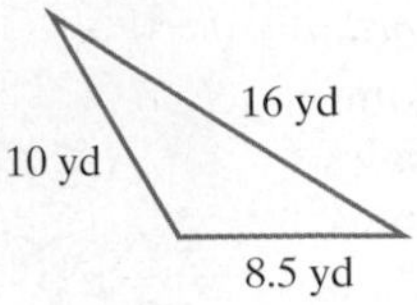

19. Equilateral triangle

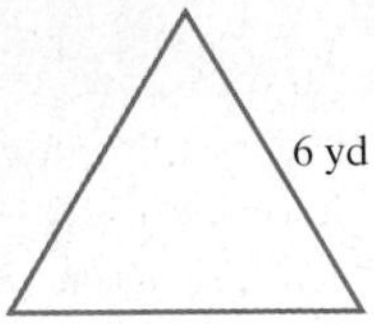

20. Regular hexagon

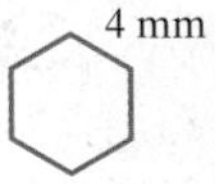

In Exercises 21–24, find the perimeter of the figure shown. Express the perimeter using the same unit of measure that appears on the given side or sides.

21.

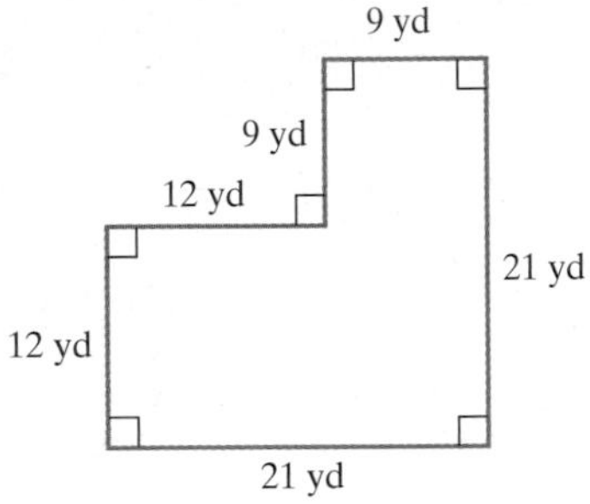

22.

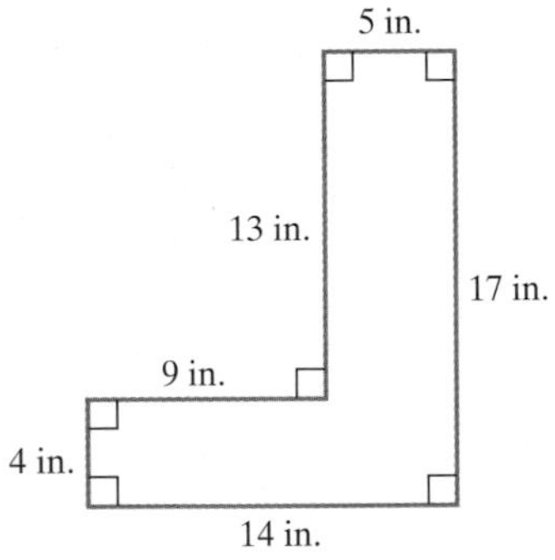

23.

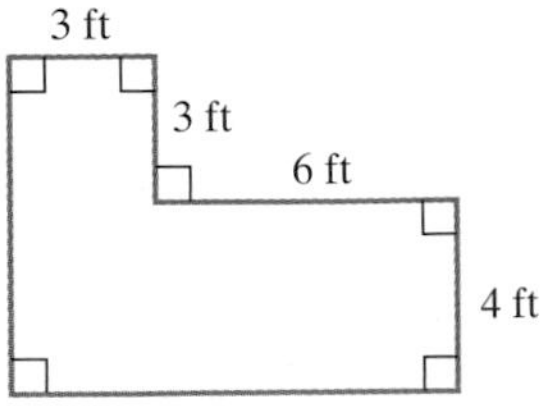

24.

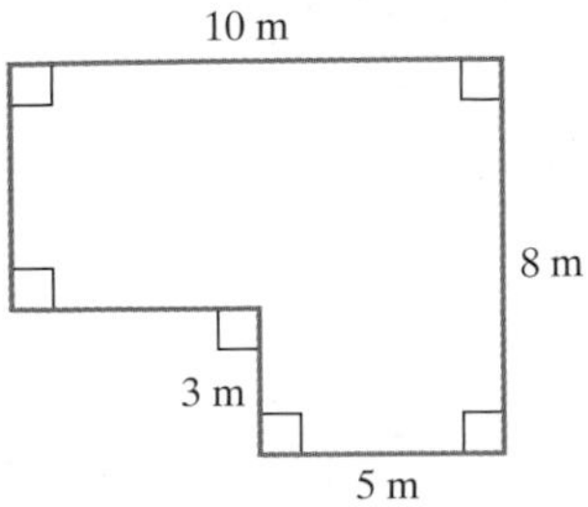

25. Find the sum of the measures of the angles of a five-sided polygon.

26. Find the sum of the measures of the angles of a six-sided polygon.

27. Find the sum of the measures of the angles of a quadrilateral.

28. Find the sum of the measures of the angles of a heptagon.

In Exercises 29–30, each figure shows a regular polygon. Find the measures of angle A and angle B.

29.

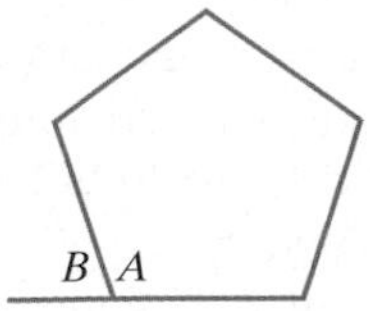

30.

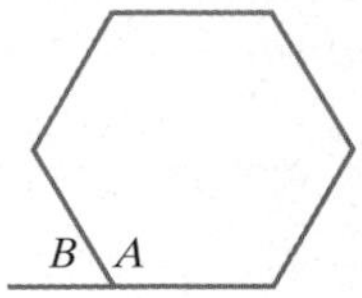

In Exercises 31–32, **a.** *Find the sum of the measures of the angles for the figure given;* **b.** *Find the measures of angle A and angle B.*

31.

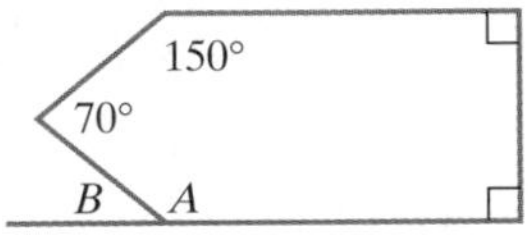

32.

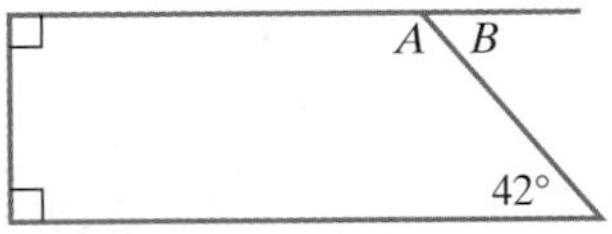

In Exercises 33–36, tessellations formed by two or more regular polygons are shown.

a. *Name the types of regular polygons that surround each vertex.*

b. *Determine the number of angles that come together at each vertex, as well as the measures of these angles.*

c. *Use the angle measures from part (b) to explain why the tessellation is possible.*

33.

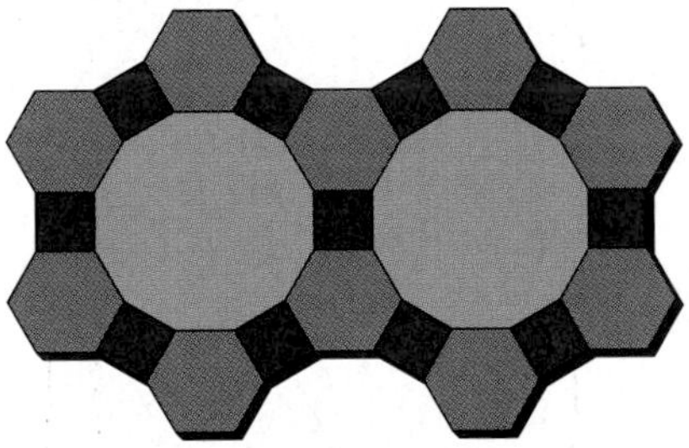

34.

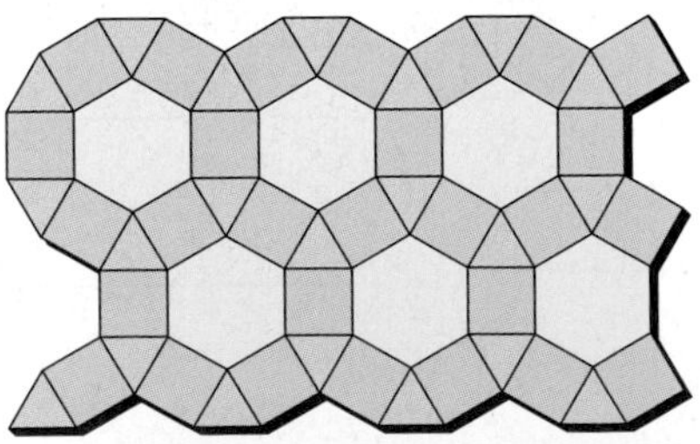

35.

36.

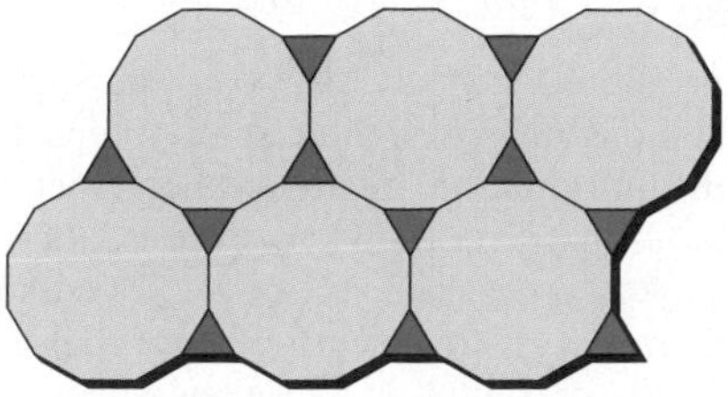

37. Can a tessellation be created using only regular nine-sided polygons? Explain your answer.

38. Can a tessellation be created using only regular ten-sided polygons? Explain your answer.

• Practice Plus

In Exercises 39–42, use an algebraic equation to determine each rectangle's dimensions.

39. A rectangular field is four times as long as it is wide. If the perimeter of the field is 500 yards, what are the field's dimensions?

40. A rectangular field is five times as long as it is wide. If the perimeter of the field is 288 yards, what are the field's dimensions?

41. An American football field is a rectangle with a perimeter of 1040 feet. The length is 200 feet more than the width. Find the width and length of the rectangular field.

42. A basketball court is a rectangle with a perimeter of 86 meters. The length is 13 meters more than the width. Find the width and length of the basketball court.

In Exercises 43–44, use algebraic equations to find the measure of each angle that is represented in terms of x.

43.

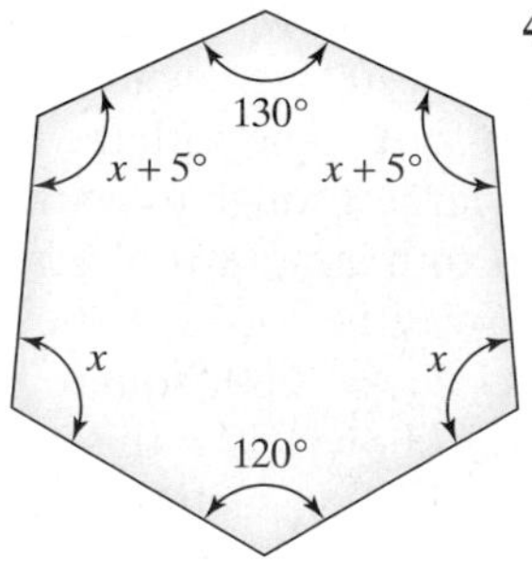

44.

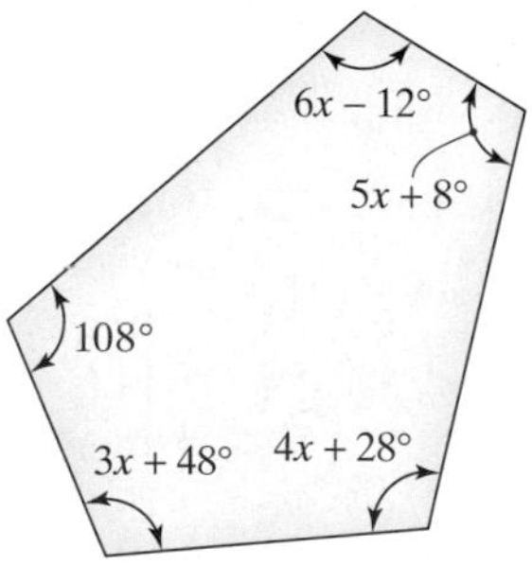

In the figure shown, the artist has cunningly distorted the "regular" polygons to create a fraudulent tessellation with discrepancies that are too subtle for the eye to notice. In Exercises 41–42, you will use mathematics, not your eyes, to observe the irregularities.

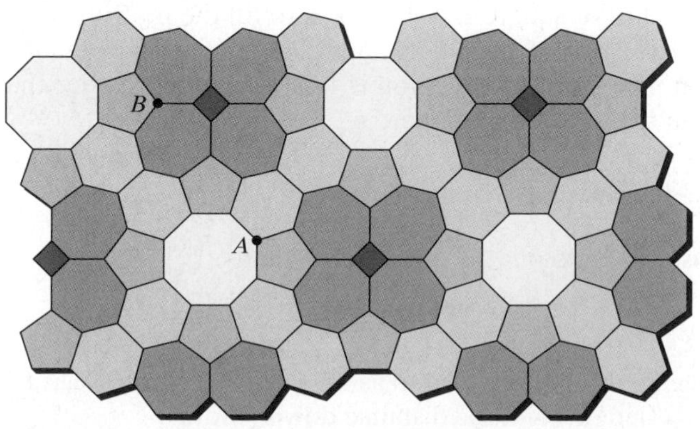

45. Find the sum of the angle measures at vertex A. Then explain why the tessellation is a fake.

46. Find the sum of the angle measures at vertex B. Then explain why the tessellation is a fake.

• Application Exercises

47. A school playground is in the shape of a rectangle 400 feet long and 200 feet wide. If fencing costs $14 per yard, what will it cost to place fencing around the playground?

48. A rectangular field is 70 feet long and 30 feet wide. If fencing costs $8 per yard, how much will it cost to enclose the field?

49. One side of a square flower bed is 8 feet long. How many plants are needed if they are to be spaced 8 inches apart around the outside of the bed?

50. What will it cost to place baseboard around the region shown if the baseboard costs $0.25 per foot? No baseboard is needed for the 2-foot doorway.

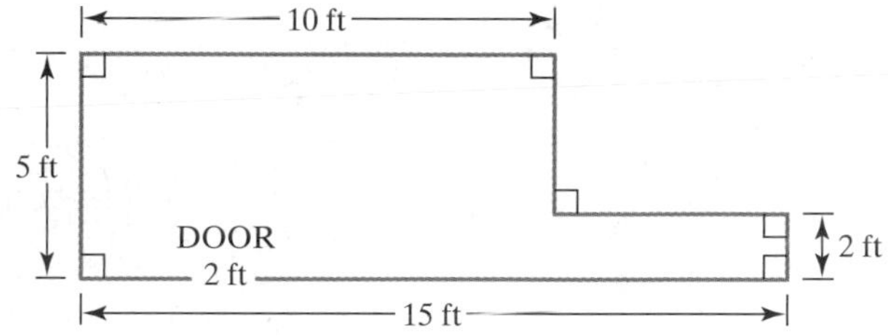

• Writing in Mathematics

51. What is a polygon?

52. Explain why rectangles and rhombuses are also parallelograms.

53. Explain why every square is a rectangle, a rhombus, a parallelogram, a quadrilateral, and a polygon.

54. Explain why a square is a regular polygon, but a rhombus is not.

55. Using words only, describe how to find the perimeter of a rectangle.

56. Describe a practical situation in which you needed to apply the concept of a geometric figure's perimeter.

57. Describe how to find the measure of an angle of a regular pentagon.

• Critical Thinking Exercises

In Exercises 58–59, write an algebraic expression that represents the perimeter of the figure shown.

58.

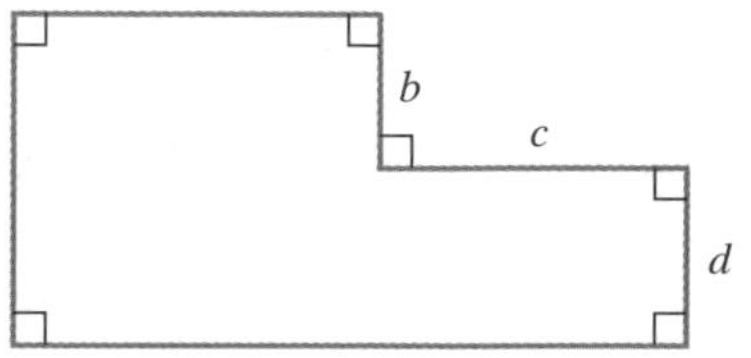

59.

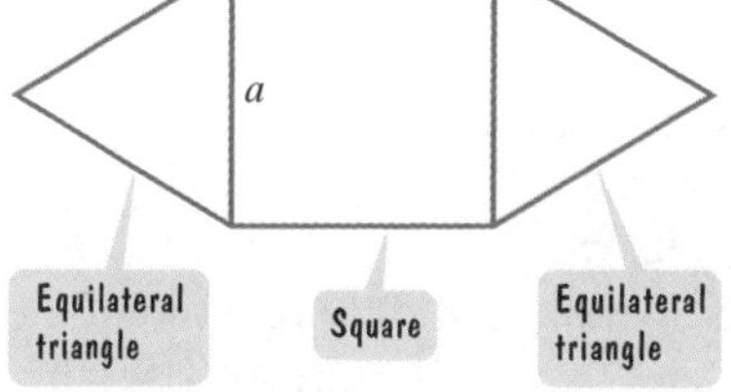

60. Find $m\measuredangle 1$ in the figure shown.

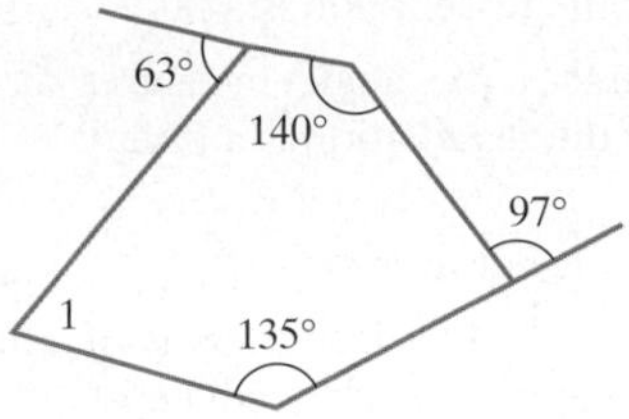

• Group Exercise

61. Group members should consult sites on the Internet devoted to tessellations, or tilings, and present a report that expands upon the information in this section. Include a discussion of cultures that have used tessellations on fabrics, wall coverings, baskets, rugs, and pottery, with examples. Include the Alhambra, a fourteenth-century palace in Granada, Spain, in the presentation, as well as works by the artist M. C. Escher. Discuss the various symmetries (translations, rotations, reflections) associated with tessellations. Demonstrate how to create unique tessellations, including Escher-type patterns. Other than creating beautiful works of art, are there any practical applications of tessellations?

SECTION 10.4 • AREA AND CIRCUMFERENCE

OBJECTIVES

1. Use area formulas to compute the areas of plane regions and solve applied problems.
2. Use formulas for a circle's circumference and area.

The size of a house is described in square feet. But how do you know from the real estate ad whether the 1200-square-foot home with the backyard pool is large enough to warrant a visit? Faced with hundreds of ads, you need some way to sort out the best bets. What does 1200 square feet mean and how is this area determined? In this section, we discuss how to compute the areas of plane regions.

1 Use area formulas to compute the areas of plane regions and solve applied problems.

Formulas for Area

In Section 9.2, we saw that the area of a two-dimensional figure is the number of square units, such as square inches or square miles, it takes to fill the interior of the figure. For example, Figure 10.32 shows that there are 12 square units contained within the rectangular region. The area of the region is 12 square units. Notice that the area can be determined in the following manner:

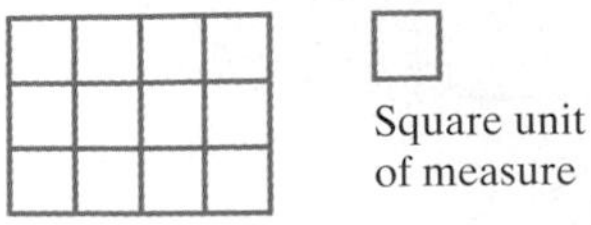

FIGURE 10.32 The area of the region on the left is 12 square units.

Distance across — Distance down

$$4 \text{ units} \times 3 \text{ units} = 4 \times 3 \times \text{units} \times \text{units}$$
$$= 12 \text{ square units.}$$

The area of a rectangular region, usually referred to as the area of a rectangle, is the product of the distance across (length) and the distance down (width).

AREA OF A RECTANGLE AND A SQUARE

The area, A, of a rectangle with length l and width w is given by the formula

$$A = lw.$$

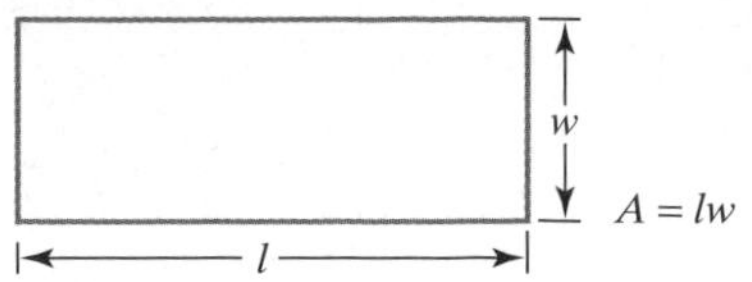

The area, A, of a square with one side measuring s linear units is given by the formula

$$A = s^2.$$

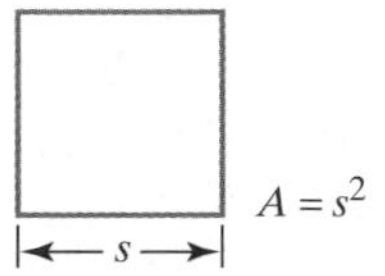

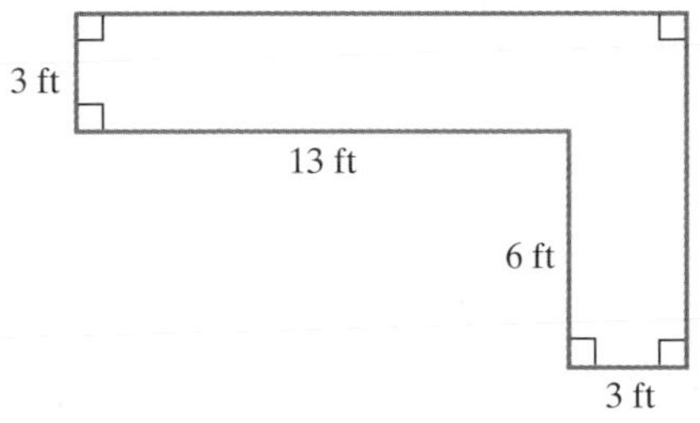

FIGURE 10.33

EXAMPLE 1 SOLVING AN AREA PROBLEM

You decide to cover the path shown in Figure 10.33 with bricks.

a. Find the area of the path.

b. If the path requires four bricks for every square foot, how many bricks are needed for the project?

SOLUTION

a. Because we have a formula for the area of a rectangle, we begin by drawing a dashed line that divides the path into two rectangles. One way of doing this is shown on the right. We then use the length and width of each rectangle to find its area. The computations for area are shown in the green and blue voice balloons.

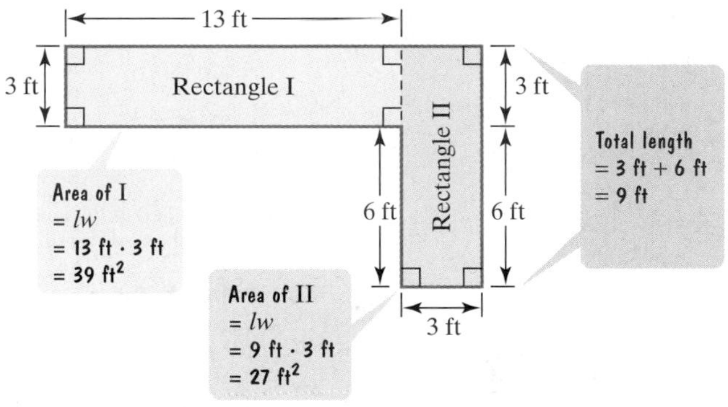

The area of the path is found by adding the areas of the two rectangles.

$$\text{Area of path} = 39 \text{ ft}^2 + 27 \text{ ft}^2 = 66 \text{ ft}^2$$

b. The path requires 4 bricks per square foot. The number of bricks needed for the project is the number of square feet in the path, its area, times 4.

$$\text{Number of bricks needed} = 66 \cancel{\text{ft}^2} \cdot \frac{4 \text{ bricks}}{\cancel{\text{ft}^2}} = 66 \cdot 4 \text{ bricks} = 264 \text{ bricks}$$

Thus, 264 bricks are needed for the project.

CHECK POINT 1 Find the area of the path described in Example 1, rendered on the right as a green region, by first measuring off a large rectangle as shown. The area of the path is the area of the large rectangle (the blue and green regions combined) minus the area of the blue rectangle. Do you get the same answer as we did in Example 1(a)?

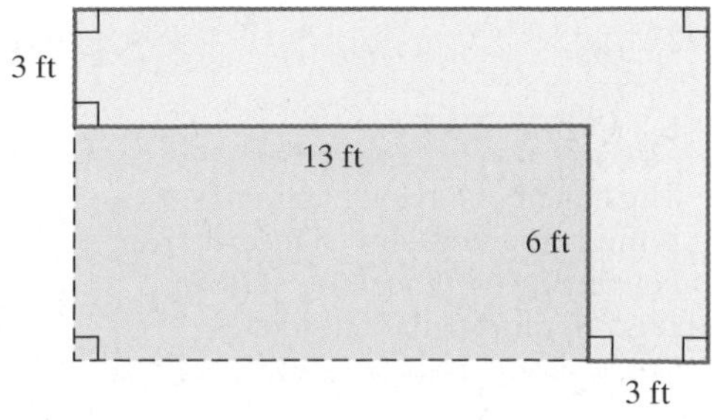

BLITZER BONUS

Appraising a House

A house is measured by an appraiser hired by a bank to help establish its value. The appraiser works from the outside, measuring off a rectangle. Then the appraiser adds the living spaces that lie outside the rectangle and subtracts the empty areas inside the rectangle. The final figure, in square feet, includes all the finished floor space in the house. Not included are the garage, outside porches, decks, or an unfinished basement.

A 1000-square-foot house is considered small, one with 1500 square feet average, and one with more than 2000 square feet pleasantly large. If a 1200-square-foot house has three bedrooms, the individual rooms might seem snug and cozy. With only one bedroom, the space may feel palatial!

In Section 9.2, we saw that although there are 3 linear feet in a linear yard, there are 9 square feet in a square yard. If a problem requires measurement of area in square yards and the linear measures are given in feet, to avoid errors, first convert feet to yards. Then apply the area formula. This idea is illustrated in Example 2.

EXAMPLE 2 SOLVING AN AREA PROBLEM

What will it cost to carpet a rectangular floor measuring 12 feet by 15 feet if the carpet costs \$18.50 per square yard?

SOLUTION We begin by converting the linear measures from feet to yards.

$$12 \text{ ft} = \frac{12 \cancel{\text{ft}}}{1} \cdot \frac{1 \text{ yd}}{3 \cancel{\text{ft}}} = \frac{12}{3} \text{yd} = 4 \text{ yd}$$

$$15 \text{ ft} = \frac{15 \cancel{\text{ft}}}{1} \cdot \frac{1 \text{ yd}}{3 \cancel{\text{ft}}} = \frac{15}{3} \text{yd} = 5 \text{ yd}$$

Next, we find the area of the rectangular floor in square yards.

$$A = lw = 5 \text{ yd} \cdot 4 \text{ yd} = 20 \text{ yd}^2$$

Finally, we find the cost of the carpet by multiplying the cost per square yard, \$18.50, by the number of square yards in the floor, 20.

$$\text{Cost of carpet} = \frac{\$18.50}{\cancel{\text{yd}^2}} \cdot \frac{20 \cancel{\text{yd}^2}}{1} = \$18.50(20) = \$370$$

It will cost \$370 to carpet the floor.

CHECK POINT 2 What will it cost to carpet a rectangular floor measuring 18 feet by 21 feet if the carpet costs \$16 per square yard?

We can use the formula for the area of a rectangle to develop formulas for areas of other polygons. We begin with a parallelogram, a quadrilateral with opposite sides equal and parallel. The **height** of a parallelogram is the perpendicular distance between two of the parallel sides. Height is denoted by h in Figure 10.34. The **base**, denoted by b, is the length of either of these parallel sides.

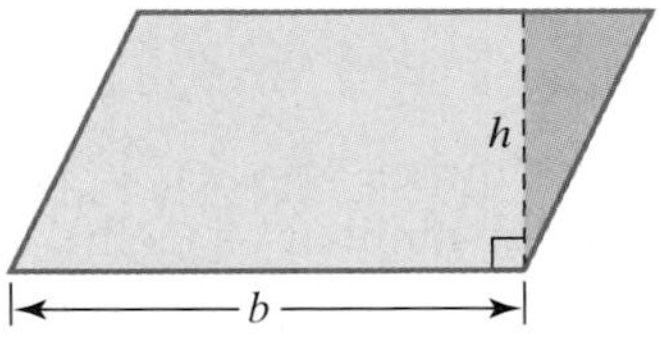

FIGURE 10.34

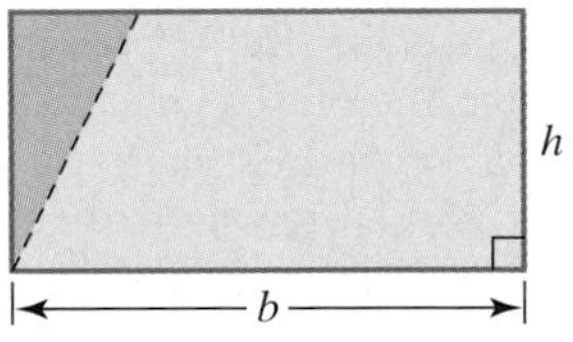

FIGURE 10.35

In Figure 10.35, the red triangular region has been cut off from the right of the parallelogram and attached to the left. The resulting figure is a rectangle with length b and width h. Because bh is the area of the rectangle, it also represents the area of the parallelogram.

STUDY TIP

The height of a parallelogram is the perpendicular distance between two of the parallel sides. It is *not* the length of a side.

AREA OF A PARALLELOGRAM

The area, A, of a parallelogram with height h and base b is given by the formula

$$A = bh.$$

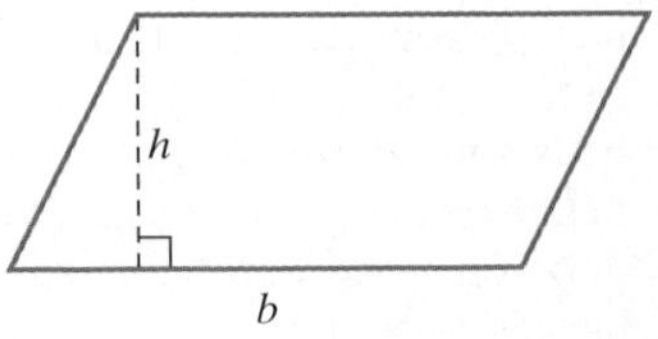

EXAMPLE 3 USING THE FORMULA FOR A PARALLELOGRAM'S AREA

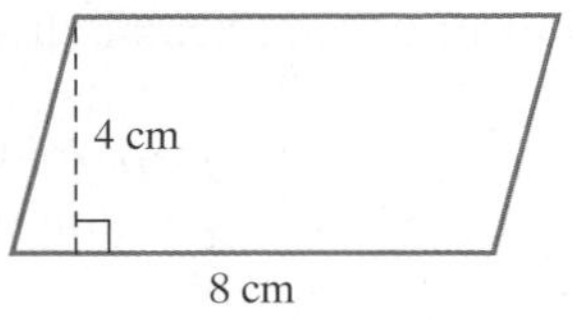

FIGURE 10.36

Find the area of the parallelogram in Figure 10.36.

SOLUTION As shown in the figure, the base is 8 centimeters and the height is 4 centimeters. Thus, $b = 8$ and $h = 4$.

$$A = bh$$
$$A = 8\text{ cm} \cdot 4\text{ cm} = 32\text{ cm}^2$$

The area is 32 cm^2.

CHECK POINT 3 Find the area of a parallelogram with a base of 10 inches and a height of 6 inches.

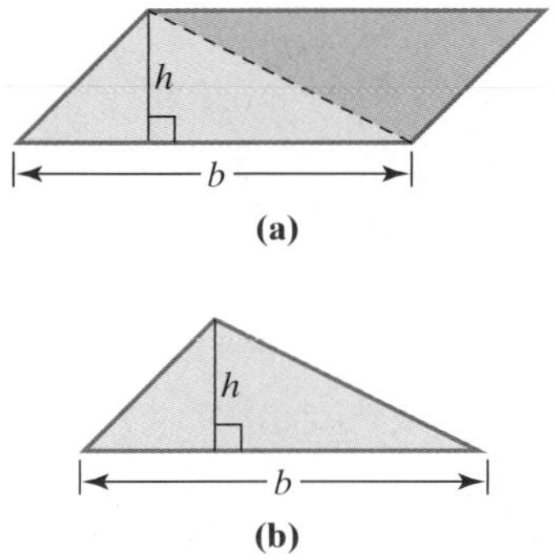

FIGURE 10.37

Figure 10.37 demonstrates how we can use the formula for the area of a parallelogram to obtain a formula for the area of a triangle. The area of the parallelogram in Figure 10.37(a) is given by $A = bh$. The diagonal shown in the parallelogram divides it into two triangles with the same size and shape. This means that the area of each triangle is one-half that of the parallelogram. Thus, the area of the triangle in Figure 10.37(b) is given by $A = \frac{1}{2}bh$.

AREA OF A TRIANGLE

The area, A, of a triangle with height h and base b is given by the formula

$$A = \frac{1}{2}bh.$$

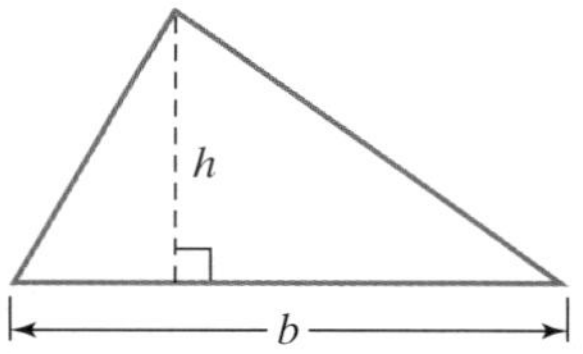

EXAMPLE 4 USING THE FORMULA FOR A TRIANGLE'S AREA

Find the area of each triangle in Figure 10.38.

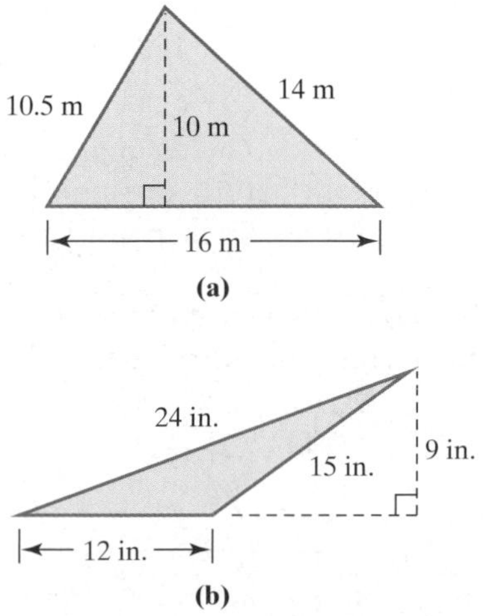

FIGURE 10.38

SOLUTION

a. In Figure 10.38(a), the base is 16 meters and the height is 10 meters, so $b = 16$ and $h = 10$. We do not need the 10.5 meters or the 14 meters to find the area. The area of the triangle is

$$A = \frac{1}{2}bh = \frac{1}{2} \cdot 16\text{ m} \cdot 10\text{ m} = 80\text{ m}^2.$$

The area is 80 square meters.

b. In Figure 10.38(b), the base is 12 inches. The base line needs to be extended to draw the height. However, we still use 12 inches for b in the area formula. The height, h, is given to be 9 inches. The area of the triangle is

$$A = \frac{1}{2}bh = \frac{1}{2} \cdot 12\text{ in.} \cdot 9\text{ in.} = 54\text{ in.}^2.$$

The area of the triangle is 54 square inches.

CHECK POINT 4 A sailboat has a triangular sail with a base of 12 feet and a height of 5 feet. Find the area of the sail.

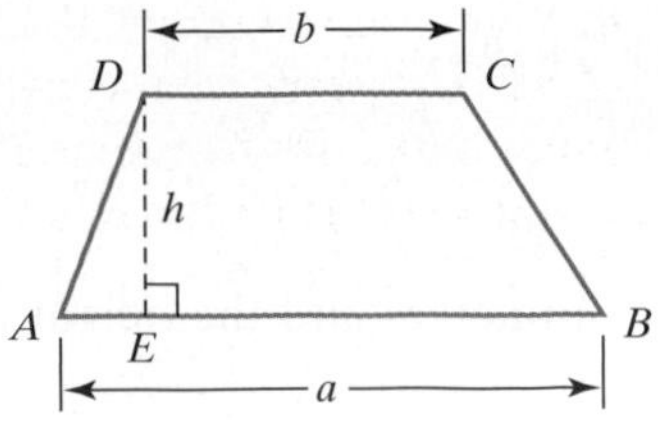

FIGURE 10.39

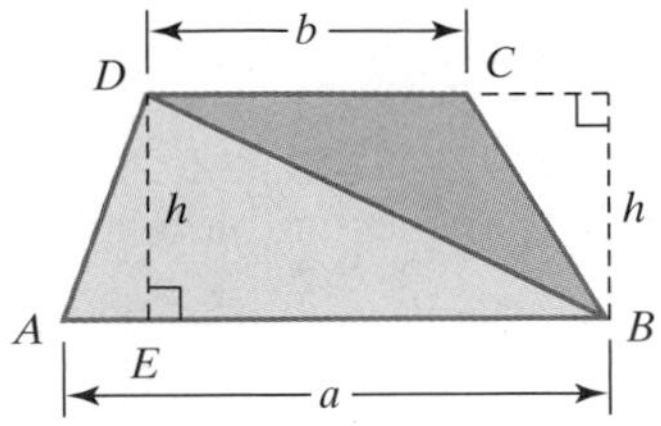

FIGURE 10.40

The formula for the area of a triangle can be used to obtain a formula for the area of a trapezoid. Consider the trapezoid shown in Figure 10.39. The lengths of the two parallel sides, called the **bases**, are represented by a (the lower base) and b (the upper base). The trapezoid's height, denoted by h, is the perpendicular distance between the two parallel sides.

In Figure 10.40, we have drawn line segment BD, dividing the trapezoid into two triangles, shown in yellow and red. The area of the trapezoid is the sum of the areas of these triangles.

Area of trapezoid = Area of yellow Δ plus Area of red Δ

$$A = \frac{1}{2}ah + \frac{1}{2}bh$$

$$= \frac{1}{2}h(a+b) \quad \text{Factor out } \frac{1}{2}h.$$

AREA OF A TRAPEZOID

The area, A, of a trapezoid with parallel bases a and b and height h is given by the formula

$$A = \frac{1}{2}h(a+b).$$

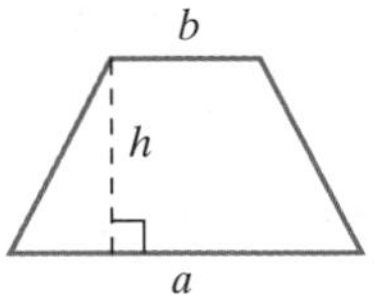

EXAMPLE 5 FINDING THE AREA OF A TRAPEZOID

Find the area of the trapezoid in Figure 10.41.

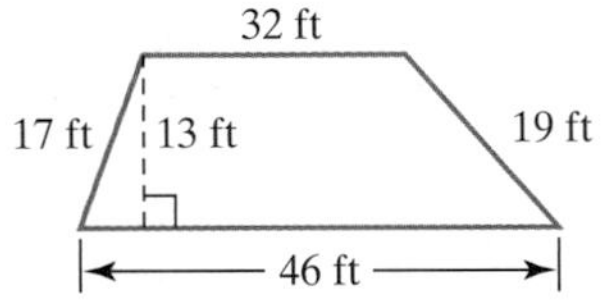

FIGURE 10.41

SOLUTION The height, h, is 13 feet. The lower base, a, is 46 feet, and the upper base, b, is 32 feet. We do not use the 17-foot and 19-foot sides in finding the trapezoid's area.

$$A = \frac{1}{2}h(a+b) = \frac{1}{2}\cdot 13\text{ ft}\cdot(46\text{ ft} + 32\text{ ft})$$

$$= \frac{1}{2}\cdot 13\text{ ft}\cdot 78\text{ ft} = 507\text{ ft}^2$$

The area of the trapezoid is 507 square feet.

CHECK POINT 5 Find the area of a trapezoid with bases of length 20 feet and 10 feet and height 7 feet.

2 Use formulas for a circle's circumference and area.

The point at which a pebble hits a flat surface of water becomes the center of a number of circular ripples.

Circles

It's a good idea to know your way around a circle. Clocks, angles, maps, and compasses are based on circles. Circles occur everywhere in nature: in ripples on water, patterns on a butterfly's wings, and cross sections of trees. Some consider the circle to be the most pleasing of all shapes.

A **circle** is a set of points in the plane equally distant from a given point, its **center**. Figure 10.42 shows two circles. The **radius** (plural: radii), r, is a line segment from the center to any point on the circle. For a given circle, all radii have the same length. The **diameter**, d, is a line segment through the center whose endpoints both lie on the circle. For a given circle, all diameters have the same length. In any circle, the **length of the diameter is twice the length of the radius**.

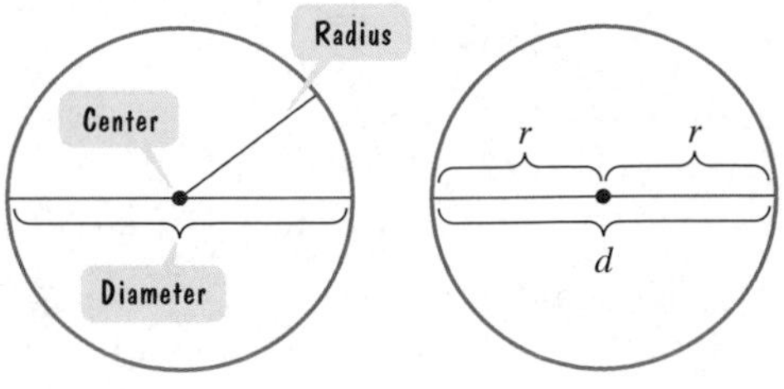

FIGURE 10.42

The words *radius* and *diameter* refer to both the line segments in Figure 10.42 as well as to their linear measures. The distance around a circle (its perimeter) is called its **circumference**, C. For all circles, if you divide the circumference by the diameter, or by twice the radius, you will get the same number. This ratio is the irrational number π and is approximately equal to 3.14:

$$\frac{C}{d} = \pi \quad \text{or} \quad \frac{C}{2r} = \pi.$$

Thus,

$$C = \pi d \quad \text{or} \quad C = 2\pi r.$$

FINDING THE DISTANCE AROUND A CIRCLE

The circumference, C, of a circle with diameter d and radius r is

$$C = \pi d \quad \text{or} \quad C = 2\pi r.$$

When computing a circle's circumference by hand, round π to 3.14. When using a calculator, use the $\boxed{\pi}$ key, which gives the value of π rounded to approximately 11 decimal places. In either case, calculations involving π give approximate answers. These answers can vary slightly depending on how π is rounded. The symbol $\approx$ (is approximately equal to) will be written in these calculations.

EXAMPLE 6 FINDING A CIRCLE'S CIRCUMFERENCE

Find the circumference of the circle in Figure 10.43.

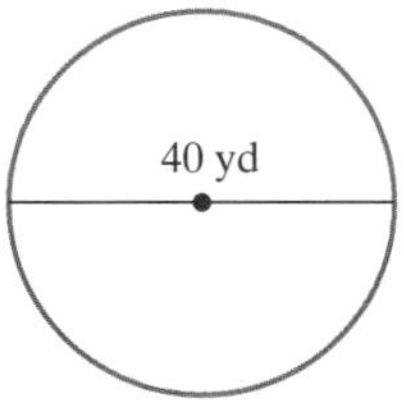

FIGURE 10.43

SOLUTION The diameter is 40 yards, so we use the formula for circumference with d in it.

$$C = \pi d = \pi(40 \text{ yd}) = 40\pi \text{ yd} \approx 125.7 \text{ yd}$$

The distance around the circle is approximately 125.7 yards.

CHECK POINT 6 Find the circumference of a circle whose diameter measures 10 inches. Express the answer in terms of π and then round to the nearest tenth of an inch.

EXAMPLE 7 USING THE CIRCUMFERENCE FORMULA

How much trim, to the nearest tenth of a foot, is needed to go around the window shown in Figure 10.44?

FIGURE 10.44

SOLUTION The trim covers the 6-foot bottom of the window, the two 8-foot sides, and the half-circle (called a semicircle) on top. The length needed is

$$6 \text{ ft} + 8 \text{ ft} + 8 \text{ ft} + \text{circumference of the semicircle.}$$

The circumference of the semicircle is half the circumference of a circle whose diameter is 6 feet.

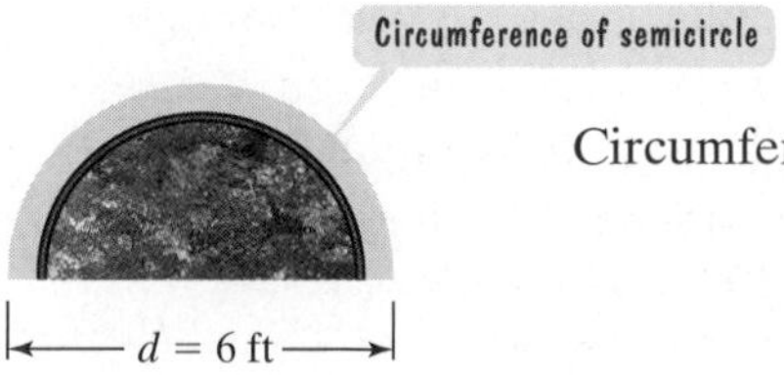

$$\text{Circumference of semicircle} = \frac{1}{2}\pi d$$

$$= \frac{1}{2}\pi(6 \text{ ft}) = 3\pi \text{ ft} \approx 9.4 \text{ ft}$$

Rounding the circumference to the nearest tenth (9.4 feet), the length of trim that is needed is approximately

$$6 \text{ ft} + 8 \text{ ft} + 8 \text{ ft} + 9.4 \text{ ft},$$

or 31.4 feet.

CHECK POINT 7 In Figure 10.44 on page 569, suppose that the dimensions are 10 feet and 12 feet for the window's bottom and side, respectively. How much trim, to the nearest tenth of a foot, is needed to go around the window?

We also use π to find the area of a circle in square units.

FINDING THE AREA OF A CIRCLE

The area, A, of a circle with radius r is

$$A = \pi r^2.$$

EXAMPLE 8 PROBLEM SOLVING USING THE FORMULA FOR A CIRCLE'S AREA

Which one of the following is the better buy: a large pizza with a 16-inch diameter for \$15.00 or a medium pizza with an 8-inch diameter for \$7.50?

SOLUTION The better buy is the pizza with the lower price per square inch. The radius of the large pizza is $\frac{1}{2} \cdot 16$ inches, or 8 inches, and the radius of the medium pizza is $\frac{1}{2} \cdot 8$ inches, or 4 inches. The area of the surface of each circular pizza is determined using the formula for the area of a circle.

$$\text{Large pizza: } A = \pi r^2 = \pi(8 \text{ in.})^2 = 64\pi \text{ in.}^2 \approx 201 \text{ in.}^2$$

$$\text{Medium pizza: } A = \pi r^2 = \pi(4 \text{ in.})^2 = 16\pi \text{ in.}^2 \approx 50 \text{ in.}^2$$

For each pizza, the price per square inch is found by dividing the price by the area:

$$\text{Price per square inch for large pizza} = \frac{\$15.00}{64\pi \text{ in.}^2} \approx \frac{\$15.00}{201 \text{ in.}^2} \approx \frac{\$0.07}{\text{in.}^2}$$

$$\text{Price per square inch for medium pizza} = \frac{\$7.50}{16\pi \text{ in.}^2} \approx \frac{\$7.50}{50 \text{ in.}^2} = \frac{\$0.15}{\text{in.}^2}.$$

The large pizza is the better buy.

TECHNOLOGY

You can use your calculator to obtain the price per square inch for each pizza in Example 8. The price per square inch for the large pizza, $\frac{15}{64\pi}$, is approximated by one of the following sequences of keystrokes:

MANY SCIENTIFIC CALCULATORS

15 [÷] [(] 64 [×] [π] [)] [=]

MANY GRAPHING CALCULATORS

15 [÷] [(] 64 [π] [)] [ENTER].

In Example 8, did you at first think that the price per square inch would be the same for the large and the medium pizzas? After all, the radius of the large pizza is twice that of the medium pizza, and the cost of the large is twice that of the medium. However, the large pizza's area, 64π square inches, is *four times the area* of the medium pizza's, 16π square inches. Doubling the radius of a circle increases its area by a factor of 2^2, or 4. In general, if the radius of a circle is increased by k times its original linear measure, the area is multiplied by k^2. The same principle is true for any two-dimensional figure: If the shape of the figure is kept the same while linear dimensions are increased k times, the area of the larger, similar, figure is k^2 times greater than the area of the original figure.

CHECK POINT 8 Which one of the following is the better buy: a large pizza with an 18-inch diameter for \$20.00 or a medium pizza with a 14-inch diameter for \$14.00?

EXERCISE SET 10.4

• Practice Exercises

In Exercises 1–14, use the formulas developed in this section to find the area of each figure.

1.

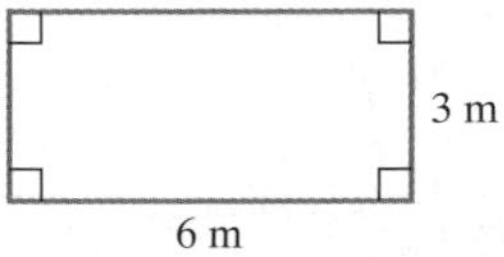

2.

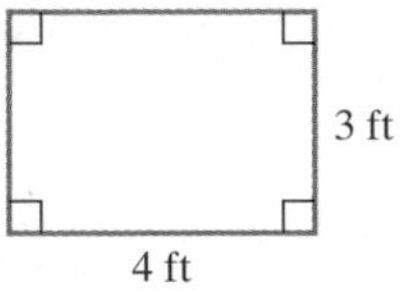

3.

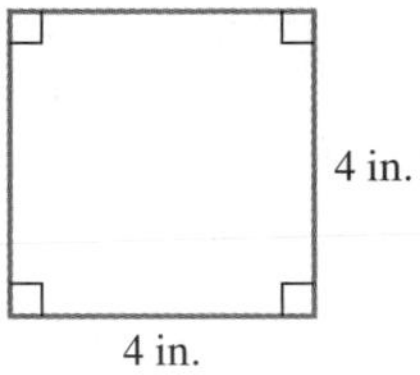

4.

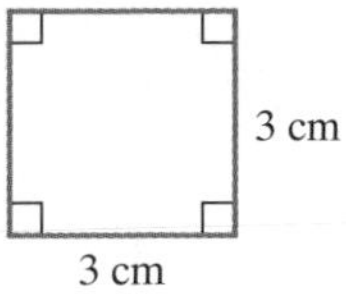

5.

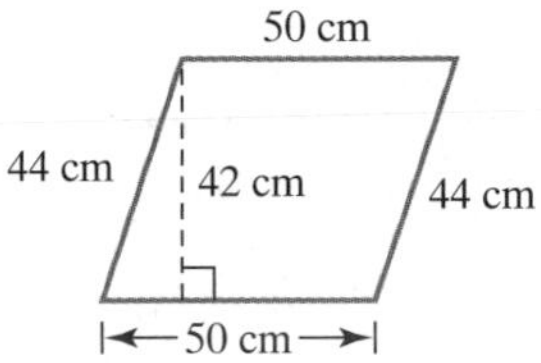

6.

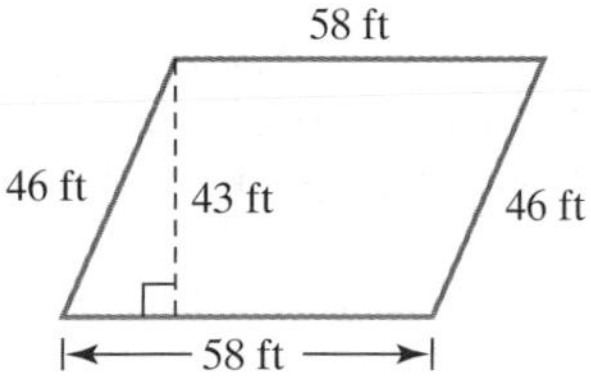

7.

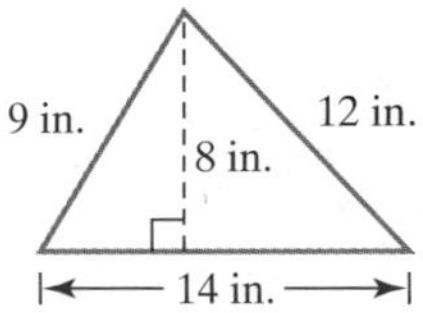

8.

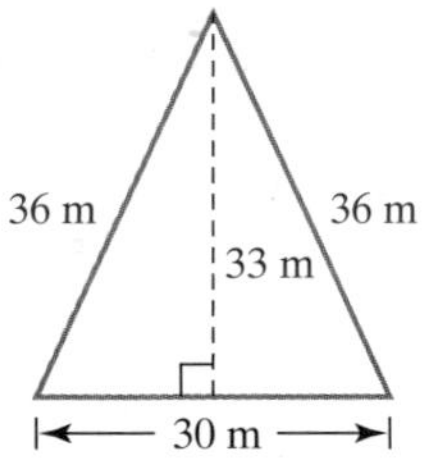

9.

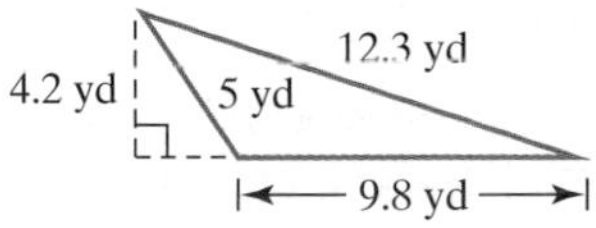

10.

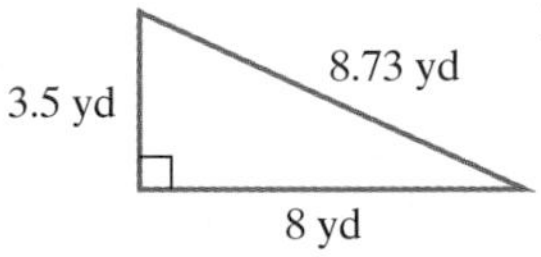

11.

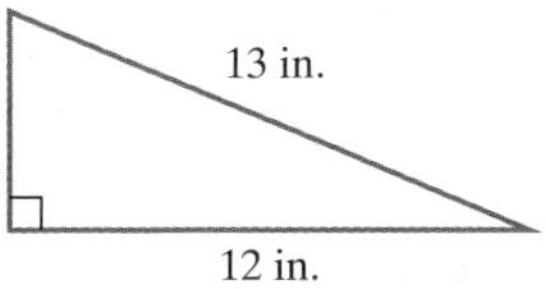

12.

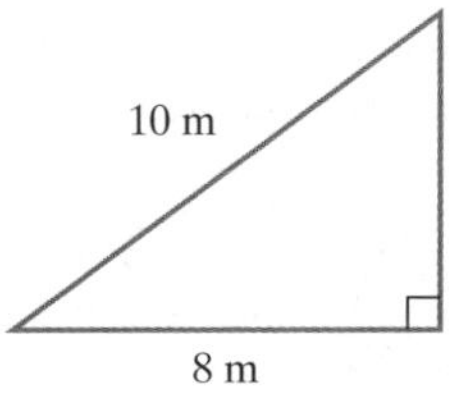

13.

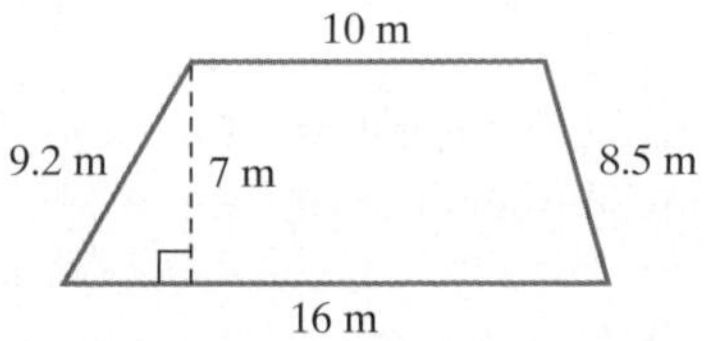

14.

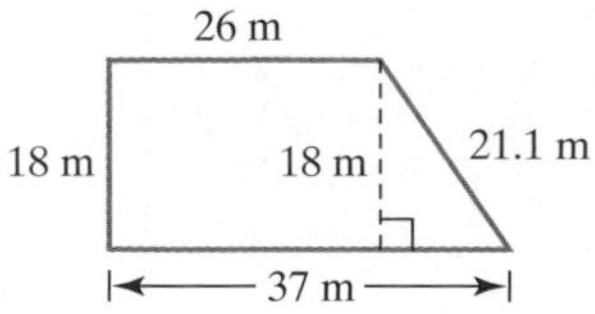

In Exercises 15–18, find the circumference and area of each circle. Express answers in terms of π and then round to the nearest tenth.

15.

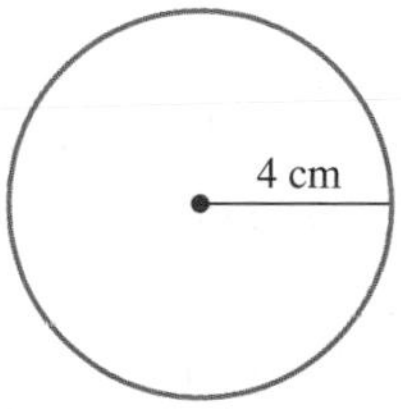

16.

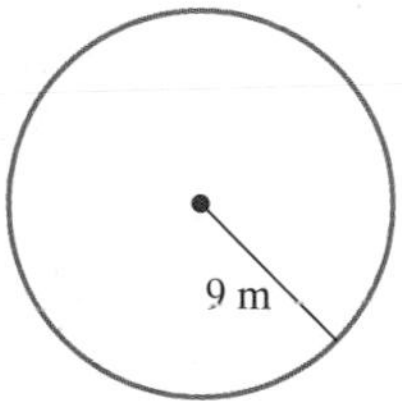

17.

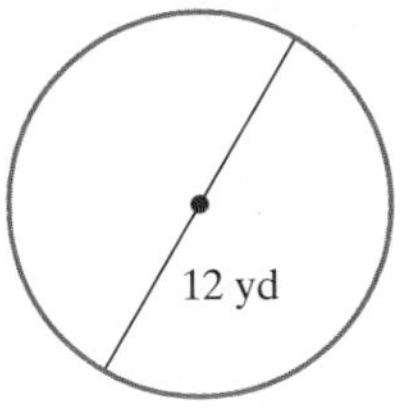

18.

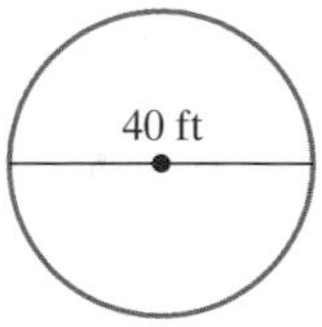

Find the area of each figure in Exercises 19–24. Where necessary, express answers in terms of π and then round to the nearest tenth.

19.

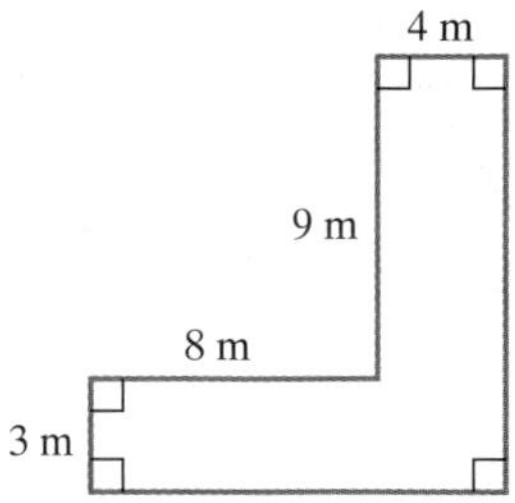

20.

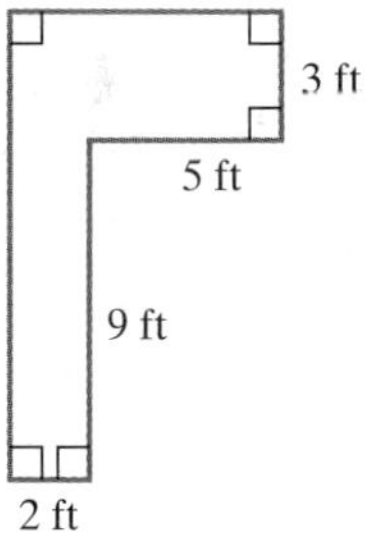

21.

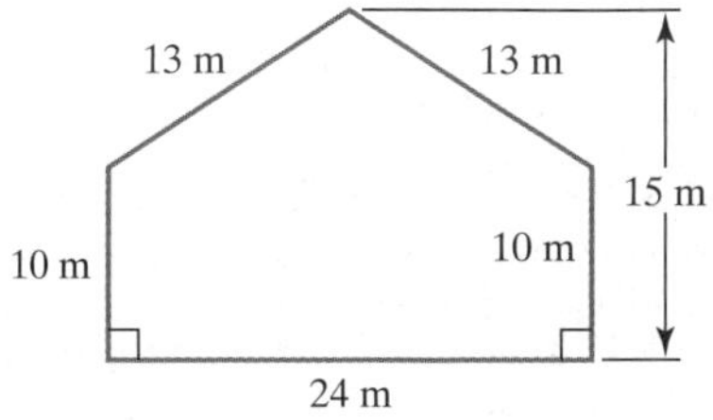

22.

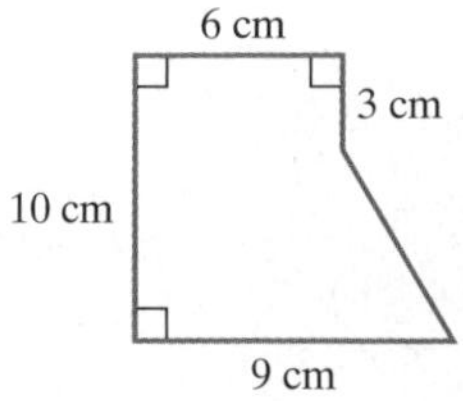

23.

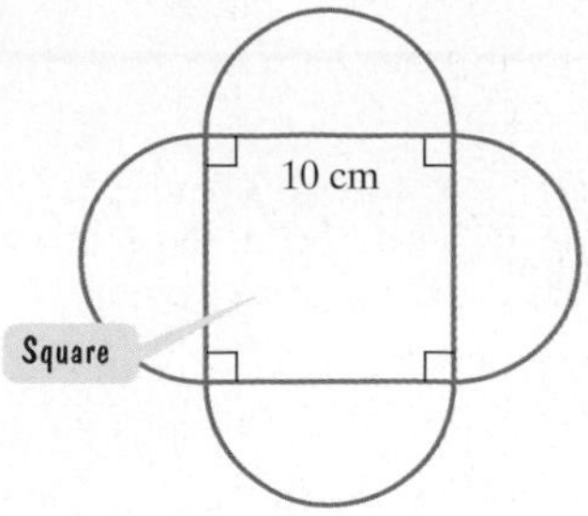

24.

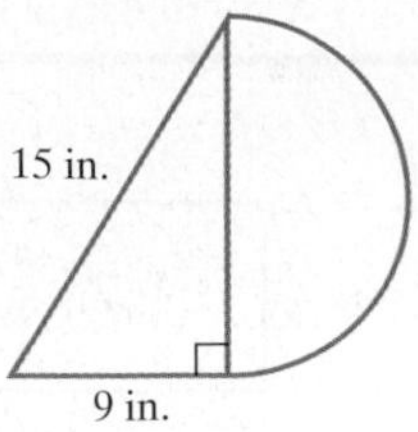

• Practice Plus

In Exercises 25–26, find the area of each shaded region.

25.

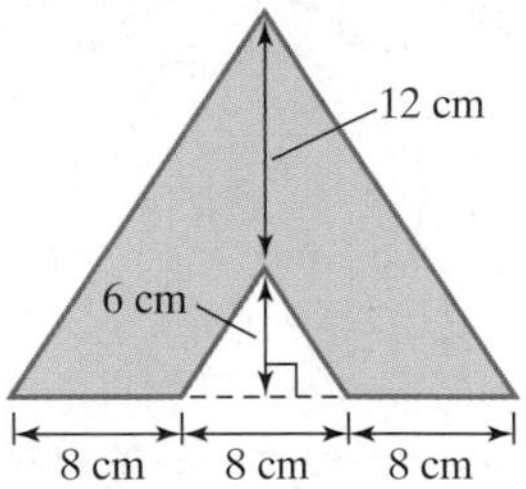

26.

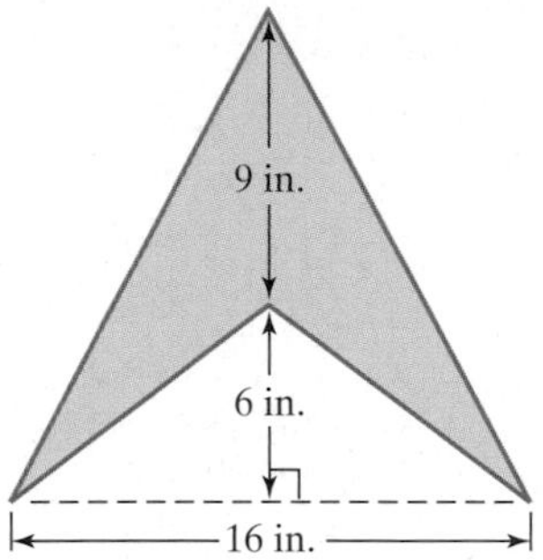

In Exercises 27–28, find the perimeter and the area of each figure. Where necessary, express answers in terms of π and round to the nearest tenth.

27.

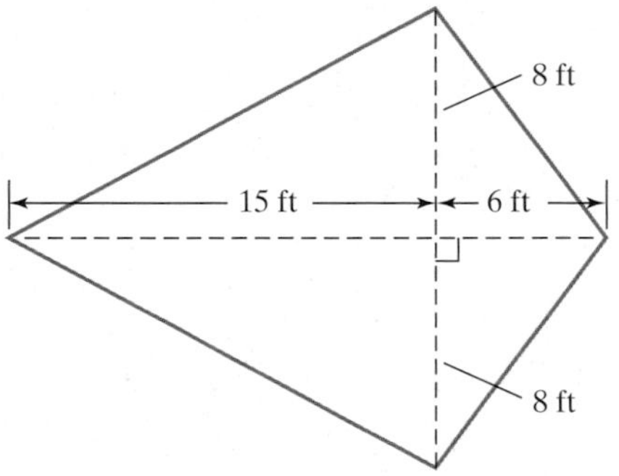

28.

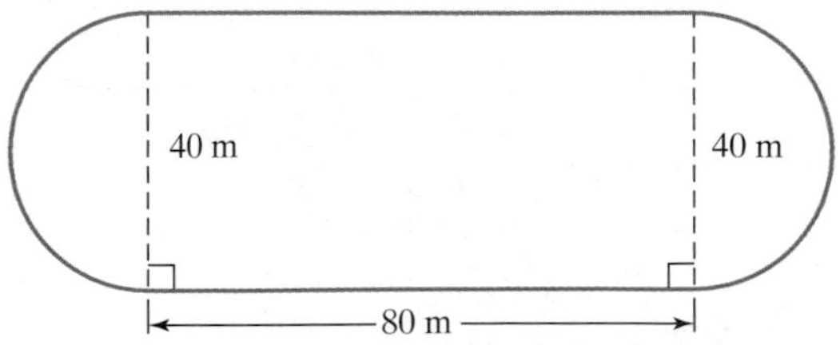

In Exercises 29–32, use a quadratic equation to solve each problem.

29. The length of a rectangular garden is 5 feet greater than the width. The area of the rectangle is 300 square feet. Find the length and the width.

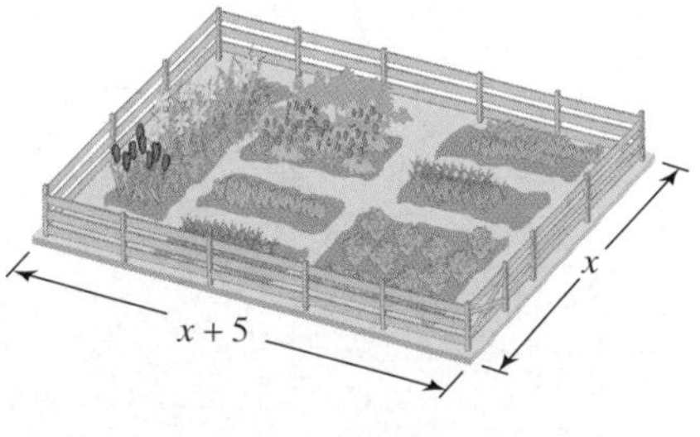

30. The length of a rectangular sign is 3 feet longer than the width. If the sign has space for 40 square feet of advertising, find its length and its width.

31. Great white sharks have triangular teeth with a height that is 1 centimeter longer than the base. If the area of one tooth is 15 square centimeters, find its base and height.

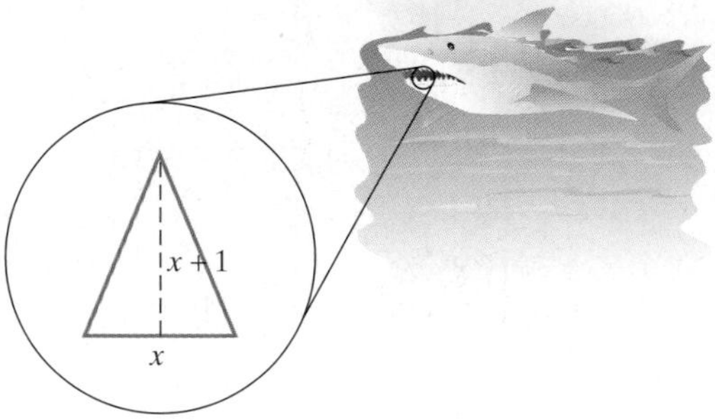

32. Each end of a glass prism is a triangle with a height that is 1 inch shorter than twice the base. If the area of the triangle is 60 square inches, how long are the base and height?

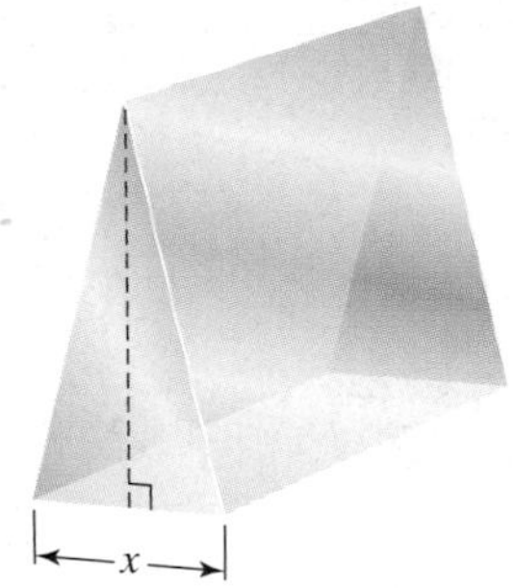

• Application Exercises

33. What will it cost to carpet a rectangular floor measuring 9 feet by 21 feet if the carpet costs $26.50 per square yard?

34. A plastering contractor charges $18 per square yard. What is the cost of plastering 60 feet of wall in a house with a 9-foot ceiling?

35. A rectangular kitchen floor measures 12 feet by 15 feet. A stove on the floor has a rectangular base measuring 3 feet by 4 feet, and a refrigerator covers a rectangular area of the floor measuring 4 feet by 5 feet. How many square feet of tile will be needed to cover the kitchen floor not counting the area used by the stove and the refrigerator?

36. A rectangular room measures 12 feet by 15 feet. The entire room is to be covered with rectangular tiles that measure 3 inches by 2 inches. If the tiles are sold at ten for 30¢, what will it cost to tile the room?

37. The lot in the figure shown at the top of the next page, except for the house, shed, and driveway, is lawn. One bag of lawn fertilizer costs $25.00 and covers 4000 square feet.

a. Determine the minimum number of bags of fertilizer needed for the lawn.

b. Find the total cost of the fertilizer.

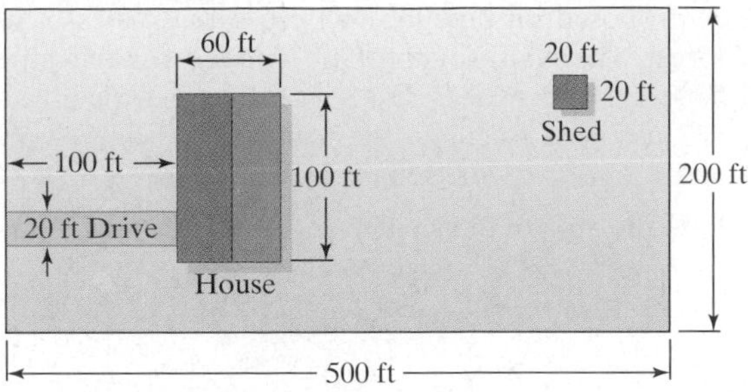

38. Taxpayers with an office in their home may deduct a percentage of their home-related expenses. This percentage is based on the ratio of the office's area to the area of the home. A taxpayer with an office in a 2200-square-foot home maintains a 20 foot by 16 foot office. If the yearly electric bills for the home come to $4800, how much of this is deductible?

39. You are planning to paint the house whose dimensions are shown in the figure.

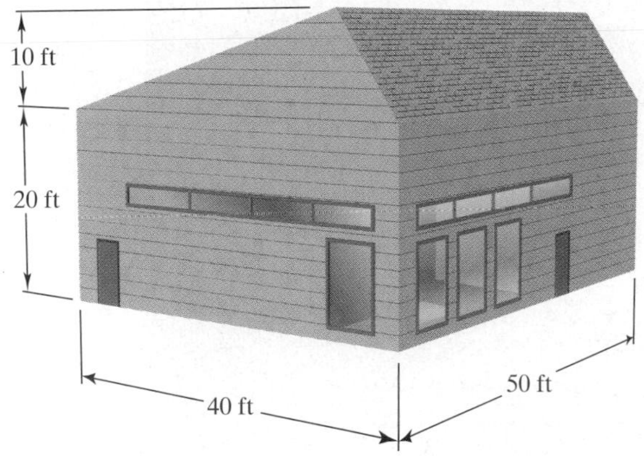

a. How many square feet will you need to paint? (There are four windows, each 8 ft by 5 ft; two windows, each 30 ft by 2 ft; and two doors, each 80 in. by 36 in., that do not require paint.)

b. The paint that you have chosen is available in gallon cans only. Each can covers 500 square feet. If you want to use two coats of paint, how many cans will you need for the project?

c. If the paint you have chosen sells for $26.95 per gallon, what will it cost to paint the house?

The diagram shows the floor plan for a one-story home. Use the given measurements to solve Exercises 40–42. (A calculator will be helpful in performing the necessary computations.)

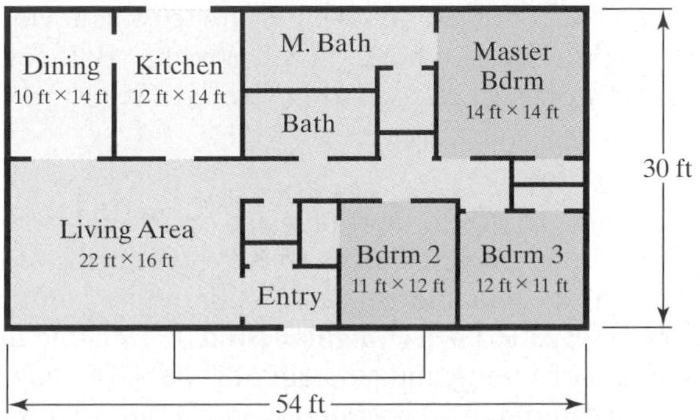

40. If construction costs $95 per square foot, find the cost of building the home.

41. If carpet costs $17.95 per square yard and is available in whole square yards only, find the cost of carpeting the three bedroom floors.

42. If ceramic tile costs $26.95 per square yard and is available in whole square yards only, find the cost of installing ceramic tile on the kitchen and dining room floors.

In Exercises 43–44, express the required calculation in terms of π and then round to the nearest tenth.

43. How much fencing is required to enclose a circular garden whose radius is 20 meters?

44. A circular rug is 6 feet in diameter. How many feet of fringe is required to edge this rug?

45. How many plants spaced every 6 inches are needed to surround a circular garden with a 30-foot radius?

46. A stained glass window is to be placed in a house. The window consists of a rectangle, 6 feet high by 3 feet wide, with a semicircle at the top. Approximately how many feet of stripping, to the nearest tenth of a foot, will be needed to frame the window?

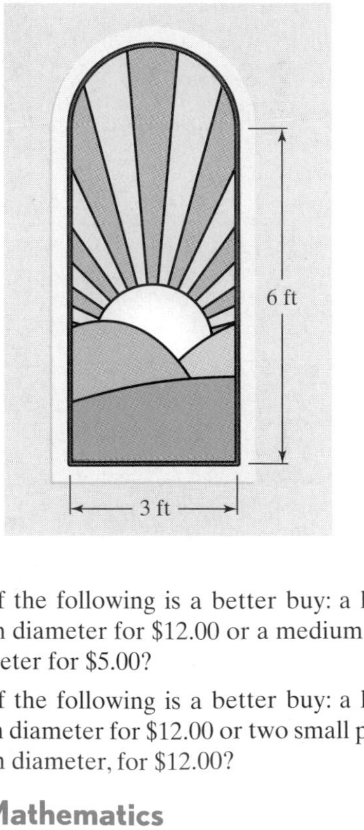

47. Which one of the following is a better buy: a large pizza with a 14-inch diameter for $12.00 or a medium pizza with a 7-inch diameter for $5.00?

48. Which one of the following is a better buy: a large pizza with a 16-inch diameter for $12.00 or two small pizzas, each with a 10-inch diameter, for $12.00?

• Writing in Mathematics

49. Using the formula for the area of a rectangle, explain how the formula for the area of a parallelogram $(A = bh)$ is obtained.

50. Using the formula for the area of a parallelogram $(A = bh)$, explain how the formula for the area of a triangle $\left(A = \frac{1}{2}bh\right)$ is obtained.

51. Using the formula for the area of a triangle, explain how the formula for the area of a trapezoid is obtained.

52. Explain why a circle is not a polygon.

53. Describe the difference between the following problems: How much fencing is needed to enclose a circular garden? How much fertilizer is needed for a circular garden?

• Critical Thinking Exercises

54. You need to enclose a rectangular region with 200 feet of fencing. Experiment with different lengths and widths to determine the maximum area you can enclose. Which quadrilateral encloses the most area?

55. Suppose you know the cost for building a rectangular deck measuring 8 feet by 10 feet. If you decide to increase the dimensions to 12 feet by 15 feet, by how much will the cost increase?

56. A rectangular swimming pool measures 14 feet by 30 feet. The pool is surrounded on all four sides by a path that is 3 feet wide. If the cost to resurface the path is \$2 per square foot, what is the total cost of resurfacing the path?

57. A proposed oil pipeline will cross 16.8 miles of national forest. The width of the land needed for the pipeline is 200 feet. If the U.S. Forest Service charges the oil company \$32 per acre, calculate the total cost. (1 mile = 5280 feet and 1 acre = 43,560 square feet.)

58. Find the area of the shaded region in terms of π.

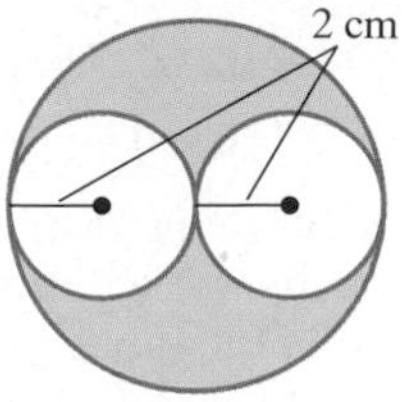

SECTION 10.5 • VOLUME

OBJECTIVES

1. Use volume formulas to compute the volumes of three-dimensional figures and solve applied problems.
2. Compute the surface area of a three-dimensional figure.

1 Use volume formulas to compute the volumes of three-dimensional figures and solve applied problems.

You are considering going to Judge Judy's Web site and filling out a case submission form to appear on her TV show. The case involves your contractor, who promised to install a water tank that holds 500 gallons of water. Upon delivery, you noticed that capacity was not printed anywhere, so you decided to do some measuring. The tank is shaped like a giant tuna can, with a circular top and bottom. You measured the radius of each circle to be 3 feet and you measured the tank's height to be 2 feet 4 inches. You know that 500 gallons is the capacity of a solid figure with a volume of about 67 cubic feet. Now you need some sort of method to compute the volume of the water tank. In this section, we discuss how to compute the volumes of various solid, three-dimensional figures. Using a formula you will learn in the section, you can determine whether the evidence indicates you can win a case against the contractor if you appear on *Judge Judy*. Or do you risk joining a cast of bozos who entertain television viewers by being loudly castigated by the judge? (Before a possible ear-piercing "Baloney, sir, you're a geometric idiot!", we suggest working Exercise 41 in Exercise Set 10.5.)

Formulas for Volume

In Section 9.2, we saw that **volume** refers to the amount of space occupied by a solid object, determined by the number of cubic units it takes to fill the interior of that object. For example, Figure 10.45 shows that there are 18 cubic units contained within the box. The volume of the box, called a **rectangular solid**, is 18 cubic units. The box has a length of 3 units, a width of 3 units, and a height of 2 units. The volume, 18 cubic units, may be determined by finding the product of the length, the width, and the height:

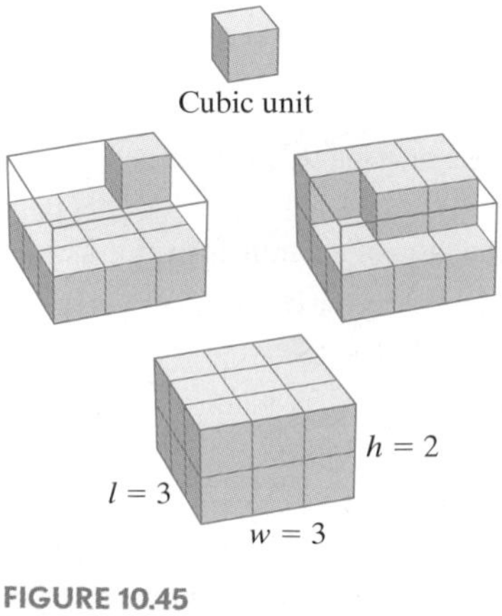

FIGURE 10.45
Volume = 18 cubic units

$$\text{Volume} = 3 \text{ units} \cdot 3 \text{ units} \cdot 2 \text{ units} = 18 \text{ units}^3.$$

In general, the volume, V, of a rectangular solid is the product of its length, l, its width, w, and its height, h:

$$V = lwh.$$

If the length, width, and height are the same, the rectangular solid is called a **cube**. Formulas for these boxlike shapes are given below.

VOLUMES OF BOXLIKE SHAPES

Rectangular solid

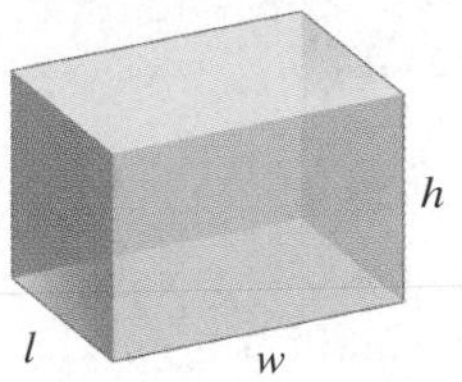

$V = lwh$

Cube

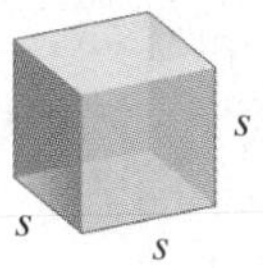

$V = sss = s^3$

EXAMPLE 1 FINDING THE VOLUME OF A RECTANGULAR SOLID

Find the volume of the rectangular solid in Figure 10.46.

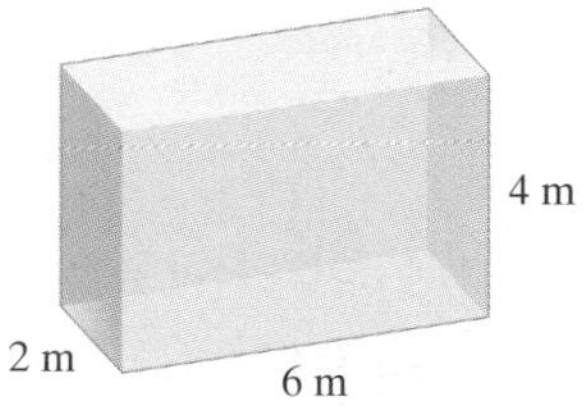

FIGURE 10.46

SOLUTION As shown in the figure, the length is 6 meters, the width is 2 meters, and the height is 4 meters. Thus, $l = 6$, $w = 2$, and $h = 4$.

$$V = lwh = 6\text{ m} \cdot 2\text{ m} \cdot 4\text{ m} = 48\text{ m}^3$$

The volume of the rectangular solid is 48 cubic meters.

CHECK POINT 1 Find the volume of a rectangular solid with length 5 feet, width 3 feet, and height 7 feet.

In Section 9.2, we saw that although there are 3 feet in a yard, there are 27 cubic feet in a cubic yard. If a problem requires measurement of volume in cubic yards and the linear measures are given in feet, to avoid errors, first convert feet to yards. Then apply the volume formula. This idea is illustrated in Example 2.

EXAMPLE 2 SOLVING A VOLUME PROBLEM

You are about to begin work on a swimming pool in your yard. The first step is to have a hole dug that is 90 feet long, 60 feet wide, and 6 feet deep. You will use a truck that can carry 10 cubic yards of dirt and charges $12 per load. How much will it cost you to have all the dirt hauled away?

SOLUTION We begin by converting feet to yards:

$$90\text{ ft} = \frac{90\,\cancel{\text{ft}}}{1} \cdot \frac{1\text{ yd}}{3\,\cancel{\text{ft}}} = \frac{90}{3}\text{yd} = 30\text{ yd}.$$

Similarly, 60 ft = 20 yd and 6 ft = 2 yd. Next, we find the volume of dirt that needs to be dug out and hauled off.

$$V = lwh = 30\text{ yd} \cdot 20\text{ yd} \cdot 2\text{ yd} = 1200\text{ yd}^3$$

Now, we find the number of loads that the truck needs to haul off all the dirt. Because the truck carries 10 cubic yards, divide the number of cubic yards of dirt by 10.

$$\text{Number of truckloads} = \frac{1200\text{ yd}^3}{\frac{10\text{ yd}^3}{\text{trip}}} = \frac{1200\,\cancel{\text{yd}^3}}{1} \cdot \frac{\text{trip}}{10\,\cancel{\text{yd}^3}} = \frac{1200}{10}\text{trips} = 120\text{ trips}$$

Because the truck charges \$12 per trip, the cost to have all the dirt hauled away is the number of trips, 120, times the cost per trip, \$12.

$$\text{Cost to haul all dirt away} = \frac{120\ \cancel{\text{trips}}}{1} \cdot \frac{\$12}{\cancel{\text{trip}}} = 120(\$12) = \$1440$$

The dirt-hauling phase of the pool project will cost you \$1440.

CHECK POINT 2 Find the volume, in cubic yards, of a cube whose edges each measure 6 feet.

FIGURE 10.47 The volume of a pyramid is $\frac{1}{3}$ the volume of a rectangular solid having the same base and the same height.

A rectangular solid is an example of a **polyhedron**, a solid figure bounded by polygons. A rectangular solid is bounded by six rectangles, called faces. By contrast, a **pyramid** is a polyhedron whose base is a polygon and whose sides are triangles. Figure 10.47 shows a pyramid with a rectangular base drawn inside a rectangular solid. The contents of three pyramids with rectangular bases exactly fill a rectangular solid of the same base and height. Thus, the formula for the volume of the pyramid is $\frac{1}{3}$ that of the rectangular solid.

VOLUME OF A PYRAMID

The volume, V, of a pyramid is given by the formula

$$V = \frac{1}{3}Bh,$$

where B is the area of the base and h is the height (the perpendicular distance from the top to the base).

Pyramid

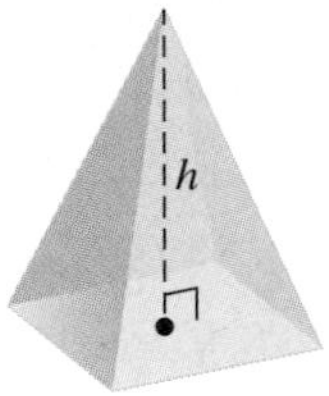

The Transamerica Tower's 3678 windows take cleaners one month to wash. Its foundation is sunk 15.5 m (52 ft) into the ground and is designed to move with earth tremors.

EXAMPLE 3 USING THE FORMULA FOR A PYRAMID'S VOLUME

Capped with a pointed spire on top of its 48 stories, the Transamerica Tower in San Francisco is a pyramid with a square base. The pyramid is 256 meters (853 feet) tall. Each side of the square base has a length of 52 meters. Although San Franciscans disliked it when it opened in 1972, they have since accepted it as part of the skyline. Find the volume of the building.

SOLUTION First find the area of the square base, represented as B in the volume formula. Because each side of the square base is 52 meters, the area of the square base is

$$B = 52\text{ m} \cdot 52\text{ m} = 2704\text{ m}^2.$$

The area of the square base is 2704 square meters. Because the pyramid is 256 meters tall, its height, h, is 256 meters. Now we apply the formula for the volume of a pyramid:

$$V = \frac{1}{3}Bh = \frac{1}{3} \cdot \frac{2704\text{ m}^2}{1} \cdot \frac{256\text{ m}}{1} = \frac{2704 \cdot 256}{3}\text{m}^3 \approx 230{,}741\text{ m}^3.$$

The volume of the building is approximately 230,741 cubic meters.

The San Francisco pyramid is relatively small compared to the Great Pyramid outside Cairo, Egypt. Built about 2550 B.C. by a labor force of 100,000, the Great Pyramid is approximately 11 times the volume of San Francisco's pyramid.

CHECK POINT 3 A pyramid is 4 feet tall. Each side of the square base has a length of 6 feet. Find the pyramid's volume.

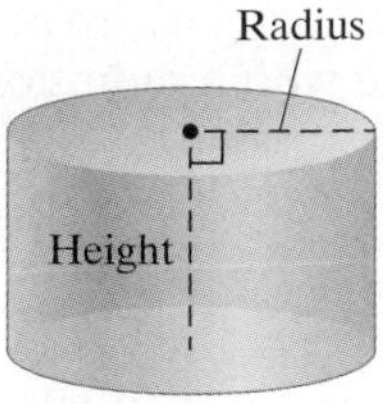

FIGURE 10.48

Not every three-dimensional figure is a polyhedron. Take, for example, the right circular cylinder shown in Figure 10.48. Its shape should remind you of a soup can or a stack of coins. The right circular cylinder is so named because the top and bottom are circles, and the side forms a right angle with the top and bottom. The formula for the volume of a right circular cylinder is given as follows:

VOLUME OF A RIGHT CIRCULAR CYLINDER

The volume, V, of a right circular cylinder is given by the formula

$$V = \pi r^2 h,$$

where r is the radius of the circle at either end and h is the height.

Right circular cylinder

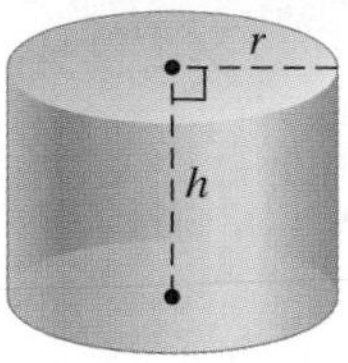

EXAMPLE 4 FINDING THE VOLUME OF A CYLINDER

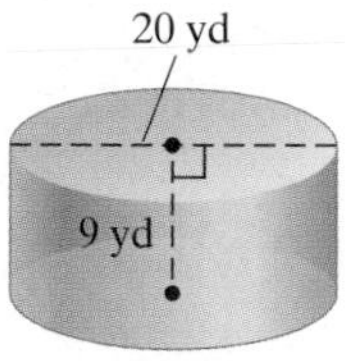

FIGURE 10.49

Find the volume of the cylinder in Figure 10.49.

SOLUTION In order to find the cylinder's volume, we need both its radius and its height. Because the diameter is 20 yards, the radius is half this length, or 10 yards. The height of the cylinder is given to be 9 yards. Thus, $r = 10$ and $h = 9$. Now we apply the formula for the volume of a cylinder.

$$V = \pi r^2 h = \pi(10 \text{ yd})^2 \cdot 9 \text{ yd} = 900\pi \text{ yd}^3 \approx 2827 \text{ yd}^3$$

The volume of the cylinder is approximately 2827 cubic yards.

CHECK POINT 4 Find the volume, to the nearest cubic inch, of a cylinder with a diameter of 8 inches and a height of 6 inches.

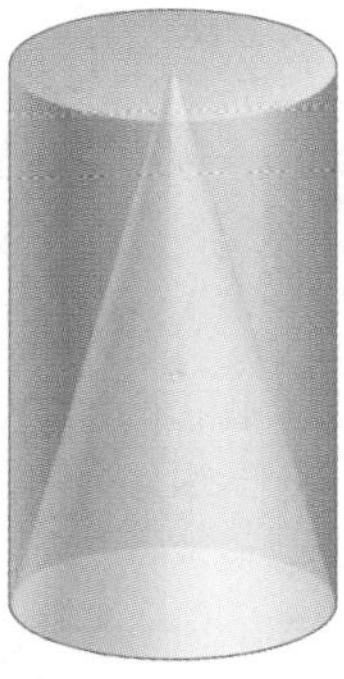

FIGURE 10.50

Figure 10.50 shows a **right circular cone** inside a cylinder, sharing the same circular base as the cylinder. The height of the cone, the perpendicular distance from the top to the circular base, is the same as that of the cylinder. Three such cones can occupy the same amount of space as the cylinder. Therefore, the formula for the volume of the cone is $\frac{1}{3}$ the volume of the cylinder.

VOLUME OF A CONE

The volume, V, of a right circular cone that has height h and radius r is given by the formula

$$V = \frac{1}{3}\pi r^2 h.$$

Cone

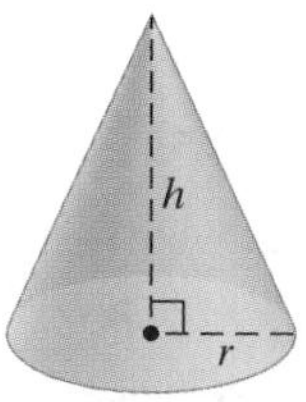

EXAMPLE 5 FINDING THE VOLUME OF A CONE

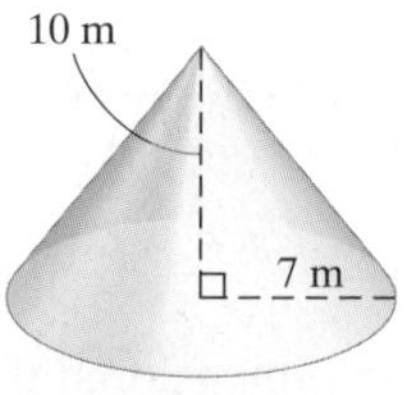

FIGURE 10.51

Find the volume of the cone in Figure 10.51.

SOLUTION The radius of the cone is 7 meters and the height is 10 meters. Thus, $r = 7$ and $h = 10$. Now we apply the formula for the volume of a cone.

$$V = \frac{1}{3}\pi r^2 h = \frac{1}{3}\pi(7 \text{ m})^2 \cdot 10 \text{ m} = \frac{490\pi}{3}\text{m}^3 \approx 513 \text{ m}^3$$

The volume of the cone is approximately 513 cubic meters.

CHECK POINT 5 Find the volume, to the nearest cubic inch, of a cone with a radius of 4 inches and a height of 6 inches.

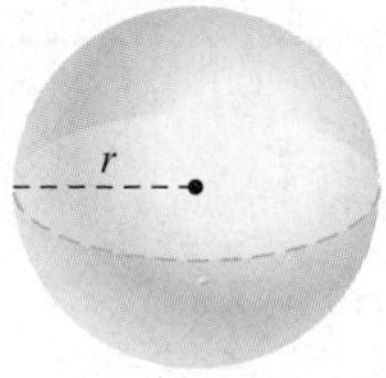

FIGURE 10.52

Figure 10.52 shows a *sphere*. Its shape may remind you of a basketball. The Earth is not a perfect sphere, but it's close. A **sphere** is the set of points in space equally distant from a given point, its **center**. The **radius** is the line segment from the center to any point on the sphere. The word *radius* is also used to refer to the length of this line segment. A sphere's volume can be found by using π and its radius.

VOLUME OF A SPHERE

The volume, V, of a sphere of radius r is given by the formula

$$V = \frac{4}{3}\pi r^3.$$

Sphere

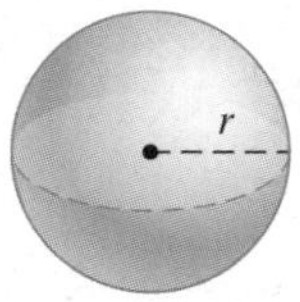

EXAMPLE 6 APPLYING VOLUME FORMULAS

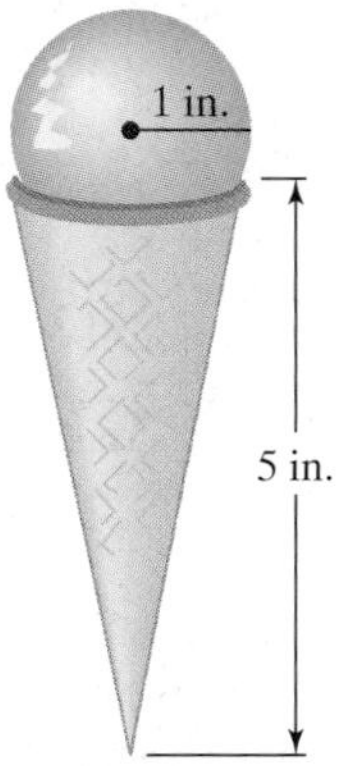

FIGURE 10.53

An ice cream cone is 5 inches deep and has a radius of 1 inch. A spherical scoop of ice cream also has a radius of 1 inch. (See Figure 10.53.) If the ice cream melts into the cone, will it overflow?

SOLUTION The ice cream will overflow if the volume of the ice cream, a sphere, is greater than the volume of the cone. Find the volume of each.

$$V_{\text{cone}} = \frac{1}{3}\pi r^2 h = \frac{1}{3}\pi(1 \text{ in.})^2 \cdot 5 \text{ in.} = \frac{5\pi}{3}\text{in.}^3 \approx 5 \text{ in.}^3$$

$$V_{\text{sphere}} = \frac{4}{3}\pi r^3 = \frac{4}{3}\pi(1 \text{ in.})^3 = \frac{4\pi}{3}\text{in.}^3 \approx 4 \text{ in.}^3$$

The volume of the spherical scoop of ice cream is less than the volume of the cone, so there will be no overflow.

CHECK POINT 6 A basketball has a radius of 4.5 inches. If the ball is filled with 350 cubic inches of air, is this enough air to fill it completely?

2 Compute the surface area of a three-dimensional figure.

Surface Area

In addition to volume, we can also measure the area of the outer surface of a three-dimensional object, called its **surface area**. Like area, surface area is measured in square units. For example, the surface area of the rectangular solid in Figure 10.54 is the sum of the areas of the six outside rectangles of the solid.

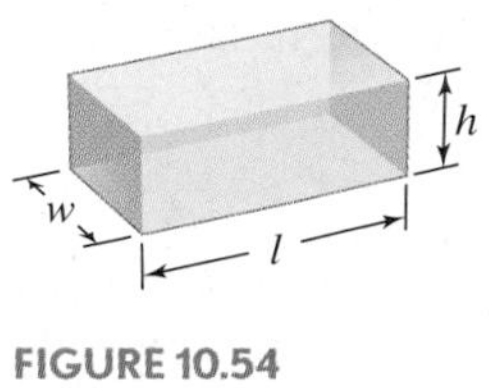

FIGURE 10.54

$$\text{Surface Area} = lw + lw + lh + lh + wh + wh$$

(Areas of top and bottom rectangles; Areas of front and back rectangles; Areas of rectangles on left and right sides)

$$= 2lw + 2lh + 2wh$$

Formulas for the surface area, abbreviated SA, of three-dimensional figures are given in Table 10.4.

TABLE 10.4 COMMON FORMULAS FOR SURFACE AREA

Cube	Rectangular Solid	Circular Cylinder
$SA = 6s^2$	$SA = 2lw + 2lh + 2wh$	$SA = 2\pi r^2 + 2\pi rh$

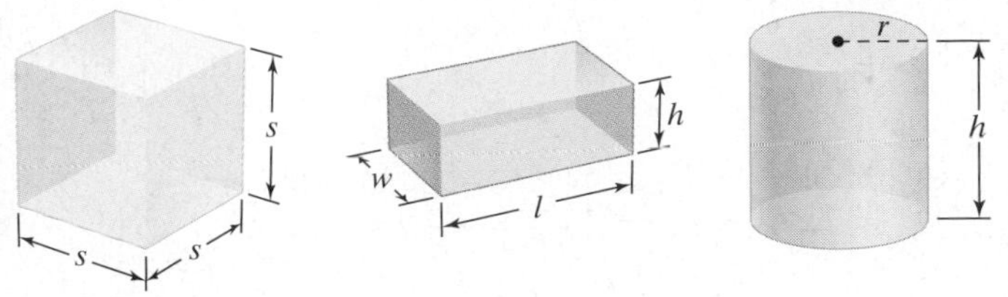

EXAMPLE 7 FINDING THE SURFACE AREA OF A SOLID

Find the surface area of the rectangular solid in Figure 10.55.

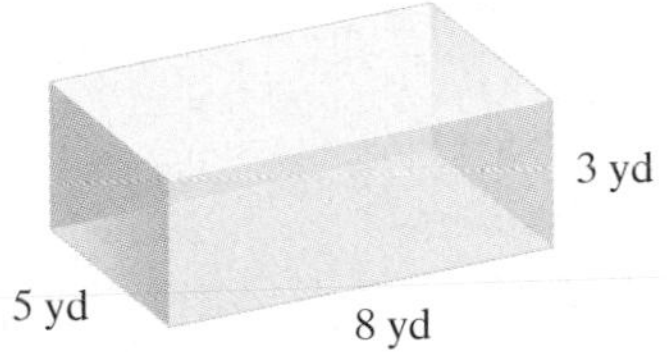

FIGURE 10.55

SOLUTION As shown in the figure, the length is 8 yards, the width is 5 yards, and the height is 3 yards. Thus, $l = 8$, $w = 5$, and $h = 3$.

$$\begin{aligned} SA &= 2lw + 2lh + 2wh \\ &= 2 \cdot 8\text{ yd} \cdot 5\text{ yd} + 2 \cdot 8\text{ yd} \cdot 3\text{ yd} + 2 \cdot 5\text{ yd} \cdot 3\text{ yd} \\ &= 80\text{ yd}^2 + 48\text{ yd}^2 + 30\text{ yd}^2 = 158\text{ yd}^2 \end{aligned}$$

The surface area is 158 square yards.

CHECK POINT 7 If the length, width, and height shown in Figure 10.55 are each doubled, find the surface area of the resulting rectangular solid.

EXERCISE SET 10.5

• Practice Exercises

In Exercises 1–20, find the volume of each figure. If necessary, express answers in terms of π and then round to the nearest whole number.

1.

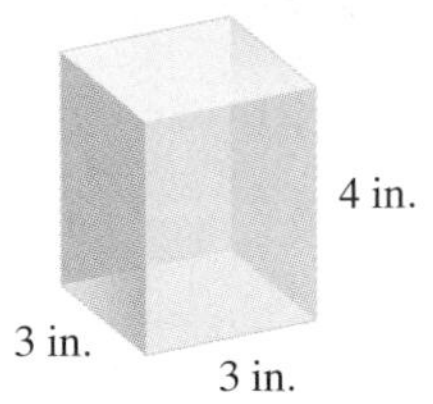

2.

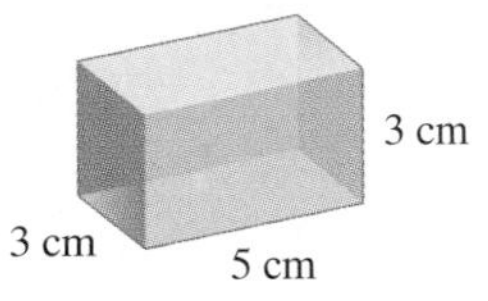

3.

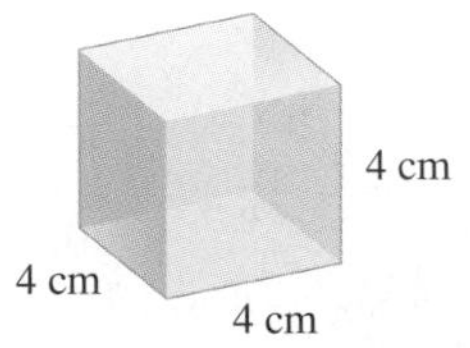

4.

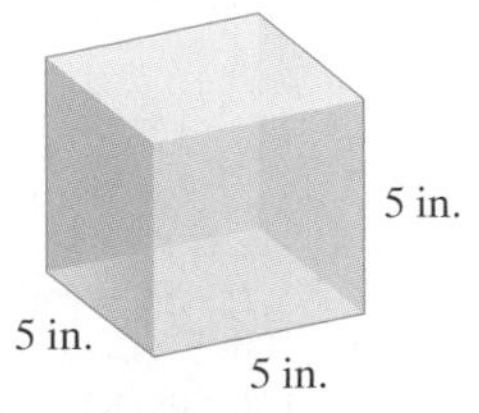

5.

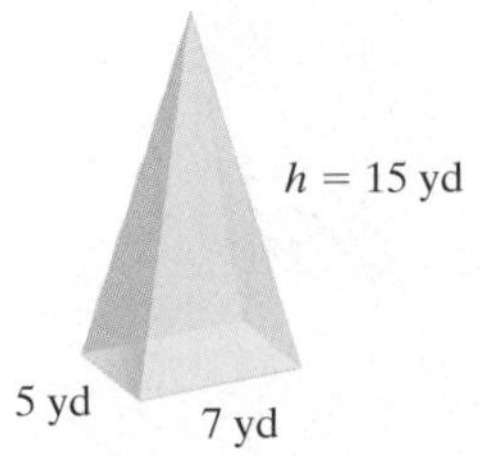

6.

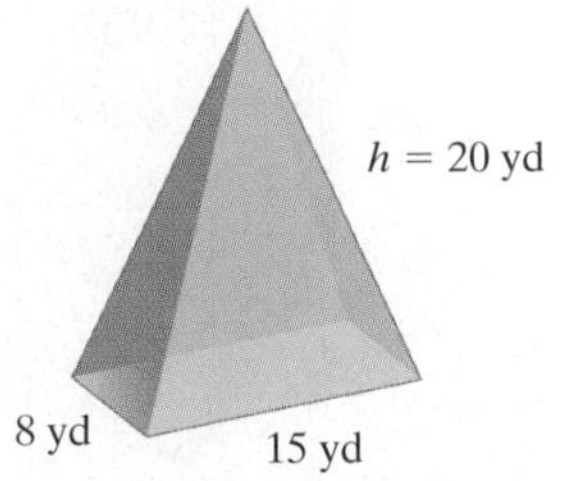

7.

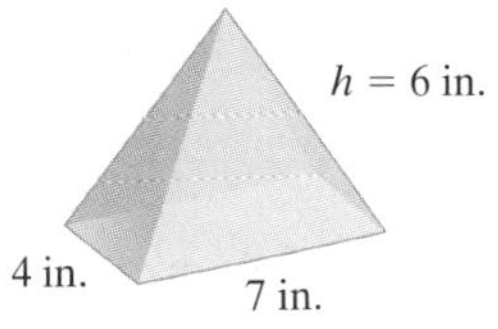

8.

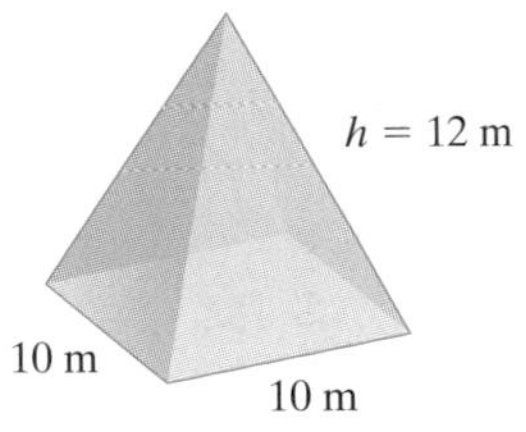

9.

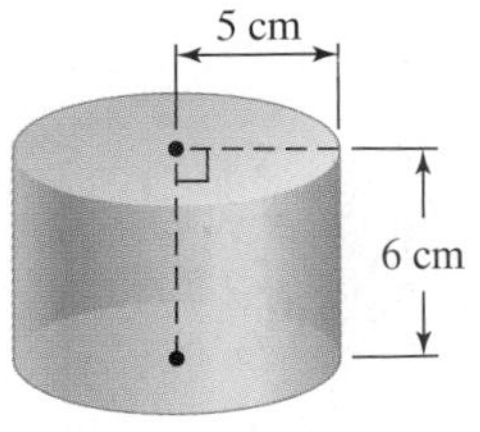

10.

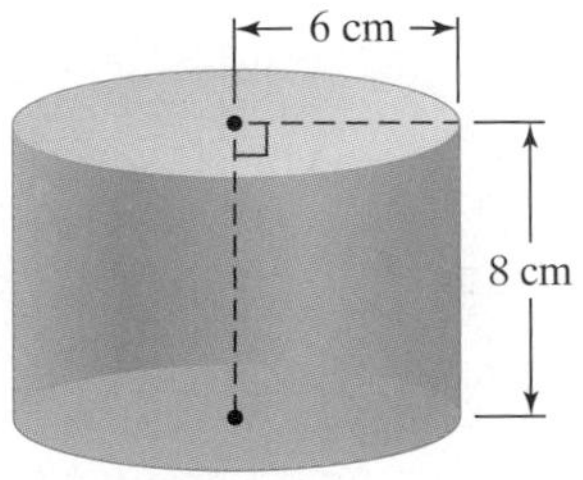

11.

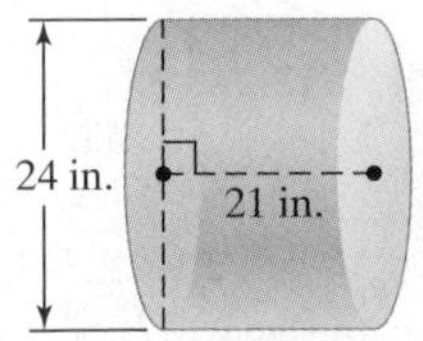

12.

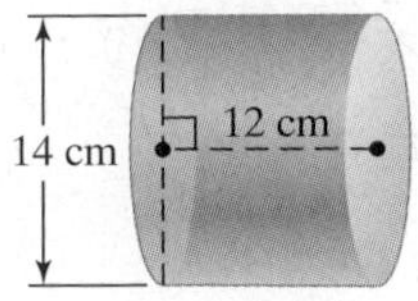

13.

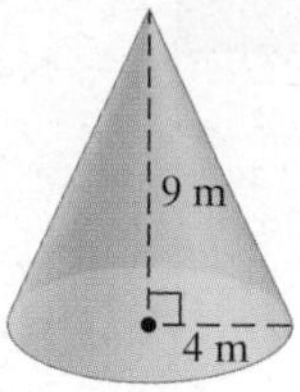

14.

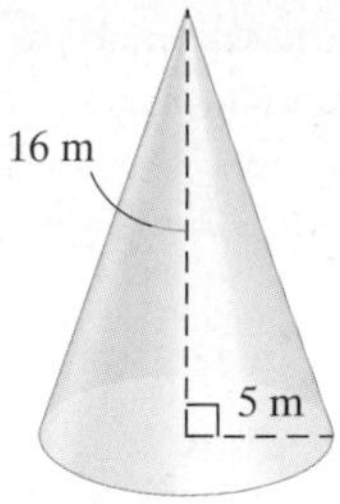

15.

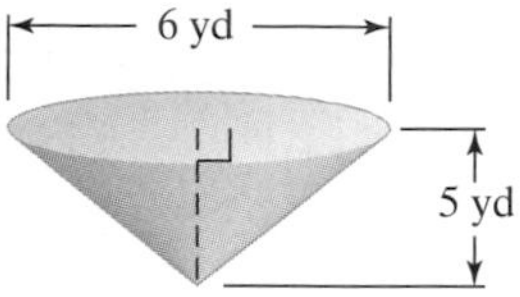

16.

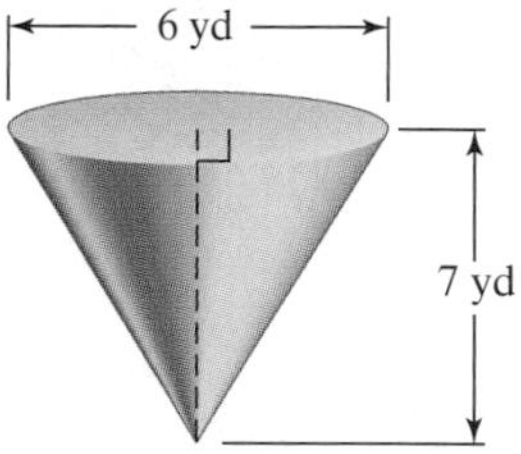

17.

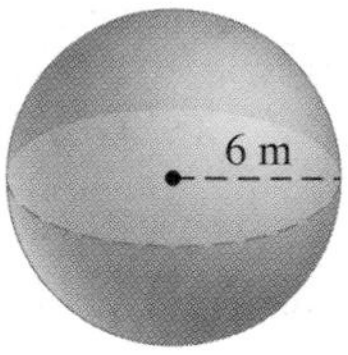

18.

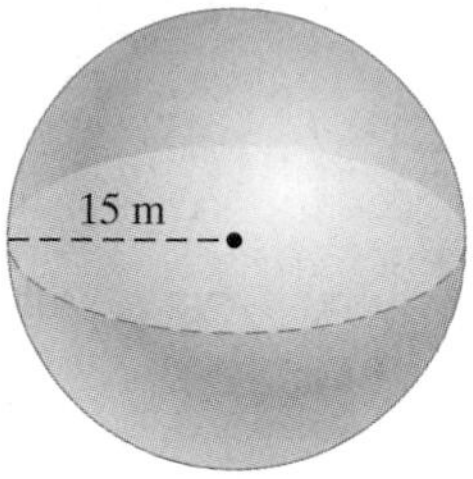

19.

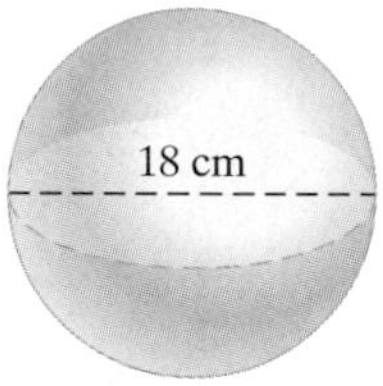

20.

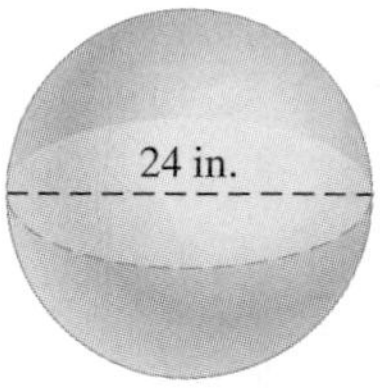

In Exercises 21–24, find the surface area of each figure.

21.

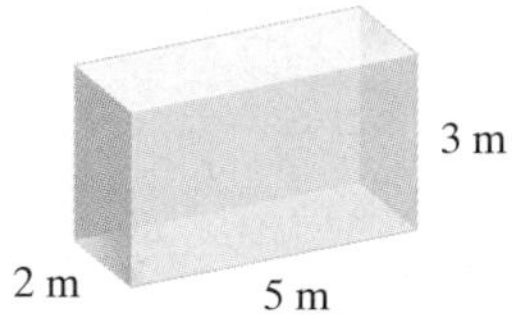

22.

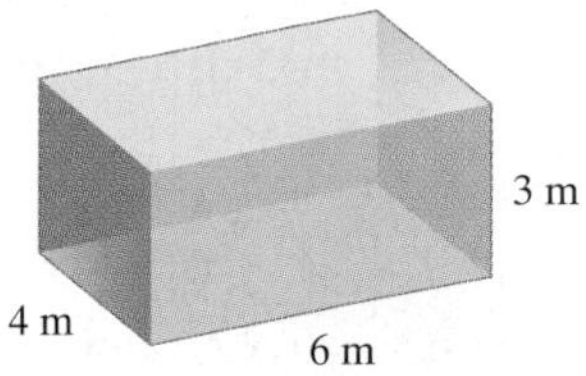

23.

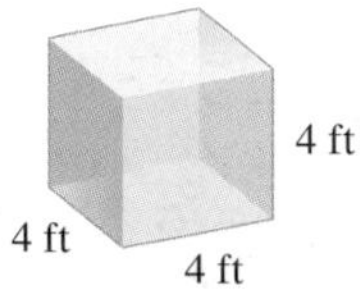

24.

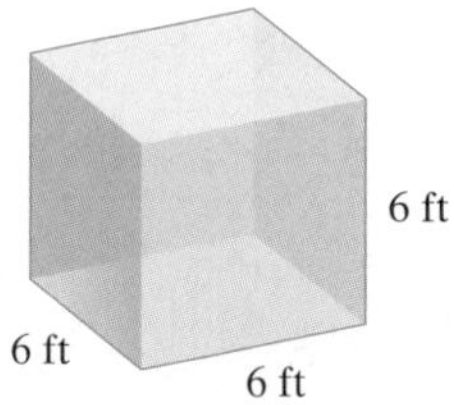

In Exercises 25–26, use two formulas for volume to find the volume of each figure. Express answers in terms of π and then round to the nearest whole number.

25.

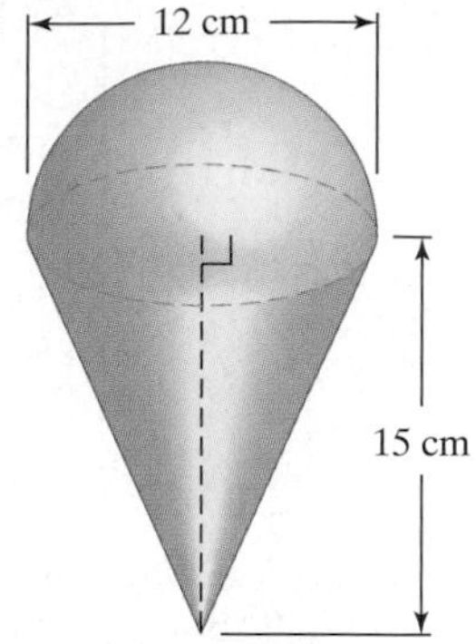

26.

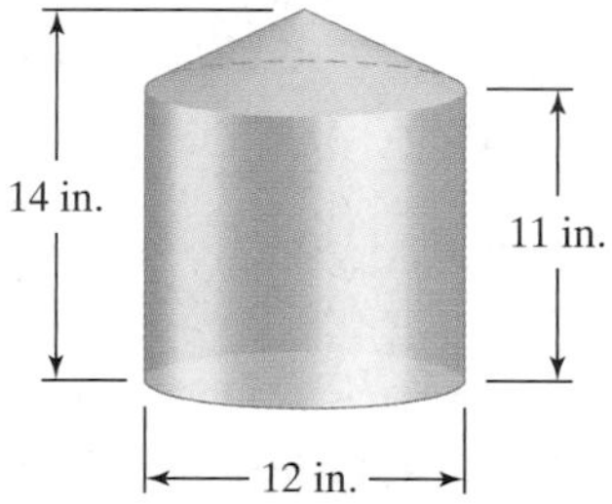

• Practice Plus

27. Find the surface area and the volume of the figure shown.

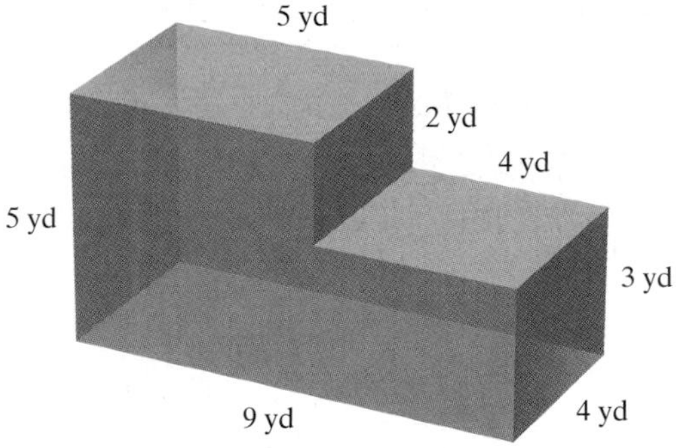

28. Find the surface area and the volume of the cement block in the figure shown.

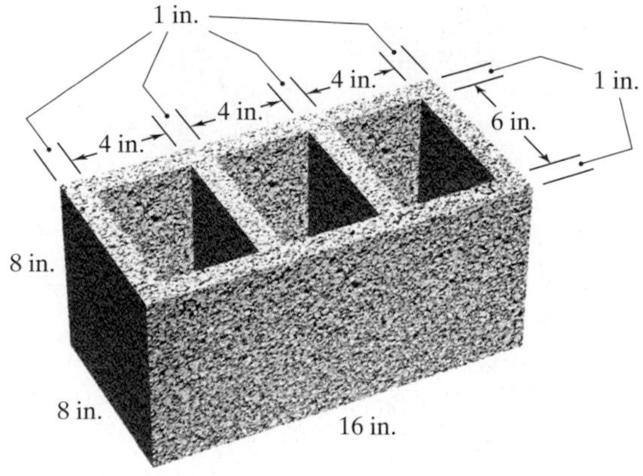

29. Find the surface area of the figure shown.

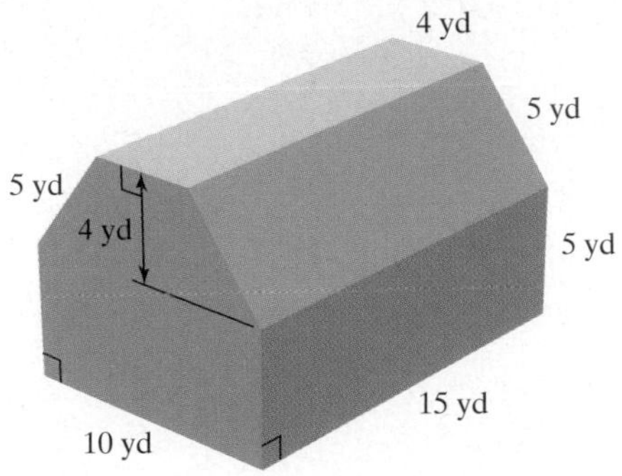

30. A machine produces open boxes using square sheets of metal measuring 12 inches on each side. The machine cuts equal-sized squares whose sides measure 2 inches from each corner. Then it shapes the metal into an open box by turning up the sides. Find the volume of the box.

31. Find the ratio, reduced to lowest terms, of the volume of a sphere with a radius of 3 inches to the volume of a sphere with a radius of 6 inches.

32. Find the ratio, reduced to lowest terms, of the volume of a sphere with a radius of 3 inches to the volume of a sphere with a radius of 9 inches.

33. A cylinder with radius 3 inches and height 4 inches has its radius tripled. How many times greater is the volume of the larger cylinder than the smaller cylinder?

34. A cylinder with radius 2 inches and height 3 inches has its radius quadrupled. How many times greater is the volume of the larger cylinder than the smaller cylinder?

• Application Exercises

35. A building contractor is to dig a foundation 12 feet long, 9 feet wide, and 6 feet deep for a toll booth. The contractor pays \$10 per load for trucks to remove the dirt. Each truck holds 6 cubic yards. What is the cost to the contractor to have all the dirt hauled away?

36. What is the cost of concrete for a walkway that is 15 feet long, 8 feet wide, and 9 inches deep if the concrete costs \$30 per cubic yard?

37. A furnace is designed to heat 10,000 cubic feet. Will this furnace be adequate for a 1400-square-foot house with a 9-foot ceiling?

38. A water reservoir is shaped like a rectangular solid with a base that is 50 yards by 30 yards, and a vertical height of 20 yards. At the start of a three-month period of no rain, the reservoir was completely full. At the end of this period, the height of the water was down to 6 yards. How much water was used in the three-month period?

39. The Great Pyramid outside Cairo, Egypt, has a square base measuring 756 feet on a side and a height of 480 feet.
   a. What is the volume of the Great Pyramid, in cubic yards?
   b. The stones used to build the Great Pyramid were limestone blocks with an average volume of 1.5 cubic yards. How many of these blocks were needed to construct the Great Pyramid?

40. Although the Eiffel Tower in Paris is not a solid pyramid, its shape approximates that of a pyramid with a square base measuring 120 feet on a side and a height of 980 feet. If it were a solid pyramid, what would be the Eiffel Tower's volume, in cubic yards?

41. You are about to sue your contractor who promised to install a water tank that holds 500 gallons of water. You know that 500 gallons is the capacity of a tank that holds 67 cubic feet. The cylindrical tank has a radius of 3 feet and a height of 2 feet 4 inches. Does the evidence indicate you can win the case against the contractor if it goes to court?

42. Two cylindrical cans of soup sell for the same price. One can has a diameter of 6 inches and a height of 5 inches. The other has a diameter of 5 inches and a height of 6 inches. Which can contains more soup and, therefore, is the better buy?

43. A circular backyard pool has a diameter of 24 feet and is 4 feet deep. One cubic foot of water has a capacity of approximately 7.48 gallons. If water costs \$2 per thousand gallons, how much, to the nearest dollar, will it cost to fill the pool?

44. The tunnel under the English Channel that connects England and France is the world's longest tunnel. There are actually three separate tunnels built side by side. Each is a half-cylinder that is 50,000 meters long and 4 meters high. How many cubic meters of dirt had to be removed to build the tunnel?

• Writing in Mathematics

45. Explain the following analogy:

   In terms of formulas used to compute volume, a pyramid is to a rectangular solid just as a cone is to a cylinder.

46. Explain why a cylinder is not a polyhedron.

• Critical Thinking Exercises

47. What happens to the volume of a sphere if its radius is doubled?

48. A scale model of a car is constructed so that its length, width, and height are each $\frac{1}{10}$ the length, width, and height of the actual car. By how many times does the volume of the car exceed its scale model?

In Exercises 49–50, find the volume of the darkly shaded region. If necessary, round to the nearest whole number.

49.

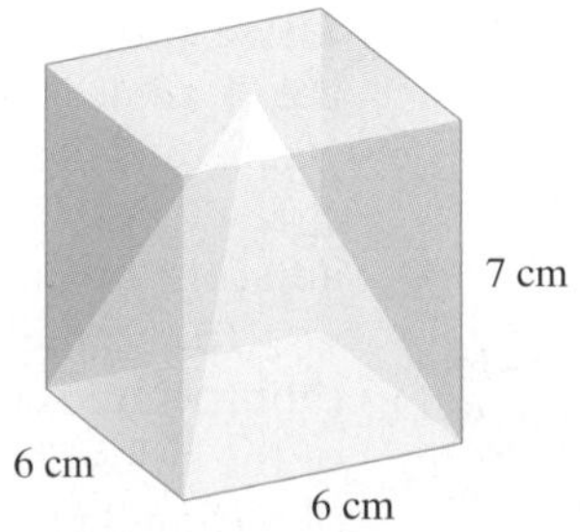

50.

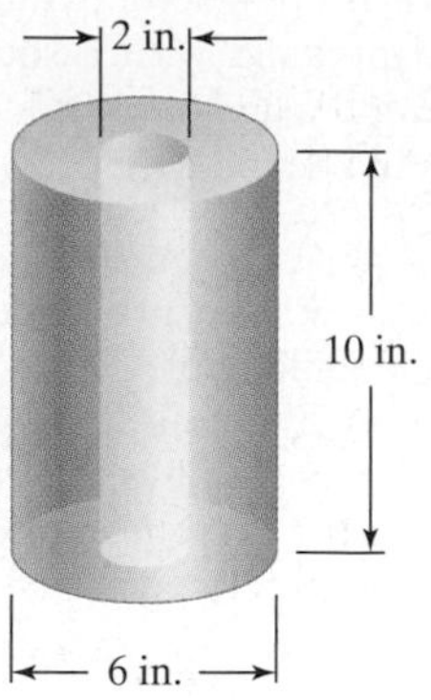

51. Find the surface area of the figure shown.

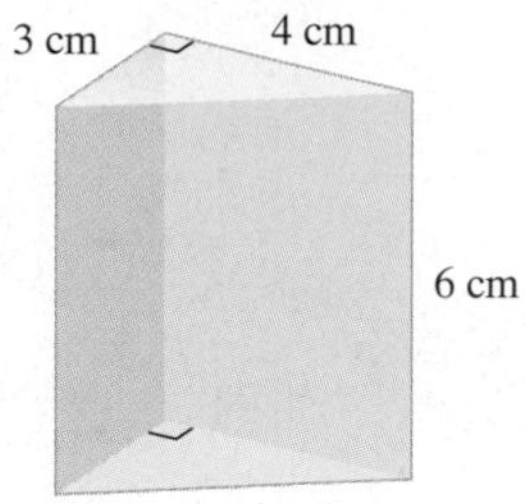

SECTION 10.6 • RIGHT TRIANGLE TRIGONOMETRY

OBJECTIVES

1. Use the lengths of the sides of a right triangle to find trigonometric ratios.
2. Use trigonometric ratios to find missing parts of right triangles.
3. Use trigonometric ratios to solve applied problems.

In the last century, Ang Rita Sherpa climbed Mount Everest ten times, all without the use of bottled oxygen.

Mountain climbers have forever been fascinated by reaching the top of Mount Everest, sometimes with tragic results. The mountain, on Asia's Tibet-Nepal border, is Earth's highest, peaking at an incredible 29,035 feet. The heights of mountains can be found using **trigonometry**. The word *trigonometry* means *measurement of triangles*. Trigonometry is used in navigation, building, and engineering. For centuries, Muslims used trigonometry and the stars to navigate across the Arabian desert to Mecca, the birthplace of the prophet Muhammad, the founder of Islam. The ancient Greeks used trigonometry to record the locations of thousands of stars and worked out the motion of the Moon relative to Earth. Today, trigonometry is used to study the structure of DNA, the master molecule that determines how we grow from a single cell to a complex, fully developed adult.

Ratios in Right Triangles

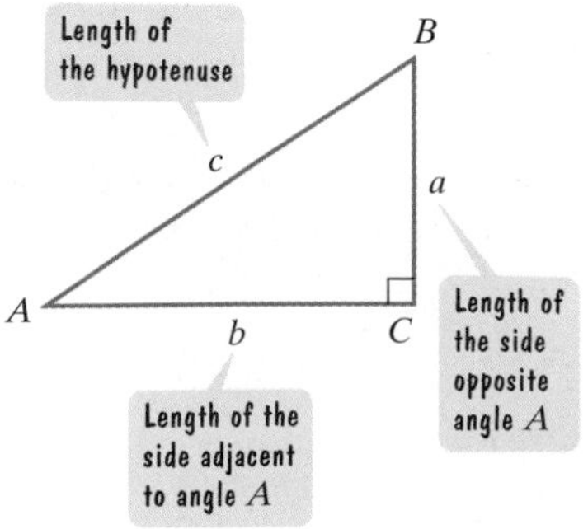

FIGURE 10.56 Naming a right triangle's sides from the point of view of an acute angle

The right triangle forms the basis of trigonometry. If either acute angle of a right triangle stays the same size, the shape of the triangle does not change even if it is made larger or smaller. Because of properties of similar triangles, this means that the ratios of certain lengths stay the same regardless of the right triangle's size. These ratios have special names and are defined in terms of the **side opposite** an acute angle, the **side adjacent** to the acute angle, and the **hypotenuse**. In Figure 10.56, the length of the hypotenuse, the side opposite the 90° angle, is represented by c. The length of the side opposite angle A is represented by a. The length of the side adjacent to angle A is represented by b.

The three fundamental trigonometric ratios, **sine** (abbreviated sin), **cosine** (abbreviated cos), and **tangent** (abbreviated tan), are defined as ratios of the lengths of the sides of a right triangle. In the box that follows on the next page, when a side of a triangle is mentioned, we are referring to the *length* of that side.

1 Use the lengths of the sides of a right triangle to find trigonometric ratios.

TRIGONOMETRIC RATIOS

Let A represent an acute angle of a right triangle, with right angle C, shown in Figure 10.56. For angle A, the trigonometric ratios are defined as follows:

sine of A
$$\sin A = \frac{\text{side opposite angle } A}{\text{hypotenuse}} = \frac{a}{c}$$

cosine of A
$$\cos A = \frac{\text{side adjacent to angle } A}{\text{hypotenuse}} = \frac{b}{c}$$

tangent of A
$$\tan A = \frac{\text{side opposite angle } A}{\text{side adjacent to angle } A} = \frac{a}{b}.$$

STUDY TIP

The word

SOHCAHTOA (pronounced: so-cah-tow-ah)

is a way to remember the definitions of the three trigonometric ratios.

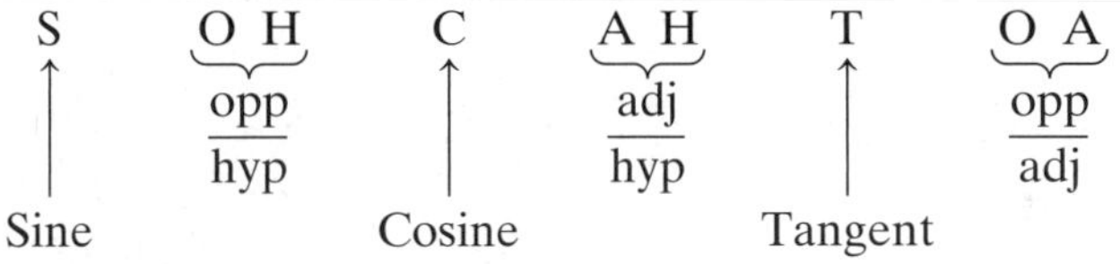

"Some Old Hog Came Around Here and Took Our Apples."

EXAMPLE 1 BECOMING FAMILIAR WITH THE TRIGONOMETRIC RATIOS

Find the sine, cosine, and tangent of A in Figure 10.57.

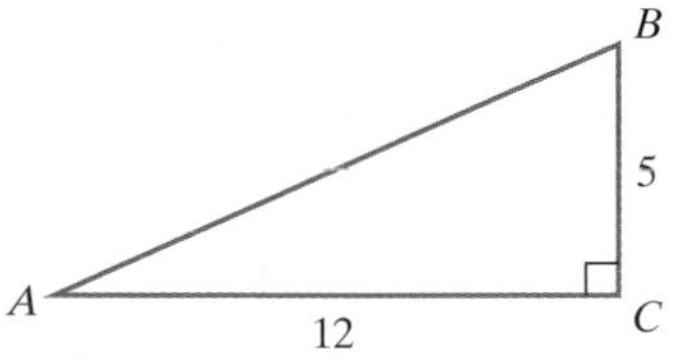

FIGURE 10.57

SOLUTION We begin by finding the measure of the hypotenuse c using the Pythagorean Theorem.

$$c^2 = a^2 + b^2 = 5^2 + 12^2 = 25 + 144 = 169$$
$$c = \sqrt{169} = 13$$

Now, we apply the definitions of the trigonometric ratios.

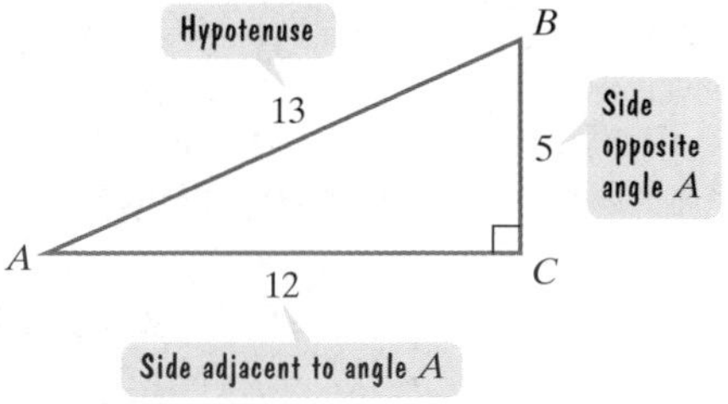

$$\sin A = \frac{\text{side opposite angle } A}{\text{hypotenuse}} = \frac{5}{13}$$
$$\cos A = \frac{\text{side adjacent to angle } A}{\text{hypotenuse}} = \frac{12}{13}$$
$$\tan A = \frac{\text{side opposite angle } A}{\text{side adjacent to angle } A} = \frac{5}{12}$$

CHECK POINT 1 Find the sine, cosine, and tangent of A in the figure shown.

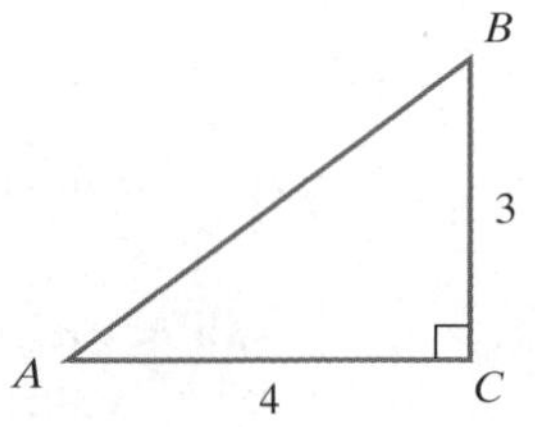

2 Use trigonometric ratios to find missing parts of right triangles.

A scientific or graphing calculator in the degree mode will give you decimal approximations for the trigonometric ratios of any angle. For example, to find an approximation for tan 37°, the tangent of 37°, a keystroke sequence similar to one of the following can be used:

Many Scientific Calculators: 37 [TAN]

Many Graphing Calculators: [TAN] 37 [ENTER].

The tangent of 37°, rounded to four decimal places, is 0.7536.

If we are given the length of one side and the measure of an acute angle of a right triangle, we can use trigonometry to solve for the length of either of the other two sides. Example 2 illustrates how this is done.

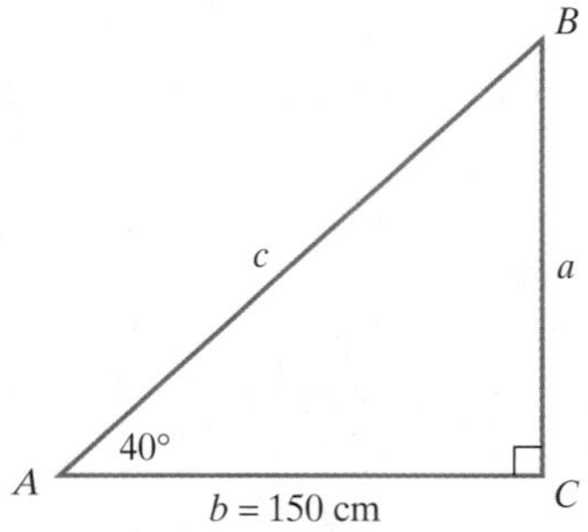

FIGURE 10.58

EXAMPLE 2 FINDING A MISSING LEG OF A RIGHT TRIANGLE

Find a in the right triangle in Figure 10.58.

SOLUTION We need to identify a trigonometric ratio that will make it possible to find a. Because we have a known angle, 40°, an unknown opposite side, a, and a known adjacent side, 150 cm, we use the tangent ratio.

$$\tan 40° = \frac{a}{150}$$

Side opposite the 40° angle

Side adjacent to the 40° angle

Now we solve for a by multiplying both sides by 150.

$$a = 150 \tan 40° \approx 126$$

The tangent ratio reveals that a is approximately 126 centimeters.

CHECK POINT 2 In Figure 10.58, let $m\angle A = 62°$ and $b = 140$ cm. Find a to the nearest centimeter.

TECHNOLOGY

Here is the keystroke sequence for 150 tan 40°:

MANY SCIENTIFIC CALCULATORS

150 [×] 40 [TAN] [=]

MANY GRAPHING CALCULATORS

150 [TAN] 40 [ENTER].

EXAMPLE 3 FINDING A MISSING HYPOTENUSE OF A RIGHT TRIANGLE

Find c in the right triangle in Figure 10.58.

SOLUTION In Example 2, we found a: $a \approx 126$. Because we are given that $b = 150$, it is possible to find c using the Pythagorean Theorem: $c^2 = a^2 + b^2$. However, if we made an error in computing a, we will perpetuate our mistake using this approach.

Instead, we will use the quantities given and identify a trigonometric ratio that will make it possible to find c. Refer to Figure 10.58. Because we have a known angle, 40°, a known adjacent side, 150 cm, and an unknown hypotenuse, c, we use the cosine ratio.

$$\cos 40° = \frac{150}{c}$$

Side adjacent to the 40° angle

Hypotenuse

$c \cos 40° = 150$ Multiply both sides by c.

$c = \dfrac{150}{\cos 40°}$ Divide both sides by cos 40°.

$c \approx 196$ Use a calculator.

The cosine ratio reveals that the hypotenuse is approximately 196 centimeters.

TECHNOLOGY

Here is the keystroke sequence for $\frac{150}{\cos 40°}$:

MANY SCIENTIFIC CALCULATORS

150 [÷] 40 [COS] [=]

MANY GRAPHING CALCULATORS

150 [÷] [COS] 40 [ENTER].

CHECK POINT 3 In Figure 10.58, let $m\angle A = 62°$ and $b = 140$ cm. Find c to the nearest centimeter.

3 Use trigonometric ratios to solve applied problems.

Applications of the Trigonometric Ratios

Trigonometry was first developed to measure heights and distances that are inconvenient or impossible to measure. These applications often involve the angle made with an imaginary horizontal line. As shown in Figure 10.59, an angle formed by a horizontal line and the line of sight to an object that is above the horizontal line is called the **angle of elevation**. The angle formed by a horizontal line and the line of sight to an object that is below the horizontal line is called the **angle of depression**. Transits and sextants are instruments used to measure such angles.

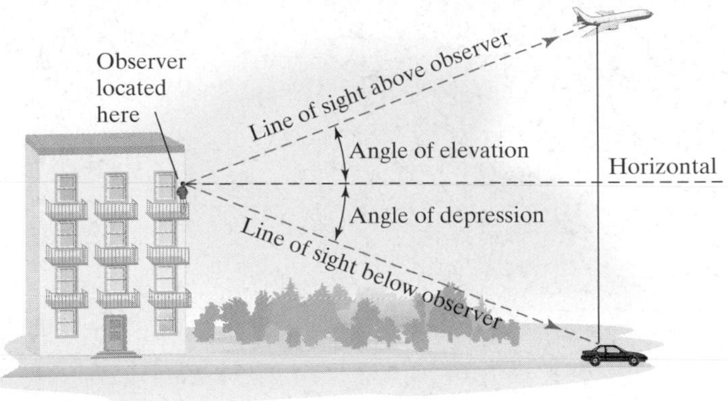

FIGURE 10.59

EXAMPLE 4 PROBLEM SOLVING USING AN ANGLE OF ELEVATION

From a point on level ground 125 feet from the base of a tower, the angle of elevation to the top of the tower is 57.2°. Approximate the height of the tower to the nearest foot.

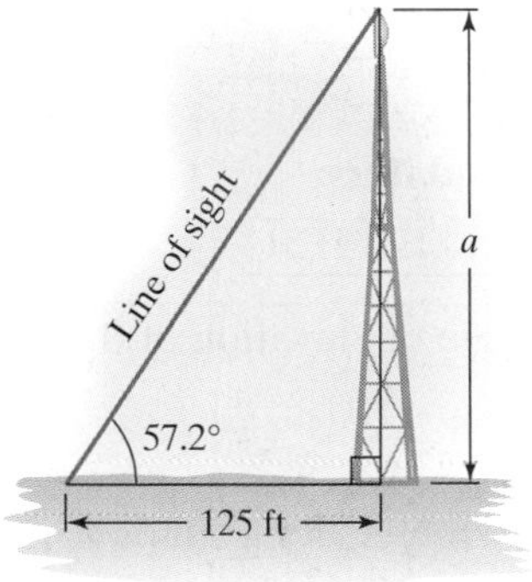

FIGURE 10.60 Determining height without using direct measurement

SOLUTION A sketch is shown in Figure 10.60, where a represents the height of the tower. In the right triangle, we have a known angle, an unknown opposite side, and a known adjacent side. Therefore, we use the tangent ratio.

$$\tan 57.2° = \frac{a}{125}$$

Side opposite the 57.2° angle

Side adjacent to the 57.2° angle

We solve for a by multiplying both sides of this equation by 125:

$$a = 125 \tan 57.2° \approx 194.$$

The tower is approximately 194 feet high.

CHECK POINT 4 From a point on level ground 80 feet from the base of the Eiffel Tower, the angle of elevation is 85.4°. Approximate the height of the Eiffel Tower to the nearest foot.

If the measures of two sides of a right triangle are known, the measures of the two acute angles can be found using the **inverse trigonometric keys** on a calculator. For example, suppose that $\sin A = 0.866$. We can find the measure of angle A by using the *inverse sine* key, usually labeled $\boxed{\text{SIN}^{-1}}$. The key $\boxed{\text{SIN}^{-1}}$ is not a button you will actually press; it is the secondary function for the button labeled $\boxed{\text{SIN}}$.

Many Scientific Calculators:

.866 $\boxed{\text{2nd}}$ $\boxed{\text{SIN}}$

Pressing $\boxed{\text{2nd}}$ $\boxed{\text{SIN}}$ accesses the inverse sine key, $\boxed{\text{SIN}^{-1}}$.

Many Graphing Calculators:

$\boxed{\text{2nd}}$ $\boxed{\text{SIN}}$ .866 $\boxed{\text{ENTER}}$

The display should show approximately 59.99°, which can be rounded to 60°. Thus, if $\sin A = 0.866$, then $m\measuredangle A \approx 60°$.

EXAMPLE 5 DETERMINING THE ANGLE OF ELEVATION

A building that is 21 meters tall casts a shadow 25 meters long. Find the angle of elevation of the sun.

SOLUTION The situation is illustrated in Figure 10.61. We are asked to find $m\measuredangle A$. We begin with the tangent ratio.

$$\tan A = \frac{21}{25}$$

Side opposite A

Side adjacent to A

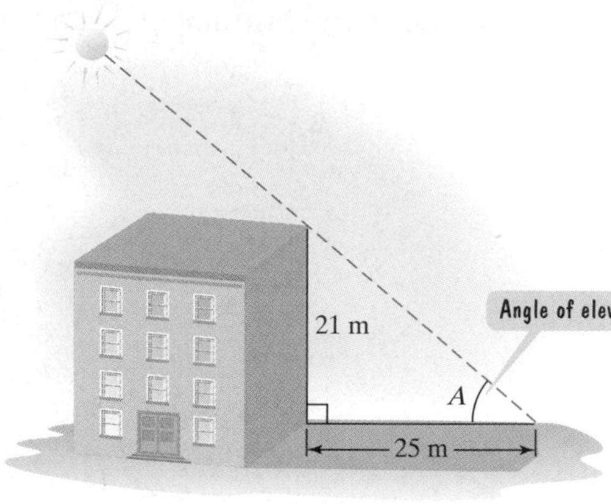

FIGURE 10.61

We use the **inverse tangent** key, $\boxed{\text{TAN}^{-1}}$, to find A.

Many Scientific Calculators:

$\boxed{(}\ 21\ \boxed{\div}\ 25\ \boxed{)}\ \boxed{\text{2nd}}\ \boxed{\text{TAN}}$

Pressing $\boxed{\text{2nd}}\boxed{\text{TAN}}$ accesses the inverse tangent key, $\boxed{\text{TAN}^{-1}}$.

Many Graphing Calculators:

$\boxed{\text{2nd}}\ \boxed{\text{TAN}}\ \boxed{(}\ 21\ \boxed{\div}\ 25\ \boxed{)}\ \boxed{\text{ENTER}}$

The display should show approximately 40. Thus, the angle of elevation of the sun is approximately 40°.

CHECK POINT 5 A flagpole that is 14 meters tall casts a shadow 10 meters long. Find the angle of elevation of the sun to the nearest degree.

BLITZER BONUS

The Mountain Man

In the 1930s, a *National Geographic* team headed by Brad Washburn used trigonometry to create a map of the 5000-square-mile region of the Yukon, near the Canadian border. The team started with aerial photography. By drawing a network of angles on the photographs, the approximate locations of the major mountains and their rough heights were determined. The expedition then spent three months on foot to find the exact heights. Team members established two base points a known distance apart, one directly under the mountain's peak. By measuring the angle of elevation from one of the base points to the peak, the tangent ratio was used to determine the peak's height. The Yukon expedition was a major advance in the way maps are made.

EXERCISE SET 10.6

• Practice Exercises

In Exercises 1–8, use the given right triangles to find ratios, in reduced form, for sin A, cos A, and tan A.

1.

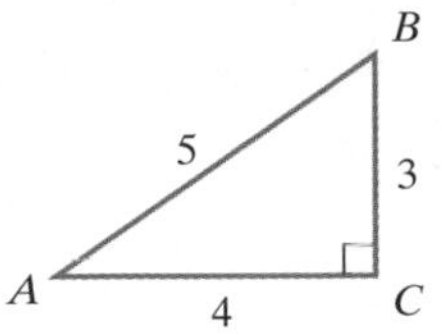

2.

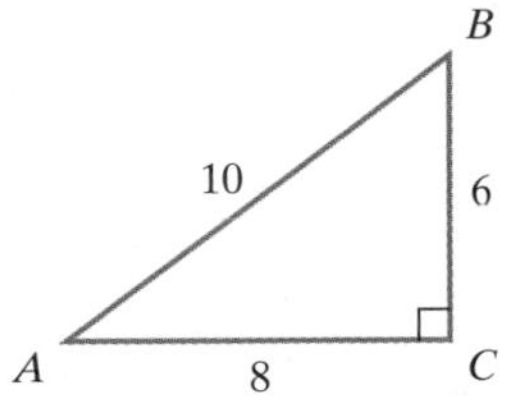

3.

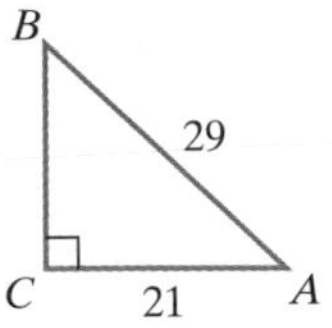

4.

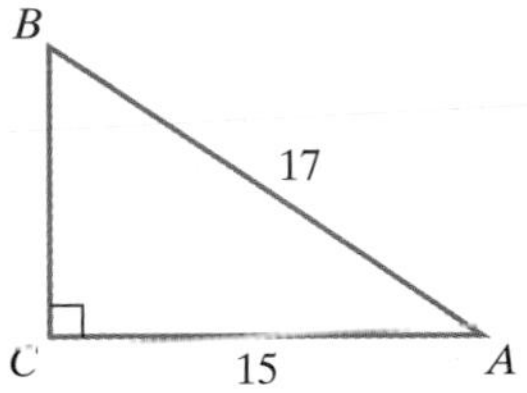

5.

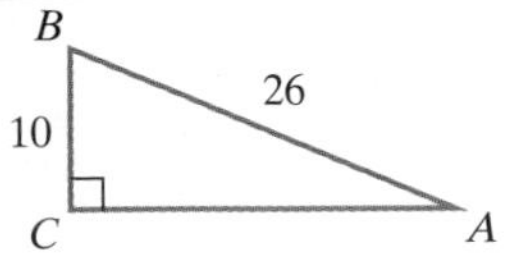

6.

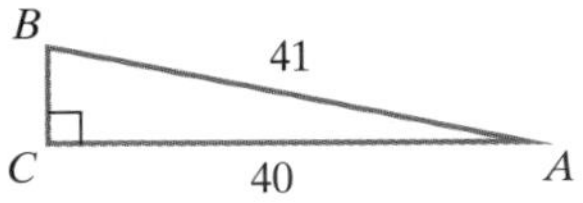

7.

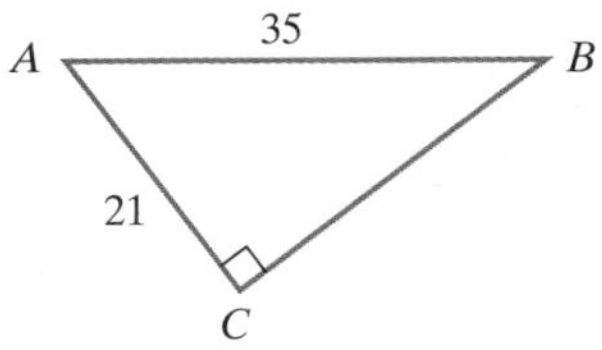

8.

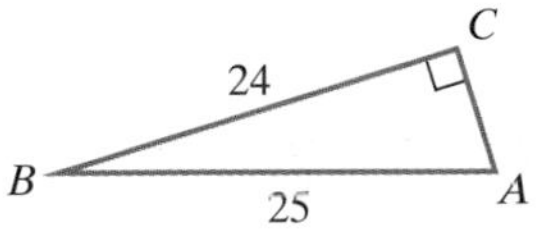

In Exercises 9–18, find the measure of the side of the right triangle whose length is designated by a lowercase letter. Round answers to the nearest whole number.

9.

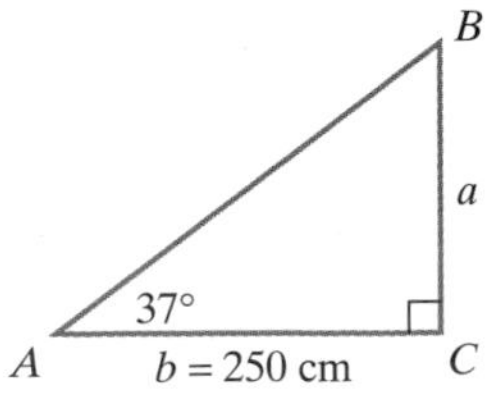

10.

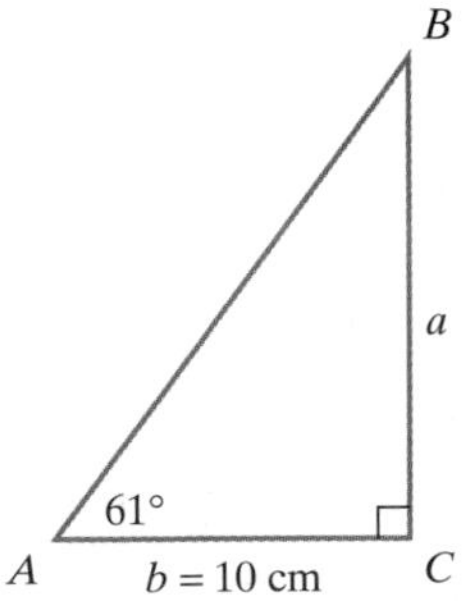

11.

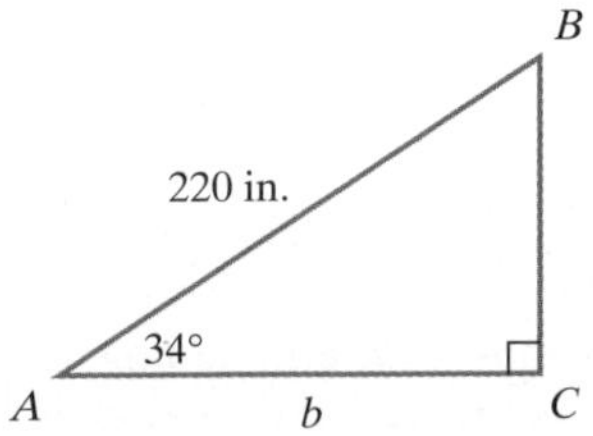

12.

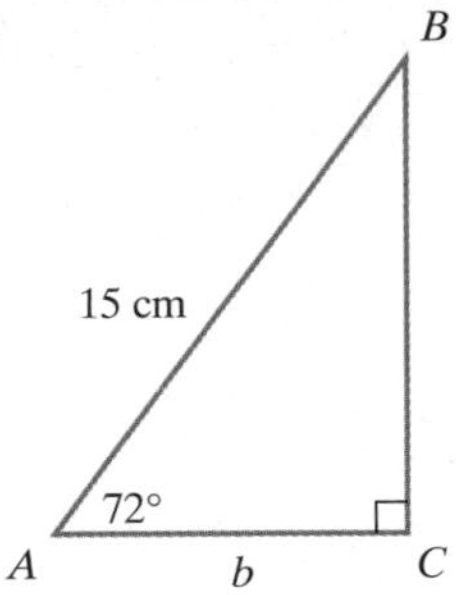

13.

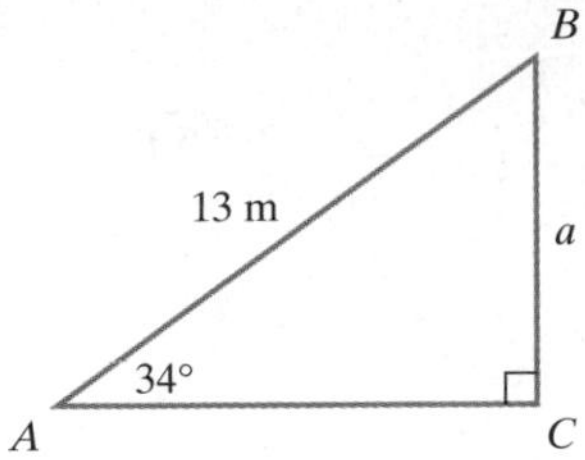

14.

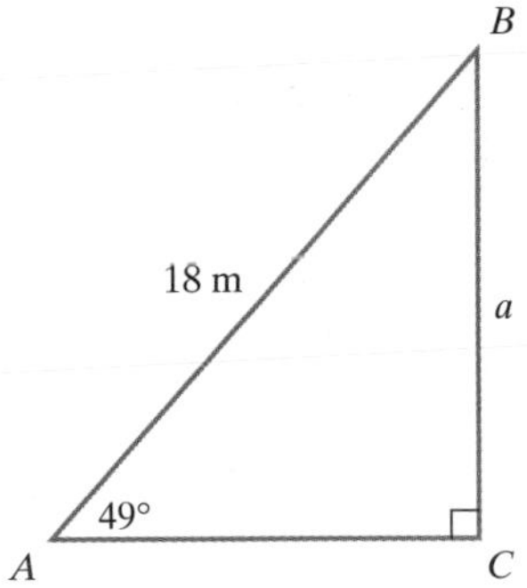

15.

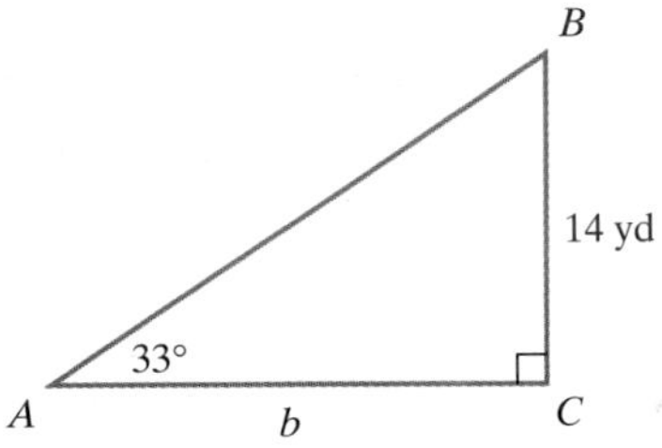

16.

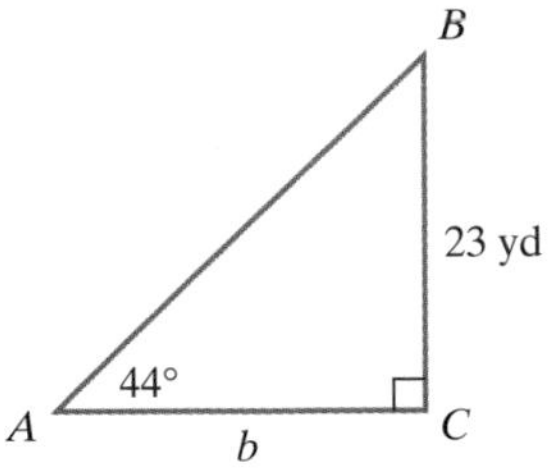

17.

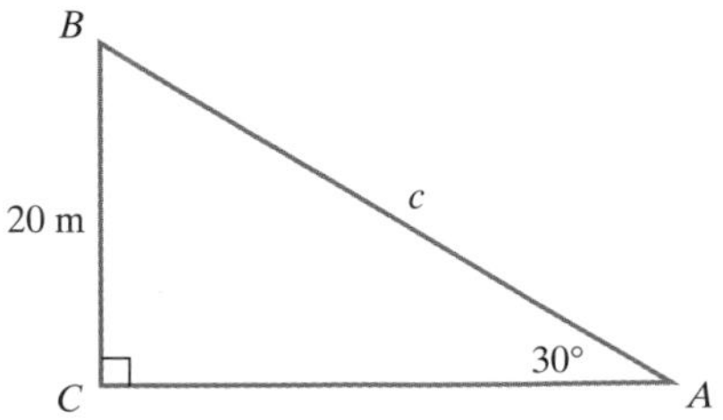

18.

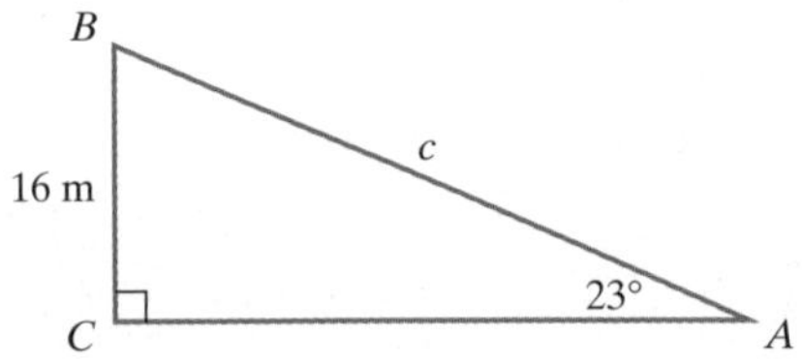

In Exercises 19–22, find the measures of the parts of the right triangle that are not given. Round all answers to the nearest whole number.

19. 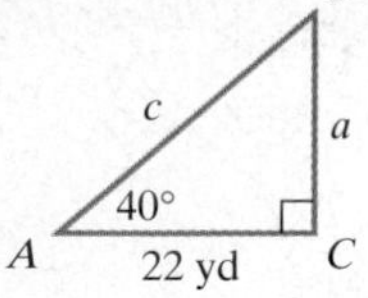

20. 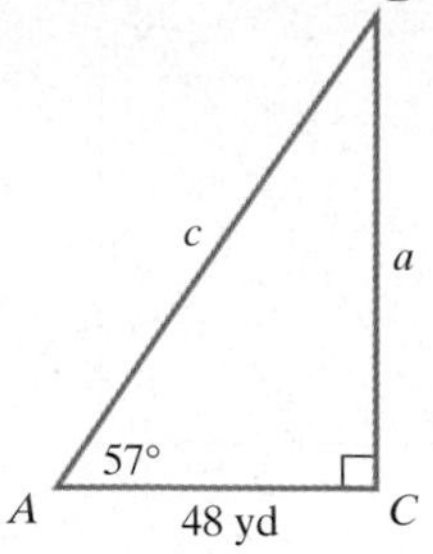

21. 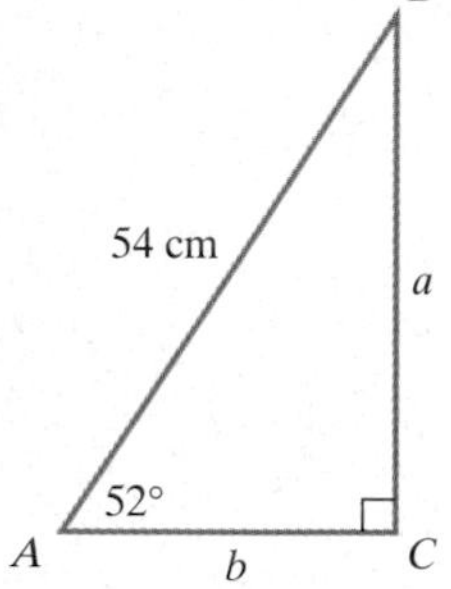

22. 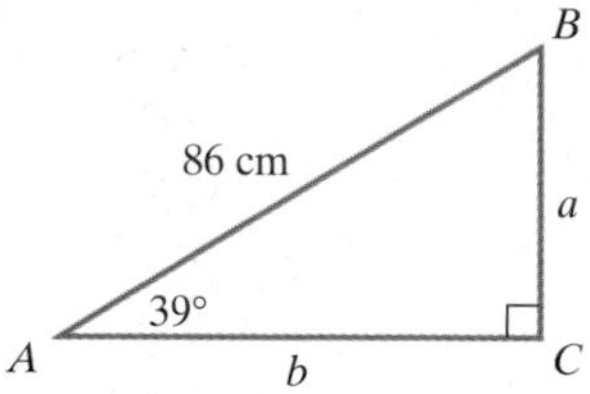

In Exercises 23–26, use the inverse trigonometric keys on a calculator to find the measure of angle A, rounded to the nearest whole degree.

23. 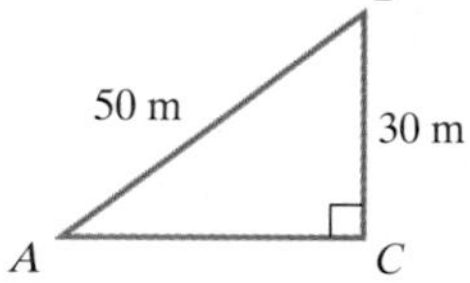

24. 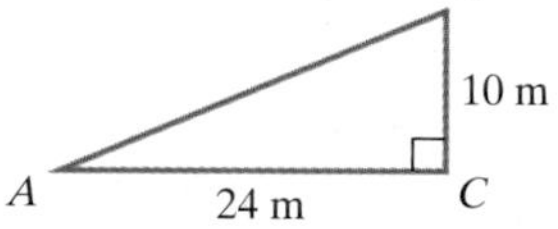

25. 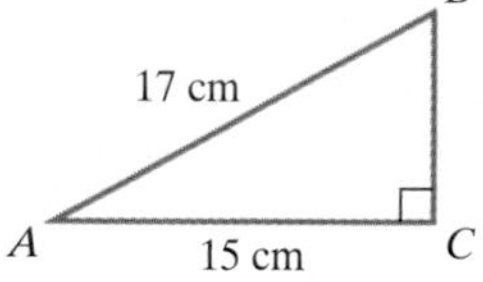

26. 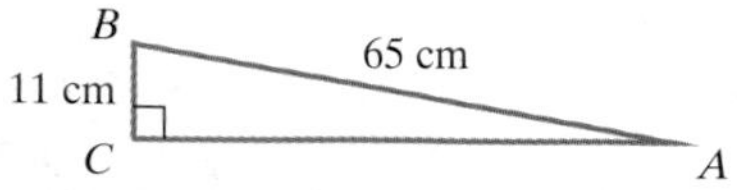

• Practice Plus

In Exercises 27–34, find the length x to the nearest whole number.

27. 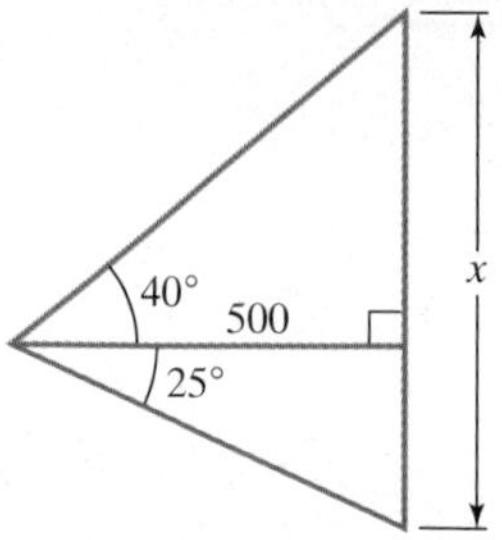

28. 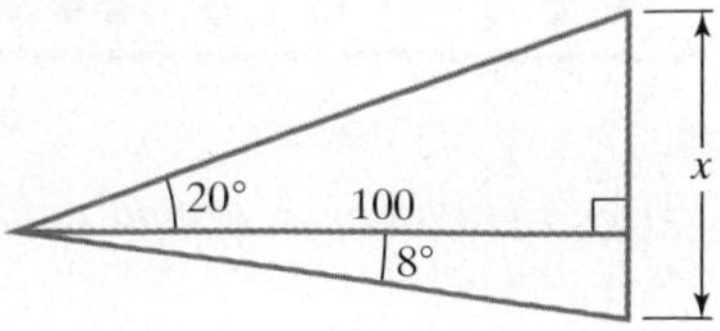

29. 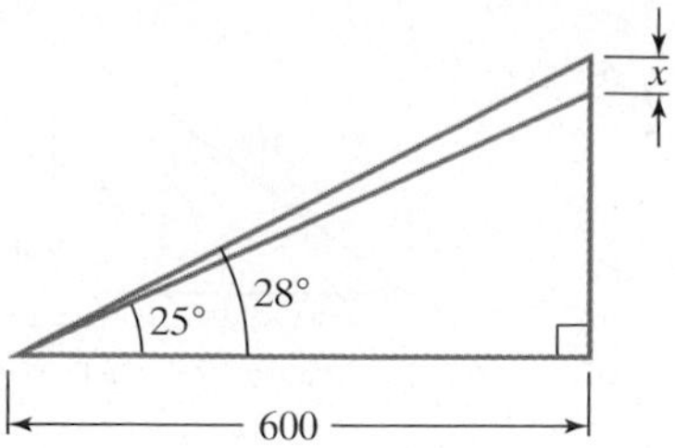

30. 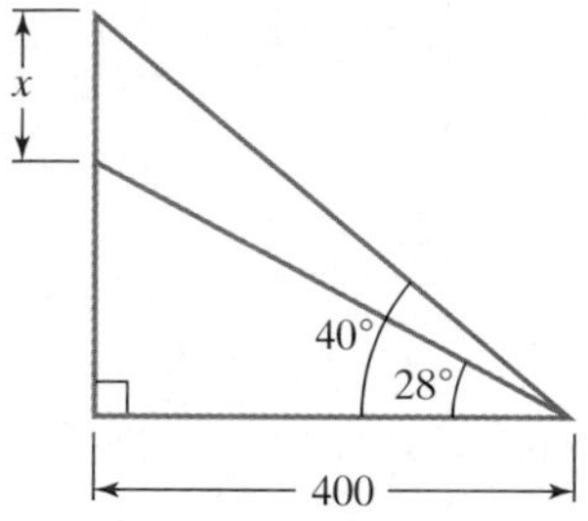

31. 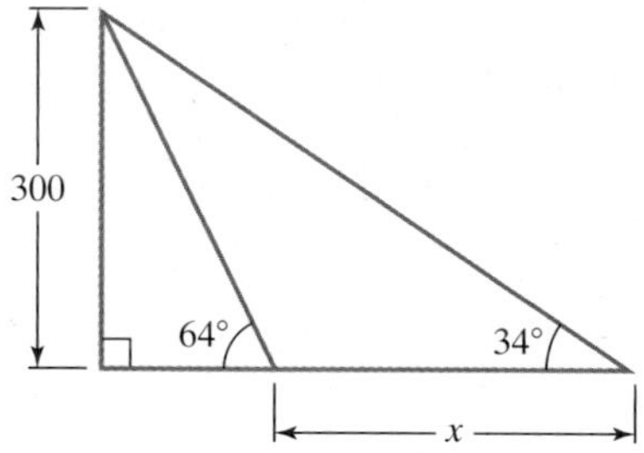

32. 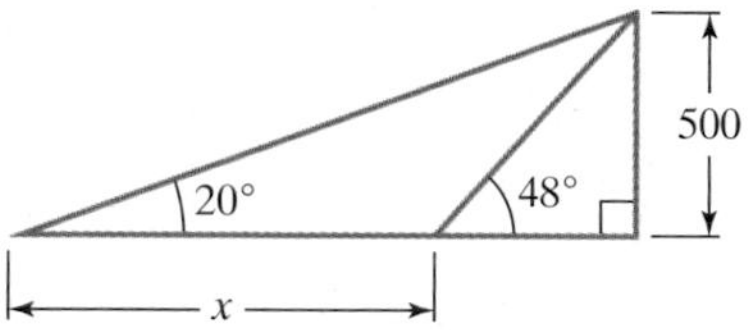

33. 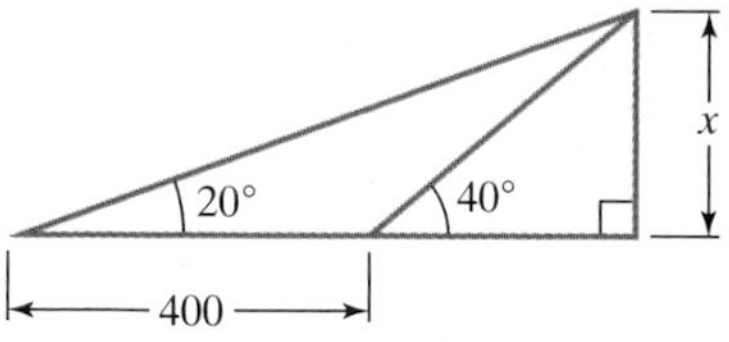

34. 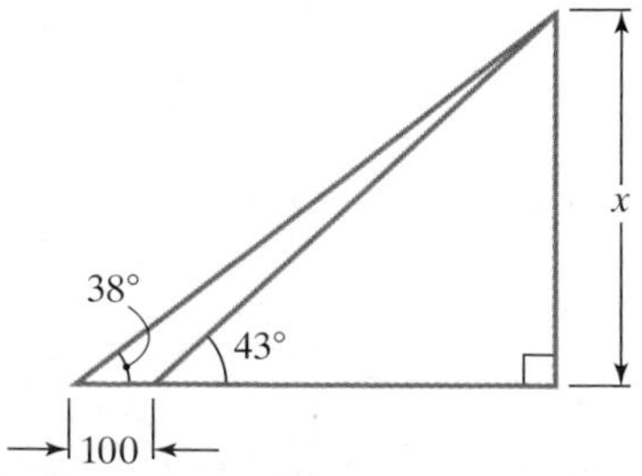

• Application Exercises

35. To find the distance across a lake, a surveyor took the measurements in the figure shown at the top of the next page. Use these measurements to determine how far it is across the lake. Round to the nearest yard.

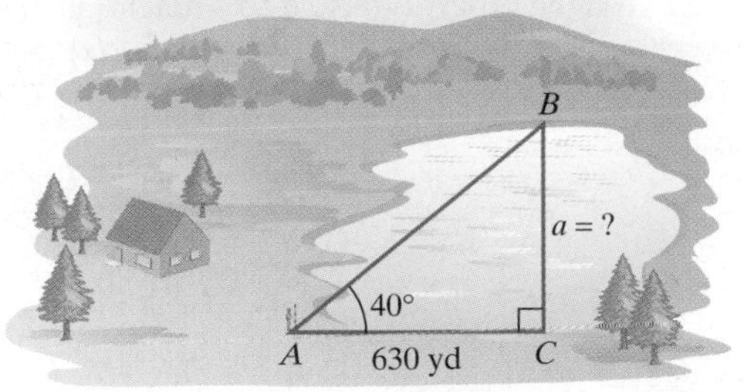

36. At a certain time of day, the angle of elevation of the sun is 40°. To the nearest foot, find the height of a tree whose shadow is 35 feet long.

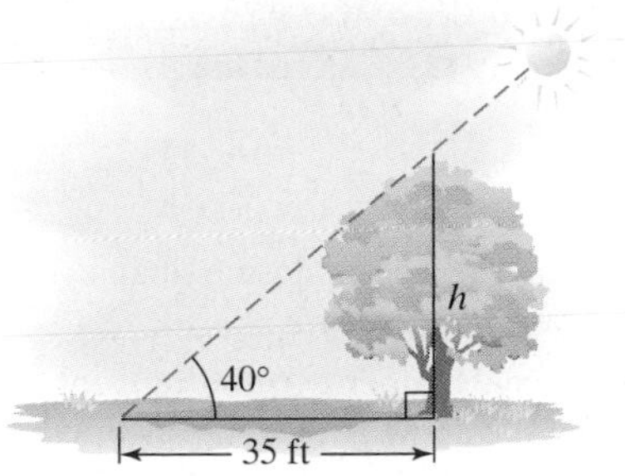

37. A plane rises from take-off and flies at an angle of 10° with the horizontal runway. When it has gained 500 feet in altitude, find the distance, to the nearest foot, the plane has flown.

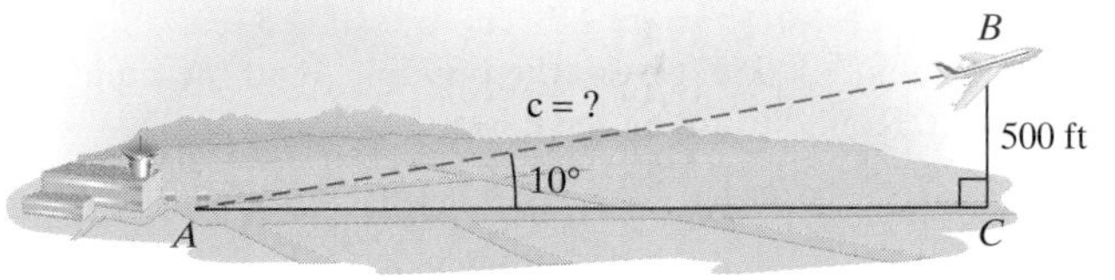

38. A road is inclined at an angle of 5°. After driving 5000 feet along this road, find the driver's increase in altitude. Round to the nearest foot.

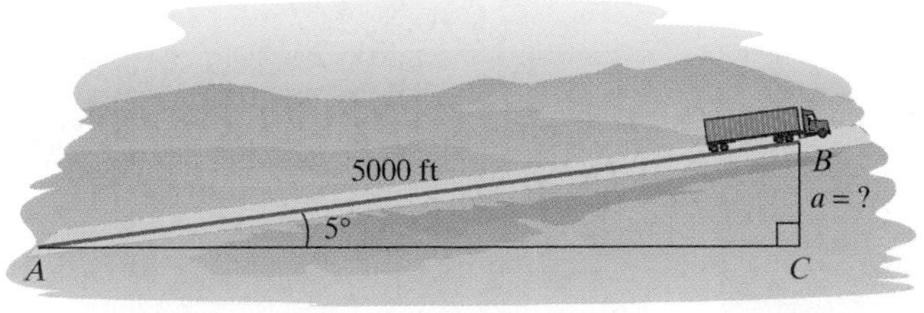

39. The tallest television transmitting tower in the world is in North Dakota. From a point on level ground 5280 feet (one mile) from the base of the tower, the angle of elevation to the top of the tower is 21.3°. Approximate the height of the tower to the nearest foot.

40. From a point on level ground 30 yards from the base of a building, the angle of elevation to the top of the building is 38.7°. Approximate the height of the building to the nearest foot.

41. The Statue of Liberty is approximately 305 feet tall. If the angle of elevation of a ship to the top of the statue is 23.7°, how far, to the nearest foot, is the ship from the statue's base?

42. A 200-foot cliff drops vertically into the ocean. If the angle of elevation of a ship to the top of the cliff is 22.3°, how far off shore, to the nearest foot, is the ship?

43. A tower that is 125 feet tall casts a shadow 172 feet long. Find the angle of elevation of the sun to the nearest degree.

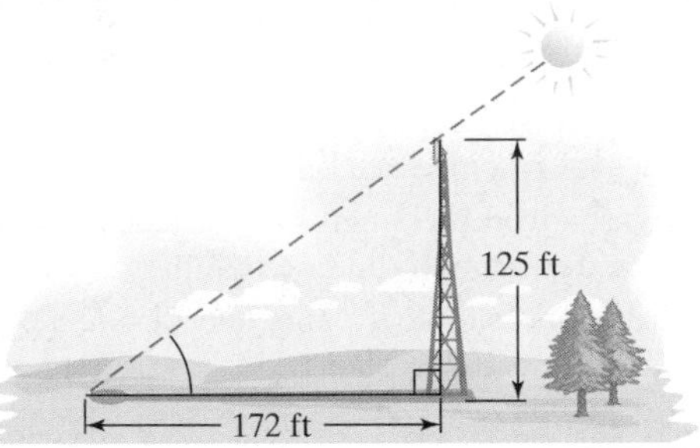

44. The Washington Monument is 555 feet high. If you stand one quarter of a mile, or 1320 feet, from the base of the monument and look to the top, find the angle of elevation to the nearest degree.

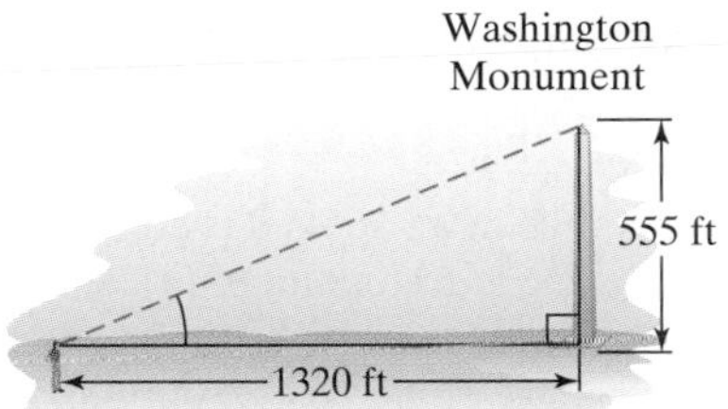

45. A helicopter hovers 1000 feet above a small island. The figure shows that the angle of depression from the helicopter to point P is 36°. How far off the coast, to the nearest foot, is the island?

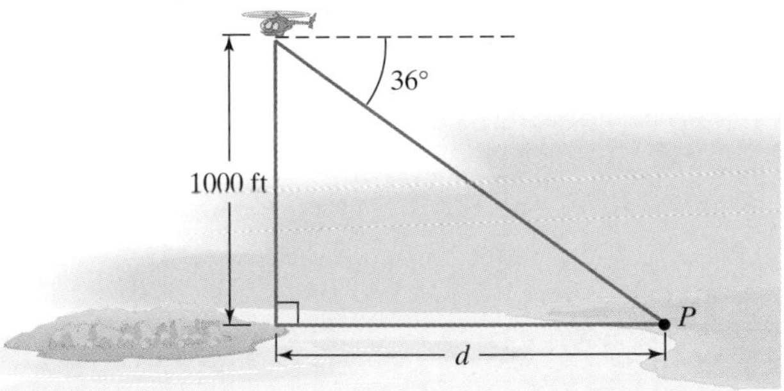

46. A police helicopter is flying at 800 feet. A stolen car is sighted at an angle of depression of 72°. Find the distance of the stolen car, to the nearest foot, from a point directly below the helicopter.

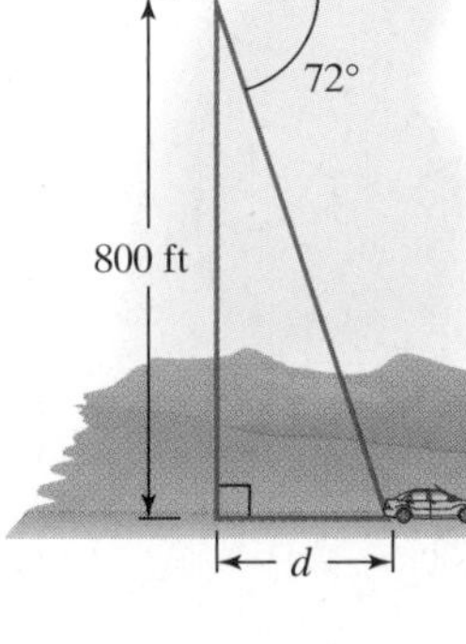

47. A wheelchair ramp is to be built beside the steps to the campus library. Find the angle of elevation of the 23-foot ramp, to the nearest tenth of a degree, if its final height is 6 feet.

48. A kite flies at a height of 30 feet when 65 feet of string is out. If the string is in a straight line, find the angle that it makes with the ground. Round to the nearest tenth of a degree.

• Writing in Mathematics

49. If you are given the lengths of the sides of a right triangle, describe how to find the sine of either acute angle.

50. Describe one similarity and one difference between the sine ratio and the cosine ratio in terms of the sides of a right triangle.

51. If one of the acute angles of a right triangle is 37°, explain why the sine ratio does not increase as the size of the triangle increases.

52. If the measure of one of the acute angles and the hypotenuse of a right triangle are known, describe how to find the measure of the remaining parts of the triangle.

53. Describe what is meant by an angle of elevation and an angle of depression.

54. Give an example of an applied problem that can be solved using one or more trigonometric ratios. Be as specific as possible.

55. Use a calculator to find each of the following: sin 32° and cos 58°; sin 17° and cos 73°; sin 50° and cos 40°; sin 88° and cos 2°. Describe what you observe. Based on your observations, what do you think the *co* in *cosine* stands for?

56. Stonehenge, the famous "stone circle" in England, was built between 2750 B.C. and 1300 B.C. using solid stone blocks weighing over 99,000 pounds each. It required 550 people to pull a single stone up a ramp inclined at a 9° angle. Describe how right triangle trigonometry can be used to determine the distance the 550 workers had to drag a stone in order to raise it to a height of 30 feet.

• Critical Thinking Exercises

57. Explain why the sine or cosine of an acute angle cannot be greater than or equal to 1.

58. Describe what happens to the tangent of an angle as the measure of the angle gets close to 90°. What happens at 90°?

59. From the top of a 250-foot lighthouse, a plane is sighted overhead and a ship is observed directly below the plane. The angle of elevation of the plane is 22° and the angle of depression of the ship is 35°. Find **a.** the distance of the ship from the lighthouse; **b.** the plane's height above the water. Round to the nearest foot.

60. Sighting the top of a building, a surveyor measured the angle of elevation to be 22°. The transit is 5 feet above the ground and 300 feet from the building. Find the building's height. Round to the nearest foot.

SECTION 10.7 • BEYOND EUCLIDEAN GEOMETRY

OBJECTIVE

1. Gain an understanding of some of the general ideas of other kinds of geometries.

Think of your favorite natural setting. During the last quarter of the twentieth century, mathematicians developed a new kind of geometry that uses the computer to produce the diverse forms of nature that we see around us. These forms are not polygons, polyhedrons, circles, or cylinders. In this section, we move beyond Euclidean geometry to explore ideas which have extended geometry beyond the boundaries first laid down by the ancient Greek scholars.

1 Gain an understanding of some of the general ideas of other kinds of geometries.

The Geometry of Graphs

In the early 1700s, the city of Königsberg, Germany, was connected by seven bridges, shown in Figure 10.62. Many people in the city were interested in finding if it were possible to walk through the city so as to cross each bridge exactly once. After a few trials, you may be convinced that the answer is no. However, it is not easy to prove your answer by trial and error because there are a large number of ways of taking such a walk.

STUDY TIP

A more detailed presentation on the geometry of graphs, called *graph theory*, can be found in Chapter 15.

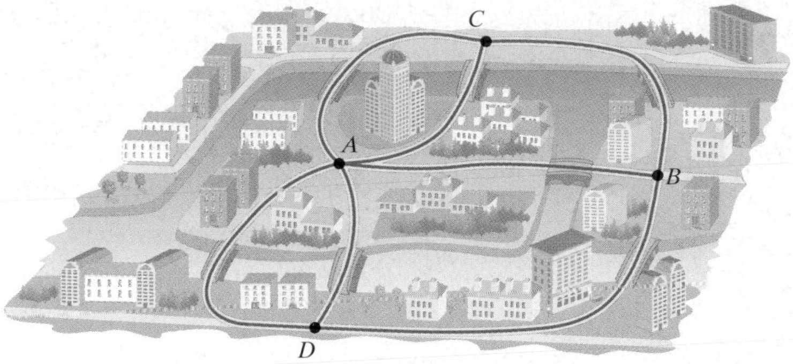

FIGURE 10.62

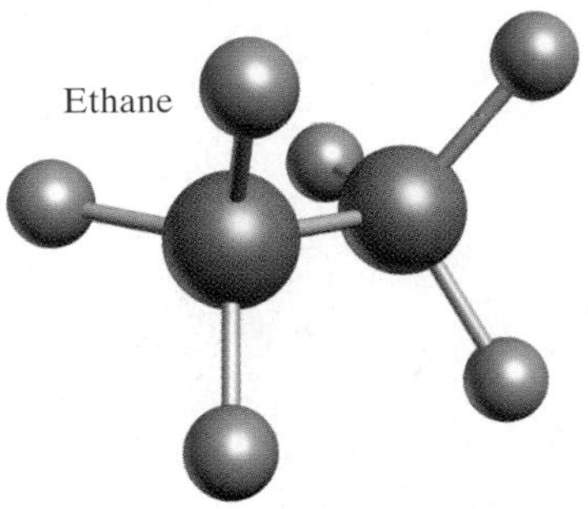

Graph theory is used to show how atoms are linked to form molecules.

The problem was taken to the Swiss mathematician Leonhard Euler (1707–1783). In the year 1736, Euler proved that it is not possible to stroll through the city and cross each bridge exactly once. His solution of the problem opened up a new kind of geometry called **graph theory**. Graph theory is now used to design city streets, analyze traffic patterns, and find the most efficient routes for public transportation.

Euler solved the problem by introducing the following definitions:

A **vertex** is a point. An **edge** is a line segment or curve that starts and ends at a vertex.

Vertices and edges form a **graph**. A vertex with an odd number of attached edges is an **odd vertex**. A vertex with an even number of attached edges is an **even vertex**.

Using these definitions, Figure 10.63 shows that the graph in the Königsberg bridge problem has four odd vertices.

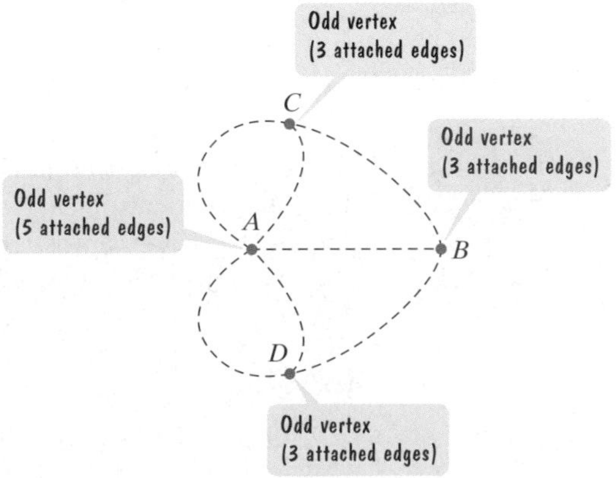

FIGURE 10.63

A graph is **traversable** if it can be traced without lifting the pencil from the paper and without tracing an edge more than once. Euler proved the following rules of traversability in solving the problem:

RULES OF TRAVERSABILITY

1. A graph with all even vertices is traversable. One can start at any vertex and end where one began.
2. A graph with two odd vertices is traversable. One must start at either of the odd vertices and finish at the other.
3. A graph with more than two odd vertices is not traversable.

Because the graph in the Königsberg bridge problem has four odd vertices, it cannot be traversed.

EXAMPLE 1 TO TRAVERSE OR NOT TO TRAVERSE?

Consider the graph in Figure 10.64.

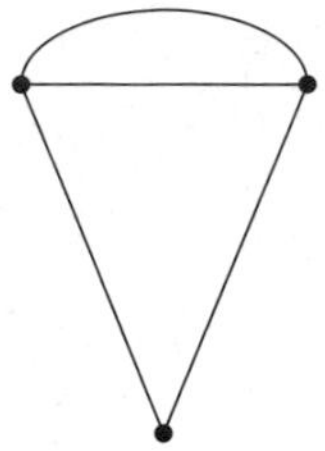

FIGURE 10.64

a. Is this graph traversable?
b. If it is, describe a path that will traverse it.

SOLUTION

a. Begin by determining if each vertex is even or odd.

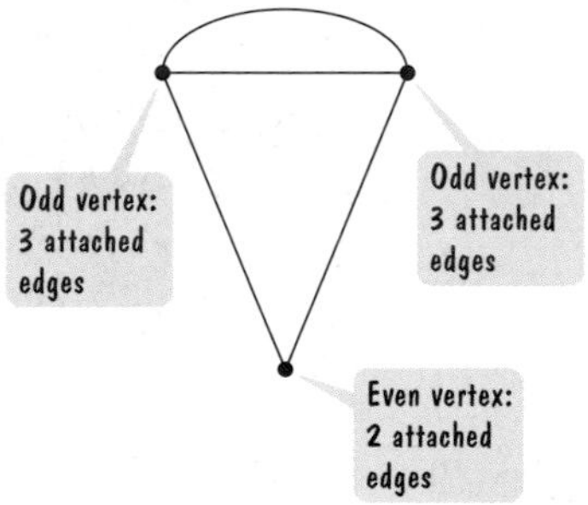

Because this graph has two odd vertices, by Euler's second rule, it is traversable.

b. In order to find a path that traverses this graph, we again use Euler's second rule. It states that we must start at either of the odd vertices and finish at the other. One of two possible paths is shown in Figure 10.65.

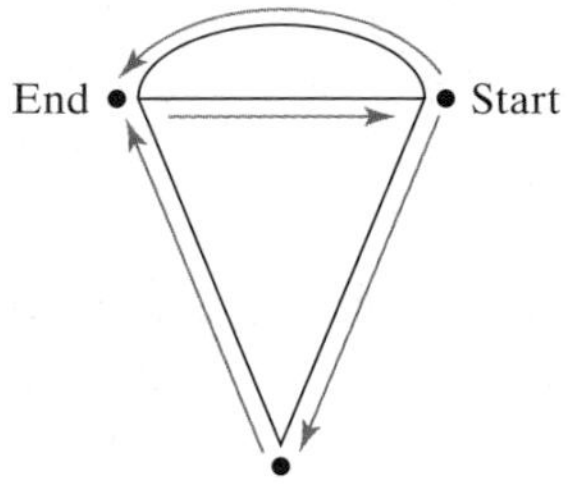

FIGURE 10.65

CHECK POINT 1 Create a graph with two even and two odd vertices. Then describe a path that will traverse it.

Graph theory is used to solve many kinds of practical problems. The first step is to create a graph that represents, or models, the problem. For example, consider a UPS driver trying to find the best way to deliver packages around town. By modeling the delivery locations as vertices and roads between locations as edges, graph theory reveals the driver's most efficient path. Graphs are powerful tools because they illustrate the important aspects of a problem and leave out unnecessary detail.

Topology

A branch of modern geometry called **topology** looks at shapes in a completely new way. In Euclidean geometry, shapes are rigid and unchanging. In topology, shapes can be twisted, stretched, bent, and shrunk. Total flexibility is the rule.

A topologist does not know the difference between a doughnut and a coffee cup! This is because, topologically speaking, there is no difference. They both have one hole, and in this strange geometry of transformations, a doughnut can be flattened, pulled, and pushed to form a coffee cup.

In topology, objects are classified according to the number of holes in them, called their **genus**. The genus gives the largest number of complete cuts that can be made in the object without cutting the object into two pieces. Objects with the same genus are **topologically equivalent**.

The three shapes shown below (sphere, cube, irregular blob) have the same genus: 0. No complete cuts can be made without cutting these objects into two pieces.

STUDY TIP

The genus of an object is the same as the number of holes in the object.

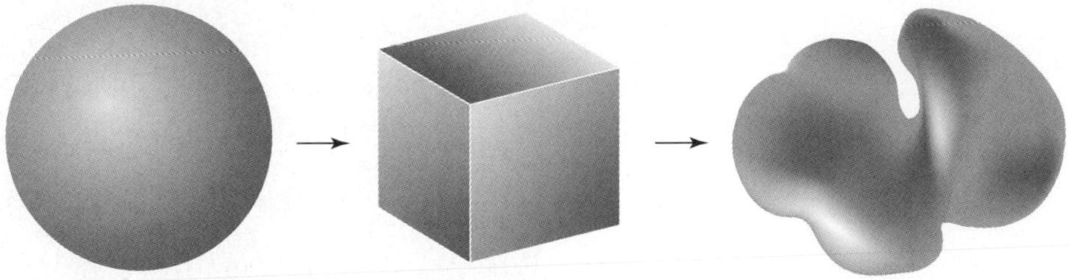

How can a doughnut be transformed into a coffee cup? It can be stretched and deformed to make a bowl part of the surface. Both the doughnut and the coffee cup have genus 1. One complete cut can be made without cutting these objects into two pieces.

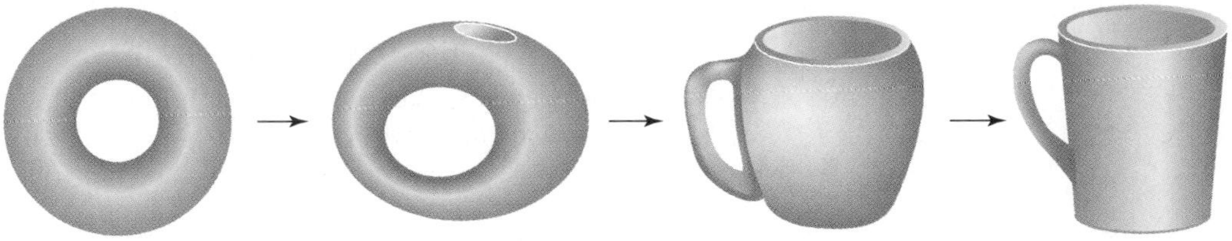

To a topologist, a lump with two holes in it is no different than a sugar bowl with two handles. Both have genus 2. Two complete cuts can be made without cutting these objects into two pieces.

Shown below is a transformation that results in a most unusual topological figure.

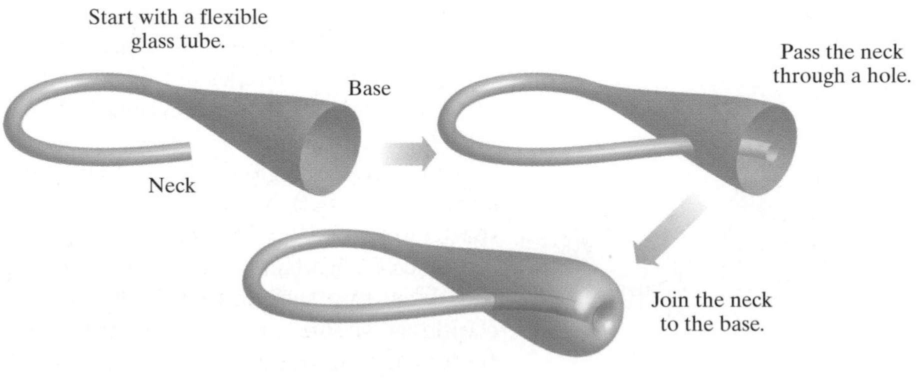

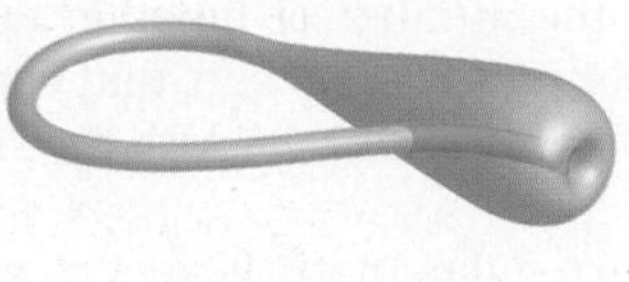
A Klein bottle

The figure that results is called a **Klein bottle**. You couldn't use one to carry water on a long hike. Because the inside surface loops back on itself to merge with the outside, it has neither an outside nor an inside and cannot hold water. A Klein bottle passes through itself without the existence of a hole, which is impossible in three-dimensional space. A true Klein bottle is visible only when generated on a computer.

A Klein bottle generated on a computer

Topology is more than an excursion in geometric fantasy. Topologists study knots and ways in which they are topologically equivalent. Knot theory is used to identify viruses and understand the ways in which they invade our cells. Such an understanding is a first step in finding vaccines for viruses ranging from the common cold to HIV.

Non-Euclidean Geometries

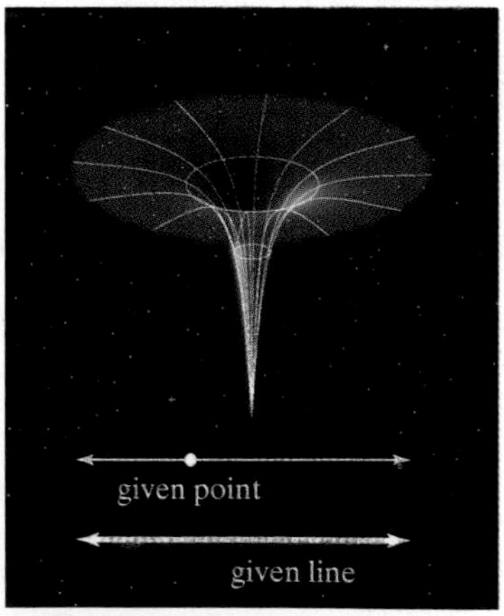

FIGURE 10.66

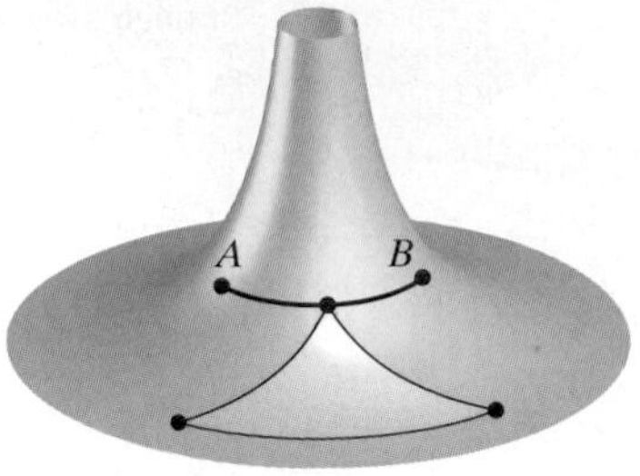

FIGURE 10.67

Imagine this: Earth is squeezed and compressed to the size of a golf ball. It becomes a **black hole**, a region in space where everything seems to disappear. Its pull of gravity is now so strong that the space near the golf ball can be thought of as a funnel with the black hole sitting at the bottom. Any object that comes near the funnel will be pulled into it by the immense gravity of the golf-ball-sized Earth. Then the object disappears! Although this sounds like science fiction, some physicists believe that there are billions of black holes in space.

Is there a geometry that describes this unusual phenomenon? Yes, although it's not the geometry of Euclid. Euclidean geometry is based on the assumption that given a point not on a line, there is one line that can be drawn through the point parallel to the given line, shown as the thinner white line in Figure 10.66. We used this assumption to prove that the sum of the measures of the three angles of any triangle is 180°.

Hyperbolic geometry was developed independently by the Russian mathematician Nikolay Lobachevsky (1792–1856) and the Hungarian mathematician Janos Bolyai (1802–1860). It is based on the assumption that given a point not on a line, there are an infinite number of lines that can be drawn through the point parallel to the given line. The shapes in this non-Euclidean geometry are not represented on a plane. Instead, they are drawn on a funnel-like surface, called a *pseudosphere*, shown in Figure 10.67. On such a surface, the shortest distance between two points is a curved line. A triangle's sides are composed of arcs, and the sum of the measures of its angles is less than 180°. The shape of the pseudosphere looks like the distorted space near a black hole.

Once the ice had been broken by Lobachevsky and Bolyai, mathematicians were stimulated to set up other non-Euclidean geometries. The best known of these was **elliptic geometry**, proposed by the German mathematician Bernhard Riemann (1826–1866). Riemann began his geometry with the assumption that there are no

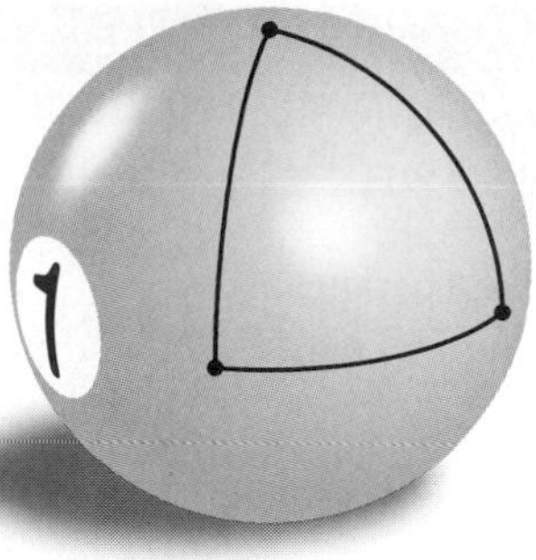

FIGURE 10.68

parallel lines. As shown in Figure 10.68, elliptic geometry is on a sphere, and the sum of the measures of the angles of a triangle is greater than 180°.

Riemann's elliptic geometry was used by Albert Einstein in his theory of the universe. One aspect of the theory states that if you set off on a journey through space and keep going in the same direction, you will eventually come back to your starting point. The same thing happens on the surface of a sphere. This means that space itself is "curved," although the idea is difficult to visualize. It is interesting that Einstein used ideas of non-Euclidean geometry more than 50 years after the system was logically developed. Mathematics often moves ahead of our understanding of the physical world.

BLITZER BONUS

Colorful Puzzles

How many different colors are needed to color a plane map so that any two regions that share a common border are colored differently? Even though no map could be found that required more than four colors, a proof that four colors would work for every map remained elusive to mathematicians for over 100 years. The conjecture that at most four colors are needed, stated in 1852, was proved by American mathematicians Kenneth Appel and Wolfgang Haken of the University of Illinois in 1976. Their proof translated maps into graphs that represented each region as a vertex and each shared common border as an edge between corresponding vertices. The proof relied heavily on computer computations that checked approximately 1500 special cases, requiring 1200 hours of computer time. Although there are recent rumors about a flaw in the proof, no one has found a proof that does not enlist the use of computer calculations.

If you take a strip of paper, give it a single half-twist, and paste the ends together, the result is a one-sided surface called a Möbius strip. A map on a Möbius strip requires six colors to make sure that no adjacent areas are the same color.

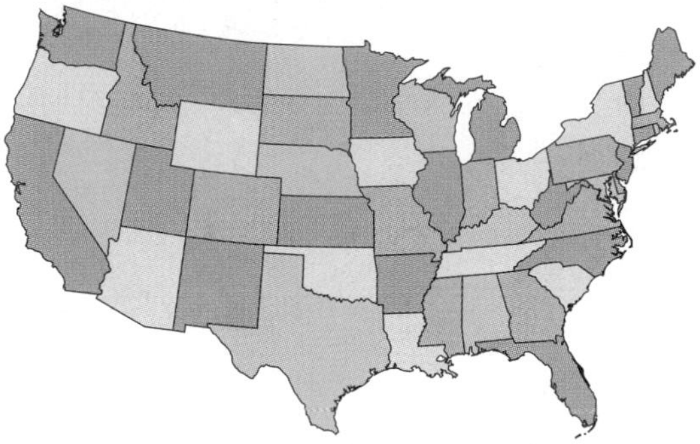

At most four colors are needed on a plane map.

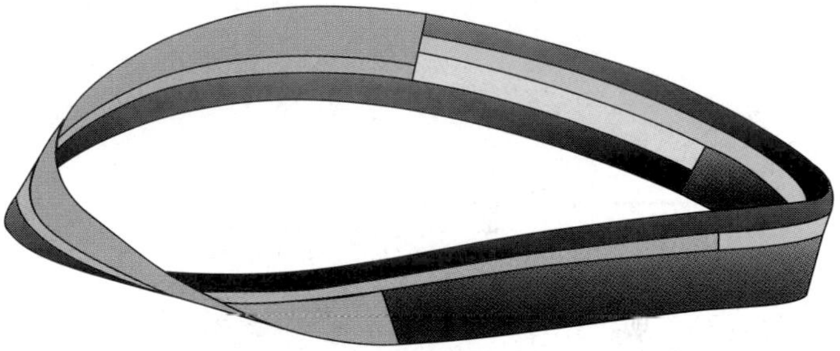

At most six colors are needed on a map drawn on a Möbius strip.

We have seen that Dutch artist M. C. Escher is known for combining art and geometry. Many of his images are based on non-Euclidean geometry. In the woodcut shown on the right, things enlarge as they approach the center and shrink proportionally as they approach the boundary. The shortest distance between two points is a curved line, and the triangles that are formed look like those from hyperbolic geometry.

Table 10.5 on the next page compares Euclidean geometry with hyperbolic and elliptic geometry.

M. C. Escher, *Circle Limit III* © 2004 The M.C. Escher Company, The Netherlands, Baarn, Holland. All rights reserved.

TABLE 10.5 COMPARING THREE SYSTEMS OF GEOMETRY

Euclidean Geometry **Euclid (300 B.C.)**	**Hyperbolic Geometry** **Lobachevsky, Bolyai (1830)**	**Elliptic Geometry** **Riemann (1850)**
Given a point not on a line, there is one and only one line through the point parallel to the given line.	Given a point not on a line, there are an infinite number of lines through the point that do not intersect the given line.	There are no parallel lines.
Geometry is on a plane: 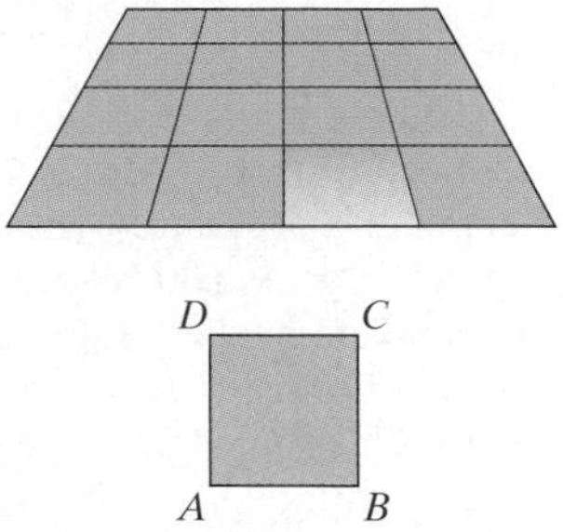	Geometry is on a pseudosphere: 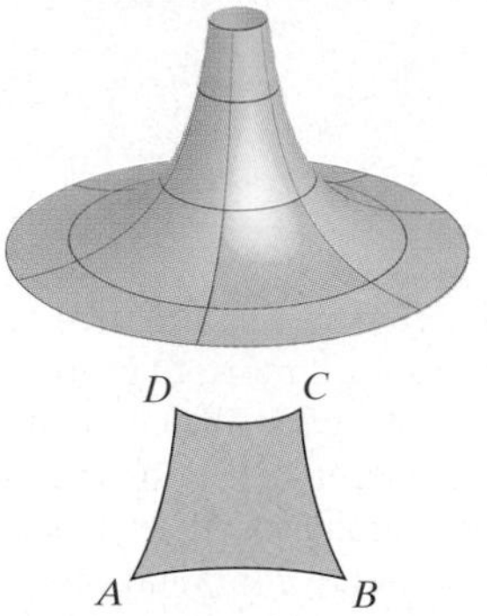	Geometry is on a sphere: 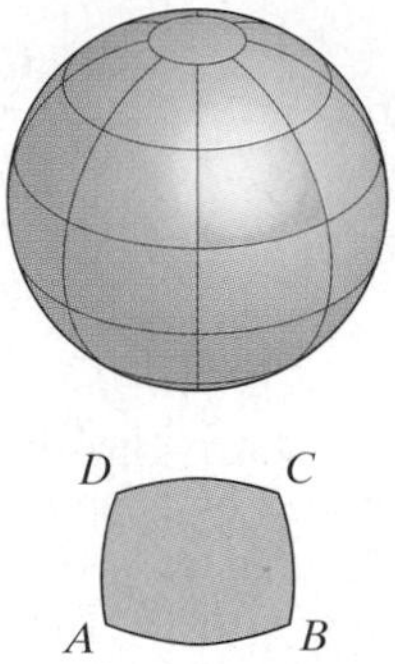
The sum of the measures of the angles of a triangle is 180°. 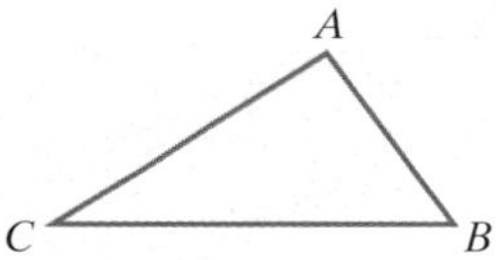	The sum of the measures of the angles of a triangle is less than 180°. 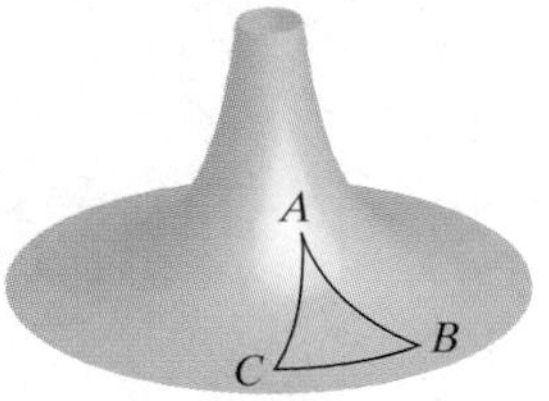	The sum of the measures of the angles of a triangle is greater than 180°. 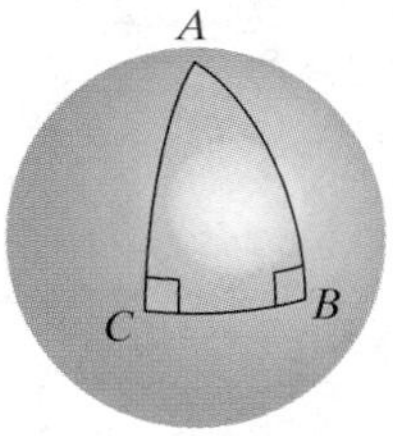

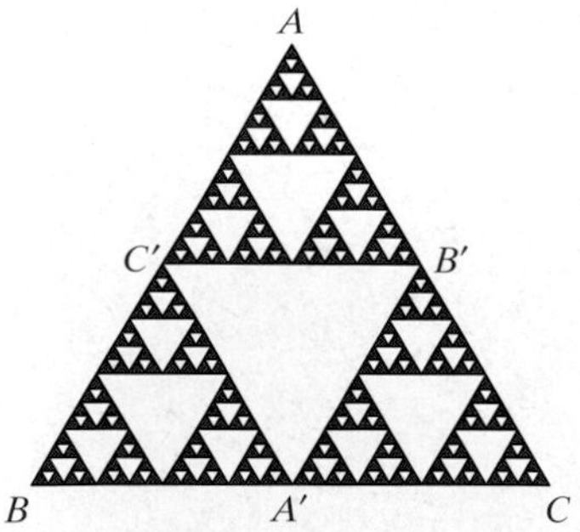

FIGURE 10.69

"I love Euclidean geometry, but it is quite clear that it does not give a reasonable presentation of the world. Mountains are not cones, clouds are not spheres, trees are not cylinders, neither does lightning travel in a straight line. Almost everything around us is non-Euclidean."

Benoit Mandelbrot

Fractal Geometry

How can geometry describe nature's complexity in objects such as ferns, coastlines, or the human circulatory system? Any magnified portion of a fern repeats much of the pattern of the whole fern, as well as new and unexpected patterns. This property is called **self-similarity**.

Magnified portion

Through the use of computers, a new geometry of natural shapes, called **fractal geometry**, has arrived. The word *fractal* is from the Latin word *fractus*, meaning "broken up," or "fragmented." The fractal shape shown in Figure 10.69 is, indeed, broken up. This shape was obtained by repeatedly subtracting triangles from within triangles. From the midpoints of the sides of triangle ABC, remove triangle $A'B'C'$.

FIGURE 10.70 Daryl H. Hepting and Allan N. Snider, "Desktop Tetrahedron" 1990. Computer generated at the University of Regina in Canada

Repeat the process for the three remaining triangles, then with each of the triangles left after that, and so on ad infinitum.

The process of repeating a rule again and again to create a self-similar fractal like the broken-up triangle is called **iteration**. The self-similar fractal shape in Figure 10.70 was generated on a computer by iteration that involved subtracting pyramids within pyramids. Computers can generate fractal shapes by carrying out thousands or millions of iterations.

In 1975, Benoit Mandelbrot (1924–), the mathematician who developed fractal geometry, published *The Fractal Geometry of Nature*. This book of beautiful computer graphics shows images that look like actual mountains, coastlines, underwater coral gardens, and flowers, all imitating nature's forms. Many of the realistic-looking landscapes that you see in movies are actually computer-generated fractal images.

These images are computer-generated fractals.

EXERCISE SET 10.7

• Practice and Application Exercises

For each graph in Exercises 1–6, **a.** *Is the graph traversable?* **b.** *If it is, describe a path that will traverse it.*

1.

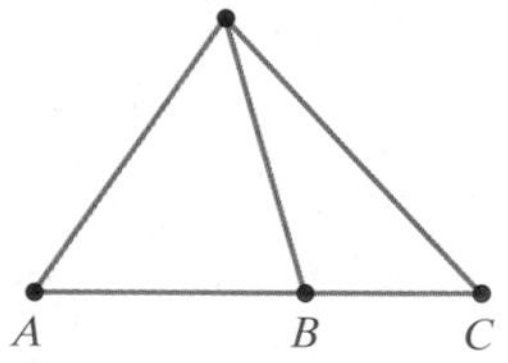

2.

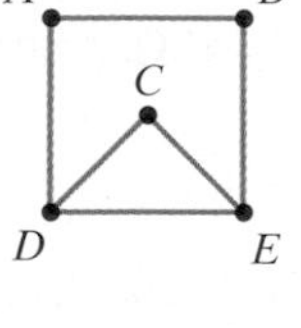

3.

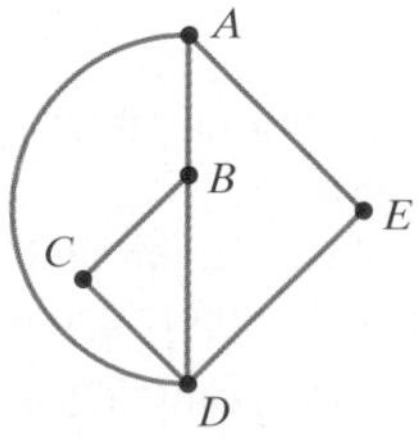

4.

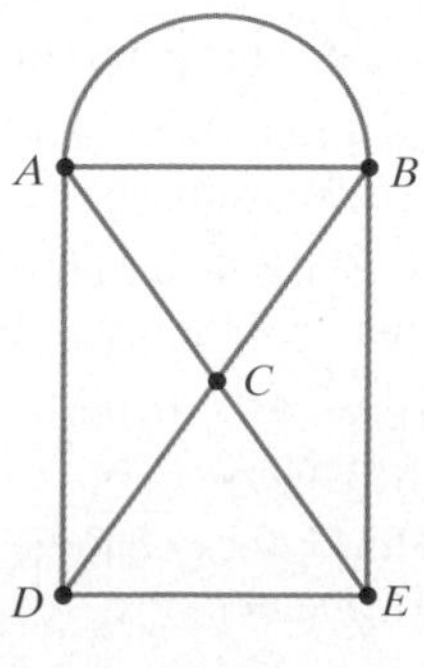

5.

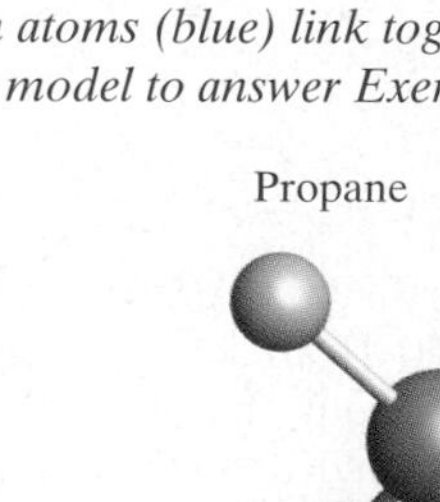

6.

The model shows the way that carbon atoms (red) and hydrogen atoms (blue) link together to form a propane molecule. Use the model to answer Exercises 7–9.

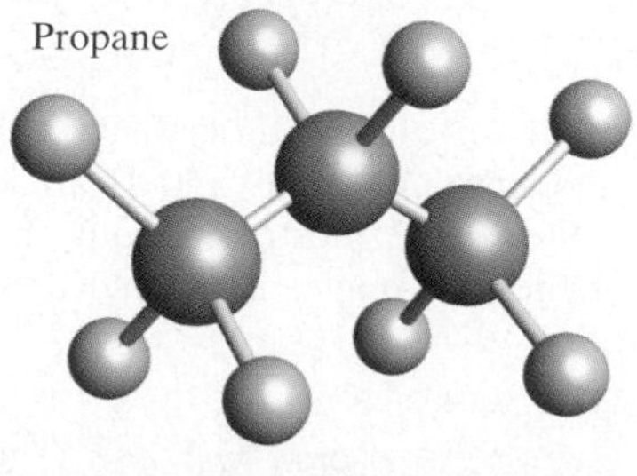

7. Using each of the three red carbon atoms as a vertex and each of the eight black hydrogen atoms as a vertex, draw a graph for the propane molecule.

8. Determine if each vertex of the network is even or odd.
9. Is the network traversable?

The figure on the left shows the floor plan of a four-room house. By representing rooms as vertices, the outside, E, as a vertex, and doors as edges, the figure on the right is a graph that models the floor plan. Use these figures to solve Exercises 10–13.

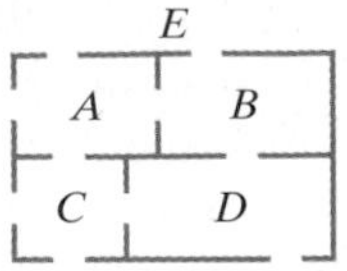

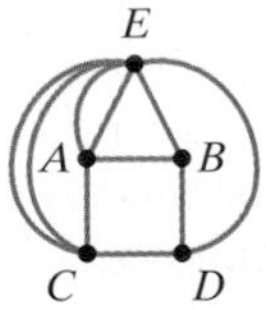

10. Use the floor plan to determine how many doors connect the outside, E, to room A. How is this shown in the graph?
11. Use the floor plan to determine how many doors connect the outside, E, to room C. How is this shown in the graph?
12. Is the graph traversable? Explain your answer.
13. If the graph is traversable, determine a path to walk through every room, using each door only once.

In Exercises 14–17, give the genus of each object.

14.

Pretzel

15.

Pitcher

16.

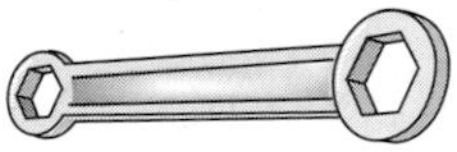

Wrench

17.

Button

18. In Exercises 14–17, which objects are topologically equivalent?
19. Draw (or find and describe) an object of genus 4 or more.
20. What does the figure shown illustrate about angles in a triangle when the triangle is drawn on a sphere?

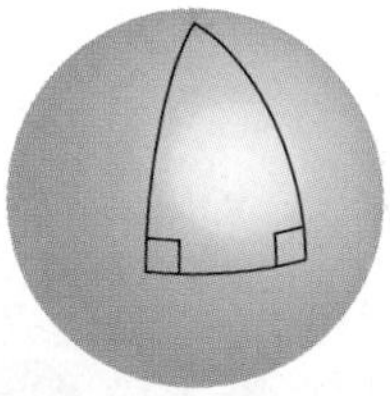

21. The figure shows a quadrilateral that was drawn on the surface of a sphere. Angles C and D are obtuse angles. What does the figure illustrate about the sum of the measures of the four angles in a quadrilateral in elliptic geometry?

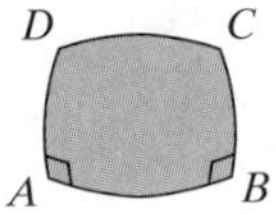

In Exercises 22–24, describe whether each figure shown exhibits self-similarity.

22.

23.

24.

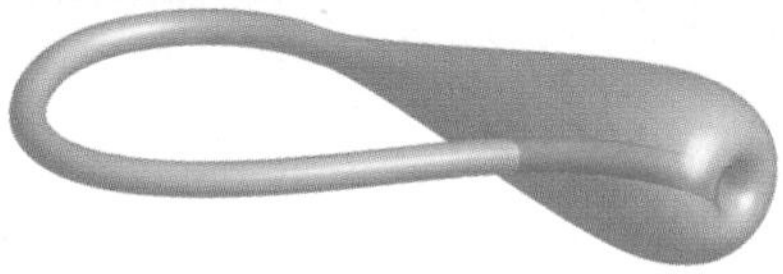

25. Consult an Internet site devoted to fractals and download two fractal images that imitate nature's forms. How is self-similarity shown in each image?

• Writing in Mathematics

26. What is a graph?
27. What does it mean if a graph is traversable?
28. How do you determine whether or not a graph is traversable?
29. Describe one way in which topology is different than Euclidean geometry.
30. What is the genus of an object?
31. Describe how a rectangular solid and a sphere are topologically equivalent.
32. State the assumption that Euclid made about parallel lines that was altered in both hyperbolic and elliptic geometry.
33. How does hyperbolic geometry differ from Euclidean geometry?
34. How does elliptic geometry differ from Euclidean geometry?

35. What is self-similarity? Describe an object in nature that has this characteristic.

36. Some suggest that nature produces its many forms through a combination of both iteration and a touch of randomness. Describe what this means.

37. Find an Internet site devoted to fractals. Use the site to write a paper on a specific use of fractals.

38. Did you know that laid end to end, the veins, arteries, and capillaries of your body would reach over 40,000 miles? However, your vascular system occupies a very small fraction of your body's volume. Describe a self-similar object in nature, such as your vascular system, with enormous length but relatively small volume.

39. Describe a difference between the shapes of man-made objects and objects that occur in nature.

40. Explain what this short poem by Jonathan Swift has to do with fractal images:

So Nat'ralists observe, A Flea
Hath Smaller Fleas that on him prey
and these have smaller Fleas to bite'em
And so proceed, ad infinitum

41. In Tom Stoppard's play *Arcadia*, the characters talk about mathematics, including ideas from fractal geometry. Read the play and write a paper on one of the ideas that the characters discuss that is related to something presented in this section.

• Group Exercises

42. This activity is suggested for two or three people. Research some of the practical applications of topology. Present the results of your research in a seminar to the entire class. You may also want to include a discussion of some of topology's more unusal figures, such as the Klein bottle and the Möbius strip.

43. Research non-Euclidean geometry and plan a seminar based on your group's research. Each group member should research one of the following five areas:

a. Present an overview of the history of the people who developed non-Euclidean geometry. Who first used the term and why did he never publish his work?

b. Present an overview of the connection between Saccheri quadrilaterals and non-Euclidean geometry. Describe the work of Girolamo Saccheri.

c. Describe how Albert Einstein applied the ideas of Gauss and Riemann. Discuss the notion of curved space and a fourth dimension.

d. Present examples of the work of M. C. Escher that provide ways of visualizing hyperbolic and elliptic geometry.

e. Describe how non-Euclidean geometry changed the direction of subsequent research in mathematics.

After all research has been completed, the group should plan the order in which each group member will speak. Each person should plan on taking about five minutes for his or her portion of the presentation.

44. Albert Einstein's theory of general relativity is concerned with the structure, or the geometry, of the universe. In order to describe the universe, Einstein discovered that he needed four variables: three variables to locate an object in space and a fourth variable describing time. This system is known as space-time.

Because we are three-dimensional beings, how can we imagine four dimensions? One interesting approach to visualizing four dimensions is to consider an analogy of a two-dimensional being struggling to understand three dimensions. This approach first appeared in a book called *Flatland* by Edwin Abbott, written around 1884.

Flatland describes an entire race of beings who are two dimensional, living on a flat plane, unaware of the existence of anything outside their universe. A house in Flatland would look like a blueprint or a line drawing to us. If we were to draw a closed circle around Flatlanders, they would be imprisoned in a cell with no way to see out or escape because there is no way to move up and over the circle. For a two-dimensional being moving only on a plane, the idea of up would be incomprehensible. We could explain that up means moving in a new direction, perpendicular to the two dimensions they know, but it would be similar to telling us we can move in the fourth dimension by traveling perpendicular to our three dimensions.

Group members should obtain copies of or excerpts from Edwin Abbott's *Flatland*. We especially recommend *The Annotated Flatland*, Perseus Publishing, 2002, with fascinating commentary by mathematician and author Ian Stewart. Once all group members have read the story, the following questions are offered for group discussion.

a. How does the sphere, the visitor from the third dimension, reflect the same narrow perspective as the Flatlanders?

b. What are some of the sociological problems raised in the story?

c. What happens when we have a certain way of seeing the world that is challenged by coming into contact with something quite different? Be as specific as possible, citing either personal examples or historical examples.

d. How are A. Square's difficulties in visualizing three dimensions similar to those of a three-dimensional dweller trying to visualize four dimensions?

e. How does the author reflect the overt sexism of his time?

f. What "upward not northward" ideas do you hold that, if shared, would result in criticism, rejection, or a fate similar to that of the narrator of *Flatland*?

CHAPTER SUMMARY, REVIEW, AND TEST

SUMMARY DEFINITIONS AND CONCEPTS — EXAMPLES

10.1 Points, Lines, Planes, and Angles

Definitions and Concepts	Examples
a. Line AB ($\overleftrightarrow{AB}$ or $\overleftrightarrow{BA}$), half-line AB ($\overset{\circ\!\!\rightarrow}{AB}$), ray AB ($\overrightarrow{AB}$), and line segment AB ($\overline{AB}$ or $\overline{BA}$) are represented in Figure 10.2 on page 539.	
b. Angles are measured in degrees. A degree, $1°$, is $\frac{1}{360}$ of a complete rotation. Acute angles measure less than $90°$, right angles $90°$, obtuse angles more than $90°$ but less than $180°$, and straight angles $180°$.	Ex. 1, p. 539
c. Complementary angles are two angles whose measures have a sum of $90°$. Supplementary angles are two angles whose measures have a sum of $180°$.	Ex. 2, p. 541; Ex. 3, p. 541
d. Vertical angles have the same measure.	Ex. 4, p. 542
e. If parallel lines are intersected by a transversal, alternate interior angles, alternate exterior angles, and corresponding angles have the same measure.	Ex. 5, p. 543

10.2 Triangles

Definitions and Concepts	Examples
a. The sum of the measures of the three angles of any triangle is $180°$.	Ex. 1, p. 547; Ex. 2, p. 548
b. Triangles can be classified by angles (acute, right, obtuse) or by sides (isosceles, equilateral, scalene). See the box on page 548.	
c. Similar triangles have the same shape, but not necessarily the same size. Corresponding angles have the same measure and corresponding sides are proportional. If the measures of two angles of one triangle are equal to those of two angles of a second triangle, then the two triangles are similar.	Ex. 3, p. 549; Ex. 4, p. 550
d. The Pythagorean Theorem: The sum of the squares of the lengths of the legs of a right triangle equals the square of the length of the hypotenuse.	Ex. 5, p. 551; Ex. 6, p. 552

10.3 Polygons, Perimeter, and Tessellations

Definitions and Concepts	Examples
a. A polygon is a closed geometric figure in a plane formed by three or more line segments. Names of some polygons, given in Table 10.2 on page 556, include triangles (three sides), quadrilaterals (four sides), pentagons (five sides), hexagons (six sides), heptagons (seven sides), and octagons (eight sides). A regular polygon is one whose sides are all the same length and whose angles all have the same measure. The perimeter of a polygon is the sum of the lengths of its sides.	Ex. 1, p. 557
b. Types of quadrilaterals, including the parallelogram, rhombus, rectangle, square, and trapezoid, and their characteristics, are given in Table 10.3 on page 557.	
c. The sum of the measures of the angles of an n-sided polygon is $(n-2)180°$. If the n-sided polygon is a regular polygon, then each angle measures $\frac{(n-2)180°}{n}$.	Ex. 2 p. 558
d. A tessellation is a pattern consisting of the repeated use of the same geometric figures to completely cover a plane, leaving no gaps and having no overlaps. The angle requirement for the formation of a tessellation is that the sum of the measures of the angles at each vertex must be $360°$.	Ex. 3, p. 560

10.4 Area and Circumference

Definitions and Concepts	Examples
a. Formulas for Area Rectangle: $A = lw$; Square: $A = s^2$; Parallelogram: $A = bh$; Triangle: $A = \frac{1}{2}bh$; Trapezoid: $A = \frac{1}{2}h(a + b)$	Ex. 1, p. 565; Ex. 2, p. 566; Ex. 3, p. 567; Ex. 4, p. 567; Ex. 5, p. 568
b. Circles Circumference: $C = 2\pi r$ or $C = \pi d$ Area: $A = \pi r^2$	Ex. 6, p. 569; Ex. 7, p. 569; Ex. 8, p. 570

10.5 Volume

a. Formulas for Volume
Rectangular Solid: $V = lwh$; Cube: $V = s^3$; Pyramid: $V = \frac{1}{3}Bh$;
Cylinder: $V = \pi r^2 h$; Cone: $V = \frac{1}{3}\pi r^2 h$;
Sphere: $V = \frac{4}{3}\pi r^3$
Ex. 1, p. 575; Ex. 2, p. 575; Ex. 3, p. 576; Ex. 4, p. 577; Ex. 5, p. 577; Ex. 6, p. 578

b. Formulas for surface area are given in Table 10.4 on page 579. Ex. 7, p. 579

10.6 Right Triangle Trigonometry

a. Trigonometric ratios, sin A, cos A, and tan A, are defined in the box on page 583. Ex. 1, p. 583

b. Given one side and the measure of an acute angle of a right triangle, the trigonometric ratios can be used to find the measures of the other parts of the right triangle. Ex. 2, p. 584; Ex. 3, p. 584; Ex. 4, p. 585

c. Given the measures of two sides of a right triangle, the measures of the acute angles can be found using the inverse trigonometric ratio keys $\boxed{\text{SIN}^{-1}}$, $\boxed{\text{COS}^{-1}}$, and $\boxed{\text{TAN}^{-1}}$, on a calculator. Ex. 5, p. 586

10.7 Beyond Euclidean Geometry

a. A vertex is a point. An edge is a line segment or curve that starts and ends at a vertex. Vertices and edges form a graph. A vertex with an odd number of edges is odd; one with an even number of edges is even. A traversable graph is one that can be traced without removing the pencil from the paper and without tracing an edge more than once. A graph with all even vertices or one with two odd vertices is traversable. With more than two odd vertices, the graph cannot be traversed. Ex. 1, p. 592

b. In topology, shapes are twisted, stretched, bent, and shrunk. The genus of an object refers to the number of holes in the object. Objects with the same genus are topologically equivalent.

c. Non-Euclidean geometries, including hyperbolic geometry and elliptic geometry, are outlined in Table 10.5 on page 596.

d. Fractal geometry includes self-similar forms; magnified portions of such forms repeat much of the pattern of the whole form.

REVIEW EXERCISES

10.1

In the figure shown, lines l and m are parallel. In Exercises 1–7, match each term with the numbered angle or angles in the figure.

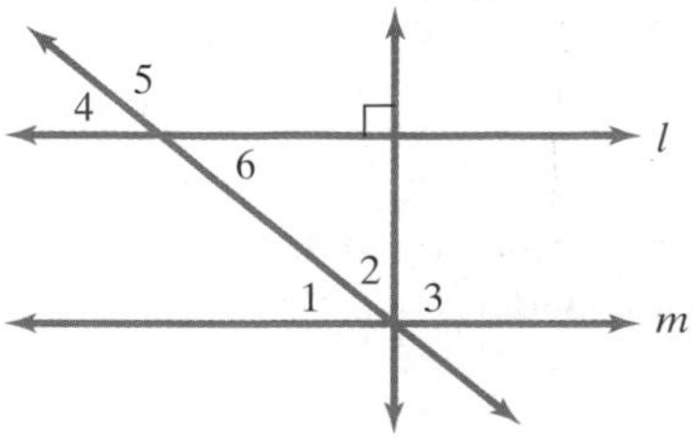

1. right angle
2. obtuse angle
3. vertical angles
4. alternate interior angles
5. corresponding angles
6. the complement of ∡1
7. the supplement of ∡6

In Exercises 8–9, find the measure of the angle in which ?° appears.

8.

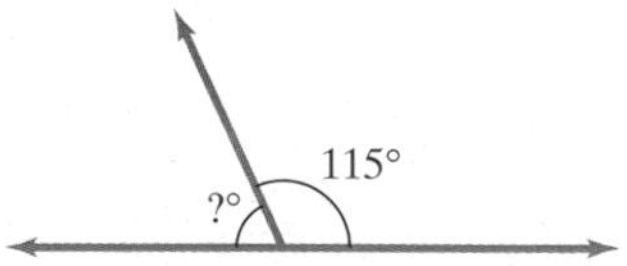

9.

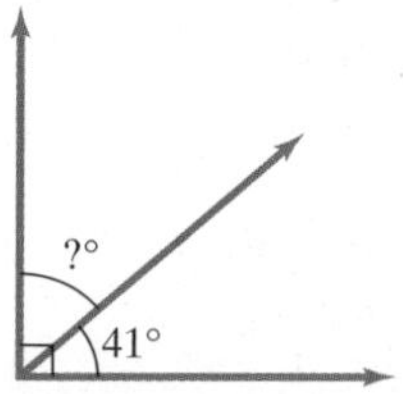

10. If an angle measures 73°, find the measure of its complement.

11. If an angle measures 46°, find the measure of its supplement.

12. In the figure shown, find the measures of angles 1, 2, and 3.

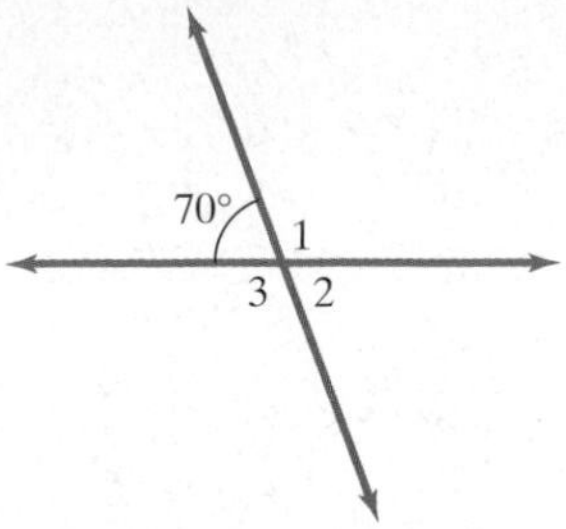

13. In the figure shown, two parallel lines are intersected by a transversal. One of the angle measures is given. Find the measure of each of the other seven angles.

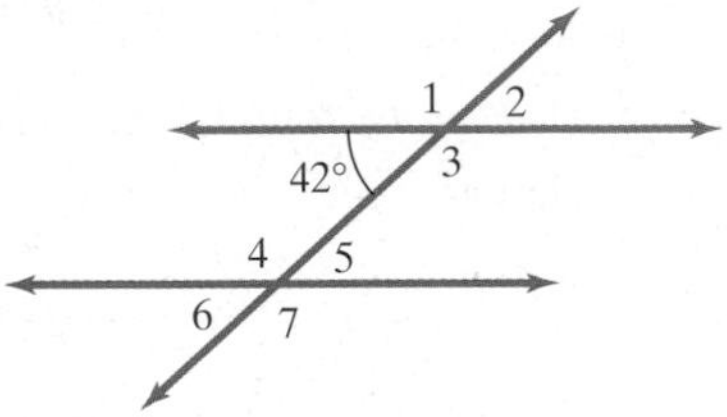

10.2

In Exercises 14–15, find the measure of angle A for the triangle shown.

14.

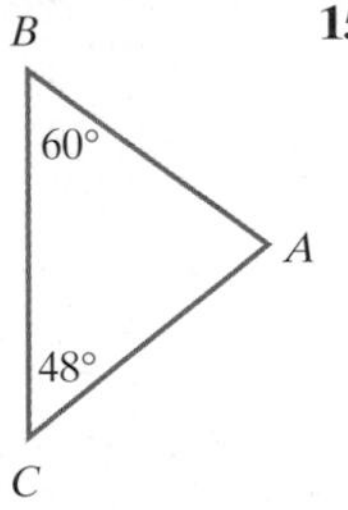

15.

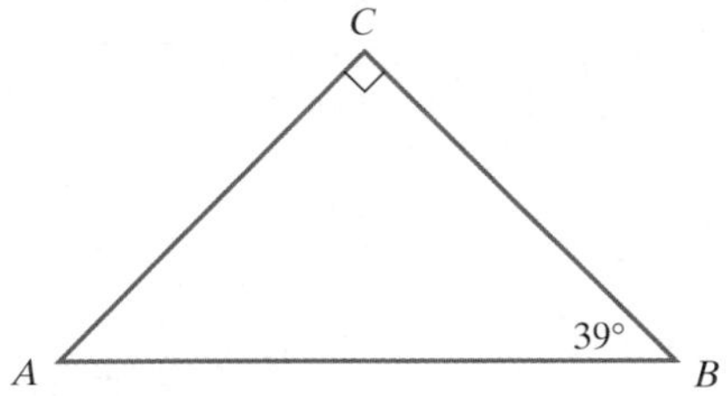

16. Find the measures of angles 1 through 5 in the figure shown.

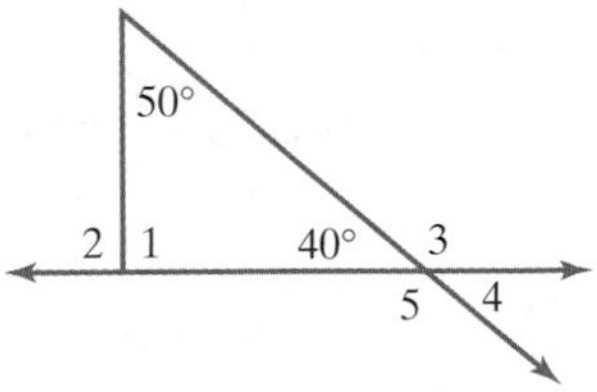

17. In the figure shown, lines l and m are parallel. Find the measure of each numbered angle.

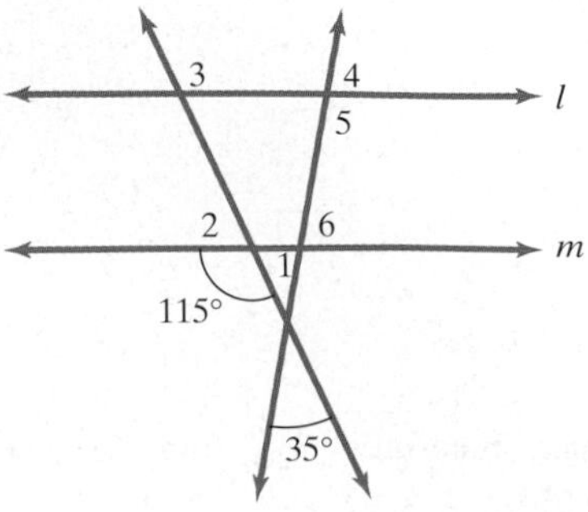

In Exercises 18–19, use similar triangles and the fact that corresponding sides are proportional to find the length of each side marked with an x.

18.

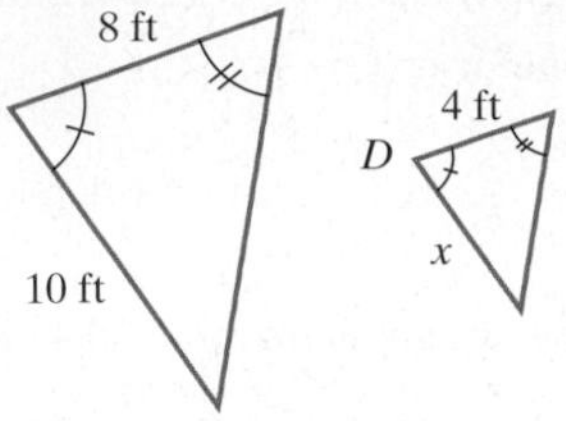

19.

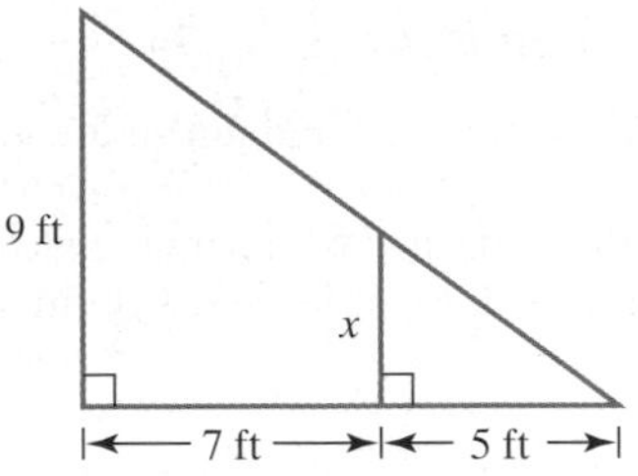

In Exercises 20–22, use the Pythagorean Theorem to find the missing length in each right triangle. Round, if necessary, to the nearest tenth.

20.

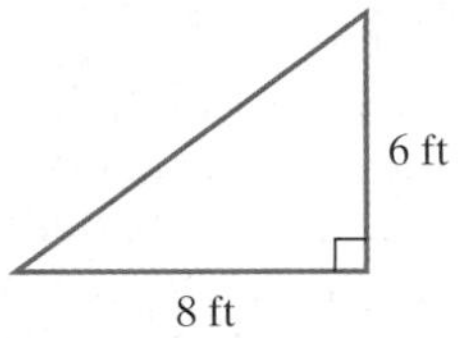

21.

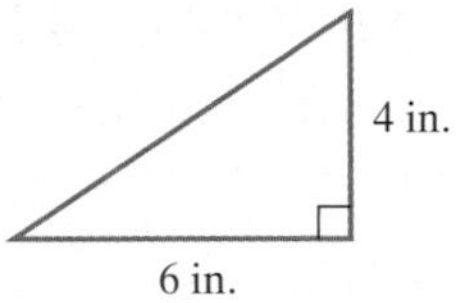

22.

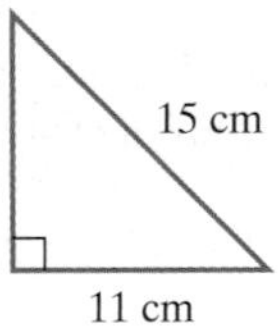

23. Find the height of the lamppost in the figure.

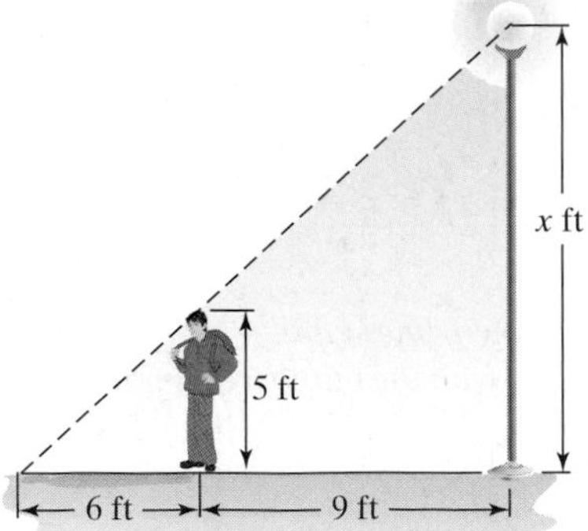

24. How far away from the building in the figure shown is the bottom of the ladder?

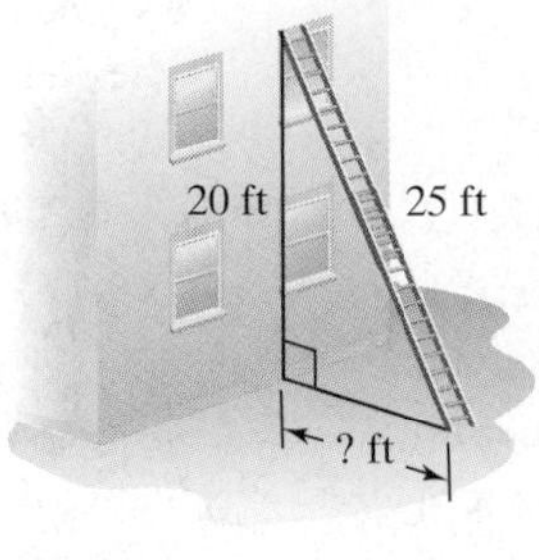

25. A vertical pole is to be supported by three wires. Each wire is 13 yards long and is anchored 5 yards from the base of the pole. How far up the pole will the wires be attached?

10.3

26. Write the names of all quadrilaterals that always have four right angles.

27. Write the names of all quadrilaterals with four sides always having the same measure.

28. Write the names of all quadrilaterals that do not always have four angles with the same measure.

In Exercises 29–31, find the perimeter of the figure shown. Express the perimeter using the same unit of measure that appears in the figure.

29.

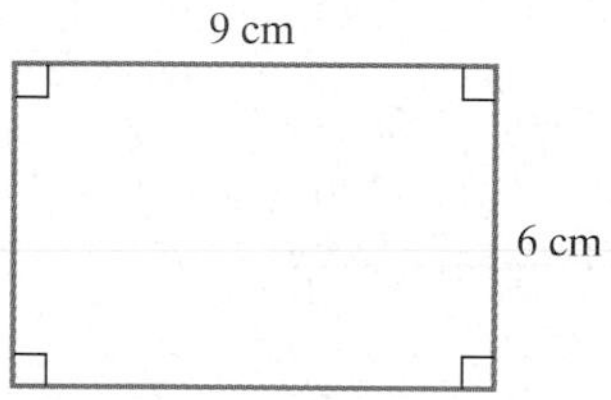

30.

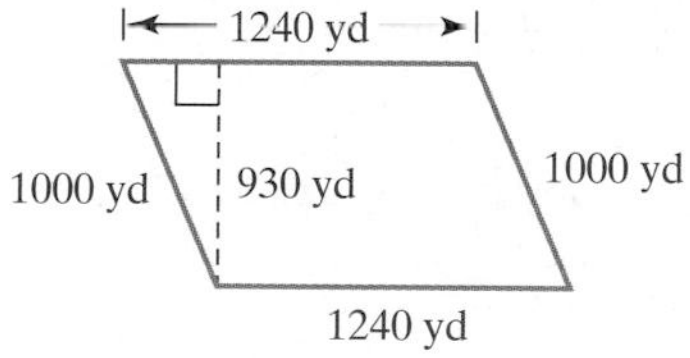

31.

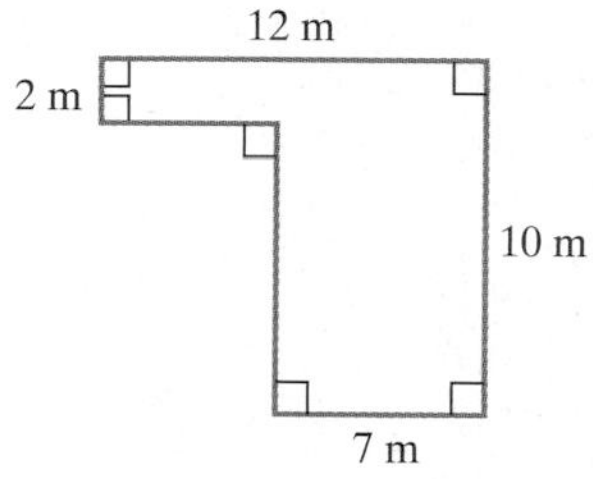

32. Find the sum of the measures of the angles of a 12-sided polygon.

33. Find the sum of the measures of the angles of an octagon.

34. The figure shown is a regular polygon. Find the measures of angle 1 and angle 2.

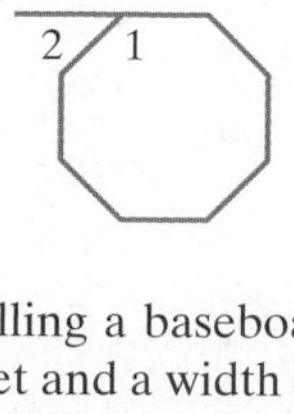

35. A carpenter is installing a baseboard around a room that has a length of 35 feet and a width of 15 feet. The room has four doorways and each doorway is 3 feet wide. If no baseboard is to be put across the doorways and the cost of the baseboard is $1.50 per foot, what is the cost of installing the baseboard around the room?

36. Use the following tessellation to solve this exercise.

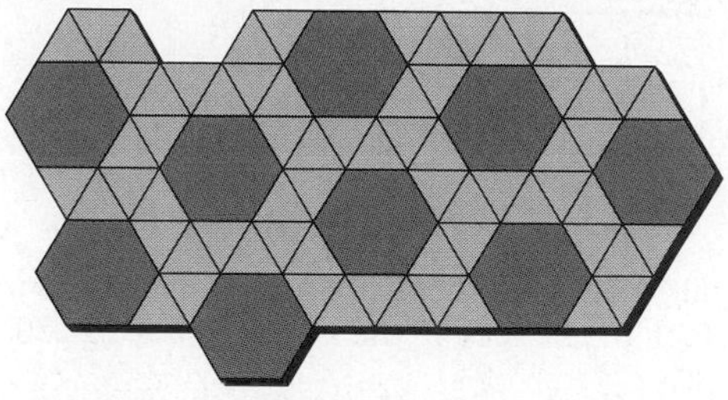

a. Name the types of regular polygons that surround each vertex.

b. Determine the number of angles that come together at each vertex, as well as the measures of these angles.

c. Use the angle measures from part (b) to explain why the tessellation is possible.

37. Can a tessellation be created using only regular hexagons? Explain your answer.

10.4

In Exercises 38–41, find the area of each figure.

38.

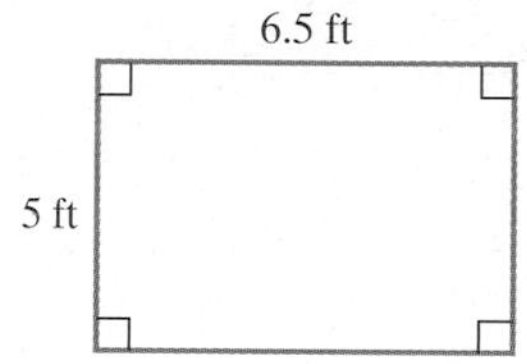

39.

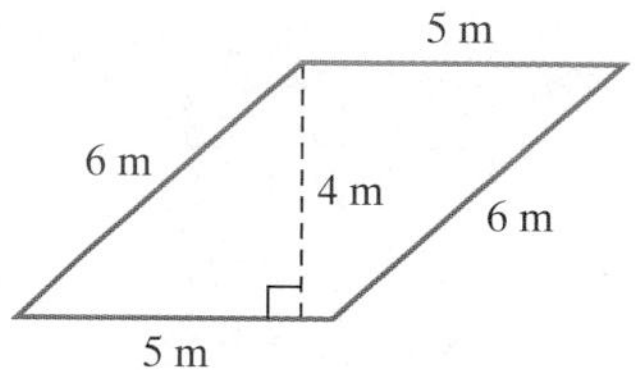

40.

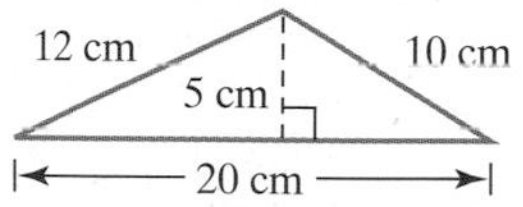

41.

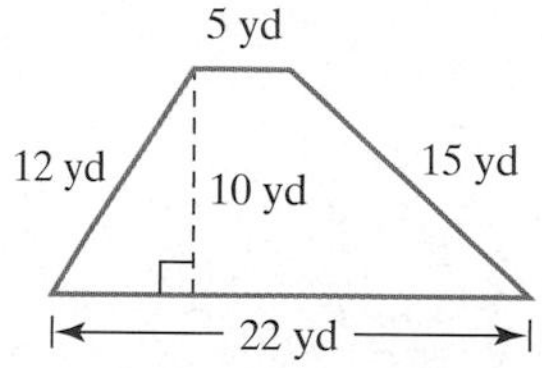

42. Find the circumference and the area of a circle with a diameter of 20 meters. Express answers in terms of π and then round to the nearest tenth.

In Exercises 43–44, find the area of each figure.

43.

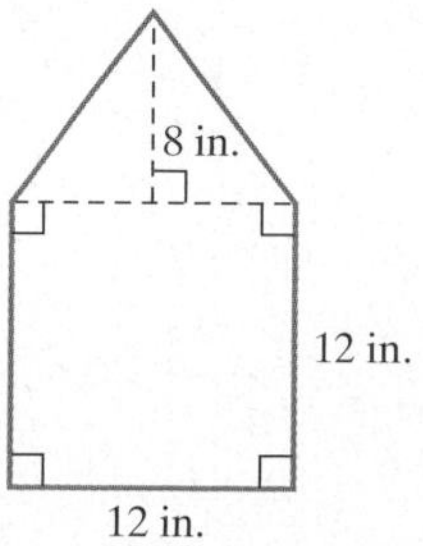

44.

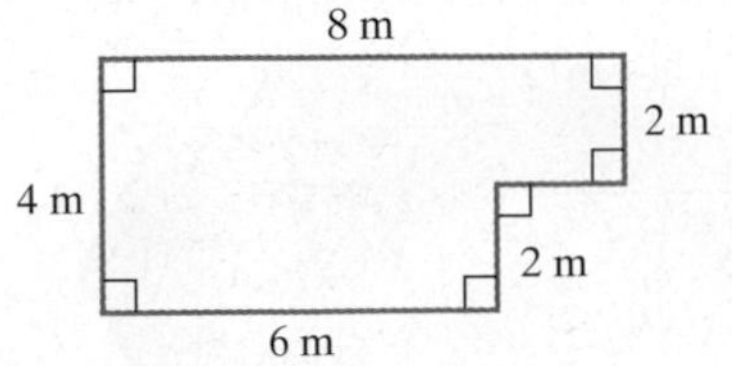

45. What will it cost to carpet a rectangular floor measuring 15 feet by 21 feet if the carpet costs $22.50 per square yard?

46. What will it cost to cover a rectangular floor measuring 40 feet by 50 feet with square tiles that measure 2 feet on each side if a package of 10 tiles costs $13 per package?

47. How much fencing, to the nearest whole yard, is needed to enclose a circular garden that measures 10 yards across?

10.5

In Exercises 48–52, find the volume of each figure. Where necessary, express answers in terms of π and then round to the nearest whole number.

48.

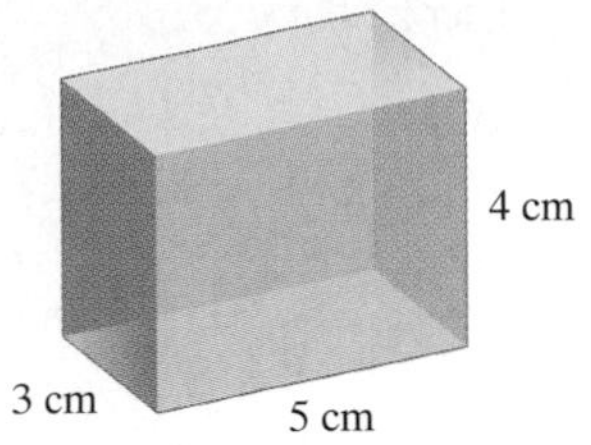

49.

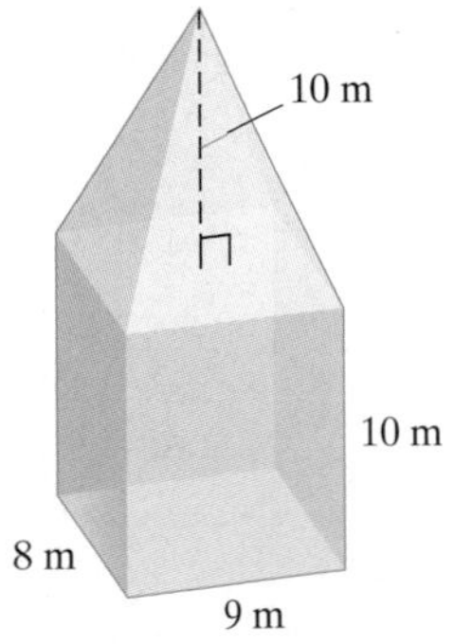

50.

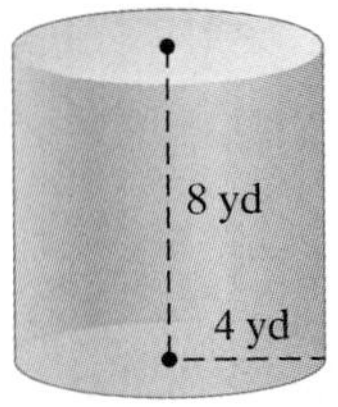

51.

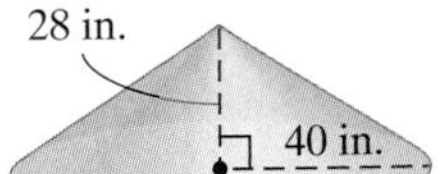

52.

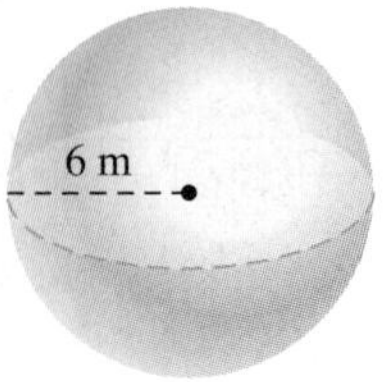

53. Find the surface area of the figure shown.

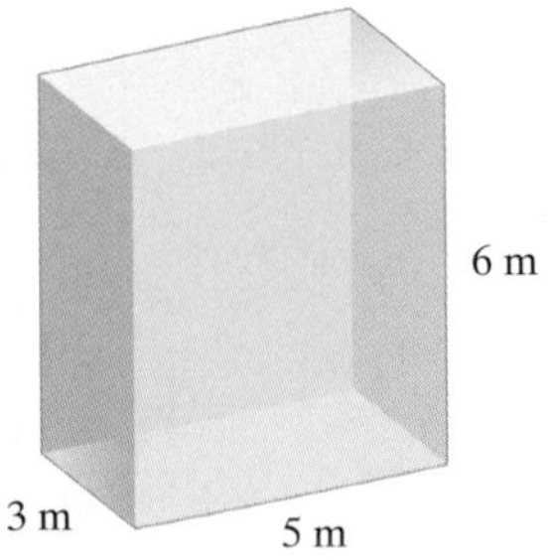

54. A train is being loaded with shipping boxes. Each box is 8 meters long, 4 meters wide, and 3 meters high. If there are 50 shipping boxes, how much space is needed?

55. An Egyptian pyramid has a square base measuring 145 meters on each side. If the height of the pyramid is 93 meters, find its volume.

56. What is the cost of concrete for a walkway that is 27 feet long, 4 feet wide, and 6 inches deep if the concrete is $40 per cubic yard?

10.6

57. Use the right triangle shown to find ratios, in reduced form, for $\sin A$, $\cos A$, and $\tan A$.

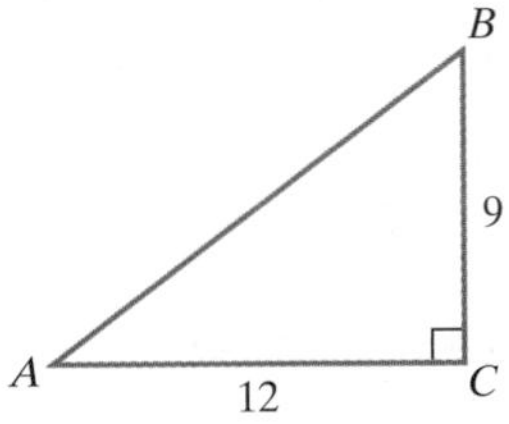

In Exercises 58–60, find the measure of the side of the right triangle whose length is designated by a lowercase letter. Round answers to the nearest whole number.

58.

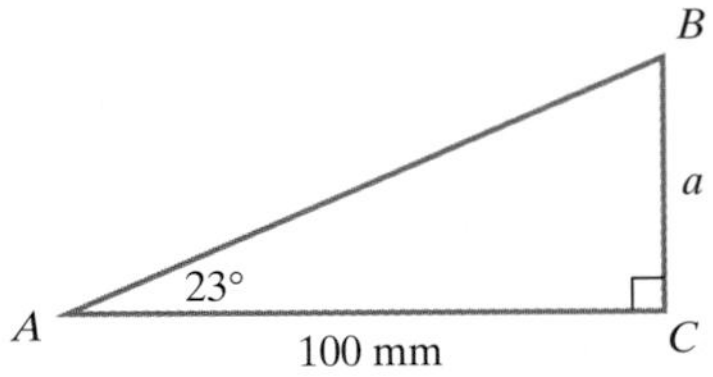

59.

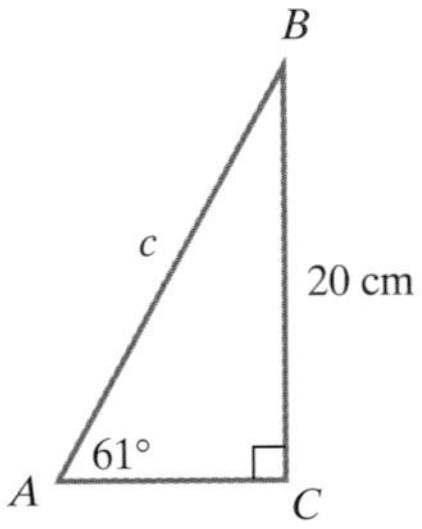

60.

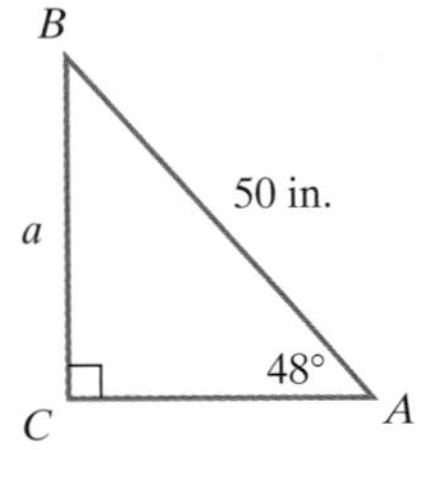

61. Find the measure of angle A in the right triangle shown. Round to the nearest whole degree.

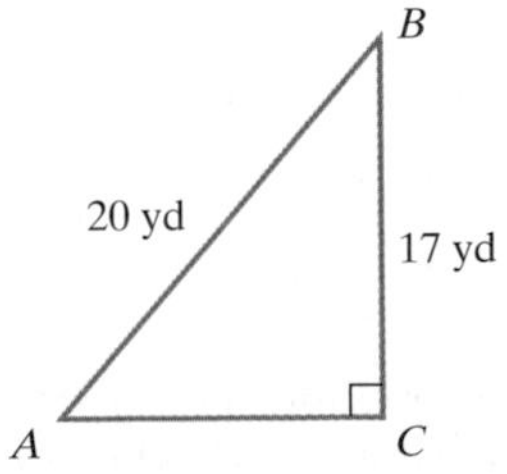

62. A hiker climbs for a half mile (2640 feet) up a slope whose inclination is 17°. How many feet of altitude, to the nearest foot, does the hiker gain?

63. To find the distance across a lake, a surveyor took the measurements in the figure shown. What is the distance across the lake? Round to the nearest meter.

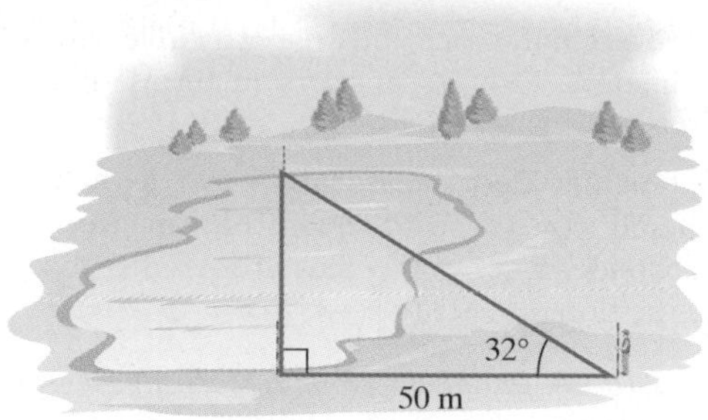

64. When a six-foot pole casts a four-foot shadow, what is the angle of elevation of the sun? Round to the nearest whole degree.

10.7

For each graph in Exercises 65–66, determine whether it is traversable. If it is, describe a path that will traverse it.

65.

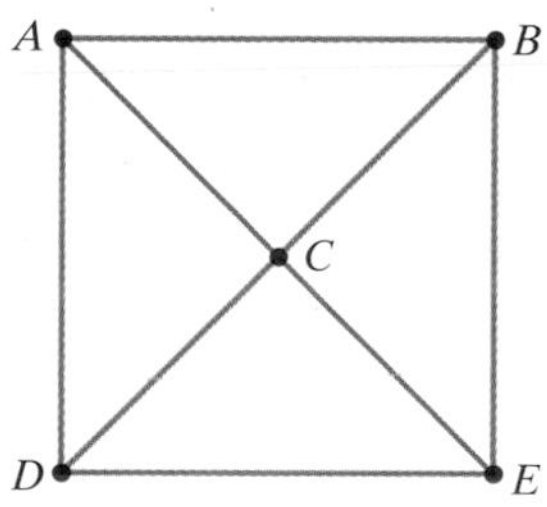

66.

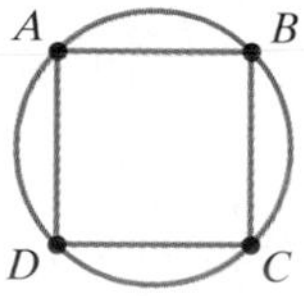

In Exercises 67–70, give the genus of each object. Which objects are topologically equivalent?

67.

68.

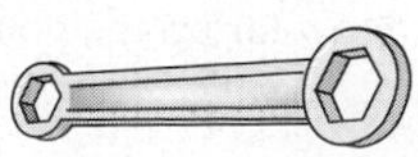

69.

70.

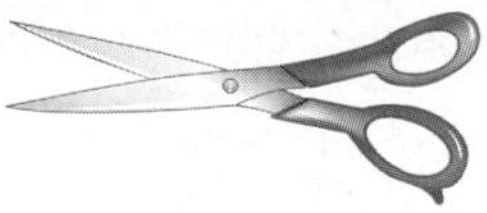

71. State Euclid's assumption about parallel lines that no longer applies in hyperbolic and elliptic geometry.

72. What is self-similarity? Describe an object in nature that has this characteristic.

CHAPTER 10 TEST

1. If an angle measures 54°, find the measure of its complement and supplement.

In Exercises 2–4, use the figure shown to find the measure of angle 1.

2.

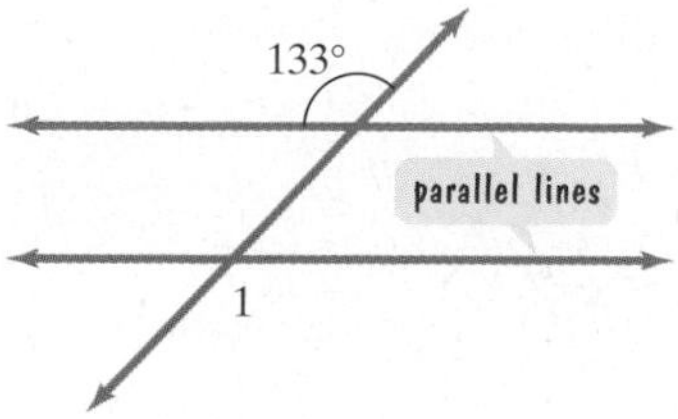

3.

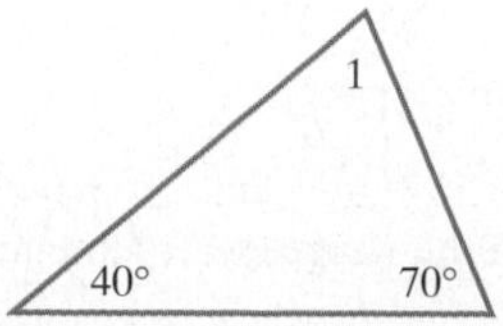

4.

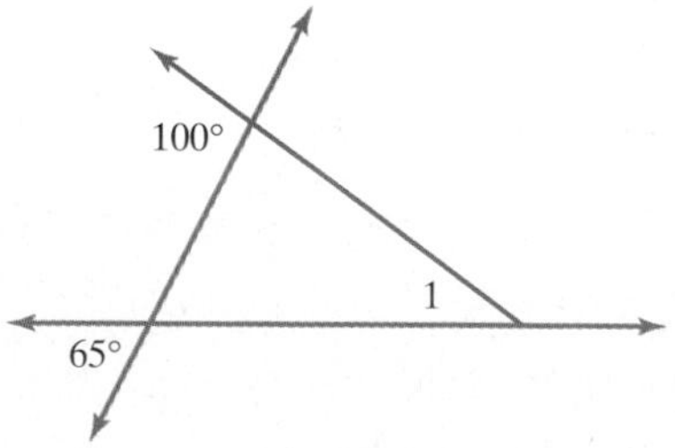

5. The triangles in the figure are similar. Find the length of the side marked with an x.

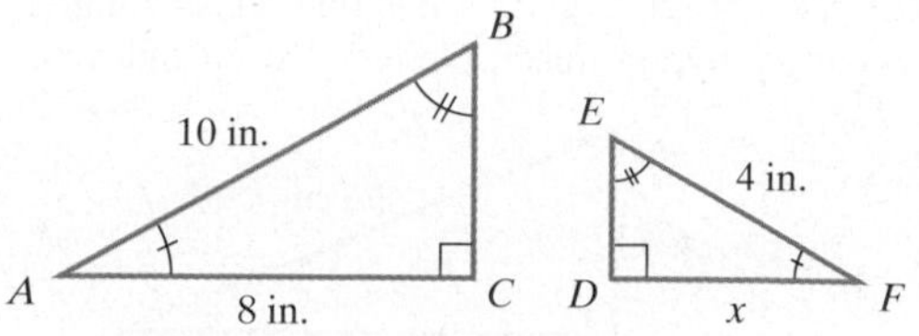

6. A vertical pole is to be supported by three wires. Each wire is 26 feet long and is anchored 24 feet from the base of the pole. How far up the pole should the wires be attached?

7. Find the sum of the measures of the angles of a ten-sided polygon.

8. Find the perimeter of the figure shown.

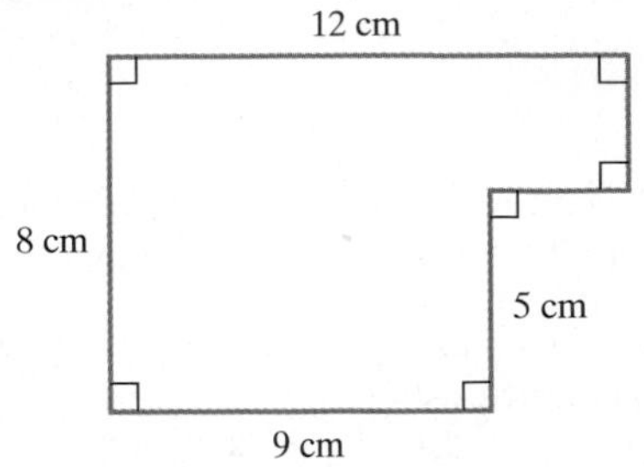

9. Which one of the following names a quadrilateral in which the sides that meet at each vertex have the same measure?

a. rectangle
b. parallelogram
c. trapezoid
d. rhombus

10. Use the following tessellation to solve this exercise.

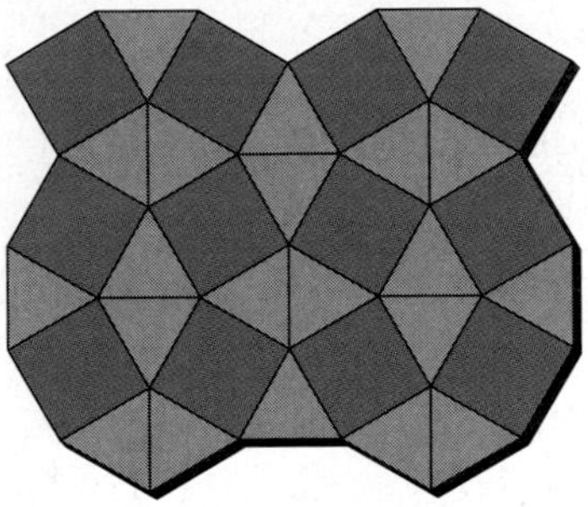

a. Name the types of regular polygons that surround each vertex.

b. Determine the number of angles that come together at each vertex, as well as the measures of these angles.

c. Use the angle measures from part (b) to explain why the tessellation is possible.

In Exercises 11–12, find the area of each figure.

11.

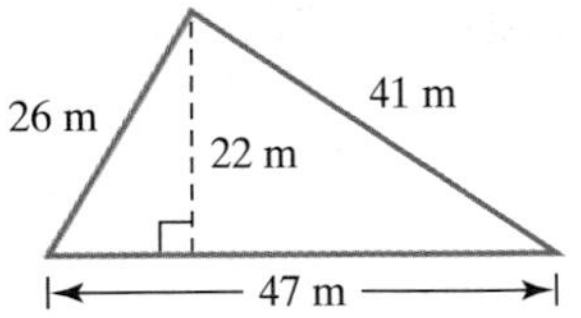

12.

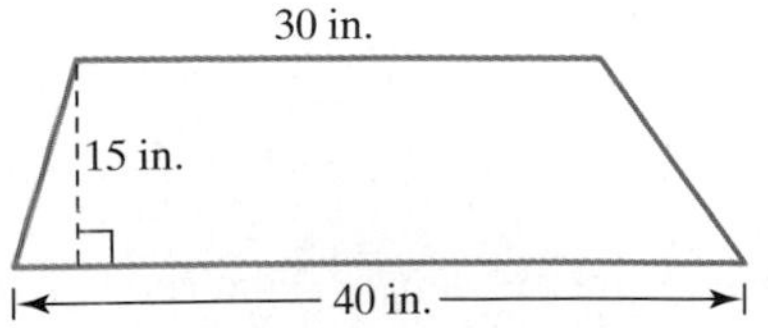

13. The right triangle shown has one leg of length 5 centimeters and a hypotenuse of length 13 centimeters.

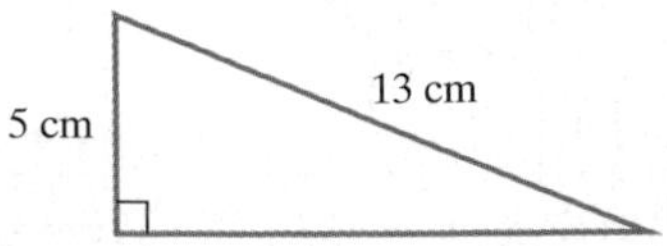

a. Find the length of the other leg.

b. What is the perimeter of the triangle?

c. What is the area of the triangle?

14. Find the circumference and area of a circle with a diameter of 40 meters. Express answers in terms of π and then round to the nearest tenth.

15. A rectangular floor measuring 8 feet by 6 feet is to be completely covered with square tiles measuring 8 inches on each side. How many tiles are needed to completely cover the floor?

In Exercises 16–18, find the volume of each figure. If necessary, express the answer in terms of π and then round to the nearest whole number.

16.

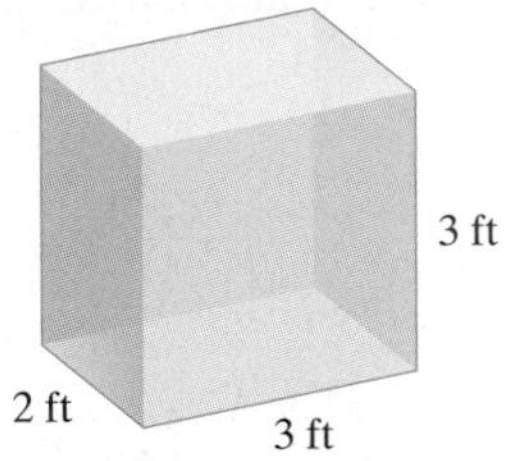

17.

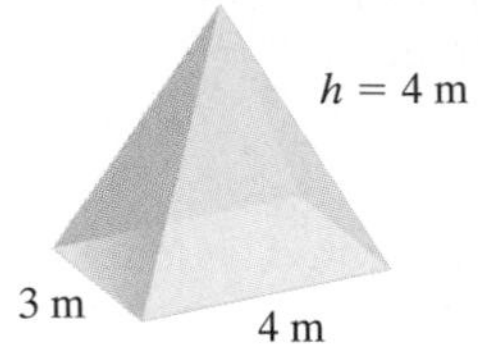

18.

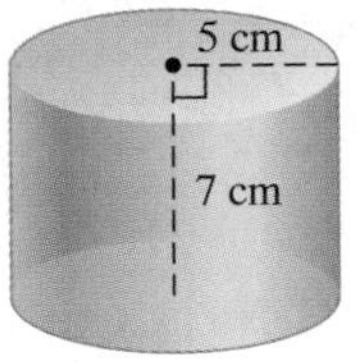

19. Find the measure, to the nearest whole number, of the side of the right triangle whose length is designated by c.

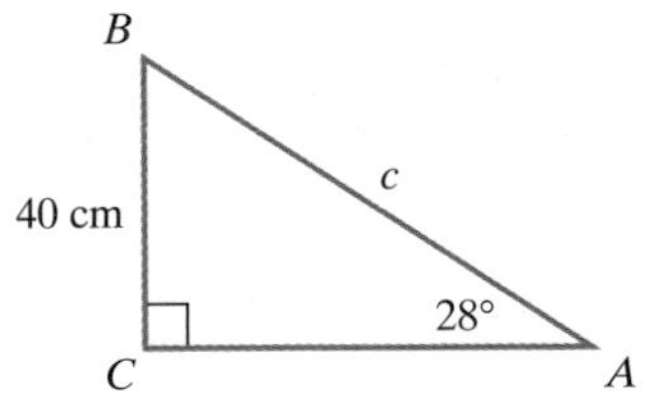

20. At a certain time of day, the angle of elevation of the sun is 34°. If a building casts a shadow measuring 104 feet, find the height of the building to the nearest foot.

21. Determine if the graph shown is traversable. If it is, describe a path that will traverse it.

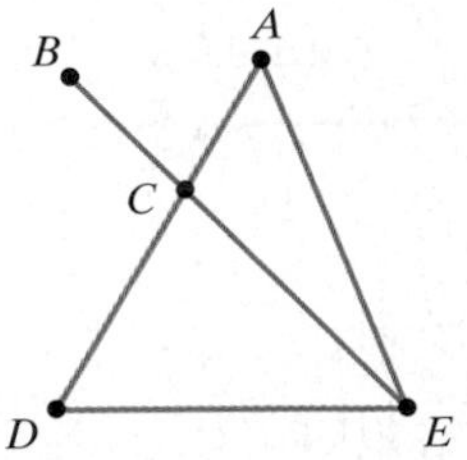

22. Describe a difference between the shapes of fractal geometry and those of Euclidean geometry.

CHAPTER 11

Counting Methods and Probability Theory

Two of America's best-loved presidents, Abraham Lincoln and John F. Kennedy, are linked by a bizarre series of coincidences:

- Lincoln was elected president in 1860. Kennedy was elected president in 1960.
- Lincoln's assassin, John Wilkes Booth, was born in 1839. Kennedy's assassin, Lee Harvey Oswald, was born in 1939.
- Lincoln's secretary, named Kennedy, warned him not to go to the theater on the night he was shot. Kennedy's secretary, named Lincoln, warned him not to go to Dallas on the day he was shot.
- Booth shot Lincoln in a theater and ran into a warehouse. Oswald shot Kennedy from a warehouse and ran into a theater.
- Both Lincoln and Kennedy were shot from behind, with their wives present.
- Andrew Johnson, who succeeded Lincoln, was born in 1808. Lyndon Johnson, who succeeded Kennedy, was born in 1908.

Source: Edward Burger and Michael Starbird, *Coincidences, Chaos, and All That Math Jazz*, W. W. Norton and Company, 2005.

Amazing coincidences? A cosmic conspiracy? Not really. In this chapter, you will see how the mathematics of uncertainty and risk, called probability theory, numerically describes situations in which to expect the unexpected. By assigning numbers to things that are extraordinarily unlikely, we can logically analyze coincidences without erroneous beliefs that strange and mystical events are occurring. We'll even see how wildly inaccurate our intuition can be about the likelihood of an event by examining an "amazing" coincidence that is nearly certain.

Coincidences are discussed in the Blitzer Bonus on page 658. Coincidences that are nearly certain are developed in Exercise 83 of Exercise Set 11.7.

SECTION 11.1 • THE FUNDAMENTAL COUNTING PRINCIPLE

OBJECTIVE

1. Use the Fundamental Counting Principle to determine the number of possible outcomes in a given situation.

Have you ever imagined what your life would be like if you won the lottery? What changes would you make? Before you fantasize about becoming a person of leisure with a staff of obedient elves, think about this: The probability of winning top prize in the lottery is about the same as the probability of being struck by lightning. There are millions of possible number combinations in lottery games, and only one way of winning the grand prize. Determining the probability of winning involves calculating the chance of getting the winning combination from all possible outcomes. In this section, we begin preparing for the surprising world of probability by looking at methods for counting possible outcomes.

1 Use the Fundamental Counting Principle to determine the number of possible outcomes in a given situation.

The Fundamental Counting Principle with Two Groups of Items

It's early morning, you're groggy, and you have to select something to wear for your 8 A.M. class. (What *were* you thinking when you signed up for a class at that hour?!) Fortunately, your "lecture wardrobe" is rather limited—just two pairs of jeans to choose from (one blue, one black) and three T-shirts to choose from (one beige, one yellow, and one blue). Your early-morning dilemma is illustrated in Figure 11.1.

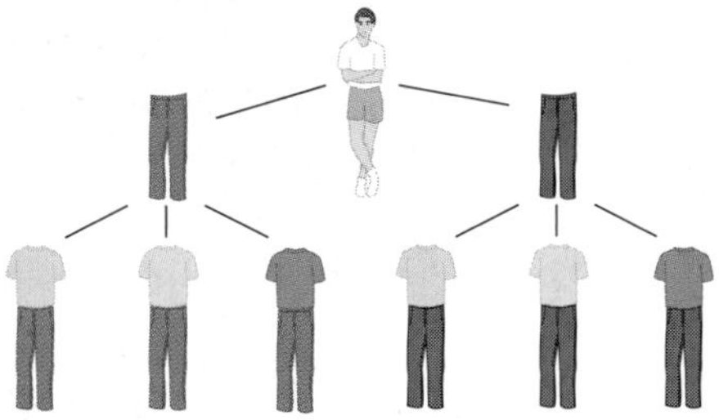

FIGURE 11.1 Selecting a wardrobe

The **tree diagram**, so named because of its branches, shows that you can form six different outfits from your two pairs of jeans and three T-shirts. Each pair of jeans can be combined with one of three T-shirts. Notice that the total number of outfits can be obtained by multiplying the number of choices for the jeans, 2, by the number of choices for the T-shirts, 3:

$$2 \cdot 3 = 6.$$

We can generalize this idea to any two groups of items—not just jeans and T-shirts—with the **Fundamental Counting Principle**.

> **THE FUNDAMENTAL COUNTING PRINCIPLE**
> If you can choose one item from a group of M items and a second item from a group of N items, then the total number of two-item choices is $M \cdot N$.

EXAMPLE 1 APPLYING THE FUNDAMENTAL COUNTING PRINCIPLE

The Greasy Spoon Restaurant offers 6 appetizers and 14 main courses. In how many ways can a person order a two-course meal?

SOLUTION Choosing from one of 6 appetizers and one of 14 main courses, the total number of two-course meals is

$$6 \cdot 14 = 84.$$

A person can order a two-course meal in 84 different ways.

CHECK POINT 1 A restaurant offers 10 appetizers and 15 main courses. In how many ways can you order a two-course meal?

EXAMPLE 2 APPLYING THE FUNDAMENTAL COUNTING PRINCIPLE

This is the semester that you will take your required psychology and social science courses. Because you decide to register early, there are 15 sections of psychology from which you can choose. Furthermore, there are 9 sections of social science that are available at times that do not conflict with those for psychology. In how many ways can you create two-course schedules that satisfy the psychology-social science requirement?

SOLUTION The number of ways that you can satisfy the requirement is found by multiplying the number of choices for each course. You can choose your psychology course from 15 sections and your social science course from 9 sections. For both courses you have

$$15 \cdot 9, \text{ or } 135$$

choices. Thus, you can satisfy the psychology-social science requirement in 135 ways.

CHECK POINT 2 Rework Example 2 given that the number of sections of psychology and nonconflicting sections of social science each decrease by 5.

The Fundamental Counting Principle with More Than Two Groups of Items

Whoops! You forgot something in choosing your lecture wardrobe—shoes! You have two pairs of sneakers to choose from—one black and one red, for that extra fashion flair! Your possible outfits, including sneakers, are shown in Figure 11.2.

The number of possible ways of playing the first four moves on each side in a game of chess is 318,979,564,000.

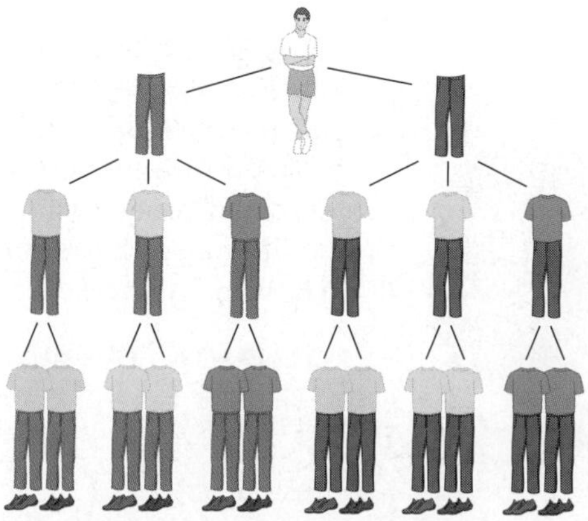

FIGURE 11.2 Increasing wardrobe selections

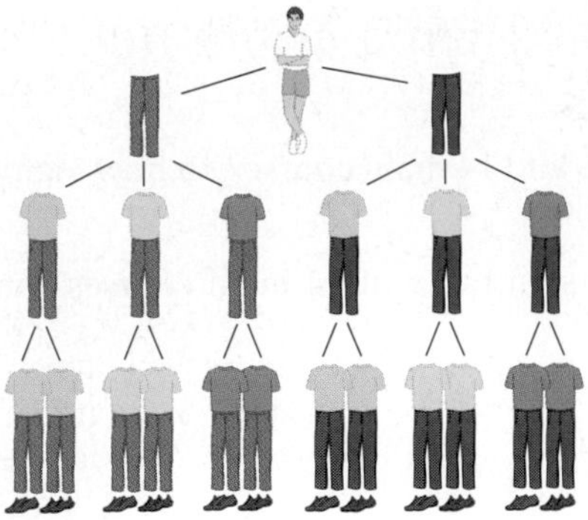

FIGURE 11.2 (repeated)

The tree diagram shows that you can form 12 outfits from your two pairs of jeans, three T-shirts, and two pairs of sneakers. Notice that the number of outfits can be obtained by multiplying the number of choices for jeans, 2, the number of choices for T-shirts, 3, and the number of choices for sneakers, 2:

$$2 \cdot 3 \cdot 2 = 12.$$

Unlike your earlier dilemma, you are now dealing with *three* groups of items. The Fundamental Counting Principle can be extended to determine the number of possible outcomes in situations in which there are three or more groups of items.

THE FUNDAMENTAL COUNTING PRINCIPLE
The number of ways in which a series of successive things can occur is found by multiplying the number of ways in which each thing can occur.

For example, if you own 30 pairs of jeans, 20 T-shirts, and 12 pairs of sneakers, you have

$$30 \cdot 20 \cdot 12 = 7200$$

choices for your wardrobe.

EXAMPLE 3 OPTIONS IN PLANNING A COURSE SCHEDULE

Next semester you are planning to take three courses—math, English, and humanities. Based on time blocks and highly recommended professors, there are 8 sections of math, 5 of English, and 4 of humanities that you find suitable. Assuming no scheduling conflicts, how many different three-course schedules are possible?

SOLUTION This situation involves making choices with three groups of items.

Math	English	Humanities
8 choices	5 choices	4 choices

We use the Fundamental Counting Principle to find the number of three-course schedules. Multiply the number of choices for each of the three groups.

$$8 \cdot 5 \cdot 4 = 160$$

Thus, there are 160 different three-course schedules.

CHECK POINT 3 A pizza can be ordered with two choices of size (medium or large), three choices of crust (thin, thick, or regular), and five choices of toppings (ground beef, sausage, pepperoni, bacon, or mushrooms). How many different one-topping pizzas can be ordered?

EXAMPLE 4 CAR OF THE FUTURE

Car manufacturers are now experimenting with lightweight three-wheel cars, designed for one person, and considered ideal for city driving. Intrigued? Suppose you could order such a car with a choice of 9 possible colors, with or without air conditioning, electric or gas powered, and with or without an onboard computer. In how many ways can this car be ordered with regard to these options?

Source: Corbin Motors (www.Corbinmotors.com)

SOLUTION This situation involves making choices with four groups of items.

Color	Air conditioning	Power	Computer
9 choices	2 choices: with or without	2 choices: electric or gas	2 choices: with or without

We use the Fundamental Counting Principle to find the number of ordering options. Multiply the number of choices for each of the four groups.

$$9 \cdot 2 \cdot 2 \cdot 2 = 72$$

Thus, the car can be ordered in 72 different ways.

CHECK POINT 4 The car in Example 4 is now available in 10 possible colors. The options involving air conditioning, power, and an onboard computer still apply. Furthermore, the car is available with or without a global positioning system (for pinpointing your location at every moment). In how many ways can this car be ordered in terms of these options?

EXAMPLE 5 A MULTIPLE-CHOICE TEST

You are taking a multiple-choice test that has ten questions. Each of the questions has four answer choices, with one correct answer per question. If you select one of these four choices for each question and leave nothing blank, in how many ways can you answer the questions?

SOLUTION This situation involves making choices with ten questions.

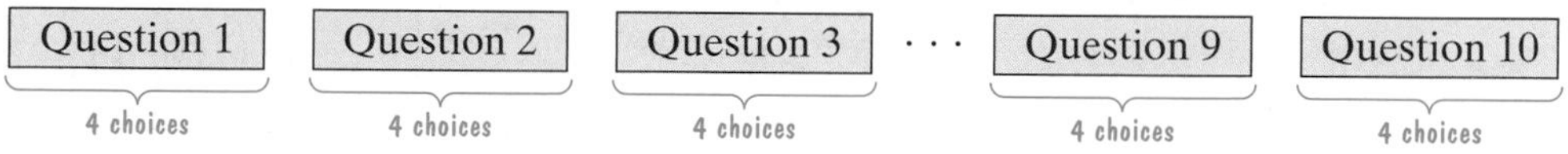

We use the Fundamental Counting Principle to determine the number of ways that you can answer the questions on the test. Multiply the number of choices, 4, for each of the ten questions.

$$4 \cdot 4 \cdot 4 \cdot 4 \cdot 4 \cdot 4 \cdot 4 \cdot 4 \cdot 4 \cdot 4 = 4^{10} = 1{,}048{,}576$$ Use a calculator: 4 y^x 10 =.

Thus, you can answer the questions in 1,048,576 different ways.

Are you surprised that there are over one million ways of answering a ten-question multiple-choice test? Of course, there is only one way to answer the test and receive a perfect score. The probability of guessing your way into a perfect score involves calculating the chance of getting a perfect score, just one way, from all 1,048,576 possible outcomes. In short, prepare for the test and do not rely on guessing!

CHECK POINT 5 You are taking a multiple-choice test that has six questions. Each of the questions has three answer choices, with one correct answer per question. If you select one of these three choices for each question and leave nothing blank, in how many ways can you answer the questions?

EXAMPLE 6 TELEPHONE NUMBERS IN THE UNITED STATES

Telephone numbers in the United States begin with three-digit area codes followed by seven-digit local telephone numbers. Area codes and local telephone numbers cannot begin with 0 or 1. How many different telephone numbers are possible?

SOLUTION This situation involves making choices with ten groups of items.

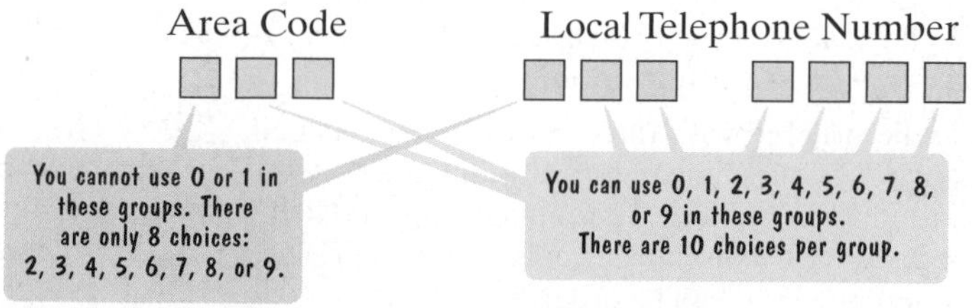

BLITZER BONUS

Running Out of Telephone Numbers

By the year 2020, portable telephones used for business and pleasure will all be videophones. At that time, U.S. population is expected to be 323 million. Faxes, beepers, cell phones, computer phone lines, and business lines may result in certain areas running out of phone numbers. Solution: Add more digits!

With or without extra digits, we expect that the 2020 videophone greeting will still be "hello," a word created by Thomas Edison in 1877. Phone inventor Alexander Graham Bell preferred "ahoy," but "hello" won out, appearing in the *Oxford English Dictionary* in 1883.

(*Source*: *New York Times*)

Here are the choices for each of the ten groups of items:

Area Code			Local Telephone Number						
8	10	10	8	10	10	10	10	10	10

We use the Fundamental Counting Principle to determine the number of different telephone numbers that are possible. The total number of telephone numbers possible is

$$8 \cdot 10 \cdot 10 \cdot 8 \cdot 10 \cdot 10 \cdot 10 \cdot 10 \cdot 10 \cdot 10 = 6{,}400{,}000{,}000.$$

There are six billion four hundred million different telephone numbers that are possible.

CHECK POINT 6 An electronic gate can be opened by entering five digits on a keypad containing the digits 0, 1, 2, 3, . . . , 8, 9. How many different keypad sequences are possible if the digit 0 cannot be used as the first digit?

EXERCISE SET 11.1

• Practice and Application Exercises

Solve Exercises 1–6 using the Fundamental Counting Principle with two groups of items.

1. A restaurant offers 8 appetizers and 10 main courses. In how many ways can a person order a two-course meal?
2. The model of the car you are thinking of buying is available in nine different colors and three different styles (hatchback, sedan, or station wagon). In how many ways can you order the car?
3. A popular brand of pen is available in three colors (red, green, or blue) and four writing tips (bold, medium, fine, or micro). How many different choices of pens do you have with this brand?
4. In how many ways can a casting director choose a female lead and a male lead from five female actors and six male actors?
5. A student is planning a two-part trip. The first leg of the trip is from San Francisco to New York, and the second leg is from New York to Paris. From San Francisco to New York, travel options include airplane, train, or bus. From New York to Paris, the options are limited to airplane or ship. In how many ways can the two-part trip be made?
6. For a temporary job between semesters, you are painting the parking spaces for a new shopping mall with a letter of the alphabet and a single digit from 1 to 9. The first parking space is A1 and the last parking space is Z9. How many parking spaces can you paint with distinct labels?

Solve Exercises 7–22 using the Fundamental Counting Principle with three or more groups of items.

7. An ice cream store sells two drinks (sodas or milk shakes), in four sizes (small, medium, large, or jumbo), and five flavors (vanilla, strawberry, chocolate, coffee, or pistachio). In how many ways can a customer order a drink?
8. A pizza can be ordered with three choices of size (small, medium, or large), four choices of crust (thin, thick, crispy, or regular), and six choices of toppings (ground beef, sausage, pepperoni, bacon, mushrooms, or onions). How many one-topping pizzas can be ordered?
9. A restaurant offers the following limited lunch menu.

Main Course	Vegetables	Beverages	Desserts
Ham	Potatoes	Coffee	Cake
Chicken	Peas	Tea	Pie
Fish	Green beans	Milk	Ice cream
Beef		Soda	

If one item is selected from each of the four groups, in how many ways can a meal be ordered? Describe two such orders.

10. An apartment complex offers apartments with four different options, designated by A through D.

A	B	C	D
one bedroom	one bathroom	first floor	lake view
two bedrooms	two bathrooms	second floor	golf course view
three bedrooms			no special view

How many apartment options are available? Describe two such options.

11. Shoppers in a large shopping mall are categorized as male or female, over 30 or 30 and under, and cash or credit card shoppers. In how many ways can the shoppers be categorized?
12. There are three highways from city A to city B, two highways from city B to city C, and four highways from city C to city D. How many different highway routes are there from city A to city D?
13. A person can order a new car with a choice of six possible colors, with or without air conditioning, with or without automatic transmission, with or without power windows, and with or without a CD player. In how many different ways can a new car be ordered with regard to these options?
14. A car model comes in nine colors, with or without air conditioning, with or without a sun roof, with or without automatic transmission, and with or without antilock brakes. In how many ways can the car be ordered with regard to these options?

15. You are taking a multiple-choice test that has five questions. Each of the questions has three answer choices, with one correct answer per question. If you select one of these three choices for each question and leave nothing blank, in how many ways can you answer the questions?

16. You are taking a multiple-choice test that has eight questions. Each of the questions has three answer choices, with one correct answer per question. If you select one of these three choices for each question and leave nothing blank, in how many ways can you answer the questions?

17. In the original plan for area codes in 1945, the first digit could be any number from 2 through 9, the second digit was either 0 or 1, and the third digit could be any number except 0. With this plan, how many different area codes are possible?

18. The local seven-digit telephone numbers in Inverness, California, have 669 as the first three digits. How many different telephone numbers are possible in Inverness?

19. License plates in a particular state display two letters followed by three numbers, such as AT-887 or BB-013. How many different license plates can be manufactured for this state?

20. How many different four-letter radio station call letters can be formed if the first letter must be W or K?

21. A stock can go up, go down, or stay unchanged. How many possibilities are there if you own seven stocks?

22. A social security number contains nine digits, such as 074-66-7795. How many different social security numbers can be formed?

• Writing in Mathematics

23. Explain the Fundamental Counting Principle.

24. Figure 11.2 on page 609 shows that a tree diagram can be used to find the total number of outfits. Describe one advantage of using the Fundamental Counting Principle rather than a tree diagram.

25. Write an original problem that can be solved using the Fundamental Counting Principle. Then solve the problem.

• Critical Thinking Exercises

26. How many four-digit odd numbers are there? Assume that the digit on the left cannot be 0.

27. In order to develop a more appealing hamburger, a franchise used taste tests with 12 different buns, 30 sauces, 4 types of lettuce, and 3 types of tomatoes. If the taste test was done at one restaurant by one tester who took 10 minutes to eat each hamburger, approximately how long would it take the tester to eat all possible hamburgers?

• Group Exercise

28. The group should select real-world situations where the Fundamental Counting Principle can be applied. These can involve the number of possible student ID numbers on your campus, the number of possible phone numbers in your community, the number of meal options at a local restaurant, the number of ways a person in the group can select outfits for class, the number of ways a condominium can be purchased in a nearby community, and so on. Once situations have been selected, group members should determine in how many ways each part of the task can be done. Group members will need to obtain menus, find out about telephone-digit requirements in the community, count shirts, pants, shoes in closets, visit condominium sales offices, and so on. Once the group reassembles, apply the Fundamental Counting Principle to determine the number of available options in each situation. Because these numbers may be quite large, use a calculator.

SECTION 11.2 • PERMUTATIONS

OBJECTIVES

1. Use the Fundamental Counting Principle to count permutations.
2. Evaluate factorial expressions.
3. Use the permutations formula.
4. Find the number of permutations of duplicate items.

Ladies and gentlemen: Please give a huge round of applause for

U2! Bruce Springsteen and the E Street Band!
Aerosmith! The Rolling Stones!

You are in charge of planning one of the most anticipated concert tours of the decade. All four of these groups will appear in concert, which will be seen in a pay-per-view cable special by millions of people throughout the world. One of your jobs is to determine the order in which the groups will perform. Each group will perform once. How many different ways can you put together this four-group concert?

1 Use the Fundamental Counting Principle to count permutations.

You are familiar with the work of all these musicians *and* you know the Fundamental Counting Principle! (Who could be better qualified for this job?) You can choose any of the four groups as the first performer. Once you've chosen the first group, you'll have three groups left to choose from for the second performer. You'll then have two groups left to choose from for the third performance. After the first three performers are determined, you'll have only one group left for the final appearance in the concert. This situation can be shown as follows:

First Group to Perform	Second Group to Perform	Third Group to Perform	Last Group to Perform
4 choices	3 choices	2 choices	1 choice

We use the Fundamental Counting Principle to find the number of ways you can put together the concert. Multiply the choices:

$$4 \cdot 3 \cdot 2 \cdot 1 = 24.$$

Thus, there are 24 different ways to arrange the concert. One of the 24 possible arrangements is

Aerosmith–Bruce Springsteen–U2–The Rolling Stones.

Such an ordered arrangement is called a *permutation* of the four rock groups.

A **permutation** is an ordered arrangement of items that occurs when

- No item is used more than once. (Each rock group performs exactly once.)
- The order of arrangement makes a difference. (It will make a difference in terms of how the concert is received if the Rolling Stones are the first group or the last group to perform.)

The Rolling Stones

EXAMPLE 1 COUNTING PERMUTATIONS

Based on their long-standing contribution to rock music, you decide that the Rolling Stones should be the last group to perform at the four-group U2, Bruce Springsteen, Aerosmith, Rolling Stones concert. Given this decision, in how many ways can you put together the concert?

SOLUTION You can now choose any one of the three groups, U2, Bruce Springsteen and the E Street Band, or Aerosmith, as the opening act. Once you've chosen the first group, you'll have two groups left to choose from for the second performance. You'll then have just one group left to choose for the third performance. There is also just one choice for the closing act—the Rolling Stones. This situation can be shown as follows:

First Group to Perform	Second Group to Perform	Third Group to Perform	Last Group to Perform
3 choices (U2, Springsteen, or Aerosmith)	2 choices	1 choice	1 choice: The Rolling Stones will close the concert.

We use the Fundamental Counting Principle to find the number of ways you can put together the concert. Multiply the choices:

$$3 \cdot 2 \cdot 1 \cdot 1 = 6.$$

Thus, there are six different ways to arrange the concert if the Rolling Stones are the final group to perform.

CHECK POINT 1 For the concert in Example 1, suppose that U2 is to be the opening act and the Rolling Stones are to be the last group to perform. In how many ways can you put together the concert?

BLITZER BONUS

How to Pass the Time for $2\frac{1}{2}$ Million Years

If you were to arrange 15 different books on a shelf and it took you one minute for each permutation, the entire task would take 2,487,965 years.

Source: Isaac Asimov's Book of Facts

EXAMPLE 2 COUNTING PERMUTATIONS

You need to arrange seven of your favorite books along a small shelf. How many different ways can you arrange the books, assuming that the order of the books makes a difference to you?

SOLUTION You may choose any of the seven books for the first position on the shelf. This leaves six choices for second position. After the first two positions are filled, there are five books to choose from for third position, four choices left for the fourth position, three choices left for the fifth position, then two choices for the sixth position, and only one choice for the last position. This situation can be shown as follows:

First Shelf Position	Second Shelf Position	Third Shelf Position	Fourth Shelf Position	Fifth Shelf Position	Sixth Shelf Position	Seventh Shelf Position
7 choices	6 choices	5 choices	4 choices	3 choices	2 choices	1 choice

We use the Fundamental Counting Principle to find the number of ways you can arrange the seven books along the shelf. Multiply the choices:

$$7\cdot6\cdot5\cdot4\cdot3\cdot2\cdot1 = 5040.$$

Thus, you can arrange the books in 5040 ways. There are 5040 different possible permutations.

CHECK POINT 2 In how many ways can you arrange five books along a shelf, assuming that the order of the books makes a difference?

2 Evaluate factorial expressions.

FACTORIALS FROM 0 THROUGH 20

0!	1
1!	1
2!	2
3!	6
4!	24
5!	120
6!	720
7!	5040
8!	40,320
9!	362,880
10!	3,628,800
11!	39,916,800
12!	479,001,600
13!	6,227,020,800
14!	87,178,291,200
15!	1,307,674,368,000
16!	20,922,789,888,000
17!	355,687,428,096,000
18!	6,402,373,705,728,000
19!	121,645,100,408,832,000
20!	2,432,902,008,176,640,000

As n increases, $n!$ grows very rapidly. Factorial growth is more explosive than exponential growth discussed in Chapter 7.

Factorial Notation

The product in Example 2,

$$7\cdot6\cdot5\cdot4\cdot3\cdot2\cdot1$$

is given a special name and symbol. It is called 7 **factorial**, and written 7!. Thus,

$$7! = 7\cdot6\cdot5\cdot4\cdot3\cdot2\cdot1.$$

In general, if n is a positive integer, then $n!$ (*n factorial*) is the product of all positive integers from n down through 1. For example,

$$1! = 1$$

$$2! = 2\cdot1 = 2$$

$$3! = 3\cdot2\cdot1 = 6$$

$$4! = 4\cdot3\cdot2\cdot1 = 24$$

$$5! = 5\cdot4\cdot3\cdot2\cdot1 = 120$$

$$6! = 6\cdot5\cdot4\cdot3\cdot2\cdot1 = 720.$$

FACTORIAL NOTATION

If n is a positive integer, the notation $n!$ (read "n factorial") is the product of all positive integers from n down through 1.

$$n! = n(n-1)(n-2)\cdots(3)(2)(1)$$

0! (zero factorial), by definition, is 1.

$$0! = 1$$

EXAMPLE 3 USING FACTORIAL NOTATION

Evaluate the following factorial expressions without using the factorial key on your calculator:

a. $\frac{8!}{5!}$ **b.** $\frac{26!}{21!}$ **c.** $\frac{500!}{499!}$.

TECHNOLOGY

Most calculators have a key or menu item for calculating factorials. Here are the keystrokes for finding 9!:

MANY SCIENTIFIC CALCULATORS:

9 [x!] [=]

MANY GRAPHING CALCULATORS:

9 [!] [ENTER].

Because $n!$ becomes quite large as n increases, your calculator will display these larger values in scientific notation.

SOLUTION

a. We can evaluate the numerator and the denominator of $\frac{8!}{5!}$. However, it is easier to use the following simplification:

$$\frac{8!}{5!} = \frac{8\cdot7\cdot6\cdot\boxed{5\cdot4\cdot3\cdot2\cdot1}}{\boxed{5\cdot4\cdot3\cdot2\cdot1}} = \frac{8\cdot7\cdot6\cdot\boxed{5!}}{\boxed{5!}} = \frac{8\cdot7\cdot6\cdot\cancel{5!}}{\cancel{5!}} = 8\cdot7\cdot6 = 336.$$

b. Rather than write out 26!, the numerator of $\frac{26!}{21!}$, as the product of all integers from 26 down to 1, we can express 26! as

$$26! = 26\cdot25\cdot24\cdot23\cdot22\cdot21!.$$

In this way, we can cancel 21! in the numerator and the denominator of the given expression.

$$\frac{26!}{21!} = \frac{26\cdot25\cdot24\cdot23\cdot22\cdot21!}{21!} = \frac{26\cdot25\cdot24\cdot23\cdot22\cdot\cancel{21!}}{\cancel{21!}}$$

$$= 26\cdot25\cdot24\cdot23\cdot22 = 7{,}893{,}600$$

c. In order to cancel identical factorials in the numerator and the denominator of $\frac{500!}{499!}$, we can express 500! as $500\cdot499!$.

$$\frac{500!}{499!} = \frac{500\cdot499!}{499!} = \frac{500\cdot\cancel{499!}}{\cancel{499!}} = 500$$

CHECK POINT 3 Evaluate without using a calculator's factorial key:

a. $\frac{9!}{6!}$ **b.** $\frac{16!}{11!}$ **c.** $\frac{100!}{99!}$.

3 Use the permutations formula.

A Formula for Permutations

You are the coach of a little league baseball team. There are 13 players on the team (and lots of parents hovering in the background, dreaming of stardom for their little "Barry Bonds"). You need to choose a batting order having 9 players. The order makes a difference, because, for instance, if bases are loaded and "Little Barry" is fourth or fifth at bat, his possible home run will drive in three additional runs. How many batting orders can you form?

You can choose any of 13 players for the first person at bat. Then you will have 12 players from which to choose the second batter, then 11 from which to choose the third batter, and so on. The situation can be shown as follows:

Batter 1	Batter 2	Batter 3	Batter 4	Batter 5	Batter 6	Batter 7	Batter 8	Batter 9
13 choices	12 choices	11 choices	10 choices	9 choices	8 choices	7 choices	6 choices	5 choices

The total number of batting orders is

$$13\cdot12\cdot11\cdot10\cdot9\cdot8\cdot7\cdot6\cdot5 = 259{,}459{,}200.$$

Nearly 260 million batting orders are possible for your 13-player little league team. Each batting order is a permutation because the order of the batters makes a difference. The number of permutations of 13 players taken 9 at a time is 259,459,200.

We can obtain a formula for finding the number of permutations by rewriting our computation:

$$13 \cdot 12 \cdot 11 \cdot 10 \cdot 9 \cdot 8 \cdot 7 \cdot 6 \cdot 5$$

$$= \frac{13 \cdot 12 \cdot 11 \cdot 10 \cdot 9 \cdot 8 \cdot 7 \cdot 6 \cdot 5 \cdot \boxed{4 \cdot 3 \cdot 2 \cdot 1}}{\boxed{4 \cdot 3 \cdot 2 \cdot 1}} = \frac{13!}{4!} = \frac{13!}{(13-9)!}.$$

Thus, the number of permutations of 13 things taken 9 at a time is $\frac{13!}{(13-9)!}$. The special notation ${}_{13}P_9$ is used to replace the phrase "the number of permutations of 13 things taken 9 at a time." Using this new notation, we can write

$${}_{13}P_9 = \frac{13!}{(13-9)!}.$$

The numerator of this expression is the factorial of the number of items, 13 team members: 13!. The denominator is also a factorial. It is the factorial of the difference between the number of items, 13, and the number of items in each permutation, 9 batters: $(13 - 9)!$.

The notation ${}_nP_r$ means the **number of permutations of n things taken r at a time**. We can generalize from the situation in which 9 batters were taken from 13 players. By generalizing, we obtain the following formula for the number of permutations if r items are taken from n items:

STUDY TIP

Because all permutation problems are also Fundamental Counting problems, they can be solved using the formula for ${}_nP_r$ or using the Fundamental Counting Principle.

PERMUTATIONS OF n THINGS TAKEN r AT A TIME

The number of possible permutations if r items are taken from n items is

$${}_nP_r = \frac{n!}{(n-r)!}.$$

EXAMPLE 4 USING THE FORMULA FOR PERMUTATIONS

You and 19 of your friends have decided to form an Internet marketing consulting firm. The group needs to choose three officers—a CEO, an operating manager, and a treasurer. In how many ways can those offices be filled?

SOLUTION Your group is choosing $r = 3$ officers from a group of $n = 20$ people (you and 19 friends). The order in which the officers are chosen matters because the CEO, the operating manager, and the treasurer each have different responsibilities. Thus, we are looking for the number of permutations of 20 things taken 3 at a time. We use the formula

$${}_nP_r = \frac{n!}{(n-r)!}$$

with $n = 20$ and $r = 3$.

$${}_{20}P_3 = \frac{20!}{(20-3)!} = \frac{20!}{17!} = \frac{20 \cdot 19 \cdot 18 \cdot 17!}{17!} = \frac{20 \cdot 19 \cdot 18 \cdot \cancel{17!}}{\cancel{17!}} = 20 \cdot 19 \cdot 18 = 6840$$

Thus, there are 6840 different ways of filling the three offices.

TECHNOLOGY

Graphing calculators have a menu item for calculating permutations, usually labeled $\boxed{{}_nP_r}$. For example, to find ${}_{20}P_3$, the keystrokes are

20 $\boxed{{}_nP_r}$ 3 $\boxed{\text{ENTER}}$.

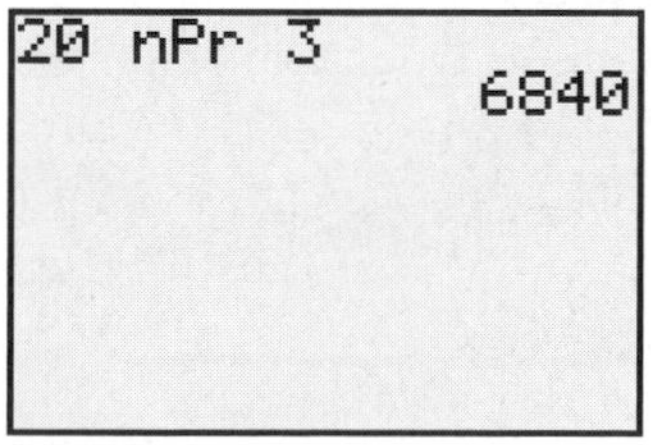

If you are using a scientific calculator, check your manual for the location of the menu item for calculating permutations and the required keystrokes.

CHECK POINT 4 A corporation has seven members on its board of directors. In how many different ways can it elect a president, vice-president, secretary, and treasurer?

EXAMPLE 5 USING THE FORMULA FOR PERMUTATIONS

You are working for The Sitcom Television Network. Your assignment is to help set up the television schedule for Monday evenings between 7 and 10 P.M. You need to schedule a show in each of six 30-minute time blocks, beginning with 7 to 7:30 and ending with 9:30 to 10:00. You can select from among the following situation comedies: *Home Improvement*, *Seinfeld*, *Mad About You*, *Cheers*, *Friends*, *Frasier*, *All in the Family*, *I Love Lucy*, *M*A*S*H*, *The Larry Sanders Show*, *The Jeffersons*, *Married with Children*, and *Happy Days*. How many different programming schedules can be arranged?

SOLUTION You are choosing $r = 6$ situation comedies from a collection of $n = 13$ classic sitcoms. The order in which the programs are aired matters. Family-oriented comedies have higher ratings when aired in earlier time blocks, such as 7 to 7:30. By contrast, comedies with adult themes do better in later time blocks. In short, we are looking for the number of permutations of 13 things taken 6 at a time. We use the formula

$$_nP_r = \frac{n!}{(n-r)!}$$

with $n = 13$ and $r = 6$.

$$_{13}P_6 = \frac{13!}{(13-6)!} = \frac{13!}{7!} = \frac{13 \cdot 12 \cdot 11 \cdot 10 \cdot 9 \cdot 8 \cdot \cancel{7!}}{\cancel{7!}} = 13 \cdot 12 \cdot 11 \cdot 10 \cdot 9 \cdot 8 = 1{,}235{,}520$$

There are 1,235,520 different programming schedules that can be arranged.

CHECK POINT 5 How many different programming schedules can be arranged by choosing 5 situation comedies from a collection of 9 classic sitcoms?

4 Find the number of permutations of duplicate items.

Permutations of Duplicate Items

The number of permutations of the letters in the word SET is 3!, or 6. The six permutations are

SET, STE, EST, ETS, TES, TSE.

Are there also six permutations of the letters in the name ANA? The answer is no. Unlike SET, with three distinct letters, ANA contains three letters, of which the two As are duplicates. If we rearrange the letters just as we did with SET, we obtain

ANA, AAN, NAA, NAA, ANA, AAN.

Without the use of color to distinguish between the two As, there are only three distinct permutations: ANA, AAN, NAA.

There is a formula for finding the number of distinct permutations when duplicate items exist:

PERMUTATIONS OF DUPLICATE ITEMS

The number of permutations of n items, where p items are identical, q items are identical, r items are identical, and so on, is given by

$$\frac{n!}{p!\,q!\,r!\ldots}.$$

For example, ANA contains three letters ($n = 3$), where two of the letters are identical ($p = 2$). The number of distinct permutations is

$$\frac{n!}{p!} = \frac{3!}{2!} = \frac{3 \cdot \cancel{2!}}{\cancel{2!}} = 3.$$

We saw that the three distinct permutations are ANA, AAN, and NAA.

TECHNOLOGY

Parentheses are necessary to enclose the factorials in the denominator when using a calculator to find

$$\frac{11!}{4!\,4!\,2!}.$$

EXAMPLE 6 USING THE FORMULA FOR PERMUTATIONS OF DUPLICATE ITEMS

In how many distinct ways can the letters of the word MISSISSIPPI be arranged?

SOLUTION The word contains 11 letters ($n = 11$), where four Is are identical ($p = 4$), four Ss are identical ($q = 4$), and 2 Ps are identical ($r = 2$). The number of distinct permutations is

$$\frac{n!}{p!\,q!\,r!} = \frac{11!}{4!\,4!\,2!} = \frac{11\cdot10\cdot9\cdot8\cdot7\cdot6\cdot5\cdot\cancel{4!}}{\cancel{4!}\,4\cdot3\cdot2\cdot1\cdot2\cdot1} = 34{,}650$$

There are 34,650 distinct ways the letters in the word MISSISSIPPI can be arranged.

CHECK POINT 6 In how many ways can the letters of the word OSMOSIS be arranged?

EXERCISE SET 11.2

• Practice and Application Exercises

Use the Fundamental Counting Principle to solve Exercises 1–12.

1. Six performers are to present their comedy acts on a weekend evening at a comedy club. How many different ways are there to schedule their appearances?
2. Five singers are to perform on a weekend evening at a night club. How many different ways are there to schedule their appearances?
3. In the *Cambridge Encyclopedia of Language* (Cambridge University Press, 1987), author David Crystal presents five sentences that make a reasonable paragraph regardless of their order. The sentences are as follows:

   Mark had told him about the foxes.
   John looked out of the window.
   Could it be a fox?
   However, nobody had seen one for months.
   He thought he saw a shape in the bushes.

   In how many different orders can the five sentences be arranged?
4. In how many different ways can a police department arrange eight suspects in a police lineup if each lineup contains all eight people?
5. As in Exercise 1, six performers are to present their comedy acts on a weekend evening at a comedy club. One of the performers insists on being the last stand-up comic of the evening. If this performer's request is granted, how many different ways are there to schedule the appearances?
6. As in Exercise 2, five singers are to perform at a night club. One of the singers insists on being the last performer of the evening. If this singer's request is granted, how many different ways are there to schedule the appearances?
7. You need to arrange nine of your favorite books along a small shelf. How many different ways can you arrange the books, assuming that the order of the books makes a difference to you?
8. You need to arrange ten of your favorite photographs on the mantel above a fireplace. How many ways can you arrange the photographs, assuming that the order of the pictures makes a difference to you?

In Exercises 9–10, use the five sentences that are given in Exercise 3.

9. How many different five-sentence paragraphs can be formed if the paragraph begins with "He thought he saw a shape in the bushes" and ends with "John looked out of the window"?
10. How many different five-sentence paragraphs can be formed if the paragraph begins with "He thought he saw a shape in the bushes" followed by "Mark had told him about the foxes"?
11. A television programmer is arranging the order that five movies will be seen between the hours of 6 P.M. and 4 A.M. Two of the movies have a G rating, and they are to be shown in the first two time blocks. One of the movies is rated NC-17, and it is to be shown in the last of the time blocks, from 2 A.M. until 4 A.M. Given these restrictions, in how many ways can the five movies be arranged during the indicated time blocks?
12. A camp counselor and six campers are to be seated along a picnic bench. In how many ways can this be done if the counselor must be seated in the middle and a camper who has a tendency to engage in food fights must sit to the counselor's immediate left?

In Exercises 13–32, evaluate each factorial expression.

13. $\frac{9!}{6!}$
14. $\frac{12!}{10!}$
15. $\frac{29!}{25!}$
16. $\frac{31!}{28!}$
17. $\frac{19!}{11!}$
18. $\frac{17!}{9!}$
19. $\frac{600!}{599!}$
20. $\frac{700!}{699!}$
21. $\frac{104!}{102!}$
22. $\frac{106!}{104!}$
23. $7! - 3!$
24. $6! - 3!$
25. $(7 - 3)!$
26. $(6 - 3)!$
27. $\left(\frac{12}{4}\right)!$
28. $\left(\frac{45}{9}\right)!$
29. $\frac{7!}{(7-2)!}$
30. $\frac{8!}{(8-5)!}$
31. $\frac{13!}{(13-3)!}$
32. $\frac{17!}{(17-3)!}$

In Exercises 33–40, use the formula for $_nP_r$ to evaluate each expression.

33. $_9P_4$ **34.** $_7P_3$ **35.** $_8P_5$

36. $_{10}P_4$ **37.** $_6P_6$ **38.** $_9P_9$

39. $_8P_0$ **40.** $_6P_0$

Use the formula for $_nP_r$ to solve Exercises 41–48.

41. A club with ten members is to choose three officers—president, vice-president, and secretary-treasurer. If each office is to be held by one person and no person can hold more than one office, in how many ways can those offices be filled?

42. A corporation has seven members on its board of directors. In how many different ways can it elect a president, vice-president, secretary, and treasurer?

43. For a segment of a radio show, a disc jockey can play 7 records. If there are 13 records to select from, in how many ways can the program for this segment be arranged?

44. Suppose you are asked to list, in order of preference, the three best movies you have seen this year. If you saw 20 movies during the year, in how many ways can the three best be chosen and ranked?

45. In a race in which six automobiles are entered and there are no ties, in how many ways can the first three finishers come in?

46. In a production of *West Side Story*, eight actors are considered for the male roles of Tony, Riff, and Bernardo. In how many ways can the director cast the male roles?

47. Nine bands have volunteered to perform at a benefit concert, but there is only enough time for five of the bands to play. How many lineups are possible?

48. How many arrangements can be made using four of the letters of the word COMBINE if no letter is to be used more than once?

Use the formula for the number of permutations of duplicate items to solve Exercises 49–56.

49. In how many distinct ways can the letters of the word DALLAS be arranged?

50. In how many distinct ways can the letters of the word SCIENCE be arranged?

51. How many distinct permutations can be formed using the letters of the word TALLAHASSEE?

52. How many distinct permutations can be formed using the letters of the word TENNESSEE?

53. In how many ways can the digits in the number 5,446,666 be arranged?

54. In how many ways can the digits in the number 5,432,435 be arranged?

In Exercises 55–56, a signal can be formed by running different colored flags up a pole, one above the other.

55. Find the number of different signals consisting of eight flags that can be made using three white flags, four red flags, and one blue flag.

56. Find the number of different signals consisting of nine flags that can be made using three white flags, five red flags, and one blue flag.

• Writing in Mathematics

57. What is a permutation?

58. Explain how to find $n!$, where n is a positive integer.

59. Explain the best way to evaluate $\frac{900!}{899!}$ without a calculator.

60. Describe what $_nP_r$ represents.

61. Write a word problem that can be solved by evaluating 5!.

62. Write a word problem that can be solved by evaluating $_7P_3$.

63. If 24 permutations can be formed using the letters in the word BAKE, why can't 24 permutations also be formed using the letters in the word BABE? How is the number of permutations in BABE determined?

• Critical Thinking Exercises

64. Ten people board an airplane that has 12 aisle seats. In how many ways can they be seated if they all select aisle seats?

65. Six horses are entered in a race. If two horses are tied for first place, and there are no ties among the other four horses, in how many ways can the six horses cross the finish line?

66. Performing at a concert are eight rock bands and eight jazz groups. How many ways can the program be arranged if the first, third, and eighth performers are jazz groups?

67. Five men and five women line up at a checkout counter in a store. In how many ways can they line up if the first person in line is a woman, and the people in line alternate woman, man, woman, man, and so on?

68. How many four-digit odd numbers less than 6000 can be formed using the digits 2, 4, 6, 7, 8, and 9?

69. Express $_nP_{n-2}$ without using factorials.

SECTION 11.3 • COMBINATIONS

OBJECTIVES

1. Distinguish between permutation and combination problems.
2. Solve problems involving combinations using the combinations formula.

As the twentieth century drew to a close, *Time* magazine presented a series of special issues on the most influential people of the century. In its issue on heroes and icons (June 14, 1999), *Time* discussed a number of people whose careers became more profitable after their tragic deaths, including Marilyn Monroe, James Dean, Jim Morrison, Kurt Cobain, and Selena.

Imagine that you ask your friends the following question: "Of these five people, which three would you select to be included in a documentary featuring the best of their work?" You are not asking your friends to rank their three favorite artists in any kind of order—they should merely select the three to be included in the documentary.

1 Distinguish between permutation and combination problems.

One friend answers, "Jim Morrison, Kurt Cobain, and Selena." Another responds, "Selena, Kurt Cobain, and Jim Morrison." These two people have the same artists in their group of selections, even if they are named in a different order. We are interested *in which artists are named, not the order in which they are named* for the documentary. Because the items are taken without regard to order, this is not a permutation problem. No ranking of any sort is involved.

Later on, you ask your roommate which three artists she would select for the documentary. She names Marilyn Monroe, James Dean, and Selena. Her selection is different from those of your two other friends because different entertainers are cited.

Mathematicians describe the group of artists given by your roommate as a *combination*. A **combination** of items occurs when

- The items are selected from the same group (the five stars who died young and tragically).
- No item is used more than once. (You may adore Selena, but your three selections cannot be Selena, Selena, and Selena.)
- The order of items makes no difference. (Morrison, Cobain, Selena is the same group in the documentary as Selena, Cobain, Morrison.)

Do you see the difference between a permutation and a combination? A permutation is an ordered arrangement of a given group of items. A combination is a group of items taken without regard to their order. **Permutation** problems involve situations in which **order matters**. **Combination** problems involve situations in which the **order** of items **makes no difference**.

Marilyn Monroe, Actress (1927–1962)

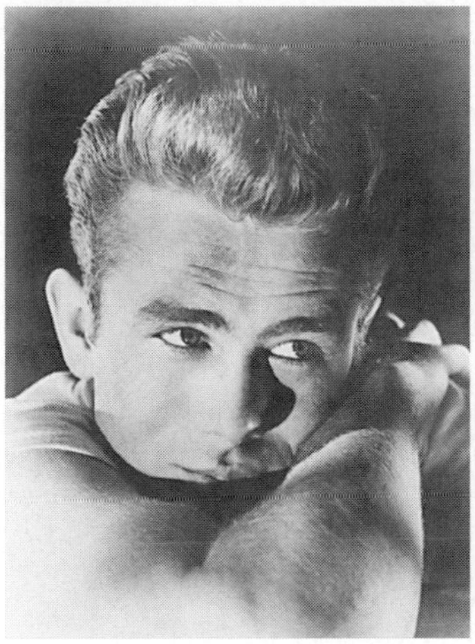

James Dean, Actor (1931–1955)

Jim Morrison, Musician and Lead Singer of The Doors (1943–1971)

Kurt Cobain, Musician and Front Man for Nirvana (1967–1994)

Selena, Musician of Tejano Music (1971–1995)

EXAMPLE 1 DISTINGUISHING BETWEEN PERMUTATIONS AND COMBINATIONS

For each of the following problems, determine whether the problem is one involving permutations or combinations. (It is not necessary to solve the problem.)

a. Six students are running for student government president, vice-president, and treasurer. The student with the greatest number of votes becomes the president, the second highest vote-getter becomes vice-president, and the student who gets the third largest number of votes will be treasurer. How many different outcomes are possible for these three positions?

b. Six people are on the board of supervisors for your neighborhood park. A three-person committee is needed to study the possibility of expanding the park. How many different committees could be formed from the six people?

c. Baskin-Robbins offers 31 different flavors of ice cream. One of their items is a bowl consisting of three scoops of ice cream, each a different flavor. How many such bowls are possible?

SOLUTION

a. Students are choosing three student government officers from six candidates. The order in which the officers are chosen makes a difference because each of the offices (president, vice-president, treasurer) is different. Order matters. This is a problem involving permutations.

b. A three-person committee is to be formed from the six-person board of supervisors. The order in which the three people are selected does not matter because they are not filling different roles on the committee. Because order makes no difference, this is a problem involving combinations.

c. A three-scoop bowl of three different flavors is to be formed from Baskin-Robbin's 31 flavors. The order in which the three scoops of ice cream are put into the bowl is irrelevant. A bowl with chocolate, vanilla, and strawberry is exactly the same as a bowl with vanilla, strawberry, and chocolate. Different orderings do not change things, and so this is a problem involving combinations.

CHECK POINT 1 For each of the following problems, determine whether the problem is one involving permutations or combinations. (It is not necessary to solve the problem.)

a. How many ways can you select 6 free DVDs from a list of 200 DVDs?

b. In a race in which there are 50 runners and no ties, in how many ways can the first three finishers come in?

2 Solve problems involving combinations using the combinations formula.

A Formula for Combinations

We have seen that the notation $_nP_r$ means the number of permutations of n things taken r at a time. Similarly, the notation **$_nC_r$ means the number of combinations of n things taken r at a time.**

We can develop a formula for $_nC_r$ by comparing permutations and combinations. Consider the letters A, B, C, and D. The number of permutations of these four letters taken three at a time is

$$_4P_3 = \frac{4!}{(4-3)!} = \frac{4!}{1!} = \frac{4 \cdot 3 \cdot 2 \cdot 1}{1} = 24.$$

Here are the 24 permutations:

ABC,	ABD,	ACD,	BCD,
ACB,	ADB,	ADC,	BDC,
BAC,	BAD,	CAD,	CBD,
BCA,	BDA,	CDA,	CDB,
CAB,	DAB,	DAC,	DBC,
CBA,	DBA,	DCA,	DCB.
This column contains only one combination, ABC.	This column contains only one combination, ABD.	This column contains only one combination, ACD.	This column contains only one combination, BCD.

Because the order of items makes no difference in determining combinations, each column of six permutations represents one combination. There are a total of four combinations:

ABC, ABD, ACD, BCD.

Thus, $_4C_3 = 4$: The number of combinations of 4 things taken 3 at a time is 4. With 24 permutations and only four combinations, there are 6, or 3!, times as many permutations as there are combinations.

In general, there are $r!$ times as many permutations of n things taken r at a time as there are combinations of n things taken r at a time. Thus, we find the number of combinations of n things taken r at a time by dividing the number of permutations of n things taken r at a time by $r!$.

$$_nC_r = \frac{_nP_r}{r!} = \frac{\frac{n!}{(n-r)!}}{r!} = \frac{n!}{(n-r)!\,r!}$$

STUDY TIP

The number of combinations if r items are taken from n items cannot be found using the Fundamental Counting Principle and requires the use of the formula shown on the right.

COMBINATIONS OF n THINGS TAKEN r AT A TIME

The number of possible combinations if r items are taken from n items is

$$_nC_r = \frac{n!}{(n-r)!\,r!}.$$

EXAMPLE 2 USING THE FORMULA FOR COMBINATIONS

A three-person committee is needed to study ways of improving public transportation. How many committees could be formed from the eight people on the board of supervisors?

SOLUTION The order in which the three people are selected does not matter. This is a problem of selecting $r = 3$ people from a group of $n = 8$ people. We are looking for the number of combinations of eight things taken three at a time. We use the formula

$$_nC_r = \frac{n!}{(n-r)!\,r!}$$

with $n = 8$ and $r = 3$.

$$_8C_3 = \frac{8!}{(8-3)!\,3!} = \frac{8!}{5!\,3!} = \frac{8\cdot7\cdot6\cdot5!}{5!\cdot3\cdot2\cdot1} = \frac{8\cdot7\cdot6\cdot\cancel{5!}}{\cancel{5!}\cdot3\cdot2\cdot1} = 56$$

Thus, 56 committees of three people each can be formed from the eight people on the board of supervisors.

CHECK POINT 2 You volunteer to pet-sit for your friend who has seven different animals. How many different pet combinations are possible if you take three of the seven pets?

TECHNOLOGY

Graphing calculators have a menu item for calculating combinations, usually labeled $_nC_r$. For example, to find $_8C_3$, the keystrokes on most graphing calculators are

8 [$_nC_r$] 3 [ENTER].

If you are using a scientific calculator, check your manual to see whether there is a menu item for calculating combinations.

If you use your calculator's factorial key to find $\frac{8!}{5!\,3!}$, be sure to enclose the factorials in the denominator with parentheses

8 [!] [÷] [(] 5 [!] [×] 3 [!] [)]

pressing [=] or [ENTER] to obtain the answer.

EXAMPLE 3 USING THE FORMULA FOR COMBINATIONS

In poker, a person is dealt 5 cards from a standard 52-card deck. The order in which you are dealt the 5 cards does not matter. How many different 5-card poker hands are possible?

SOLUTION Because the order in which the 5 cards are dealt does not matter, this is a problem involving combinations. We are looking for the number of combinations of $n = 52$ cards drawn $r = 5$ at a time. We use the formula

$$_nC_r = \frac{n!}{(n-r)!\,r!}$$

with $n = 52$ and $r = 5$.

$$_{52}C_5 = \frac{52!}{(52-5)!\,5!} = \frac{52!}{47!\,5!} = \frac{52\cdot51\cdot50\cdot49\cdot48\cdot\cancel{47!}}{\cancel{47!}\cdot5\cdot4\cdot3\cdot2\cdot1} = 2{,}598{,}960$$

Thus, there are 2,598,960 different 5-card poker hands possible. It surprises many people that more than 2.5 million 5-card hands can be dealt from a mere 52 cards.

FIGURE 11.3 A royal flush

If you are a card player, it does not get any better than to be dealt the 5-card poker hand shown in Figure 11.3. This hand is called a *royal flush*. It consists of an ace, king, queen, jack, and 10, all of the same suit: all hearts, all diamonds, all clubs, or all spades. The probability of being dealt a royal flush involves calculating the number of ways of being dealt such a hand: just 4 of all 2,598,960 possible hands. In the next section, we move from counting possibilities to computing probabilities.

CHECK POINT 3 How many different 4-card hands can be dealt from a deck that has 16 different cards?

There are situations in which both the formula for combinations and the Fundamental Counting Principle are used together. Let's say that the U.S. Senate, with 100 members, consists of 54 Republicans and 46 Democrats. We want to form a committee of 3 Republicans and 2 Democrats.

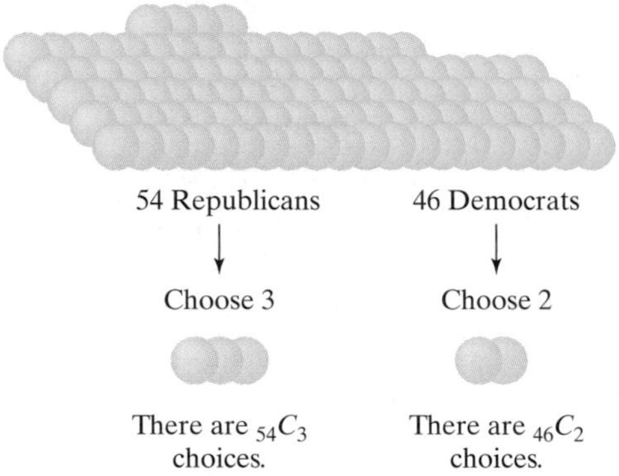

By the Fundamental Counting Principle, the number of ways of choosing 3 Republicans and 2 Democrats is given by

$$_{54}C_3 \cdot {}_{46}C_2.$$

In Example 4, we develop these ideas in more detail.

EXAMPLE 4 USING THE FORMULA FOR COMBINATIONS AND THE FUNDAMENTAL COUNTING PRINCIPLE

The U.S. Senate of the 104th Congress consisted of 54 Republicans and 46 Democrats. How many committees can be formed if each committee must have 3 Republicans and 2 Democrats?

SOLUTION The order in which the members are selected does not matter. Thus, this is a problem involving combinations.

We begin with the number of ways of selecting 3 Republicans out of 54 Republicans without regard to order. We are looking for the number of combinations of $n = 54$ people taken $r = 3$ people at a time. We use the formula

$$_nC_r = \frac{n!}{(n-r)!\,r!}$$

with $n = 54$ and $r = 3$.

$$_{54}C_3 = \frac{54!}{(54-3)!\,3!} = \frac{54!}{51!\,3!} = \frac{54 \cdot 53 \cdot 52 \cdot \cancel{51!}}{\cancel{51!} \cdot 3 \cdot 2 \cdot 1} = \frac{54 \cdot 53 \cdot 52}{3 \cdot 2 \cdot 1} = 24{,}804$$

There are 24,804 choices for forming 3-member Republican committees.

Next, we find the number of ways of selecting 2 Democrats out of 46 Democrats without regard to order. We are looking for the number of combinations of $n = 46$ people taken $r = 2$ people at a time. Once again, we use the formula

$$_nC_r = \frac{n!}{(n-r)!\,r!}.$$

This time, $n = 46$ and $r = 2$.

$$_{46}C_2 = \frac{46!}{(46-2)!\,2!} = \frac{46!}{44!\,2!} = \frac{46 \cdot 45 \cdot \cancel{44!}}{\cancel{44!} \cdot 2 \cdot 1} = 1035$$

There are 1035 choices for forming 2-member Democratic committees.

We use the Fundamental Counting Principle to find the number of committees that can be formed:

$$_{54}C_3 \cdot {}_{46}C_2 = 24{,}804 \cdot 1035 = 25{,}672{,}140.$$

Thus, 25,672,140 committees can be formed.

CHECK POINT 4 The U.S. Senate of the 107th Congress consisted of 50 Democrats, 49 Republicans, and one Independent. How many committees can be formed if each committee must have 3 Democrats and 2 Republicans?

EXERCISE SET 11.3

• Practice Exercises

In Exercises 1–4, does the problem involve permutations or combinations? Explain your answer. (It is not necessary to solve the problem.)

1. A medical researcher needs 6 people to test the effectiveness of an experimental drug. If 13 people have volunteered for the test, in how many ways can 6 people be selected?
2. Fifty people purchase raffle tickets. Three winning tickets are selected at random. If first prize is \$1000, second prize is \$500, and third prize is \$100, in how many different ways can the prizes be awarded?
3. How many different four-letter passwords can be formed from the letters A, B, C, D, E, F, and G if no repetition of letters is allowed?
4. Fifty people purchase raffle tickets. Three winning tickets are selected at random. If each prize is \$500, in how many different ways can the prizes be awarded?

In Exercises 5–20, use the formula for $_nC_r$ to evaluate each expression.

5. $_6C_5$ 6. $_8C_7$ 7. $_9C_5$ 8. $_{10}C_6$
9. $_{11}C_4$ 10. $_{12}C_5$ 11. $_8C_1$ 12. $_7C_1$
13. $_7C_7$ 14. $_4C_4$ 15. $_{30}C_3$ 16. $_{25}C_4$
17. $_5C_0$ 18. $_6C_0$ 19. $\frac{_7C_3}{_5C_4}$ 20. $\frac{_{10}C_3}{_6C_4}$

• Practice Plus

In Exercises 21–28, evaluate each expression.

21. $\frac{_7P_3}{3!} - {}_7C_3$ 22. $\frac{_{20}P_2}{2!} - {}_{20}C_2$ 23. $1 - \frac{_3P_2}{_4P_3}$
24. $1 - \frac{_5P_3}{_{10}P_4}$ 25. $\frac{_7C_3}{_5C_4} - \frac{98!}{96!}$ 26. $\frac{_{10}C_3}{_6C_4} - \frac{46!}{44!}$
27. $\frac{_4C_2 \cdot {}_6C_1}{_{18}C_3}$ 28. $\frac{_5C_1 \cdot {}_7C_2}{_{12}C_3}$

• Application Exercises

Use the formula for $_nC_r$ to solve Exercises 29–36.

29. An election ballot asks voters to select three city commissioners from a group of six candidates. In how many ways can this be done?
30. A four-person committee is to be elected from an organization's membership of 11 people. How many different committees are possible?
31. Of 12 possible books, you plan to take 4 with you on vacation. How many different collections of 4 books can you take?
32. There are 14 standbys who hope to get seats on a flight, but only 6 seats are available on the plane. How many different ways can the 6 people be selected?
33. You volunteer to help drive children at a charity event to the zoo, but you can fit only 8 of the 17 children present in your van. How many different groups of 8 children can you drive?
34. Of the 100 people in the U.S. Senate, 18 serve on the Foreign Relations Committee. How many ways are there to select Senate members for this committee (assuming party affiliation is not a factor in the selection)?
35. To win at LOTTO in the state of Florida, one must correctly select 6 numbers from a collection of 53 numbers (1 through 53). The order in which the selection is made does not matter. How many different selections are possible?

36. To win in the New York State lottery, one must correctly select 6 numbers from 59 numbers. The order in which the selection is made does not matter. How many different selections are possible?

In Exercises 37–46, solve by the method of your choice.

37. In a race in which six automobiles are entered and there are no ties, in how many ways can the first four finishers come in?

38. A book club offers a choice of 8 books from a list of 40. In how many ways can a member make a selection?

39. A medical researcher needs 6 people to test the effectiveness of an experimental drug. If 13 people have volunteered for the test, in how many ways can 6 people be selected?

40. Fifty people purchase raffle tickets. Three winning tickets are selected at random. If first prize is $1000, second prize is $500, and third prize is $100, in how many different ways can the prizes be awarded?

41. From a club of 20 people, in how many ways can a group of three members be selected to attend a conference?

42. Fifty people purchase raffle tickets. Three winning tickets are selected at random. If each prize is $500, in how many different ways can the prizes be awarded?

43. How many different four-letter passwords can be formed from the letters A, B, C, D, E, F, and G if no repetition of letters is allowed?

44. Nine comedy acts will perform over two evenings. Five of the acts will perform on the first evening. How many ways can the schedule for the first evening be made?

45. Using 15 flavors of ice cream, how many cones with three different flavors can you create if it is important to you which flavor goes on the top, middle, and bottom?

46. Baskin-Robbins offers 31 different flavors of ice cream. One of its items is a bowl consisting of three scoops of ice cream, each a different flavor. How many such bowls are possible?

Use the formula for ${}_nC_r$ and the Fundamental Counting Principle to solve Exercises 47–50.

47. In how many ways can a committee of four men and five women be formed from a group of seven men and seven women?

48. How many different committees can be formed from 5 professors and 15 students if each committee is made up of 2 professors and 10 students?

49. The U.S. Senate of the 109th Congress consisted of 55 Republicans, 44 Democrats, and 1 Independent. How many committees can be formed if each committee must have 4 Republicans and 3 Democrats?

50. A mathematics exam consists of 10 multiple-choice questions and 5 open-ended problems in which all work must be shown. If an examinee must answer 8 of the multiple-choice questions and 3 of the open-ended problems, in how many ways can the questions and problems be chosen?

Thousands of jokes have been told about marriage and divorce. Exercises 51–58 are based on the following observations:

- *"By all means, marry; if you get a good wife, you'll be happy. If you get a bad one, you'll become a philosopher." - Socrates*
- *"My wife and I were happy for 20 years. Then we met." - Rodney Dangerfield*
- *"Whatever you may look like, marry a man your own age. As your beauty fades, so will his eyesight." - Phyllis Diller*
- *"Why do Jewish divorces cost so much? Because they're worth it." - Henny Youngman*
- *"I think men who have a pierced ear are better prepared for marriage. They've experienced pain and bought jewelry." - Rita Rudner*
- *"For a while we pondered whether to take a vacation or get a divorce. We decided that a trip to Bermuda is over in two weeks, but a divorce is something you always have." - Woody Allen*

51. In how many ways can these six jokes be ranked from best to worst?

52. If Socrates's thoughts about marriage are excluded, in how many ways can the remaining five jokes be ranked from best to worst?

53. In how many ways can people select their three favorite jokes from these thoughts about marriage and divorce?

54. In how many ways can people select their two favorite jokes from these thoughts about marriage and divorce?

55. If the order in which these jokes are told makes a difference in terms of how they are received, how many ways can they be delivered if Socrates's comments are scheduled first and Dangerfield's joke is told last?

56. If the order in which these jokes are told makes a difference in terms of how they are received, how many ways can they be delivered if a joke by a woman (Rudner or Diller) is told first?

57. In how many ways can people select their favorite joke told by a woman (Rudner or Diller) and their two favorite jokes told by a man?

58. In how many ways can people select their favorite joke told by a woman (Rudner or Diller) and their three favorite jokes told by a man?

• Writing in Mathematics

59. What is a combination?

60. Explain how to distinguish between permutation and combination problems.

61. Write a word problem that can be solved by evaluating ${}_7C_3$.

• Critical Thinking Exercises

62. Write a word problem that can be solved by evaluating ${}_{10}C_3 \cdot {}_7C_2$.

63. A 6/53 lottery involves choosing 6 of the numbers from 1 through 53 and a 5/36 lottery involves choosing 5 of the numbers from 1 through 36. The order in which the numbers are chosen does not matter. Which lottery is easier to win? Explain your answer.

64. If the number of permutations of n objects taken r at a time is six times the number of combinations of n objects taken r at a time, determine the value of r. Is there enough information to determine the value of n? Why or why not?

65. In a group of 20 people, how long will it take each person to shake hands with each of the other persons in the group, assuming that it takes three seconds for each shake and only 2 people can shake hands at a time? What if the group is increased to 40 people?

66. A sample of 4 telephones is selected from a shipment of 20 phones. There are 5 defective telephones in the shipment. How many of the samples of 4 phones do not include any of the defective ones?

SECTION 11.4 • FUNDAMENTALS OF PROBABILITY

OBJECTIVES

1. Compute theoretical probability.
2. Compute empirical probability.

TABLE 11.1 THE HOURS OF SLEEP AMERICANS GET ON A TYPICAL NIGHT

Hours of Sleep	Number of Americans, in millions
4 or less	12
5	27
6	75
7	90
8	81
9	9
10 or more	6

Total: 300

Source: Discovery Health Media

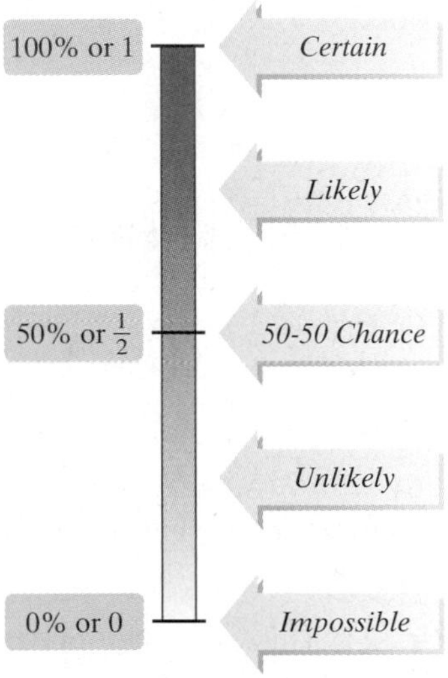

Possible Values for Probabilities

How many hours of sleep do you typically get each night? Table 11.1 indicates that 75 million out of 300 million Americans are getting six hours of sleep on a typical night. The *probability* of an American getting six hours of sleep on a typical night is $\frac{75}{300}$. This fraction can be reduced to $\frac{1}{4}$, or expressed as 0.25, or 25%. Thus, 25% of Americans get six hours of sleep each night.

We find a probability by dividing one number by another. Probabilities are assigned to an *event*, such as getting six hours of sleep on a typical night. Events that are certain to occur are assigned probabilities of 1, or 100%. For example, the probability that a given individual will eventually die is 1. Although Woody Allen whined, "I don't want to achieve immortality through my work. I want to achieve it through not dying," death (and taxes) are always certain. By contrast, if an event cannot occur, its probability is 0. Regrettably, the probability that Elvis will return and serenade us with one final reprise of "Don't Be Cruel" (and we hope we're not) is 0.

Probabilities of events are expressed as numbers ranging from 0 to 1, or 0% to 100%. The closer the probability of a given event is to 1, the more likely it is that the event will occur. The closer the probability of a given event is to 0, the less likely it is that the event will occur.

1 Compute theoretical probability.

Theoretical Probability

You toss a coin. Although it is equally likely to land either heads up, denoted by H, or tails up, denoted by T, the actual outcome is uncertain. Any occurrence for which the outcome is uncertain is called an **experiment**. Thus, tossing a coin is an example of an experiment. The set of all possible outcomes of an experiment is the **sample space** of the experiment, denoted by S. The sample space for the coin-tossing experiment is

$$S = \{H, T\}.$$

Lands heads up — Lands tails up

An **event**, denoted by E, is any subset of a sample space. For example, the subset $E = \{T\}$ is the event of landing tails up when a coin is tossed.

Theoretical probability applies to situations like this, in which the sample space only contains equally likely outcomes, all of which are known. To calculate the theoretical probability of an event, we divide the number of outcomes resulting in the event by the total number of outcomes in the sample space.

COMPUTING THEORETICAL PROBABILITY

If an event E has $n(E)$ equally likely outcomes and its sample space S has $n(S)$ equally likely outcomes, the **theoretical probability** of event E, denoted by $P(E)$, is

$$P(E) = \frac{\text{number of outcomes in event } E}{\text{total number of possible outcomes}} = \frac{n(E)}{n(S)}.$$

How can we use this formula to compute the probability of a coin landing tails up? We use the following sets:

$$E = \{T\} \qquad S = \{H, T\}.$$

This is the event of landing tails up.

This is the sample space with all equally likely outcomes.

The probability of a coin landing tails up is

$$P(E) = \frac{\text{number of outcomes that result in tails up}}{\text{total number of possible outcomes}} = \frac{n(E)}{n(S)} = \frac{1}{2}.$$

FIGURE 11.4 Outcomes when a die is rolled

Theoretical probability applies to many games of chance, including dice rolling, lotteries, card games, and roulette. We begin with rolling a die. Figure 11.4 illustrates that when a die is rolled, there are six equally likely possible outcomes. The sample space can be shown as

$$S = \{1, 2, 3, 4, 5, 6\}.$$

EXAMPLE 1 COMPUTING THEORETICAL PROBABILITY

A die is rolled once. Find the probability of rolling

a. a 3. **b.** an even number. **c.** a number less than 5.
d. a number less than 10. **e.** a number greater than 6.

SOLUTION The sample space is $S = \{1, 2, 3, 4, 5, 6\}$ with $n(S) = 6$. We will use 6, the total number of possible outcomes, in the denominator of each probability fraction.

a. The phrase "rolling a 3" describes the event $E = \{3\}$. This event can occur in one way: $n(E) = 1$.

$$P(3) = \frac{\text{number of outcomes that result in 3}}{\text{total number of possible outcomes}} = \frac{n(E)}{n(S)} = \frac{1}{6}$$

The probability of rolling a 3 is $\frac{1}{6}$.

b. The phrase "rolling an even number" describes the event $E = \{2, 4, 6\}$. This event can occur in three ways: $n(E) = 3$.

$$P(\text{even number}) = \frac{\text{number of outcomes that result in an even number}}{\text{total number of possible outcomes}} = \frac{n(E)}{n(S)} = \frac{3}{6} = \frac{1}{2}$$

The probability of rolling an even number is $\frac{1}{2}$.

c. The phrase "rolling a number less than 5" describes the event $E = \{1, 2, 3, 4\}$. This event can occur in four ways: $n(E) = 4$.

$$P(\text{less than } 5) = \frac{\text{number of outcomes that are less than 5}}{\text{total number of possible outcomes}} = \frac{n(E)}{n(S)} = \frac{4}{6} = \frac{2}{3}$$

The probability of rolling a number less than 5 is $\frac{2}{3}$.

d. The phrase "rolling a number less than 10" describes the event $E = \{1, 2, 3, 4, 5, 6\}$. This event can occur in six ways: $n(E) = 6$. Can you see that all of the possible outcomes are less than 10? This event is certain to occur.

$$P(\text{less than } 10) = \frac{\text{number of outcomes that are less than 10}}{\text{total number of possible outcomes}} = \frac{n(E)}{n(S)} = \frac{6}{6} = 1$$

The probability of any certain event is 1.

e. The phrase "rolling a number greater than 6" describes an event that cannot occur, or the empty set. Thus, $E = \emptyset$ and $n(E) = 0$.

$$P(\text{greater than } 6) = \frac{\text{number of outcomes that are greater than 6}}{\text{total number of possible outcomes}} = \frac{n(E)}{n(S)} = \frac{0}{6} = 0$$

The probability of an event that cannot occur is 0.

In Example 1, there are six possible outcomes, each with a probability of $\frac{1}{6}$:

$$P(1) = \frac{1}{6} \quad P(2) = \frac{1}{6} \quad P(3) = \frac{1}{6} \quad P(4) = \frac{1}{6} \quad P(5) = \frac{1}{6} \quad P(6) = \frac{1}{6}.$$

The sum of these probabilities is 1: $\frac{1}{6} + \frac{1}{6} + \frac{1}{6} + \frac{1}{6} + \frac{1}{6} + \frac{1}{6} = 1$. In general, **the sum of the theoretical probabilities of all possible outcomes in the sample space is 1**.

CHECK POINT 1 A die is rolled once. Find the probability of rolling

a. a 2.

b. a number less than 4.

c. a number greater than 7.

d. a number less than 7.

Our next example involves a standard 52-card bridge deck, illustrated in Figure 11.5. The deck has four suits: Hearts and diamonds are red, and clubs and spades are black. Each suit has 13 different face values—A(ace), 2, 3, 4, 5, 6, 7, 8, 9, 10, J(jack), Q(queen), and K(king). Jacks, queens, and kings are called **picture cards** or **face cards**.

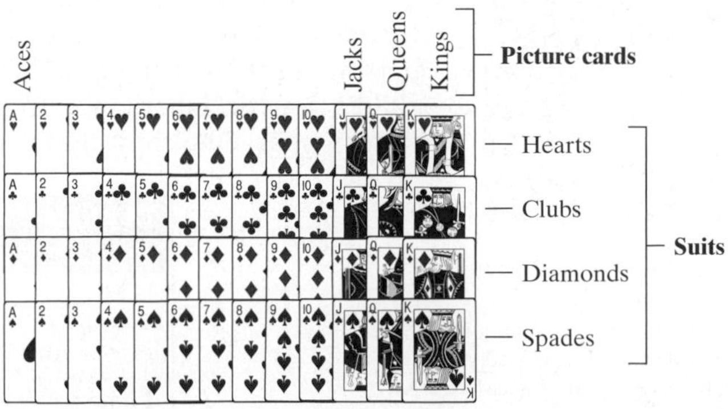

FIGURE 11.5 A standard 52-card bridge deck

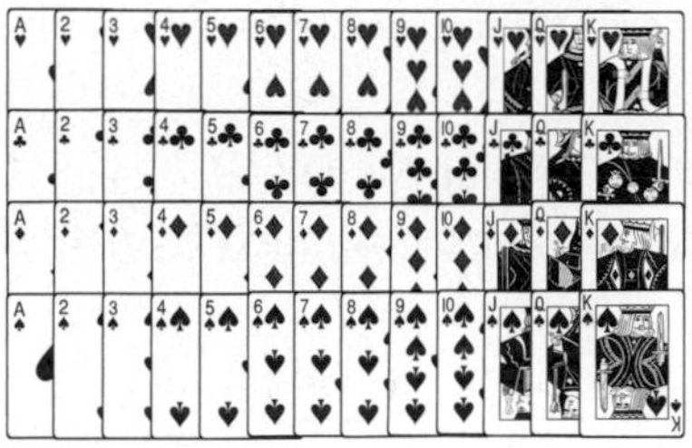

FIGURE 11.5 (repeated)

EXAMPLE 2 PROBABILITY AND A DECK OF 52 CARDS

You are dealt one card from a standard 52-card deck. Find the probability of being dealt

a. a king. **b.** a heart. **c.** the king of hearts.

SOLUTION Because there are 52 cards in the deck, the total number of possible ways of being dealt a single card is 52. The number of outcomes in the sample space is 52: $n(S) = 52$. We use 52 as the denominator of each probability fraction.

a. Let E be the event of being dealt a king. Because there are four kings in the deck, this event can occur in four ways: $n(E) = 4$.

$$P(\text{king}) = \frac{\text{number of outcomes that result in a king}}{\text{total number of possible outcomes}} = \frac{n(E)}{n(S)} = \frac{4}{52} = \frac{1}{13}$$

The probability of being dealt a king is $\frac{1}{13}$.

b. Let E be the event of being dealt a heart. Because there are 13 hearts in the deck, this event can occur in 13 ways: $n(E) = 13$.

$$P(\text{heart}) = \frac{\text{number of outcomes that result in a heart}}{\text{total number of possible outcomes}} = \frac{n(E)}{n(S)} = \frac{13}{52} = \frac{1}{4}$$

The probability of being dealt a heart is $\frac{1}{4}$.

c. Let E be the event of being dealt the king of hearts. Because there is only one card in the deck that is the king of hearts, this event can occur in just one way: $n(E) = 1$.

$$P(\text{king of hearts}) = \frac{\text{number of outcomes that result in the king of hearts}}{\text{total number of possible outcomes}} = \frac{n(E)}{n(S)} = \frac{1}{52}$$

The probability of being dealt the king of hearts is $\frac{1}{52}$.

BLITZER BONUS

Try to Bench Press This at the Gym

You have a deck of cards for every permutation of the 52 cards. If each deck weighed only as much as a single hydrogen atom, all the decks together would weigh a billion times as much as the sun.

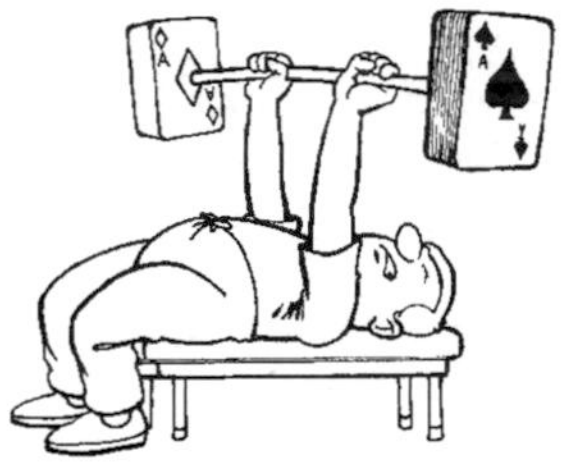

Source: Isaac Asimov's Book of Facts

CHECK POINT 2 You are dealt one card from a standard 52-card deck. Find the probability of being dealt

a. an ace. **b.** a red card. **c.** a red king.

Probabilities play a valuable role in the science of genetics. Example 3 deals with cystic fibrosis, an inherited lung disease occurring in about 1 out of every 2000 births among Caucasians and in about 1 out of every 250,000 births among non-Caucasians.

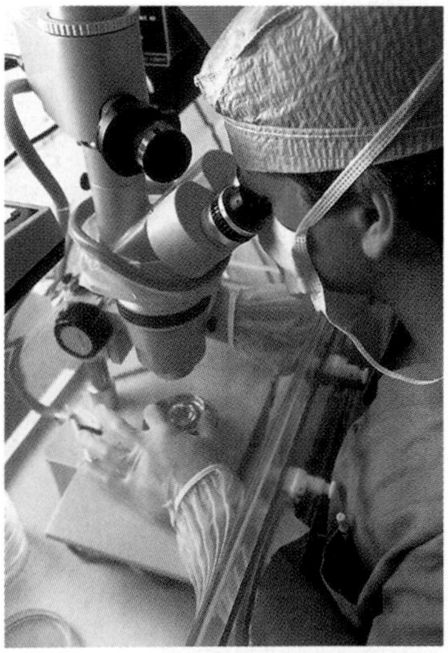

Genetic engineering offers some hope for cystic fibrosis patients. Geneticists can now isolate the c gene, the gene responsible for the disease. It is hoped that it will soon be possible to replace the defective c gene with a normal C gene.

EXAMPLE 3 PROBABILITIES IN GENETICS

Each person carries two genes that are related to the absence or presence of the disease cystic fibrosis. Most Americans have two normal genes for this trait and are unaffected by cystic fibrosis. However, 1 in 25 Americans carries one normal gene and one defective gene. If we use c to represent a defective gene and C a normal gene, such a carrier can be designated as Cc. Thus, CC is a person who neither carries nor has cystic fibrosis, Cc is a carrier who is not actually sick, and cc is a person sick with the disease. Table 11.2 shows the four equally likely outcomes for a child's genetic inheritance from two parents who are both carrying one cystic fibrosis gene. One copy of each gene is passed on to the child from the parents.

TABLE 11.2 CYSTIC FIBROSIS AND GENETIC INHERITANCE

		Second Parent	
		C	c
First Parent	C	CC	Cc
	c	cC	cc

Shown in the table are the four possibilities for a child whose parents each carry one cystic fibrosis gene.

If each parent carries one cystic fibrosis gene, what is the probability that their child will have cystic fibrosis?

SOLUTION Table 11.2 shows that there are four equally likely outcomes. The sample space is $S = \{CC, Cc, cC, cc\}$ and $n(S) = 4$. The phrase "will have cystic fibrosis" describes only the *cc* child. Thus, $E = \{cc\}$ and $n(E) = 1$.

$$P(\text{cystic fibrosis}) = \frac{\text{number of outcomes that result in cystic fibrosis}}{\text{total number of possible outcomes}} = \frac{n(E)}{n(S)} = \frac{1}{4}$$

If each parent carries one cystic fibrosis gene, the probability that their child will have cystic fibrosis is $\frac{1}{4}$.

CHECK POINT 3 Use Table 11.2 in Example 3 to solve this exercise. If each parent carries one cystic fibrosis gene, find the probability that their child will be a carrier of the disease who is not actually sick.

2 Compute empirical probability.

Empirical Probability

Theoretical probability is based on a set of equally likely outcomes and the number of elements in the set. By contrast, *empirical probability* applies to situations in which we observe how frequently an event occurs. We use the following formula to compute the empirical probability of an event:

COMPUTING EMPIRICAL PROBABILITY

The empirical probability of event E is

$$P(E) = \frac{\text{observed number of times } E \text{ occurs}}{\text{total number of observed occurrences}}.$$

EXAMPLE 4 COMPUTING EMPIRICAL PROBABILITY

Table 11.3 shows the distribution, by marital status and gender, of the 212.5 million Americans ages 18 or older.

TABLE 11.3 MARITAL STATUS OF THE U.S. POPULATION, AGES 18 OR OLDER, IN MILLIONS

	Never Married	Married	Widowed	Divorced	Total
Male	28.6	62.1	2.7	9.0	102.4
Female	23.3	62.8	11.3	12.7	110.1
Total	51.9	124.9	14.0	21.7	212.5

Total male: $28.6 + 62.1 + 2.7 + 9.0 = 102.4$

Total female: $23.3 + 62.8 + 11.3 + 12.7 = 110.1$

Total never married: $28.6 + 23.3 = 51.9$

Total widowed: $2.7 + 11.3 = 14.0$

Total adult population: $102.4 + 110.1 = 212.5$

Total married: $62.1 + 62.8 = 124.9$

Total divorced: $9.0 + 12.7 = 21.7$

Source: U.S. Census Bureau

STUDY TIP

Our selection from the U.S. adult population is *random*. This means that every person in the population has an equal chance of being chosen. We'll have much more to say about random selections in Chapter 12, Statistics.

If one person is randomly selected from the population described in Table 11.3, find the probability, to the nearest hundredth, that the person

a. is divorced. **b.** is female.

SOLUTION

a. The probability of selecting a divorced person is the observed number of divorced people, 21.7 (million), divided by the total number of U.S. adults, 212.5 (million).

$$P(\text{selecting a divorced person from the U.S. adult population}) = \frac{\text{number of divorced people}}{\text{total number of U.S. adults}} = \frac{21.7}{212.5} \approx 0.10$$

The empirical probability of selecting a divorced person from the U.S. adult population is approximately 0.10.

b. Be sure to refer to Table 11.3 on the previous page. The probability of selecting a female is the observed number of females, 110.1 (million), divided by the total number of U.S. adults, 212.5 (million).

$$P(\text{selecting a female from the U.S. adult population}) = \frac{\text{number of females}}{\text{total number of U.S. adults}} = \frac{110.1}{212.5} \approx 0.52$$

The empirical probability of selecting a female from the U.S. adult population is approximately 0.52.

CHECK POINT 4 If one person is randomly selected from the population described in Table 11.3 on page 631, find the probability, expressed as a decimal rounded to the nearest hundredth, that the person

a. has never been married. **b.** is male.

In certain situations, we can establish a relationship between the two kinds of probability. Consider, for example, a coin that is equally likely to land heads or tails. Such a coin is called a **fair coin**. Empirical probability can be used to determine whether a coin is fair. Suppose we toss a coin 10, 50, 100, 1000, 10,000, and 100,000 times. We record the number of heads observed, shown in Table 11.4. For each of the six cases in the table, the empirical probability of heads is determined by dividing the number of heads observed by the number of tosses.

TABLE 11.4 EMPIRICAL PROBABILITIES OF HEADS AS THE NUMBER OF TOSSES INCREASES

Number of Tosses	Number of Heads Observed	Empirical Probability of Heads, or $P(H)$
10	4	$P(H) = \frac{4}{10} = 0.4$
50	27	$P(H) = \frac{27}{50} = 0.54$
100	44	$P(H) = \frac{44}{100} = 0.44$
1000	530	$P(H) = \frac{530}{1000} = 0.53$
10,000	4851	$P(H) = \frac{4851}{10{,}000} = 0.4851$
100,000	49,880	$P(H) = \frac{49{,}880}{100{,}000} = 0.4988$

A pattern is exhibited by the empirical probabilities in the right-hand column of Table 11.4. As the number of tosses increases, the empirical probabilities tend to get closer to 0.5, the theoretical probability. These results give us no reason to suspect that the coin is not fair.

Table 11.4 illustrates an important principle when observing uncertain outcomes such as the event of a coin landing on heads. As an experiment is repeated more and more times, the empirical probability of an event tends to get closer to the theoretical probability of that event. This principle is known as the **law of large numbers**.

EXERCISE SET 11.4

• Practice and Application Exercises

Exercises 1–54 involve theoretical probability. Use the theoretical probability formula to solve each exercise. Express each probability as a fraction reduced to lowest terms.

In Exercises 1–10, a die is rolled. The set of equally likely outcomes is $\{1, 2, 3, 4, 5, 6\}$. *Find the probability of rolling*

1. a 4.

2. a 5.

3. an odd number.

4. a number greater than 3.

5. a number less than 3.

6. a number greater than 4.

7. a number less than 7.

8. a number less than 8.

9. a number greater than 7.

10. a number greater than 8.

In Exercises 11–20, you are dealt one card from a standard 52-card deck. Find the probability of being dealt

11. a queen.

12. a jack.

13. a club.

14. a diamond.

15. a picture card.

16. a card greater than 3 and less than 7.

17. the queen of spades.

18. the ace of clubs.

19. a diamond and a spade.

20. a card with a green heart.

In Exercises 21–26, a fair coin is tossed two times in succession. The set of equally likely outcomes is $\{HH, HT, TH, TT\}$. *Find the probability of getting*

21. two heads.

22. two tails.

23. the same outcome on each toss.

24. different outcomes on each toss.

25. a head on the second toss.

26. at least one head.

In Exercises 27–34, you select a family with three children. If M represents a male child and F a female child, the set of equally likely outcomes for the children's genders is $\{MMM, MMF, MFM, MFF, FMM, FMF, FFM, FFF\}$. *Find the probability of selecting a family with*

27. exactly one female child.

28. exactly one male child.

29. exactly two male children.

30. exactly two female children.

31. at least one male child.

32. at least two female children.

33. four male children.

34. fewer than four female children.

In Exercises 35–40, a single die is rolled twice. The 36 equally likely outcomes are shown as follows:

		Second Roll					
		⚀	⚁	⚂	⚃	⚄	⚅
First Roll	⚀	(1, 1)	(1, 2)	(1, 3)	(1, 4)	(1, 5)	(1, 6)
	⚁	(2, 1)	(2, 2)	(2, 3)	(2, 4)	(2, 5)	(2, 6)
	⚂	(3, 1)	(3, 2)	(3, 3)	(3, 4)	(3, 5)	(3, 6)
	⚃	(4, 1)	(4, 2)	(4, 3)	(4, 4)	(4, 5)	(4, 6)
	⚄	(5, 1)	(5, 2)	(5, 3)	(5, 4)	(5, 5)	(5, 6)
	⚅	(6, 1)	(6, 2)	(6, 3)	(6, 4)	(6, 5)	(6, 6)

Find the probability of getting

35. two even numbers.

36. two odd numbers.

37. two numbers whose sum is 5.

38. two numbers whose sum is 6.

39. two numbers whose sum exceeds 12.

40. two numbers whose sum is less than 13.

Use the spinner shown to answer Exercises 41–48. Assume that it is equally probable that the pointer will land on any one of the ten colored regions. If the pointer lands on a borderline, spin again.

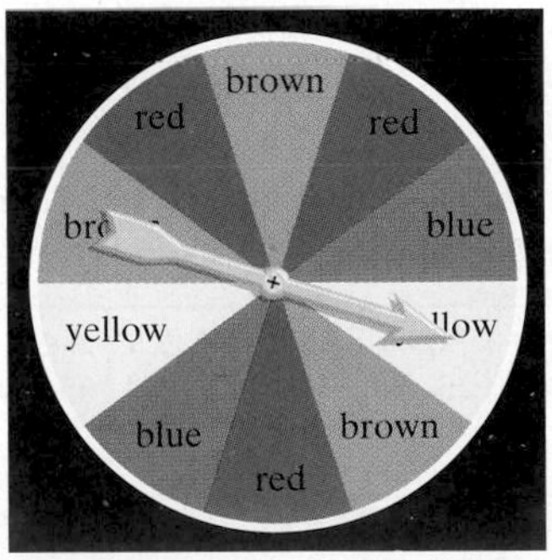

Find the probability that the spinner lands in

41. a red region.

42. a yellow region.

43. a blue region.

44. a brown region.

45. a region that is red or blue.

46. a region that is yellow or brown.

47. a region that is red and blue.

48. a region that is yellow and brown.

Exercises 49–54 deal with sickle cell anemia, an inherited disease in which red blood cells become distorted and deprived of oxygen. Approximately 1 in every 500 African-American infants is born with the disease; only 1 in 160,000 white infants has the disease. A person with two sickle cell genes will have the disease, but a person with only one sickle cell gene will have a mild, nonfatal anemia called sickle cell trait. (Approximately 8%–10% of the African-American population has this trait.)

		Second Parent S	s
First	*S*	*SS*	*Ss*
Parent	*s*	*sS*	*ss*

If we use s to represent a sickle cell gene and S a healthy gene, the table shows the four possibilities for the children of two Ss parents. Each parent has only one sickle cell gene, so each has the relatively mild sickle cell trait. Find the probability that these parents give birth to a child who

49. has sickle cell anemia. **50.** has sickle cell trait.

51. is healthy.

In Exercises 52–54, use the following table that shows the four possibilities for the children of one healthy, SS, parent, and one parent with sickle cell trait, Ss.

		Second Parent (with Sickle Cell Trait) S	s
Healthy	*S*	*SS*	*Ss*
First Parent	*S*	*SS*	*Ss*

Find the probability that these parents give birth to a child who

52. has sickle cell anemia. **53.** has sickle cell trait.

54. is healthy.

The table shows the distribution, by age and gender, of the 29.3 million Americans who live alone. Use the data in the table to solve Exercises 55–60.

NUMBER OF PEOPLE IN THE UNITED STATES LIVING ALONE, IN MILLIONS

	Ages 15–24	Ages 25–34	Ages 35–44	Ages 45–64	Ages 65–74	Ages ≥75	Total
Male	0.7	2.2	2.6	4.3	1.3	1.4	12.5
Female	0.8	1.6	1.6	5.0	2.9	4.9	16.8
Total	1.5	3.8	4.2	9.3	4.2	6.3	29.3

Source: U.S. Census Bureau

Find the probability, expressed as a decimal rounded to the nearest hundredth, that a randomly selected American living alone is

55. male. **56.** female.

57. in the 25–34 age range.

58. in the 35–44 age range.

59. a woman in the 15–24 age range.

60. a man in the 45–64 age range.

The table shows the number of Americans who moved in 2004, categorized by where they moved and whether they were an owner or a renter. Use the data in the table, expressed in millions, to solve Exercises 61–66.

NUMBER OF PEOPLE IN THE UNITED STATES WHO MOVED IN 2004, IN MILLIONS

	Moved to Same State	Moved to Different State	Moved to Different Country
Owner	11.7	2.8	0.3
Renter	18.7	4.5	1.0

Source: U.S. Census Bureau

Find the probability, expressed as a decimal rounded to the nearest hundredth, that a randomly selected American who moved in 2004 was

61. an owner.

62. a renter.

63. a person who moved within the same state.

64. a person who moved to a different country.

65. a renter who moved to a different state.

66. an owner who moved to a different state.

• Writing in Mathematics

67. What is the sample space of an experiment? What is an event?

68. How is the theoretical probability of an event computed?

69. Describe the difference between theoretical probability and empirical probability.

70. Give an example of an event whose probability must be determined empirically rather than theoretically.

71. Use the definition of theoretical probability to explain why the probability of an event that cannot occur is 0.

72. Use the definition of theoretical probability to explain why the probability of an event that is certain to occur is 1.

73. Write a probability word problem whose answer is one of the following fractions: $\frac{1}{6}$ or $\frac{1}{4}$ or $\frac{1}{3}$.

74. The president of a large company with 10,000 employees is considering mandatory cocaine testing for every employee. The test that would be used is 90% accurate, meaning that it will detect 90% of the cocaine users who are tested, and that 90% of the nonusers will test negative. This also means that the test gives 10% false positive. Suppose that 1% of the employees actually use cocaine. Find the probability that someone who tests positive for cocaine use is, indeed, a user.

Hint: Find the following probability fraction:

$$\frac{\text{the number of employees who test positive and are cocaine users}}{\text{the number of employes who test positive}}.$$

This fraction is given by

$$\frac{90\% \text{ of } 1\% \text{ of } 10{,}000}{\text{the number who test positive who actually use cocaine plus the number who test positive who do not use cocaine}}.$$

What does this probability indicate in terms of the percentage of employees who test positive who are not actually users? Discuss these numbers in terms of the issue of mandatory drug testing. Write a paper either in favor of or against mandatory drug testing, incorporating the actual percentage accuracy for such tests.

• Critical Thinking Exercises

75. The target in the figure shown in the next column contains four squares. If a dart thrown at random hits the target, find the probability that it will land in an orange region.

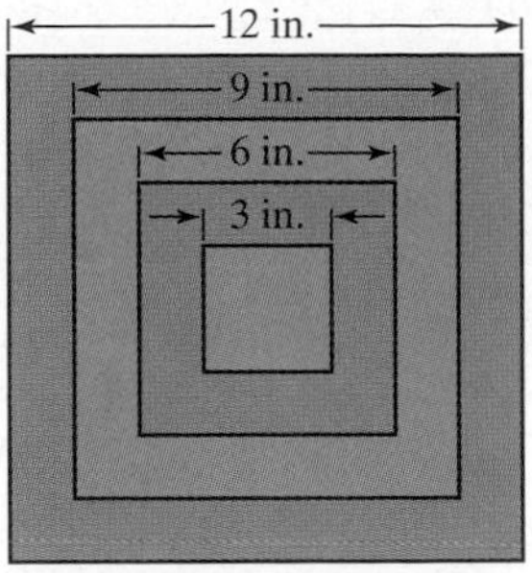

76. Some three-digit numbers, such as 101 and 313, read the same forward and backward. If you select a number from all three-digit numbers, find the probability that it will read the same forward and backward.

SECTION 11.5 • PROBABILITY WITH THE FUNDAMENTAL COUNTING PRINCIPLE, PERMUTATIONS, AND COMBINATIONS

OBJECTIVES

1. Compute probabilities with permutations.
2. Compute probabilities with combinations.

George Tooker (b. 1920) "*Mirror II*" *1963, egg tempera on gesso panel, 20 × 20 in., 1968.4. Gift of R. H. Donnelley Erdman (PA 1956). Addison Gallery of American Art, Phillips Academy, Andover, Massachusetts. All Rights Reserved.*

PROBABILITY OF DYING AT ANY GIVEN AGE

Age	Probability of Male Death	Probability of Female Death
10	0.00013	0.00010
20	0.00140	0.00050
30	0.00153	0.00050
40	0.00193	0.00095
50	0.00567	0.00305
60	0.01299	0.00792
70	0.03473	0.01764
80	0.07644	0.03966
90	0.15787	0.11250
100	0.26876	0.23969
110	0.39770	0.39043

Source: George Shaffner, *The Arithmetic of Life and Death*

According to actuarial tables, there is no year in which death is as likely as continued life, at least until the age of 115. Until that age, the probability of dying in any one year ranges from a low of 0.00009 for a girl at age 11 to a high of 0.465 for either gender at age 114. For a healthy 30-year-old, how does the probability of dying this year compare to the probability of winning the top prize in a state lottery game? In this section, we provide the surprising answer to this question, as we study probability with the Fundamental Counting Principle, permutations, and combinations.

1 Compute probabilities with permutations.

Probability with Permutations

We return to our concert tour with U2, Bruce Springsteen and the E Street Band, Aerosmith, and the Rolling Stones. Now, the two surviving members of the Beatles have agreed to join the tour! You really have your work cut out for you. In which order should the five groups in the concert perform? Because order makes a difference, this is a permutation situation. Example 1 is based on this scenario, and uses permutations to solve a probability problem.

EXAMPLE 1 PROBABILITY AND PERMUTATIONS

The five groups in the tour agree to determine the order of performance based on a random selection. Each band's name is written on one of five cards. The cards are placed in a hat and then five cards are drawn, one at a time. The order in which the cards are drawn determines the order in which the bands perform. What is the probability of the Rolling Stones performing fourth and the Beatles last?

SOLUTION We begin by applying the definition of probability to this situation.

P(Rolling Stones fourth, Beatles last)

$$= \frac{\text{number of permutations with Rolling Stones fourth, Beatles last}}{\text{total number of possible permutations}}$$

We can use the Fundamental Counting Principle to find the total number of possible permutations. This represents the number of ways you can put together the concert.

First Group to Perform	Second Group to Perform	Third Group to Perform	Fourth Group to Perform	Last Group to Perform
5 choices	4 choices	3 choices	2 choices	1 choice

There are $5 \cdot 4 \cdot 3 \cdot 2 \cdot 1$, or 120, possible permutations. Equivalently, the five groups can perform in 120 different orders.

We can also use the Fundamental Counting Principle to find the number of permutations with the Rolling Stones performing fourth and the Beatles performing last. You can choose any one of the three groups, U2, Bruce Springsteen and the E Street Band, or Aerosmith, as the opening act. This leaves two choices for the second group to perform, and only one choice for the third group to perform. There is only one choice for the fourth group—the Rolling Stones, and one choice for the closing act—the Beatles:

First Group to Perform	Second Group to Perform	Third Group to Perform	Fourth Group to Perform	Last Group to Perform
3 choices (U2, Springsteen, or Aerosmith)	2 choices	1 choice	1 choice: The Rolling Stones	1 choice: The Beatles

Thus, there are $3 \cdot 2 \cdot 1 \cdot 1 \cdot 1$, or 6 possible permutations. Equivalently, there are 6 lineups with the Rolling Stones performing fourth and the Beatles last.

Now we can return to our probability fraction.

P(Rolling Stones fourth, Beatles last)

$$= \frac{\text{number of permutations with Rolling Stones fourth, Beatles last}}{\text{total number of possible permutations}}$$

$$= \frac{6}{120} = \frac{1}{20}$$

The probability of the Rolling Stones performing fourth and the Beatles last is $\frac{1}{20}$.

CHECK POINT 1 Use the information given in Example 1 to find the probability of U2 performing first, the Rolling Stones performing fourth, and the Beatles last.

BLITZER BONUS

Permutations and Rubik's Cube

First developed in Hungary in the 1970s by Erno Rubik, a Rubik's cube contains 26 small cubes. The square faces of the cubes are colored in six different colors. The cubes can be twisted horizontally or vertically. When first purchased, the cube is arranged so that each face shows a single color. To do the puzzle, you first turn columns and rows in a random way until all of the six faces are multicolored. To solve the puzzle, you must return the cube to its original state—that is, a single color on each of the six faces. With 115,880,067,072,000 arrangements, this is no easy task! If it takes one-half second for each of these arrangements, it would require over 1,800,000 years to move the cube into all possible arrangements.

2 Compute probabilities with combinations.

In 2004, Americans spent $49.4 billion on lotteries set up by revenue-hungry states. Once prizes and administrative costs were paid, $15.1 billion was left in revenue for the states. Throughout the United States, 64% of lottery profits go to education funding.
Source: North American Association of State and Provincial Lotteries

Probability with Combinations

In 2006, 41 states and Washington, D.C., had lotteries, and several states were considering selling lottery tickets on the Internet. If your state has a lottery drawing each week, the probability that someone will win the top prize is relatively high. If there is no winner this week, it is virtually certain that eventually someone will be graced with millions of dollars. So, why are you so unlucky compared to this undisclosed someone? In Example 2, we provide an answer to this question.

EXAMPLE 2 PROBABILITY AND COMBINATIONS: WINNING THE LOTTERY

Florida's lottery game, LOTTO, is set up so that each player chooses six different numbers from 1 to 53. If the six numbers chosen match the six numbers drawn randomly, the player wins (or shares) the top cash prize. (As of this writing, the top cash prize has ranged from $7 million to $106.5 million.) With one LOTTO ticket, what is the probability of winning this prize?

SOLUTION Because the order of the six numbers does not matter, this is a situation involving combinations. We begin with the formula for probability.

$$P(\text{winning}) = \frac{\text{number of ways of winning}}{\text{total number of possible combinations}}$$

We can use the combinations formula

$$_nC_r = \frac{n!}{(n-r)!\,r!}$$

to find the total number of possible combinations. We are selecting $r = 6$ numbers from a collection of $n = 53$ numbers.

$$_{53}C_6 = \frac{53!}{(53-6)!\,6!} = \frac{53!}{47!\,6!} = \frac{53 \cdot 52 \cdot 51 \cdot 50 \cdot 49 \cdot 48 \cdot \cancel{47!}}{\cancel{47!} \cdot 6 \cdot 5 \cdot 4 \cdot 3 \cdot 2 \cdot 1} = 22{,}957{,}480$$

There are nearly 23 million number combinations possible in LOTTO. If a person buys one LOTTO ticket, that person has selected only one combination of the six numbers. With one LOTTO ticket, there is only one way of winning.

Now we can return to our probability fraction.

$$P(\text{winning}) = \frac{\text{number of ways of winning}}{\text{total number of possible combinations}} = \frac{1}{22{,}957{,}480} \approx 0.0000000436$$

The probability of winning the top prize with one LOTTO ticket is $\frac{1}{22{,}957{,}480}$, or about 1 in 23 million.

Suppose that a person buys 5000 different tickets in Florida's LOTTO. Because that person has selected 5000 different combinations of the six numbers, the probability of winning is

$$\frac{5000}{22{,}957{,}480} \approx 0.000218.$$

The chances of winning top prize are about 218 in a million. At $1 per LOTTO ticket, it is highly probable that our LOTTO player will be $5000 poorer. Knowing a little probability helps a lotto.

BLITZER BONUS

Comparing the Probability of Dying to the Probability of Winning Florida's LOTTO

As a healthy nonsmoking 30-year-old, your probability of dying this year is approximately 0.001. Divide this probability by the probability of winning LOTTO with one ticket:

$$\frac{0.001}{0.0000000436} \approx 22{,}936.$$

A healthy 30-year-old is nearly 23,000 times more likely to die this year than to win Florida's lottery.

CHECK POINT 2 People lose interest when they do not win at games of chance, including Florida's LOTTO. With drawings twice weekly instead of once, the game described in Example 2 was brought in to bring back lost players and increase ticket sales. The original LOTTO was set up so that each player chose six different numbers from 1 to 49, rather than from 1 to 53, with a lottery drawing only once a week. With one LOTTO ticket, what was the probability of winning the top cash prize in Florida's original LOTTO? Express the answer as a fraction and as a decimal correct to ten places.

EXAMPLE 3 PROBABILITY AND COMBINATIONS

A club consists of five men and seven women. Three members are selected at random to attend a conference. Find the probability that the selected group consists of

a. three men.

b. one man and two women.

SOLUTION The order in which the three people are selected does not matter, so this is a problem involving combinations.

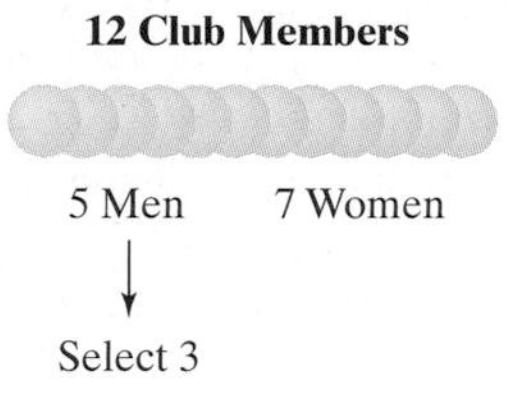

a. We begin with the probability of selecting three men.

$$P(3\text{ men}) = \frac{\text{number of ways of selecting 3 men}}{\text{total number of possible combinations}}$$

First, we consider the denominator of the probability fraction. We are selecting $r = 3$ people from a total group of $n = 12$ people (five men and seven women). The total number of possible combinations is

$$_{12}C_3 = \frac{12!}{(12-3)!\,3!} = \frac{12!}{9!\,3!} = \frac{12\cdot 11\cdot 10\cdot \cancel{9!}}{\cancel{9!}\cdot 3\cdot 2\cdot 1} = 220.$$

Thus, there are 220 possible three-person selections.

Next, we consider the numerator of the probability fraction. We are interested in the number of ways of selecting three men from five men. We are selecting $r = 3$ men from a total group of $n = 5$ men. The number of possible combinations of three men is

$$_5C_3 = \frac{5!}{(5-3)!\,3!} = \frac{5!}{2!\,3!} = \frac{5\cdot 4\cdot \cancel{3!}}{2\cdot 1\cdot \cancel{3!}} = 10.$$

Thus, there are 10 ways of selecting three men from five men. Now we can fill in the numbers in the numerator and the denominator of our probability fraction.

$$P(3\text{ men}) = \frac{\text{number of ways of selecting 3 men}}{\text{total number of possible combinations}} = \frac{10}{220} = \frac{1}{22}$$

The probability that the group selected to attend the conference consists of three men is $\frac{1}{22}$.

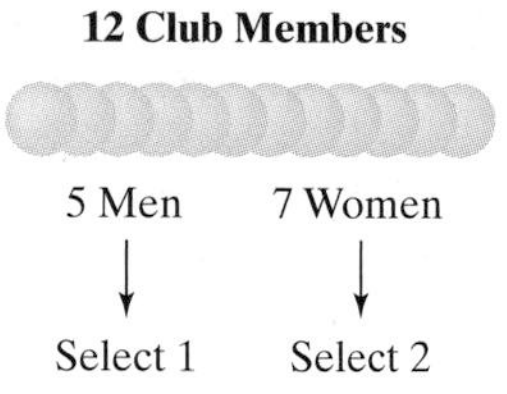

b. We set up the fraction for the probability that the selected group consists of one man and two women.

$$P(1\text{ man, 2 women}) = \frac{\text{number of ways of selecting 1 man and 2 women}}{\text{total number of possible combinations}}$$

The denominator of this fraction is the same as the denominator in part (a). The total number of possible combinations is found by selecting $r = 3$ people from $n = 12$ people: $_{12}C_3 = 220$.

Next, we move to the numerator of the probability fraction. The number of ways of selecting $r = 1$ man from $n = 5$ men is

$$_5C_1 = \frac{5!}{(5-1)!\,1!} = \frac{5!}{4!\,1!} = \frac{5\cdot \cancel{4!}}{\cancel{4!}\cdot 1} = 5.$$

The number of ways of selecting $r = 2$ women from $n = 7$ women is

$$_7C_2 = \frac{7!}{(7-2)!\,2!} = \frac{7!}{5!\,2!} = \frac{7\cdot 6\cdot \cancel{5!}}{\cancel{5!}\cdot 2\cdot 1} = 21.$$

By the Fundamental Counting Principle, the number of ways of selecting 1 man and 2 women is

$$_5C_1 \cdot {_7C_2} = 5\cdot 21 = 105.$$

Now we can fill in the numbers in the numerator and the denominator of our probability fraction.

$$P(1 \text{ man, } 2 \text{ women}) = \frac{\text{number of ways of selecting 1 man and 2 women}}{\text{total number of possible combinations}} = \frac{{}_5C_1 \cdot {}_7C_2}{{}_{12}C_3} = \frac{105}{220} = \frac{21}{44}$$

The probability that the group selected to attend the conference consists of one man and two women is $\frac{21}{44}$.

CHECK POINT 3 A club consists of six men and four women. Three members are selected at random to attend a conference. Find the probability that the selected group consists of

a. three men.

b. two men and one woman.

EXERCISE SET 11.5

• Practice and Application Exercises

1. Martha, Lee, Nancy, Paul, and Armando have all been invited to a dinner party. They arrive randomly and each person arrives at a different time.
   a. In how many ways can they arrive?
   b. In how many ways can Martha arrive first and Armando last?
   c. Find the probability that Martha will arrive first and Armando last.
2. Three men and three women line up at a checkout counter in a store.
   a. In how many ways can they line up?
   b. In how many ways can they line up if the first person in line is a woman, and then the line alternates by gender—that is a woman, a man, a woman, a man, and so on?
   c. Find the probability that the first person in line is a woman and the line alternates by gender.
3. Six stand-up comics, A, B, C, D, E, and F, are to perform on a single evening at a comedy club. The order of performance is determined by random selection. Find the probability that
   a. Comic E will perform first.
   b. Comic C will perform fifth and comic B will perform last.
   c. The comedians will perform in the following order: D, E, C, A, B, F.
   d. Comic A or comic B will perform first.
4. Seven performers, A, B, C, D, E, F, and G, are to appear in a fund raiser. The order of performance is determined by random selection. Find the probability that
   a. D will perform first.
   b. E will perform sixth and B will perform last.
   c. They will perform in the following order: C, D, B, A, G, F, E.
   d. F or G will perform first.
5. A group consists of four men and five women. Three people are selected to attend a conference.
   a. In how many ways can three people be selected from this group of nine?
   b. In how many ways can three women be selected from the five women?
   c. Find the probability that the selected group will consist of all women.
6. A political discussion group consists of five Democrats and six Republicans. Four people are selected to attend a conference.
   a. In how many ways can four people be selected from this group of eleven?
   b. In how many ways can four Republicans be selected from the six Republicans?
   c. Find the probability that the selected group will consist of all Republicans.
7. To play the California lottery, a person has to correctly select 6 out of 51 numbers, paying \$1 for each six-number selection. If the six numbers picked are the same as the ones drawn by the lottery, mountains of money are bestowed. What is the probability that a person with one combination of six numbers will win? What is the probability of winning if 100 different lottery tickets are purchased?
8. A state lottery is designed so that a player chooses five numbers from 1 to 30 on one lottery ticket. What is the probability that a player with one lottery ticket will win? What is the probability of winning if 100 different lottery tickets are purchased?
9. A box contains 25 transistors, 6 of which are defective. If 6 are selected at random, find the probability that
   a. all are defective.
   b. none are defective.
10. A committee of five people is to be formed from six lawyers and seven teachers. Find the probability that
    a. all are lawyers.
    b. none are lawyers.

11. A city council consists of six Democrats and four Republicans. If a committee of three people is selected, find the probability of selecting one Democrat and two Republicans.

12. A parent-teacher committee consisting of four people is to be selected from fifteen parents and five teachers. Find the probability of selecting two parents and two teachers.

Exercises 13–18 involve a deck of 52 cards. If necessary, refer to the picture of a deck of cards, Figure 11.5 on page 629.

13. A poker hand consists of five cards.

a. Find the total number of possible five-card poker hands.

b. A diamond flush is a five-card hand consisting of all diamonds. Find the number of possible diamond flushes.

c. Find the probability of being dealt a diamond flush.

14. A poker hand consists of five cards.

a. Find the total number of possible five-card poker hands.

b. Find the number of ways in which four aces can be selected.

c. Find the number of ways in which one king can be selected.

d. Use the Fundamental Counting Principle and your answers from parts (b) and (c) to find the number of ways of getting four aces and one king.

e. Find the probability of getting a poker hand consisting of four aces and one king.

15. If you are dealt 3 cards from a shuffled deck of 52 cards, find the probability that all 3 cards are picture cards.

16. If you are dealt 4 cards from a shuffled deck of 52 cards, find the probability that all 4 are hearts.

17. If you are dealt 4 cards from a shuffled deck of 52 cards, find the probability of getting two queens and two kings.

18. If you are dealt 4 cards from a shuffled deck of 52 cards, find the probability of getting three jacks and one queen.

• Writing in Mathematics

19. If people understood the mathematics involving probabilities and lotteries, as you now do, do you think they would continue to spend hundreds of dollars per year on lottery tickets? Explain your answer.

20. Write and solve an original problem involving probability and permutations.

21. Write and solve an original problem involving probability and combinations whose solution requires $\frac{{}_{14}C_{10}}{{}_{20}C_{10}}$.

• Critical Thinking Exercises

22. An apartment complex offers apartments with four different options, designated by A through D. There are an equal number of apartments with each combination of options.

A	B	C	D
one bedroom two bedrooms three bedrooms	one bathroom two bathrooms	first floor second floor	lake view golf course view no special view

If there is only one apartment left, what is the probability that it is precisely what a person is looking for, namely two bedrooms, two bathrooms, first floor, and a lake or golf course view?

23. Reread Exercise 7. How much must a person spend so that the probability of winning the California lottery is $\frac{1}{2}$?

24. Suppose that it is a week in which the cash prize in Florida's LOTTO is promised to exceed \$50 million. If a person purchases 22,957,480 tickets in LOTTO at \$1 per ticket (all possible combinations), isn't this a guarantee of winning the lottery? Because the probability in this situation is 1, what's wrong with doing this?

25. The digits 1, 2, 3, 4, and 5 are randomly arranged to form a three-digit number. (Digits are not repeated.) Find the probability that the number is even and greater than 500.

26. In a five-card poker hand, what is the probability of being dealt exactly one ace and no picture cards?

• Group Exercise

27. Research and present a group report on state lotteries. Include answers to some or all of the following questions. As always, make the report interesting and informative. Which states do not have lotteries? Why not? How much is spent per capita on lotteries? What are some of the lottery games? What is the probability of winning top prize in these games? What income groups spend the greatest amount of money on lotteries? If your state has a lottery, what does it do with the money it makes? Is the way the money is spent what was promised when the lottery first began?

SECTION 11.6 • EVENTS INVOLVING *NOT* AND *OR*; ODDS

OBJECTIVES

1. Find the probability that an event will not occur.
2. Find the probability of one event or a second event occurring.
3. Understand and use odds.

You take your first trip to London. You are surprised to learn that the British gamble on everything. Shops with bookmakers are available everywhere for placing bets. In such a shop, you overhear a conversation about turning up the king of hearts in a deck of cards. You are expecting to hear something about a probability of $\frac{1}{52}$. Instead, you hear the phrase "51 to 1 against." Are you having difficulty understanding the British accents or did you miss something in your liberal arts math course? Whatever happened to probability?

No, it's not the accent. There are several ways to express the likelihood of an event. For example, we can discuss the probability of an event. We can also discuss *odds against* an event and *odds in favor* of an event. In this section, we expand our knowledge of probability and explain the meaning of odds.

1 Find the probability that an event will not occur.

Probability of an Event Not Occurring

If we know $P(E)$, the probability of an event E, we can determine the probability that the event will not occur, denoted by $P(\text{not } E)$. The event *not* E is the **complement** of E because it is the set of all outcomes in the sample space S that are not outcomes in the event E. In any experiment, an event must occur or its complement must occur. Thus, the sum of the probability that an event will occur and the probability that it will not occur is 1:

$$P(E) + P(\text{not } E) = 1.$$

Solving for $P(E)$ or for $P(\text{not } E)$, we obtain the following formulas:

COMPLEMENT RULES OF PROBABILITY

- The probability that an event E will not occur is equal to 1 minus the probability that it will occur.

$$P(\text{not } E) = 1 - P(E)$$

- The probability that an event E will occur is equal to 1 minus the probability that it will not occur.

$$P(E) = 1 - P(\text{not } E)$$

Using set notation, if E' is the complement of E, then $P(E') = 1 - P(E)$ and $P(E) = 1 - P(E')$.

EXAMPLE 1 THE PROBABILITY OF AN EVENT NOT OCCURRING

If you are dealt one card from a standard 52-card deck, find the probability that you are not dealt a queen.

SOLUTION Because

$$P(\text{not } E) = 1 - P(E)$$

then

$$P(\text{not a queen}) = 1 - P(\text{queen}).$$

There are four queens in a deck of 52 cards. The probability of being dealt a queen is $\frac{4}{52} = \frac{1}{13}$. Thus,

$$P(\text{not a queen}) = 1 - P(\text{queen}) = 1 - \frac{1}{13} = \frac{13}{13} - \frac{1}{13} = \frac{12}{13}.$$

The probability that you are not dealt a queen is $\frac{12}{13}$.

STUDY TIP

You can work Example 1 without using the formula for $P(\text{not } E)$. Here is how it's done:

$$P(\text{not a queen}) = \frac{\text{number of ways a non-queen can occur}}{\text{total number of outcomes}}$$

$$= \frac{48}{52}$$

With 4 queens, 52 − 4 = 48 cards are not queens.

$$= \frac{4 \cdot 12}{4 \cdot 13} = \frac{12}{13}.$$

CHECK POINT 1 If you are dealt one card from a standard 52-card deck, find the probability that you are not dealt a diamond.

EXAMPLE 2 USING THE COMPLEMENT RULES

The circle graph in Figure 11.6 shows the distribution, by age group, of the 191 million car drivers in the United States, with all numbers rounded to the nearest million. If one driver is randomly selected from this population, find the probability that the person

a. is not in the 20–29 age group.

b. is less than 80 years old.

Express probabilities as simplified fractions.

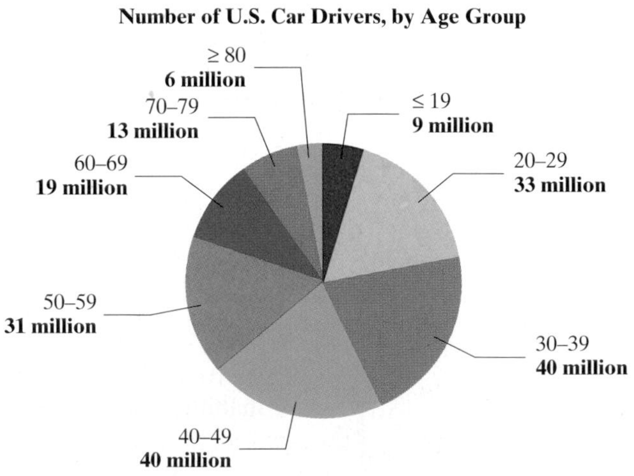

FIGURE 11.6
Source: U.S. Census Bureau

SOLUTION

a. We begin with the probability that a randomly selected driver is not in the 20–29 age group.

$$P(\text{not in 20–29 age group})$$
$$= 1 - P(\text{in 20–29 age group})$$
$$= 1 - \frac{33}{191}$$

The graph shows 33 million drivers in the 20–29 age group.

This number, 191 million drivers, was given, but can be obtained by adding the numbers in the eight sectors.

$$= \frac{191}{191} - \frac{33}{191} = \frac{158}{191}$$

The probability that a randomly selected driver is not in the 20–29 age group is $\frac{158}{191}$.

b. We could compute the probability that a randomly selected driver is less than 80 years old by adding the numbers in each of the seven sectors representing drivers less than 80 and dividing this sum by 191 (million). However, it is easier to use complements. The complement of selecting a driver less than 80 years old is selecting a driver 80 or older.

$$P(\text{less than 80 years old})$$
$$= 1 - P(\text{80 or older})$$
$$= 1 - \frac{6}{191}$$

The graph shows 6 million drivers 80 or older.

$$= \frac{191}{191} - \frac{6}{191} = \frac{185}{191}$$

The probability that a randomly selected driver is less than 80 years old is $\frac{185}{191}$.

CHECK POINT 2 If one driver is randomly selected from the population represented in Figure 11.6, find the probability, expressed as a simplified fraction, that the person

a. is not in the 50–59 age group.

b. is at least 20 years old.

2 Find the probability of one event or a second event occurring.

Or Probabilities with Mutually Exclusive Events

Suppose that you randomly select one card from a deck of 52 cards. Let A be the event of selecting a king and B be the event of selecting a queen. Only one card is selected, so it is impossible to get both a king and a queen. The events of selecting a king and a queen cannot occur simultaneously. They are called *mutually exclusive events*.

MUTUALLY EXCLUSIVE EVENTS

If it is impossible for events A and B to occur simultaneously, the events are said to be **mutually exclusive**.

In general, if A and B are mutually exclusive events, the probability that either A or B will occur is determined by adding their individual probabilities.

***OR* PROBABILITIES WITH MUTUALLY EXCLUSIVE EVENTS**

If A and B are mutually exclusive events, then

$$P(A \text{ or } B) = P(A) + P(B).$$

Using set notation, $P(A \cup B) = P(A) + P(B)$.

EXAMPLE 3 THE PROBABILITY OF EITHER OF TWO MUTUALLY EXCLUSIVE EVENTS OCCURRING

If one card is randomly selected from a deck of cards, what is the probability of selecting a king or a queen?

SOLUTION We find the probability that either of these mutually exclusive events will occur by adding their individual probabilities.

$$P(\text{king or queen}) = P(\text{king}) + P(\text{queen}) = \frac{4}{52} + \frac{4}{52} = \frac{8}{52} = \frac{2}{13}$$

The probability of selecting a king or a queen is $\frac{2}{13}$.

CHECK POINT 3 If you roll a single, six-sided die, what is the probability of getting either a 4 or a 5?

Or Probabilities with Events That Are Not Mutually Exclusive

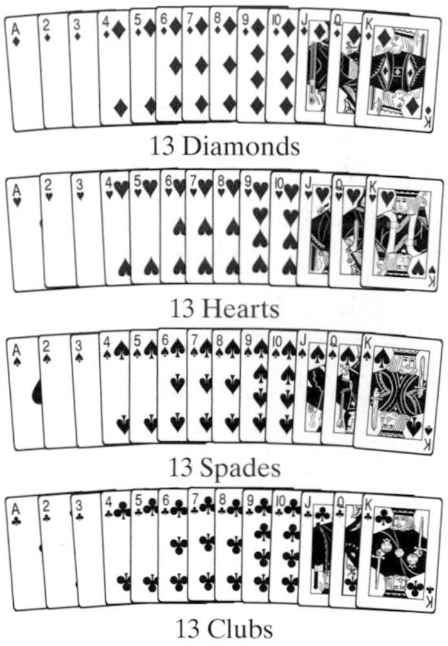

FIGURE 11.7 A deck of 52 cards

Consider the deck of 52 cards shown in Figure 11.7. Suppose that these cards are shuffled and you randomly select one card from the deck. What is the probability of selecting a diamond or a picture card (jack, queen, king)? Begin by adding their individual probabilities.

$$P(\text{diamond}) + P(\text{picture card}) = \frac{13}{52} + \frac{12}{52}$$

There are 13 diamonds in the deck of 52 cards.

There are 12 picture cards in the deck of 52 cards.

FIGURE 11.8 Three diamonds are picture cards.

However, this sum is not the probability of selecting a diamond or a picture card. The problem is that there are three cards that are *simultaneously* diamonds and picture cards, shown in Figure 11.8. The events of selecting a diamond and selecting a picture card are not mutually exclusive. It is possible to select a card that is both a diamond and a picture card.

The situation is illustrated in the Venn diagram in Figure 11.9. Why can't we find the probability of selecting a diamond or a picture card by adding their individual probabilities? The Venn diagram shows that three of the cards, the three diamonds that are picture cards, get counted twice when we add the individual probabilities. First the three cards get counted as diamonds, and then they get counted as picture cards. In order to avoid the error of counting the three cards twice, we need to subtract the probability of getting a diamond and a picture card, $\frac{3}{52}$, as follows:

$$P(\text{diamond or picture card})$$
$$= P(\text{diamond}) + P(\text{picture card}) - P(\text{diamond and picture card})$$
$$= \frac{13}{52} + \frac{12}{52} - \frac{3}{52} = \frac{13 + 12 - 3}{52} = \frac{22}{52} = \frac{11}{26}.$$

Thus, the probability of selecting a diamond or a picture card is $\frac{11}{26}$.

In general, if A and B are events that are not mutually exclusive, the probability that A or B will occur is determined by adding their individual probabilities and then subtracting the probability that A and B occur simultaneously.

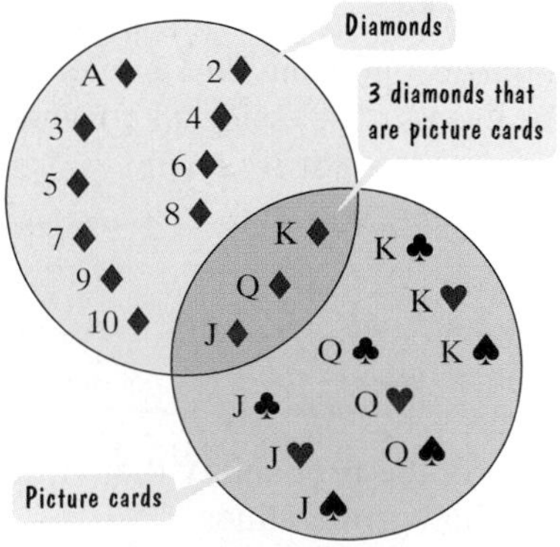

FIGURE 11.9

***OR* PROBABILITIES WITH EVENTS THAT ARE NOT MUTUALLY EXCLUSIVE**

If A and B are not mutually exclusive events, then

$$P(A \text{ or } B) = P(A) + P(B) - P(A \text{ and } B).$$

Using set notation,

$$P(A \cup B) = P(A) + P(B) - P(A \cap B).$$

EXAMPLE 4 AN *OR* PROBABILITY WITH EVENTS THAT ARE NOT MUTUALLY EXCLUSIVE

In a group of 25 baboons, 18 enjoy grooming their neighbors, 16 enjoy screeching wildly, while 10 enjoy grooming their neighbors and screeching wildly. If one baboon is selected at random from the group, find the probability that it enjoys grooming its neighbors or screeching wildly.

SOLUTION It is possible for a baboon in the group to enjoy both grooming its neighbors and screeching wildly. Ten of the brutes are given to engage in both activities. These events are not mutually exclusive.

$$P\left(\begin{array}{c}\text{grooming}\\ \text{or screeching}\end{array}\right) = P(\text{grooming}) + P(\text{screeching}) - P\left(\begin{array}{c}\text{grooming}\\ \text{and screeching}\end{array}\right)$$

$$= \frac{18}{25} + \frac{16}{25} - \frac{10}{25}$$

18 of the 25 baboons enjoy grooming.

16 of the 25 baboons enjoy screeching.

10 of the 25 baboons enjoy both.

$$= \frac{18 + 16 - 10}{25} = \frac{24}{25}$$

The probability that a baboon in the group enjoys grooming its neighbors or screeching wildly is $\frac{24}{25}$.

CHECK POINT 4 In a group of 50 students, 23 take math, 11 take psychology, and 7 take both math and psychology. If one student is selected at random, find the probability that the student takes math or psychology.

EXAMPLE 5 AN *OR* PROBABILITY WITH EVENTS THAT ARE NOT MUTUALLY EXCLUSIVE

FIGURE 11.10 It is equally probable that the pointer will land on any one of the eight regions.

Figure 11.10 illustrates a spinner. It is equally probable that the pointer will land on any one of the eight regions, numbered 1 through 8. If the pointer lands on a borderline, spin again. Find the probability that the pointer will stop on an even number or on a number greater than 5.

SOLUTION It is possible for the pointer to land on a number that is both even and greater than 5. Two of the numbers, 6 and 8, are even and greater than 5. These events are not mutually exclusive. The probability of landing on a number that is even or greater than 5 is calculated as follows:

$$P\left(\begin{array}{c}\text{even or}\\ \text{greater than 5}\end{array}\right) = P(\text{even}) + P(\text{greater than 5}) - P\left(\begin{array}{c}\text{even and}\\ \text{greater than 5}\end{array}\right)$$

$$= \frac{4}{8} + \frac{3}{8} - \frac{2}{8}$$

Four of the eight numbers, 2, 4, 6, and 8, are even.

Three of the eight numbers, 6, 7, and 8, are greater than 5.

Two of the eight numbers, 6 and 8, are even and greater than 5.

$$= \frac{4 + 3 - 2}{8} = \frac{5}{8}.$$

The probability that the pointer will stop on an even number or a number greater than 5 is $\frac{5}{8}$.

CHECK POINT 5 Use Figure 11.10 to find the probability that the pointer will stop on an odd number or a number less than 5.

EXAMPLE 6 *OR* PROBABILITIES WITH REAL-WORLD DATA

Each year the Internal Revenue Service audits a sample of tax forms to verify their accuracy. Table 11.5 shows the number of tax returns filed and audited in 2003, by taxable income.

TABLE 11.5 TAX RETURNS FILED AND AUDITED, BY TAXABLE INCOME, 2003

	<$25,000	$25,000–$49,999	$50,000–$99,999	≥$100,000	Total
Audit	414,357	135,041	113,944	151,969	815,311
No audit	52,792,911	30,964,967	25,502,542	10,775,542	120,035,962
Total	53,207,268	31,100,008	25,616,486	10,927,511	120,851,273

Source: Internal Revenue Service

If one person is randomly selected from the population represented in Table 11.5, find the probability that

a. the taxpayer had a taxable income less than $25,000 or was audited.

b. the taxpayer had a taxable income less than $25,000 or at least $100,000.

Express probabilities as decimals rounded to the nearest hundredth.

SOLUTION

a. It is possible to select a taxpayer who both earned less than $25,000 and was audited. Thus, these events are not mutually exclusive.

P (less than $25,000 or audited)

$$= P(\text{less than } \$25{,}000) + P(\text{audited}) - P(\text{less than } \$25{,}000 \text{ and audited})$$

$$= \frac{53{,}207{,}268}{120{,}851{,}273} + \frac{815{,}311}{120{,}851{,}273} - \frac{414{,}357}{120{,}851{,}273}$$

Of the 120,851,273 taxpayers, 53,207,268 had taxable incomes less than $25,000.

Of the 120,851,273 taxpayers, 815,311 were audited.

Of the 120,851,273 taxpayers, 414,357 earned less than $25,000 and were audited.

$$= \frac{53{,}608{,}222}{120{,}851{,}273} \approx 0.44$$

The probability that a taxpayer had a taxable income less than $25,000 or was audited is approximately 0.44.

b. A taxable income of *at least* $100,000 means $100,000 or more. Thus, it is not possible to select a taxpayer with both a taxable income of less than $25,000 and at least $100,000. These events are mutually exclusive.

P(less than $25,000 or at least $100,000)

$$= P(\text{less than } \$25{,}000) + P(\text{at least } \$100{,}000)$$

$$= \frac{53{,}207{,}268}{120{,}851{,}273} + \frac{10{,}927{,}511}{120{,}851{,}273}$$

Of the 120,851,273 taxpayers, 53,207,268 had taxable incomes less than $25,000.

Of the 120,851,273 taxpayers, 10,927,511 had taxable incomes of $100,000 or more.

$$= \frac{64{,}134{,}779}{120{,}851{,}273} \approx 0.53$$

The probability that a taxpayer had a taxable income less than $25,000 or at least $100,000 is approximately 0.53.

CHECK POINT 6 If one person is randomly selected from the population represented in Table 11.5, find the probability, expressed as a decimal rounded to the nearest hundredth, that

a. the taxpayer had a taxable income of at least \$100,000 or was not audited.

b. the taxpayer had a taxable income less than \$25,000 or between \$50,000 and \$99,999, inclusive.

3 Understand and use odds.

Odds

If we know the probability of an event E, we can also speak of the *odds in favor*, or the *odds against*, the event. The following definitions link together the concepts of odds and probabilities:

PROBABILITY TO ODDS

If $P(E)$ is the probability of an event E occurring, then

1. The **odds in favor of E** are found by taking the probability that E will occur and dividing by the probability that E will not occur.

$$\text{Odds in favor of } E = \frac{P(E)}{P(\text{not } E)}$$

2. The **odds against E** are found by taking the probability that E will not occur and dividing by the probability that E will occur.

$$\text{Odds against } E = \frac{P(\text{not } E)}{P(E)}$$

The odds against E can also be found by reversing the ratio representing the odds in favor of E.

EXAMPLE 7 FROM PROBABILITY TO ODDS

You roll a single, six-sided die.

a. Find the odds in favor of rolling a 2.

b. Find the odds against rolling a 2.

SOLUTION Let E represent the event of rolling a 2. In order to determine odds, we must first find the probability of E occurring and the probability of E not occurring. With $S = \{1, 2, 3, 4, 5, 6\}$ and $E = \{2\}$, we see that

$$P(E) = \frac{1}{6}$$

$$\text{and} \quad P(\text{not } E) = 1 - \frac{1}{6} = \frac{6}{6} - \frac{1}{6} = \frac{5}{6}.$$

Now we are ready to construct the ratios for the odds in favor of E and the odds against E.

a. $$\text{Odds in favor of } E(\text{rolling a 2}) = \frac{P(E)}{P(\text{not } E)} = \frac{\frac{1}{6}}{\frac{5}{6}} = \frac{1}{6} \cdot \frac{6}{5} = \frac{1}{5}$$

STUDY TIP

When computing odds, the denominators of the two probabilities will always divide out.

The odds in favor of rolling a 2 are $\frac{1}{5}$. The ratio $\frac{1}{5}$ is usually written 1:5 and is read "1 to 5." Thus, the odds in favor of rolling a 2 are 1 to 5.

b. Now that we have the odds in favor of rolling a 2, namely $\frac{1}{5}$ or 1:5, we can find the odds against rolling a 2 by reversing this ratio. Thus,

$$\text{Odds against } E(\text{rolling a } 2) = \frac{5}{1} \quad \text{or} \quad 5:1.$$

The odds against rolling a 2 are 5 to 1.

CHECK POINT 7 You are dealt one card from a 52-card deck.

a. Find the odds in favor of getting a red queen.

b. Find the odds against getting a red queen.

EXAMPLE 8 FROM PROBABILITY TO ODDS

The winner of a raffle will receive a new sports utility vehicle. If 500 raffle tickets were sold and you purchased ten tickets, what are the odds against your winning the car?

SOLUTION Let E represent the event of winning the SUV. Because you purchased ten tickets and 500 tickets were sold,

$$P(E) = \frac{10}{500} = \frac{1}{50} \quad \text{and} \quad P(\text{not } E) = 1 - \frac{1}{50} = \frac{50}{50} - \frac{1}{50} = \frac{49}{50}.$$

Now we are ready to construct the ratio for the odds against E (winning the SUV).

$$\text{Odds against } E = \frac{P(\text{not } E)}{P(E)} = \frac{\frac{49}{50}}{\frac{1}{50}} = \frac{49}{50} \cdot \frac{50}{1} = \frac{49}{1}$$

The odds against winning the SUV are 49 to 1, written 49:1.

CHECK POINT 8 The winner of a raffle will receive a two-year scholarship to the college of his or her choice. If 1000 raffle tickets were sold and you purchased five tickets, what are the odds against your winning the scholarship?

Odds enable us to play and bet fairly on games. For example, we have seen that the odds in favor of getting 2 when you roll a die are 1 to 5. Suppose this is a gaming situation and you bet \$1 on a 2 turning up. In terms of your bet, there is one favorable outcome, rolling 2, and five unfavorable outcomes, rolling 1, 3, 4, 5, or 6. The odds in favor of getting 2, 1 to 5, compares the number of favorable outcomes, one, to the number of unfavorable outcomes, five.

Using odds in a gaming situation where money is waged, we can determine if the game is *fair*. If the odds in favor of an event E are a to b, the **game is fair** if a bet of \$$a$ is lost if event E does not occur, but a win of \$$b$ (as well as returning the bet of \$$a$) is realized if event E does occur. For example, the odds in favor of getting 2 on a die roll are 1 to 5. If you bet \$1 on a 2 turning up and the game is fair, you should win \$5 (and have your bet of \$1 returned) if a 2 turns up.

Now that we know how to convert from probability to odds, let's see how to convert from odds to probability. Suppose that the odds in favor of event E occurring are a to b. This means that

$$\frac{P(E)}{P(\text{not } E)} = \frac{a}{b} \quad \text{or} \quad \frac{P(E)}{1 - P(E)} = \frac{a}{b}.$$

By solving the equation on the right for $P(E)$, we obtain the following formula for converting from odds to probability:

BLITZER BONUS

House Odds

The odds given at horse races and at all games of chance are usually *odds against*. The horse in Example 9, with odds of winning at 2 to 5, has odds against winning at 5 to 2. At a horse race, the odds on this particular horse are given simply as 5 to 2. These **house odds** tell a gambler what the payoff is on a bet. For every \$2 bet on the horse, the gambler would win \$5 if the horse won, in addition to having the \$2 bet returned.

ODDS TO PROBABILITY

If the odds in favor of event E are a to b, then the probability of the event is given by

$$P(E) = \frac{a}{a+b}.$$

EXAMPLE 9 FROM ODDS TO PROBABILITY

The odds in favor of a particular horse winning a race are 2 to 5. What is the probability that this horse will win the race?

SOLUTION Because odds in favor, a to b, means a probability of $\frac{a}{a+b}$, then odds in favor, 2 to 5, means a probability of

$$\frac{2}{2+5} = \frac{2}{7}.$$

The probability that this horse will win the race is $\frac{2}{7}$.

CHECK POINT 9 The odds against a particular horse winning a race are 15 to 1. Find the odds in favor of the horse winning the race and the probability of the horse winning the race.

EXERCISE SET 11.6

• Practice and Application Exercises

In Exercises 1–6, you are dealt one card from a 52-card deck. Find the probability that you are not dealt

1. an ace. **2.** a 3. **3.** a heart. **4.** a club. **5.** a picture card. **6.** a red picture card.

In 5-card poker, played with a standard 52-card deck, ${}_{52}C_5$, or 2,598,960, different hands are possible. The probability of being dealt various hands is the number of different ways they can occur divided by 2,598,960. Shown in Exercises 7–10 are various types of poker hands and their probabilities. In each exercise, find the probability of not being dealt this type of hand.

Type of Hand	Illustration	Number of Ways the Hand Can Occur	Probability
7. Straight flush: 5 cards with consecutive numbers, all in the same suit (excluding royal flush)		36	$\frac{36}{2{,}598{,}960}$
8. Four of a kind: 4 cards with the same number, plus 1 additional card		624	$\frac{624}{2{,}598{,}960}$
9. Full house: 3 cards of one number and 2 cards of a second number		3744	$\frac{3744}{2{,}598{,}960}$
10. Flush: 5 cards of the same suit (excluding royal flush and straight flush)		5108	$\frac{5108}{2{,}598{,}960}$

The graph shows the probability of cardiovascular disease, by age and gender. Use the information in the graph to solve Exercises 11–12. Express all probabilities as decimals, estimated to two decimal places.

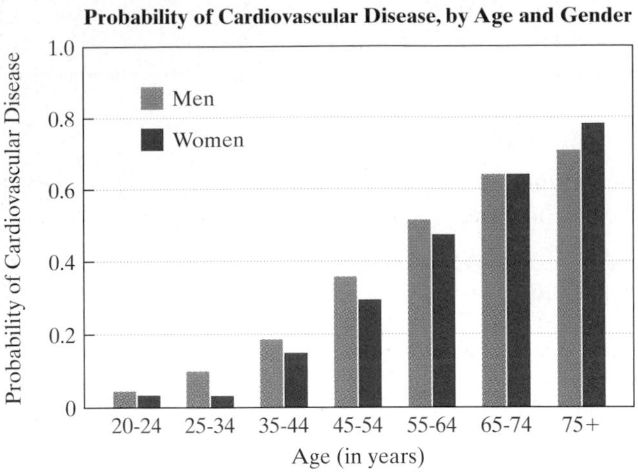

Source: American Heart Association

11. a. What is the probability that a randomly selected man between the ages of 25 and 34 has cardiovascular disease?

b. What is the probability that a randomly selected man between the ages of 25 and 34 does not have cardiovascular disease?

12. a. What is the probability that a randomly selected woman, 75 or older, has cardiovascular disease?

b. What is the probability that a randomly selected woman, 75 or older, does not have cardiovascular disease?

The table shows the distribution, by annual income, of the 112 million households in the United States in 2003, with all numbers rounded to the nearest million. Use this distribution to solve Exercises 13–16.

INCOME DISTRIBUTION OF U.S. HOUSEHOLDS, IN MILLIONS

Annual Income	Number	Annual Income	Number
Less than $10,000	10	$35,000–$49,999	17
$10,000–$14,999	8	$50,000–$74,999	20
$15,000–$24,999	15	$75,000–$99,999	12
$25,000–$34,999	13	$100,000 or more	17

Source: U.S. Census Bureau

If one household is randomly selected from this population, find the probability, expressed as a simplified fraction, that

13. the household income is not in the $50,000–$74,999 range.

14. the household income is not in the $15,000–$24,999 range.

15. the household income is less than $100,000.

16. the household income is at least $10,000.

In Exercises 17–22, you randomly select one card from a 52-card deck. Find the probability of selecting

17. a 2 or a 3.

18. a 7 or an 8.

19. a red 2 or a black 3.

20. a red 7 or a black 8.

21. the 2 of hearts or the 3 of spades.

22. the 7 of hearts or the 8 of spades.

23. The mathematics faculty at a college consists of 8 professors, 12 associate professors, 14 assistant professors, and 10 instructors. If one faculty member is randomly selected, find the probability of choosing a professor or an instructor.

24. A political discussion group consists of 30 Republicans, 25 Democrats, 8 Independents, and 4 members of the Green party. If one person is randomly selected from the group, find the probability of choosing an Independent or a Green.

In Exercises 25–26, a single die is rolled. Find the probability of rolling

25. an even number or a number less than 5.

26. an odd number or a number less than 4.

In Exercises 27–30, you are dealt one card from a 52-card deck. Find the probability that you are dealt

27. a 7 or a red card.

28. a 5 or a black card.

29. a heart or a picture card.

30. a card greater than 2 and less than 7, or a diamond.

In Exercises 31–34, it is equally probable that the pointer on the spinner shown will land on any one of the eight regions, numbered 1 through 8. If the pointer lands on a borderline, spin again.

Find the probability that the pointer will stop on

31. an odd number or a number less than 6.

32. an odd number or a number greater than 3.

33. an even number or a number greater than 5.

34. an even number or a number less than 4.

Use this information to solve Exercises 35–38. The mathematics department of a college has 8 male professors, 11 female professors, 14 male teaching assistants, and 7 female teaching assistants. If a person is selected at random from the group, find the probability that the selected person is

35. a professor or a male.

36. a professor or a female.

37. a teaching assistant or a female.

38. a teaching assistant or a male.

39. In a class of 50 students, 29 are Democrats, 11 are business majors, and 5 of the business majors are Democrats. If one student is randomly selected from the class, find the probability of choosing a Democrat or a business major.

40. A student is selected at random from a group of 200 students in which 135 take math, 85 take English, and 65 take both math and English. Find the probability that the selected student takes math or English.

The table shows the educational attainment of the U.S. population, ages 25 and over, in 2004. Use the data in the table, expressed in millions, to solve Exercises 41–48.

EDUCATIONAL ATTAINMENT OF THE U.S. POPULATION, AGES 25 AND OVER, IN MILLIONS

	Less Than 4 Years High School	4 Years High School Only	Some College (Less than 4 years)	4 Years College (or More)	Total
Male	14	28	22	26	90
Female	14	32	26	25	97
Total	28	60	48	51	187

Source: U.S. Census Bureau

Find the probability, expressed as a simplified fraction, that a randomly selected American, aged 25 or over,

41. has not completed four years (or more) of college.

42. has not completed four years of high school.

43. has completed four years of high school only or less than four years of college.

44. has completed less than four years of high school or four years of high school only.

45. has completed four years of high school only or is a man.

46. has completed four years of high school only or is a woman.

Find the odds in favor and the odds against a randomly selected American, aged 25 and over, with

47. four years (or more) of college.

48. less than four years of high school.

The graph shows the distribution, by branch and gender, of the 1.43 million, or 1430 thousand, active-duty personnel in the U.S. military in 2003. Numbers are given in thousands and rounded to the nearest ten thousand. Use the data to solve Exercises 49–60.

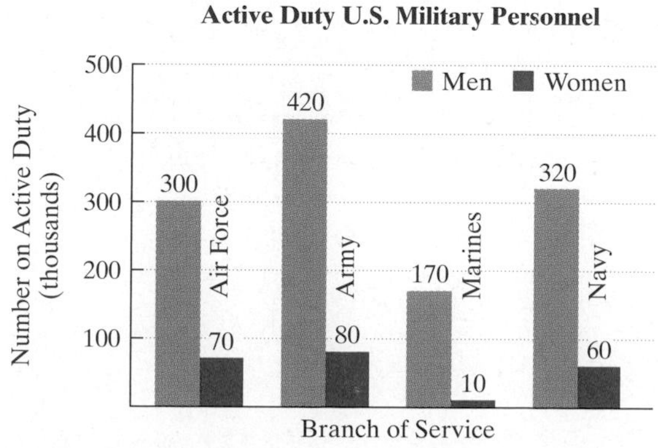

Source: U.S. Defense Department

If one person is randomly selected from the population represented in the bar graph in the previous column, find the probability, expressed as a simplified fraction, that the person

49. is not in the Army.

50. is not in the Marines.

51. is in the Navy or is a man.

52. is in the Army or is a woman.

53. is in the Air Force or the Marines.

54. is in the Army or the Navy.

Find the odds in favor and the odds against a randomly selected person from the population represented in the bar graph in the previous column being

55. in the Navy.

56. in the Army.

57. a woman in the Marines.

58. a woman in the Air Force.

59. a man.

60. a woman.

In Exercises 61–64, a single die is rolled. Find the odds

61. in favor of rolling a number greater than 2.

62. in favor of rolling a number less than 5.

63. against rolling a number greater than 2.

64. against rolling a number less than 5.

The circle graphs show the percentage of children in the United States whose parents are college graduates in one-parent households and two-parent households. Use the information shown to solve Exercises 65–66.

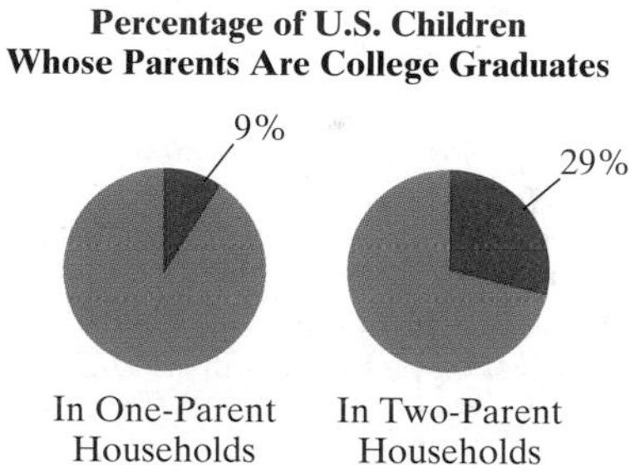

Source: U.S. Census Bureau

65. a. What are the odds in favor of a child in a one-parent household having a parent who is a college graduate?

b. What are the odds against a child in a one-parent household having a parent who is a college graduate?

66. a. What are the odds in favor of a child in a two-parent household having parents who are college graduates?

b. What are the odds against a child in a two-parent household having parents who are college graduates?

In Exercises 67–76, one card is randomly selected from a deck of cards. Find the odds

67. in favor of drawing a heart.

68. in favor of drawing a picture card.

69. in favor of drawing a red card.

70. in favor of drawing a black card.

71. against drawing a 9.

72. against drawing a 5.

73. against drawing a black king.

74. against drawing a red jack.

75. against drawing a spade greater than 3 and less than 9.

76. against drawing a club greater than 4 and less than 10.

77. The winner of a raffle will receive a 21-foot outboard boat. If 1000 raffle tickets were sold and you purchased 20 tickets, what are the odds against your winning the boat?

78. The winner of a raffle will receive a 30-day all-expense-paid trip throughout Europe. If 5000 raffle tickets were sold and you purchased 30 tickets, what are the odds against your winning the trip?

Of the 38 plays attributed to Shakespeare, 18 are comedies, 10 are tragedies, and 10 are histories. In Exercises 79–86, one play is randomly selected from Shakespeare's 38 plays. Find the odds

79. in favor of selecting a comedy.

80. in favor of selecting a tragedy.

81. against selecting a history.

82. against selecting a comedy.

83. in favor of selecting a comedy or a tragedy.

84. in favor of selecting a tragedy or a history.

85. against selecting a tragedy or a history.

86. against selecting a comedy or a history.

87. If you are given odds of 3 to 4 in favor of winning a bet, what is the probability of winning the bet?

88. If you are given odds of 3 to 7 in favor of winning a bet, what is the probability of winning the bet?

89. Based on his skills in basketball, it was computed that when Michael Jordan shot a free throw, the odds in favor of his making it were 21 to 4. Find the probability that when Michael Jordan shot a free throw, he missed it. Out of every 100 free throws he attempted, on the average how many did he make?

90. The odds in favor of a person who is alive at age 20 still being alive at age 70 are 193 to 270. Find the probability that a person who is alive at age 20 will still be alive at age 70.

Exercises 91–92 give the odds against various flight risks. (Source: Men's Health, August 2005) Use these odds to determine the probability of the underlined event for those in flight.

91. odds against <u>contracting an airborne disease</u>: 999 to 1

92. odds against <u>deep-vein thrombosis</u> (blood clot in the leg): 28 to 1

• Writing in Mathematics

93. Explain how to find the probability of an event not occurring. Give an example.

94. What are mutually exclusive events? Give an example of two events that are mutually exclusive.

95. Explain how to find *or* probabilities with mutually exclusive events. Give an example.

96. Give an example of two events that are not mutually exclusive.

97. Explain how to find *or* probabilities with events that are not mutually exclusive. Give an example.

98. Explain how to find the odds in favor of an event if you know the probability that the event will occur.

99. Explain how to find the probability of an event if you know the odds in favor of that event.

• Critical Thinking Exercises

100. In Exercise 39, find the probability of choosing **a**. a Democrat who is not a business major; **b**. a student who is neither a Democrat nor a business major.

101. On New Year's Eve, the probability of a person driving while intoxicated or having a driving accident is 0.35. If the probability of driving while intoxicated is 0.32 and the probability of having a driving accident is 0.09, find the probability of a person having a driving accident while intoxicated.

102. The formula for converting from odds to probability is given in the box on page 649. Read the paragraph on the bottom of page 648 that precedes this box and derive the formula.

SECTION 11.7 • EVENTS INVOLVING *AND*; CONDITIONAL PROBABILITY

OBJECTIVES

1. Find the probability of one event and a second event occurring.
2. Compute conditional probabilities.

You are considering a job offer in South Florida. You were thrilled by images of Miami on MTV's *The Real World*. The job offer is just what you wanted and you are excited about living in the midst of Miami's tropical diversity. However, there is just one thing: the risk of hurricanes. If you expect to stay in Miami ten years and buy a home, what is the probability that South Florida will be hit by a hurricane at least once in the next ten years?

In this section, we look at the probability that an event occurs at least once by expanding our discussion of probability to events involving *and*.

1 Find the probability of one event and a second event occurring.

And Probabilities with Independent Events

Consider tossing a fair coin two times in succession. The outcome of the first toss, heads or tails, does not affect what happens when you toss the coin a second time. For example, the occurrence of tails on the first toss does not make tails more likely or less likely to occur on the second toss. The repeated toss of a coin produces *independent events* because the outcome of one toss does not affect the outcome of others.

STUDY TIP

Do not confuse *independent events* and *mutually exclusive events.* Mutually exclusive events cannot occur at the same time. Independent events occur at different times, although they have no effect on each other.

INDEPENDENT EVENTS

Two events are **independent events** if the occurrence of either of them has no effect on the probability of the other.

When a fair coin is tossed two times in succession, the set of equally likely outcomes is

$$\{\text{heads heads, heads tails, tails heads, tails tails}\}.$$

We can use this set to find the probability of getting heads on the first toss and heads on the second toss:

$$P(\text{heads and heads}) = \frac{\text{number of ways two heads can occur}}{\text{total number of possible outcomes}} = \frac{1}{4}.$$

We can also determine the probability of two heads, $\frac{1}{4}$, without having to list all the equally likely outcomes. The probability of heads on the first toss is $\frac{1}{2}$. The probability of heads on the second toss is also $\frac{1}{2}$. The product of these probabilities, $\frac{1}{2} \cdot \frac{1}{2}$, results in the probability of two heads, namely $\frac{1}{4}$. Thus,

$$P(\text{heads and heads}) = P(\text{heads}) \cdot P(\text{heads}).$$

In general, if two events are independent, we can calculate the probability of the first occurring and the second occurring by multiplying their probabilities.

AND PROBABILITIES WITH INDEPENDENT EVENTS

If A and B are independent events, then

$$P(A \text{ and } B) = P(A) \cdot P(B).$$

EXAMPLE 1 INDEPENDENT EVENTS ON A ROULETTE WHEEL

FIGURE 11.11 A U.S. roulette wheel

Figure 11.11 shows a U.S. roulette wheel that has 38 numbered slots (1 through 36, 0, and 00). Of the 38 compartments, 18 are black, 18 are red, and 2 are green. A play has the dealer spin the wheel and a small ball in opposite directions. As the ball slows to a stop, it can land with equal probability on any one of the 38 numbered slots. Find the probability of red occurring on two consecutive plays.

SOLUTION The wheel has 38 equally likely outcomes and 18 are red. Thus, the probability of red occurring on a play is $\frac{18}{38}$, or $\frac{9}{19}$. The result that occurs on each play is independent of all previous results. Thus,

$$P(\text{red and red}) = P(\text{red}) \cdot P(\text{red}) = \frac{9}{19} \cdot \frac{9}{19} = \frac{81}{361} \approx 0.224.$$

The probability of red occurring on two consecutive plays is $\frac{81}{361}$.

Some roulette players incorrectly believe that if red occurs on two consecutive plays, then another color is "due." Because the events are independent, the outcomes of previous spins have no effect on any other spins.

CHECK POINT 1 Find the probability of green occurring on two consecutive plays on a roulette wheel.

The *and* rule for independent events can be extended to cover three or more events. Thus, if A, B, and C are independent events, then

$$P(A \text{ and } B \text{ and } C) = P(A) \cdot P(B) \cdot P(C).$$

EXAMPLE 2 INDEPENDENT EVENTS IN A FAMILY

The picture in the margin shows a family that had nine girls in a row. Find the probability of this occurrence.

SOLUTION If two or more events are independent, we can find the probability of them all occurring by multiplying their probabilities. The probability of a baby girl is $\frac{1}{2}$, so the probability of nine girls in a row is $\frac{1}{2}$ used as a factor nine times.

$$P(\text{nine girls in a row}) = \frac{1}{2} \cdot \frac{1}{2} \cdot \frac{1}{2} \cdot \frac{1}{2} \cdot \frac{1}{2} \cdot \frac{1}{2} \cdot \frac{1}{2} \cdot \frac{1}{2} \cdot \frac{1}{2}$$

$$= \left(\frac{1}{2}\right)^9 = \frac{1}{512}$$

The probability of a run of nine girls in a row is $\frac{1}{512}$. (If another child is born into the family, this event is independent of the other nine and the probability of a girl is still $\frac{1}{2}$.)

CHECK POINT 2 Find the probability of a family having four boys in a row.

TABLE 11.6 THE SAFFIR/SIMPSON HURRICANE SCALE

Category	Winds (Miles per Hour)
1	74–95
2	96–110
3	111–130
4	131–155
5	>155

Now let us return to the hurricane problem that opened this section. The Saffir/Simpson scale assigns numbers 1 through 5 to measure the disaster potential of a hurricane's winds. Table 11.6 describes the scale. According to the National Hurricane Center, the probability that South Florida will be hit by a category 1 hurricane or higher in any single year is $\frac{5}{19}$, or approximately 0.26. In Example 3, we explore the risks of living in "Hurricane Alley."

EXAMPLE 3 HURRICANES AND PROBABILITIES

If the probability that South Florida will be hit by a hurricane in any single year is $\frac{5}{19}$,

a. What is the probability that South Florida will be hit by a hurricane in three consecutive years?

b. What is the probability that South Florida will not be hit by a hurricane in the next ten years?

SOLUTION

a. The probability that South Florida will be hit by a hurricane in three consecutive years is

$$P(\text{hurricane and hurricane and hurricane})$$

$$= P(\text{hurricane}) \cdot P(\text{hurricane}) \cdot P(\text{hurricane}) = \frac{5}{19} \cdot \frac{5}{19} \cdot \frac{5}{19} = \frac{125}{6859} \approx 0.018.$$

b. We will first find the probability that South Florida will not be hit by a hurricane in any single year.

$$P(\text{no hurricane}) = 1 - P(\text{hurricane}) = 1 - \frac{5}{19} = \frac{14}{19} \approx 0.737$$

The probability of not being hit by a hurricane in a single year is $\frac{14}{19}$. Therefore, the probability of not being hit by a hurricane ten years in a row is $\frac{14}{19}$ used as a factor ten times.

$$P(\text{no hurricanes for ten years})$$

$$= P\begin{pmatrix}\text{no hurricane}\\ \text{for year 1}\end{pmatrix} \cdot P\begin{pmatrix}\text{no hurricane}\\ \text{for year 2}\end{pmatrix} \cdot P\begin{pmatrix}\text{no hurricane}\\ \text{for year 3}\end{pmatrix} \cdot \cdots \cdot P\begin{pmatrix}\text{no hurricane}\\ \text{for year 10}\end{pmatrix}$$

$$= \frac{14}{19} \cdot \frac{14}{19} \cdot \frac{14}{19} \cdot \cdots \cdot \frac{14}{19}$$

$$= \left(\frac{14}{19}\right)^{10} \approx (0.737)^{10} \approx 0.047$$

The probability that South Florida will not be hit by a hurricane in the next ten years is approximately 0.047.

Now we are ready to answer your question:

What is the probability that South Florida will be hit by a hurricane at least once in the next ten years?

Because $P(\text{not } E) = 1 - P(E)$,

$$P(\text{no hurricane for ten years}) = 1 - P(\text{at least one hurricane in ten years}).$$

In our logic chapter, we saw that the negation of "at least one" is "no."

Equivalently,

$$P(\text{at least one hurricane in ten years}) = 1 - P(\text{no hurricane for ten years}) = 1 - 0.047 = 0.953.$$

With a probability of 0.953, it is nearly certain that South Florida will be hit by a hurricane at least once in the next ten years.

STUDY TIP

When solving probability problems, begin by deciding whether to use the *or* formulas or the *and* formulas.

- *Or* problems usually have the word *or* in the statement of the problem. These problems involve only one selection.

Example:

If one person is selected, find the probability of selecting a man or a Canadian.

- *And* problems often do not have the word *and* in the statement of the problem. These problems involve more than one selection.

Example:

If two people are selected, find the probability that both are men.

THE PROBABILITY OF AN EVENT HAPPENING AT LEAST ONCE

$$P(\text{event happening at least once}) = 1 - P(\text{event does not happen})$$

CHECK POINT 3 If the probability that South Florida will be hit by a hurricane in any single year is $\frac{5}{19}$,

a. What is the probability that South Florida will be hit by a hurricane in four consecutive years?

b. What is the probability that South Florida will not be hit by a hurricane in the next four years?

c. What is the probability that South Florida will be hit by a hurricane at least once in the next four years?

Express all probabilities as fractions and as decimals rounded to three places.

And Probabilities with Dependent Events

5 chocolate-covered cherries lie within the 20 pieces.

Once a chocolate-covered cherry is selected, only 4 chocolate-covered cherries lie within the remaining 19 pieces.

Chocolate lovers, please help yourselves! There are 20 mouth-watering tidbits to select from. What's that? You want 2? And you prefer chocolate-covered cherries? The problem is that there are only 5 chocolate-covered cherries, and it's impossible to tell what is inside each piece. They're all shaped exactly alike. At any rate, reach in, select a piece, enjoy, choose another piece, eat, and be well. There is nothing like savoring a good piece of chocolate in the midst of all this chit-chat about probability and hurricanes.

Another question? You want to know what your chances are of selecting 2 chocolate-covered cherries? Well, let's see. Five of the 20 pieces are chocolate-covered cherries, so the probability of getting one of them on your first selection is $\frac{5}{20}$, or $\frac{1}{4}$. Now, suppose that you did choose a chocolate-covered cherry on your first pick. Eat it slowly; there's no guarantee that you'll select your favorite on the second selection. There are now only 19 pieces of chocolate left. Only 4 are chocolate-covered cherries. The probability of getting a chocolate-covered cherry on your second try is 4 out of 19, or $\frac{4}{19}$. This is a different probability than the $\frac{1}{4}$ probability on your first selection. Selecting a chocolate-covered cherry the first time changes what is in the candy box. The probability of what you select the second time *is* affected by the outcome of the first event. For this reason, we say that these are *dependent events*.

DEPENDENT EVENTS

Two events are **dependent events** if the occurrence of one of them has an effect on the probability of the other.

The probability of selecting two chocolate-covered cherries in a row can be found by multiplying the $\frac{1}{4}$ probability on the first selection by the $\frac{4}{19}$ probability on the second selection:

$P(\text{chocolate-covered cherry and chocolate-covered cherry})$

$$= P(\text{chocolate-covered cherry}) \cdot P\left(\begin{matrix}\text{chocolate-covered cherry} \\ \text{given that one was selected}\end{matrix}\right)$$

$$= \frac{1}{4} \cdot \frac{4}{19} = \frac{1}{19}.$$

The probability of selecting two chocolate-covered cherries in a row is $\frac{1}{19}$. This is a special case of finding the probability that each of two dependent events occurs.

AND PROBABILITIES WITH DEPENDENT EVENTS

If A and B are dependent events, then

$$P(A \text{ and } B) = P(A) \cdot P(B \text{ given that } A \text{ has occurred}).$$

EXAMPLE 4 AN *AND* PROBABILITY WITH DEPENDENT EVENTS

Good news: You won a free trip to Madrid and can take two people with you, all expenses paid. Bad news: Ten of your cousins have appeared out of nowhere and are begging you to take them. You write each cousin's name on a card, place the cards in a hat, and select one name. Then you select a second name without replacing the first card. If three of your ten cousins speak Spanish, find the probability of selecting two Spanish-speaking cousins.

SOLUTION Because $P(A \text{ and } B) = P(A) \cdot P(B \text{ given that } A \text{ has occurred})$, then $P(\text{two Spanish-speaking cousins})$

$$= P(\text{speaks Spanish and speaks Spanish})$$

$$= P(\text{speaks Spanish}) \cdot P\left(\begin{array}{c}\text{speaks Spanish given that a Spanish-speaking} \\ \text{cousin was selected first}\end{array}\right)$$

$$= \frac{3}{10} \cdot \frac{2}{9}$$

There are ten cousins, three of whom speak Spanish.

After picking a Spanish-speaking cousin, there are nine cousins left, two of whom speak Spanish.

$$= \frac{6}{90} = \frac{1}{15} \approx 0.067.$$

The probability of selecting two Spanish-speaking cousins is $\frac{1}{15}$.

STUDY TIP

Example 4 can also be solved using the combinations formula.

$$P(\text{two Spanish speakers}) = \frac{\text{number of ways of selecting 2 Spanish-speaking cousins}}{\text{number of ways of selecting 2 cousins}}$$

$$= \frac{_3C_2}{_{10}C_2}$$

2 Spanish speakers selected from 3 Spanish-speaking cousins

2 cousins selected from 10 cousins

$$= \frac{3}{45} = \frac{1}{15}$$

CHECK POINT 4 You are dealt two cards from a 52-card deck. Find the probability of getting two kings.

The multiplication rule for dependent events can be extended to cover three or more dependent events. For example, in the case of three such events,

$$P(A \text{ and } B \text{ and } C)$$
$$= P(A) \cdot P(B \text{ given that } A \text{ occurred}) \cdot P(C \text{ given that } A \text{ and } B \text{ occurred}).$$

EXAMPLE 5 AN *AND* PROBABILITY WITH THREE DEPENDENT EVENTS

Three people are randomly selected, one person at a time, from five freshmen, two sophomores, and four juniors. Find the probability that the first two people selected are freshmen and the third is a junior.

5 freshmen
2 sophomores
4 juniors
The given numbers (repeated)

SOLUTION

P(first two are freshmen and the third is a junior)

$= P(\text{freshman}) \cdot P\left(\begin{array}{c}\text{freshman given that a}\\ \text{freshman was selected first}\end{array}\right) \cdot P\left(\begin{array}{c}\text{junior given that a freshman was}\\ \text{selected first and a freshman was}\\ \text{selected second}\end{array}\right)$

$= \frac{5}{11} \cdot \frac{4}{10} \cdot \frac{4}{9}$

There are 11 people, five of whom are freshmen.

After picking a freshman, there are 10 people left, four of whom are freshmen.

After the first two selections, 9 people are left, four of whom are juniors.

$= \frac{8}{99}$

The probability that the first two people selected are freshmen and the third is a junior is $\frac{8}{99}$.

2 Compute conditional probabilities.

CHECK POINT 5 You are dealt three cards from a 52-card deck. Find the probability of getting three hearts.

Conditional Probability

We have seen that for any two dependent events A and B,

$$P(A \text{ and } B) = P(A) \cdot P(B \text{ given that } A \text{ occurs}).$$

The probability of B given that A occurs is called *conditional probability*, denoted by $P(B|A)$.

CONDITIONAL PROBABILITY

The probability of event B, assuming that the event A has already occurred, is called the **conditional probability** of B, given A. This probability is denoted by $P(B|A)$.

It is helpful to think of the conditional probability $P(B|A)$ as the **probability that event B occurs if the sample space is restricted to the outcomes associated with event A.**

BLITZER BONUS

Coincidences

The phone rings and it's the friend you were just thinking of. You're driving down the road and a song you were humming in your head comes on the radio. Although these coincidences seem strange, perhaps even mystical, they're not. Coincidences are bound to happen. Ours is a world in which there are a great many potential coincidences, each with a low probability of occurring. When these surprising coincidences happen, we are amazed and remember them. However, we pay little attention to the countless number of noncoincidences: How often do you think of your friend and she doesn't call, or how often does she call when you're not thinking about her? By noticing the hits and ignoring the misses, we incorrectly perceive that there is a relationship between the occurrence of two independent events.

Another problem is that we often underestimate the probabilities of coincidences in certain situations, acting with more surprise than we should when they occur. For example, in a group of only 23 people, the probability that two individuals share a birthday (same month and day) is greater than $\frac{1}{2}$. Above 50 people, the probability of any two people sharing a birthday approaches certainty. You can verify the probabilities behind the coincidence of shared birthdays in relatively small groups by working Exercise 83 in Exercise Set 11.7.

EXAMPLE 6 FINDING CONDITIONAL PROBABILITY

A letter is randomly selected from the letters of the English alphabet. Find the probability of selecting a vowel, given that the outcome is a letter that precedes h.

SOLUTION We are looking for

$$P(\text{vowel}|\text{letter precedes h}).$$

This is the probability of a vowel if the sample space is restricted to the set of letters that precede h. Thus, the sample space is given by

$$S = \{a, b, c, d, e, f, g\}.$$

There are seven possible outcomes in the sample space. We can select a vowel from this set in one of two ways: a or e. Therefore, the probability of selecting a vowel, given that the outcome is a letter that precedes h, is $\frac{2}{7}$.

$$P(\text{vowel}|\text{letter precedes h}) = \frac{2}{7}$$

CHECK POINT 6 You are dealt one card from a 52-card deck. Find the probability of getting a heart, given that the card you were dealt is a red card.

EXAMPLE 7 CONDITIONAL PROBABILITIES WITH REAL-WORLD DATA

When women turn 40, their gynecologists typically remind them that it is time to undergo mammography screening for breast cancer. The data in Table 11.7 are based on 100,000 U.S. women, ages 40 to 50, who participated in mammography screening.

TABLE 11.7 MAMMOGRAPHY SCREENING ON 100,000 U.S. WOMEN, AGES 40 TO 50

	Breast Cancer	No Breast Cancer	Total
Positive Mammogram	720	6944	7664
Negative Mammogram	80	92,256	92,336
Total	800	99,200	100,000

Source: Gerd Gigerenzer, *Calculated Risks*. Simon and Schuster, 2002

Assuming that these numbers are representative of all U.S. women ages 40 to 50, find the probability that a woman in this age range

a. has a positive mammogram, given that she does not have breast cancer.

b. does not have breast cancer, given that she has a positive mammogram.

SOLUTION

a. We begin with the probability that a U.S. woman aged 40 to 50 has a positive mammogram, given that she does not have breast cancer:

$$P(\text{positive mammogram}|\text{no breast cancer}).$$

This is the probability of a positive mammogram if the data are restricted to women without breast cancer:

	No Breast Cancer
Positive Mammogram	6944
Negative Mammogram	92,256
Total	99,200

Within the restricted data, there are 6944 women with positive mammograms and 6944 + 92,256, or 99,200 women without breast cancer. Thus,

$$P(\text{positive mammogram}|\text{no breast cancer}) = \frac{6944}{99{,}200} = 0.07.$$

Among women without breast cancer, the probability of a positive mammogram is 0.07.

b. Now, we find the probability that a U.S. woman aged 40 to 50 does not have breast cancer, given that she has a positive mammogram:

$$P(\text{no breast cancer}|\text{positive mammogram}).$$

This is the probability of not having breast cancer if the data are restricted to women with positive mammograms:

	Breast Cancer	No Breast Cancer	Total
Positive Mammogram	720	6944	7664

Within the restricted data, there are 6944 women without breast cancer and 720 + 6944, or 7664 women with positive mammograms. Thus,

$$P(\text{no breast cancer}|\text{positive mammogram}) = \frac{6944}{7664} \approx 0.906.$$

Among women with positive mammograms, the probability of not having breast cancer is $\frac{6944}{7664}$, or approximately 0.906.

STUDY TIP

Example 7 shows that the probability of a positive mammogram among women without breast cancer, 0.07, is not the same as the probability of not having breast cancer among women with positive mammograms, approximately 0.9. In general, the conditional probability of B, given A, is not the same as the conditional probability of A, given B:

$$P(B|A) \neq P(A|B).$$

CHECK POINT 7 Use the data in Table 11.7 at the top of the previous page to find the probability that a U.S. woman aged 40 to 50

a. has a positive mammogram, given that she has breast cancer.

b. has breast cancer, given that she has a positive mammogram.

Express probabilities as decimals and, if necessary, round to three decimal places.

We have seen that $P(B|A)$ is the probability that event B occurs if the sample space is restricted to event A. Thus,

$$P(B|A) = \frac{\text{number of outcomes of } B \text{ that are in the restricted sample space } A}{\text{number of outcomes in the restricted sample space } A}.$$

This can be stated in terms of the following formula:

A FORMULA FOR CONDITIONAL PROBABILITY

$$P(B|A) = \frac{n(B \cap A)}{n(A)} = \frac{\text{number of outcomes common to } B \text{ and } A}{\text{number of outcomes in } A}$$

EXERCISE SET 11.7

• Practice and Application Exercises

Exercises 1–26 involve probabilities with independent events.

Use the spinner shown to solve Exercises 1–10. It is equally probable that the pointer will land on any one of the six regions. If the pointer lands on a borderline, spin again. If the pointer is spun twice, find the probability it will land on

1. green and then red.

2. yellow and then green.

3. yellow and then yellow.

4. red and then red.

5. a color other than red each time.

6. a color other than green each time.

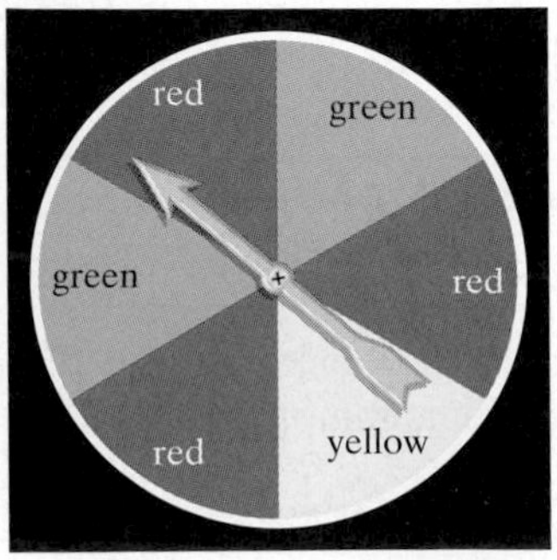

If the pointer is spun three times, find the probability it will land on

7. green and then red and then yellow.

8. red and then red and then green.

9. red every time.

10. green every time.

In Exercises 11–14, a single die is rolled twice. Find the probability of rolling

11. a 2 the first time and a 3 the second time.

12. a 5 the first time and a 1 the second time.

13. an even number the first time and a number greater than 2 the second time.

14. an odd number the first time and a number less than 3 the second time.

In Exercises 15–20, you draw one card from a 52-card deck. Then the card is replaced in the deck, the deck is shuffled, and you draw again. Find the probability of drawing

15. a picture card the first time and a heart the second time.

16. a jack the first time and a club the second time.

17. a king each time.

18. a 3 each time.

19. a red card each time.

20. a black card each time.

21. If you toss a fair coin six times, what is the probability of getting all heads?

22. If you toss a fair coin seven times, what is the probability of getting all tails?

In Exercises 23–24, a coin is tossed and a die is rolled. Find the probability of getting

23. a head and a number greater than 4.

24. a tail and a number less than 5.

25. The probability that South Florida will be hit by a major hurricane (category 4 or 5) in any single year is $\frac{1}{16}$. (*Source:* National Hurricane Center)

a. What is the probability that South Florida will be hit by a major hurricane two years in a row?

b. What is the probability that South Florida will be hit by a major hurricane in three consecutive years?

c. What is the probability that South Florida will not be hit by a major hurricane in the next ten years?

d. What is the probability that South Florida will be hit by a major hurricane at least once in the next ten years?

26. The probability that a region prone to flooding will flood in any single year is $\frac{1}{10}$.

a. What is the probability of a flood two years in a row?

b. What is the probability of flooding in three consecutive years?

c. What is the probability of no flooding for ten consecutive years?

d. What is the probability of flooding at least once in the next ten years?

The graph shows that U.S. adults dependent on tobacco have a greater probability of suffering from some ailments than the general adult population. When making two or more selections from populations with large numbers, such as the U.S. adult population or the population dependent on tobacco, we assume that each selection is independent of every other selection. In Exercises 27–32, assume that the selections are independent events.

Probability That U.S. Adults Suffer from Various Ailments

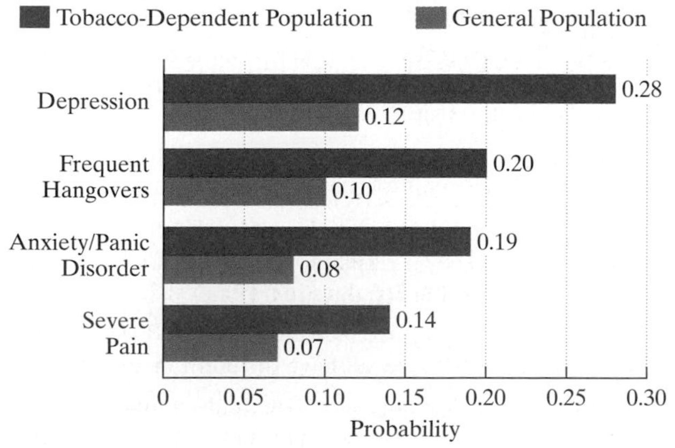

Source: MARS 2005 OTC/DTC

27. If two adults are randomly selected from the general population, what is the probability that they both suffer from depression?

28. If two adults are randomly selected from the population of cigarette smokers, what is the probability that they both suffer from depression?

29. If three adults are randomly selected from the population of cigarette smokers, what is the probability that they all suffer from frequent hangovers?

30. If three adults are randomly selected from the general population, what is the probability that they all suffer from frequent hangovers?

31. If three adults are randomly selected from the population of cigarette smokers, what is the probability, expressed as a decimal correct to four places, that at least one person suffers from anxiety/panic disorder?

32. If three adults are randomly selected from the population of cigarette smokers, what is the probability, expressed as a decimal correct to four places, that at least one person suffers from severe pain?

Exercises 33–48 involve probabilities with dependent events.

In Exercises 33–36, we return to our box of chocolates. There are 30 chocolates in the box, all identically shaped. Five are filled with coconut, 10 with caramel, and 15 are solid chocolate. You randomly select one piece, eat it, and then select a second piece. Find the probability of selecting

33. two solid chocolates in a row.

34. two caramel-filled chocolates in a row.

35. a coconut-filled chocolate followed by a caramel-filled chocolate.

36. a coconut-filled chocolate followed by a solid chocolate.

In Exercises 37–42, consider a political discussion group consisting of 5 Democrats, 6 Republicans, and 4 Independents. Suppose that two group members are randomly selected, in succession, to attend a political convention. Find the probability of selecting

37. two Democrats.

38. two Republicans.

39. an Independent and then a Republican.

40. an Independent and then a Democrat.

41. no Independents.

42. no Democrats.

In Exercises 43–48, an ice chest contains six cans of apple juice, eight cans of grape juice, four cans of orange juice, and two cans of mango juice. Suppose that you reach into the container and randomly select three cans in succession. Find the probability of selecting

43. three cans of apple juice.

44. three cans of grape juice.

45. a can of grape juice, then a can of orange juice, then a can of mango juice.

46. a can of apple juice, then a can of grape juice, then a can of orange juice.

47. no grape juice.

48. no apple juice.

In Exercises 49–56, the numbered disks shown are placed in a box and one disk is selected at random.

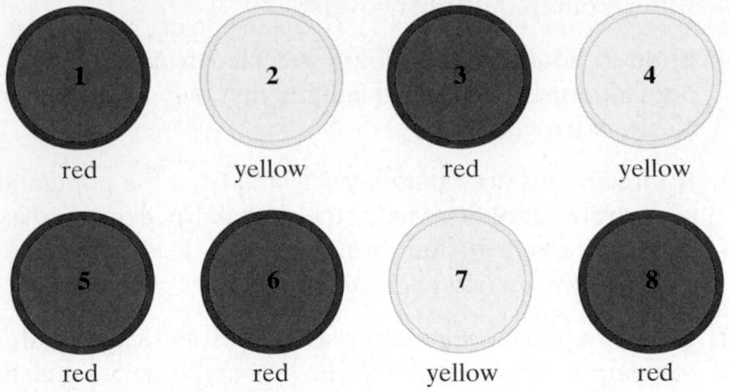

Find the probability of selecting

49. a 3, given that a red disk is selected.

50. a 7, given that a yellow disk is selected.

51. an even number, given that a yellow disk is selected.

52. an odd number, given that a red disk is selected.

53. a red disk, given that an odd number is selected.

54. a yellow disk, given that an odd number is selected.

55. a red disk, given that the number selected is at least 5.

56. a yellow disk, given that the number selected is at most 3.

The table shows the outcome of car accidents in Florida for a recent year by whether or not the driver wore a seat belt. Use the data to solve Exercises 57–60. Express probabilities as fractions and as decimals rounded to three places.

CAR ACCIDENTS IN FLORIDA

	Wore Seat Belt	No Seat Belt	Total
Driver Survived	412,368	162,527	574,895
Driver Died	510	1601	2111
Total	412,878	164,128	577,006

Source: Alan Agresti and Christine Franklin, *Statistics*, Prentice Hall, 2007

57. Find the probability of surviving a car accident, given that the driver wore a seat belt.

58. Find the probability of not surviving a car accident, given that the driver did not wear a seat belt.

59. Find the probability of wearing a seat belt, given that a driver survived a car accident.

60. Find the probability of not wearing a seat belt, given that a driver did not survive a car accident.

In Exercises 61–72, we return to the table showing the distribution, by marital status and gender, of the 212.5 million Americans ages 18 or older.

MARITAL STATUS OF THE U.S. POPULATION, AGES 18 OR OLDER, IN MILLIONS

	Never Married	Married	Widowed	Divorced	Total
Male	28.6	62.1	2.7	9.0	102.4
Female	23.3	62.8	11.3	12.7	110.1
Total	51.9	124.9	14.0	21.7	212.5

Source: U.S. Census Bureau

If one person is selected from the population described in the table at the bottom of the previous column, find the probability, expressed as a decimal rounded to three places, that the person

61. is not divorced.

62. is not widowed.

63. is widowed or divorced.

64. had never been married or is divorced.

65. is male or divorced.

66. is female or divorced.

67. is male, given that this person is divorced.

68. is female, given that this person is divorced.

69. is widowed, given that this person is a woman.

70. is divorced, given that this person is a man.

71. had never been married or is married, given that this person is a man.

72. had never been married or is married, given that this person is a woman.

• Writing in Mathematics

73. Explain how to find *and* probabilities with independent events. Give an example.

74. Explain how to find *and* probabilities with dependent events. Give an example.

75. What does $P(B|A)$ mean? Give an example.

In Exercises 76–80, write a probability problem involving the word "and" whose solution results in the probability fractions shown.

76. $\frac{1}{2} \cdot \frac{1}{2}$

77. $\frac{1}{6} \cdot \frac{1}{6} \cdot \frac{1}{6}$

78. $\frac{1}{2} \cdot \frac{1}{6}$

79. $\frac{13}{52} \cdot \frac{12}{51}$

80. $\frac{1}{4} \cdot \frac{3}{5}$

• Critical Thinking Exercises

81. If the probability of being hospitalized during a year is 0.1, find the probability that no one in a family of five will be hospitalized in a year.

82. If a single die is rolled five times, what is the probability it lands on 2 on the first, third, and fourth rolls, but not on any of the other rolls?

83. Probabilities and Coincidence of Shared Birthdays

a. If two people are selected at random, the probability that they do not have the same birthday (day and month) is $\frac{365}{365} \cdot \frac{364}{365}$. Explain why this is so. (Ignore leap years and assume 365 days in a year.)

b. If three people are selected at random, find the probability that they all have different birthdays.

c. If three people are selected at random, find the probability that at least two of them have the same birthday.

d. If 20 people are selected at random, find the probability that at least 2 of them have the same birthday.

e. How large a group is needed to give a 0.5 chance of at least two people having the same birthday?

84. Nine cards numbered from 1 through 9 are placed into a box and two cards are selected without replacement. Find the probability that both numbers selected are odd, given that their sum is even.

• Group Exercises

85. Do you live in an area prone to catastrophes, such as earthquakes, fires, tornados, hurricanes, or floods? If so, research the probability of this catastrophe occurring in a single year. Group members should then use this probability to write and solve a problem similar to Exercise 25 in this exercise set.

86. Group members should use the table for Exercises 61–72 to write and solve four probability problems different than those in the exercises. Two should involve *or* (one with events that are mutually exclusive and one with events that are not), one should involve *and*—that is, events in succession—and one should involve conditional probability.

SECTION 11.8 • EXPECTED VALUE

OBJECTIVES

1. Compute expected value.
2. Use expected value to solve applied problems.
3. Use expected value to determine the average payoff or loss in a game of chance.

1 Compute expected value.

Would you be willing to spend \$50 a year for an insurance policy that pays \$200,000 if you become too ill to continue your education? It is unlikely that this will occur. Insurance companies make money by compensating us for events that have a low probability. If one in every 5000 students needs to quit college due to serious illness, the probability of this event is $\frac{1}{5000}$. Multiplying the amount of the claim, \$200,000, by its probability, $\frac{1}{5000}$, tells the insurance company what to expect on average for each policy:

$$\$200{,}000 \times \frac{1}{5000} = \$40.$$

Amount of the claim — Probability of paying the claim

Over the long run, the insurance company can expect to pay \$40 for each policy it sells. By selling the policy for \$50, the expected profit is \$10 per policy. If 400,000 students choose to take out this insurance, the company can expect to make 400,000 × \$10, or \$4,000,000.

Expected value is a mathematical way to use probabilities to determine what to expect in various situations over the long run. Expected value is used to determine premiums on insurance policies, weigh the risks versus the benefits of alternatives in business ventures, and indicate to a player of any game of chance what will happen if the game is played repeatedly.

The standard way to find expected value is to multiply each possible outcome by its probability, and then add these products. We use the letter E to represent expected value.

EXAMPLE 1 COMPUTING EXPECTED VALUE

Find the expected value for the outcome of the roll of a fair die.

SOLUTION The outcomes are 1, 2, 3, 4, 5, and 6, each with a probability of $\frac{1}{6}$. The expected value, E, is computed by multiplying each outcome by its probability and then adding these products.

$$E = 1\cdot\frac{1}{6} + 2\cdot\frac{1}{6} + 3\cdot\frac{1}{6} + 4\cdot\frac{1}{6} + 5\cdot\frac{1}{6} + 6\cdot\frac{1}{6}$$
$$= \frac{1+2+3+4+5+6}{6} = \frac{21}{6} = 3.5$$

The expected value of the roll of a fair die is 3.5. This means that if the die is rolled repeatedly, there are an average of 3.5 dots per roll over the long run. This expected value cannot occur on a single roll of the die. However, it is a long-run average of the various outcomes that can occur when a fair die is rolled.

CHECK POINT 1 It is equally probable that a pointer will land on any one of four regions, numbered 1 through 4. Find the expected value for where the pointer will stop.

TABLE 11.8 OUTCOMES AND PROBABILITIES FOR THE NUMBER OF GIRLS IN A THREE-CHILD FAMILY

Outcome: Number of Girls	Probability
0	$\frac{1}{8}$
1	$\frac{3}{8}$
2	$\frac{3}{8}$
3	$\frac{1}{8}$

EXAMPLE 2 COMPUTING EXPECTED VALUE

Find the expected value for the number of girls for a family with three children.

SOLUTION A family with three children can have 0, 1, 2, or 3 girls. There are eight ways these outcomes can occur.

No girls : Boy Boy Boy (One way)
One girl : Girl Boy Boy, Boy Girl Boy, Boy Boy Girl (Three ways)
Two girls : Girl Girl Boy, Girl Boy Girl, Boy Girl Girl (Three ways)
Three girls : Girl Girl Girl (One way)

Table 11.8 shows the probabilities for 0, 1, 2, and 3 girls.

The expected value, E, is computed by multiplying each outcome by its probability and then adding these products.

$$E = 0\cdot\frac{1}{8} + 1\cdot\frac{3}{8} + 2\cdot\frac{3}{8} + 3\cdot\frac{1}{8} = \frac{0+3+6+3}{8} = \frac{12}{8} = \frac{3}{2} = 1.5$$

The expected value is 1.5. This means that if we record the number of girls in many different three-child families, the average number of girls for all these families will be 1.5. In a three-child family, half the children are expected to be girls, so the expected value of 1.5 is consistent with this observation.

TABLE 11.9

Number of Heads	Probability
0	$\frac{1}{16}$
1	$\frac{4}{16}$
2	$\frac{6}{16}$
3	$\frac{4}{16}$
4	$\frac{1}{16}$

CHECK POINT 2 A fair coin is tossed four times in succession. Table 11.9 shows the probabilities for the different number of heads that can arise. Find the expected value for the number of heads.

2 Use expected value to solve applied problems.

Applications of Expected Value

Empirical probabilities can be determined in many situations by examining what has occurred in the past. For example, an insurance company can tally various claim amounts over many years. If 15% of these amounts are for a \$2000 claim, then the probability of this claim amount is 0.15. By studying sales of similar houses in a particular area, a realtor can determine the probability that he or she will sell a listed house, another agent will sell the house, or the listed house will remain unsold. Once probabilities have been assigned to all possible outcomes, expected value can indicate what is expected to happen in the long run. These ideas are illustrated in Examples 3 and 4.

TABLE 11.10 PROBABILITIES FOR AUTO CLAIMS

Amount of Claim (to the nearest $2000)	Probability
$0	0.70
$2000	0.15
$4000	0.08
$6000	0.05
$8000	0.01
$10,000	0.01

EXAMPLE 3 DETERMINING AN INSURANCE PREMIUM

An automobile insurance company has determined the probabilities for various claim amounts for drivers ages 16 through 21, shown in Table 11.10.

a. Calculate the expected value and describe what this means in practical terms.

b. How much should the company charge as an average premium so that it does not lose or gain money on its claim costs?

SOLUTION

a. The expected value, E, is computed by multiplying each outcome by its probability, and then adding these products.

$$\begin{aligned} E &= \$0(0.70) + \$2000(0.15) + \$4000(0.08) + \$6000(0.05) \\ &\quad + \$8000(0.01) + \$10{,}000(0.01) \\ &= \$0 + \$300 + \$320 + \$300 + \$80 + \$100 \\ &= \$1100 \end{aligned}$$

The expected value is $1100. This means that in the long run the average cost of a claim is $1100. The insurance company should expect to pay $1100 per car insured to people in the 16–21 age group.

b. At the very least, the amount that the company should charge as an average premium for each person in the 16–21 group is $1100. In this way, it will not lose or gain money on its claims costs. It's quite probable that the company will charge more, moving from break-even to profit.

CHECK POINT 3 Work Example 3 again if the probabilities for claims of $0 and $10,000 are reversed. Thus, the probability of a $0 claim is 0.01 and the probability of a $10,000 claim is 0.70.

Business decisions are interpreted in terms of dollars and cents. In these situations, **expected value is calculated by multiplying the gain or loss for each possible outcome by its probability. The sum of these products is the expected value.**

EXAMPLE 4 EXPECTATION IN A BUSINESS DECISION

You are a realtor considering listing a $500,000 house. The cost of advertising and providing food for other realtors during open showings is anticipated to cost you $5000. The house is quite unusual, and you are given a four-month listing. If the house is unsold after four months, you lose the listing and receive nothing. You anticipate that the probability you sell your own listed house is 0.3, the probability that another agent sells your listing is 0.2, and the probability that the house is unsold after 4 months is 0.5. If you sell your own listed house, the commission is a hefty $30,000. If another realtor sells your listing, the commission is $15,000. The bottom line: You will not take the listing unless you anticipate earning at least $6000. Should you list the house?

SOLUTION Shown in the margin is a summary of the amounts of money and probabilities that will determine your decision. The expected value in this situation is the sum of each income possibility times its probability. The expected value represents the amount you can anticipate earning if you take the listing. If the expected value is not at least $6000, you should not list the house.

THE REALTOR'S SUMMARY SHEET

My Cost:	$5000
My Possible Income:	
I sell house:	$30,000
Another agent sells house:	$15,000
House unsold after 4 months:	$0
The Probabilities:	
I sell house:	0.3
Another agent sells house:	0.2
House unsold after 4 months:	0.5
My Bottom Line:	
I take the listing only if I anticipate earning at least $6000.	

THE REALTOR'S SUMMARY SHEET (repeated)

My Cost:	$5000
My Possible Income:	
I sell house:	$30,000
Another agent sells house:	$15,000
House unsold after 4 months:	$0
The Probabilities:	
I sell house:	0.3
Another agent sells house:	0.2
House unsold after 4 months:	0.5
My Bottom Line:	
I take the listing only if I anticipate earning at least $6000.	

The possible incomes listed in the margin, $30,000, $15,000, and $0, do not take into account your $5000 costs. Because of these costs, each amount needs to be reduced by $5000. Thus, you can gain $30,000 − $5000, or $25,000, or you can gain $15,000 − $5000, or $10,000. Because $0 − $5000 = −$5000, you can also lose $5000. Table 11.11 summarizes possible outcomes if you take the listing, and their respective probabilities.

TABLE 11.11 GAINS, LOSSES, AND PROBABILITIES FOR LISTING A $500,000 HOUSE

Outcome	Gain or Loss	Probability
Sells house	$25,000	0.3
Another agent sells house	$10,000	0.2
House doesn't sell	−$5000	0.5

The expected value, E, is computed by multiplying each gain or loss in Table 11.11 by its probability, and then adding these results.

$$E = \$25{,}000(0.3) + \$10{,}000(0.2) + (-\$5000)(0.5)$$
$$= \$7500 + \$2000 + (-\$2500) = \$7000$$

You can expect to earn $7000 by listing the house. Because the expected value exceeds $6000, you should list the house.

CHECK POINT 4 The SAT is a multiple-choice test. Each question has five possible answers. The test taker must select one answer for each question or not answer the question. One point is awarded for each correct response and $\frac{1}{4}$ point is subtracted for each wrong answer. No points are added or subtracted for answers left blank. Table 11.12 summarizes the information for the outcomes of a random guess on an SAT question. Find the expected point value of a random guess. Is there anything to gain or lose on average by guessing? Explain your answer.

TABLE 11.12 GAINS AND LOSSES FOR GUESSING ON THE SAT

Outcome	Gain or Loss	Probability
Guess correctly	1	$\frac{1}{5}$
Guess incorrectly	$-\frac{1}{4}$	$\frac{4}{5}$

3 Use expected value to determine the average payoff or loss in a game of chance.

Expected Value and Games of Chance

Expected value can be interpreted as the average payoff in a contest or game when either is played a large number of times. **To find the expected value of a game, multiply the gain or loss for each possible outcome by its probability. Then add the products.**

EXAMPLE 5 EXPECTED VALUE AS AVERAGE PAYOFF

A game is played using one die. If the die is rolled and shows 1, 2, or 3, the player wins nothing. If the die shows 4 or 5, the player wins $3. If the die shows 6, the player wins $9. If there is a charge of $1 to play the game, what is the game's expected value? Describe what this means in practical terms.

SOLUTION Because there is a charge of $1 to play the game, a player who wins $9 gains $9 − $1, or $8. A player who wins $3 gains $3 − $1, or $2. If the player gets $0, there is a loss of $1 because $0 − $1 = −$1. The outcomes for the die, with their respective gains, losses, and probabilities, are summarized in Table 11.13.

BLITZER BONUS

Gambling It Away

Games in gambling casinos have probabilities and payoffs that result in negative expected values. This means that players will lose money in the long run. With no clocks on the walls or windows to look out of, casinos bet that players will forget about time and play longer. This brings casino owners closer to what they can expect to earn, while negative expected values sneak up on losing patrons. (No wonder they provide free beverages!)

A Potpourri of Gambling-Related Data

- Population of Las Vegas: 535,000
- Slot Machines in Las Vegas: 150,000
- Average Earnings per Slot Machine per Year: $100,000
- Average Amount Lost per Hour in Las Vegas Casinos: $696,000
- Average Amount an American Adult Loses Gambling per Year: $350
- Average Amount a Nevada Resident Loses Gambling per Year: $1000

Source: Paul Grobman, *Vital Statistics*, Plume, 2005

TABLE 11.13 GAINS, LOSSES, AND PROBABILITIES IN A GAME OF CHANCE

Outcome	Gain or Loss	Probability
1, 2, or 3	−$1	$\frac{3}{6}$
4 or 5	$2	$\frac{2}{6}$
6	$8	$\frac{1}{6}$

Expected value, E, is computed by multiplying each gain or loss in Table 11.13 by its probability and then adding these results.

$$E = (-\$1)\left(\frac{3}{6}\right) + \$2\left(\frac{2}{6}\right) + \$8\left(\frac{1}{6}\right)$$

$$= \frac{-\$3 + \$4 + \$8}{6} = \frac{\$9}{6} = \$1.50$$

The expected value is $1.50. This means that in the long run, a player can expect to win an average of $1.50 for each game played. However, this does not mean that the player will win $1.50 on any single game. It does mean that if the game is played repeatedly, then, in the long run, the player should expect to win about $1.50 per play on the average. If 1000 games are played, one could expect to win $1500. However, if only three games are played, one's net winnings can range between −$3 and $24, even though the expected winnings are $1.50(3), or $4.50.

CHECK POINT 5 A charity is holding a raffle and sells 1000 raffle tickets for $2 each. One of the tickets will be selected to win a grand prize of $1000. Two other tickets will be selected to win consolation prizes of $50 each. Fill in the missing column in Table 11.14. Then find the expected value if you buy one raffle ticket. Describe what this means in practical terms. What can you expect to happen if you purchase five tickets?

TABLE 11.14 GAINS, LOSSES, AND PROBABILITIES IN A RAFFLE

Outcome	Gain or Loss	Probability
Win Grand Prize		$\frac{1}{1000}$
Win Consolation Prize		$\frac{2}{1000}$
Win Nothing		$\frac{997}{1000}$

Unlike the game in Example 5, games in gambling casinos are set up so that players will lose in the long run. These games have negative expected values. Such a game is roulette, French for "little wheel." We first saw the roulette wheel in Section 11.7. It is shown again in Figure 11.12. Recall that the wheel has 38 numbered slots (1 through 36, 0, and 00). In each play of the game, the dealer spins the wheel and a small ball in opposite directions. The ball is equally likely to come to rest in any one of the slots, which are colored black, red, or green. Gamblers can place a number of different bets in roulette. Example 6 illustrates one gambling option.

FIGURE 11.12 A U.S. roulette wheel

BLITZER BONUS

How to Win at Roulette

A player may win or lose at roulette, but in the long run the casino always wins. Casinos make an average of three cents on every dollar spent by gamblers. There *is* a way to win at roulette in the long run: Own the casino.

EXAMPLE 6 EXPECTED VALUE AND ROULETTE

One way to bet in roulette is to place \$1 on a single number. If the ball lands on that number, you are awarded \$35 and get to keep the \$1 that you paid to play the game. If the ball lands on any one of the other 37 slots, you are awarded nothing and the \$1 that you bet is collected. Find the expected value for playing roulette if you bet \$1 on number 20. Describe what this means.

SOLUTION Table 11.15 contains the two outcomes of interest: the ball landing on your number, 20, and the ball landing elsewhere (in any one of the other 37 slots). The outcomes, their respective gains, losses, and probabilities, are summarized in the table.

TABLE 11.15 PLAYING ONE NUMBER WITH A 35 TO 1 PAYOFF IN ROULETTE

Outcome	Gain or Loss	Probability
Ball lands on 20	\$35	$\frac{1}{38}$
Ball does not land on 20	−\$1	$\frac{37}{38}$

Expected value, E, is computed by multiplying each gain or loss in Table 11.15 by its probability and then adding these results.

$$E = \$35\left(\frac{1}{38}\right) + (-\$1)\left(\frac{37}{38}\right) = \frac{\$35 - \$37}{38} = \frac{-\$2}{38} \approx -\$0.05$$

The expected value is approximately −\$0.05. This means that in the long run, a player can expect to lose about 5¢ for each game played. If 2000 games are played, one could expect to lose \$100.

CHECK POINT 6 In the game of one-spot keno, a card is purchased for \$1. It allows a player to choose one number from 1 to 80. A dealer then chooses twenty numbers at random. If the player's number is among those chosen, the player is paid \$3.20, but does not get to keep the \$1 paid to play the game. Find the expected value of a \$1 bet. Describe what this means.

EXERCISE SET 11.8

• Practice and Application Exercises

In Exercises 1–2, the numbers that each pointer can land on and their respective probabilities are shown. Compute the expected value for the number on which each pointer lands.

1.

Outcome	Probability
1	$\frac{1}{2}$
2	$\frac{1}{4}$
3	$\frac{1}{4}$

2.

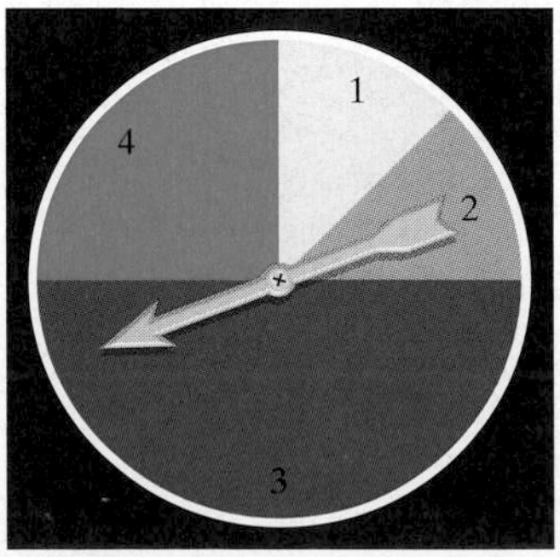

Outcome	Probability
1	$\frac{1}{8}$
2	$\frac{1}{8}$
3	$\frac{1}{2}$
4	$\frac{1}{4}$

The tables in Exercises 3–4 show claims and their probabilities for an insurance company.

a. *Calculate the expected value and describe what this means in practical terms.*

b. *How much should the company charge as an average premium so that it breaks even on its claim costs?*

c. *How much should the company charge to make a profit of $50 per policy?*

3. PROBABILITIES FOR HOMEOWNERS' INSURANCE CLAIMS

Amount of Claim (to the nearest $50,000)	Probability
$0	0.65
$50,000	0.20
$100,000	0.10
$150,000	0.03
$200,000	0.01
$250,000	0.01

4. PROBABILITIES FOR MEDICAL INSURANCE CLAIMS

Amount of Claim (to the nearest $20,000)	Probability
$0	0.70
$20,000	0.20
$40,000	0.06
$60,000	0.02
$80,000	0.01
$100,000	0.01

5. An architect is considering bidding for the design of a new museum. The cost of drawing plans and submitting a model is $10,000. The probability of being awarded the bid is 0.1, and anticipated profits are $100,000, resulting in a possible gain of this amount minus the $10,000 cost for plans and a model. What is the expected value in this situation? Describe what this value means.

6. A construction company is planning to bid on a building contract. The bid costs the company $1500. The probability that the bid is accepted is $\frac{1}{5}$. If the bid is accepted, the company will make $40,000 minus the cost of the bid. Find the expected value in this situation. Describe what this value means.

7. It is estimated that there are 27 deaths for every 10 million people who use airplanes. A company that sells flight insurance provides $100,000 in case of death in a plane crash. A policy can be purchased for $1. Calculate the expected value and thereby determine how much the insurance company can make over the long run for each policy that it sells.

8. A 25-year-old can purchase a one-year life insurance policy for $10,000 at a cost of $100. Past history indicates that the probability of a person dying at age 25 is 0.002. Determine the company's expected gain per policy.

Exercises 9–10 are related to the SAT, described in Check Point 4 on page 666.

9. Suppose that you can eliminate one of the possible five answers. Modify the two probabilities shown in the final column in Table 11.12 on page 666 by finding the probabilities of guessing correctly and guessing incorrectly under these circumstances. What is the expected point value of a random guess? Is it advantageous to guess under these circumstances?

10. Suppose that you can eliminate two of the possible five answers. Modify the two probabilities shown in the final column in Table 11.12 on page 666 by finding the probabilities of guessing correctly and guessing incorrectly under these circumstances. What is the expected point value of a random guess? Is it advantageous to guess under these circumstances?

11. A store specializing in mountain bikes is to open in one of two malls. If the first mall is selected, the store anticipates a yearly profit of $300,000 if successful and a yearly loss of $100,000 otherwise. The probability of success is $\frac{1}{2}$. If the second mall is selected, it is estimated that the yearly profit will be $200,000 if successful; otherwise, the annual loss will be $60,000. The probability of success at the second mall is $\frac{3}{4}$. Which mall should be chosen in order to maximize the expected profit?

12. An oil company is considering two sites on which to drill, described as follows:

Site A: Profit if oil is found: $80 million
Loss if no oil is found: $10 million
Probability of finding oil: 0.2

Site B: Profit if oil is found: $120 million
Loss if no oil is found: $18 million
Probability of finding oil: 0.1

Which site has the larger expected profit? By how much?

13. In a product liability case, a company can settle out of court for a loss of $350,000, or go to trial, losing $700,000 if found guilty and nothing if found not guilty. Lawyers for the company estimate the probability of a not-guilty verdict to be 0.8.

a. Find the expected value of the amount the company can lose by taking the case to court.

b. Should the company settle out of court?

14. A service that repairs air conditioners sells maintenance agreements for $80 a year. The average cost for repairing an air conditioner is $350 and 1 in every 100 people who purchase maintenance agreements have air conditioners that require repair. Find the service's expected profit per maintenance agreement.

Exercises 15–19 involve computing expected values in games of chance.

15. A game is played using one die. If the die is rolled and shows 1, the player wins $5. If the die shows any number other than 1, the player wins nothing. If there is a charge of $1 to play the game, what is the game's expected value? What does this value mean?

16. A game is played using one die. If the die is rolled and shows 1, the player wins $1; if 2, the player wins $2; if 3, the player wins $3. If the die shows 4, 5, or 6, the player wins nothing. If there is a charge of $1.25 to play the game, what is the game's expected value? What does this value mean?

17. Another option in a roulette game (see Example 6 on page 668) is to bet $1 on red. (There are 18 red compartments, 18 black compartments, and 2 compartments that are neither red nor black.) If the ball lands on red, you get to keep the $1 that you paid to play the game and you are awarded $1. If the ball lands elsewhere, you are awarded nothing and the $1 that you bet is collected. Find the expected value for playing roulette if you bet $1 on red. Describe what this number means.

18. The spinner on a wheel of fortune can land with an equal chance on any one of ten regions. Three regions are red, four are blue, two are yellow, and one is green. A player wins $4 if the spinner stops on red and $2 if it stops on green. The player loses $2 if it stops on blue and $3 if it stops on yellow. What is the expected value? What does this mean if the game is played ten times?

19. For many years, organized crime ran a numbers game that is now run legally by many state governments. The player selects a three-digit number from 000 to 999. There are 1000 such numbers. A bet of $1 is placed on a number, say number 115. If the number is selected, the player wins $500. If any other number is selected, the player wins nothing. Find the expected value for this game and describe what this means.

• Writing in Mathematics

20. What does the expected value for the outcome of the roll of a fair die represent?

21. Explain how to find the expected value for the number of girls for a family with two children. What is the expected value?

22. How do insurance companies use expected value to determine what to charge for a policy?

23. Describe a situation in which a business can use expected value.

24. If the expected value of a game is negative, what does this mean? Also describe the meaning of a positive and a zero expected value.

25. The expected value for purchasing a ticket in a raffle is −$0.75. Describe what this means. Will a person who purchases a ticket lose $0.75?

• Critical Thinking Exercises

26. A popular state lottery is the 5/35 lottery, played in Arizona, Connecticut, Illinois, Iowa, Kentucky, Maine, Massachusetts, New Hampshire, South Dakota, and Vermont. In Arizona's version of the game, prizes are set: First prize is $50,000, second prize is $500, and third prize is $5. To win first prize, you must select all five of the winning numbers, numbered from 1 to 35. Second prize is awarded to players who select any four of the five winning numbers, and third prize is awarded to players who select any three of the winning numbers. The cost to purchase a lottery ticket is $1. Find the expected value of Arizona's "Fantasy Five" game, and describe what this means in terms of buying a lottery ticket over the long run.

27. Refer to the probabilities of dying at any given age on page 635 to solve this exercise. A 20-year-old woman wants to purchase a $200,000 one-year life insurance policy. What should the insurance company charge the woman for the policy if it wants an expected profit of $60?

• Group Exercise

28. This activity is a group research project intended for people interested in games of chance at casinos. The research should culminate in a seminar on games of chance and their expected values. The seminar is intended to last about 30 minutes and should result in an interesting and informative presentation made to the entire class.

Each member of the group should research a game available at a typical casino. Describe the game to the class and compute its expected value. After each member has done this, so that class members now have an idea of those games with the greatest and smallest house advantages, a final group member might want to research and present ways for currently treating people whose addiction to these games has caused their lives to swirl out of control.

CHAPTER SUMMARY, REVIEW, AND TEST

• SUMMARY

DEFINITIONS AND CONCEPTS	EXAMPLES
11.1 The Fundamental Counting Principle	
The number of ways in which a series of successive things can occur is found by multiplying the number of ways in which each thing can occur.	Ex. 1, p. 609; Ex. 2, p. 609; Ex. 3, p. 610; Ex. 4, p. 610; Ex. 5, p. 611; Ex. 6, p. 611
11.2 Permutations	
a. A permutation from a group of items occurs when no item is used more than once and the order of arrangement makes a difference. The Fundamental Counting Principle can be used to determine the number of permutations possible.	Ex. 1, p. 614; Ex. 2, p. 615

b. Factorial Notation — Ex. 3, p. 616

$$n! = n(n-1)(n-2)\cdots(3)(2)(1) \text{ and } 0! = 1$$

c. Permutations Formula — Ex. 4, p. 617; Ex. 5, p. 618

The number of permutations possible if r items are taken from n items is ${}_nP_r = \dfrac{n!}{(n-r)!}$.

d. Permutations of Duplicate Items — Ex. 6, p. 619

The number of permutations of n items, where p items are identical, q items are identical, r items are identical, and so on, is

$$\frac{n!}{p!\,q!\,r!\ldots}.$$

11.3 Combinations

a. A combination from a group of items occurs when no item is used more than once and the order of items makes no difference. — Ex. 1, p. 621

b. Combinations Formula — Ex. 2, p. 623; Ex. 3, p. 623; Ex. 4, p. 624

The number of combinations possible if r items are taken from n items is ${}_nC_r = \dfrac{n!}{(n-r)!\,r!}$.

11.4 Fundamentals of Probability

a. Theoretical probability applies to experiments in which the set of all equally likely outcomes, called the sample space, is known. An event is any subset of the sample space.

b. The theoretical probability of event E with sample space S is — Ex. 1, p. 628; Ex. 2, p. 630; Ex. 3, p. 630

$$P(E) = \frac{\text{number of outcomes in } E}{\text{total number of possible outcomes}} = \frac{n(E)}{n(S)}.$$

c. Empirical probability applies to situations in which we observe the frequency of the occurrence of an event.

d. The empirical probability of event E is — Ex. 4, p. 631

$$P(E) = \frac{\text{observed number of times } E \text{ occurs}}{\text{total number of observed occurrences}}.$$

11.5 Probability with the Fundamental Counting Principle, Permutations, and Combinations

a. Probability of a permutation — Ex. 1, p. 636

$$= \frac{\text{the number of ways the permutation can occur}}{\text{total number of possible permutations}}.$$

b. Probability of a combination — Ex. 2, p. 637; Ex. 3, p. 638

$$= \frac{\text{the number of ways the combination can occur}}{\text{total number of possible combinations}}.$$

11.6 Events Involving *Not* and *Or*; Odds

a. Complement Rules of Probability — Ex. 1, p. 642; Ex. 2, p. 642

$$P(\text{not } E) = 1 - P(E) \quad \text{and} \quad P(E) = 1 - P(\text{not } E)$$

b. If it is impossible for events A and B to occur simultaneously, the events are mutually exclusive.

c. If A and B are mutually exclusive events, then $P(A \text{ or } B) = P(A) + P(B)$. — Ex. 3, p. 644; Ex. 6(b), p. 646

d. If A and B are not mutually exclusive events, then

$$P(A \text{ or } B) = P(A) + P(B) - P(A \text{ and } B).$$

Ex. 4, p. 645;
Ex. 5, p. 645;
Ex. 6(a), p. 646

e. Probability to Odds

1. Odds in favor of $E = \dfrac{P(E)}{P(\text{not } E)}$ **2.** Odds against $E = \dfrac{P(\text{not } E)}{P(E)}$

Ex. 7, p. 647;
Ex. 8, p. 648

f. Odds to Probability

If odds in favor of E are a to b, then $P(E) = \dfrac{a}{a+b}$.

Ex. 9. p. 649

11.7 Events Involving *And*; Conditional Probability

a. Two events are independent if the occurrence of either of them has no effect on the probability of the other.

b. If A and B are independent events,

$$P(A \text{ and } B) = P(A) \cdot P(B).$$

Ex. 1, p. 654

c. The probability of a succession of independent events is the product of each of their probabilities.

Ex. 2, p. 654;
Ex. 3, p. 655

d. Two events are dependent if the occurrence of one of them has an effect on the probability of the other.

e. If A and B are dependent events,

$$P(A \text{ and } B) = P(A) \cdot P(B \text{ given that } A \text{ has occurred}).$$

Ex. 4, p. 657

f. The multiplication rule for dependent events can be extended to cover three or more dependent events. In the case of three such events,

$$P(A \text{ and } B \text{ and } C)$$
$$= P(A) \cdot P(B \text{ given } A \text{ occurred}) \cdot P(C \text{ given } A \text{ and } B \text{ occurred}).$$

Ex. 5, p. 657

g. The conditional probability of B, given A, written $P(B|A)$, is the probability of B if the sample space is restricted to A.

$$P(B|A) = \frac{n(B \cap A)}{n(A)} = \frac{\text{number of outcomes common to } B \text{ and } A}{\text{number of outcomes in } A}$$

Ex. 6, p. 658;
Ex. 7, p. 659

11.8 Expected Value

a. Expected value, E, is found by multiplying every possible outcome by its probability and then adding these products.

Ex. 1, p. 664;
Ex. 2, p. 664;
Ex. 3, p. 665

b. In situations involving business decisions, expected value is calculated by multiplying the gain or loss for each possible outcome by its probability. The sum of these products is the expected value.

Ex. 4, p. 665

c. In a game of chance, expected value is the average payoff when the game is played a large number of times. To find the expected value of a game, multiply the gain or loss for each possible outcome by its probability. Then add the products.

Ex. 5, p. 666;
Ex. 6, p. 668

REVIEW EXERCISES

11.1

1. A restaurant offers 20 appetizers and 40 main courses. In how many ways can a person order a two-course meal?

2. A popular brand of pen comes in red, green, blue, or black ink. The writing tip can be chosen from extra bold, bold, regular, fine, or micro. How many different choices of pens do you have with this brand?

3. In how many ways can first and second prize be awarded in a contest with 100 people, assuming that each prize is awarded to a different person?

4. You are answering three multiple-choice questions. Each question has five answer choices, with one correct answer per question. If you select one of these five choices for each question and leave nothing blank, in how many ways can you answer the questions?

5. A stock can go up, go down, or stay unchanged. How many possibilities are there if you own five stocks?

6. A person can purchase a condominium with a choice of five kinds of carpeting, with or without a pool, with or without a porch, and with one, two, or three bedrooms. How many different options are there for the condominium?

11.2

7. Six acts are scheduled to perform in a variety show. How many different ways are there to schedule their appearances?

8. In how many ways can five airplanes line up for departure on a runway?

9. You need to arrange seven of your favorite books along a small shelf. Although you are not arranging the books by height, the tallest of the books is to be placed at the left end and the shortest of the books at the right end. How many different ways can you arrange the books?

In Exercises 10–13, evaluate each factorial expression.

10. $\frac{16!}{14!}$ **11.** $\frac{800!}{799!}$

12. $5! - 3!$ **13.** $\frac{11!}{(11-3)!}$

In Exercises 14–15, use the formula for ${}_nP_r$ to evaluate each expression.

14. ${}_{10}P_6$ **15.** ${}_{100}P_2$

Use the formula for ${}_nP_r$ to solve Exercises 16–17.

16. A club with 15 members is to choose four officers—president, vice-president, secretary, and treasurer. In how many ways can these offices be filled?

17. Suppose you are asked to list, in order of preference, the five favorite CDs you purchased in the past 12 months. If you bought 20 CDs over this time period, in how many ways can the five favorite be ranked?

Use the formula for the number of permutations with duplicate items to solve Exercises 18–19.

18. In how many distinct ways can the letters of the word TORONTO be arranged?

19. In how many ways can the digits in the number 335,557 be arranged?

11.3

In Exercises 20–22, does the problem involve permutations or combinations? Explain your answer. (It is not necessary to solve the problem.)

20. How many different 4-card hands can be dealt from a 52-card deck?

21. How many different ways can a director select from 20 male actors to cast the roles of Mark, Roger, Angel, and Collins in the musical *Rent*?

22. How many different ways can a director select 4 actors from a group of 20 actors to attend a workshop on performing in rock musicals?

In Exercises 23–24, use the formula for ${}_nC_r$ to evaluate each expression.

23. ${}_{11}C_7$ **24.** ${}_{14}C_5$

Use the formula for ${}_nC_r$ to solve Exercises 25–28.

25. An election ballot asks voters to select four city commissioners from a group of ten candidates. In how many ways can this be done?

26. How many different 5-card hands can be dealt from a deck that has only hearts (13 different cards)?

27. From the 20 CDs that you've bought during the past year, you plan to take 3 with you on vacation. How many different sets of three CDs can you take?

28. A political discussion group consists of 12 Republicans and 8 Democrats. In how many ways can 5 Republicans and 4 Democrats be selected to attend a conference on politics and social issues?

11.4

In Exercises 29–32, a die is rolled. Find the probability of rolling

29. a 6.

30. a number less than 5.

31. a number less than 7.

32. a number greater than 6.

In Exercises 33–37, you are dealt one card from a 52-card deck. Find the probability of being dealt

33. a 5.

34. a picture card.

35. a card greater than 4 and less than 8.

36. a 4 of diamonds.

37. a red ace.

In Exercises 38–40, suppose that you reach into a bag and randomly select one piece of candy from 15 chocolates, 10 caramels, and 5 peppermints. Find the probability of selecting

38. a chocolate.

39. a caramel.

40. a peppermint.

41. Tay-Sachs disease occurs in 1 of every 3600 births among Jews from central and eastern Europe, and in 1 in 600,000 births in other populations. The disease causes abnormal accumulation of certain fat compounds in the spinal cord and brain, resulting in paralysis, blindness, and mental impairment. Death generally occurs before the age of five. If we use t to represent a Tay-Sachs gene and T a healthy gene, the table below shows the four possibilities for the children of one healthy, TT, parent, and one parent who carries the disease, Tt, but is not sick.

a. Find the probability that a child of these parents will be a carrier without the disease.

b. Find the probability that a child of these parents will have the disease.

		Second Parent T	t
First	T	TT	Tt
Parent	T	TT	Tt

The table shows the employment status of the U.S. civilian labor force in 2004, by gender. Use the data in the table, expressed in millions, to solve Exercises 42–44.

EMPLOYMENT STATUS OF THE U.S. LABOR FORCE, IN MILLIONS, IN 2004

	Employed	Unemployed	Total
Male	74.5	33.2	107.7
Female	64.7	51.0	115.7
Total	139.2	84.2	223.4

Source: U.S. Bureau of Labor Statistics

Find the probability, expressed as a decimal rounded to three places, that a randomly selected person from the civilian labor force represented in the table

42. is employed.

43. is female.

44. is an unemployed male.

11.5

45. If cities A, B, C, and D are visited in random order, each city visited once, find the probability that city D will be visited first, city B second, city A third, and city C last.

In Exercises 46–49, suppose that six singers are being lined up to perform at a charity. Call the singers A, B, C, D, E, and F. The order of performance is determined by writing each singer's name on one of six cards, placing the cards in a hat, and then drawing one card at a time. The order in which the cards are drawn determines the order in which the singers perform. Find the probability that

46. singer C will perform last.

47. singer B will perform first and singer A will perform last.

48. the singers will perform in the following order: F, E, A, D, C, B.

49. the performance will begin with singer A or C.

50. A lottery game is set up so that each player chooses five different numbers from 1 to 20. If the five numbers match the five numbers drawn in the lottery, the player wins (or shares) the top cash prize. What is the probability of winning the prize

a. with one lottery ticket?

b. with 100 different lottery tickets?

51. A committee of four people is to be selected from six Democrats and four Republicans. Find the probability that

a. all are Democrats.

b. two are Democrats and two are Republicans.

52. If you are dealt 3 cards from a shuffled deck of red cards (26 different cards), find the probability of getting exactly 2 picture cards.

11.6

In Exercises 53–57, a die is rolled. Find the probability of

53. not rolling a 5.

54. not rolling a number less than 4.

55. rolling a 3 or a 5.

56. rolling a number less than 3 or greater than 4.

57. rolling a number less than 5 or greater than 2.

In Exercises 58–63, you draw one card from a 52-card deck. Find the probability of

58. not drawing a picture card.

59. not drawing a diamond.

60. drawing an ace or a king.

61. drawing a black 6 or a red 7.

62. drawing a queen or a red card.

63. drawing a club or a picture card.

In Exercises 64–69, it is equally probable that the pointer on the spinner shown will land on any one of the six regions, numbered 1 through 6, and colored as shown. If the pointer lands on a borderline, spin again. Find the probability of

64. not stopping on 4.

65. not stopping on yellow.

66. not stopping on red.

67. stopping on red or yellow.

68. stopping on red or an even number.

69. stopping on red or a number greater than 3.

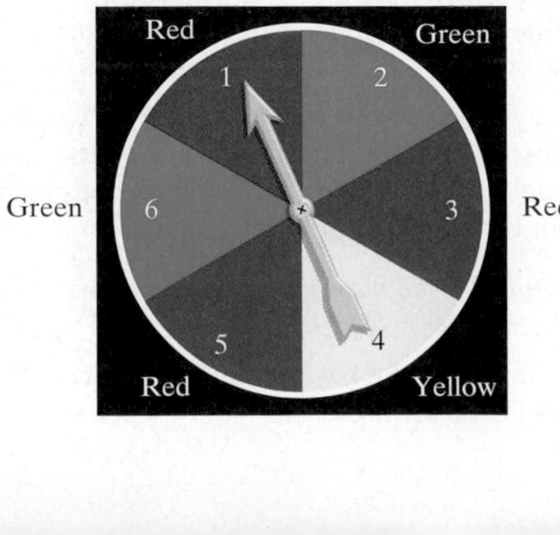

Use this information to solve Exercises 70–71. At a workshop on police work and the African-American community, there are 50 African-American male police officers, 20 African-American female police officers, 90 white male police officers, and 40 white female police officers. If one police officer is selected at random from the people at the workshop, find the probability that the selected person is

70. African American or male.

71. female or white.

Suppose that a survey of 350 college students is taken. Each student is asked the type of college attended (public or private) and the family's income level (low, middle, high). Use the data in the table to solve Exercises 72–75. Express probabilities as simplified fractions.

	Public	Private	Total
Low	120	20	140
Middle	110	50	160
High	22	28	50
Total	252	98	350

Find the probability that a randomly selected student in the survey

72. attends a public college.

73. is not from a high-income family.

74. is from a middle-income or a high-income family.

75. attends a private college or is from a high-income family.

76. One card is randomly selected from a deck of 52 cards. Find the odds in favor and the odds against getting a queen.

77. The winner of a raffle will receive a two-year scholarship to any college of the winner's choice. If 2000 raffle tickets were sold and you purchased 20 tickets, what are the odds against your winning the scholarship?

78. The odds in favor of a candidate winning an election are given at 3 to 1. What is the probability that this candidate will win the election?

11.7

Use the spinner shown to solve Exercises 79–83. It is equally likely that the pointer will land on any one of the six regions, numbered 1 through 6, and colored as shown. If the pointer lands on a borderline, spin again. If the pointer is spun twice, find the probability it will land on

79. yellow and then red.

80. 1 and then 3.

81. yellow both times.

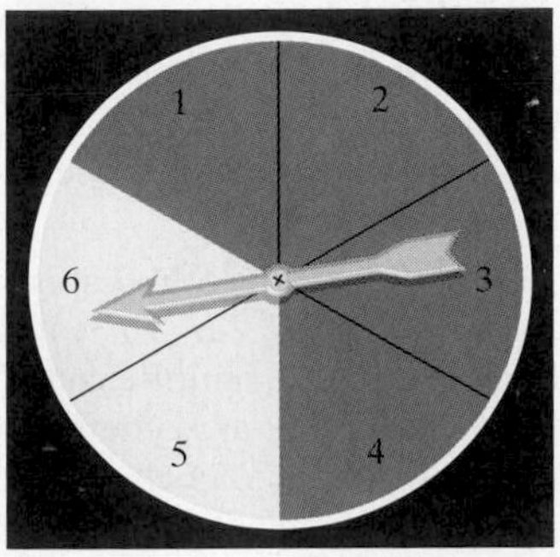

If the pointer is spun three times, find the probability it will land on

82. yellow and then 4 and then an odd number.

83. red every time.

84. What is the probability of a family having five boys born in a row?

85. The probability of a flood in any given year in a region prone to flooding is 0.2.

a. What is the probability of a flood two years in a row?

b. What is the probability of a flood for three consecutive years?

c. What is the probability of no flooding for four consecutive years?

d. What is the probability of a flood at least once in the next four years?

In Exercises 86–87, two students are selected from a group of four psychology majors, three business majors, and two music majors. The two students are to meet with the campus cafeteria manager to voice the group's concerns about food prices and quality. One student is randomly selected and leaves for the cafeteria manager's office. Then, a second student is selected. Find the probability of selecting

86. a music major and then a psychology major.

87. two business majors.

88. A final visit to the box of chocolates: It's now grown to a box of 50, of which 30 are solid chocolate, 15 are filled with jelly, and 5 are filled with cherries. The story is still the same: They all look alike. You select a piece, eat it, select a second piece, eat it, and help yourself to a final sugar rush. Find the probability of selecting a solid chocolate followed by two cherry-filled chocolates.

89. A single die is tossed. Find the probability that the tossed die shows 5, given that the outcome is an odd number.

90. A letter is randomly selected from the letters of the English alphabet. Find the probability of selecting a vowel, given that the outcome is a letter that precedes k.

91. The numbers shown below are each written on a colored chip. The chips are placed into a bag and one chip is selected at random. Find the probability of selecting

a. an odd number, given that a red chip is selected.

b. a yellow chip, given that the number selected is at least 3.

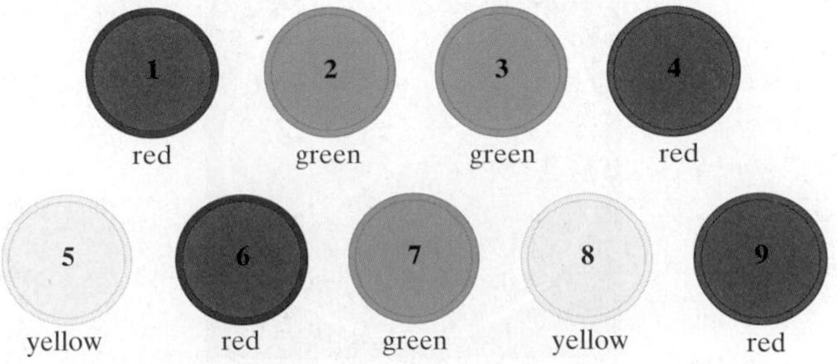

The data in the table are based on 145 Americans tested for tuberculosis. Use the data to solve Exercises 92–99. Express probabilities as simplified fractions.

	TB	No TB
Positive Screening Test	9	11
Negative Screening Test	1	124

Source: Deborah J. Bennett, *Randomness*, Harvard University Press, 1998

Find the probability that a randomly selected person from this group

92. does not have TB.
93. tests positive.
94. does not have TB or tests positive.
95. does not have TB, given a positive test.
96. has a positive test, given no TB.
97. has TB, given a negative test.

Suppose that two people are randomly selected, in succession, from this group. Find the probability of selecting

98. two people with TB.
99. two people with positive screening tests.

11.4 and 11.6–11.7

The table shows the distribution, by age and gender, of the 30,242 deaths in the United States involving firearms in 2002.

DEATHS IN THE UNITED STATES INVOLVING FIREARMS, 2002

	Under Age 5	Ages 5–14	Ages 15–19	Ages 20–24	Ages 25–44	Ages 45–64	Ages 65–74	Age ≥75	Total
Male	42	242	2209	3887	9850	5875	1768	2225	26,098
Female	29	106	265	419	1736	1165	225	199	4144
Total	71	348	2474	4306	11,586	7040	1993	2424	30,242

Source: National Safety Council

In Exercises 100–106, use the data in the table to find the probability, expressed as a fraction and as a decimal rounded to three places, that a firearm death in the United States

100. involved a male.

101. involved a person in the 25–44 age range.

102. involved a person less than 75 years old.

103. involved a person in the 20–24 age range or in the 25–44 age range.

104. involved a female or a person younger than 5.

105. involved a person in the 20–24 age range, given that this person was a male.

106. involved a male, given that this person was at least 75.

11.8

107. The numbers that the pointer can land on and their respective probabilities are shown below and in the next column.

Outcome	Probability
1	$\frac{1}{4}$
2	$\frac{1}{8}$
3	$\frac{1}{8}$
4	$\frac{1}{4}$
5	$\frac{1}{4}$

Compute the expected value for the number on which the pointer lands.

108. The table shows claims and their probabilities for an insurance company.

LIFE INSURANCE FOR AN AIRLINE FLIGHT

Amount of Claim	Probability
\$0	0.9999995
\$1,000,000	0.0000005

a. Calculate the expected value and describe what this value means.

b. How much should the company charge to make a profit of \$9.50 per policy?

109. A construction company is planning to bid on a building contract. The bid costs the company \$3000. The probability that the bid is accepted is $\frac{1}{4}$. If the bid is accepted, the company will make \$30,000 minus the cost of the bid. Find the expected value in this situation. Describe what this value means.

110. A game is played using a fair coin that is tossed twice. The sample space is $\{HH, HT, TH, TT\}$. If exactly one head occurs, the player wins \$5, and if exactly two tails occur, the player also wins \$5. For any other outcome, the player receives nothing. There is a \$4 charge to play the game. What is the expected value? What does this value mean?

CHAPTER 11 TEST

1. A person can purchase a particular model of a new car with a choice of ten colors, with or without automatic transmission, with or without four-wheel drive, with or without air conditioning, and with two, three, or four radio-CD speakers. How many different options are there for this model of the car?

2. Four acts are scheduled to perform in a variety show. How many different ways are there to schedule their appearances?

3. In how many ways can seven airplanes line up for a departure on a runway if the plane with the greatest number of passengers must depart first?

4. A human resource manager has 11 applicants to fill three different positions. Assuming that all applicants are equally qualified for any of the three positions, in how many ways can this be done?

5. From the ten books that you've recently bought but not read, you plan to take four with you on vacation. How many different sets of four books can you take?

6. In how many distinct ways can the letters of the word ATLANTA be arranged?

In Exercises 7–9, one student is selected at random from a group of 12 freshmen, 16 sophomores, 20 juniors, and 2 seniors. Find the probability that the person selected is

7. a freshman. **8.** not a sophomore.

9. a junior or a senior.

10. If you are dealt one card from a 52-card deck, find the probability of being dealt a card greater than 4 and less than 10.

11. Seven movies (A, B, C, D, E, F, and G) are being scheduled for showing. The order of showing is determined by random selection. Find the probability that film C will be shown first, film A next-to-last, and film E last.

12. A lottery game is set up so that each player chooses six different numbers from 1 to 15. If the six numbers match the six numbers drawn in the lottery, the player wins (or shares) the top cash prize. What is the probability of winning the prize with 50 different lottery tickets?

In Exercises 13–14, it is equally probable that the pointer on the spinner shown will land on any one of the eight colored regions. If the pointer lands on a borderline, spin again.

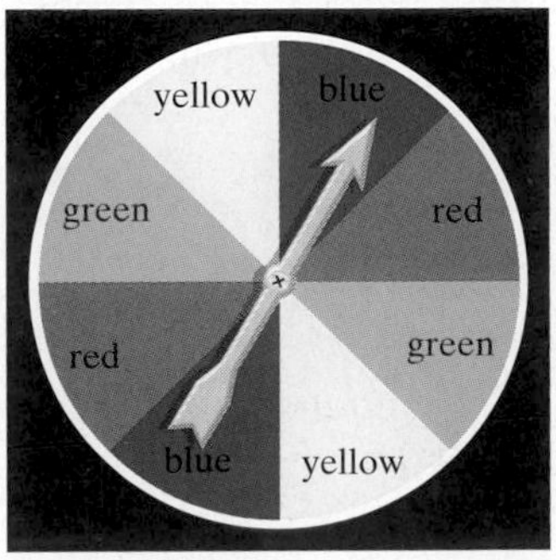

13. If the spinner is spun once, find the probability that the pointer will land on red or blue.

14. If the spinner is spun twice, find the probability that the pointer lands on red on the first spin and blue on the second spin.

15. A region is prone to flooding once every 20 years. The probability of flooding in any one year is $\frac{1}{20}$. What is the probability of flooding for three consecutive years?

16. One card is randomly selected from a deck of 52 cards. Find the probability of selecting a black card or a picture card.

17. A group of students consists of 10 male freshmen, 15 female freshmen, 20 male sophomores, and 5 female sophomores. If one person is randomly selected from the group, find the probability of selecting a freshman or a female.

18. A box contains five red balls, six green balls, and nine yellow balls. Suppose you select one ball at random from the box and do not replace it. Then you randomly select a second ball. Find the probability that both balls selected are red.

19. A quiz consisting of four multiple-choice questions has four available options (a, b, c, or d) for each question. If a person guesses at every question, what is the probability of answering *all* questions correctly?

20. A group is comprised of 20 men and 15 women. If one person is randomly selected from the group, find the odds against the person being a man.

21. The odds against a candidate winning an election are given at 1 to 4.

a. What are the odds in favor of the candidate winning?

b. What is the probability that the candidate will win the election?

A class is collecting data on eye color and gender. They organize the data they collected into the table shown. Numbers in the table represent the number of students from the class that belong to each of the categories. Use the data to solve Exercises 22–26. Express probabilities as simplified fractions.

	Brown	**Blue**	**Green**
Male	22	18	10
Female	18	20	12

Find the probability that a randomly selected student from this class

22. does not have brown eyes.

23. has brown eyes or blue eyes.

24. is female or has green eyes.

25. is male, given the student has blue eyes.

26. If two people are randomly selected, in succession, from the students in this class, find the probability that they both have green eyes.

27. An architect is considering bidding for the design of a new theater. The cost of drawing plans and submitting a model is $15,000. The probability of being awarded the bid is 0.2, and anticipated profits are $80,000, resulting in a possible gain of this amount minus the $15,000 cost for plans and models. What is the expected value if the architect decides to bid for the design? Describe what this value means.

28. A game is played by selecting one bill at random from a bag that contains ten $1 bills, five $2 bills, three $5 bills, one $10 bill, and one $100 bill. The player gets to keep the selected bill. There is a $20 charge to play the game. What is the expected value? What does this value mean?

CHAPTER 12

Statistics

In a 1996 study, researchers found that employees described as plain had salaries below the median level and those described as attractive had salaries above the median level.

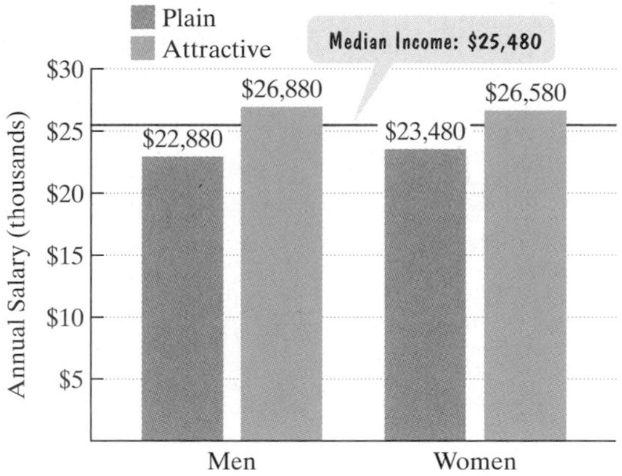

Source: Jeff Biddle and Daniel Hamermesh, CompPsych Survey

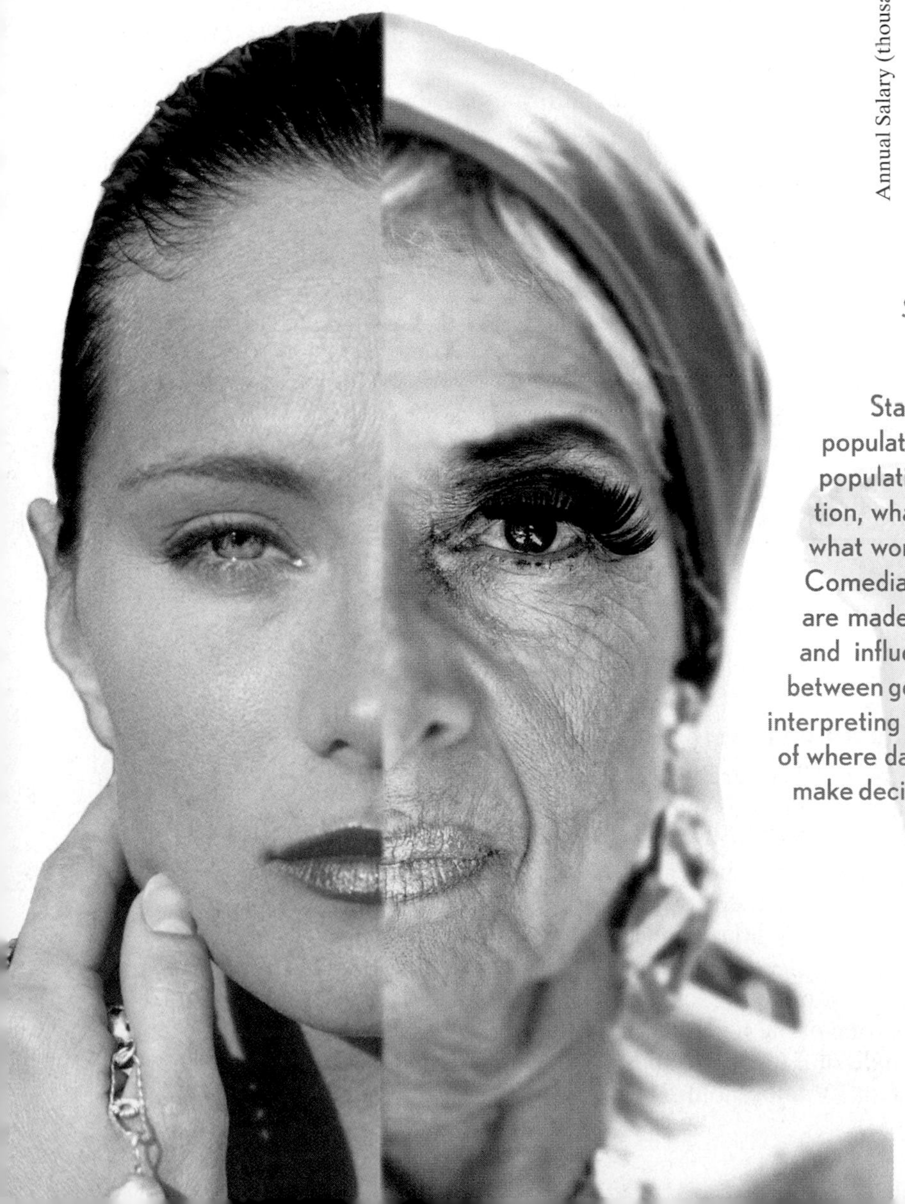

Statisticians collect numerical data from subgroups of populations to find out everything imaginable about the population as a whole, including whom they favor in an election, what they watch on TV, how much money they make, what worries them, and even how being attractive pays off. Comedians and statisticians joke that 62.38% of all statistics are made up on the spot. Because statisticians both record and influence our behavior, it is important to distinguish between good and bad methods for collecting, presenting, and interpreting data. In this chapter, you will gain an understanding of where data come from and how these numbers are used to make decisions.

SECTION 12.1 • SAMPLING, FREQUENCY DISTRIBUTIONS, AND GRAPHS

OBJECTIVES

1. Describe the population whose properties are to be analyzed.
2. Select an appropriate sampling technique.
3. Organize and present data.
4. Identify deceptions in visual displays of data.

*M*A*S*H* took place in the early 1950s, during the Korean War. By the final episode, the show had lasted four times as long as the Korean War.

At the end of the twentieth century, there were 94 million households in the United States with television sets. The television program viewed by the greatest percentage of such households in that century was the final episode of *M*A*S*H*. Over 50 million American households watched this program.

Numerical information, such as the information about the top three TV shows of the twentieth century, shown in Table 12.1, is called **data**. The word **statistics** is often used when referring to data. However, statistics has a second meaning: Statistics is also a method for collecting, organizing, analyzing, and interpreting data, as well as drawing conclusions based on the data. This methodology divides statistics into two main areas. **Descriptive statistics** is concerned with collecting, organizing, summarizing, and presenting data. **Inferential statistics** has to do with making generalizations about and drawing conclusions from the data collected.

TABLE 12.1 TV PROGRAMS WITH THE GREATEST U.S. AUDIENCE VIEWING PERCENTAGE OF THE TWENTIETH CENTURY

Program	Total Households	Viewing Percentage
1. *M*A*S*H* Feb. 28, 1983	50,150,000	60.2%
2. *Dallas* Nov. 21, 1980	41,470,000	53.3%
3. *Roots Part 8* Jan. 30, 1977	36,380,000	51.1%

Source: Nielsen Media Research

1 Describe the population whose properties are to be analyzed.

Populations and Samples

Consider the set of all American TV households. Such a set is called the *population*. In general, a **population** is the set containing all the people or objects whose properties are to be described and analyzed by the data collector.

The population of American TV households is huge. At the time of the *M*A*S*H* conclusion, there were nearly 84 million such households. Did over 50 million American TV households really watch the final episode of *M*A*S*H*? A friendly phone call to each household ("So, how are you? What's new? Watch any good television last night? If so, what?") is, of course, absurd. A **sample**, which is a subset or subgroup of the population, is needed. In this case, it would be appropriate to have a sample of a few thousand TV households to draw conclusions about the population of all TV households.

BLITZER BONUS

A Sampling Fiasco

Cover of the *Literary Digest*, October 31, 1936. General Research Division, The New York Public Library, Astor, Lenox and Tilden Foundations. The New York Public Library/Art Resource, NY

In 1936, the *Literary Digest* mailed out over ten million ballots to voters throughout the country. The results poured in, and the magazine predicted a landslide victory for Republican Alf Landon over Democrat Franklin Roosevelt. However, the prediction of the *Literary Digest* was wrong. Why? The mailing lists the editors used included people from their own subscriber list, directories of automobile owners, and telephone books. As a result, its sample was anything but random. It excluded most of the poor, who were unlikely to subscribe to the *Literary Digest*, or to own a car or telephone in the heart of the Depression. Prosperous people in 1936 were more likely to be Republican than the poor. Thus, although the sample was massive, it included a higher percentage of affluent individuals than the population as a whole did. A victim of both the Depression and the 1936 sampling fiasco, the *Literary Digest* folded in 1937.

EXAMPLE 1 POPULATIONS AND SAMPLES

A group of hotel owners in a large city decide to conduct a survey among citizens of the city to discover their opinions about casino gambling.

a. Describe the population.

b. One of the hotel owners suggests obtaining a sample by surveying all the people at six of the largest nightclubs in the city on a Saturday night. Each person will be asked to express his or her opinion on casino gambling. Does this seem like a good idea?

SOLUTION

a. The population is the set containing all the citizens of the city.

b. Questioning people at six of the city's largest nightclubs is a terrible idea. The nightclub subset is probably more likely to have a positive attitude toward casino gambling than the population of all the city's citizens.

CHECK POINT 1 A city government wants to conduct a survey among the city's homeless to discover their opinions about required residence in city shelters from midnight until 6 A.M.

a. Describe the population.

b. A city commissioner suggests obtaining a sample by surveying all the homeless people at the city's largest shelter on a Sunday night. Does this seem like a good idea? Explain your answer.

Random Sampling

There is a way to use a small sample to make generalizations about a large population: Guarantee that every member of the population has an equal chance to be selected for the sample. Surveying people at six of the city's largest nightclubs does not provide this guarantee. Unless it can be established that all citizens of the city frequent these clubs, which seems unlikely, this sampling scheme does not permit each citizen an equal chance of selection.

RANDOM SAMPLES

A **random sample** is a sample obtained in such a way that every element in the population has an equal chance of being selected for the sample.

Suppose that you are elated with the quality of one of your courses. Although it's an auditorium section with 120 students, you feel that the professor is lecturing right to you. During a wonderful lecture, you look around the auditorium to see if any of the other students are sharing your enthusiasm. Based on body language, it's hard to tell. You really want to know the opinion of the population of 120 students taking this course. You think about asking students to grade the course on an A to F scale, anticipating a unanimous A. You cannot survey everyone. Eureka! Suddenly you have an idea on how to take a sample. Place cards numbered from 1 through 120, one number per card, in a box. Because the course has assigned seating by number, each numbered card corresponds to a student in the class. Reach in and randomly select six cards. Each card, and therefore each student, has an equal chance of being selected. Then use the opinions about the course from the six randomly selected students to generalize about the course opinion for the entire 120-student population.

Your idea is precisely how random samples are obtained. In random sampling, each element in the population must be identified and assigned a number. The numbers are generally assigned in order. The way to sample from the larger numbered population is to generate random numbers using a computer or calculator.

Each numbered element from the population that corresponds to one of the generated random numbers is selected for the sample.

Call-in polls on radio and television are not reliable because those polled do not represent the larger population. A person who calls in is likely to have feelings about an issue that are consistent with the politics of the show's host. For a poll to be accurate, the sample must be chosen randomly from the larger population. The A. C. Nielsen Company uses a random sample of approximately 5000 TV households to measure the percentage of households tuned in to a television program.

2 Select an appropriate sampling technique.

EXAMPLE 2 SELECTING AN APPROPRIATE SAMPLING TECHNIQUE

We return to the hotel owners in the large city who are interested in how the city's citizens feel about casino gambling. Which of the following would be the most appropriate way to select a random sample?

a. Randomly survey people who live in the oceanfront condominiums in the city.

b. Survey the first 200 people whose names appear in the city's telephone directory.

c. Randomly select neighborhoods of the city and then randomly survey people within the selected neighborhoods.

SOLUTION Keep in mind that the population is the set containing all the city's citizens. A random sample must give each citizen an equal chance of being selected.

a. Randomly selecting people who live in the city's oceanfront condominiums is not a good idea. Many hotels lie along the oceanfront, and the oceanfront property owners might object to the traffic and noise as a result of casino gambling. Furthermore, this sample does not give each citizen of the city an equal chance of being selected.

b. If the hotel owners survey the first 200 names in the city's telephone directory, all citizens do not have an equal chance of selection. For example, individuals whose last name begins with a letter toward the end of the alphabet have no chance of being selected.

c. Randomly selecting neighborhoods of the city and then randomly surveying people within the selected neighborhoods is an appropriate technique. Using this method, each citizen has an equal chance of being selected.

In summary, given the three options, the sampling technique in part (c) is the most appropriate.

Surveys and polls involve data from a sample of some population. Regardless of the sampling technique used, the sample should exhibit characteristics typical of those possessed by the target population. This type of sample is called a **representative sample**.

BLITZER BONUS

The United States Census

A census is a survey that attempts to include the entire population. The U.S. Constitution requires a census of the American population every ten years. The 2000 census form was mailed to all households in the country. A census "long form" that asks many more questions than the basic census form is sent to a random sample of one-sixth of all households.

Although the census generates volumes of statistics, its main purpose is to give the government block-by-block population figures to create election districts with equal populations needs. The U.S. census is not foolproof. The 1990 census missed 1.6% of the American population, including an estimated 4.4% of the African American population, largely in inner cities.

CHECK POINT 2 Explain why the sampling technique described in Check Point 1(b) on page 681 is not a random sample. Then describe an appropriate way to select a random sample of the city's homeless.

3 Organize and present data.

Frequency Distributions

After data have been collected from a sample of the population, the next task facing the statistician is to present the data in a condensed and manageable form. In this way, the data can be more easily interpreted.

Suppose, for example, that researchers are interested in determining the age at which adolescent males show the greatest rate of physical growth. A random sample of 35 ten-year-old boys is measured for height and then remeasured each year until they reach 18. The age of maximum yearly growth for each subject is as follows:

12, 14, 13, 14, 16, 14, 14, 17, 13, 10, 13, 18, 12, 15, 14, 15, 15, 14, 14, 13, 15, 16, 15, 12, 13, 16, 11, 15, 12, 13, 12, 11, 13, 14, 14.

A piece of data is called a **data item**. This list of data has 35 data items. Some of the data items are identical. Two of the data items are 11 and 11. Thus, we can say that the **data value** 11 occurs twice. Similarly, because five of the data items are 12, 12, 12, 12, and 12, the data value 12 occurs five times.

Collected data can be presented using a **frequency distribution**. Such a distribution consists of two columns. The data values are listed in one column. Numerical data are generally listed from smallest to largest. The adjacent column is labeled **frequency** and indicates the number of times each value occurs.

TABLE 12.2 A FREQUENCY DISTRIBUTION FOR A BOY'S AGE OF MAXIMUM YEARLY GROWTH

Age of Maximum Growth	Number of Boys (Frequency)
10	1
11	2
12	5
13	7
14	9
15	6
16	3
17	1
18	1
Total:	$n = 35$

35 is the sum of the frequencies.

EXAMPLE 3 CONSTRUCTING A FREQUENCY DISTRIBUTION

Construct a frequency distribution for the data of the age of maximum yearly growth for 35 boys:

12, 14, 13, 14, 16, 14, 14, 17, 13, 10, 13, 18, 12, 15, 14, 15, 15, 14, 14, 13, 15, 16, 15, 12, 13, 16, 11, 15, 12, 13, 12, 11, 13, 14, 14.

SOLUTION It is difficult to determine trends in the data above in its current format. Perhaps we can make sense of the data by organizing it into a frequency distribution. Let us create two columns. One lists all possible data values, from smallest (10) to largest (18). The other column indicates the number of times the value occurs in the sample. The frequency distribution is shown in Table 12.2.

The frequency distribution indicates that one subject had maximum growth at age 10, two at age 11, five at age 12, seven at age 13, and so on. The maximum growth for most of the subjects occurred between the ages of 12 and 15. Nine boys experienced maximum growth at age 14, more than at any other age within the sample. The sum of the frequencies, 35, is equal to the original number of data items.

The trend shown by the frequency distribution in Table 12.2 indicates that the number of boys who attain their maximum yearly growth at a given age increases until age 14 and decreases after that. This trend is not evident in the data in its original format.

CHECK POINT 3 Construct a frequency distribution for the data showing final course grades for students in a precalculus course, listed alphabetically by student name in a grade book:

F, A, B, B, C, C, B, C, A, A, C, C, D, C, B, D, C, C, B, C.

A frequency distribution that lists all possible data items can be quite cumbersome when there are many such items. For example, consider the following data items. These are statistics test scores for a class of 40 students.

82	47	75	64	57	82	63	93
76	68	84	54	88	77	79	80
94	92	94	80	94	66	81	67
75	73	66	87	76	45	43	56
57	74	50	78	71	84	59	76

It's difficult to determine how well the group did when the grades are displayed like this. Because there are so many data items, one way to organize these data so that the results are more meaningful is to arrange the grades into groups, or **classes**, based on something that interests us. Many grading systems assign an A to grades in the 90–100 class, B to grades in the 80–89 class, C to grades in the 70–79 class, and so on. These classes provide one way to organize the data.

Looking at the 40 statistics test scores, we see that they range from a low of 43 to a high of 94. We can use classes that run from 40 through 49, 50 through 59, 60 through 69, and so on up to 90 through 99, to organize the scores. In Example 4, we go through the data and tally each item into the appropriate class. This method for organizing data is called a **grouped frequency distribution**.

EXAMPLE 4 CONSTRUCTING A GROUPED FREQUENCY DISTRIBUTION

Use the classes 40–49, 50–59, 60–69, 70–79, 80–89, and 90–99 to construct a grouped frequency distribution for the 40 test scores on the previous page.

SOLUTION We use the 40 given scores and tally the number of scores in each class.

Test Scores (Class)	Tally	Number of Students (Frequency)
40–49	|||	3
50–59	~~||||~~ |	6
60–69	~~||||~~ |	6
70–79	~~||||~~ ~~||||~~ |	11
80–89	~~||||~~ ||||	9
90–99	~~||||~~	5

The second score in the list, 47, is shown as the first tally in this row.

The first score in the list, 82, is shown as the first tally in this row.

TABLE 12.3

Class	Frequency
40–49	3
50–59	6
60–69	6
70–79	11
80–89	9
90–99	5
Total:	$n = 40$

40, the sum of the frequencies, is the number of data items.

Omitting the tally column results in the grouped frequency distribution in Table 12.3. The distribution shows that the greatest frequency of students scored in the 70–79 class. The number of students decreases in classes that contain successively lower and higher scores. The sum of the frequencies, 40, is equal to the original number of data items.

The leftmost number in each class of a grouped frequency distribution is called the **lower class limit**. For example, in Table 12.3, the lower limit of the first class is 40 and the lower limit of the third class is 60. The rightmost number in each class is called the **upper class limit**. In Table 12.3, 49 and 69 are the upper limits for the first and third classes, respectively. Notice that if we take the difference between any two consecutive lower class limits, we get the same number:

$$50 - 40 = 10,\ 60 - 50 = 10,\ 70 - 60 = 10,\ 80 - 70 = 10,\ 90 - 80 = 10.$$

The number 10 is called the **class width**.

When setting up class limits, each class, with the possible exception of the first or last, should have the same width. Because each data item must fall into exactly one class, it is sometimes helpful to vary the width of the first or last class to allow for items that fall far above or below most of the data.

CHECK POINT 4 Use the classes in Table 12.3 to construct a grouped frequency distribution for the following 37 exam scores:

73	58	68	75	94	79	96	79
87	83	89	52	99	97	89	58
95	77	75	81	75	73	73	62
69	76	77	71	50	57	41	98
77	71	69	90	75.			

TABLE 12.2 (repeated) A FREQUENCY DISTRIBUTION FOR A BOY'S AGE OF MAXIMUM YEARLY GROWTH

Age of Maximum Growth	Number of Boys (Frequency)
10	1
11	2
12	5
13	7
14	9
15	6
16	3
17	1
18	1
Total:	$n = 35$

Histograms and Frequency Polygons

Take a second look at the frequency distribution for the age of a boy's maximum yearly growth, repeated in Table 12.2. A bar graph with bars that touch can be used to visually display the data. Such a graph is called a **histogram**. Figure 12.1 illustrates a histogram that was constructed using the frequency distribution in Table 12.2. A series of rectangles whose heights represent the frequencies are placed next to each other. For example, the height of the bar for the data value 10, shown in Figure 12.1, is 1. This corresponds to the frequency for 10 given in Table 12.2. The higher the bar, the more frequent the age. The break along the horizontal axis, symbolized by -⁄\/-, eliminates listing the ages 1 through 9.

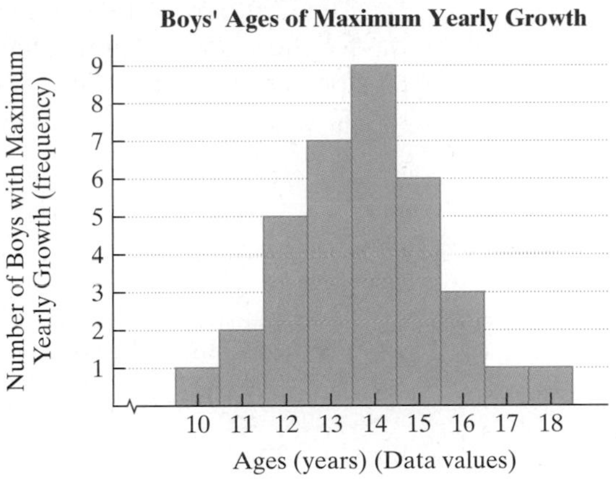

FIGURE 12.1 A histogram for a boy's age of maximum yearly growth

A line graph called a **frequency polygon** can also be used to visually convey the information shown in Figure 12.1. The axes are labeled just like those in a histogram. Thus, the horizontal axis shows data values and the vertical axis shows frequencies. Once a histogram has been constructed, it's fairly easy to draw a frequency polygon. Figure 12.2 shows a histogram with a dot at the top of each rectangle at its midpoint. Connect each of these midpoints with a straight line. To complete the frequency polygon at both ends, the lines should be drawn down to touch the horizontal axis. The completed frequency polygon is shown in Figure 12.3.

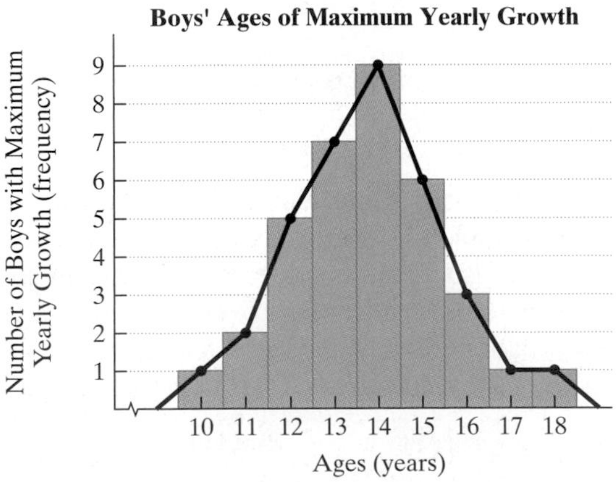

FIGURE 12.2 A histogram with a superimposed frequency polygon

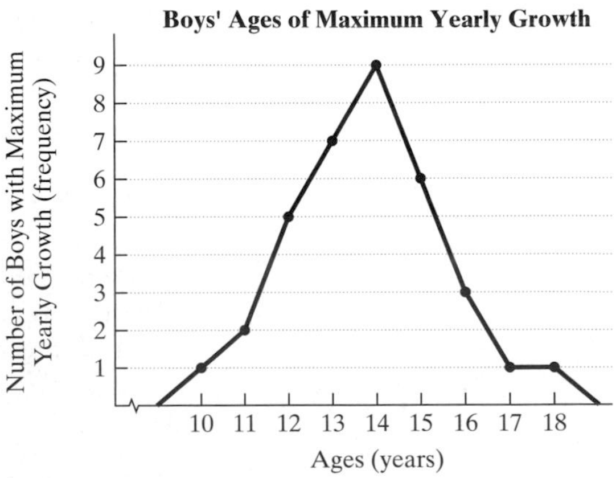

FIGURE 12.3 A frequency polygon

Stem-and-Leaf Plots

A unique way of displaying data uses a tool called a **stem-and-leaf plot**. Example 5 illustrates how we sort the data, revealing the same visual impression created by a histogram.

EXAMPLE 5 CONSTRUCTING A STEM-AND-LEAF PLOT

Use the data showing statistics test scores for 40 students to construct a stem-and-leaf plot:

82	47	75	64	57	82	63	93
76	68	84	54	88	77	79	80
94	92	94	80	94	66	81	67
75	73	66	87	76	45	43	56
57	74	50	78	71	84	59	76.

SOLUTION The plot is constructed by separating each data item into two parts. The first part is the *stem*. The **stem** consists of the tens digit. For example, the stem for the score of 82 is 8. The second part is the *leaf*. The **leaf** consists of the units digit for a given value. For the score of 82, the leaf is 2. The possible stems for the 40 scores are 4, 5, 6, 7, 8, and 9, entered in the left column of the plot.

Begin by entering each data item in the first row:

82 47 75 64 57 82 63 93.

Entering 82:

Stems	Leaves
4	
5	
6	
7	
8	2
9	

Adding 47:

Stems	Leaves
4	7
5	
6	
7	
8	2
9	

Adding 75:

Stems	Leaves
4	7
5	
6	
7	5
8	2
9	

Adding 64:

Stems	Leaves
4	7
5	
6	4
7	5
8	2
9	

Adding 57:

Stems	Leaves
4	7
5	7
6	4
7	5
8	2
9	

Adding 82:

Stems	Leaves
4	7
5	7
6	4
7	5
8	22
9	

Adding 63:

Stems	Leaves
4	7
5	7
6	43
7	5
8	22
9	

Adding 93:

Stems	Leaves
4	7
5	7
6	43
7	5
8	22
9	3

We continue in this manner and enter all the data items. Figure 12.4 shows the completed stem-and-leaf plot. If you turn the page so that the left margin is on the bottom and facing you, the visual impression created by the enclosed leaves is the same as that created by a histogram. An advantage over the histogram is that the stem-and-leaf plot preserves exact data items. The enclosed leaves extend farthest to the right when the stem is 7. This shows that the greatest frequency of students scored in the 70s.

Tens digit — Units digit

Stems	Leaves
4	7 5 3
5	7 4 6 7 0 9
6	4 3 8 6 7 6
7	5 6 7 9 5 3 6 4 8 1 6
8	2 2 4 8 0 0 1 7 4
9	3 4 2 4 4

FIGURE 12.4 A stem-and-leaf plot displaying 40 test scores

CHECK POINT 5 Construct a stem-and-leaf plot for the data in Check Point 4 on page 684.

4 Identify deceptions in visual displays of data.

Deceptions in Visual Displays of Data

Benjamin Disraeli, Queen Victoria's prime minister, stated that there are "lies, damned lies, and statistics." The problem is not that statistics lie, but rather that liars use statistics. Graphs can be used to distort the underlying data, making it difficult for the viewer to learn the truth. One potential source of misunderstanding is the scale on the vertical axis used to draw the graph. This scale is important because it lets a researcher "inflate" or "deflate" a trend. For example, both graphs in Figure 12.5 present identical data for the percentage of people in the United States living below the poverty level from 2000 through 2004. The graph on the left stretches the scale on the vertical axis to create an overall impression of a poverty rate increasing rapidly over time. The graph on the right compresses the scale on the vertical axis to create an impression of a poverty rate that is slowly increasing, and beginning to level off, over time.

Percentage of People in the United States Living below the Poverty Level, 2000-2004

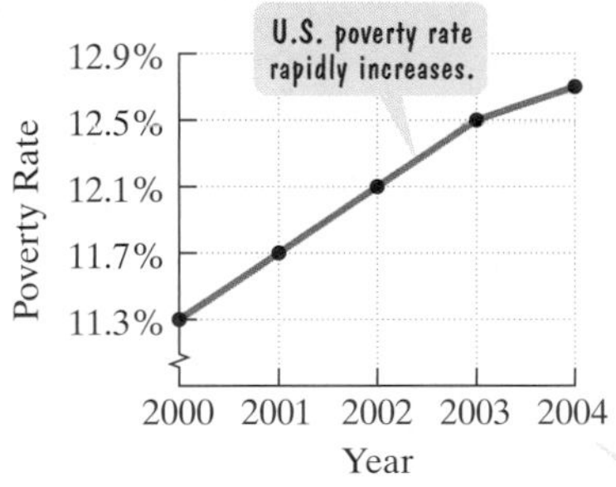

Year	Poverty Rate
2000	11.3%
2001	11.7%
2002	12.1%
2003	12.5%
2004	12.7%

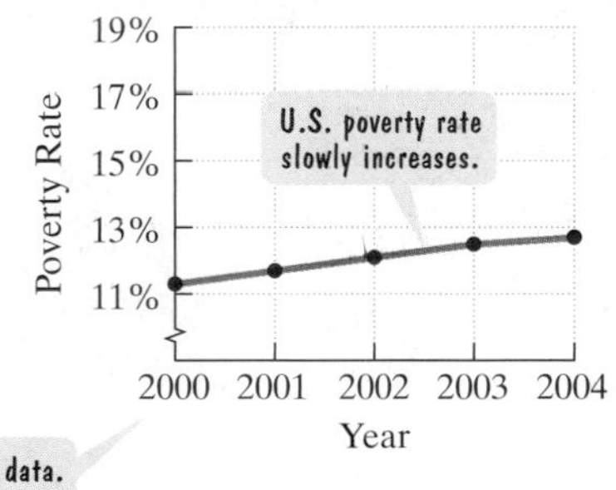

The graph in both figures present this data.

FIGURE 12.5
Source: U.S. Census Bureau

THINGS TO WATCH FOR IN VISUAL DISPLAYS OF DATA

1. Is there a title that explains what is being displayed?
2. Are numbers lined up with tick marks on the vertical axis that clearly indicate the scale? Has the scale been varied to create a more or less dramatic impression than shown by the actual data?
3. Do too many design and cosmetic effects draw attention from or distort the data?
4. Has the wrong impression been created about how the data are changing because equally spaced time intervals are not used on the horizontal axis?
5. Are bar sizes scaled proportionately in terms of the data they represent?
6. Is there a source that indicates where the data in the display came from? Do the data come from an entire population or a sample? Was a random sample used and, if so, are there possible differences between what is displayed in the graph and what is occurring in the entire population? (We'll discuss these *margins of error* in Section 12.4.) Who is presenting the visual display, and does that person have a special case to make for or against the trend shown by the graph?

Table 12.4 on the next page contains two examples of misleading visual displays.

TABLE 12.4 EXAMPLES OF MISLEADING VISUAL DISPLAYS

Graphic Display	Presentation Problems
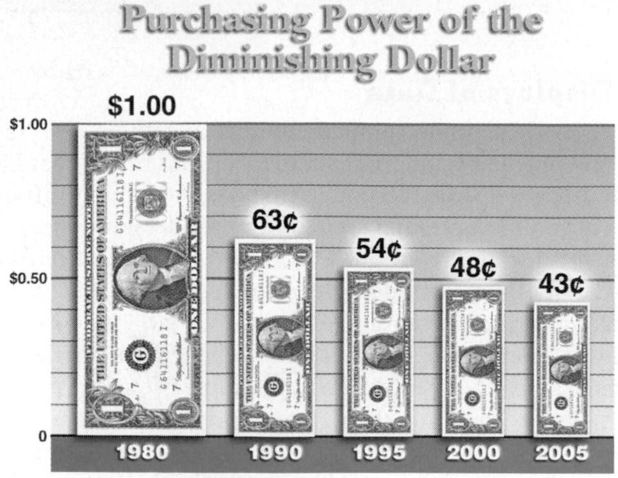 *Source:* Bureau of Labor Statistics	Although the length of each dollar bill is proportional to its spending power, the visual display varies both the length *and width* of the bills to show the diminishing power of the dollar over time. Because our eyes focus on the *areas* of the dollar-shaped bars, this creates the impression that the purchasing power of the dollar diminished even more than it really did. If the area of the dollar were drawn to reflect its purchasing power, the 2005 dollar would be approximately twice as large as the one shown in the graphic display.
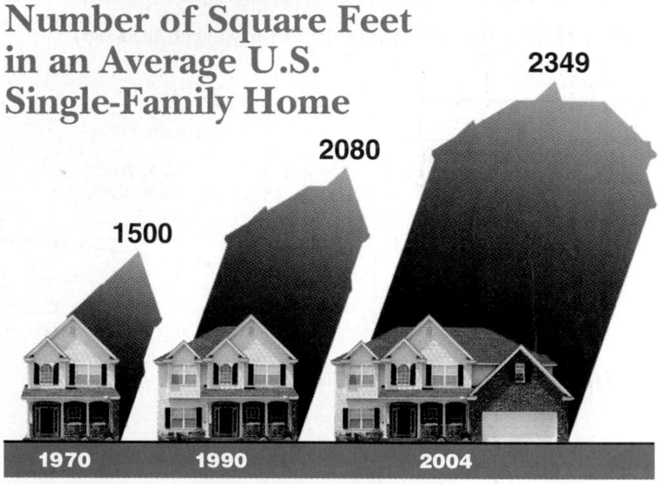 *Source:* National Association of Home Builders	Cosmetic effects of homes with equal heights, but different frontal additions and shadow lengths, make it impossible to tell if they proportionately depict the given areas. Time intervals on the horizontal axis are not uniform in size, making it appear that dwelling swelling has been linear from 1970 through 2004. The data indicate that this is not the case. There was a greater increase in area from 1970 through 1980, averaging 29 square feet per year, than from 1990 through 2004, averaging approximately 19.2 square feet per year.

BLITZER BONUS

Creating an Inaccurate Picture by Leaving Something Out

On Monday, October 19, 1987, the Dow Jones Industrial Average plunged 508 points, losing 22.6% of its value. The graph shown on the left, which appeared in a major newspaper following "Black Monday" (as it was instantly dubbed), creates the impression that the Dow average had been "bullish" from 1972 through 1987, increasing throughout this period. The graph creates this inaccurate picture by leaving something out. The graph on the right illustrates that the stock market rose and fell sharply over these years. The impressively smooth curve on the left was obtained by plotting only three of the data points. By ignoring most of the data, increases and decreases are not accounted for and the actual behavior of the market over the 15 years leading to "Black Monday" is inaccurately conveyed.

The Dow Jones Industrial Average: 1972–1987

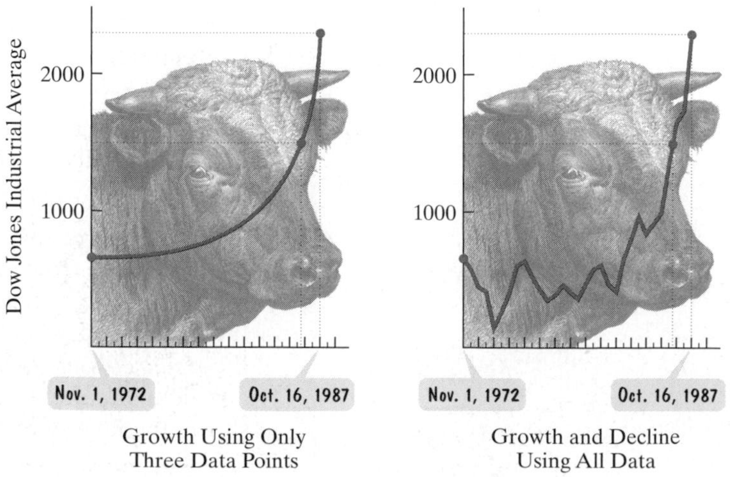

Growth Using Only Three Data Points

Growth and Decline Using All Data

Source: A. K. Dewdney, *200% of Nothing*, John Wiley and Sons, 1993

EXERCISE SET 12.1

• Practice and Application Exercises

1. "The Man Poll" of 1014 randomly selected American men ages 18 and older was taken by *Newsweek* June 2–4, 2003. The data shown below are from the poll.

IN GENERAL, HOW WOULD YOU DESCRIBE YOUR HEALTH?

	Age		
	18–34	**35–55**	**≥56**
Excellent	23%	19%	15%
Very good	37	39	32
Good	28	28	28
Fair	10	10	16
Poor	2	4	8
Don't know	0	0	1

a. Describe the population and the sample of this poll.

b. For each man, what variable is measured? Are the data quantitative (numerical) or qualitative (nonnumerical categories)?

2. The *American Association of Nurse Anesthetists Journal* (Feb. 2000) published the results of a study on the use of herbal medicines before surgery. Of 500 surgical patients who were randomly selected for the study, 51% used herbal or alternative medicines prior to surgery.

a. Describe the population and the sample of this study.

b. Is the sample representative of the population? Explain your answer.

c. For each patient, what variable is measured? Are the data quantitative (numerical) or qualitative (nonnumerical categorics)?

3. The government of a large city needs to determine whether the city's residents will support the construction of a new jail. The government decides to conduct a survey of a sample of the city's residents. Which one of the following procedures would be most appropriate for obtaining a sample of the city's residents?

a. Survey a random sample of the employees and inmates at the old jail.

b. Survey every fifth person who walks into City Hall on a given day.

c. Survey a random sample of persons within each geographic region of the city.

d. Survey the first 200 people listed in the city's telephone directory.

4. The city council of a large city needs to know whether its residents will support the building of three new schools. The council decides to conduct a survey of a sample of the city's residents. Which procedure would be most appropriate for obtaining a sample of the city's residents?

a. Survey a random sample of teachers who live in the city.

b. Survey 100 individuals who are randomly selected from a list of all people living in the state in which the city in question is located.

c. Survey a random sample of persons within each neighborhood of the city.

d. Survey every tenth person who enters City Hall on a randomly selected day.

A questionnaire was given to students in an introductory statistics class during the first week of the course. One question asked, "How stressed have you been in the last $2\frac{1}{2}$ weeks, on a scale of 0 to 10, with 0 being not at all stressed and 10 being as stressed as possible?" The students' responses are shown in the frequency distribution. Use this frequency distribution to solve Exercises 5–8.

Stress Rating	Frequency
0	2
1	1
2	3
3	12
4	16
5	18
6	13
7	31
8	26
9	15
10	14

Source: Journal of Personality and Social Psychology, 69, 1102–1112

5. Which stress rating describes the greatest number of students? How many students responded with this rating?

6. Which stress rating describes the least number of students? How many responded with this rating?

7. How many students were involved in this study?

8. How many students had a stress rating of 8 or more?

9. A random sample of 30 college students is selected. Each student is asked how much time he or she spent on homework during the previous week. The following times (in hours) are obtained:

16, 24, 18, 21, 18, 16, 18, 17, 15, 21, 19, 17, 17, 16, 19, 18,
15, 15, 20, 17, 15, 17, 24, 19, 16, 20, 16, 19, 18, 17.

Construct a frequency distribution for the data.

10. A random sample of 30 male college students is selected. Each student is asked his height (to the nearest inch). The heights are as follows:

72, 70, 68, 72, 71, 71, 71, 69, 73, 71, 73, 75, 66, 67, 75,
74, 73, 71, 72, 67, 72, 68, 67, 71, 73, 71, 72, 70, 73, 70.

Construct a frequency distribution for the data.

A college professor had students keep a diary of their social interactions for a week. Excluding family and work situations, the number of social interactions of ten minutes or longer over the week is shown in the following grouped frequency distribution. Use this information to solve Exercises 11–18.

Number of Social Interactions	Frequency
0–4	12
5–9	16
10–14	16
15–19	16
20–24	10
25–29	11
30–34	4
35–39	3
40–44	3
45–49	3

Source: Society for Personality and Social Psychology

11. Identify the lower class limit for each class.

12. Identify the upper class limit for each class.

13. What is the class width?

14. How many students were involved in this study?

15. How many students had at least 30 social interactions for the week?

16. How many students had at most 14 social interactions for the week?

17. Among the classes with the greatest frequency, which class has the least number of social interactions?

18. Among the classes with the smallest frequency, which class has the least number of social interactions?

19. As of 2007, the following are the ages, in chronological order, at which U.S. presidents were inaugurated:

57, 61, 57, 57, 58, 57, 61, 54, 68, 51, 49, 64, 50, 48, 65, 52, 56, 46, 54, 49, 50, 47, 55, 55, 54, 42, 51, 56, 55, 51, 54, 51, 60, 62, 43, 55, 56, 61, 52, 69, 64, 46, 54.

Source: Time Almanac

Construct a grouped frequency distribution for the data. Use 41–45 for the first class and use the same width for each subsequent class.

20. The IQ scores of 70 students enrolled in a liberal arts course at a college are as follows:

102, 100, 103, 86, 120, 117, 111, 101, 93, 97, 99, 95, 95, 104, 104, 105, 106, 109, 109, 89, 94, 95, 99, 99, 103, 104, 105, 109, 110, 114, 124, 123, 118, 117, 116, 110, 114, 114, 96, 99, 103, 103, 104, 107, 107, 110, 111, 112, 113, 117, 115, 116, 100, 104, 102, 94, 93, 93, 96, 96, 111, 116, 107, 109, 105, 106, 97, 106, 107, 108.

Construct a grouped frequency distribution for the data. Use 85–89 for the first class and use the same width for each subsequent class.

21. Construct a histogram and a frequency polygon for the data involving stress ratings in Exercises 5–8.

22. Construct a histogram and a frequency polygon for the data in Exercise 9.

23. Construct a histogram and a frequency polygon for the data in Exercise 10.

24. The histogram shows the distribution of starting salaries (rounded to the nearest thousand dollars) for college graduates based on a random sample of recent graduates.

Starting Salaries of Recent College Graduates

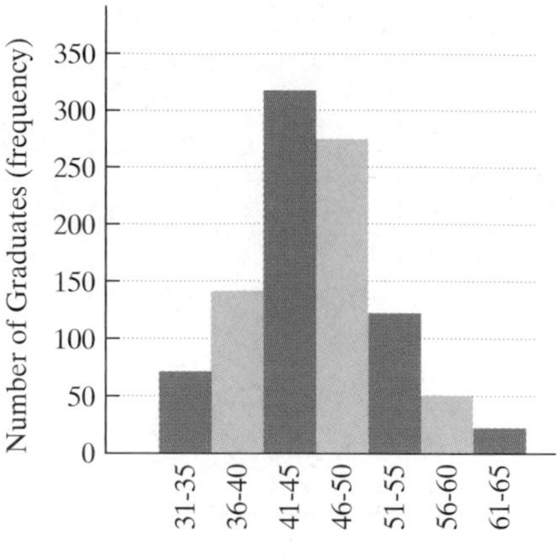

Which one of the following is true according to the graph?

a. The graph is based on a sample of approximately 500 recent college graduates.

b. More college graduates had starting salaries in the \$51,000–\$55,000 range than in the \$36,000–\$40,000 range.

c. If the sample is truly representative, then for a group of 400 college graduates, we can expect about 28 of them to have starting salaries in the \$31,000–\$35,000 range.

d. The percentage of starting salaries falling above those shown by any rectangular bar is equal to the percentage of starting salaries falling below that bar.

25. The frequency polygon shows a distribution of IQ scores. Which one of the following is true based upon the graph?

a. The graph is based on a sample of approximately 50 people.

b. More people had an IQ score of 100 than any other IQ score, and as the deviation from 100 increases or decreases, the scores fall off in a symmetrical manner.

c. More people had an IQ score of 110 than a score of 90.

d. The percentage of scores above any IQ score is equal to the percentage of scores below that score.

Distribution of IQ Scores

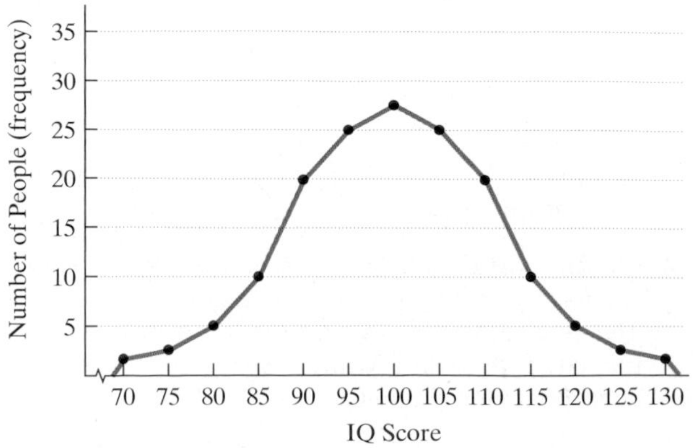

26. Construct a stem-and-leaf plot for the data in Exercise 19 showing the ages at which U.S. presidents were inaugurated.

27. A random sample of 40 college professors is selected from all professors at a university. The following list gives their ages:

63, 48, 42, 42, 38, 59, 41, 44, 45, 28, 54, 62, 51, 44, 63, 66, 59, 46, 51, 28, 37, 66, 42, 40, 30, 31, 48, 32, 29, 42, 63, 37, 36, 47, 25, 34, 49, 30, 35, 50.

Construct a stem-and-leaf plot for the data. What does the shape of the display reveal about the ages of the professors?

28. In "Ages of Oscar-Winning Best Actors and Actresses" (*Mathematics Teacher* magazine) by Richard Brown and Gretchen Davis, the stem-and-leaf plots shown compare the ages of actors and actresses for 30 winners of the Oscar at the time they won the award.

Actors	Stems	Actresses
	2	146667
98753221	3	00113344455778
88776543322100	4	11129
6651	5	
210	6	011
6	7	4
	8	0

a. What is the age of the youngest actor to win an Oscar?

b. What is the age difference between the oldest and the youngest actress to win an Oscar?

c. What is the oldest age shared by two actors to win an Oscar?

d. What differences do you observe between the two stem-and-leaf plots? What explanations can you offer for these differences?

In Exercises 29–33, describe what is misleading in each visual display of data.

29.

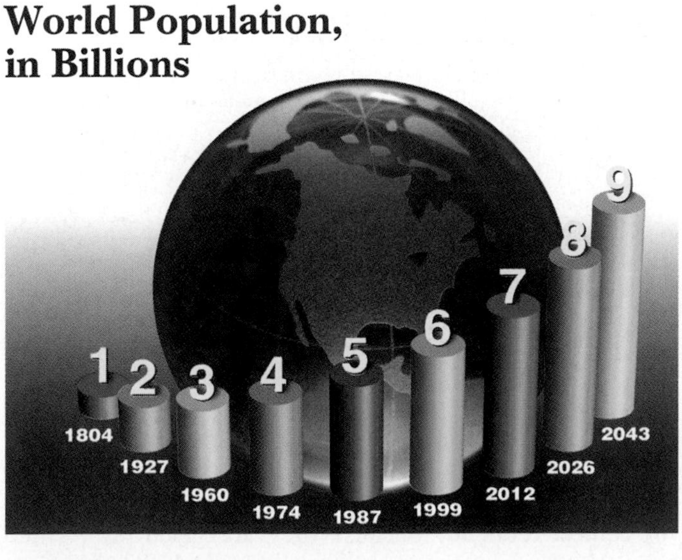

Source: U.S. Census Bureau

30.

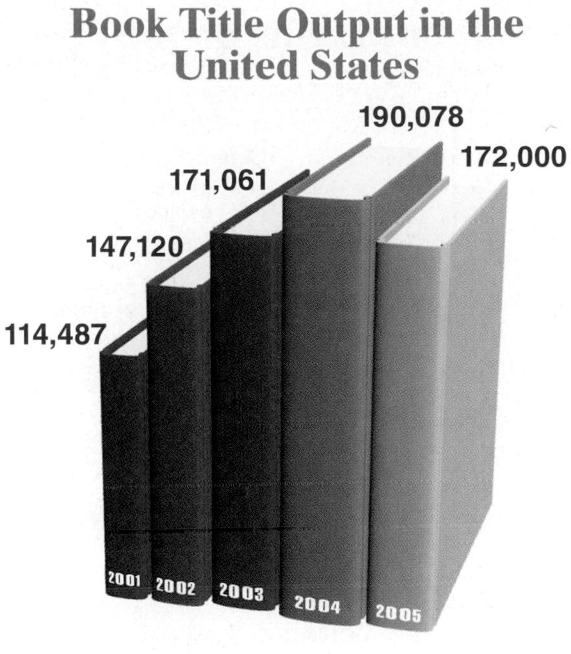

Source: R. R. Bowker

31.

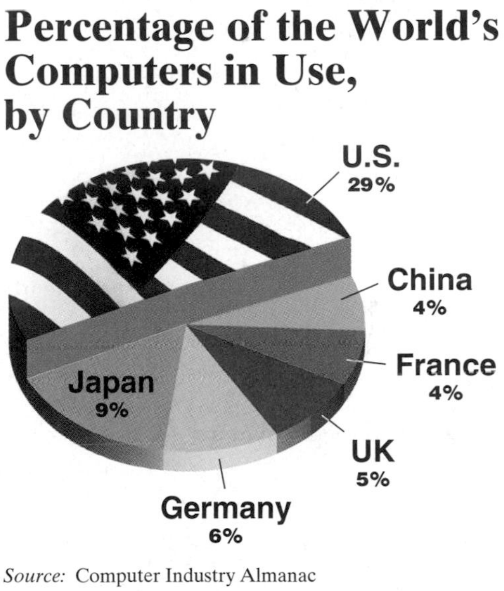

Source: Computer Industry Almanac

32.

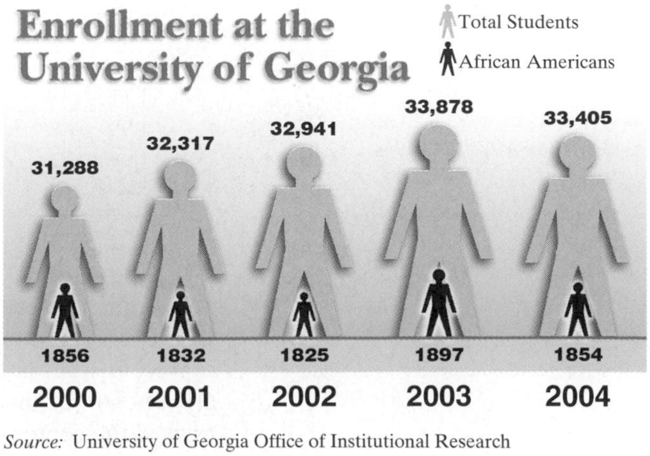

Source: University of Georgia Office of Institutional Research

33.

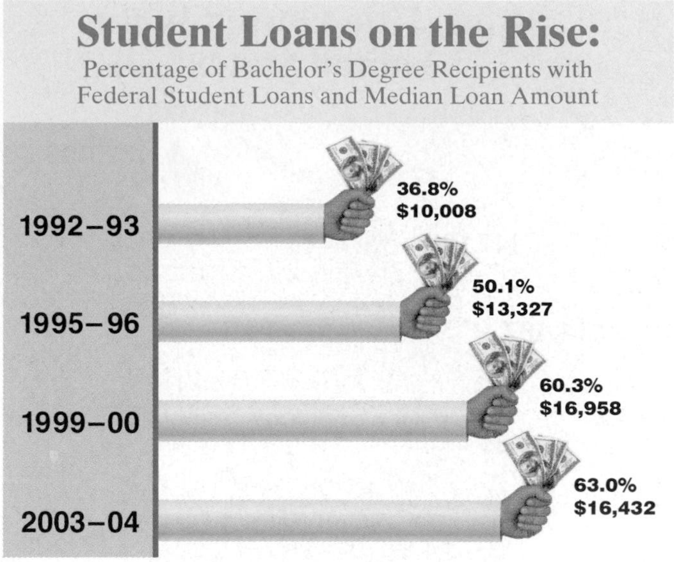

Source: American Council on Education

• Writing in Mathematics

34. What is a population? What is a sample?

35. Describe what is meant by a random sample.

36. Suppose you are interested in whether or not the students at your college would favor a grading system in which students may receive final grades of A+, A, A−, B+, B, B−, C+, C, C−, and so on. Describe how you might obtain a random sample of 100 students from the entire student population.

37. For Exercise 36, would questioning every fifth student as he or she is leaving the campus library until 100 students are interviewed be a good way to obtain a random sample? Explain your answer.

38. What is a frequency distribution?

39. What is a histogram?

40. What is a frequency polygon?

41. Describe how to construct a frequency polygon from a histogram.

42. Describe how to construct a stem-and-leaf plot from a set of data.

43. Describe two ways that graphs can be misleading.

• Critical Thinking Exercises

44. Construct a grouped frequency distribution for the following data, showing the length, in miles, of the 25 longest rivers in the United States. Use five classes that have the same width.

2540	2340	1980	1900	1900
1460	1450	1420	1310	1290
1280	1240	1040	990	926
906	886	862	800	774
743	724	692	659	649

Source: U.S. Department of the Interior

45. Use two line graphs drawn in the same coordinate system that show a better way to portray the enrollment information for 2000 through 2004 in Exercise 32.

• Group Exercises

46. The classic book on distortion using statistics is *How to Lie with Statistics* by Darrell Huff. This activity is designed for five people. Each person should select two chapters from Huff's book and then present to the class the common methods of statistical manipulation and distortion that Huff discusses.

47. Each group member should find one example of a graph that presents data with integrity and one example of a graph that is misleading. Use newspapers, magazines, the Internet, books, and so forth. Once graphs have been collected, each member should share his or her graphs with the entire group. Be sure to explain why one graph depicts data in a forthright manner and how the other graph misleads the viewer.

SECTION 12.2 • MEASURES OF CENTRAL TENDENCY

OBJECTIVES

1. Determine the mean for a data set.
2. Determine the median for a data set.
3. Determine the mode for a data set.
4. Determine the midrange for a data set.

According to researchers, "Robert," the average American guy, is 31 years old, 5 feet 10 inches, 172 pounds, works 6.1 hours daily, and sleeps 7.7 hours. These numbers represent what is "average" or "typical" of American men. In statistics, such values are known as **measures of central tendency** because they are generally located toward the center of a distribution. Four such measures are discussed in this section:

the mean, the median, the mode, and the midrange. Each measure of central tendency is calculated in a different way. Thus, it is better to use a specific term (mean, median, mode, or midrange) than to use the generic descriptive term "average."

1 Determine the mean for a data set.

The Mean

By far the most commonly used measure of central tendency is the *mean*. The **mean** is obtained by adding all the data items and then dividing the sum by the number of items. The Greek letter sigma, Σ, called a **symbol of summation**, is used to indicate the sum of data items. The notation Σx, read "the sum of x," means to add all the data items in a given data set. We can use this symbol to give a formula for calculating the mean.

THE MEAN

The **mean** is the sum of the data items divided by the number of items.

$$\text{Mean} = \frac{\Sigma x}{n},$$

where Σx represents the sum of all the data items and n represents the number of items.

EXAMPLE 1 CALCULATING THE MEAN

Table 12.5 shows the ten youngest male singers in the United States to have a number 1 single. Find the mean age of these male singers at the time of their number 1 single.

TABLE 12.5 YOUNGEST U.S. MALE SINGERS TO HAVE A NUMBER 1 SINGLE

Artist/Year	Title	Age
Stevie Wonder, 1963	"Fingertips"	13
Donny Osmond, 1971	"Go Away Little Girl"	13
Michael Jackson, 1972	"Ben"	14
Laurie London, 1958	"He's Got the Whole World in His Hands"	14
Paul Anka, 1957	"Diana"	16
Brian Hyland, 1960	"Itsy Bitsy Teenie Weenie Yellow Polkadot Bikini"	16
Shaun Cassidy, 1977	"Da Doo Ron Ron"	17
Bobby Vee, 1961	"Take Good Care of My Baby"	18
Usher, 1998	"Nice & Slow"	19
Andy Gibb, 1977	"I Just Want to Be Your Everything"	19

Source: Russell Ash, *The Top 10 of Everything*

SOLUTION We find the mean by adding the ages and dividing this sum by 10, the number of data items.

$$\text{Mean} = \frac{\Sigma x}{n} = \frac{13 + 13 + 14 + 14 + 16 + 16 + 17 + 18 + 19 + 19}{10} = \frac{159}{10} = 15.9$$

The mean age of the ten youngest singers to have a number 1 single is 15.9.

One and only one mean can be calculated for any group of numerical data. The mean may or may not be one of the actual data items. In Example 1, the mean was 15.9, although no data item is 15.9.

CHECK POINT 1 Find the mean for each group of data items:

a. 10, 20, 30, 40, 50 **b.** 3, 10, 10, 10, 117.

BLITZER BONUS

The Mean American Millionaire

According to a study involving a random sample of 1300 of America's 2,270,000 millionaires, the average millionaire lives in a $300,000 home in an upper-middle-class neighborhood, is 54 years old, drives a four-year-old American car, and had an SAT score of 1190.

Source: Stanley, *The Millionaire Next Door*

In Example 1, some of the data items were identical. We can use multiplication when computing the mean for these identical items:

$$\text{Mean} = \frac{13 + 13 + 14 + 14 + 16 + 16 + 17 + 18 + 19 + 19}{10}$$

$$= \frac{13 \cdot 2 + 14 \cdot 2 + 16 \cdot 2 + 17 \cdot 1 + 18 \cdot 1 + 19 \cdot 2}{10}$$

The data values 13, 14, 16, and 19 each have a frequency of 2.

When many data values occur more than once and a frequency distribution is used to organize the data, we can use the following formula to calculate the mean:

CALCULATING THE MEAN FOR A FREQUENCY DISTRIBUTION

$$\text{Mean} = \frac{\Sigma xf}{n},$$

where

x represents a data value.

f represents the frequency of that data value.

Σxf represents the sum of all the products obtained by multiplying each data value by its frequency.

n represents the *total frequency* of the distribution.

TABLE 12.6 STUDENTS' STRESS-LEVEL RATINGS

Stress Rating x	Frequency f
0	2
1	1
2	3
3	12
4	16
5	18
6	13
7	31
8	26
9	15
10	14

Source: Journal of Personality and Social Psychology, 69, 1102–1112

EXAMPLE 2 CALCULATING THE MEAN FOR A FREQUENCY DISTRIBUTION

In the previous exercise set, we mentioned a questionnaire given to students in an introductory statistics class during the first week of the course. One question asked, "How stressed have you been in the last $2\frac{1}{2}$ weeks, on a scale of 0 to 10, with 0 being not at all stressed and 10 being as stressed as possible?" Table 12.6 shows the students' responses. Use this frequency distribution to find the mean of the stress-level ratings.

SOLUTION We use the formula

$$\text{Mean} = \frac{\Sigma xf}{n}.$$

First, we must find xf, obtained by multiplying each data value, x, by its frequency, f. Then, we need to find the sum of these products, Σxf. We can use the frequency distribution to organize these computations. Add a third column in which each data value is multiplied by its frequency. This column, shown on the right, is headed xf. Then, find the sum of the values, Σxf, in this column.

x	f	xf
0	2	$0 \cdot 2 = 0$
1	1	$1 \cdot 1 = 1$
2	3	$2 \cdot 3 = 6$
3	12	$3 \cdot 12 = 36$
4	16	$4 \cdot 16 = 64$
5	18	$5 \cdot 18 = 90$
6	13	$6 \cdot 13 = 78$
7	31	$7 \cdot 31 = 217$
8	26	$8 \cdot 26 = 208$
9	15	$9 \cdot 15 = 135$
10	14	$10 \cdot 14 = 140$
Totals:	$n = 151$	$\Sigma xf = 975$

Σxf is the sum of the numbers in the third column.

This value, the sum of the numbers in the second column, is the total frequency of the distribution.

Now, substitute these values into the formula for the mean. Remember that n is the *total frequency* of the distribution, or 151.

$$\text{Mean} = \frac{\Sigma xf}{n} = \frac{975}{151} \approx 6.46$$

The mean of the 0 to 10 stress-level ratings is approximately 6.46. Notice that the mean is greater than 5, the middle of the 0 to 10 scale.

CHECK POINT 2 Find the mean for the data items in the frequency distribution. (In order to save space, we've written the frequency distribution horizontally.)

Score, x	30	33	40	50
Frequency, f	3	4	4	1

2 Determine the median for a data set.

The Median

The *median* age in the United States is 35.3. The oldest state by median age is Florida (38.7) and the youngest state is Utah (27.1). To find these values, researchers begin with appropriate random samples. The data items—that is, the ages—are arranged from youngest to oldest. The median age is the data item in the middle of each set of ranked, or ordered, data.

THE MEDIAN

To find the **median** of a group of data items,

1. Arrange the data items in order, from smallest to largest.
2. If the number of data items is odd, the median is the data item in the middle of the list.
3. If the number of data items is even, the median is the mean of the two middle data items.

EXAMPLE 3 FINDING THE MEDIAN

Find the median for each of the following groups of data:

a. 84, 90, 98, 95, 88

b. 68, 74, 7, 13, 15, 25, 28, 59, 34, 47.

SOLUTION

a. Arrange the data items in order, from smallest to largest. The number of data items in the list, five, is odd. Thus, the median is the middle number.

84, 88, 90, 95, 98

Middle data item

The median is 90. Notice that two data items lie above 90 and two data items lie below 90.

b. Arrange the data items in order, from smallest to largest. The number of data items in the list, ten, is even. Thus, the median is the mean of the two middle data items.

7, 13, 15, 25, 28, 34, 47, 59, 68, 74

Middle data items are 28 and 34.

$$\text{Median} = \frac{28 + 34}{2} = \frac{62}{2} = 31$$

The median is 31. Five data items lie above 31 and five data items lie below 31.

7 13 15 25 28 | 34 47 59 68 74

Five data items lie below 31.

Five data items lie above 31.

Median is 31.

CHECK POINT 3 Find the median for each of the following groups of data:

a. 28, 42, 40, 25, 35

b. 72, 61, 85, 93, 79, 87.

If a relatively long list of data items is arranged in order, it may be difficult to identify the item or items in the middle. In cases like this, the median can be found by determining its position in the list of items.

STUDY TIP

The formula

$$\frac{n+1}{2}$$

gives the *position* of the median, and not the actual value of the median. When finding the median, be sure to first arrange the data items in order from smallest to largest.

POSITION OF THE MEDIAN

If n data items are arranged in order, from smallest to largest, the median is the value in the

$$\frac{n+1}{2}$$

position.

EXAMPLE 4 FINDING THE MEDIAN USING THE POSITION FORMULA

Listed below are the points scored per season by the 13 top point scorers in the National Football League. Find the median points scored per season for the top 13 scorers.

144, 144, 145, 145, 145, 146, 147, 149, 150, 155, 161, 164, 176

SOLUTION The data items are arranged from smallest to largest. There are 13 data items, so $n = 13$. The median is the value in the

$$\frac{n+1}{2} \text{ position} = \frac{13+1}{2} \text{ position} = \frac{14}{2} \text{ position} = \text{seventh position.}$$

We find the median by selecting the data item in the seventh position.

Position 3 Position 4 Position 7

144, 144, 145, 145, 145, 146, 147, 149, 150, 155, 161, 164, 176

Position 1 Position 2 Position 5 Position 6

The median is 147. Notice that six data items lie above 147 and six data items lie below it. The median points scored per season for the top 13 scorers in the National Football League is 147.

CHECK POINT 4 Find the median for the following group of data items:

1, 2, 2, 2, 3, 3, 3, 3, 3, 5, 6, 7, 7, 10, 11, 13, 19, 24, 26.

TABLE 12.7 NUMBER OF HOME RUNS BY BASEBALL TEAMS IN THE NATIONAL LEAGUE, 2005

Team	Home Runs
Washington Nationals	117
Florida Marlins	128
San Francisco Giants	128
San Diego Padres	130
Pittsburgh Pirates	139
Los Angeles Dodgers	149
Colorado Rockies	150
Houston Astros	161
Philadelphia Phillies	167
St. Louis Cardinals	170
Milwaukee Brewers	175
New York Mets	175
Atlanta Braves	184
Arizona Diamondbacks	191
Chicago Cubs	194
Cincinnati Reds	222

Source: The World Almanac

EXAMPLE 5 FINDING THE MEDIAN USING THE POSITION FORMULA

Table 12.7 gives the number of home runs for the 16 baseball teams in the National League in 2005. Find the median number of home runs for these teams.

SOLUTION The data items are arranged from smallest to largest. There are 16 data items, so $n = 16$. The median is the value in the

$$\frac{n+1}{2} \text{ position} = \frac{16+1}{2} \text{ position} = \frac{17}{2} \text{ position} = 8.5 \text{ position.}$$

This means that the median is the mean of the data items in positions 8 and 9.

Position 3 · Position 4 · Position 7 · Position 8 · Position 9

117, 128, 128, 130, 139, 149, 150, [161, 167,] 170, 175, 175, 184, 191, 194, 222

Position 1 · Position 2 · Position 5 · Position 6

$$\text{Median} = \frac{161 + 167}{2} = \frac{328}{2} = 164$$

The median number of home runs for the teams in the National League in 2005 was 164.

CHECK POINT 5 Listed below are the number of home runs for each of the 14 baseball teams in the American League in 2005. Find the median number of home runs for these teams.

126, 130, 134, 136, 147, 155, 157, 168, 189, 199, 200, 207, 229, 260

When individual data items are listed from smallest to largest, you can find the median by identifying the item or items in the middle or by using the $\frac{n+1}{2}$ formula for its position. However, the formula for the position of the median is useful when data items are organized in a frequency distribution.

EXAMPLE 6 FINDING THE MEDIAN FOR A FREQUENCY DISTRIBUTION

The frequency distribution for the stress-level ratings of 151 students is repeated below using a horizontal format. Find the median stress-level rating.

Stress rating	x	0	1	2	3	4	5	6	7	8	9	10
Number of college students	f	2	1	3	12	16	18	13	31	26	15	14

Total: $n = 151$

SOLUTION There are 151 data items, so $n = 151$. The median is the value in the

$$\frac{n+1}{2} \text{ position} = \frac{151+1}{2} \text{ position} = \frac{152}{2} \text{ position} = 76\text{th position.}$$

We find the median by selecting the data item in the 76th position. The frequency distribution indicates that the data items begin with

0, 0, 1, 2, 2, 2, ...

We can write the data items all out and then select the median, the 76th data item. A more efficient way to proceed is to count down the frequency column in the distribution until we identify the 76th data item:

x	f	We count down the frequency column.
0	2	1, 2
1	1	3
2	3	4, 5, 6
3	12	7, 8, 9, 10, 11, 12, 13, 14, 15, 16, 17, 18
4	16	19, 20, 21, 22, 23, 24, 25, 26, 27, 28, 29, 30, 31, 32, 33, 34
5	18	35, 36, 37, 38, 39, 40, 41, 42, 43, 44, 45, 46, 47, 48, 49, 50, 51, 52,
6	13	53, 54, 55, 56, 57, 58, 59, 60, 61, 62, 63, 64, 65
7	31	66, 67, 68, 69, 70, 71, 72, 73, 74, 75, 76
8	26	
9	15	
10	14	

Stop counting. We've reached the 76th data item.

The 76th data item is 7. The median stress-level rating is 7.

CHECK POINT 6 Find the median for the following frequency distribution.

Age at presidential inauguration

Number of U.S. presidents assuming office in the 20th century with the given age

x	42	43	46	51	52	54	55	56	60	61	64	69
f	1	1	1	3	1	2	2	2	1	2	1	1

Statisticians generally use the median, rather than the mean, when reporting income. Why? Our next example will help to answer this question.

EXAMPLE 7 COMPARING THE MEDIAN AND THE MEAN

Five employees in the assembly section of a television manufacturing company earn salaries of \$19,700, \$20,400, \$21,500, \$22,600, and \$23,000 annually. The section manager has an annual salary of \$95,000.

a. Find the median annual salary for the six people.

b. Find the mean annual salary for the six people.

SOLUTION

a. To compute the median, first arrange the salaries in order:

\$19,700, \$20,400, \$21,500, \$22,600, \$23,000, \$95,000.

Because the list contains an even number of data items, six, the median is the mean of the two middle items.

$$\text{Median} = \frac{\$21{,}500 + \$22{,}600}{2} = \frac{\$44{,}100}{2} = \$22{,}050$$

The median annual salary is \$22,050.

b. We find the mean annual salary by adding the six annual salaries and dividing by 6.

$$\text{Mean} = \frac{\$19{,}700 + \$20{,}400 + \$21{,}500 + \$22{,}600 + \$23{,}000 + \$95{,}000}{6}$$

$$= \frac{\$202{,}200}{6} = \$33{,}700$$

The mean annual salary is \$33,700.

In Example 7, the median annual salary is $22,050 and the mean annual salary is $33,700. Why such a big difference between these two measures of central tendency? The relatively high annual salary of the section manager, $95,000, pulls the mean salary to a value considerably higher than the median salary. When one or more data items are much greater than the other items, these extreme values can greatly influence the mean. In cases like this, the median is often more representative of the data.

This is why the median, rather than the mean, is used to summarize the incomes, by gender and race, shown in Figure 12.6. Because no one can earn less than $0, the distribution of income must come to an end at $0 for each of these eight groups. By contrast, there is no upper limit on income on the high side. In the United States, the wealthiest 5% of the population earn about 21% of the total income. The relatively few people with very high annual incomes tend to pull the mean income to a value considerably greater than the median income. Reporting mean incomes in Figure 12.6 would inflate the numbers shown, making them nonrepresentative of the millions of workers in each of the eight groups.

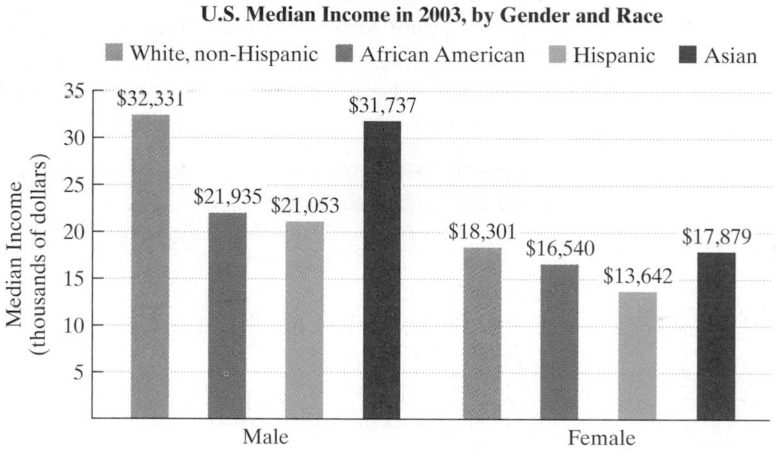

FIGURE 12.6
Source: U.S. Census Bureau

CHECK POINT 7 The ten countries in Table 12.8 accounted for 75% of the nearly $900 billion spent in 2003 on defense worldwide.

TABLE 12.8 TOP TEN MILITARY SPENDERS, 2003

Country	National Expenditure (billions of dollars)	Dollars Spent per Resident	Percentage of Global Military Spending
United States	$417.4	$1419	47%
Japan	$ 46.9	$ 367	5%
UK	$ 37.1	$ 627	4%
France	$ 35.0	$ 583	4%
China	$ 32.8	$ 25	4%
Germany	$ 27.2	$ 329	3%
Italy	$ 20.8	$ 362	2%
Iran	$ 19.2	$ 279	2%
Saudi Arabia	$ 19.1	$ 789	2%
South Korea	$ 13.9	$ 292	2%

Source: SIPRI, "The Major Spenders in 2003"

a. Find the mean national expenditure on defense, in billions of dollars, for the ten countries.

b. Find the median national expenditure on defense, in billions of dollars, for the ten countries.

c. Describe why one of the measures of central tendency is so much greater than the other.

3 Determine the mode for a data set.

The Mode

Let's take one final look at the frequency distribution for the stress-level ratings of 151 college students.

Stress rating

Number of college students

x	0	1	2	3	4	5	6	7	8	9	10
f	2	1	3	12	16	18	13	31	26	15	14

7 is the stress rating with the greatest frequency.

The data value that occurs most often in this distribution is 7, the stress rating for 31 of the 151 students. We call 7 the *mode* of this distribution.

THE MODE

The **mode** is the data value that occurs most often in a data set. If no data items are repeated, then the data set has no mode. If more than one data value has the highest frequency, then each of these data values is a mode.

EXAMPLE 8 FINDING THE MODE

Find the mode for the following group of data:

$$7, 2, 4, 7, 8, 10.$$

SOLUTION The number 7 occurs more often than any other. Therefore, 7 is the mode.

CHECK POINT 8 Find the mode for the following group of data:

$$8, 6, 2, 4, 6, 8, 10, 8.$$

4 Determine the midrange for a data set.

Be aware that a data set might not have a mode. For example, no data item in 2, 1, 4, 5, 3 is repeated, so this data group has no mode. By contrast, 3, 3, 4, 5, 6, 6 has two data values with the highest frequency, namely 3 and 6. Each of these data values is a mode and the data set is said to be **bimodal**.

TABLE 12.9 TEN HOTTEST U.S. CITIES

City	Mean Temperature
Key West, FL	77.8°
Miami, FL	75.9°
West Palm Beach, FL	74.7°
Fort Myers, FL	74.4°
Yuma, AZ	74.2°
Brownsville, TX	73.8°
Phoenix, AZ	72.6°
Vero Beach, FL	72.4°
Orlando, FL	72.3°
Tampa, FL	72.3°

Source: National Oceanic and Atmospheric Administration

The Midrange

Table 12.9 shows the ten hottest cities in the United States. Because temperature is constantly changing, you might wonder how the mean temperatures shown in the table are obtained.

First, we need to find a representative daily temperature. This is obtained by adding the lowest and highest temperatures for the day and then dividing this sum by 2. Next, we take the representative daily temperatures for all 365 days, add them, and divide the sum by 365. These are the mean temperatures that appear in Table 12.9.

Representative daily temperature,

$$\frac{\text{lowest daily temperature} + \text{highest daily temperature}}{2},$$

is an example of a measure of central tendency called the *midrange*.

THE MIDRANGE

The **midrange** is found by adding the lowest and highest data values and dividing the sum by 2.

$$\text{Midrange} = \frac{\text{lowest data value} + \text{highest data value}}{2}$$

EXAMPLE 9 FINDING THE MIDRANGE

One criticism of major league baseball is that the discrepancy between team payrolls hampers fair competition. In 2006, the New York Yankees had the greatest payroll, a record $194,663,100 (median salary: $2,925,000). The Florida Marlins were the worst paid team, with a payroll of $14,998,500 (median salary: $327,000). Find the midrange for the annual payroll of major league baseball teams in 2006.
(*Source*: usatoday.com)

SOLUTION

$$\text{Midrange} = \frac{\text{lowest annual payroll} + \text{highest annual payroll}}{2}$$

$$= \frac{\$14{,}998{,}500 + \$194{,}663{,}100}{2} = \frac{\$209{,}661{,}600}{2} = \$104{,}830{,}800$$

The midrange for the annual payroll of major league baseball teams in 2006 was $104,830,800.

We can find the mean annual payroll of the 30 professional baseball teams in 2006 by adding up the payrolls of all 30 teams and then dividing the sum by 30. It is much faster to calculate the midrange, which is often used as an estimate for the mean.

CHECK POINT 9 The best paid state governor is in New York, earning $179,000 annually. The worst paid is the governor of Maine, earning $70,000 annually. Find the midrange for annual salaries of U.S. governors.

EXAMPLE 10 FINDING THE FOUR MEASURES OF CENTRAL TENDENCY

Suppose your six exam grades in a course are

52, 69, 75, 86, 86, and 92.

Compute your final course grade (90–100 = A, 80–89 = B, 70–79 = C, 60–69 = D, below 60 = F) using the

a. mean. **b.** median. **c.** mode. **d.** midrange.

SOLUTION

a. The mean is the sum of the data items divided by the number of items, 6.

$$\text{Mean} = \frac{52 + 69 + 75 + 86 + 86 + 92}{6} = \frac{460}{6} \approx 76.67$$

Using the mean, your final course grade is C.

b. The six data items, 52, 69, 75, 86, 86, and 92, are arranged in order. Because the number of data items is even, the median is the mean of the two middle items.

$$\text{Median} = \frac{75 + 86}{2} = \frac{161}{2} = 80.5$$

Using the median, your final course grade is B.

c. The mode is the data value that occurs most frequently. Because 86 occurs most often, the mode is 86. Using the mode, your final course grade is B.

d. The midrange is the mean of the lowest and highest data values.

$$\text{Midrange} = \frac{52 + 92}{2} = \frac{144}{2} = 72$$

Using the midrange, your final course grade is C.

CHECK POINT 10 *Consumer Reports* magazine gave the following data for the number of calories in a meat hot dog for each of 17 brands:

173, 191, 182, 190, 172, 147, 146, 138, 175, 136, 179, 153, 107, 195, 135, 140, 138.

Find the mean, median, mode, and midrange for the number of calories in a meat hot dog for the 17 brands. If necessary, round answers to the nearest tenth of a calorie.

EXERCISE SET 12.2

• Practice Exercises

In Exercises 1–8, find the mean for each group of data items.

1. 7, 4, 3, 2, 8, 5, 1, 3
2. 11, 6, 4, 0, 2, 1, 12, 0, 0
3. 91, 95, 99, 97, 93, 95
4. 100, 100, 90, 30, 70, 100
5. 100, 40, 70, 40, 60
6. 1, 3, 5, 10, 8, 5, 6, 8
7. 1.6, 3.8, 5.0, 2.7, 4.2, 4.2, 3.2, 4.7, 3.6, 2.5, 2.5
8. 1.4, 2.1, 1.6, 3.0, 1.4, 2.2, 1.4, 9.0, 9.0, 1.8

In Exercises 9–12, find the mean for the data items in the given frequency distribution.

9.

Score x	Frequency f
1	1
2	3
3	4
4	4
5	6
6	5
7	3
8	2

10.

Score x	Frequency f
1	2
2	4
3	5
4	7
5	6
6	4
7	3

11.

Score x	Frequency f
1	1
2	1
3	2
4	5
5	7
6	9
7	8
8	6
9	4
10	3

12.

Score x	Frequency f
1	3
2	4
3	6
4	8
5	9
6	7
7	5
8	2
9	1
10	1

In Exercises 13–20, find the median for each group of data items.

13. 7, 4, 3, 2, 8, 5, 1, 3
14. 11, 6, 4, 0, 2, 1, 12, 0, 0
15. 91, 95, 99, 97, 93, 95
16. 100, 100, 90, 30, 70, 100
17. 100, 40, 70, 40, 60
18. 1, 3, 5, 10, 8, 5, 6, 8
19. 1.6, 3.8, 5.0, 2.7, 4.2, 4.2, 3.2, 4.7, 3.6, 2.5, 2.5
20. 1.4, 2.1, 1.6, 3.0, 1.4, 2.2, 1.4, 9.0, 9.0, 1.8

Find the median for the data items in the frequency distribution in

21. Exercise 9.
22. Exercise 10.
23. Exercise 11.
24. Exercise 12.

In Exercises 25–32, find the mode for each group of data items. If there is no mode, so state.

25. 7, 4, 3, 2, 8, 5, 1, 3
26. 11, 6, 4, 0, 2, 1, 12, 0, 0
27. 91, 95, 99, 97, 93, 95
28. 100, 100, 90, 30, 70, 100
29. 100, 40, 70, 40, 60
30. 1, 3, 5, 10, 8, 5, 6, 8
31. 1.6, 3.8, 5.0, 2.7, 4.2, 4.2, 3.2, 4.7, 3.6, 2.5, 2.5
32. 1.4, 2.1, 1.6, 3.0, 1.4, 2.2, 1.4, 9.0, 9.0, 1.8

Find the mode for the data items in the frequency distribution in

33. Exercise 9.
34. Exercise 10.
35. Exercise 11.
36. Exercise 12.

In Exercises 37–44, find the midrange for each group of data items.

37. 7, 4, 3, 2, 8, 5, 1, 3
38. 11, 6, 4, 0, 2, 1, 12, 0, 0
39. 91, 95, 99, 97, 93, 95
40. 100, 100, 90, 30, 70, 100
41. 100, 40, 70, 40, 60
42. 1, 3, 5, 10, 8, 5, 6, 8
43. 1.6, 3.8, 5.0, 2.7, 4.2, 4.2, 3.2, 4.7, 3.6, 2.5, 2.5
44. 1.4, 2.1, 1.6, 3.0, 1.4, 2.2, 1.4, 9.0, 9.0, 1.8

Find the midrange for the data items in the frequency distribution in

45. Exercise 9.

46. Exercise 10.

47. Exercise 11.

48. Exercise 12.

• Practice Plus

In Exercises 49–54, use each display of data items to find the mean, median, mode, and midrange.

49.

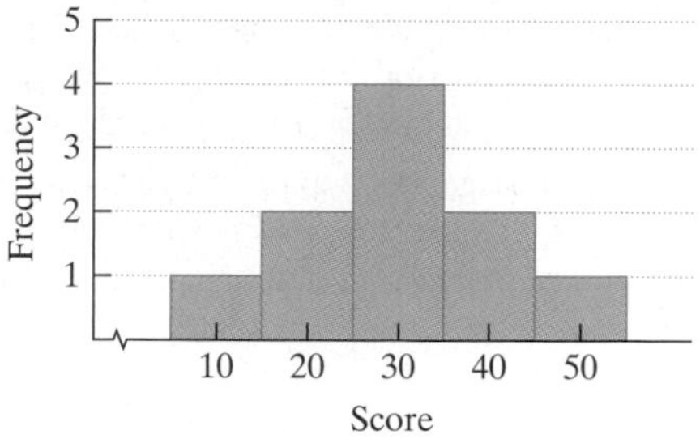

50.

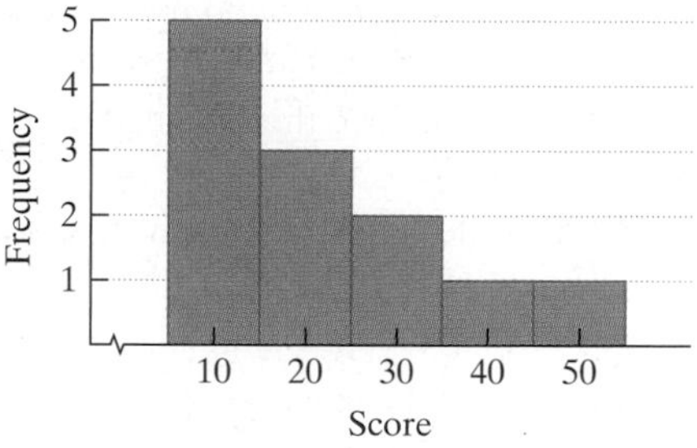

51.

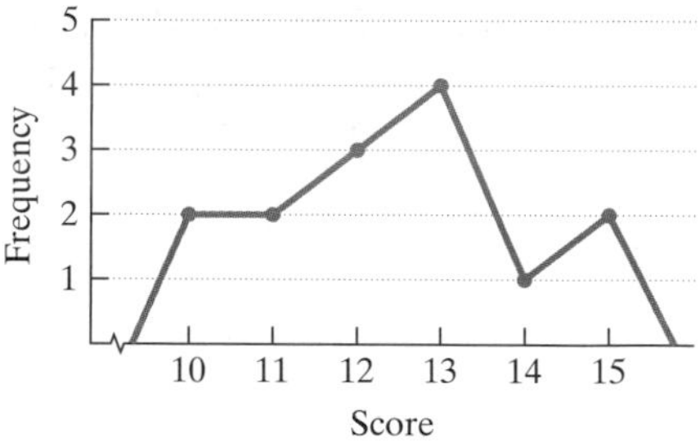

52.

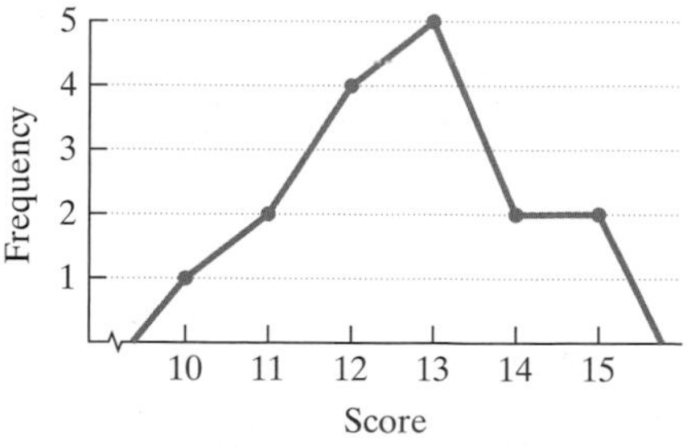

53.

Stems	Leaves			
2	1	4	5	
3	0	1	1	3
4	2	5		

54.

Stems	Leaves			
2	8			
3	2	4	4	9
4	0	1	5	7

• Application Exercises

Exercises 55–59 present data on a variety of topics. For each data set described in boldface, find the

a. *mean.*
b. *median.*
c. *mode (or state that there is no mode).*
d. *midrange.*

55. Ages of the Justices of the United States Supreme Court in 2007

Roberts (52), Stevens (87), Scalia (71), Kennedy (71), Souter (68), Thomas (59), Ginsburg (74), Breyer (69), Alito (56)

56. Number of Reported Violent Attacks against the Homeless in the United States for Various Years from 1995 through 2005

60, 63, 52, 36, 70, 105, 86

Source: National Coalition for the Homeless

57. Number of Home Runs Hit by Each of the 12 Batters for the New York Yankees in 2005

0, 4, 8, 12, 14, 17, 19, 19, 23, 32, 34, 48

Source: The World Almanac

58. Number of Home Runs Hit by Each of the Ten Batters for the Florida Marlins in 2005

2, 3, 4, 5, 6, 8, 9, 16, 33, 33

Source: The World Almanac

59. Number of Social Interactions of College Students In Exercise Set 12.1, we presented a grouped frequency distribution showing the number of social interactions of ten minutes or longer over a one-week period for a group of college students. (These interactions excluded family and work situations.) Use the frequency distribution shown to solve this exercise. (This distribution was obtained by replacing the classes in the grouped frequency distribution previously shown with the midpoints of the classes.)

Social interactions in a week (x); Number of college students (f)

x	2	7	12	17	22	27	32	37	42	47
f	12	16	16	16	10	11	4	3	3	3

The weights (to the nearest five pounds) of 40 randomly selected male college students are organized in a histogram with a superimposed frequency polygon. Use the graph to answer Exercises 60–63.

60. Find the mean weight.

61. Find the median weight.

62. Find the modal weight.

63. Find the midrange weight.

Weights of 40 Male College Students

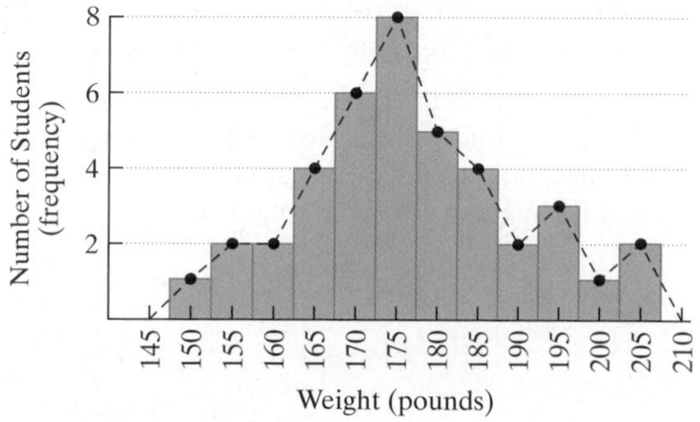

64. An advertisement for a speed-reading course claimed that the "average" reading speed for people completing the course was 1000 words per minute. Shown below are the actual data for the reading speeds per minute for a sample of 24 people who completed the course.

1000	900	800	1000	900	850
650	1000	1050	800	1000	850
700	750	800	850	900	950
600	1100	950	700	750	650

a. Find the mean, median, mode, and midrange. (If you prefer, first organize the data in a frequency distribution.)

b. Which measure of central tendency was given in the advertisement?

c. Which measure of central tendency is the best indicator of the "average" reading speed in this situation? Explain your answer.

65. In one common system for finding a grade-point average, or GPA,

$$A = 4, B = 3, C = 2, D = 1, F = 0.$$

The GPA is calculated by multiplying the number of credit hours for a course and the number assigned to each grade, and then adding these products. Then divide this sum by the total number of credit hours. Because each course grade is weighted according to the number of credits of the course, GPA is called a *weighted mean*. Calculate the GPA for this transcript:

Sociology: 3 cr. A; Biology: 3.5 cr. C; Music: 1 cr. B; Math: 4 cr. B; English: 3 cr. C.

• Writing in Mathematics

66. What is the mean and how is it obtained?

67. What is the median and how is it obtained?

68. What is the mode and how is it obtained?

69. What is the midrange and how is it obtained?

70. The "average" income in the United States can be given by the mean or the median.

a. Which measure would be used in anti-U.S. propaganda? Explain your answer.

b. Which measure would be used in pro-U.S. propaganda? Explain your answer.

71. In a class of 40 students, 21 have examination scores of 77%. Which measure or measures of central tendency can you immediately determine? Explain your answer.

72. You read an article that states, "Of the 411 players in the National Basketball Association, only 138 make more than the average salary of $3.12 million." Is $3.12 million the mean or the median salary? Explain your answer.

73. A student's parents promise to pay for next semester's tuition if an A average is earned in chemistry. With examination grades of 97%, 97%, 75%, 70%, and 55%, the student reports that an A average has been earned. Which measure of central tendency is the student reporting as the average? How is this student misrepresenting the course performance with statistics?

74. According to the National Oceanic and Atmospheric Administration, the coldest city in the United States is International Falls, Minnesota, with a mean Fahrenheit temperature of 36.8°. Explain how this mean is obtained.

75. Using Table 12.8 on page 699, explain why the mean amount spent on defense per resident is so much greater than the median amount spent on defense per resident for the ten countries.

• Critical Thinking Exercises

76. Give an example of a set of six examination grades (from 0 to 100) with each of the following characteristics:

a. The mean and the median have the same value, but the mode has a different value.

b. The mean and the mode have the same value, but the median has a different value.

c. The mean is greater than the median.

d. The mode is greater than the mean.

e. The mean, median, and mode have the same value.

f. The mean and mode have values of 72.

77. On an examination given to 30 students, no student scored below the mean. Describe how this occurred.

• Group Exercises

78. Select a characteristic, such as shoe size or height, for which each member of the group can provide a number. Choose a characteristic of genuine interest to the group. For this characteristic, organize the data collected into a frequency distribution and a graph. Compute the mean, median, mode, and midrange. Discuss any differences among these values. What happens if the group is divided (men and women, or people under a certain age and people over a certain age) and these measures of central tendency are computed for each of the subgroups? Attempt to use measures of central tendency to discover something interesting about the entire group or the subgroups.

79. A recent book on spotting bad statistics and learning to think critically about these influential numbers is *Damn Lies and Statistics* by Joel Best (University of California Press, 2001). This activity is designed for six people. Each person should select one chapter from Best's book. The group report should include examples of the use, misuse, and abuse of statistical information. Explain exactly how and why bad statistics emerge, spread, and come to shape policy debates. What specific ways does Best recommend to detect bad statistics?

SECTION 12.3 • MEASURES OF DISPERSION

OBJECTIVES

1. Determine the range for a data set.
2. Determine the standard deviation for a data set.

When you think of Houston, Texas and Honolulu, Hawaii, do balmy temperatures come to mind? Both cities have a mean temperature of 75°. However, the mean temperature does not tell the whole story. The temperature in Houston differs seasonally from a low of about 40° in January to a high of close to 100° in July and August. By contrast, Honolulu's temperature varies less throughout the year, usually ranging between 60° and 90°.

Measures of dispersion are used to describe the spread of data items in a data set. Two of the most common measures of dispersion, the *range* and the *standard deviation*, are discussed in this section.

1 Determine the range for a data set.

The Range

A quick but rough measure of dispersion is the **range**, the difference between the highest and lowest data values in a data set. For example, if Houston's hottest annual temperature is 103° and its coldest annual temperature is 33°, the range in temperature is

$$103° - 33°, \quad \text{or} \quad 70°.$$

If Honolulu's hottest day is 89° and its coldest day 61°, the range in temperature is

$$89° - 61°, \quad \text{or} \quad 28°.$$

THE RANGE

The **range**, the difference between the highest and lowest data values in a data set, indicates the total spread of the data.

$$\text{Range} = \text{highest data value} - \text{lowest data value}$$

EXAMPLE 1 COMPUTING THE RANGE

Figure 12.7 shows the number of workers, in millions, for the five countries with the largest labor forces. Find the range of workers, in millions, for these five countries.

Countries with the Most Workers

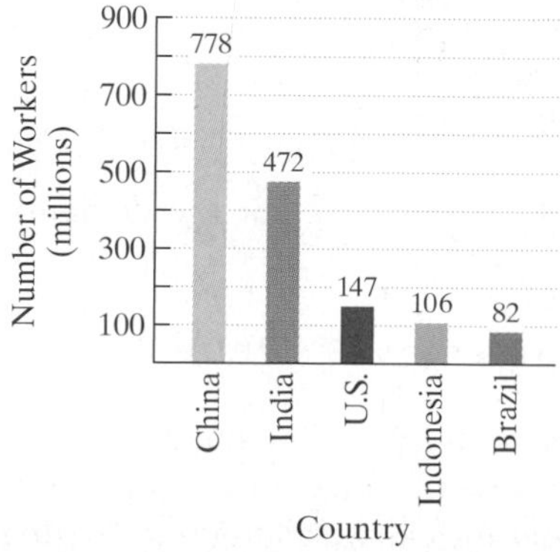

FIGURE 12.7
Source: Central Intelligence Agency

SOLUTION

$$\begin{aligned}\text{Range} &= \text{highest data value} - \text{lowest data value}\\ &= 778 - 82 = 696\end{aligned}$$

The range is 696 million workers.

CHECK POINT 1 Find the range for the following group of data items:

4, 2, 11, 7.

The Standard Deviation

A second measure of dispersion, and one that is dependent on *all* of the data items, is called the **standard deviation**. The standard deviation is found by determining how much each data item differs from the mean.

In order to compute the standard deviation, it is necessary to find by how much each data item deviates from the mean. First compute the mean. Then subtract the mean from each data item. Example 2 shows how this is done. In Example 3, we will use this skill to actually find the standard deviation.

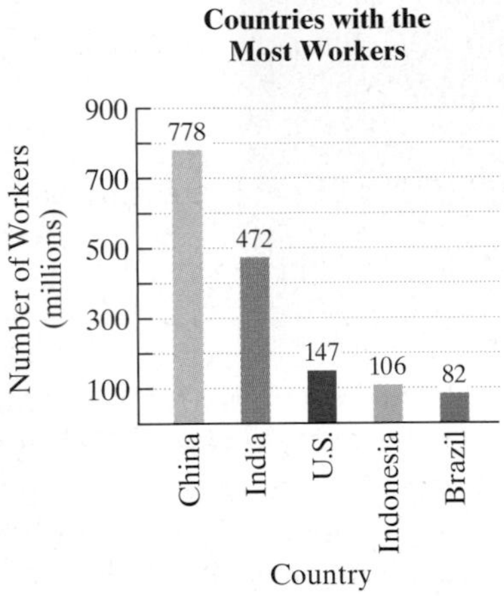

FIGURE 12.7 (repeated)
Source: Central Intelligence Agency

TABLE 12.10 DEVIATIONS FROM THE MEAN

Data item	Deviation: data item − mean
778	778 − 317 = 461
472	472 − 317 = 155
147	147 − 317 = −170
106	106 − 317 = −211
82	82 − 317 = −235

EXAMPLE 2 PREPARING TO FIND THE STANDARD DEVIATION; FINDING DEVIATIONS FROM THE MEAN

Find the deviations from the mean for the five data items 778, 472, 147, 106, and 82, shown in Figure 12.7.

SOLUTION First, calculate the mean.

$$\text{Mean} = \frac{\Sigma x}{n} = \frac{778 + 472 + 147 + 106 + 82}{5} = \frac{1585}{5} = 317$$

The mean for the five countries with the largest labor forces is 317 million workers. Now, let's find by how much each of the five data items in Figure 12.7 differs from 317, the mean. For China, with 778 million workers, the computation is shown as follows:

$$\begin{aligned}\text{Deviation from mean} &= \text{data item} - \text{mean}\\ &= 778 - 317 = 461.\end{aligned}$$

This indicates that the labor force in China exceeds the mean by 461 million workers.

The computation for the United States, with 147 million workers, is given by

$$\begin{aligned}\text{Deviation from mean} &= \text{data item} - \text{mean}\\ &= 147 - 317 = -170.\end{aligned}$$

This indicates that the labor force in the United States is 170 million workers below the mean.

The deviations from the mean for each of the five given data items are shown in Table 12.10.

CHECK POINT 2 Compute the mean for the following group of data items:

2, 4, 7, 11.

Then find the deviations from the mean for the four data items. Organize your work in table form just like Table 12.10. Keep track of these computations. You will be using them in Check Point 3.

The sum of the deviations for a set of data is always zero. For the deviations shown in Table 12.10,

$$461 + 155 + (-170) + (-211) + (-235) = 616 + (-616) = 0.$$

This shows that we cannot find a measure of dispersion by finding the mean of the deviations, because this value is always zero. However, a kind of average of the deviations from the mean, called the **standard deviation**, can be computed. We do so by squaring each deviation and later introducing a square root in the computation. Here are the details on how to find the standard deviation for a set of data:

2 Determine the standard deviation for a data set.

COMPUTING THE STANDARD DEVIATION FOR A DATA SET

1. Find the mean of the data items.
2. Find the deviation of each data item from the mean:
$$\text{data item} - \text{mean}.$$
3. Square each deviation:
$$(\text{data item} - \text{mean})^2.$$
4. Sum the squared deviations:
$$\Sigma(\text{data item} - \text{mean})^2.$$
5. Divide the sum in step 4 by $n - 1$, where n represents the number of data items:
$$\frac{\Sigma(\text{data item} - \text{mean})^2}{n - 1}.$$
6. Take the square root of the quotient in step 5. This value is the standard deviation for the data set.
$$\text{Standard deviation} = \sqrt{\frac{\Sigma(\text{data item} - \text{mean})^2}{n - 1}}$$

The computation of the standard deviation can be organized using a table with three columns:

Data item	Deviation: Data item − mean	$(\text{Deviation})^2$: $(\text{Data item} - \text{mean})^2$

In Example 2, we worked out the first two columns of such a table. Let's continue working with the data for the countries with the most workers and compute the standard deviation.

EXAMPLE 3 COMPUTING THE STANDARD DEVIATION

Figure 12.7, showing the number of workers, in millions, for the five countries with the largest labor forces, appears in the margin on page 706. Find the standard deviation, in millions, for these five countries.

SOLUTION

Step 1. Find the mean. From our work in Example 2, the mean is 317.

Step 2. Find the deviation of each data item from the mean: data item − mean. This, too, was done in Example 2 for each of the five data items.

Step 3. Square each deviation: $(\text{data item} - \text{mean})^2$. We square each of the numbers in the (data item − mean) column, shown in Table 12.11. Notice that squaring the difference always results in a positive number.

TABLE 12.11 COMPUTING THE STANDARD DEVIATION

Data item	Deviation: data item − mean	$(\text{Deviation})^2$: $(\text{data item} - \text{mean})^2$
778	$778 - 317 = 461$	$461^2 = 461 \cdot 461 = 212{,}521$
472	$472 - 317 = 155$	$155^2 = 155 \cdot 155 = 24{,}025$
147	$147 - 317 = -170$	$(-170)^2 = (-170)(-170) = 28{,}900$
106	$106 - 317 = -211$	$(-211)^2 = (-211)(-211) = 44{,}521$
82	$82 - 317 = -235$	$(-235)^2 = (-235)(-235) = 55{,}225$
Totals:	0	365,192

The sum of the deviations for a set of data is always zero.

Adding the five numbers in the third column gives the sum of the squared deviations: $\Sigma(\text{data item} - \text{mean})^2$.

TECHNOLOGY

Almost all scientific and graphing calculators compute the standard deviation of a set of data. Using the data items in Example 3,

778, 472, 147, 106, 82,

the keystrokes for obtaining the standard deviation on many scientific calculators are as follows:

778 [Σ+] 472 [Σ+] 147 [Σ+]

106 [Σ+] 82 [Σ+] [2nd] [$\sigma n - 1$].

Graphing calculators require that you specify if data items are from an entire population or a sample of the population.

Step 4. Sum the squared deviations: $\Sigma(\text{data item} - \text{mean})^2$. This step is shown in Table 12.11 on the previous page. The squares in the third column were added, resulting in a sum of 365,192.

Step 5. Divide the sum in step 4 by $n - 1$, where n represents the number of data items. The number of data items is 5 so we divide by 4.

$$\frac{\Sigma(\text{data item} - \text{mean})^2}{n-1} = \frac{365{,}192}{5-1} = \frac{365{,}192}{4} = 91{,}298$$

Step 6. The standard deviation is the square root of the quotient in step 5.

$$\text{Standard deviation} = \sqrt{\frac{\Sigma(\text{data item} - \text{mean})^2}{n-1}} = \sqrt{91{,}298} \approx 302.16$$

The standard deviation for the five countries with the largest labor forces is approximately 302.16 million workers.

CHECK POINT 3 Find the standard deviation for the group of data items in Check Point 2 on page 706. Round to two decimal places.

Example 4 illustrates that as the spread of data items increases, the standard deviation gets larger.

EXAMPLE 4 COMPUTING THE STANDARD DEVIATION

Find the standard deviation of the data items in each of the samples shown below.

Sample A	**Sample B**
17, 18, 19, 20, 21, 22, 23	5, 10, 15, 20, 25, 30, 35

SOLUTION Begin by finding the mean for each sample.

Sample A:

$$\text{Mean} = \frac{17 + 18 + 19 + 20 + 21 + 22 + 23}{7} = \frac{140}{7} = 20$$

Sample B:

$$\text{Mean} = \frac{5 + 10 + 15 + 20 + 25 + 30 + 35}{7} = \frac{140}{7} = 20$$

Although both samples have the same mean, the data items in sample B are more spread out. Thus, we would expect sample B to have the greater standard deviation. The computation of the standard deviation requires that we find $\Sigma(\text{data item} - \text{mean})^2$, shown in Table 12.12.

TABLE 12.12 COMPUTING STANDARD DEVIATIONS FOR TWO SAMPLES

Sample A			Sample B		
Data item	**Deviation: data item − mean**	**(Deviation)^2: (data item − mean)^2**	**Data item**	**Deviation: data item − mean**	**(Deviation)^2: (data item − mean)^2**
17	$17 - 20 = -3$	$(-3)^2 = 9$	5	$5 - 20 = -15$	$(-15)^2 = 225$
18	$18 - 20 = -2$	$(-2)^2 = 4$	10	$10 - 20 = -10$	$(-10)^2 = 100$
19	$19 - 20 = -1$	$(-1)^2 = 1$	15	$15 - 20 = -5$	$(-5)^2 = 25$
20	$20 - 20 = 0$	$0^2 = 0$	20	$20 - 20 = 0$	$0^2 = 0$
21	$21 - 20 = 1$	$1^2 = 1$	25	$25 - 20 = 5$	$5^2 = 25$
22	$22 - 20 = 2$	$2^2 = 4$	30	$30 - 20 = 10$	$10^2 = 100$
23	$23 - 20 = 3$	$3^2 = 9$	35	$35 - 20 = 15$	$15^2 = 225$
Totals:		$\Sigma(\text{data item} - \text{mean})^2 = 28$			$\Sigma(\text{data item} - \text{mean})^2 = 700$

Each sample contains seven data items, so we compute the standard deviation by dividing the sums in Table 12.12, 28 and 700, by 7 − 1, or 6. Then we take the square root of each quotient.

$$\text{Standard deviation} = \sqrt{\frac{\Sigma(\text{data item} - \text{mean})^2}{n - 1}}$$

Sample A:

$$\text{Standard deviation} = \sqrt{\frac{28}{6}} \approx 2.16$$

Sample B:

$$\text{Standard deviation} = \sqrt{\frac{700}{6}} \approx 10.80$$

Sample A has a standard deviation of approximately 2.16 and sample B has a standard deviation of approximately 10.80. The scores in sample B are more spread out than those in sample A.

CHECK POINT 4 Find the standard deviation of the data items in each of the samples shown below. Round to two decimal places.

Sample A: 73, 75, 77, 79, 81, 83

Sample B: 40, 44, 92, 94, 98, 100

Figure 12.8 illustrates four sets of data items organized in histograms. From left to right, the data items are

Figure 12.8(a): 4, 4, 4, 4, 4, 4, 4

Figure 12.8(b): 3, 3, 4, 4, 4, 5, 5

Figure 12.8(c): 3, 3, 3, 4, 5, 5, 5

Figure 12.8(d): 1, 1, 1, 4, 7, 7, 7.

Each data set has a mean of 4. However, as the spread of data items increases, the standard deviation gets larger. Observe that when all the data items are the same, the standard deviation is 0.

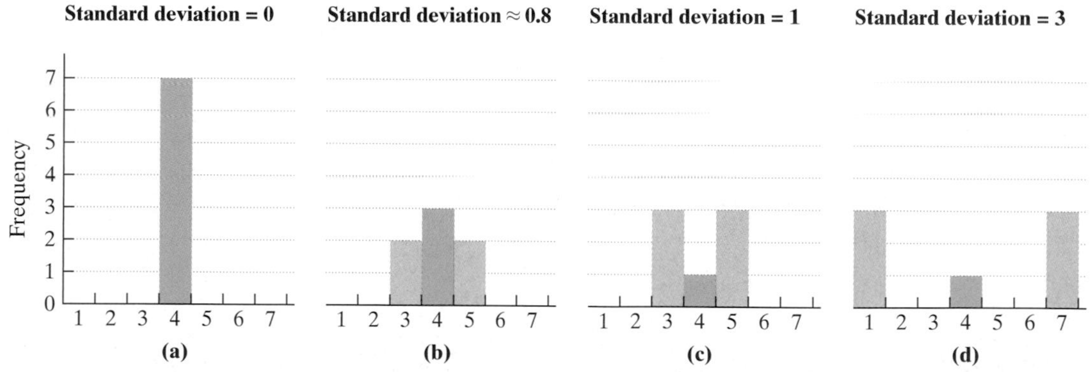

FIGURE 12.8 The standard deviation gets larger with increased dispersion among data items. In each case, the mean is 4.

EXAMPLE 5 INTERPRETING STANDARD DEVIATION

Two fifth-grade classes have nearly identical mean scores on an aptitude test, but one class has a standard deviation three times that of the other. All other factors being equal, which class is easier to teach, and why?

SOLUTION The class with the smaller standard deviation is easier to teach because there is less variation among student aptitudes. Course work can be aimed at the average student without too much concern that the work will be too easy for some or too difficult for others. By contrast, the class with greater dispersion poses a greater challenge. By teaching to the average student, the students whose scores are significantly above the mean will be bored; students whose scores are significantly below the mean will be confused.

CHECK POINT 5 Shown below are the means and standard deviations of the yearly returns on two investments from 1926 through 2004.

Investment	Mean Yearly Interest	Standard Deviation
Small-Company Stocks	17.5%	33.3%
Large-Company Stocks	12.4%	20.4%

Source: Summary Statistics of Annual Total Returns 1926 to 2004 Yearbook, Ibbotson Associates, Chicago

a. Use the means to determine which investment provided the greater yearly return.

b. Use the standard deviations to determine which investment had the greater risk. Explain your answer.

EXERCISE SET 12.3

• Practice Exercises

In Exercises 1–6, find the range for each group of data items.

1. 1, 2, 3, 4, 5
2. 16, 17, 18, 19, 20
3. 7, 9, 9, 15
4. 11, 13, 14, 15, 17
5. 3, 3, 4, 4, 5, 5
6. 3, 3, 3, 4, 5, 5, 5

In Exercises 7–10, a group of data items and their mean are given.

a. *Find the deviation from the mean for each of the data items.*

b. *Find the sum of the deviations in part (a).*

7. 3, 5, 7, 12, 18, 27; Mean = 12
8. 84, 88, 90, 95, 98; Mean = 91
9. 29, 38, 48, 49, 53, 77; Mean = 49
10. 60, 60, 62, 65, 65, 65, 66, 67, 70, 70; Mean = 65

In Exercises 11–16, find **a.** *the mean;* **b.** *the deviation from the mean for each data item; and* **c.** *the sum of the deviations in part (b).*

11. 85, 95, 90, 85, 100
12. 94, 62, 88, 85, 91
13. 146, 153, 155, 160, 161
14. 150, 132, 144, 122
15. 2.25, 3.50, 2.75, 3.10, 1.90
16. 0.35, 0.37, 0.41, 0.39, 0.43

In Exercises 17–26, find the standard deviation for each group of data items. Round answers to two decimal places.

17. 1, 2, 3, 4, 5
18. 16, 17, 18, 19, 20
19. 7, 9, 9, 15
20. 11, 13, 14, 15, 17
21. 3, 3, 4, 4, 5, 5
22. 3, 3, 3, 4, 5, 5, 5
23. 1, 1, 1, 4, 7, 7, 7
24. 6, 6, 6, 6, 7, 7, 7, 4, 8, 3
25. 9, 5, 9, 5, 9, 5, 9, 5
26. 6, 10, 6, 10, 6, 10, 6, 10

In Exercises 27–28, compute the mean, range, and standard deviation for the data items in each of the three samples. Then describe one way in which the samples are alike and one way in which they are different.

27. Sample A: 6, 8, 10, 12, 14, 16, 18
Sample B: 6, 7, 8, 12, 16, 17, 18
Sample C: 6, 6, 6, 12, 18, 18, 18

28. Sample A: 8, 10, 12, 14, 16, 18, 20
Sample B: 8, 9, 10, 14, 18, 19, 20
Sample C: 8, 8, 8, 14, 20, 20, 20

• Practice Plus

In Exercises 29–36, use each display of data items to find the standard deviation. Where necessary, round answers to two decimal places.

29.

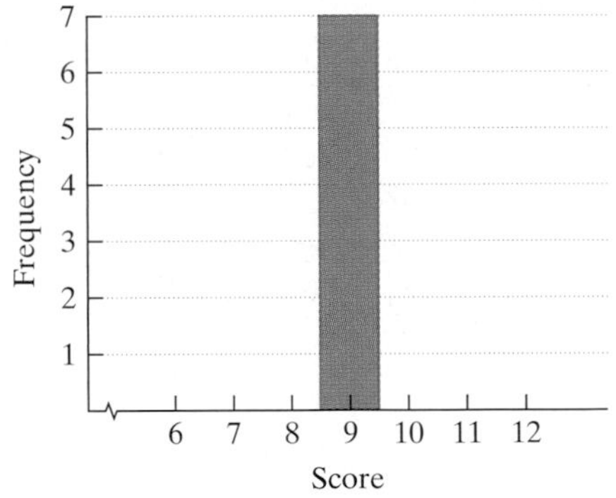

30.

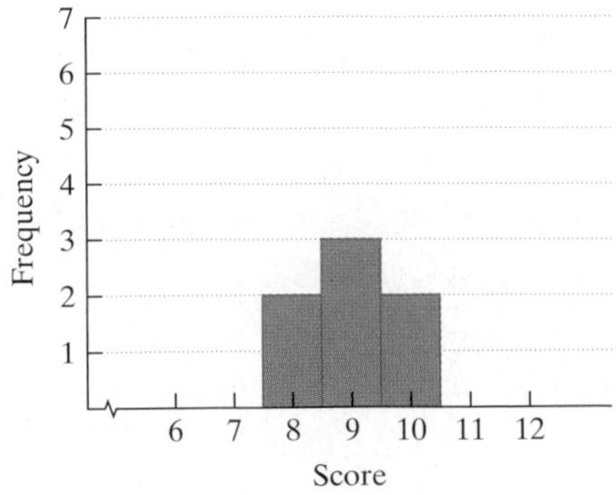

31.

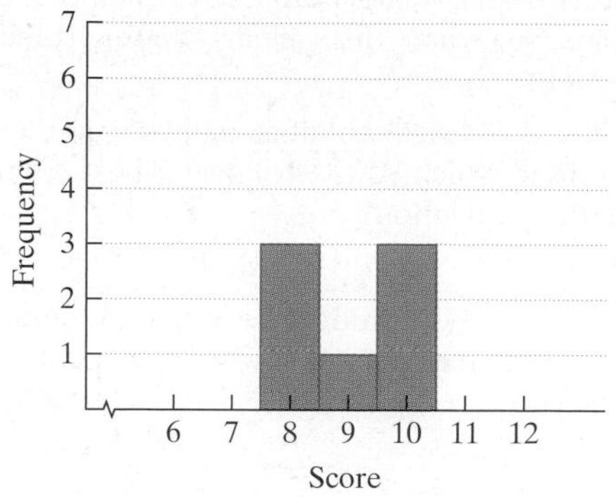

32.

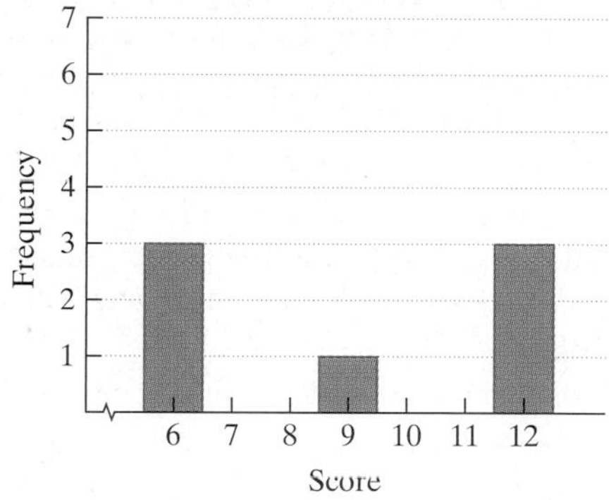

33.

Stems	Leaves
0	5
1	0 5
2	0 5

34.

Stems	Leaves
0	4 8
1	2 6
2	0

35.

Stems	Leaves
1	8 9 9 8 7 8
2	0 1 0 2

36.

Stems	Leaves
1	3 5 3 8 3 4
2	3 0 0 4

• Application Exercises

37. The data sets give the ages of Oscar winners from 1999 through 2005 at the time of the award.

Year	Best Actor	Age
1999	Kevin Spacey	40
2000	Russell Crowe	36
2001	Denzel Washington	47
2002	Adrien Brody	29
2003	Sean Penn	43
2004	Jamie Foxx	37
2005	Philip Seymour Hoffman	38

Year	Best Actress	Age
1999	Hilary Swank	25
2000	Julia Roberts	33
2001	Halle Berry	35
2002	Nicole Kidman	35
2003	Charlize Theron	28
2004	Hilary Swank	30
2005	Reese Witherspoon	29

Source: www.oscars.org

a. Without calculating, which data set has the greater mean age? Explain your answer.

b. Verify your conjecture from part (a) by calculating the mean age for each data set. Round answers to two decimal places.

c. Without calculating, which data set has the greater standard deviation? Explain your answer.

d. Verify your conjecture from part (c) by calculating the standard deviation for each data set. Round answers to two decimal places.

38. The data sets give the ages of the first six U.S. presidents and the last six U.S. presidents (through G. W. Bush).

AGE OF FIRST SIX U.S. PRESIDENTS AT INAUGURATION

President	Age
Washington	57
J. Adams	61
Jefferson	57
Madison	57
Monroe	58
J. Q. Adams	57

AGE OF LAST SIX U.S. PRESIDENTS AT INAUGURATION

President	Age
Ford	61
Carter	52
Reagan	69
G. H. W. Bush	64
Clinton	46
G. W. Bush	54

Source: Time Almanac

a. Without calculating, which set has the greater standard deviation? Explain your answer.

b. Verify your conjecture from part (b) by calculating the standard deviation for each data set. Round answers to two decimal places.

• Writing in Mathematics

39. Describe how to find the range of a data set.

40. Describe why the range might not be the best measure of dispersion.

41. Describe how the standard deviation is computed.

42. Describe what the standard deviation reveals about a data set.

43. If a set of test scores has a standard deviation of zero, what does this mean about the scores?

44. Two classes took a statistics test. Both classes had a mean score of 73. The scores of class A had a standard deviation of 5 and those of class B had a standard deviation of 10. Discuss the difference between the two classes' performance on the test.

45. A sample of cereals indicates a mean potassium content per serving of 93 milligrams and a standard deviation of 2 milligrams. Write a description of what this means for a person who knows nothing about statistics.

46. Over a one-month period, stock A had a mean daily closing price of 124.7 and a standard deviation of 12.5. By contrast, stock B had a mean daily closing price of 78.2 and a standard deviation of 6.1. Which stock was more volatile? Explain your answer.

• Critical Thinking Exercises

47. Which one of the following is true?
   - **a.** If the same number is added to each data item in a set of data, the standard deviation does not change.
   - **b.** If each number in a data set is multiplied by 4, the standard deviation is doubled.
   - **c.** It is possible for a set of scores to have a negative standard deviation.
   - **d.** Data sets with different means cannot have the same standard deviation.

48. Describe a situation in which a relatively large standard deviation is desirable.

49. If a set of test scores has a large range but a small standard deviation, describe what this means about students' performance on the test.

50. Use the data 1, 2, 3, 5, 6, 7. Without actually computing the standard deviation, which of the following best approximates the standard deviation?

   a. 2 **b.** 6 **c.** 10 **d.** 20

51. Use the data 0, 1, 3, 4, 4, 6. Add 2 to each of the numbers. How does this affect the mean? How does this affect the standard deviation?

• Group Exercises

52. As a follow-up to Group Exercise 78 on page 704, the group should reassemble and compute the standard deviation for each data set whose mean you previously determined. Does the standard deviation tell you anything new or interesting about the entire group or subgroups that you did not discover during the previous group activity?

53. Group members should consult a current almanac or the Internet and select intriguing data. The group's function is to use statistics to tell a story. Once "intriguing" data are identified, as a group
   - **a.** Summarize the data. Use words, frequency distributions, and graphic displays.
   - **b.** Compute measures of central tendency and dispersion, using these statistics to discuss the data.

SECTION 12.4 • THE NORMAL DISTRIBUTION

OBJECTIVES

1. Recognize characteristics of normal distributions.
2. Understand the 68–95–99.7 Rule.
3. Find scores at a specified standard deviation from the mean.
4. Use the 68–95–99.7 Rule.
5. Convert a data item to a z-score.
6. Understand percentiles and quartiles.
7. Solve applied problems involving normal distributions.
8. Use and interpret margins of error.
9. Recognize distributions that are not normal.

Mean Adult Heights

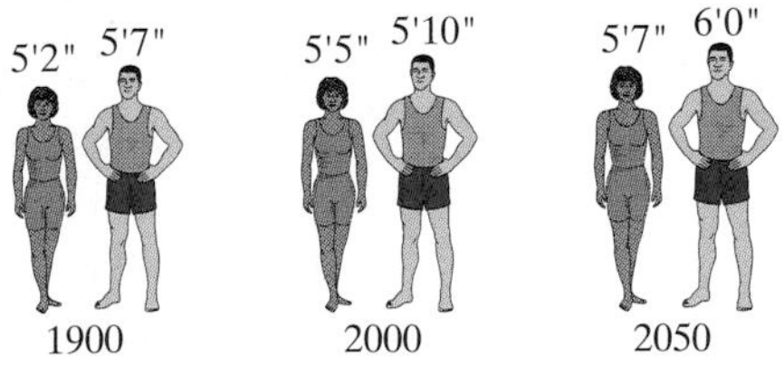

Source: National Center for Health Statistics

Our heights are on the rise! In one million B.C., the mean height for men was 4 feet 6 inches. The mean height for women was 4 feet 2 inches. Because of improved diets and medical care, the mean height for men is now 5 feet 10 inches and for women it is 5 feet 5 inches. Mean adult heights are expected to plateau by 2050.

Suppose that a researcher selects a random sample of 100 adult men, measures their heights, and constructs a histogram. The graph is shown in Figure 12.9 at the top of the next page. Figure 12.9 illustrates what happens as the sample size increases. In Figure 12.9(c), if you were to fold the graph down the middle, the left side would fit the right side. As we move out from the middle, the heights of the bars are the same to the left and right. Such a histogram is called **symmetric**. As the sample size increases, so does the graph's symmetry. If it were possible to measure

1 Recognize characteristics of normal distributions.

the heights of all adult males, the entire population, the histogram would approach what is called the **normal distribution**, shown in Figure 12.9(d). This distribution is also called the **bell curve** or the **Gaussian distribution**, named for the German mathematician Carl Friedrich Gauss (1777–1855).

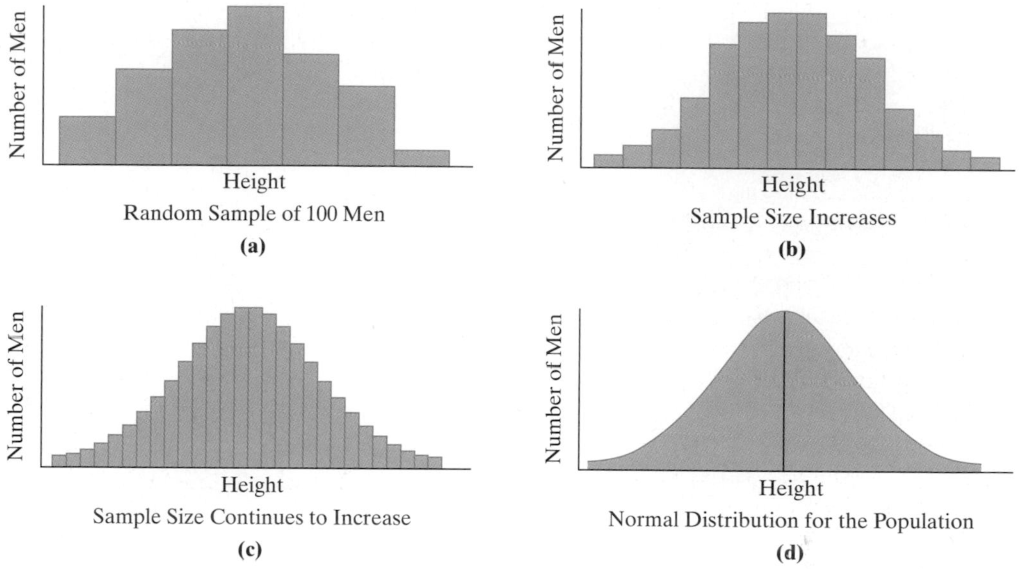

FIGURE 12.9 Heights of adult males

Figure 12.9(d) illustrates that the normal distribution is bell shaped and symmetric about a vertical line through its center. Furthermore, **the mean, median, and mode** of a normal distribution **are all equal** and located at the center of the distribution.

The shape of the normal distribution depends on the mean and the standard deviation. Figure 12.10 illustrates three normal distributions with the same mean, but different standard deviations. As the standard deviation increases, the distribution becomes more dispersed, or spread out, but retains its symmetric bell shape.

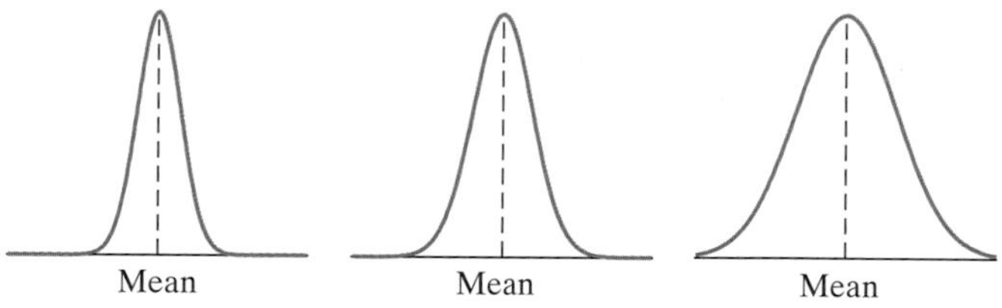

FIGURE 12.10

The normal distribution provides a wonderful model for all kinds of phenomena because many sets of data items closely resemble this population distribution. Examples include heights and weights of adult males, intelligence quotients, SAT scores, prices paid for a new car model, and life spans of light bulbs. In these distributions, the data items tend to cluster around the mean. The more an item differs from the mean, the less likely it is to occur.

The normal distribution is used to make predictions about an entire population using data from a sample. In this section, we focus on the characteristics and applications of the normal distribution.

2 Understand the 68–95–99.7 Rule.

The Standard Deviation and z-Scores in Normal Distributions

The standard deviation plays a crucial role in the normal distribution, summarized by the **68–95–99.7 Rule**. This rule is illustrated in Figure 12.11 on the next page.

BLITZER BONUS

Well-Worn Steps and the Normal Distribution

These ancient steps each take on the shape of a normal distribution when the picture is viewed upside down. The center of each step is more worn than the outer edges. The greatest number of people have walked in the center, making this the mean, median, and mode for where people have walked.

THE 68-95-99.7 RULE FOR THE NORMAL DISTRIBUTION

1. Approximately 68% of the data items fall within 1 standard deviation of the mean (in both directions).
2. Approximately 95% of the data items fall within 2 standard deviations of the mean.
3. Approximately 99.7% of the data items fall within 3 standard deviations of the mean.

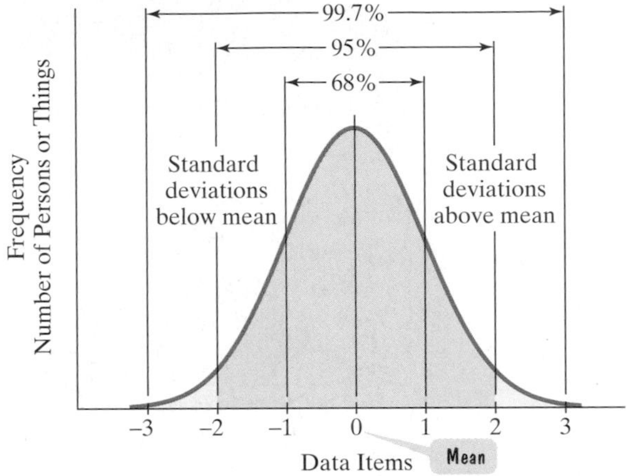

FIGURE 12.11

Figure 12.11 illustrates that a very small percentage of the data in a normal distribution lies more than 3 standard deviations above or below the mean. As we move from the mean, the curve falls rapidly, and then more and more gradually, toward the horizontal axis. The tails of the curve approach, but never touch, the horizontal axis, although they are quite close to the axis at 3 standard deviations from the mean. The range of the normal distribution is infinite. No matter how far out from the mean we move, there is always the probability (although very small) of a data item occurring even farther out.

3 Find scores at a specified standard deviation from the mean.

EXAMPLE 1 FINDING SCORES AT A SPECIFIED STANDARD DEVIATION FROM THE MEAN

Male adult heights in North America are approximately normally distributed with a mean of 70 inches and a standard deviation of 4 inches. Find the height that is

a. 2 standard deviations above the mean.

b. 3 standard deviations below the mean.

SOLUTION

a. First, let us find the height that is 2 standard deviations above the mean.

$$\begin{aligned}\text{Height} &= \text{mean} + 2 \cdot \text{standard deviation}\\ &= 70 + 2 \cdot 4 = 70 + 8 = 78\end{aligned}$$

A height of 78 inches is 2 standard deviations above the mean.

b. Next, let us find the height that is 3 standard deviations below the mean.

$$\begin{aligned}\text{Height} &= \text{mean} - 3 \cdot \text{standard deviation}\\ &= 70 - 3 \cdot 4 = 70 - 12 = 58\end{aligned}$$

A height of 58 inches is 3 standard deviations below the mean.

The distribution of male adult heights in North America is illustrated as a normal distribution in Figure 12.12.

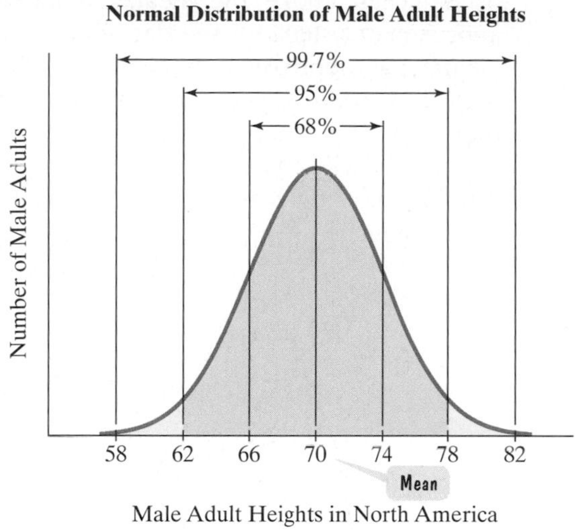

FIGURE 12.12

CHECK POINT 1 Female adult heights in North America are approximately normally distributed with a mean of 65 inches and a standard deviation of 3.5 inches. Find the height that is

a. 3 standard deviations above the mean.

b. 2 standard deviations below the mean.

4 Use the 68–95–99.7 Rule.

EXAMPLE 2 USING THE 68–95–99.7 RULE

Use the distribution of male adult heights in Figure 12.12 to find the percentage of men in North America with heights

a. between 66 inches and 74 inches.

b. between 70 inches and 74 inches.

c. above 78 inches.

SOLUTION

a. The 68–95–99.7 Rule states that approximately 68% of the data items fall within 1 standard deviation, 4, of the mean, 70.

$$\text{mean} - 1 \cdot \text{standard deviation} = 70 - 1 \cdot 4 = 70 - 4 = 66$$
$$\text{mean} + 1 \cdot \text{standard deviation} = 70 + 1 \cdot 4 = 70 + 4 = 74$$

Figure 12.12 shows that 68% of male adults have heights between 66 inches and 74 inches.

b. The percentage of men with heights between 70 inches and 74 inches is not given directly in Figure 12.12 or Figure 12.13. Because of the distribution's symmetry, the percentage with heights between 66 inches and 70 inches is the same as the percentage with heights between 70 and 74 inches. Figure 12.13 indicates that 68% have heights between 66 inches and 74 inches. Thus, half of 68%, or 34%, of men have heights between 70 inches and 74 inches.

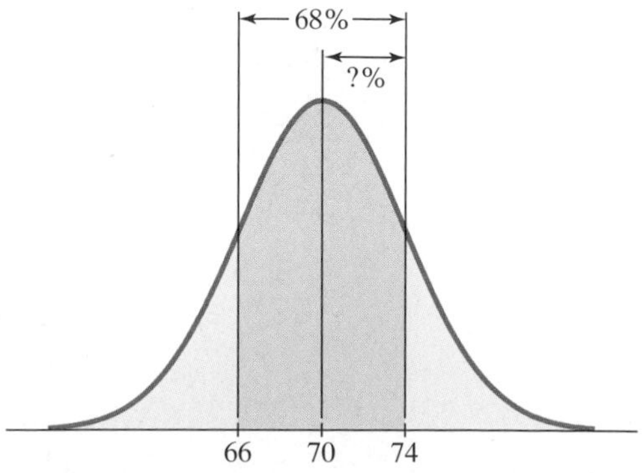

FIGURE 12.13 What percentage have heights between 70 inches and 74 inches?

c. The percentage of men with heights above 78 inches is not given directly in Figure 12.12 or Figure 12.14. A height of 78 inches is 2 standard deviations, $2 \cdot 4$, or 8 inches, above the mean, 70 inches. The 68–95–99.7 Rule states that approximately 95% of the data items fall within 2 standard deviations of the mean. Thus, approximately 100% − 95%, or 5%, of the data items are farther than 2 standard deviations from the mean. The 5% of the data items are represented by the two shaded green regions in Figure 12.14. Because of the distribution's symmetry, half of 5%, or 2.5%, of the data items are more than 2 standard deviations above the mean. This means that 2.5% of men have heights above 78 inches.

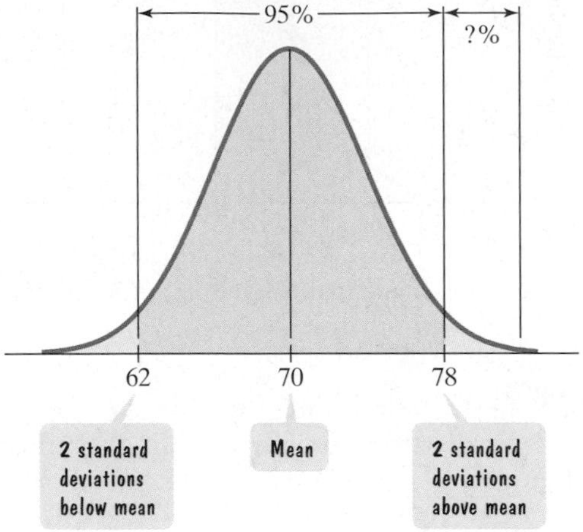

FIGURE 12.14 What percentage have heights above 78 inches?

CHECK POINT 2 Use the distribution of male adult heights in North America in Figure 12.12 on page 715 to find the percentage of men with heights

a. between 62 inches and 78 inches.

b. between 70 inches and 78 inches.

c. above 74 inches.

Because the normal distribution of male adult heights in North America has a mean of 70 inches and a standard deviation of 4 inches, a height of 78 inches lies 2 standard deviations above the mean. In a normal distribution, a ***z*-score** describes how many standard deviations a particular data item lies above or below the mean. Thus, the z-score for the data item 78 is 2.

5 Convert a data item to a z-score.

The following formula can be used to express a data item in a normal distribution as a z-score:

COMPUTING z-SCORES

A z-score describes how many standard deviations a data item in a normal distribution lies above or below the mean. The z-score can be obtained using

$$z\text{-score} = \frac{\text{data item} - \text{mean}}{\text{standard deviation}}.$$

Data items above the mean have positive z-scores. Data items below the mean have negative z-scores. The z-score for the mean is 0.

EXAMPLE 3 COMPUTING z-SCORES

The mean weight of newborn infants is 7 pounds and the standard deviation is 0.8 pound. The weights of newborn infants are normally distributed. Find the z-score for a weight of

a. 9 pounds. **b.** 7 pounds. **c.** 6 pounds.

SOLUTION We compute the z-score for each weight by using the z-score formula. The mean is 7 and the standard deviation is 0.8.

a. The z-score for a weight of 9 pounds, written z_9, is

$$z_9 = \frac{\text{data item} - \text{mean}}{\text{standard deviation}} = \frac{9-7}{0.8} = \frac{2}{0.8} = 2.5.$$

The z-score of a data item greater than the mean is always positive. A 9-pound infant is a chubby little tyke, with a weight that is 2.5 standard deviations above the mean.

b. The z-score for a weight of 7 pounds is

$$z_7 = \frac{\text{data item} - \text{mean}}{\text{standard deviation}} = \frac{7-7}{0.8} = \frac{0}{0.8} = 0.$$

The z-score for the mean is always 0. A 7-pound infant is right at the mean, deviating 0 pounds above or below it.

c. The z-score for a weight of 6 pounds is

$$z_6 = \frac{\text{data item} - \text{mean}}{\text{standard deviation}} = \frac{6-7}{0.8} = \frac{-1}{0.8} = -1.25.$$

The z-score of a data item less than the mean is always negative. A 6-pound infant's weight is 1.25 standard deviations below the mean.

Figure 12.15 shows the normal distribution of weights of newborn infants. The horizontal axis is labeled in terms of weights and z-scores.

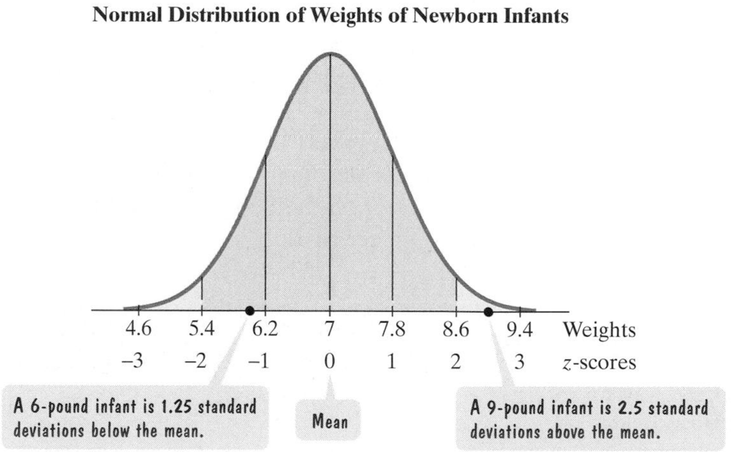

FIGURE 12.15 Infants' weights are normally distributed.

CHECK POINT 3 The length of horse pregnancies from conception to birth is normally distributed with a mean of 336 days and a standard deviation of 3 days. Find the z-score for a horse pregnancy of

a. 342 days. **b.** 336 days. **c.** 333 days.

In Example 4, we consider two normally distributed sets of test scores, in which a higher score generally indicates a better result. To compare scores on two different tests in relation to the mean on each test, we can use z-scores. The better score is the item with the greater z-score.

EXAMPLE 4 USING AND INTERPRETING z-SCORES

A student scores 70 on an arithmetic test and 66 on a vocabulary test. The scores for both tests are normally distributed. The arithmetic test has a mean of 60 and a standard deviation of 20. The vocabulary test has a mean of 60 and a standard deviation of 2. On which test did the student have the better score?

SOLUTION To answer the question, we need to find the student's z-score on each test, using

$$z = \frac{\text{data item} - \text{mean}}{\text{standard deviation}}.$$

The arithmetic test has a mean of 60 and a standard deviation of 20.

$$z\text{-score for } 70 = z_{70} = \frac{70 - 60}{20} = \frac{10}{20} = 0.5$$

The vocabulary test has a mean of 60 and a standard deviation of 2.

$$z\text{-score for } 66 = z_{66} = \frac{66 - 60}{2} = \frac{6}{2} = 3$$

The arithmetic score, 70, is half a standard deviation above the mean, whereas the vocabulary score, 66, is 3 standard deviations above the mean. The student did much better than the mean on the vocabulary test.

CHECK POINT 4 The SAT (Scholastic Aptitude Test) has a mean of 500 and a standard deviation of 100. The ACT (American College Test) has a mean of 18 and a standard deviation of 6. Both tests measure the same kind of ability, with scores that are normally distributed. Suppose that you score 550 on the SAT and 24 on the ACT. On which test did you have the better score?

EXAMPLE 5 UNDERSTANDING z-SCORES

Intelligence quotients (IQs) on the Stanford-Binet intelligence test are normally distributed with a mean of 100 and a standard deviation of 16.

a. What is the IQ corresponding to a z-score of -1.5?

b. Mensa is a group of people with high IQs whose members have z-scores of 2.05 or greater on the Stanford-Binet intelligence test. What is the IQ corresponding to a z-score of 2.05?

SOLUTION

a. We begin with the IQ corresponding to a z-score of -1.5. The negative sign in -1.5 tells us that the IQ is $1\frac{1}{2}$ standard deviations below the mean.

$$\begin{aligned} \text{IQ} &= \text{mean} - 1.5 \cdot \text{standard deviation} \\ &= 100 - 1.5(16) = 100 - 24 = 76 \end{aligned}$$

The IQ corresponding to a z-score of -1.5 is 76.

b. Next, we find the IQ corresponding to a z-score of 2.05. The positive sign implied in 2.05 tells us that the IQ is 2.05 standard deviations above the mean.

$$\begin{aligned} \text{IQ} &= \text{mean} + 2.05 \cdot \text{standard deviation} \\ &= 100 + 2.05(16) = 100 + 32.8 = 132.8 \end{aligned}$$

The IQ corresponding to a z-score of 2.05 is 132.8. (An IQ score of at least 133 is required to join Mensa.)

CHECK POINT 5 Use the information in Example 5 to find the IQ corresponding to a z-score of

a. -2.25. **b.** 1.75.

BLITZER BONUS

The IQ Controversy

Is intelligence something we are born with or is it a quality that can be manipulated through education? Can it be measured accurately and is IQ the way to measure it? There are no clear answers to these questions.

In a study by Carolyn Bird (*Pygmalion in the Classroom*), a group of third-grade teachers was told that they had classes of students with IQs well above the mean. These classes made incredible progress throughout the year. In reality, these were not gifted kids, but, rather, a random sample of all third-graders. It was the teachers' expectations, and not the IQs of the students, that resulted in increased performance.

6 Understand percentiles and quartiles.

Percentiles and Quartiles

A z-score measures a data item's position in a normal distribution. Another measure of a data item's position is its **percentile**. Percentiles are often associated with scores on standardized tests. If a score is in the 45th percentile, this means that 45% of the scores are less than this score. If a score is in the 95th percentile, this indicates that 95% of the scores are less than this score.

PERCENTILES

If n% of the items in a distribution are less than a particular data item, we say that the data item is in the ***n*th percentile** of the distribution.

STUDY TIP

A score in the 98th percentile does *not* mean that 98% of the answers are correct. Nor does it mean that the score was 98%.

EXAMPLE 6 INTERPRETING PERCENTILE

The cutoff IQ score for Mensa membership, 132.8, is in the 98th percentile. What does this mean?

SOLUTION Because 132.8 is in the 98th percentile, this means that 98% of IQ scores fall below 132.8.

CHECK POINT 6 A student scored in the 75th percentile on the SAT. What does this mean?

Three commonly encountered percentiles are the *quartiles*. **Quartiles** divide data sets into four equal parts. The 25th percentile is the **first quartile**: 25% of the data fall below the first quartile. The 50th percentile is the **second quartile**: 50% of the data fall below the second quartile, so the second quartile is equivalent to the median. The 75th percentile is the **third quartile**: 75% of the data fall below the third quartile. Figure 12.16 illustrates the concept of quartiles for the normal distribution.

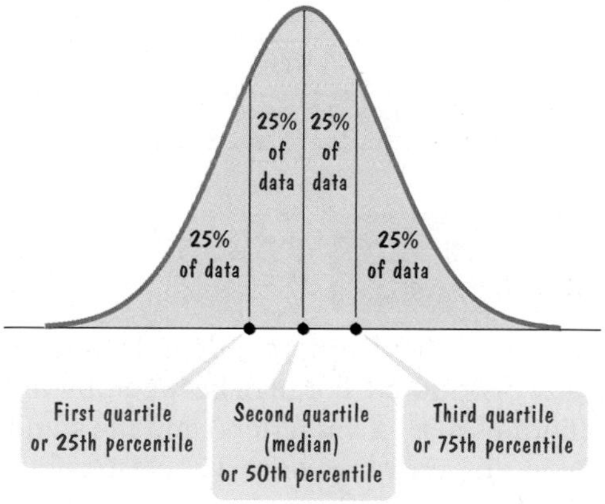

FIGURE 12.16 Quartiles

7 Solve applied problems involving normal distributions.

Problem Solving Using z-Scores and Percentiles

Table 12.13 on the next page gives a percentile interpretation for z-scores. For example, the portion of the table in the margin indicates that the corresponding percentile for a data item with a z-score of 2 is 97.72. A student with this score on a test whose results are normally distributed outperformed 97.72% of those who took the test.

In a normal distribution, the mean, median, and mode all have a corresponding z-score of 0. Table 12.13 shows that the percentile for a z-score of 0 is 50.00. Thus, 50% of the data items in a normal distribution are less than the mean, median, and mode. Consequently, 50% of the data items are greater than or equal to the mean, median, and mode.

Two entries from Table 12.13. The complete table is on the next page.

z-Score	Percentile
2.0	97.72
0.0	50.00

Table 12.13 can be used to find the percentage of data items that are less than any data item in a normal distribution. Begin by converting the data item to a z-score. Then, use the table to find the percentile for this z-score. This percentile is the percentage of data items that are less than the data item in question.

TABLE 12.13 z-SCORES AND PERCENTILES

z-Score	Percentile	z-Score	Percentile	z-Score	Percentile	z-Score	Percentile
−4.0	0.003	−1.0	15.87	0.0	50.00	1.1	86.43
−3.5	0.02	−0.95	17.11	0.05	51.99	1.2	88.49
−3.0	0.13	−0.90	18.41	0.10	53.98	1.3	90.32
−2.9	0.19	−0.85	19.77	0.15	55.96	1.4	91.92
−2.8	0.26	−0.80	21.19	0.20	57.93	1.5	93.32
−2.7	0.35	−0.75	22.66	0.25	59.87	1.6	94.52
−2.6	0.47	−0.70	24.20	0.30	61.79	1.7	95.54
−2.5	0.62	−0.65	25.78	0.35	63.68	1.8	96.41
−2.4	0.82	−0.60	27.43	0.40	65.54	1.9	97.13
−2.3	1.07	−0.55	29.12	0.45	67.36	2.0	97.72
−2.2	1.39	−0.50	30.85	0.50	69.15	2.1	98.21
−2.1	1.79	−0.45	32.64	0.55	70.88	2.2	98.61
−2.0	2.28	−0.40	34.46	0.60	72.57	2.3	98.93
−1.9	2.87	−0.35	36.32	0.65	74.22	2.4	99.18
−1.8	3.59	−0.30	38.21	0.70	75.80	2.5	99.38
−1.7	4.46	−0.25	40.13	0.75	77.34	2.6	99.53
−1.6	5.48	−0.20	42.07	0.80	78.81	2.7	99.65
−1.5	6.68	−0.15	44.04	0.85	80.23	2.8	99.74
−1.4	8.08	−0.10	46.02	0.90	81.59	2.9	99.81
−1.3	9.68	−0.05	48.01	0.95	82.89	3.0	99.87
−1.2	11.51	0.0	50.00	1.0	84.13	3.5	99.98
−1.1	13.57					4.0	99.997

EXAMPLE 7 FINDING THE PERCENTAGE OF DATA ITEMS LESS THAN A GIVEN DATA ITEM

According to the Department of Health and Education, cholesterol levels are normally distributed. For men between 18 and 24 years, the mean is 178.1 (measured in milligrams per 100 milliliters) and the standard deviation is 40.7. What percentage of men in this age range have a cholesterol level less than 239.15?

SOLUTION If you are familiar with your own cholesterol level, you probably recognize that a level of 239.15 is fairly high for a young man. Because of this, we would expect most young men to have a level less than 239.15. Let's see if this is so. Table 12.13 requires that we use z-scores. We compute the z-score for a 239.15 cholesterol level by using the z-score formula.

$$z_{239.15} = \frac{\text{data item} - \text{mean}}{\text{standard deviation}} = \frac{239.15 - 178.1}{40.7} = \frac{61.05}{40.7} = 1.5$$

A man between 18 and 24 with a 239.15 cholesterol level is 1.5 standard deviations above the mean, illustrated in Figure 12.17(a). The question mark indicates that we must find the percentage of men with a cholesterol level less than $z = 1.5$, the z-score for a 239.15 cholesterol level. Table 12.13 gives this percentage as a percentile.

Find 1.5 in the z-score column in the right portion of the table. The percentile given to the right of 1.5 is 93.32. Thus, 93.32% of men between 18 and 24 have a cholesterol level less than 239.15, shown in Figure 12.17(b).

A PORTION OF TABLE 12.13

z-Score	Percentile
1.4	91.92
1.5	93.32
1.6	94.52

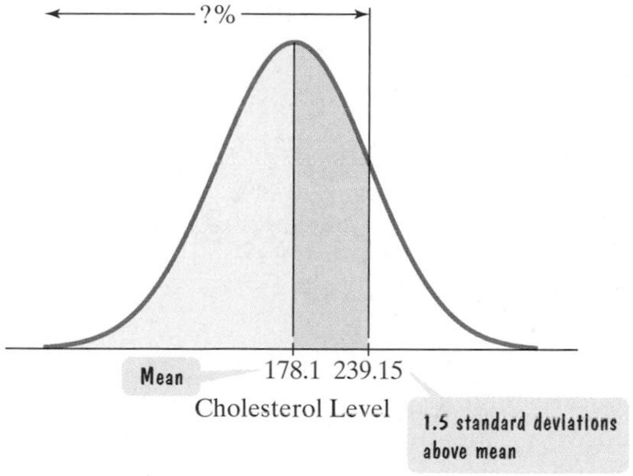

FIGURE 12.17(a)

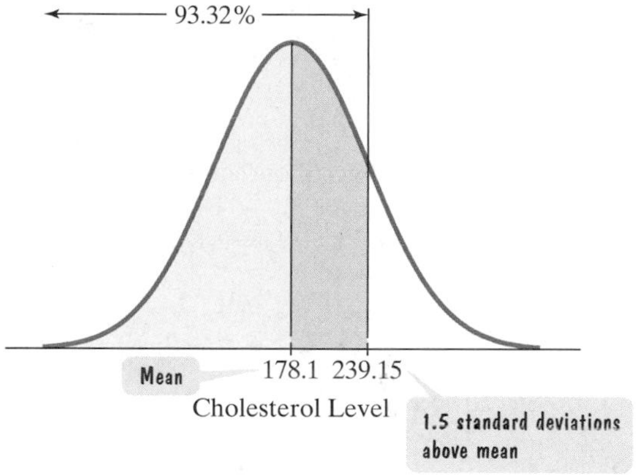

FIGURE 12.17(b)

CHECK POINT 7 The distribution of monthly charges for cellphone plans in the United States is approximately normal with a mean of \$62 and a standard deviation of \$18. What percentage of plans have charges that are less than \$83.60?

The normal distribution accounts for all data items, meaning 100% of the scores. This means that Table 12.13 can also be used to find the percentage of data items that are greater than any data item in a normal distribution. Use the percentile in the table to determine the percentage of data items less than the data item in question. Then subtract this percentage from 100% to find the percentage of data items greater than the item in question. In using this technique, we will treat the phrases "greater than" and "greater than or equal to" as equivalent.

EXAMPLE 8 FINDING THE PERCENTAGE OF DATA ITEMS GREATER THAN A GIVEN DATA ITEM

Lengths of pregnancies of women are normally distributed with a mean of 266 days and a standard deviation of 16 days. What percentage of children are born from pregnancies lasting more than 274 days?

SOLUTION Table 12.13 requires that we use z-scores. We compute the z-score for a 274-day pregnancy by using the z-score formula.

$$z_{274} = \frac{\text{data item} - \text{mean}}{\text{standard deviation}} = \frac{274 - 266}{16} = \frac{8}{16} = 0.5$$

A 274-day pregnancy is 0.5 standard deviation above the mean. Table 12.13 gives the percentile corresponding to 0.50 as 69.15. This means that 69.15% of pregnancies last less than 274 days, illustrated in Figure 12.18. We must find the number of pregnancies lasting more than 274 days by subtracting 69.15% from 100%.

$$100\% - 69.15\% = 30.85\%$$

Thus, 30.85% of children are born from pregnancies lasting more than 274 days.

A Portion of Table 12.13

z-Score	Percentile
0.45	67.36
0.50	69.15
0.55	70.88

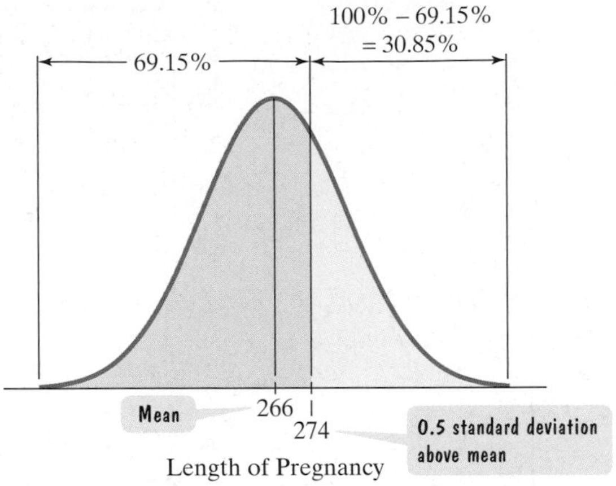

FIGURE 12.18

CHECK POINT 8 Female adult heights in North America are approximately normally distributed with a mean of 65 inches and a standard deviation of 3.5 inches. What percentage of North American women have heights that exceed 69.9 inches?

We have seen how Table 12.13 is used to find the percentage of data items that are less than or greater than any given item. The table can also be used to find the percentage of data items *between* two given items. Because the percentile for each item is the percentage of data items less than the given item, the percentage of data between the two given items is found by subtracting the lesser percent from the greater percent. This is illustrated in Figure 12.19.

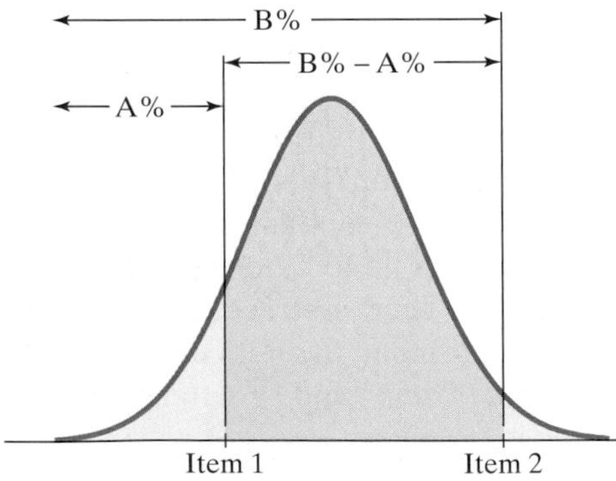

FIGURE 12.19 The percentile for data item 1 is A. The percentile for data item 2 is B. The percentage of data items between item 1 and item 2 is B% − A%.

FINDING THE PERCENTAGE OF DATA ITEMS BETWEEN TWO GIVEN ITEMS IN A NORMAL DISTRIBUTION

1. Convert each given data item to a z-score:

$$z = \frac{\text{data item} - \text{mean}}{\text{standard deviation}}.$$

2. Use Table 12.13 to find the percentile corresponding to each z-score in step 1.
3. Subtract the lesser percentile from the greater percentile and attach a % sign.

EXAMPLE 9 FINDING THE PERCENTAGE OF DATA ITEMS BETWEEN TWO GIVEN DATA ITEMS

The amount of time that self-employed Americans work each week is normally distributed with a mean of 44.6 hours and a standard deviation of 14.4 hours. What percentage of self-employed individuals in the United States work between 37.4 and 80.6 hours per week?

SOLUTION

Step 1. Convert each given data item to a z-score.

$$z_{37.4} = \frac{\text{data item} - \text{mean}}{\text{standard deviation}} = \frac{37.4 - 44.6}{14.4} = \frac{-7.2}{14.4} = -0.5$$

$$z_{80.6} = \frac{\text{data item} - \text{mean}}{\text{standard deviation}} = \frac{80.6 - 44.6}{14.4} = \frac{36}{14.4} = 2.5$$

A Portion of Table 12.13

z-Score	Percentile
−0.55	29.12
−0.50	30.85
−0.45	32.64

Step 2. Use Table 12.13 to find the percentile corresponding to these z-scores. The percentile given to the right of −0.50 is 30.85. This means that 30.85% of self-employed Americans work less than 37.4 hours per week.

A Portion of Table 12.13

z-Score	Percentile
2.4	99.18
2.5	99.38
2.6	99.53

Table 12.13 also gives the percentile corresponding to $z = 2.5$. Find 2.5 in the z-score column in the far-right portion of the table. The percentile given to the right of 2.5 is 99.38. This means that 99.38% of self-employed Americans work less than 80.6 hours per week.

Step 3. Subtract the lesser percentile from the greater percentile and attach a % sign. Subtracting percentiles, we obtain

$$99.38 - 30.85 = 68.53.$$

Thus, 68.53% of self-employed Americans work between 37.4 and 80.6 hours per week. The solution is illustrated in Figure 12.20.

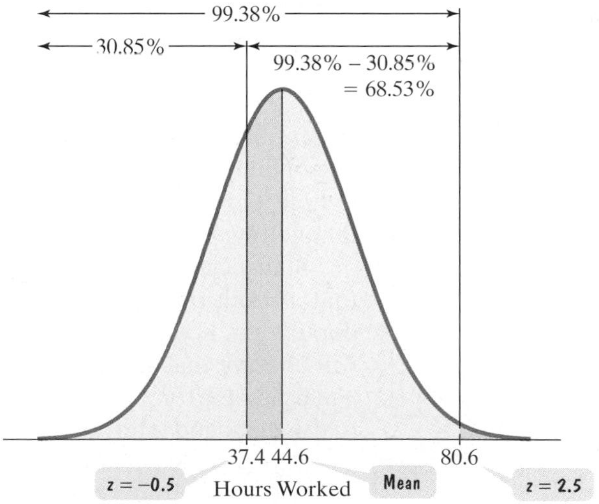

FIGURE 12.20

CHECK POINT 9 The distribution for the life of refrigerators is approximately normal with a mean of 14 years and a standard deviation of 2.5 years. What percentage of refrigerators have lives between 11 years and 18 years?

Our work in Examples 7 through 9 is summarized as follows:

COMPUTING PERCENTAGE OF DATA ITEMS FOR NORMAL DISTRIBUTIONS

Description of Percentage	Graph	Computation of Percentage
Percentage of data items less than a given data item with $z = b$	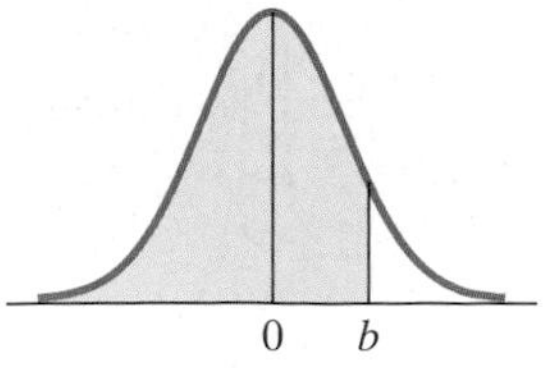	Use the table percentile for $z = b$ and add a % sign.
Percentage of data items greater than a given data item with $z = a$	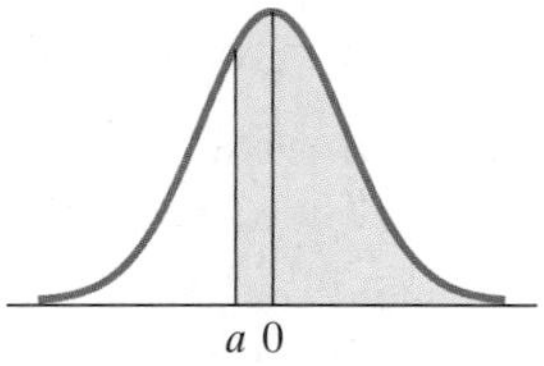	Subtract the table percentile for $z = a$ from 100 and add a % sign.
Percentage of data items between two given data items with $z = a$ and $z = b$	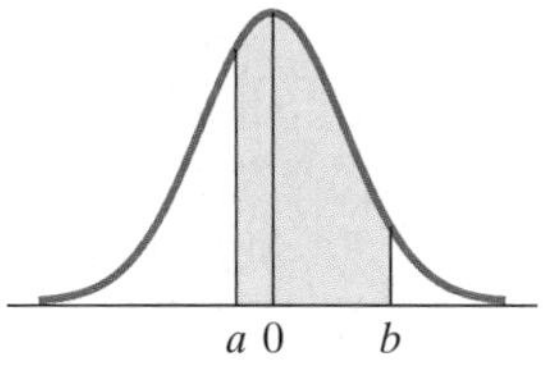	Subtract the table percentile for $z = a$ from the table percentile for $z = b$ and add a % sign.

8 Use and interpret margins of error.

Polls and Margins of Error

When you were between the ages of 6 and 14, how would you have responded to this question:

What is bad about being a kid?

What Is Bad about Being a Kid?

Kids Say	
Getting bossed around	17%
School, homework	15%
Can't do everything I want	11%
Chores	9%
Being grounded	9%

Source: Penn, Schoen, and Berland using 1172 interviews with children ages 6 to 14 from May 14 to June 1, 1999, Margin of error: ±2.9%

Note the margin of error.

In a random sample of 1172 children ages 6 through 14, 17% of the children responded, "Getting bossed around." The problem is that this is a single random sample. Do 17% of kids in the entire population of children ages 6 through 14 think that getting bossed around is a bad thing?

Statisticians use properties of the normal distribution to estimate the probability that a result obtained from a single sample reflects what is truly happening in the population. If you look at the results of a poll like the one shown in the margin, you will observe that a *margin of error* is reported. Surveys and opinion polls often give a margin of error. Let's use our understanding of the normal distribution to see how to calculate and interpret margins of error.

Suppose that $p\%$ of the population of children ages 6 through 14 hold the opinion that getting bossed around is a bad thing about being a kid. Instead of taking only one random sample of 1172 children, we repeat the process of selecting a random sample of 1172 children hundreds of times. Then, we calculate the percentage of children for each sample who think being bossed around is bad. With random sampling, we expect to find the percentage in many of the samples close to $p\%$, with relatively few samples having percentages far from $p\%$. Figure 12.21 on the next page shows that the percentages of children from the hundreds of samples can be modeled by a normal distribution. The mean of this distribution is the actual population percent, $p\%$, and is the most frequent result from the samples.

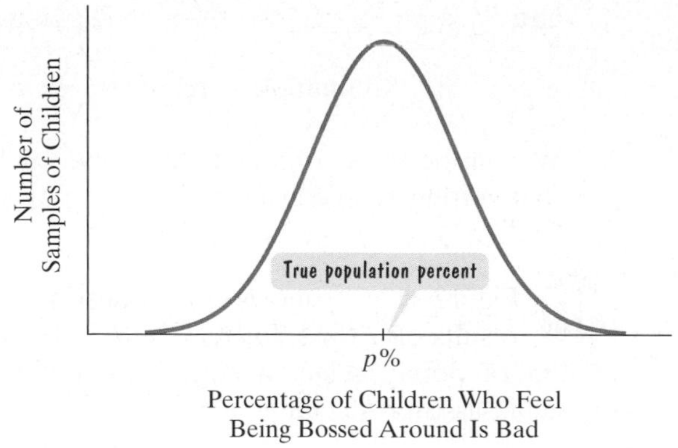

FIGURE 12.21 Percentage of children who feel being bossed around is bad

Mathematicians have shown that the standard deviation of a normal distribution of samples like the one in Figure 12.21 is approximately $\frac{1}{2\sqrt{n}}$, where n is the sample size. Using the 68–95–99.7 Rule, approximately 95% of the samples have a percentage within 2 standard deviations of the true population percentage, $p\%$:

$$2 \text{ standard deviations} = 2 \cdot \frac{1}{2\sqrt{n}} = \frac{1}{\sqrt{n}}.$$

If we use a single random sample of size n, there is a 95% probability that the percent obtained will lie within two standard deviations, or $\frac{1}{\sqrt{n}}$, of the true population percent. We can be 95% confident that the true population percent lies between

$$\text{the sample percent} - \frac{1}{\sqrt{n}}$$

and

$$\text{the sample percent} + \frac{1}{\sqrt{n}}.$$

We call $\pm\frac{1}{\sqrt{n}}$ the **margin of error**.

MARGIN OF ERROR IN A SURVEY

If a statistic is obtained from a random sample of size n, there is a 95% probability that it lies within $\frac{1}{\sqrt{n}}$ of the true population statistic, where $\pm\frac{1}{\sqrt{n}}$ is called the **margin of error**.

EXAMPLE 10 USING AND INTERPRETING MARGIN OF ERROR

In a random sample of 1172 children ages 6 through 14, 17% of the children said getting bossed around is a bad thing about being a kid.

a. Verify the margin of error that was given for this survey.

b. Write a statement about the percentage of children in the population who feel that getting bossed around is a bad thing about being a kid.

SOLUTION

a. The sample size is $n = 1172$. The margin of error is

$$\pm\frac{1}{\sqrt{n}} = \pm\frac{1}{\sqrt{1172}} \approx \pm 0.029 = \pm 2.9\%.$$

b. There is a 95% probability that the true population percentage lies between

$$\text{the sample percent} - \frac{1}{\sqrt{n}} = 17\% - 2.9\% = 14.1\%$$

WHAT IS BAD ABOUT BEING A KID?

Kids Say	
Getting bossed around	17%
School, homework	15%
Can't do everything I want	11%
Chores	9%
Being grounded	9%

Source: Penn, Schoen, and Berland using 1172 interviews with children ages 6 to 14 from May 14 to June 1, 1999, Margin of error: ±2.9%

9 Recognize distributions that are not normal.

and

$$\text{the sample percent} + \frac{1}{\sqrt{n}} = 17\% + 2.9\% = 19.9\%.$$

We can be 95% confident that between 14.1% and 19.9% of all children feel that getting bossed around is a bad thing about being a kid.

BLITZER BONUS

A Caveat Giving a True Picture of a Poll's Accuracy

Unlike the precise calculation of a poll's margin of error, certain polling imperfections cannot be determined exactly. One problem is that people do not always respond to polls honestly and accurately. Some people are embarrassed to say "undecided," so they make up an answer. Other people may try to respond to questions in the way they think will make the pollster happy, just to be "nice." Perhaps the following caveat, applied to the poll in Example 10, would give the public a truer picture of its accuracy:

> The poll results are 14.1% to 19.9% at the 95% confidence level, but it's only under ideal conditions that we can be 95% confident that the true numbers are within 2.9% of the poll's results. The true error span is probably greater than 2.9% due to limitations that are inherent in this and every poll, but, unfortunately, this additional error amount cannot be calculated precisely. Warning: Five percent of the time—that's one time out of 20—the error will be greater than 2.9%. We remind readers of the poll that things occurring "only" 5% of the time do, indeed, happen.

We suspect that the public would tire of hearing this.

CHECK POINT 10 Figure 12.22 shows the question and results of a *USA Today,* CNN/Gallup poll of 485 randomly selected American adults on physician-assisted suicide.

a. Find the margin of error for this survey. Round to the nearest tenth of a percent.

b. Write a statement about the percentage of American adults in the population who support physician-assisted suicide.

c. Based on your answer to part (b), explain how the title given with the circle graph in Figure 12.22 is misleading.

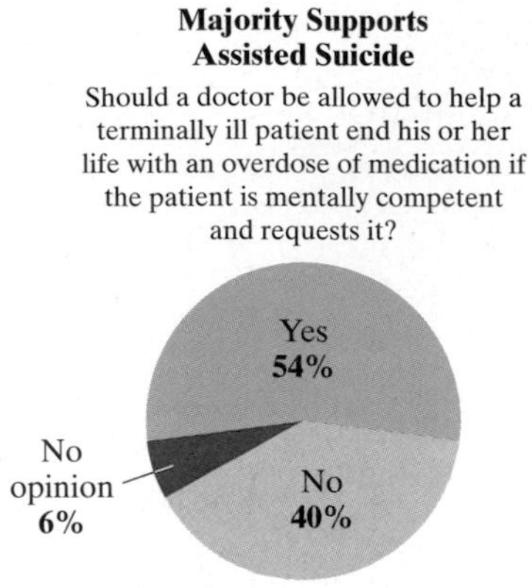

FIGURE 12.22
Source: USA Today, CNN/Gallup Poll

Other Kinds of Distributions

The histogram in Figure 12.23 represents the frequencies of the ages of women interviewed by Kinsey and his colleagues in their study of female sexual behavior. This distribution is not symmetric. The greatest frequency of women interviewed was in the 16–20 age range. The bars get shorter and shorter after this. The shorter bars fall on the right, indicating that relatively few older women were included in Kinsey's interviews.

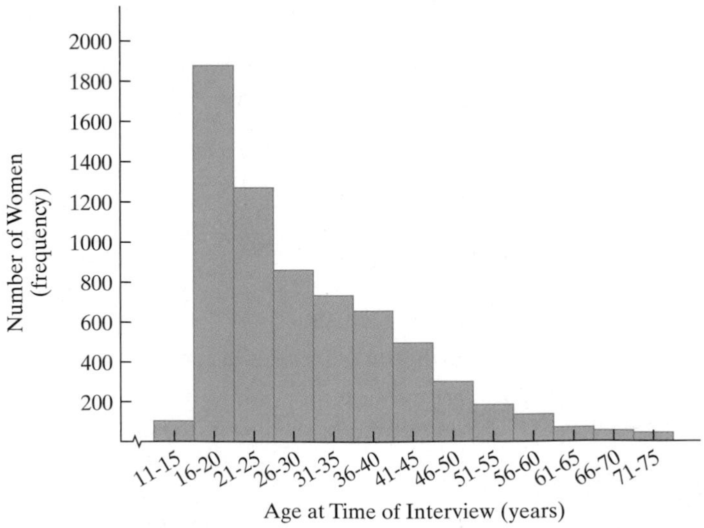

FIGURE 12.23 Histogram of the ages of females interviewed by Kinsey and his associates

Although the normal distribution is the most important of all distributions in terms of analyzing data, not all data can be approximated by this symmetric distribution with its mean, median, and mode all having the same value.

In our discussion of measures of central tendency, we mentioned that the median, rather than the mean, is used to summarize income. Figure 12.24 at the top of the next page illustrates the population distribution of weekly earnings in the

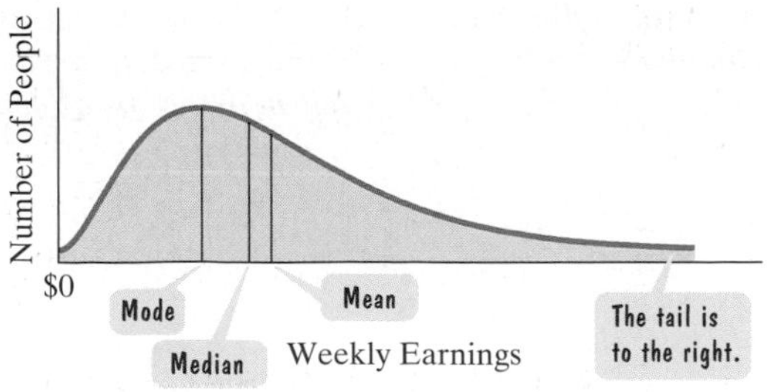

FIGURE 12.24 Skewed to the right

United States. There is no upper limit on weekly earnings. The relatively few people with very high weekly incomes tend to pull the mean income to a value greater than the median. The most frequent income, the mode, occurs toward the low end of the data items. The mean, median, and mode do not have the same value, and a normal distribution is not an appropriate model for describing weekly earnings in the United States.

The distribution in Figure 12.24 is called a *skewed distribution*. A distribution of data is **skewed** if a large number of data items are piled up at one end or the other, with a "tail" at the opposite end. In the distribution of weekly earnings in Figure 12.24, the tail is to the right. Such a distribution is said to be **skewed to the right**.

By contrast to the distribution of weekly earnings, the distribution in Figure 12.25 has more data items at the high end of the scale than at the low end. The tail of this distribution is to the left. The distribution is said to be **skewed to the left**. In many colleges, an example of a distribution skewed to the left is based on the student ratings of faculty teaching performance. Most professors are given rather high ratings, while only a few are rated terrible. These low ratings pull the value of the mean lower than the median.

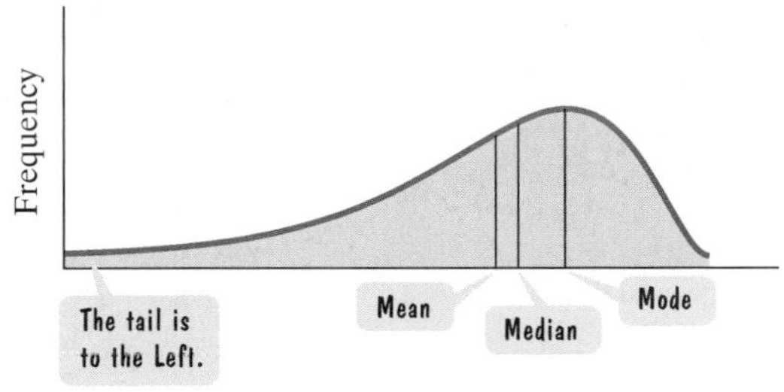

FIGURE 12.25 Skewed to the left

EXERCISE SET 12.4

• Practice and Application Exercises

The scores on a test are normally distributed with a mean of 100 and a standard deviation of 20. In Exercises 1–10, find the score that is

1. 1 standard deviation above the mean.

2. 2 standard deviations above the mean.

3. 3 standard deviations above the mean.

4. $1\frac{1}{2}$ standard deviations above the mean.

5. $2\frac{1}{2}$ standard deviations above the mean.

6. 1 standard deviation below the mean.

7. 2 standard deviations below the mean.

8. 3 standard deviations below the mean.

9. one-half a standard deviation below the mean.

10. $2\frac{1}{2}$ standard deviations below the mean.

Not everyone pays the same price for the same model of a car. The figure illustrates a normal distribution for the prices paid for a particular model of a new car. The mean is $17,000 and the standard deviation is $500.

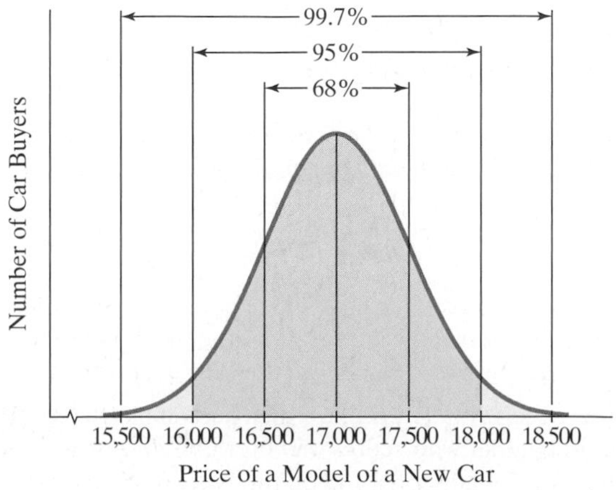

In Exercises 11–22, use the 68–95–99.7 Rule, illustrated in the figure at the bottom of the previous page, to find the percentage of buyers who paid

11. between \$16,500 and \$17,500.

12. between \$16,000 and \$18,000.

13. between \$17,000 and \$17,500.

14. between \$17,000 and \$18,000.

15. between \$16,000 and \$17,000.

16. between \$16,500 and \$17,000.

17. between \$15,500 and \$17,000.

18. between \$17,000 and \$18,500.

19. more than \$17,500.

20. more than \$18,000.

21. less than \$16,000.

22. less than \$16,500.

Intelligence quotients (IQs) on the Stanford-Binet intelligence test are normally distributed with a mean of 100 and a standard deviation of 16. In Exercises 23–32, use the 68–95–99.7 Rule to find the percentage of people with IQs

23. between 68 and 132. **24.** between 84 and 116.

25. between 68 and 100. **26.** between 84 and 100.

27. above 116. **28.** above 132.

29. below 68. **30.** below 84.

31. above 148. **32.** below 52.

A set of data items is normally distributed with a mean of 60 and a standard deviation of 8. In Exercises 33–48, convert each data item to a z-score.

33. 68 **34.** 76 **35.** 84 **36.** 92

37. 64 **38.** 72 **39.** 74 **40.** 78

41. 60 **42.** 100 **43.** 52 **44.** 44

45. 48 **46.** 40 **47.** 34 **48.** 30

Yearly returns on large-company stocks are normally distributed with mean yearly interest at 12.4% and a standard deviation of 20.4%. In Exercises 49–56, find the z-score for an investment that

49. earns 43% annually. **50.** earns 48.1% annually.

51. earns 58.3% annually. **52.** earns 78.7% annually.

53. loses 13.1% annually. **54.** loses 2.9% annually.

55. loses 18.2% annually. **56.** loses 38.6% annually.

Intelligence quotients on the Stanford-Binet intelligence test are normally distributed with a mean of 100 and a standard deviation of 16. Intelligence quotients on the Wechsler intelligence test are normally distributed with a mean of 100 and a standard deviation of 15. Use this information to solve Exercises 57–58.

57. Use z-scores to determine which person has the higher IQ: an individual who scores 128 on the Stanford-Binet or an individual who scores 127 on the Wechsler.

58. Use z-scores to determine which person has the higher IQ: an individual who scores 150 on the Stanford-Binet or an individual who scores 148 on the Wechsler.

A set of data items is normally distributed with a mean of 400 and a standard deviation of 50. In Exercises 59–66, find the data item in this distribution that corresponds to the given z-score.

59. $z = 2$ **60.** $z = 3$

61. $z = 1.5$ **62.** $z = 2.5$

63. $z = -3$ **64.** $z = -2$

65. $z = -2.5$ **66.** $z = -1.5$

Use Table 12.13 on page 720 to solve Exercises 67–82.

In Exercises 67–74, find the percentage of data items in a normal distribution that lie **a.** *below and* **b.** *above the given z-score.*

67. $z = 0.6$ **68.** $z = 0.8$

69. $z = 1.2$ **70.** $z = 1.4$

71. $z = -0.7$ **72.** $z = -0.4$

73. $z = -1.2$ **74.** $z = -1.8$

In Exercises 75–82, find the percentage of data items in a normal distribution that lie between

75. $z = 0.2$ and $z = 1.4$. **76.** $z = 0.3$ and $z = 2.1$.

77. $z = 1$ and $z = 3$. **78.** $z = 2$ and $z = 3$.

79. $z = -1.5$ and $z = 1.5$. **80.** $z = -1.2$ and $z = 1.2$.

81. $z = -2$ and $z = -0.5$. **82.** $z = -2.2$ and $z = -0.3$.

Systolic blood pressure readings are normally distributed with a mean of 121 and a standard deviation of 15. (A reading above 140 is considered to be high blood pressure.) In Exercises 83–92, begin by converting any given blood pressure reading or readings into z-scores. Then use Table 12.13 on page 720 to find the percentage of people with blood pressure readings

83. below 142. **84.** below 148.

85. above 130. **86.** above 133.

87. above 103. **88.** above 100.

89. between 142 and 154. **90.** between 145 and 157.

91. between 112 and 130. **92.** between 109 and 133.

The weights for 12-month-old baby boys are normally distributed with a mean of 22.5 pounds and a standard deviation of 2.2 pounds. In Exercises 93–96, use Table 12.13 on page 720 to find the percentage of 12-month-old baby boys who weigh

93. more than 25.8 pounds.

94. more than 23.6 pounds.

95. between 19.2 and 21.4 pounds.

96. between 18.1 and 19.2 pounds.

97. Using a random sample of 2272 American adults with children, a Harris survey asked respondents to name their dream job for their child or children. The top five responses and the percentage of parents who named each of these jobs are shown in the bar graph at the top of the next page.

What is Your Dream Job for Your Child/Children? Top Responses

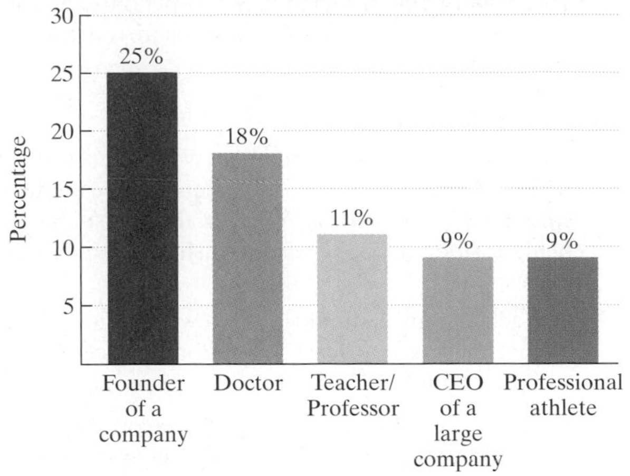

a. Find the margin of error, to the nearest tenth of a percent, for this survey.

b. Write a statement about the percentage of parents in the population who consider a doctor as the dream job for their child.

98. Using a random sample of 2297 American adults, an NBC *Today Show* poll asked respondents if they got enough sleep at night. The responses are shown in the circle graph.

Do You Get Enough Sleep at Night?

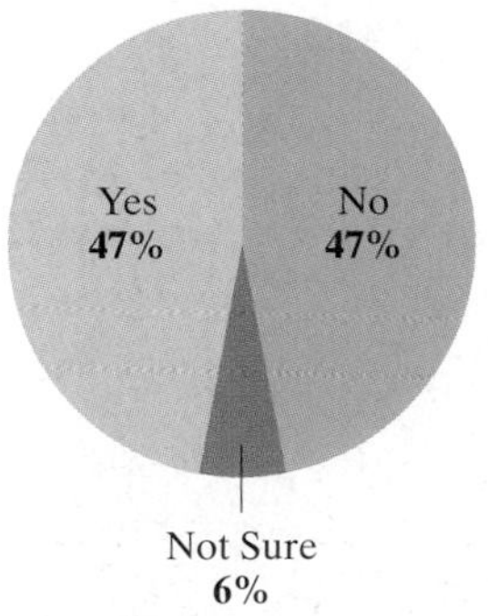

a. Find the margin of error, to the nearest tenth of a percent, for this survey.

b. Write a statement about the percentage of American adults in the population who do not get enough sleep at night.

99. Using a random sample of 4000 TV households, Nielsen Media Research found that 60.2% watched the final episode of *M*A*S*H*.

a. Find the margin of error in this percent.

b. Write a statement about the percentage of TV households in the population who tuned into the final episode of *M*A*S*H*.

100. Using a random sample of 4000 TV households, Nielsen Media Research found that 51.1% watched *Roots, Part 8*.

a. Find the margin of error in this percent.

b. Write a statement about the percentage of TV households in the population who tuned into *Roots, Part 8*.

101. In 1997, Nielsen Media Research increased its random sample to 5000 TV households. By how much, to the nearest tenth of a percent, did this improve the margin of error over that in Exercises 99 and 100?

102. If Nielsen Media Research were to increase its random sample from 5000 to 10,000 TV households, by how much, to the nearest tenth of a percent, would this improve the margin of error?

103. The histogram shows murder rates per 100,000 residents and the number of U.S. states that had these rates in 2003.

U.S. Murder Rates per 100,000 Residents, by State and Washington, D.C.

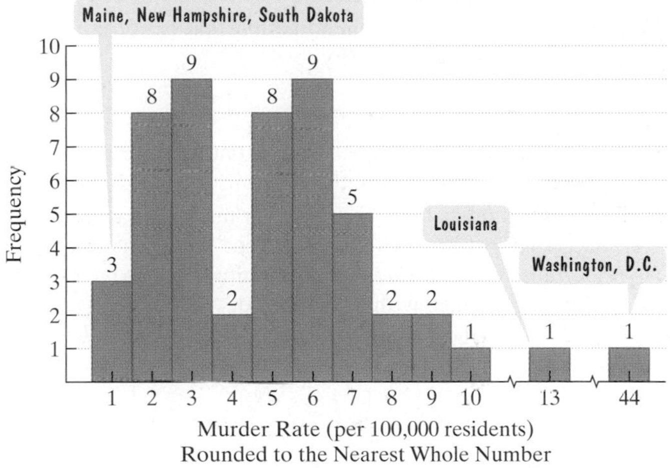

Source: FBI, *Crime in the United States*

a. Is the shape of this distribution best classified as normal, skewed to the right, or skewed to the left?

b. Calculate the mean murder rate per 100,000 residents for the 50 states and Washington, D.C.

c. Find the median murder rate per 100,000 residents for the 50 states and Washington, D.C.

d. Are the mean and median murder rates consistent with the shape of the distribution that you described in part (a)? Explain your answer.

e. The standard deviation for the data is approximately 6.1. If the distribution were roughly normal, what would be the z-score, rounded to one decimal place, for Washington, D.C.? Does this seem unusually high? Explain your answer.

• Writing in Mathematics

104. What is a symmetric histogram?

105. Describe the normal distribution and discuss some of its properties.

106. Describe the 68–95–99.7 Rule.

107. Describe how to determine the z-score for a data item in a normal distribution.

108. What does a z-score measure?

109. Give an example of both a commonly occurring and an infrequently occurring z-score. Explain how you arrived at these examples.

110. Describe when a z-score is negative.

111. If you score in the 83rd percentile, what does this mean?

112. If your weight is in the third quartile, what does this mean?

113. Explain how to find the percentage of data items between the first quartile and the third quartile.

114. Two students have scores with the same percentile, but for different administrations of the SAT. Does this mean that the students have the same score on the SAT? Explain your answer.

115. Give an example of a phenomenon that is normally distributed. Explain why. (Try to be creative and not use one of the distributions discussed in this section.) Estimate what the mean and the standard deviation might be and describe how you determined these estimates.

116. Give an example of a phenomenon that is not normally distributed and explain why.

• Critical Thinking Exercises

117. Find two z-scores so that 40% of the data in the distribution lies between them. (More than one answer is possible.)

118. A woman insists that she will never marry a man as short or shorter than she, knowing that only one man in 400 falls into this category. Assuming a mean height of 69 inches for men with a standard deviation of 2.5 inches (and a normal distribution), approximately how tall is the woman?

119. The placement test for a college has scores that are normally distributed with a mean of 500 and a standard deviation of 100. If the college accepts only the top 10% of examinees, what is the cutoff score on the test for admission?

• Group Exercise

120. For this activity, group members will conduct interviews with a random sample of students on campus. Each student is to be asked. "What is the worst thing about being a student?" One response should be recorded for each student.

a. Each member should interview enough students so that there are at least 50 randomly selected students in the sample.

b. After all responses have been recorded, the group should organize the four most common answers. For each answer, compute the percentage of students in the sample who felt that this is the worst thing about being a student.

c. Find the margin of error for your survey.

d. For each of the four most common answers, write a statement about the percentage of all students on your campus who feel that this is the worst thing about being a student.

SECTION 12.5 • SCATTER PLOTS, CORRELATION, AND REGRESSION LINES

OBJECTIVES

1. Make a scatter plot for a table of data items.
2. Interpret information given in a scatter plot.
3. Compute the correlation coefficient.
4. Write the equation of the regression line.
5. Use a sample's correlation coefficient to determine whether there is a correlation in the population.

Surprised by the number of people smoking cigarettes in movies and television shows made in the 1940s and 1950s? At that time, there was little awareness of the relationship between tobacco use and numerous diseases. Cigarette smoking was seen as a healthy way to relax and help digest a hearty meal. Then, in 1964, an equation changed everything. To understand the mathematics behind this turning point in public health, we need to explore situations involving data collected on two variables.

Up to this point in the chapter, we have studied situations in which data sets involve a single variable, such as heights, weights, cholesterol levels, and lengths of pregnancies. By contrast, the 1964 study involved data collected on two variables from 11 countries—annual cigarette consumption for each adult male and deaths per million males from lung cancer. In this section, we consider situations in which there are two data items for each randomly selected person or thing. Our interest is in determining whether or not there is a relationship between the two variables and, if so, the strength of that relationship.

1 Make a scatter plot for a table of data items.

Scatter Plots and Correlation

Is there a relationship between education and prejudice? With increased education, does a person's level of prejudice tend to decrease? Notice that we are interested in two quantities—years of education and level of prejudice. For each person in our sample, we will record the number of years of school completed and the score on a test measuring prejudice. Higher scores on this 1-to-10 test indicate greater prejudice. Using x to represent years of education and y to represent scores on a test measuring prejudice, Table 12.14 shows these two quantities for a random sample of ten people.

TABLE 12.14 RECORDING TWO QUANTITIES IN A SAMPLE OF TEN PEOPLE

Respondent	A	B	C	D	E	F	G	H	I	J
Years of education (x)	12	5	14	13	8	10	16	11	12	4
Score on prejudice test (y)	1	7	2	3	5	4	1	2	3	10

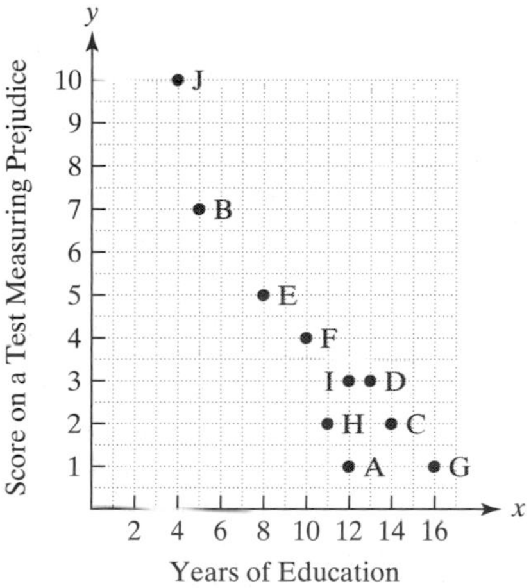

FIGURE 12.26 A scatter plot for education-prejudice data

When two data items are collected for every person or object in a sample, the data items can be visually displayed using a *scatter plot*. A **scatter plot** is a collection of data points, one data point per person or object. We can make a scatter plot of the data in Table 12.14 by drawing a horizontal axis to represent years of education and a vertical axis to represent scores on a test measuring prejudice. We then represent each of the ten respondents with a single point on the graph. For example, the dot for respondent A is located to represent 12 years of education on the horizontal axis and 1 on the prejudice test on the vertical axis. Plotting each of the ten pieces of data in a rectangular coordinate system results in the scatter plot shown in Figure 12.26.

A scatter plot like the one in Figure 12.26 can be used to determine whether two quantities are related. If there is a clear relationship, the quantities are said to be **correlated**. The scatter plot shows a downward trend among the data points, although there are a few exceptions. People with increased education tend to have a lower score on the test measuring prejudice. **Correlation** is used to determine if there is a relationship between two variables and, if so, the strength and direction of that relationship.

Correlation and Causal Connections

Correlations can often be seen when data items are displayed on a scatter plot. Although the scatter plot in Figure 12.26 indicates a correlation between education and prejudice, we cannot conclude that increased education causes a person's level of prejudice to decrease. There are at least three possible explanations:

STUDY TIP

The numbered list on the right represents three possibilities. Perhaps you can provide a better explanation about decreasing prejudice with increased education.

1. The correlation between increased education and decreased prejudice is simply a coincidence.
2. Education usually involves classrooms with a variety of different kinds of people. Increased exposure to diversity in the classroom setting, which accompanies increased levels of education, might be an underlying cause for decreased prejudice.
3. Education, the process of acquiring knowledge, requires people to look at new ideas and see things in different ways. Thus, education causes one to be more tolerant and less prejudiced.

Establishing that one thing causes another is extremely difficult, even if there is a strong correlation between these things. For example, as the air temperature increases, there is an increase in the number of people stung by jellyfish at the beach. This does not mean that an increase in air temperature causes more people to be stung. It might mean that because it is hotter, more people go into the water. With an increased number of swimmers, more people are likely to be stung. In short, correlation is not necessarily causation.

Regression Lines and Correlation Coefficients

Figure 12.27 shows the scatter plot for the education-prejudice data. Also shown is a straight line that seems to approximately "fit" the data points. Most of the data points lie either near or on this line. A line that best fits the data points in a scatter plot is called a **regression line**. The regression line is the particular line in which the spread of the data points around it is as small as possible.

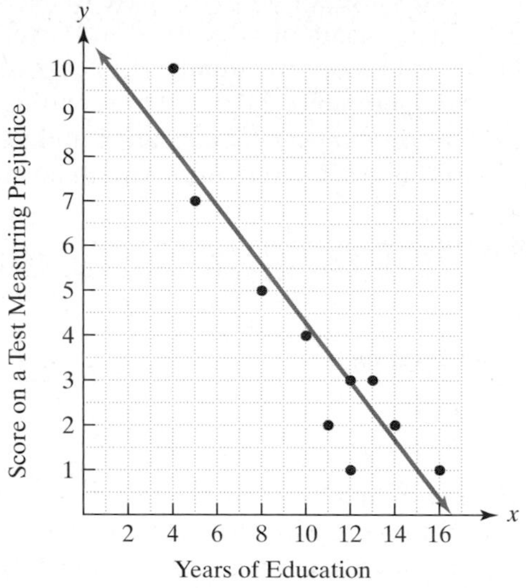

FIGURE 12.27 A scatter plot with a regression line

2 Interpret information given in a scatter plot.

A measure that is used to describe the strength and direction of a relationship between variables whose data points lie on or near a line is called the **correlation coefficient**, designated by r. Figure 12.28 shows scatter plots and correlation coefficients. Variables are **positively correlated** if they tend to increase or decrease together, as in Figure 12.28 (a), (b), and (c). By contrast, variables are **negatively correlated** if one variable tends to decrease while the other increases, as in Figure 12.28 (e), (f), and (g). Figure 12.28 illustrates that a correlation coefficient, r, is a number between -1 and 1, inclusive. Figure 12.28(a) shows a value of 1. This indicates a **perfect positive correlation** in which all points in the scatter plot lie precisely on the regression line that rises from left to right. Figure 12.28(g) shows a value of -1. This indicates a **perfect negative correlation** in which all points in the scatter plot lie precisely on the regression line that falls from left to right.

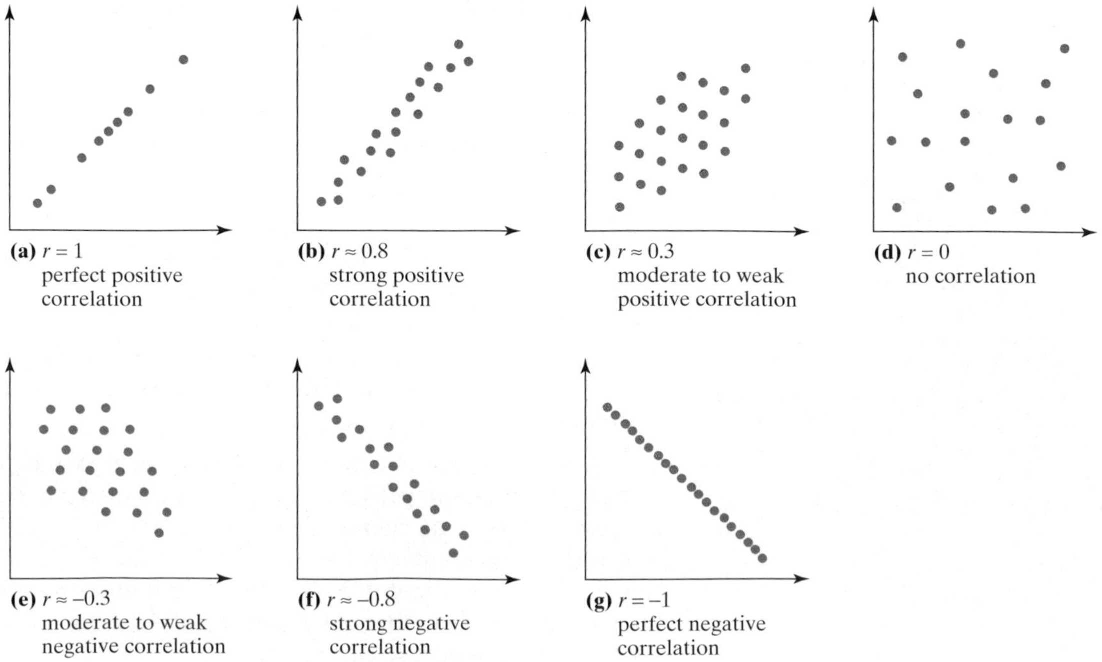

FIGURE 12.28 Scatter plots and correlation coefficients

BLITZER BONUS

Beneficial Uses of Correlation Coefficients

- A Florida study showed a high positive correlation between the number of powerboats and the number of manatee deaths. Many of these deaths were seen to be caused by boats' propellers gashing into the manatees' bodies. Based on this study, Florida set up coastal sanctuaries where powerboats are prohibited so that these large gentle mammals that float just below the water's surface could thrive.
- In 1986, researchers studied how psychiatric patients readjusted to their community after their release from a mental hospital. A moderate positive correlation ($r = 0.38$) was found between patients' attractiveness and their postdischarge social adjustment. The better-looking patients were better off. The researchers suggested that physical attractiveness plays a role in patients' readjustment to community living because good-looking people tend to be treated better by others than homely people are.

Take another look at Figure 12.28. If r is between 0 and 1, as in (b) and (c), the two variables are positively correlated, but not perfectly. Although all the data points will not lie on the regression line, as in (a), an increase in one variable tends to be accompanied by an increase in the other.

Negative correlations are also illustrated in Figure 12.28. If r is between 0 and -1, as in (e) and (f), the two variables are negatively correlated, but not perfectly. Although all the data points will not lie on the regression line, as in (g), an increase in one variable tends to be accompanied by a decrease in the other.

EXAMPLE 1 INTERPRETING A CORRELATION COEFFICIENT

In a 1971 study involving 232 subjects, researchers found a relationship between the subjects' level of stress and how often they became ill. The correlation coefficient in this study was 0.32. Does this indicate a strong relationship between stress and illness?

SOLUTION The correlation coefficient $r = 0.32$ means that as stress increases, frequency of illness also tends to increase. However, 0.32 is only a moderate correlation, illustrated in Figure 12.28(c). There is not, based on this study, a strong relationship between stress and illness. In this study, the relationship is somewhat weak.

CHECK POINT 1 In a 1996 study involving obesity in mothers and daughters, researchers found a relationship between a high body-mass index for the girls and their mothers. (Body-mass index is a measure of weight relative to height. People with a high body-mass index are overweight or obese.) The correlation coefficient in this study was 0.51. Does this indicate a weak relationship between the body-mass index of daughters and the body-mass index of their mothers?

How to Obtain the Correlation Coefficient and the Equation of the Regression Line

3 Compute the correlation coefficient.

The easiest way to find the correlation coefficient and the equation of the regression line is to use a graphing or statistical calculator. Graphing calculators have statistical menus that enable you to enter the x and y data items for the variables. Based on this information, you can instruct the calculator to display a scatter plot, the equation of the regression line, and the correlation coefficient.

We can also compute the correlation coefficient and the equation of the regression line by hand using formulas. First, we compute the correlation coefficient.

COMPUTING THE CORRELATION COEFFICIENT BY HAND

The following formula is used to calculate the correlation coefficient, r:

$$r = \frac{n(\Sigma xy) - (\Sigma x)(\Sigma y)}{\sqrt{n(\Sigma x^2) - (\Sigma x)^2}\sqrt{n(\Sigma y^2) - (\Sigma y)^2}}.$$

In the formula,

n = the number of data points, (x, y)
Σx = the sum of the x-values
Σy = the sum of the y-values
Σxy = the sum of the product of x and y in each pair
Σx^2 = the sum of the squares of the x-values
Σy^2 = the sum of the squares of the y-values
$(\Sigma x)^2$ = the square of the sum of the x-values
$(\Sigma y)^2$ = the square of the sum of the y-values

When computing the correlation coefficient by hand, organize your work in five columns:

x	y	xy	x^2	y^2

Find the sum of the numbers in each column. Then, substitute these values into the formula for r. Example 2 illustrates computing the correlation coefficient for the education-prejudice test data.

EXAMPLE 2 COMPUTING THE CORRELATION COEFFICIENT

Shown below are the data involving the number of years of school, x, completed by ten randomly selected people and their scores on a test measuring prejudice, y. Recall that higher scores on the measure of prejudice (1 to 10) indicate greater levels of prejudice. Determine the correlation coefficient between years of education and scores on a prejudice test.

Respondent	A	B	C	D	E	F	G	H	I	J
Years of education (x)	12	5	14	13	8	10	16	11	12	4
Score on prejudice test (y)	1	7	2	3	5	4	1	2	3	10

SOLUTION As suggested, organize the work in five columns.

x	y	xy	x^2	y^2
12	1	12	144	1
5	7	35	25	49
14	2	28	196	4
13	3	39	169	9
8	5	40	64	25
10	4	40	100	16
16	1	16	256	1
11	2	22	121	4
12	3	36	144	9
4	10	40	16	100
$\Sigma x = 105$	$\Sigma y = 38$	$\Sigma xy = 308$	$\Sigma x^2 = 1235$	$\Sigma y^2 = 218$

Add all values in the x-column. Add all values in the y-column. Add all values in the xy-column. Add all values in the x^2-column. Add all values in the y^2-column.

We use these five sums to calculate the correlation coefficient.

Another value in the formula for r that we have not yet determined is n, the number of data points (x, y). Because there are ten items in the x-column and ten items in the y-column, the number of data points (x, y) is ten. Thus, $n = 10$.

In order to calculate r, we also need to find the square of the sum of the x-values and the y-values:

$$(\Sigma x)^2 = (105)^2 = 11{,}025 \quad \text{and} \quad (\Sigma y)^2 = (38)^2 = 1444.$$

We are ready to determine the value for r.

$$\begin{aligned} r &= \frac{n(\Sigma xy) - (\Sigma x)(\Sigma y)}{\sqrt{n(\Sigma x^2) - (\Sigma x)^2}\sqrt{n(\Sigma y^2) - (\Sigma y)^2}} \\ &= \frac{10(308) - 105(38)}{\sqrt{10(1235) - 11{,}025}\sqrt{10(218) - 1444}} \\ &= \frac{-910}{\sqrt{1325}\sqrt{736}} \\ &\approx -0.92 \end{aligned}$$

TECHNOLOGY

GRAPHING CALCULATORS, SCATTER PLOTS, AND REGRESSION LINES

You can use a graphing calculator to display a scatter plot and the regression line. After entering the x and y data items for years of education and scores on a prejudice test, the calculator shows the scatter plot of the data and the regression line.

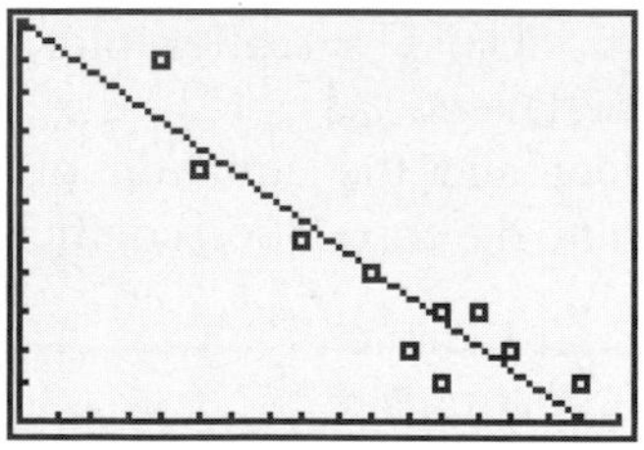

Also displayed below is the regression line's equation and the correlation coefficient, r. The slope shown below is approximately -0.69. The negative slope reinforces the fact that there is a negative correlation between the variables in Example 2.

"Common wisdom among statisticians is that at least 5% of all data points are corrupted, either when they are initially recorded or when they are entered into the computer."

Jessica Utts, STATISTICIAN

The value for r, approximately -0.92, is fairly close to -1 and indicates a strong negative correlation. This means that the more education a person has, the less prejudiced that person is (based on scores on the test measuring levels of prejudice).

CHECK POINT 2 Is there a relationship between alcohol from moderate wine consumption and heart disease death rate? The table gives data from 19 developed countries. Using a calculator, determine the correlation coefficient between these variables. Round to two decimal places.

France (G) U.S. (R)

Country	A	B	C	D	E	F	G	H	I	J	K	L	M	N	O	P	Q	R	S
Liters of alcohol from drinking wine, per person per year (x)	2.5	3.9	2.9	2.4	2.9	0.8	9.1	0.8	0.7	7.9	1.8	1.9	0.8	6.5	1.6	5.8	1.3	1.2	2.7
Deaths from heart disease, per 100,000 people per year (y)	211	167	131	191	220	297	71	211	300	107	167	266	227	86	207	115	285	199	172

Source: *New York Times*, December 28, 1994

Once we have determined that two variables are related, we can use the equation of the regression line to determine the exact relationship. Here is the formula for writing the equation of the line that best fits the data:

4 Write the equation of the regression line.

WRITING THE EQUATION OF THE REGRESSION LINE BY HAND

The equation of the regression line is

$$y = mx + b,$$

where

$$m = \frac{n(\Sigma xy) - (\Sigma x)(\Sigma y)}{n(\Sigma x^2) - (\Sigma x)^2} \quad \text{and} \quad b = \frac{\Sigma y - m(\Sigma x)}{n}.$$

EXAMPLE 3 WRITING THE EQUATION OF THE REGRESSION LINE

a. Shown, again, in Figure 12.27 is the scatter plot and the regression line for the data in Example 2. Use the data to find the equation of the regression line that relates years of education and scores on a prejudice test.

b. Approximately what score on the test can be anticipated by a person with nine years of education?

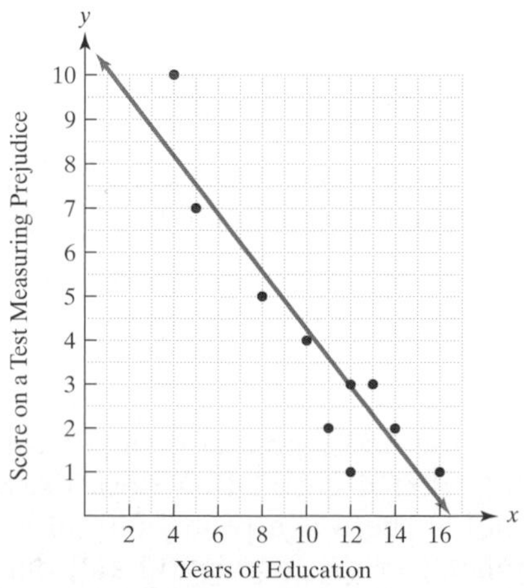

FIGURE 12.27 (repeated)

SOLUTION

a. We use the sums obtained in Example 2. We begin by computing m.

$$m = \frac{n(\Sigma xy) - (\Sigma x)(\Sigma y)}{n(\Sigma x^2) - (\Sigma x)^2} = \frac{10(308) - 105(38)}{10(1235) - (105)^2} = \frac{-910}{1325} \approx -0.69$$

With a negative correlation coefficient, it makes sense that the slope of the regression line is negative. This line falls from left to right, indicating a negative correlation.

Now, we find the y-intercept, b.

$$b = \frac{\Sigma y - m(\Sigma x)}{n} = \frac{38 - (-0.69)(105)}{10} = \frac{110.45}{10} \approx 11.05$$

Using $m \approx -0.69$ and $b \approx 11.05$, the equation of the regression line, $y = mx + b$, is

$$y = -0.69x + 11.05,$$

where x represents the number of years of education and y represents the score on the prejudice test.

b. To anticipate the score on the prejudice test for a person with nine years of education, substitute 9 for x in the regression line's equation.

$$y = -0.69x + 11.05$$
$$y = -0.69(9) + 11.05 = 4.84$$

A person with nine years of education is anticipated to have a score close to 5 on the prejudice test.

5 Use a sample's correlation coefficient to determine whether there is a correlation in the population.

CHECK POINT 3 Use the data in Check Point 2 on page 735 to find the equation of the regression line. Use the equation to predict the heart disease death rate in a country where adults average 10 liters of alcohol per person per year.

TABLE 12.15 VALUES FOR DETERMINING CORRELATIONS IN A POPULATION

n	$\alpha = 0.05$	$\alpha = 0.01$
4	0.950	0.990
5	0.878	0.959
6	0.811	0.917
7	0.754	0.875
8	0.707	0.834
9	0.666	0.798
10	0.632	0.765
11	0.602	0.735
12	0.576	0.708
13	0.553	0.684
14	0.532	0.661
15	0.514	0.641
16	0.497	0.623
17	0.482	0.606
18	0.468	0.590
19	0.456	0.575
20	0.444	0.561
22	0.423	0.537
27	0.381	0.487
32	0.349	0.449
37	0.325	0.418
42	0.304	0.393
47	0.288	0.372
52	0.273	0.354
62	0.250	0.325
72	0.232	0.302
82	0.217	0.283
92	0.205	0.267
102	0.195	0.254

The larger the sample size, n, the smaller is the value of r needed for a correlation in the population.

The Level of Significance of r

In Example 2, we found a strong negative correlation between education and prejudice, computing the correlation coefficient, r, to be -0.92. However, the sample size ($n = 10$) was relatively small. With such a small sample, can we truly conclude that a correlation exists in the population? Or could it be that education and prejudice are not related? Perhaps the results we obtained were simply due to sampling error and chance.

Mathematicians have identified values to determine whether r, the correlation coefficient for a sample, can be attributed to a relationship between variables in the population. These values are shown in the second and third columns of Table 12.15. They depend on the sample size, n, listed in the left column. If $|r|$, the absolute value of the correlation coefficient computed for the sample, is greater than the value given in the table, a correlation exists between the variables in the population. The column headed $\alpha = 0.05$ denotes a **significance level of 5%**, meaning that there is a 0.05 probability that, when the statistician says the variables are correlated, they are actually not related in the population. The column on the right, headed $\alpha = 0.01$, denotes a **significance level of 1%**, meaning that there is a 0.01 probability that, when the statistician says the variables are correlated, they are actually not related in the population. Values in the $\alpha = 0.01$ column are greater than those in the $\alpha = 0.05$ column. Because of the possibility of sampling error, there is always a probability that when we say the variables are related, there is actually not a correlation in the population from which the sample was randomly selected.

EXAMPLE 4 DETERMINING A CORRELATION IN THE POPULATION

In Example 2, we computed $r = -0.92$ for $n = 10$. Can we conclude that there is a negative correlation between education and prejudice in the population?

SOLUTION Begin by taking the absolute value of the calculated correlation coefficient.

$$|r| = |-0.92| = 0.92$$

Now, look to the right of $n = 10$ in Table 12.15. Because 0.92 is greater than both of these values (0.632 and 0.765), we may conclude that a correlation does exist between education and prejudice in the population. (There is a probability of at most 0.01 that the variables are not really correlated in the population and our results could be attributed to chance.)

CHECK POINT 4 If you worked Check Point 2 correctly, you should have found that $r \approx -0.84$ for $n = 19$. Can you conclude that there is a negative correlation between moderate wine consumption and heart disease death rate?

BLITZER BONUS

Cigarettes and Lung Cancer

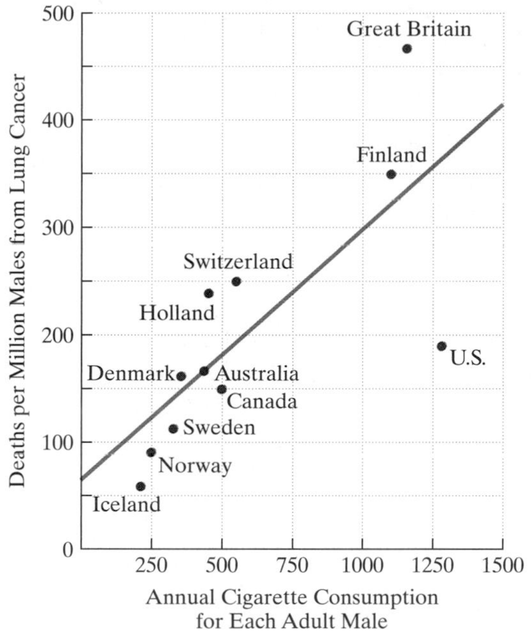

Source: Smoking and Health, Washington, D.C., 1964

This scatter plot shows a relationship between cigarette consumption among males and deaths due to lung cancer per million males. The data are from 11 countries and date back to a 1964 report by the U.S. Surgeon General. The scatter plot can be modeled by a line whose slope indicates an increasing death rate from lung cancer with increased cigarette consumption. At that time, the tobacco industry argued that in spite of this regression line, tobacco use is not the cause of cancer. Recent data do, indeed, show a causal effect between tobacco use and numerous diseases.

EXERCISE SET 12.5

• Practice and Application Exercises

In Exercises 1–8, make a scatter plot for the given data. Use the scatter plot to describe whether or not the variables appear to be related.

1.

x	1	6	4	3	7	2
y	2	5	3	3	4	1

2.

x	2	1	6	3	4
y	4	5	10	8	9

3.

x	8	6	1	5	4	10	3
y	2	4	10	5	6	2	9

4.

x	4	5	2	1
y	1	3	5	4

5.

Respondent	A	B	C	D	E	F	G
Years of education of parent (x)	13	9	7	12	12	10	11
Years of education of child (y)	13	11	7	16	17	8	17

6.

Respondent	A	B	C	D	E
IQ (x)	110	115	120	125	135
Annual income(y) (in thousands of dollars)	30	32	36	40	44

7. The data show the number of registered automatic weapons, in thousands, and the murder rate, in murders per 100,000, for eight randomly selected states.

Automatic weapons, x	11.6	8.3	6.9	3.6	2.6	2.5	2.4	0.6
Murder rate, y	13.1	10.6	11.5	10.1	5.3	6.6	3.6	4.4

Source: FBI and Bureau of Alcohol, Tobacco, and Firearms

8. The data show the number of employed and unemployed male workers, 20 years and older, in thousands, for six selected years in the United States.

Year	1995	1996	1997	1998	1999	2000
Employed, x	64,085	64,897	66,524	67,134	67,761	68,580
Unemployed, y	3239	3147	2826	2580	2433	2350

Source: Bureau of Labor Statistics

The scatter plot in the figure shows the relationship between the percentage of married women of child-bearing age using contraceptives and births per woman in selected countries. Use the scatter plot to determine whether each of the statements in Exercises 9–18 is true or false.

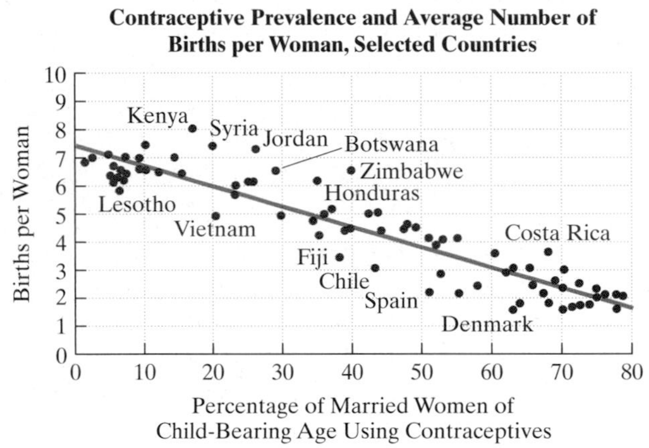

Source: Population Reference Bureau

9. There is a strong positive correlation between contraceptive use and births per woman.

10. There is no correlation between contraceptive use and births per woman.

11. There is a strong negative correlation between contraceptive use and births per woman.

12. There is a causal relationship between contraceptive use and births per woman.

13. With approximately 43% of women of child-bearing age using contraceptives, there are 3 births per woman in Chile.

14. With 20% of women of child-bearing age using contraceptives, there are 6 births per woman in Vietnam.

15. No two countries have a different number of births per woman with the same percentage of married women using contraceptives.

16. The country with the greatest number of births per woman also has the smallest percentage of women using contraceptives.

17. Most of the data points do not lie on the regression line.

18. The number of selected countries shown in the scatter plot is approximately 20.

Just as money doesn't buy happiness for individuals, the two don't necessarily go together for countries either. However, the scatter plot does show a relationship between a country's annual per capita income and the percentage of people in that country who call themselves "happy." Use the scatter plot to determine whether each of the statements in Exercises 19–26 is true or false.

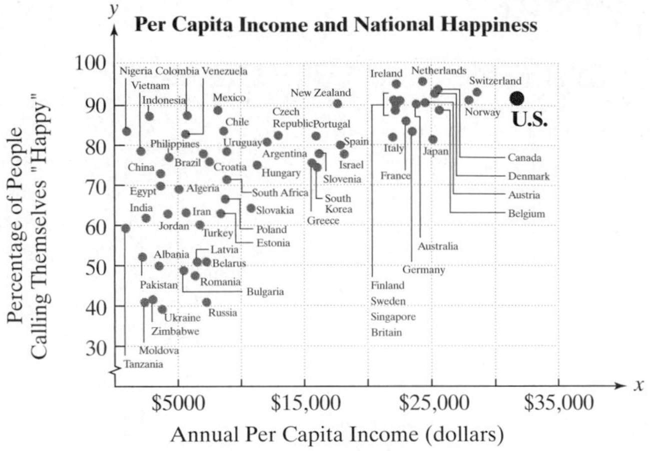

Source: Richard Layard, *Happiness: Lessons from a New Science*, Penguin, 2005

19. There is no correlation between per capita income and the percentage of people who call themselves "happy."

20. There is an almost-perfect positive correlation between per capita income and the percentage of people who call themselves "happy."

21. There is a positive correlation between per capita income and the percentage of people who call themselves "happy."

22. As per capita income decreases, the percentage of people who call themselves "happy" also tends to decrease.

23. The country with the lowest per capita income has the least percentage of people who call themselves "happy."

24. The country with the highest per capita income has the greatest percentage of people who call themselves "happy."

25. A reasonable estimate of the correlation coefficient for the data is 0.8.

26. A reasonable estimate of the correlation coefficient for the data is -0.3.

Use the scatter plots shown, labeled (a)–(f), to solve Exercises 27–30.

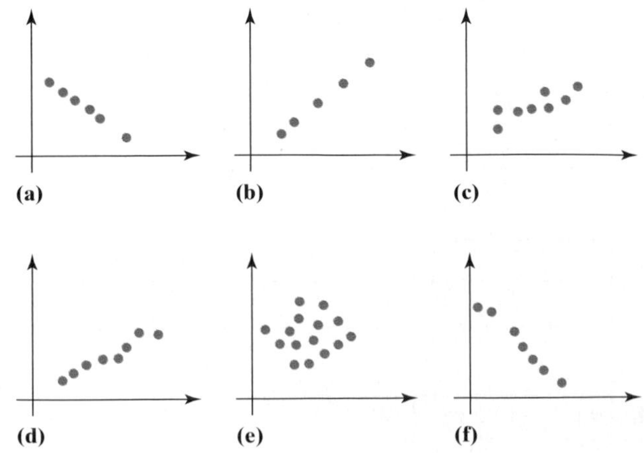

27. Which scatter plot indicates a perfect negative correlation?

28. Which scatter plot indicates a perfect positive correlation?

29. In which scatter plot is $r = 0.9$?

30. In which scatter plot is $r = 0.01$?

Compute r, the correlation coefficient, rounded to the nearest thousandth, for the data in

31. Exercise 1.

32. Exercise 2.

33. Exercise 3.

34. Exercise 4.

35. Use the data in Exercise 5 to solve this exercise.

a. Determine the correlation coefficient between years of education of parent and child.

b. Find the equation of the regression line for years of education of parent and child.

c. Approximately how many years of education can we predict for a child with a parent who has 16 years of education?

36. Use the data in Exercise 6 to solve this exercise.

a. Determine the correlation coefficient between IQ and income.

b. Find the equation of the regression line for IQ and income.

c. Approximately what annual income can be anticipated by a person whose IQ is 123?

37. Use the data in Exercise 7 to solve this exercise.

a. Determine the correlation coefficient between the number of automatic weapons and the murder rate.

b. Find the equation of the regression line.

c. Approximately what murder rate can we anticipate in a state that has 14 thousand registered weapons?

38. Use the data in Exercise 8 to solve this exercise.

a. Determine the correlation coefficient between the number of employed males and the number of unemployed males.

b. Find the equation of the regression line.

c. Approximately how many unemployed males can we anticipate for a year in which there are 70,000 thousand employed males?

In Exercises 39–45, the correlation coefficient, r, is given for a sample of n data points. Use the $\alpha = 0.05$ *column in Table 12.15 on page 736 to determine whether or not we may conclude that a correlation does exist in the population. (Using the* $\alpha = 0.05$ *column, there is a probability of 0.05 that the variables are not really correlated in the population and our results could be attributed to chance. Ignore this possibility when concluding whether or not there is a correlation in the population.)*

39. $n = 20, r = 0.5$

40. $n = 27, r = 0.4$

41. $n = 12, r = 0.5$

42. $n = 22, r = 0.04$

43. $n = 72, r = -0.351$

44. $n = 37, r = -0.37$

45. $n = 20, r = -0.37$

46. In the 1964 study on cigarette consumption and deaths due to lung cancer (see the Blitzer Bonus on page 737), $n = 11$ and $r = 0.73$. What can you conclude using the $\alpha = 0.05$ column in Table 12.15?

• Writing in Mathematics

47. What is a scatter plot?

48. How does a scatter plot indicate that two variables are correlated?

49. Give an example of two variables with a strong positive correlation and explain why this is so.

50. Give an example of two variables with a strong negative correlation and explain why this is so.

51. What is meant by a regression line?

52. When all points in a scatter plot fall on the regression line, what is the value of the correlation coefficient? Describe what this means.

For the pairs of quantities in Exercises 53–56, describe whether a scatter plot will show a positive correlation, a negative correlation, or no correlation. If there is a correlation, is it strong, moderate, or weak? Explain your answers.

53. Height and weight

54. Number of days absent and grade in a course

55. Height and grade in a course

56. Hours of television watched and grade in a course

57. Explain how to use the correlation coefficient for a sample to determine if there is a correlation in the population.

• Critical Thinking Exercises

58. Which one of the following is true?

a. A scatter plot need not define y as a function of x.

b. The correlation coefficient and the slope of the regression line for the same set of data can have opposite signs.

c. When all points in a scatter plot fall on the regression line, the value of the correlation coefficient is 0.

d. If the same number is subtracted from each x-item, but the y-item stays the same, the correlation coefficient for these new data points decreases.

59. Give an example of two variables with a strong correlation, where each variable is not the cause of the other.

• Technology Exercise

60. Use the linear regression feature of a graphing calculator to verify your work in any two exercises from Exercises 35–38, parts (a) and (b).

• Group Exercises

61. The group should select two variables related to people on your campus that it believes have a strong positive or negative correlation. Once these variables have been determined,

a. Collect at least 30 ordered pairs of data (x, y) from a sample of people on your campus.

b. Draw a scatter plot for the data collected.

c. Does the scatter plot indicate a positive correlation, a negative correlation, or no relationship between the variables?

d. Calculate r. Does the value of r reinforce the impression conveyed by the scatter plot?

e. Find the equation of the regression line.

f. Use the regression line's equation to make a prediction about a y-value given an x-value.

g. Are the results of this project consistent with the group's original belief about the correlation between the variables, or are there some surprises in the data collected?

62. What is the opinion of students on your campus about . . . ? Group members should begin by deciding on some aspect of college life around which student opinion can be polled. The poll should consist of the question, "What is your opinion of . . . ?" Be sure to provide options such as excellent, good, average, poor, horrible, or a 1-to-10 scale, or possibly grades of A, B, C, D, F. Use a random sample of students on your campus and conduct the opinion survey. After collecting the data, present and interpret it using as many of the skills and techniques learned in this chapter as possible.

CHAPTER SUMMARY, REVIEW, AND TEST

SUMMARY

DEFINITIONS AND CONCEPTS	EXAMPLES
12.1 Sampling, Frequency Distributions, and Graphs	
a. A population is the set containing all objects whose properties are to be described and analyzed. A sample is a subset of the population.	Ex. 1, p. 681
b. Random samples are obtained in such a way that each member of the population has an equal chance of being selected.	Ex. 2, p. 682
c. Data can be organized and presented in frequency distributions, grouped frequency distributions, histograms, frequency polygons, and stem-and-leaf plots.	Ex. 3, p. 683; Ex. 4, p. 684; Figures 12.2 and 12.3, p. 685; Ex. 5, p. 686
d. The box on page 687 lists some things to watch for in visual displays of data.	Table 12.4, p. 688
12.2 Measures of Central Tendency	
a. The mean is the sum of the data items divided by the number of items. Mean $= \frac{\Sigma x}{n}$.	Ex. 1, p. 693
b. The mean of a frequency distribution is computed using $\text{Mean} = \frac{\Sigma xf}{n}$, where x is each data value, f is its frequency, and n is the total frequency of the distribution.	Ex. 2, p. 694
c. The median of ranked data is the item in the middle or the mean of the two middlemost items. The median is the value in the $\frac{n+1}{2}$ position in the list of ranked data.	Ex. 3, p. 695; Ex. 4, p. 696; Ex. 5, p. 697; Ex. 6, p. 697
d. When one or more data items are much greater than or much less than the other items, these extreme values greatly influence the mean, often making the median more representative of the data.	Ex. 7, p. 698
e. The mode of a data set is the value that occurs most often. If there is no such value, there is no mode. If more than one data value has the highest frequency, then each of these data values is a mode.	Ex. 8, p. 700
f. The midrange is computed using $\frac{\text{lowest data value} + \text{highest data value}}{2}$.	Ex. 9, p. 701; Ex. 10, p. 701
12.3 Measures of Dispersion	
a. Range = highest data value − lowest data value	Ex. 1, p. 705

b. Standard deviation $= \sqrt{\dfrac{\Sigma(\text{data item} - \text{mean})^2}{n - 1}}$ — Ex. 2, p. 706; Ex. 3, p. 707; Ex. 4, p. 708

c. As the spread of data items increases, the standard deviation gets larger. — Ex. 5, p. 709

12.4 The Normal Distribution

a. The normal distribution is a theoretical distribution for the entire population. The distribution is bell shaped and symmetric about a vertical line through its center, where the mean, median, and mode are located.

b. The 68–95–99.7 Rule — Ex. 1, p. 714; Ex. 2, p. 715

Approximately 68% of the data items fall within 1 standard deviation of the mean,
95% of the data items fall within 2 standard deviations of the mean, and
99.7% of the data items fall within 3 standard deviations of the mean.

c. A z-score describes how many standard deviations a data item in a normal distribution lies above or below the mean. — Ex. 3, p. 716; Ex. 4, p. 718; Ex. 5, p. 718

$$z\text{-score} = \frac{\text{data item} - \text{mean}}{\text{standard deviation}}$$

d. If n% of the items in a distribution are less than a particular data item, that data item is in the nth percentile of the distribution. The 25th percentile is the first quartile, the 50th percentile, or the median, is the second quartile, and the 75th percentile is the third quartile. — Ex. 6, p. 719; Figure 12.16, p. 719

e. A table showing z-scores and their percentiles can be used to find the percentage of data items less than or greater than a given data item in a normal distribution, as well as the percentage of data items between two given items. See the boxed summary on computing percentage of data items on page 724. — Ex. 7, p. 720; Ex. 8, p. 721; Ex. 9, p. 723

f. If a statistic is obtained from a random sample of size n, there is a 95% probability that it lies within $\frac{1}{\sqrt{n}}$ of the true population statistic. $\pm\frac{1}{\sqrt{n}}$ is called the margin of error. — Ex. 10, p. 725

g. A distribution of data is skewed if a large number of data items are piled up at one end or the other, with a "tail" at the opposite end. — Figure 12.24, p. 727; Figure 12.25, p. 727

12.5 Scatter Plots, Correlation, and Regression Lines

a. A plot of data points is called a scatter plot. If the points lie approximately along a line, the line that best fits the data is called a regression line.

b. A correlation coefficient, r, measures the strength and direction of a possible relationship between variables. If $r = 1$, there is a perfect positive correlation, and if $r = -1$, there is a perfect negative correlation. If $r = 0$, there is no relationship between the variables. Table 12.15 on page 736 indicates whether r denotes a correlation in the population. — Ex. 1, p. 733; Ex. 4, p. 736

c. The formula for computing the correlation coefficient, r, is given in the box on page 733. The equation of the regression line is given in the box on page 735. — Ex. 2, p. 734; Ex. 3, p. 735

REVIEW EXERCISES

12.1

A survey of 1511 randomly selected American women ages 25 through 60 was taken by CyberPulse Advisory Panel. The data below are from the poll. Use this information to solve Exercises 1–2.

How Often Do You Entertain Guests for Dinner?

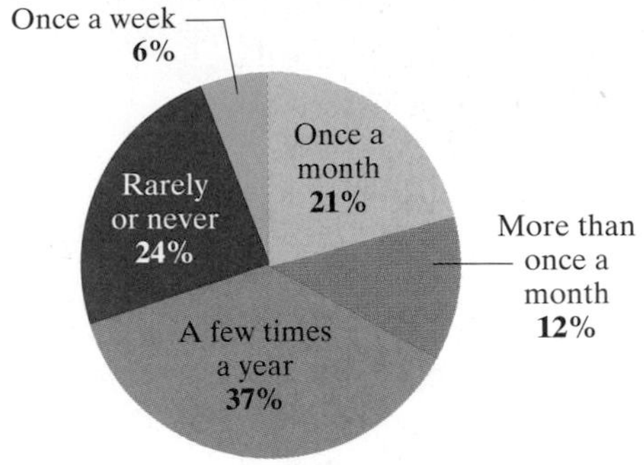

1. Describe the population and the sample of this poll.
2. For each woman polled, what variable is measured?
3. The government of a large city wants to know if its citizens will support a three-year tax increase to provide additional support to the city's community college system. The government decides to conduct a survey of the city's residents before placing a tax increase initiative on the ballot. Which one of the following is most appropriate for obtaining a sample of the city's residents?
   a. Survey a random sample of persons within each geographic region of the city.
   b. Survey a random sample of community college professors living in the city.
   c. Survey every tenth person who walks into the city's government center on two randomly selected days of the week.
   d. Survey a random sample of persons within each geographic region of the state in which the city is located.

A random sample of ten college students is selected and each student is asked how much time he or she spent on homework during the previous weekend. The following times, in hours, are obtained:

$$8, 10, 9, 7, 9, 8, 7, 6, 8, 7.$$

Use these data items to solve Exercises 4–6.

4. Construct a frequency distribution for the data.
5. Construct a histogram for the data.
6. Construct a frequency polygon for the data.

The 50 grades on a physiology test are shown. Use the data to solve Exercises 7–8.

44	24	54	81	18
34	39	63	67	60
72	36	91	47	75
57	74	87	49	86
59	14	26	41	90
13	29	13	31	68
63	35	29	70	22
95	17	50	42	27
73	11	42	31	69
56	40	31	45	51

7. Construct a grouped frequency distribution for the data. Use 0–39 for the first class, 40–49 for the second class, and make each subsequent class width the same as the second class.
8. Construct a stem-and-leaf plot for the data.
9. Describe what is misleading about the size of the barrels in the following visual display.

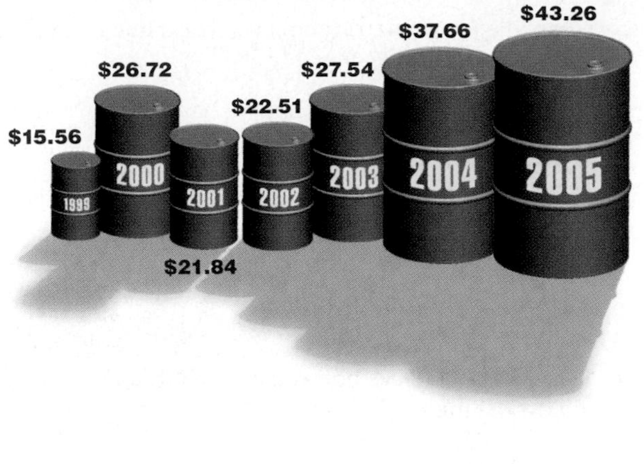

Source: U.S. Department of Energy

12.2

In Exercises 10–11, find the mean for each group of data items.

10. 84, 90, 95, 89, 98
11. 33, 27, 9, 10, 6, 7, 11, 23, 27
12. Find the mean for the data items in the given frequency distribution.

Score x	Frequency f
1	2
2	4
3	3
4	1

In Exercises 13–14, find the median for each group of data items.

13. 33, 27, 9, 10, 6, 7, 11, 23, 27
14. 28, 16, 22, 28, 34
15. Find the median for the data items in the frequency distribution in Exercise 12.

In Exercises 16–17, find the mode for each group of data items. If there is no mode, so state.

16. 33, 27, 9, 10, 6, 7, 11, 23, 27
17. 582, 585, 583, 585, 587, 587, 589
18. Find the mode for the data items in the frequency distribution in Exercise 12.

In Exercises 19–20, find the midrange for each group of data items.

19. 84, 90, 95, 88, 98
20. 33, 27, 9, 10, 6, 7, 11, 23, 27
21. Find the midrange for the data items in the frequency distribution in Exercise 12.

22. Researchers at Emory University studied national health-care data from 14,000 Americans in 1987 and 2002. Explain how the research team obtained the mean annual health-care costs shown in the bar graph.

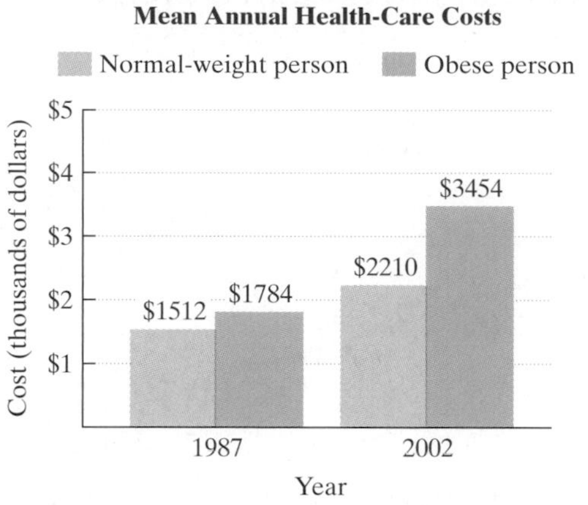

Source: Kenneth Thorpe, Emory University

23. A student took seven tests in a course, scoring between 90% and 95% on three of the tests, between 80% and 89% on three of the tests, and below 40% on one of the tests. In this distribution, is the mean or the median more representative of the student's overall performance in the course? Explain your answer.

24. The data items below are the ages of U.S. presidents at the time of their first inauguration.

57	61	57	57	58	57	61	54	68	51	49	64	50	48
65	52	56	46	54	49	51	47	55	55	54	42	51	56
55	51	54	51	60	62	43	55	56	61	52	69	64	46 54

a. Organize the data in a frequency distribution.

b. Use the frequency distribution to find the mean age, median age, modal age, and midrange age of the presidents when they were inaugurated.

12.3

In Exercises 25–26, find the range for each group of data items.

25. 28, 34, 16, 22, 28

26. 312, 783, 219, 312, 426, 219

27. The mean for the data items 29, 9, 8, 22, 46, 51, 48, 42, 53, 42 is 35. Find **a.** the deviation from the mean for each data item and **b.** the sum of the deviations in part (a).

28. Use the data items 36, 26, 24, 90, and 74 to find **a.** the mean, **b.** the deviation from the mean for each data item, and **c.** the sum of the deviations in part (b).

In Exercises 29–30, find the standard deviation for each group of data items.

29. 3, 3, 5, 8, 10, 13

30. 20, 27, 23, 26, 28, 32, 33, 35

31. A test measuring anxiety levels is administered to a sample of ten college students with the following results. (High scores indicate high anxiety.)

10, 30, 37, 40, 43, 44, 45, 69, 86, 86

Find the mean, range, and standard deviation for the data.

32. Compute the mean and the standard deviation for each of the following data sets. Then, write a brief description of similarities and differences between the two sets based on each of your computations.

Set A: 80, 80, 80, 80   Set B: 70, 70, 90, 90

33. Describe how you would determine

a. which of the two groups, men or women, at your college has a higher mean grade point average.

b. which of the groups is more consistently close to its mean grade point average.

12.4

The scores on a test are normally distributed with a mean of 70 and a standard deviation of 8. In Exercises 34–36, find the score that is

34. 2 standard deviations above the mean.

35. $3\frac{1}{2}$ standard deviations above the mean.

36. $1\frac{1}{4}$ standard deviations below the mean.

The ages of people living in a retirement community are normally distributed with a mean age of 68 years and a standard deviation of 4 years. In Exercises 37–43, use the 68–95–99.7 Rule to find the percentage of people in the community whose ages

37. are between 64 and 72.
38. are between 60 and 76.
39. are between 68 and 72.
40. are between 56 and 80.
41. exceed 72.
42. are less than 72.
43. exceed 76.

A set of data items is normally distributed with a mean of 50 and a standard deviation of 5. In Exercises 44–48, convert each data item to a z-score.

44. 50
45. 60
46. 58
47. 35
48. 44

49. A student scores 60 on a vocabulary test and 80 on a grammar test. The data items for both tests are normally distributed. The vocabulary test has a mean of 50 and a standard deviation of 5. The grammar test has a mean of 72 and a standard deviation of 6. On which test did the student have the better score? Explain why this is so.

The number of miles that a particular brand of car tires lasts is normally distributed with a mean of 32,000 miles and a standard deviation of 4000 miles. In Exercises 50–52, find the data item in this distribution that corresponds to the given z-score.

50. $z = 1.5$
51. $z = 2.25$
52. $z = -2.5$

The mean cholesterol level for all men in the United States is 200 and the standard deviation is 15. In Exercises 53–56, use Table 12.13 on page 720 to find the percentage of U.S. men whose cholesterol level

53. is less than 221.
54. is greater than 173.
55. is between 173 and 221.
56. is between 164 and 182.

Use the percentiles for the weights of adult men over 40 to solve Exercises 57–59.

Weight	Percentile
235	86
227	third quartile
180	second quartile
173	first quartile

Find the percentage of men over 40 who weigh

57. less than 227 pounds.
58. more than 235 pounds.
59. between 227 and 235 pounds.

60. Using a random sample of 2041 executives of American companies, a Korn/Ferry survey asked respondents if their career was related to the area of their college degree. The poll indicated that 85% of the executives responded "yes" and 15% said "no."

a. Find the margin of error, to the nearest tenth of a percent, for this survey.

b. Write a statement about the percentage of American executives in the population whose career is not related to their college degree.

61. The histogram indicates the frequencies of the number of syllables per word for 100 randomly selected words in Japanese.

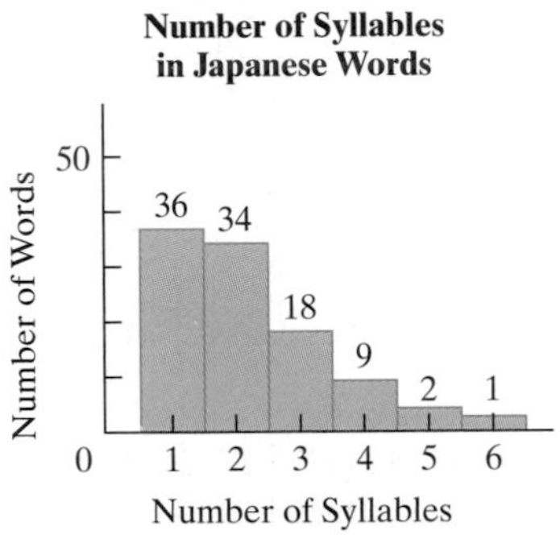

a. Is the shape of this distribution best classified as normal, skewed to the right, or skewed to the left?

b. Find the mean, median, and mode for the number of syllables in the sample of Japanese words.

c. Are the measures of central tendency from part (b) consistent with the shape of the distribution that you described in part (a)? Explain your answer.

12.5

In Exercises 62–63, make a scatter plot for the given data. Use the scatter plot to describe whether or not the variables appear to be related.

62.

x	1	3	4	6	8	9
y	1	2	3	3	5	5

63.

Country	Canada	U.S.	Mexico	Brazil	Costa Rica	Denmark	China	Egypt	Pakistan	Bangladesh	Australia	Japan	Russia
Life expectancy in years, x	79	76	72	64	76	76	70	62	59	57	80	80	65
Infant deaths per 1000 births, y	5.6	6.4	25.9	40.0	13.1	6.8	45.5	69.3	93.5	97.7	5.3	4.1	23.3

Source: U.S. Bureau of the Census International Database

The scatter plot in the figure shows the relationship between the percentage of adult females in a country who are literate and the mortality of children under five. Also shown is the regression line. Use this information to determine whether each of the statements in Exercises 64–70 is true or false.

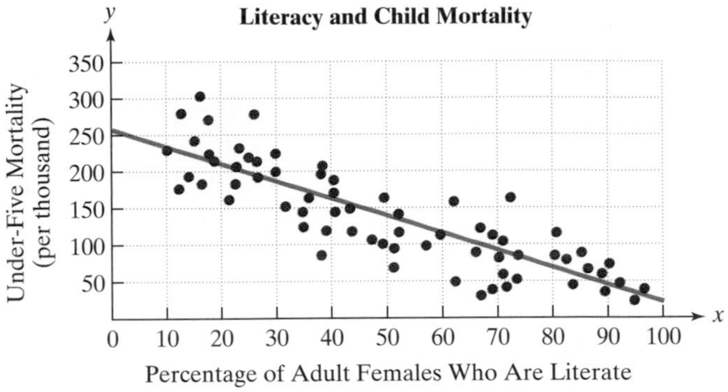

Source: United Nations

64. There is a perfect negative correlation between the percentage of adult females who are literate and under-five mortality.

65. As the percentage of adult females who are literate increases, under-five mortality tends to decrease.

66. The country with the least percentage of adult females who are literate has the greatest under-five mortality.

67. No two countries have the same percentage of adult females who are literate but different under-five mortalities.

68. There are more than 20 countries in this sample.

69. There is no correlation between the percentage of adult females who are literate and under-five mortality.

70. The country with the greatest percentage of adult females who are literate has an under-five mortality rate that is less than 50 children per thousand.

71. Which one of the following scatter plots indicates a correlation coefficient of approximately −0.9?

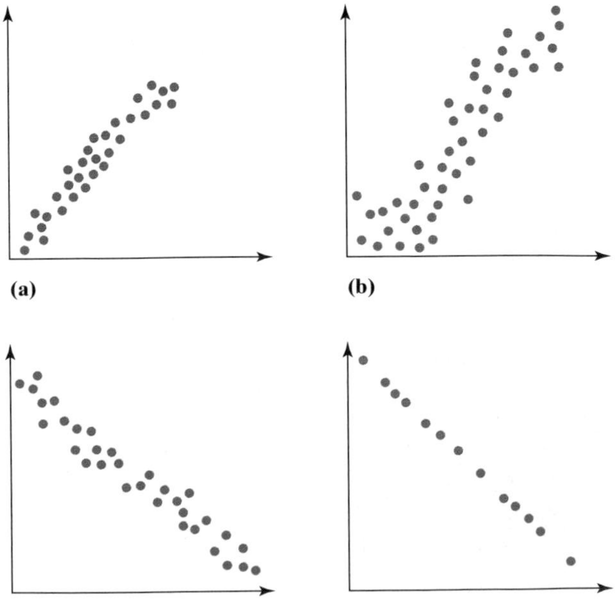

(a) (b) (c) (d)

72. Use the data in Exercise 62 to solve the exercise.

a. Compute r, the correlation coefficient, rounded to the nearest thousandth.

b. Find the equation of the regression line.

73. The graph, based on Nielsen Media Research 2005 data taken from random samples of Americans at various ages, indicates that as we get older, we watch more television.

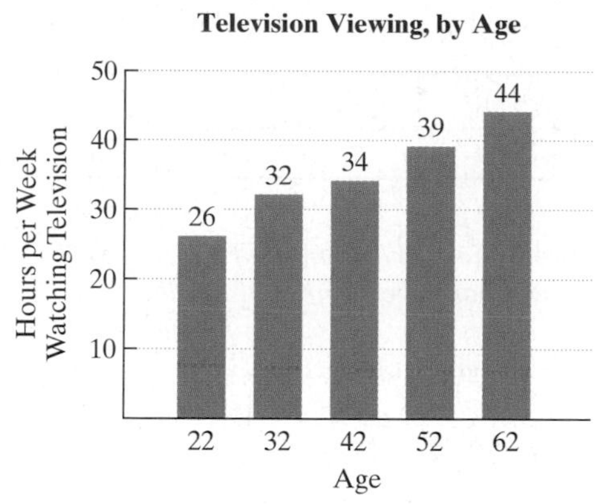

Source: Nielsen Media Research

a. Let x represent one's age and let y represent hours per week watching television. Calculate the correlation coefficient.

b. Using Table 12.15 on page 736 and the $\alpha = 0.05$ column, determine whether there is a correlation between age and time spent watching television in the American population.

CHAPTER 12 TEST

1. Politicians in the Florida Keys need to know if the residents of Key Largo think the amount of money charged for water is reasonable. The politicians decide to conduct a survey of a sample of Key Largo's residents. Which procedure would be most appropriate for a sample of Key Largo's residents?

a. Survey all water customers who pay their water bills at Key Largo City Hall on the third day of the month.

b. Survey a random sample of executives who work for the water company in Key Largo.

c. Survey 5000 individuals who are randomly selected from a list of all people living in Georgia and Florida.

d. Survey a random sample of persons within each neighborhood of Key Largo.

Use these scores on a ten-point quiz to solve Exercises 2–4.

$$8, 5, 3, 6, 5, 10, 6, 9, 4, 5, 7, 9, 7, 4, 8, 8$$

2. Construct a frequency distribution for the data.

3. Construct a histogram for the data.

4. Construct a frequency polygon for the data.

Use the 30 test scores listed below to solve Exercises 5–6.

79	51	67	50	78
62	89	83	73	80
88	48	60	71	79
89	63	55	93	71
41	81	46	50	61
59	50	90	75	61

5. Construct a grouped frequency distribution for the data. Use 40–49 for the first class and use the same width for each subsequent class.

6. Construct a stem-and-leaf display for the data.

7. The graph shows the percentage of students in the United States through grade 12 who were home-schooled in 1999 and 2003. What impression does the roofline in the visual display imply about what occurred in 2000 through 2002? How might this be misleading?

Source: National Center for Education Statistics

Use the six data items listed below to solve Exercises 8–11.

$$3, 6, 2, 1, 7, 3$$

8. Find the mean.

9. Find the median.

10. Find the midrange.

11. Find the standard deviation.

Use the frequency distribution shown to solve Exercises 12–14.

Score x	Frequency f
1	3
2	5
3	2
4	2

12. Find the mean.

13. Find the median.

14. Find the mode.

15. The annual salaries of four salespeople and the owner of a bookstore are

$17,500, $19,000, $22,000, $27,500, $98,500.

Is the mean or the median more representative of the five annual salaries? Briefly explain your answer.

According to the American Freshman, *the number of hours that college freshmen spend studying each week is normally distributed with a mean of 7 hours and a standard deviation of 5.3 hours. In Exercises 16–17, use the 68–95–99.7 Rule to find the percentage of college freshmen who study*

16. between 7 and 12.3 hours each week.

17. more than 17.6 hours each week.

18. IQ scores are normally distributed in the population. Who has a higher IQ: a student with a 120 IQ on a scale where 100 is the mean and 10 is the standard deviation, or a professor with a 128 IQ on a scale where 100 is the mean and 15 is the standard deviation? Briefly explain your answer.

19. Use the z-scores and the corresponding percentiles shown below to solve this exercise. Test scores are normally distributed with a mean of 74 and a standard deviation of 10. What percentage of the scores are above 88?

z-Score	Percentile
1.1	86.43
1.2	88.49
1.3	90.32
1.4	91.92
1.5	93.32

20. Use the percentiles in the table shown below to find the percentage of scores between 630 and 690.

Score	Percentile
780	99
750	87
720	72
690	49
660	26
630	8
600	1

21. Using a random sample of 100 students from a campus of approximately 12,000 students, 60% of the students in the sample said they were very satisfied with their professors.

a. Find the margin of error in this percent.

b. Write a statement about the percentage of the entire population of students from this campus who are very satisfied with their professors.

22. Make a scatter plot for the given data. Use the scatter plot to describe whether or not the variables appear to be related.

x	1	4	3	5	2
y	5	2	2	1	4

The scatter plot shows the number of minutes each of 16 people exercise per week and the number of headaches per month each person experiences. Use the scatter plot to determine whether each of the statements in Exercises 23–25 is true or false.

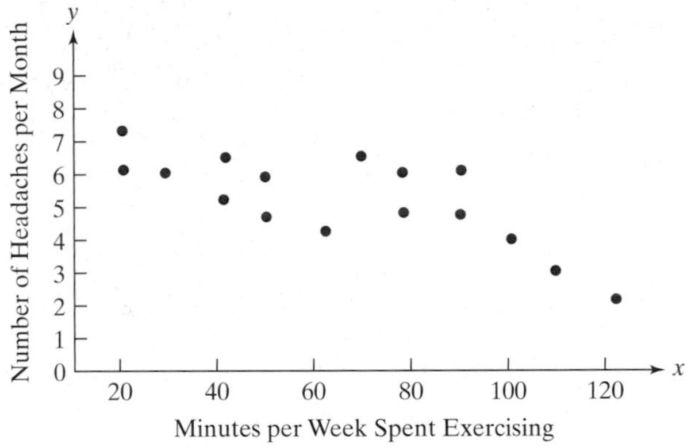

23. An increase in the number of minutes devoted to exercise causes a decrease in headaches.

24. There is a perfect negative correlation between time spent exercising and number of headaches.

25. The person who exercised most per week had the least number of headaches per month.

26. Is the relationship between the price of gas and the number of people visiting our national parks a positive correlation, a negative correlation, or is there no correlation? Explain your answer.

Answers to Selected Exercises

CHAPTER 1

Section 1.1

Check Point Exercises

1. a. Each number in the list is obtained by adding 6 to the previous number.; 33 **b.** Each number in the list is obtained by multiplying the previous number by 5.; 1250 **c.** To get the second number, multiply the previous number by 2. Then multiply by 3 and then by 4. Then multiply by 2, then by 3, and then by 4, repeatedly.; 3456 **d.** To get the second number, add 8 to the previous number. Then add 8 and then subtract 14. Then add 8, then add 8, and then subtract 14, repeatedly.; 7 **2. a.** Starting with the third number, each number is the sum of the previous two numbers.; 76 **b.** Starting with the second number, each number is one less than twice the previous number.; 257
3. The figures alternate between rectangles and triangles, and the number of appendages follows the pattern: one, two, three, one, two, three, etc.;

4. a. The result of the process is two times the original number selected.
b. Representing the original number as n, we have

Select a number: n
Multiply the number by 4: $4n$
Add 6 to the product: $4n + 6$
Divide this sum by 2: $\dfrac{4n+6}{2} = 2n + 3$
Subtract 3 from the quotient: $2n + 3 - 3 = 2n$.

Exercise Set 1.1

1. Each number in the list is obtained by adding 4 to the previous number.; 28
3. Each number in the list is obtained by subtracting 5 from the previous number.; 12
5. Each number in the list is obtained by multiplying the previous number by 3.; 729
7. Each number in the list is obtained by multiplying the previous number by 2.; 32
9. The numbers in the list alternate between 1 and numbers obtained by multiplying the number prior to the previous number by 2.; 32
11. Each number in the list is obtained by subtracting 2 from the previous number.; -6
13. Each number in the list is obtained by adding 4 to the denominator of the previous fraction.; $\frac{1}{22}$
15. Each number in the list is obtained by multiplying the previous number by $\frac{1}{3}$.; $\frac{1}{81}$
17. The second number is obtained by adding 4 to the first number. The third number is obtained by adding 5 to the second number. The number being added to the previous number increases by 1 each time.; 42 **19.** The second number is obtained by adding 3 to the first number. The third number is obtained by adding 5 to the second number. The number being added to the previous number increases by 2 each time.; 51
21. Starting with the third number, each number is the sum of the previous two numbers.; 71 **23.** To get the second number, add 5 to the previous number. Then add 5 and then subtract 7. Then add 5, then add 5, and then subtract 7, repeatedly.; 18 **25.** The second number is obtained by multiplying the first number by 2. The third number is obtained by subtracting 1 from the second number. Then multiply by 2 and then subtract 1, repeatedly.; 33 **27.** Each number in the list is obtained by multiplying the previous number by $-\frac{1}{4}$.; $\frac{1}{4}$ **29.** For each pair in the list, the second number is obtained by subtracting 4 from the first number.; -1

31. The pattern is: square, triangle, circle, square, triangle, circle, etc.;

33. Each figure contains the letter of the alphabet following the letter in the previous figure with one more occurrence than in the previous figure.;

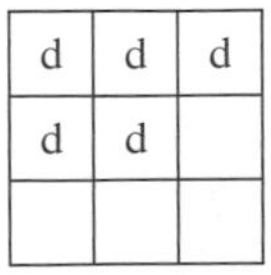

35. a. The result of the process is two times the original number selected.
b. Representing the original number as n, we have

Select a number: n
Multiply the number by 4: $4n$
Add 8 to the product: $4n + 8$
Divide this sum by 2: $\dfrac{4n+8}{2} = 2n + 4$
Subtract 4 from the quotient: $2n + 4 - 4 = 2n$.

37. a. The result of the process is 3.
b. Representing the original number as n, we have

Select a number: n
Add 5: $n + 5$
Double the result: $2(n + 5) = 2n + 10$
Subtract 4: $2n + 10 - 4 = 2n + 6$
Divide by 2: $\dfrac{2n+6}{2} = n + 3$
Subtract n: $n + 3 - n = 3$.

39. $1 + 2 + 3 + 4 + 5 + 6 = \frac{6 \times 7}{2}; 21 = 21$ **41.** $1 + 3 + 5 + 7 + 9 + 11 = 6 \times 6; 36 = 36$ **43.** $98{,}765 \times 9 + 3 = 888{,}888$; correct **45.** $165 \times 3367 = 555{,}555$; correct **47.** b **49.** c **51.** deductive reasoning; Answers will vary. **53.** inductive reasoning; Answers will vary. **55. a.** 28, 36, 45, 55, 66 **b.** 36, 49, 64, 81, 100 **c.** 35, 51, 70, 92, 117 **d.** square **61.** $(11 - 7)^2 = 121 - 154 + 49$ **63.** Answers will vary; an example is: 1, 5, 1, 10, 1, ... **65. a.** 36; 4356;443,556; 44,435,556 **b.** In each multiplication, a number is multiplied by itself; this number has one more digit than the number in the previous multiplication; all such digits are 6.; Each product has one more digit of 4 than the previous product, followed by a digit of 3, followed by one more digit of 5 than the previous product, ending in a digit of 6; the first product has zero digits of 4 and zero digits of 5. **c.** $66{,}666 \times 66{,}666 = 4{,}444{,}355{,}556$; $666{,}666 \times 666{,}666 = 444{,}443{,}555{,}556$ **d.** inductive reasoning; Answers will vary.

Section 1.2

Check Point Exercises

1. a. 300,000,000 **b.** 295,700,000 **2. a.** 3.1 **b.** 3.1416 **3. a.** \$2, \$1, \$5, \$4, \$1, \$2, and \$3; ≈ \$18 **b.** no **4. a.** ≈ \$2000 per wk **b.** ≈ \$100,000 per yr **5. a.** $0.63 \times 178{,}586{,}613$ **b.** $0.6 \times 200{,}000{,}000 = 120{,}000{,}000$; ≈ 120,000,000 (120 million) non-owners **6. a.** ≈ 0.17 yr for each subsequent birth year **b.** ≈ 88.1 yr **7. a.** ≈ 118 democracies **b.** 1981–1985 **c.** 1977 **8. a.** ≈ 0.12 million motorcycles per yr **b.** $M = 0.4 + 0.12x$ **c.** ≈ 2.2 million motorcycles

Exercise Set 1.2

1. a. 47,451,900 **b.** 47,452,000 **c.** 47,450,000 **d.** 47,500,000 **e.** 47,000,000 **f.** 50,000,000 **3.** 2.718 **5.** 2.71828 **7.** 2.718281828 **9.** $350 + 600 = 950$; 955; reasonably well **11.** $9 + 1 + 19 = 29$; 29.23; quite well **13.** $32 - 11 = 21$; 20.911; quite well **15.** $40 \times 6 = 240$; 218.185; not so well **17.** $0.8 \times 400 = 320$; 327.06; reasonably well **19.** $48 \div 3 = 16$; ≈ 16.49; quite well **21.** 30% of 200,000 is 60,000.; 59,920.96; quite well **23.** ≈ \$43 **25.** ≈ \$40,000 per yr **27.** ≈ \$24,000 **29.** ≈ \$1000 **31.** ≈ \$30 per hr **33.** ≈ 700,800 hr **35.** ≈ 40; ≈ 42.03; quite reasonable **37.** b **39.** c **41.** ≈ 3 hr **43.** ≈ 100,000,000 American adults **45. a.** ≈ 85 people per 100 **b.** ≈ 5400 people **47. a.** ≈ \$13 per yr **b.** ≈ \$326 **49. a.** 1960; ≈ 4100 cigarettes per adult **b.** 1940–1950 **c.** 1930 **51. a.** ≈ \$857 per yr **b.** $C = 14{,}000 + 857x$ **c.** ≈ \$25,998 **67.** a **69.** b **71.** ≈ 667 days; ≈ 1.8 yr

Section 1.3

Check Point Exercises

1. the amount of money given to the cashier **2.** The 128-ounce bottle at approximately 4¢ an ounce is the better value. **3.** 14 months **4.** 5 combinations **5.** 6 outfits **6.** A route that will cost less than \$1460 is *A, D, E, C, B, A*.

Trick Questions

1. 12 **2.** 12 **3.** sister and brother **4.** match

Exercise Set 1.3

1. the price of the computer **3.** the number of words on the page **5.** unnecessary information: weekly salary of \$350; extra pay: \$180 **7.** unnecessary information: \$20 given to the parking attendant; charge: \$4.50 **9. a.** 24-ounce box for \$4.59 **b.** 22¢ per ounce for the 15.3-ounce box and \$3.06 per pound for the 24-ounce box **c.** no; Answers will vary. **11.** \$3000 **13.** \$50 **15.** \$90 **17.** \$4525 **19.** \$565 **21.** 4 mi **23.** \$104 **25.** \$14,300 **27.** 5 ways **29.** 6 ways **31.** 9 ways **33.** 10 different total scores **35.** B owes \$18 and C owes \$2.; A is owed \$14, D is owed \$4, and E is owed \$2.; B should give A \$14 and D \$4, while C should give E \$2. **37.** 4 ways **39.** Andy, Darnell, Caleb, Beth, Ella **41.** Home, Bank, Post Office, Dry Cleaners, Home

43. Sample answer:
CO, WY, UT, AZ, NM, CO, UT

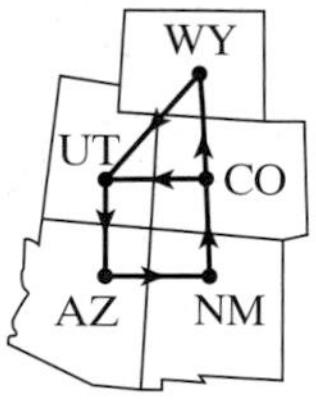

45. Bob's major is psychology.

47. a.

5	22	18
28	15	2
12	8	25

b.

4	9	8
11	7	3
6	5	10

49.

9	6	7
8	1	4
3	2	5

51.

```
     156
28)4368
   28
   156
   140
    168
    168
      0
```

57. the dentist with poor dental work **59.** Friday

61. Sample answer:

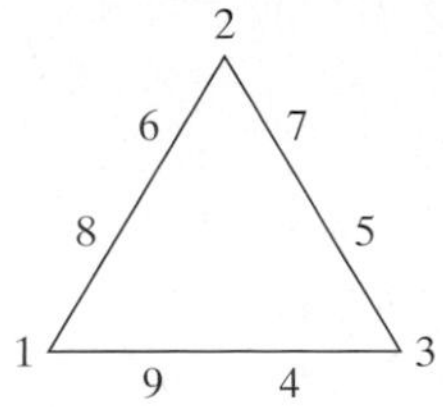

63. There is no missing dollar; in the end, the customers paid a total of \$27 of which \$25 went to the restaurant and \$2 was stolen by the waiter.

65. Answers will vary; an example is

State	A	B	C	D
Congressional Seats	4	6	8	12

Chapter 1 Review Exercises

1. deductive reasoning: Answers will vary. **2.** inductive reasoning; Answers will vary. **3.** Each number in the list is obtained by adding 5 to the previous number.; 24 **4.** Each number in the list is obtained by multiplying the previous number by 2.; 112 **5.** The successive differences are consecutive counting numbers beginning with 2.; 21 **6.** Each number in the list is obtained by writing a fraction with a denominator that is one more than the denominator of the previous fraction before it is reduced to lowest terms.; $\frac{3}{8}$ **7.** Each number in the list is obtained by multiplying the previous number by $-\frac{1}{2}$.; $\frac{5}{2}$ **8.** Each number in the list is obtained by subtracting 60 from the previous number; −200. **9.** Each number beginning with the third number is the sum of the two previous numbers.; 42 **10.** To get the second number, multiply the first number by 3. Then multiply the second number by 2 to get the third number. Then multiply by 3 and then by 2, repeatedly.; 432 **11.** The figures alternate between squares and circles, and in each figure the tick mark has been rotated 90° clockwise from its position in the previous figure.; 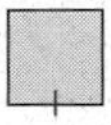
12. $2 + 4 + 8 + 16 + 32 = 64 - 2$; correct **13.** $444 \div 12 = 37$; correct

14. a. The result is the original number.
b. Representing the original number as n, we have

Select a number:	n
Double the number:	$2n$
Add 4 to the product:	$2n + 4$
Divide the sum by 2:	$\frac{2n+4}{2} = n + 2$

Subtract 2 from the quotient: $n + 2 - 2 = n$.

15. a. 4,115,600 **b.** 4,116,000 **c.** 4,100,000 **d.** 4,000,000 **16. a.** 1.5 **b.** 1.51 **c.** 1.507 **d.** 1.5065917 **17.** ≈ 16; 15.71; quite reasonable **18.** ≈ 450; 432.67; somewhat reasonable **19.** ≈ 5; ≈ 4.76; quite reasonable **20.** ≈ 2400; 2397.0548; quite reasonable **21.** ≈ \$18.00 **22.** ≈ \$560 **23.** ≈ \$60 **24.** ≈ 1,600,000 liberals **25.** b **26.** c **27. a.** called gay, lesbian, or a homophobic name; women: 13%; men: 37% **b.** ≈ 3,600,000 women **28. a.** ≈ 1.5 million Americans per yr **b.** ≈ 57.8 million Americans **29. a.** 1900; 400,000 dropouts **b.** 1985–1990 **c.** 1985 **30. a.** ≈ 0.26 billion dollars per yr **b.** $L = 1.7 + 0.26x$ **c.** ≈ \$5.34 billion **31.** the weight of the child **32.** unnecessary information: \$20 given to driver; cost of trip: \$8.00 **33.** 8 lb **34.** \$885 **35.** Plan A; \$90 **36.** 5.75 hr or 5 hr 45 min **37.** \$15,500 **38.** 6 combinations

Chapter 1 Test

1. deductive **2.** inductive **3.** Each number in the list is obtained by adding 5 to the previous number.; 20 **4.** Each number in the list is obtained by multiplying the previous number by $\frac{1}{2}$.; $\frac{1}{96}$ **5.** $3367 \times 15 = 50{,}505$ **6.** The outer figure is always a square; the inner figure follows the pattern: triangle, circle, square, triangle, circle, square, etc.; the number of appendages on the outer square alternates between 1 and 2.; 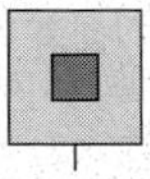

7. a. The original number is doubled.
b. Representing the original number as n, we have

Select a number:	n
Multiply the number by 4:	$4n$
Add 8 to the product:	$4n + 8$
Divide the sum by 2:	$\frac{4n+8}{2} = 2n + 4$

Subtract 4 from the quotient: $2n + 4 - 4 = 2n$.

8. 3,300,000 **9.** 706.38 **10.** ≈ \$90 **11.** ≈ \$25,000 per person **12.** ≈ 60 **13.** ≈ 28,000,000 cases **14.** a **15. a.** 2001; ≈ 1220 discharges **b.** 1996 **c.** ≈ 9500 discharges **16. a.** ≈ 0.5% per yr decrease **b.** $S = 37.4 - 0.5x$ **c.** ≈ 17.4% **17.** Estes Rental; \$12 **18.** \$14,080 **19.** 26 weeks **20.** Belgium; 160,000 people

CHAPTER 2

Section 2.1

Check Point Exercises

1. L is the set of the first six letters of the alphabet. **2.** M = {April, August} **3.** $O = \{1, 3, 5, 7, 9\}$ **4. a.** not the empty set **b.** empty set **c.** not the empty set **d.** not the empty set **5. a.** true **b.** true **c.** false **6. a.** $A = \{1, 2, 3\}$

b. $B = \{15, 16, 17, 18, \ldots\}$ **c.** $O = \{1, 3, 5, 7, \ldots\}$ **7. a.** $\{1, 2, 3, 4, \ldots, 199\}$ **b.** $\{51, 52, 53, 54, \ldots, 200\}$ **8. a.** $n(A) = 5$ **b.** $n(B) = 1$ **c.** $n(C) = 8$ **d.** $n(D) = 0$ **9.** Yes; each language in the table is paired with a distinct number of 15–24-year olds. **10. a.** true **b.** false

Exercise Set 2.1

1. well defined; set **3.** not well defined; not a set **5.** well defined; set **7.** the set of planets in our solar system **9.** the set of months that begin with J **11.** the set of natural numbers greater than 5 **13.** the set of natural numbers between 6 and 20, inclusive **15.** {winter, spring, summer, fall} **17.** {September, October, November, December} **19.** $\{1, 2, 3\}$ **21.** $\{1, 3, 5, 7, 9, 11\}$ **23.** $\{1, 2, 3, 4, 5\}$ **25.** $\{6, 7, 8, 9, \ldots\}$ **27.** $\{7, 8, 9, 10\}$ **29.** $\{10, 11, 12, 13, \ldots, 79\}$ **31.** $\{2\}$ **33.** not the empty set **35.** empty set **37.** not the empty set **39.** empty set **41.** empty set **43.** not the empty set **45.** not the empty set **47.** true **49.** true **51.** false **53.** true **55.** false **57.** false **59.** true **61.** false **63.** false **65.** true **67.** 5 **69.** 15 **71.** 0 **73.** 1 **75.** 4 **77.** 5 **79.** 0 **81. a.** not equivalent; Answers will vary. **b.** not equal; Answers will vary. **83. a.** equivalent; Answers will vary. **b.** not equal; Answers will vary. **85. a.** equivalent; Answers will vary. **b.** equal; Answers will vary. **87. a.** equivalent; Answers will vary. **b.** not equal; Answers will vary. **89. a.** equivalent; Answers will vary. **b.** equal; Answers will vary. **91.** infinite **93.** finite **95.** finite **97.** $\{x \mid x \in \mathbf{N} \text{ and } x \geq 61\}$ **99.** $\{x \mid x \in \mathbf{N} \text{ and } 61 \leq x \leq 89\}$ **101.** Answers will vary; an example is: $\{0, 1, 2, 3\}$ and $\{1, 2, 3, 4\}$. **103.** impossible; Answers will vary. **105.** {New Zealand, Australia, United States} **107.** {Australia, United States, United Kingdom, Switzerland, Ireland} **109.** {United Kingdom, Switzerland, Ireland} **111.** $\varnothing$ or { } **113.** $\{12, 19\}$ **115.** $\{20, 21\}$ **117.** no one-to-one correspondence; not equivalent **125.** a

Section 2.2

Check Point Exercises

1. a. $\not\subseteq$ **b.** $\subseteq$ **c.** $\subseteq$ **2. a.** $\subseteq$, $\subset$ **b.** $\subseteq$, $\subset$ **3.** yes **4. a.** 16; 15 **b.** 64; 63 **5. a.** 8; the number of different combinations of the books that you can take on vacation **b.** $\varnothing$, {*The Da Vinci Code*}, {*The Lord of the Rings*}, {*America (The Book)*}, {*The Da Vinci Code, The Lord of the Rings*}, {*The Da Vinci Code, America (The Book)*}, {*The Lord of the Rings, America (The Book)*}, {*The Da Vinci Code, The Lord of the Rings, America (The Book)*} **c.** 7

Exercise Set 2.2

1. $\subseteq$ **3.** $\not\subseteq$ **5.** $\not\subseteq$ **7.** $\not\subseteq$ **9.** $\subseteq$ **11.** $\not\subseteq$ **13.** both **15.** $\subseteq$ **17.** both **19.** $\subseteq$ **21.** neither **23.** true **25.** false; Answers will vary. **27.** true **29.** false; Answers will vary. **31.** true **33.** false; Answers will vary. **35.** true **37.** $\varnothing$, {border collie}, {poodle}, {border collie, poodle} **39.** $\varnothing$, {t}, {a}, {b}, {t, a}, {t, b}, {a, b}, {t, a, b} **41.** $\varnothing$ and $\{0\}$ **43.** 16; 15 **45.** 64; 63 **47.** 128; 127 **49.** 8; 7 **51.** false; The set $\{1, 2, 3, \ldots, 1000\}$ has $2^{1000} - 1$ proper subsets. **53.** true **55.** false; $\varnothing \subseteq \{\varnothing, \{\varnothing\}\}$ **57.** true **59.** true **61.** true **63.** false; The set of subsets of {a, e, i, o, u} contains 32 elements. **65.** false; $D \subseteq T$ **67.** true **69.** false; If $x \in W$, then $x \in D$. **71.** true **73.** true **75.** 32 **77.** 64 **79.** 256 **87.** b **89.** 7

Section 2.3

Check Point Exercises

1. a. $\{1, 5, 6, 7, 9\}$ **b.** $\{1, 5, 6\}$ **c.** $\{7, 9\}$ **2. a.** {a, b, c, d} **b.** {e} **c.** {e, f, g} **d.** {f, g} **3.** {b, c, e} **4. a.** $\{7, 10\}$ **b.** $\varnothing$ **c.** $\varnothing$ **5. a.** $\{1, 3, 5, 6, 7, 10, 11\}$ **b.** $\{1, 2, 3, 4, 5, 6, 7\}$ **c.** $\{1, 2, 3\}$ **6. a.** {a, d} **b.** {a, d} **7. a.** $\{5\}$ **b.** $\{2, 3, 7, 11, 13, 17, 19\}$ **c.** $\{2, 3, 5, 7, 11, 13\}$ **d.** $\{17, 19\}$ **e.** $\{5, 7, 11, 13, 17, 19\}$ **f.** $\{2, 3\}$ **8.** 385 students

Exercise Set 2.3

1. the set of all composers **3.** the set of all brands of soft drinks **5.** {c, d, e} **7.** {b, c, d, e, f} **9.** $\{6, 7, 8, 9, \ldots, 20\}$ **11.** $\{2, 4, 6, 8, \ldots, 20\}$ **13.** $\{21, 22, 23, 24, \ldots\}$ **15.** $\{1, 3, 5, 7, \ldots\}$ **17.** $\{1, 3\}$ **19.** $\{1, 2, 3, 5, 7\}$ **21.** $\{2, 4, 6\}$ **23.** $\{4, 6\}$ **25.** $\{1, 3, 5, 7\}$ or A **27.** $\{1, 2, 4, 6, 7\}$ **29.** $\{1, 2, 4, 6, 7\}$ **31.** $\{4, 6\}$ **33.** $\{1, 3, 5, 7\}$ or A **35.** $\varnothing$ **37.** $\{1, 2, 3, 4, 5, 6, 7\}$ or U **39.** $\{1, 3, 5, 7\}$ or A **41.** {g, h} **43.** {a, b, g, h} **45.** {b, c, d, e, f} or C **47.** {c, d, e, f} **49.** {a, g, h} or A **51.** {a, b, c, d, e, f, g, h} or U **53.** {a, b, c, d, e, f, g, h} or U **55.** {c, d, e, f} **57.** {a, g, h} or A **59.** $\varnothing$ **61.** {a, b, c, d, e, f, g, h} or U **63.** {a, g, h} or A **65.** {a, c, d, e, f, g, h} **67.** $\{1, 3, 4, 7\}$ **69.** $\{1, 2, 3, 4, 5, 6, 7, 8, 9\}$ **71.** $\{3, 7\}$ **73.** $\{1, 4, 8, 9\}$ **75.** $\{8, 9\}$ **77.** $\{1, 4\}$ **79.** {$\triangle$, two, four, six} **81.** {$\triangle$, #, \$, two, four, six} **83.** 6 **85.** 5 **87.** {#, \$, two, four, six, 10, 01} **89.** {two, four, six} **91.** 4 **93.** 31 **95.** 27 **97.** $\{1, 2, 3, 4, 5, 6, 7, 8\}$ or U **99.** $\{1, 3, 5, 7\}$ or A **101.** $\{1, 7\}$ **103.** $\{1, 3, 5, 6, 7, 8\}$ **105.** $\{23, 29, 31, 37, 41, 43, 53, 59, 61, 67, 71\}$ **107.** 60 **109.** {Ashley, Mike, Josh} **111.** {Ashley, Mike, Josh, Emily, Hanna, Ethan} **113.** {Ashley} **115.** {Jacob} **117.** I **119.** I **121.** IV **123.** I **125.** IV **127.** II **129.** III **131.** I **133.** {spacial-temporal toys, sports equipment, toy cars and trucks} **135.** {dollhouses, spacial-temporal toys, sports equipment, toy cars and trucks} **137.** $\varnothing$ **139.** 283 people **153.** d

155.

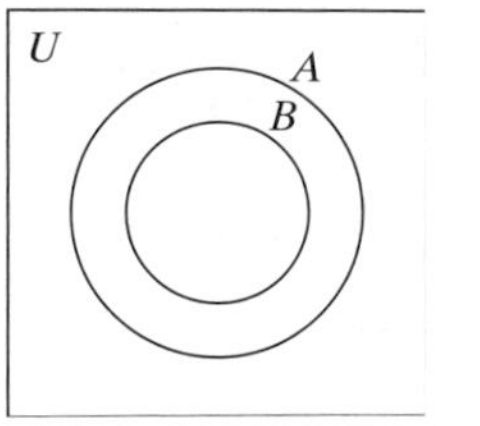

157.

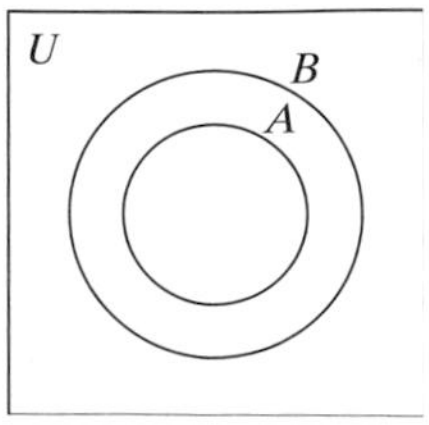

Section 2.4

Check Point Exercises

1. a. {a, b, c, d, f} **b.** {a, b, c, d, f} **c.** {a, b, d}
2. a. {5, 6, 7, 8, 9} **b.** {1, 2, 5, 6, 7, 8, 9, 10, 12} **c.** {5, 6, 7} **d.** {3, 4, 6, 8, 11} **e.** {1, 2, 3, 5, 6, 7, 8, 9, 10, 11, 12}
3.

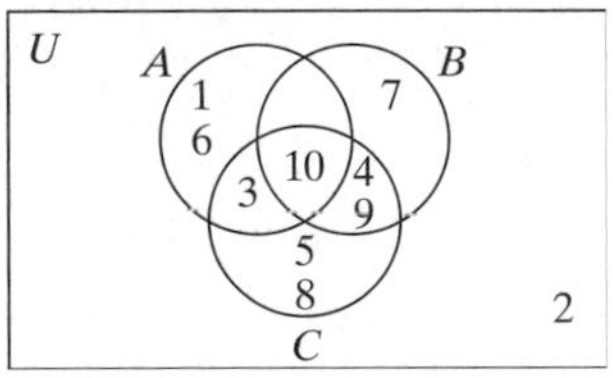

4. a. IV **b.** IV **c.** $(A \cup B)' = A' \cap B'$ **5. a.** II, IV, and V **b.** II, IV, and V **c.** $A \cap (B \cup C) = (A \cap B) \cup (A \cap C)$

Exercise Set 2.4

1. {1, 2, 3, 5, 7} **3.** {1, 2, 3, 5, 7} **5.** {2} **7.** {2} **9.** ∅ **11.** {4, 6} **13.** {a, b, g, h} **15.** {a, b, g, h} **17.** {b} **19.** {b} **21.** ∅ **23.** {c, d, e, f} **25.** II, III, V, and VI **27.** I, II, IV, V, VI, and VII **29.** II and V **31.** I, IV, VII, and VIII **33.** {1, 2, 3, 4, 5, 6, 7, 8} **35.** {1, 2, 3, 4, 5, 6, 7, 8, 9, 10, 11} **37.** {12, 13} **39.** {4, 5, 6} **41.** {6} **43.** {1, 2, 3, 4, 5, 7, 8, 9, 10, 11, 12, 13}
45.

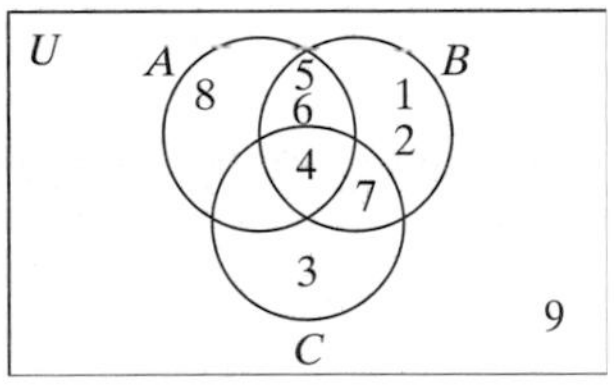

47.

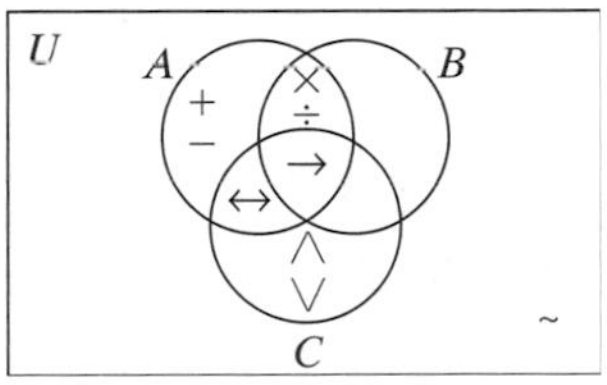

49. a. II **b.** II **c.** $A \cap B = B \cap A$ **51. a.** I, III, and IV **b.** IV **c.** no; Answers will vary. **53.** not equal **55.** not equal **57.** equal **59. a.** II, IV, V, VI, and VII **b.** II, IV, V, VI, and VII **c.** $(A \cap B) \cup C = (A \cup C) \cap (B \cup C)$ **61. a.** II, IV, and V **b.** I, II, IV, V, and VI **c.** no; Answers will vary. **63.** not true **65.** true; theorem **67.** true; theorem **69. a.** {c, e, f}; {c, e, f} **b.** {1, 3, 5, 7, 8}; {1, 3, 5, 7, 8} **c.** $A \cup (B' \cap C') = (A \cup B') \cap (A \cup C')$ **d.** theorem **71.** $(A \cap B)' \cap (A \cup B)$ **73.** $A' \cup B$ **75.** $(A \cap B) \cup C$ **77.** $A' \cap (B \cup C)$ **79.** {Ann, Jose, Al, Gavin, Amy, Ron, Grace} **81.** {Jose} **83.** {Lily, Emma} **85.** {Lily, Emma, Ann, Jose, Lee, Maria, Fred, Ben, Sheila, Ellen, Gary} **87.** {Lily, Emma, Al, Gavin, Amy, Lee, Maria} **89.** {Al, Gavin, Amy} **91.** The set of students who scored 90% or above on exam 1 and exam 3 but not on exam 2 **93.** II **95.** V **97.** I **99.** III **101.** V **103.** VII **105.**

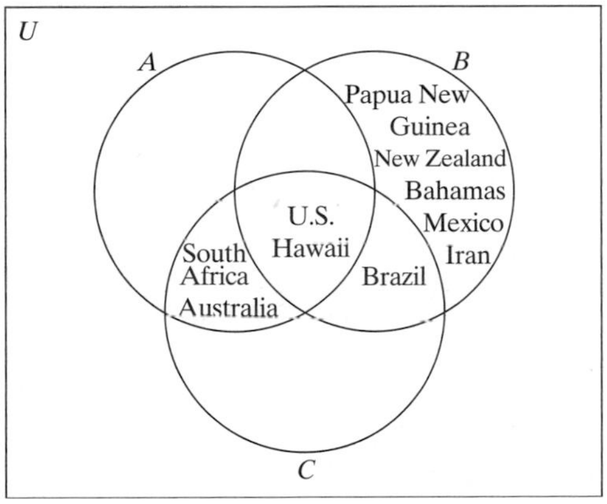

109. AB^+ **111.** no

Section 2.5

Check Point Exercises

1. a. 75 **b.** 90 **c.** 20 **d.** 145 **e.** 55 **f.** 70 **g.** 30 **h.** 175 **2. a.** 490 men **b.** 510 men
3.

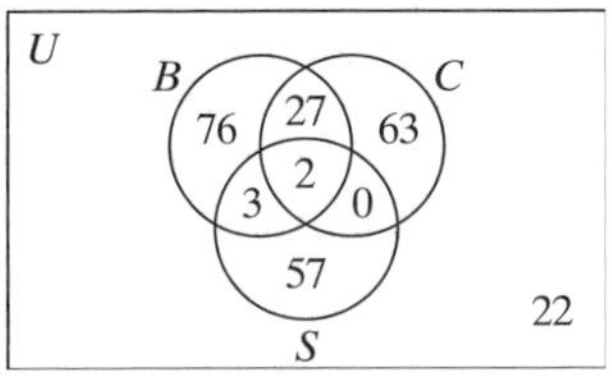

4. a. 63 **b.** 3 **c.** 136 **d.** 30 **e.** 228 **f.** 22

Exercise Set 2.5

1. 26 **3.** 17 **5.** 37 **7.** 7 **9.** I: 14; III: 22; IV: 5 **11.** 17 **13.** 6 **15.** 28 **17.** 9 **19.** 3 **21.** 19 **23.** 21 **25.** 34

27. I: 5; II: 1; III: 4; IV: 3; VI: 1; VII: 8; VIII: 6 **29.** I: 5; II: 10; III: 3; IV: 4; V: 7; VI: 1; VII: 6; VIII: 2 **31.** impossible; There are only 10 elements in set A but there are 13 elements in set A that are also in sets B or C. A similar problem exists for set C. **33.** 18 **35.** 9 **37.** 9

39. a–d.

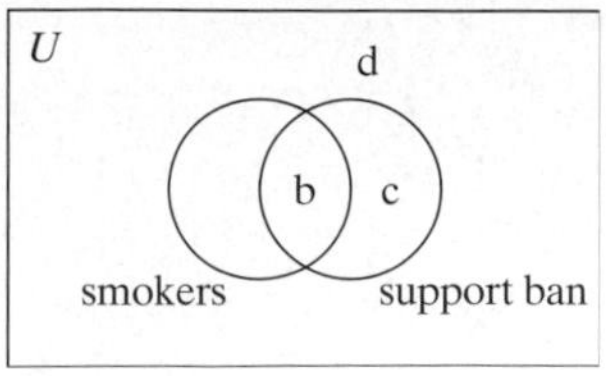

41. a–d.

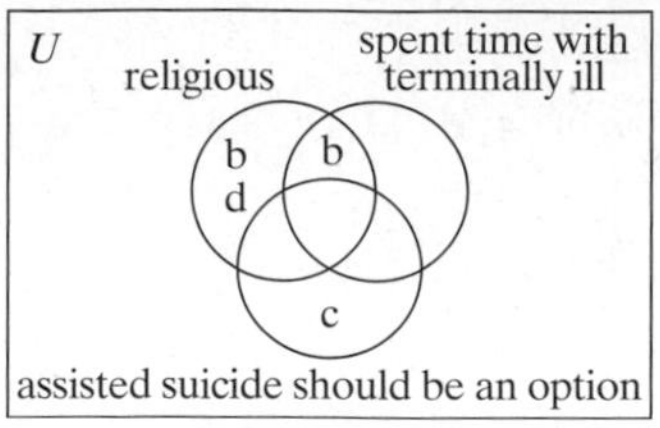

e. Answers will vary.

43.

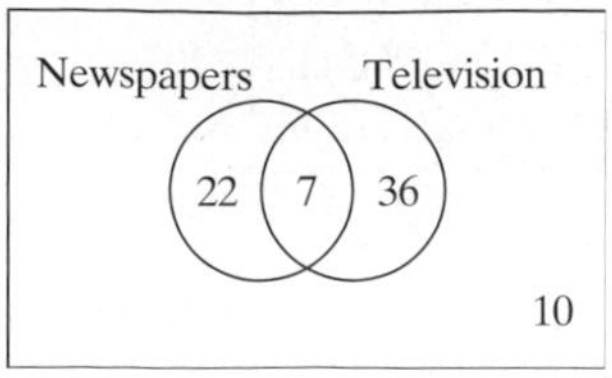

a. 22 **b.** 36 **c.** 65 **d.** 10

45.

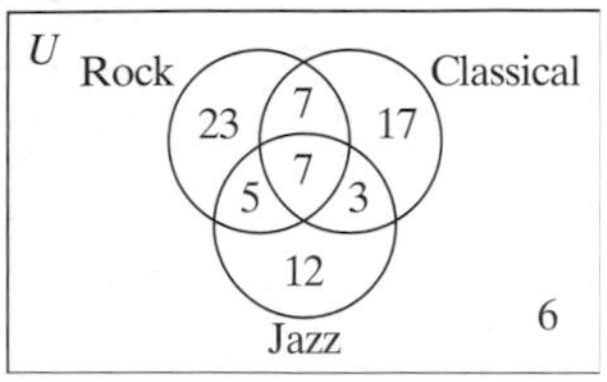

a. 23 **b.** 3 **c.** 32 **d.** 52
e. 22 **f.** 6

47. a. 1500 **b.** 1135 **c.** 56 **d.** 327 **e.** 526 **f.** 366 **g.** 1191 **51.** b **53.** Under the conditions given concerning enrollment in math, chemistry, and psychology courses, the total number of students is 100, not 90.

Chapter 2 Review Exercises

1. the set of days of the week beginning with the letter T **2.** the set of natural numbers between 1 and 10, inclusive **3.** $\{m, i, s\}$ **4.** $\{8, 9, 10, 11, 12\}$ **5.** $\{1, 2, 3, \ldots, 30\}$ **6.** not empty **7.** empty set **8.** $\in$ **9.** $\notin$ **10.** 12 **11.** 15 **12.** $\neq$ **13.** $\neq$ **14.** equivalent **15.** both **16.** finite **17.** infinite **18.** $\subseteq$ **19.** $\not\subseteq$ **20.** $\subseteq$ **21.** $\subseteq$ **22.** both **23.** false; Answers will vary. **24.** false; Answers will vary. **25.** true **26.** false; Answers will vary. **27.** true **28.** false; It has $2^1 = 2$ subsets. **29.** true **30.** $\varnothing, \{1\}, \{5\}, \{1, 5\}; \{1, 5\}$ **31.** 32; 31 **32.** 8; 7 **33.** $\{1, 2, 4\}$ **34.** $\{1, 2, 3, 4, 6, 7, 8\}$ **35.** $\{5\}$ **36.** $\{6, 7, 8\}$ **37.** $\{6, 7, 8\}$ **38.** $\{4, 5, 6\}$ **39.** $\{2, 3, 6, 7\}$ **40.** $\{1, 4, 5, 6, 8, 9\}$ **41.** $\{4, 5\}$ **42.** $\{1, 2, 3, 6, 7, 8, 9\}$ **43.** $\{2, 3, 7\}$ **44.** $\{6\}$ **45.** $\{1, 2, 3, 4, 5, 6, 7, 8, 9\}$ **46.** 33 **47.** $\{1, 2, 3, 4, 5\}$ **48.** $\{1, 2, 3, 4, 5, 6, 7, 8\}$ or U **49.** $\{c, d, e, f, k, p, r\}$ **50.** $\{f, p\}$ **51.** $\{c, d, f, k, p, r\}$ **52.** $\{c, d, e\}$ **53.** $\{a, b, c, d, e, g, h, p, r\}$ **54.** $\{f\}$ **55.**

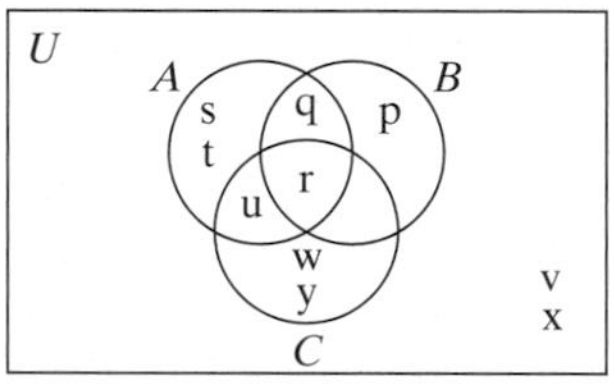

56. Use Figure 2.21 on page 84.

Set	Regions in the Venn Diagram
A	I, II
B	II, III
$A \cup B$	I, II, III
$(A \cup B)'$	IV

Set	Regions in the Venn Diagram
A'	III, IV
B'	I, IV
$A' \cap B'$	IV

Since $(A \cup B)'$ and $A' \cap B'$ represent the same region, $(A \cup B)' = A' \cap B'$.

57. Use Figure 2.22 on page 85.

Set	Regions in the Venn Diagram
A	I, II, IV, V
B	II, III, V, VI
C	IV, V, VI, VII
$B \cup C$	II, III, IV, V, VI, VII
$A \cap (B \cup C)$	II, IV, V

Set	Regions in the Venn Diagram
A	I, II, IV, V
B	II, III, V, VI
C	IV, V, VI, VII
$B \cap C$	V, VI
$A \cup (B \cap C)$	I, II, IV, V, VI

Since $A \cap (B \cup C)$ and $A \cup (B \cap C)$ do not represent the same regions, $A \cap (B \cup C) = A \cup (B \cap C)$ is false.

58. a. I **b.** III **c.** VIII **d.** II **e.** V

59. a–c.

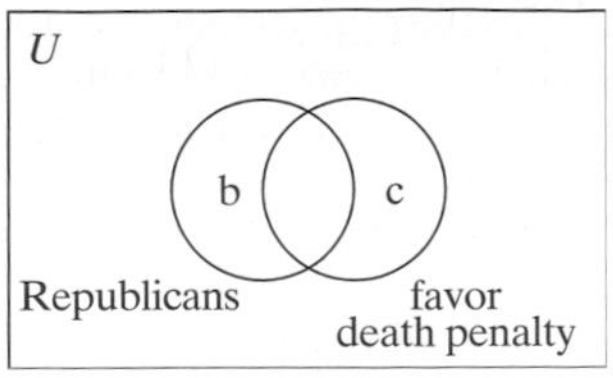

60. a. 250 **b.** 800 **c.** 200 **61. a.** 50 **b.** 26 **c.** 130 **d.** 46 **e.** 0

Chapter 2 Test

1. {18, 19, 20, 21, 22, 23, 24} **2.** false; Answers will vary. **3.** true **4.** true **5.** false; Answers will vary. **6.** true **7.** false; Answers will vary. **8.** false; Answers will vary. **9.** false; Answers will vary. **10.** ∅, {6}, {9}, {6, 9}; {6, 9} **11.** {a, b, c, d, e, f} **12.** {a, b, c, d, f, g} **13.** {b, c, d} **14.** {a, e} **15.** 5 **16.** {b, c, d, i, j, k} **17.** {a} **18.** {a, f, h}

19.

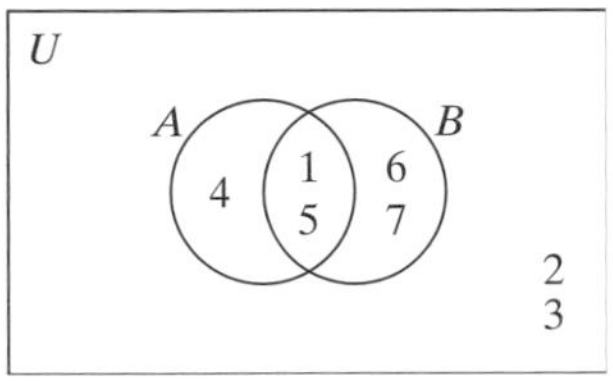

20. theorem **21. a.** V **b.** VII **c.** IV **d.** I **e.** VI

22. a.

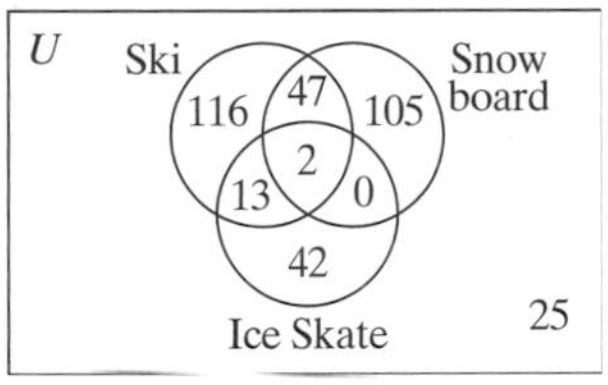

b. 263 **c.** 25 **d.** 62 **e.** 0 **f.** 147 **g.** 116

CHAPTER 3

Section 3.1

Check Point Exercises

1. a. Paris is not the capital of Spain. **b.** July is a month. **2. a.** $\sim p$ **b.** $\sim q$ **3.** Chicago O'Hare is not the world's busiest airport. **4.** Some new tax dollars will not be used to improve education.; At least one new tax dollar will not be used to improve education.

Exercise Set 3.1

1. statement **3.** statement **5.** not a statement **7.** statement **9.** not a statement **11.** statement **13.** statement **15.** It is not raining. **17.** The Dallas Cowboys are the team with the most Super Bowl wins. **19.** Chocolate in moderation is good for the heart. **21.** $\sim p$ **23.** $\sim r$ **25.** Listening to classical music does not make infants smarter. **27.** Sigmund Freud's father was 20 years older than his mother **29. a.** There are no whales that are not mammals. **b.** Some whales are not mammals. **31. a.** At least one student is a business major. **b.** No students are business majors. **33. a.** At least one thief is not a criminal. **b.** All thieves are criminals. **35. a.** All Democratic presidents have not been impeached. **b.** Some Democratic presidents have been impeached. **37.** Some Africans have Jewish ancestry. **39.** Some rap is not hip-hop. **41. a.** All birds are parrots. **b.** false; Some birds are not parrots. **43. a.** No college students are business majors. **b.** false; Some college students are business majors. **45. a.** All people like Sara Lee. **b.** Some people don't like Sara Lee. **47. a.** No safe thing is exciting. **b.** Some safe things are exciting. **49. a.** Some great actors are not Tom Hanks **b.** All great actors are Tom Hanks. **51.** b **53.** true **55.** false; Some college students in the United States are willing to marry without romantic love. **57.** true **59.** false; The sentence "5% of college students in Australia are willing to marry without romantic love" is a statement. **69.** Answers will vary.

Section 3.2

Check Point Exercises

1. a. $q \wedge p$ **b.** $\sim p \wedge q$ **2. a.** $p \vee q$ **b.** $q \vee \sim p$ **3. a.** $\sim p \rightarrow \sim q$ **b.** $q \rightarrow \sim p$ **4.** $\sim q \rightarrow p$ **5. a.** $q \leftrightarrow p$ **b.** $\sim p \leftrightarrow \sim q$ **6. a.** It is not true that he earns $105,000 yearly and that he is often happy. **b.** He is not often happy and he earns $105,000 yearly. **c.** It is not true that if he is often happy then he earns $105,000 yearly. **7. a.** If the plant is fertilized and watered, then it will not wilt. **b.** The plant is fertilized, and if it is watered then it will not wilt. **8.** p: There is too much homework.; q: A teacher is boring.; r: I take the class. **a.** $(p \vee q) \rightarrow \sim r$ **b.** $p \vee (q \rightarrow \sim r)$

Exercise Set 3.2

1. $p \wedge q$ **3.** $q \wedge \sim p$ **5.** $\sim q \wedge p$ **7.** $p \vee q$ **9.** $p \vee \sim q$ **11.** $p \rightarrow q$ **13.** $\sim p \rightarrow \sim q$ **15.** $\sim q \rightarrow \sim p$ **17.** $p \rightarrow q$ **19.** $p \rightarrow \sim q$ **21.** $q \rightarrow \sim p$ **23.** $p \rightarrow \sim q$ **25.** $q \rightarrow \sim p$ **27.** $p \leftrightarrow q$ **29.** $\sim q \leftrightarrow \sim p$ **31.** $q \leftrightarrow p$ **33.** The heater is not working and the house is cold. **35.** The heater is working or the house is not cold. **37.** If the heater is working, then the house is not cold. **39.** The heater is working if and only if the house is not cold. **41.** It is July 4th and we are not having a barbecue. **43.** It is not July 4th or we are having a barbecue. **45.** If we are having a barbecue, then it is not July 4th. **47.** It is not July 4th if and only if we are having a barbecue. **49.** It is not true that Romeo loves Juliet and Juliet loves Romeo. **51.** Romeo does not love Juliet and Juliet loves Romeo. **53.** Neither Juliet loves Romeo nor Romeo loves Juliet. **55.** Juliet does not love Romeo or Romeo loves Juliet. **57.** Romeo does not love Juliet and Juliet does not love Romeo. **59.** $(p \vee q) \vee r$ **61.** $(p \vee \sim q) \rightarrow r$ **63.** $r \leftrightarrow (p \wedge \sim q)$ **65.** $(p \wedge \sim q) \rightarrow r$ **67.** If the temperature is above 85° and we have finished studying, then we will go to the beach. **69.** The temperature is above 85°, and if we have finished studying then we will go to the beach. **71.** $\sim r \rightarrow (\sim p \vee \sim q)$; If we do not go to the beach, then the temperature is not above 85° or we have not finished studying. **73.** If we do not go to the beach then we have not finished studying, or the temperature is above 85°. **75.** $r \leftrightarrow (p \wedge q)$; We will go to the beach if and only if the temperature is above 85° and we have finished studying. **77.** The temperature is above 85° if and only if we have finished studying, and we go to the beach. **79.** If we do not go to the beach, then it is not true that both the temperature is above 85° and we have finished studying.

81. p: I like the teacher.; q: The course is interesting.; r: I miss class.; $(p \vee q) \rightarrow \sim r$ **83.** p: I like the teacher.; q: The course is interesting.; r: I miss class.; $p \vee (q \rightarrow \sim r)$ **85.** p: I like the teacher.; q: The course is interesting.; r: I miss class.; $r \leftrightarrow \sim (p \wedge q)$ **87.** p: I like the teacher.; q: The course is interesting.; r: I miss class.; $p \rightarrow (\sim r \leftrightarrow q)$ **89.** p: I like the teacher.; q: The course is interesting.; r: I miss class.; s: I spend extra time reading the book.; $(\sim p \wedge r) \rightarrow (\sim q \vee s)$ **91.** p: Being French is necessary for being a Parisian.; q: Being German is necessary for being a Berliner.; $\sim p \rightarrow \sim q$ **93.** p: You file an income tax report.; q: You file a complete statement of earnings.; r: You are a taxpayer.; s: You are an authorized tax preparer.; $(r \vee s) \rightarrow (p \wedge q)$ **95.** p: You are wealthy.; q: You are happy.; r: You live contentedly.; $\sim (p \rightarrow (q \wedge r))$ **97.** $[p \rightarrow (q \vee r)] \leftrightarrow (p \wedge r)$ **99.** $(p \rightarrow p) \leftrightarrow [(p \wedge p) \rightarrow \sim p]$ **101.** $\sim p \rightarrow q$ **103.** $(p \rightarrow q) \wedge \sim q$ **105.** $((p \rightarrow q) \wedge \sim p) \rightarrow \sim q$ **115.** p: Shooting unarmed citizens is morally justifiable.; q: Bombing unarmed citizens is morally justifiable.; $((p \leftrightarrow q) \wedge \sim p) \rightarrow \sim q$

Section 3.3

Check Point Exercises

1. a. false **b.** true **c.** false **d.** true

2.

p	q	$p \vee q$	$\sim (p \vee q)$
T	T	T	F
T	F	T	F
F	T	T	F
F	F	F	T

$\sim (p \vee q)$ is true when both p and q are false; otherwise, $\sim (p \vee q)$ is false.

3.

p	q	$\sim p$	$\sim q$	$\sim p \wedge \sim q$
T	T	F	F	F
T	F	F	T	F
F	T	T	F	F
F	F	T	T	T

$\sim p \wedge \sim q$ is true when both p and q are false; otherwise, $\sim p \wedge \sim q$ is false.

4.

p	q	$\sim q$	$p \wedge \sim q$	$\sim p$	$(p \wedge \sim q) \vee \sim p$
T	T	F	F	F	F
T	F	T	T	F	T
F	T	F	F	T	T
F	F	T	F	T	T

$(p \wedge \sim q) \vee \sim p$ is false when both p and q are true; otherwise, $(p \wedge \sim q) \vee \sim p$ is true.

5.

p	$\sim p$	$p \wedge \sim p$
T	F	F
F	T	F

$p \wedge \sim p$ is false in all cases.

6. p: I study hard.; q: I ace the final.; r: I fail the course.

a.

p	q	r	$q \vee r$	$p \wedge (q \vee r)$
T	T	T	T	T
T	T	F	T	T
T	F	T	T	T
T	F	F	F	F
F	T	T	T	F
F	T	F	T	F
F	F	T	T	F
F	F	F	F	F

b. false

7. true

Exercise Set 3.3

1. true **3.** false **5.** false **7.** false **9.** true **11.** true **13.** true **15.** true

17.

p	$\sim p$	$\sim p \wedge p$
T	F	F
F	T	F

19.

p	q	$\sim p$	$\sim p \wedge q$
T	T	F	F
T	F	F	F
F	T	T	T
F	F	T	F

21.

p	q	$p \vee q$	$\sim(p \vee q)$
T	T	T	F
T	F	T	F
F	T	T	F
F	F	F	T

23.

p	q	$\sim p$	$\sim q$	$\sim p \wedge \sim q$
T	T	F	F	F
T	F	F	T	F
F	T	T	F	F
F	F	T	T	T

25.

p	q	$\sim q$	$p \vee \sim q$
T	T	F	T
T	F	T	T
F	T	F	F
F	F	T	T

27.

p	q	$\sim p$	$\sim p \vee q$	$\sim(\sim p \vee q)$
T	T	F	T	F
T	F	F	F	T
F	T	T	T	F
F	F	T	T	F

29.

p	q	$\sim p$	$p \vee q$	$(p \vee q) \wedge \sim p$
T	T	F	T	F
T	F	F	T	F
F	T	T	T	T
F	F	T	F	F

31.

p	q	$\sim p$	$\sim q$	$p \wedge \sim q$	$\sim p \vee (p \wedge \sim q)$
T	T	F	F	F	F
T	F	F	T	T	T
F	T	T	F	F	T
F	F	T	T	F	T

33.

p	q	$\sim p$	$\sim q$	$p \vee q$	$\sim p \vee \sim q$	$(p \vee q) \wedge (\sim p \vee \sim q)$
T	T	F	F	T	F	F
T	F	F	T	T	T	T
F	T	T	F	T	T	T
F	F	T	T	F	T	F

35.

p	q	$\sim q$	$p \wedge \sim q$	$p \wedge q$	$(p \wedge \sim q) \vee (p \wedge q)$
T	T	F	F	T	T
T	F	T	T	F	T
F	T	F	F	F	F
F	F	T	F	F	F

37.

p	q	r	$\sim q$	$\sim q \vee r$	$p \wedge (\sim q \vee r)$
T	T	T	F	T	T
T	T	F	F	F	F
T	F	T	T	T	T
T	F	F	T	T	T
F	T	T	F	T	F
F	T	F	F	F	F
F	F	T	T	T	F
F	F	F	T	T	F

39.

p	q	r	$\sim p$	$\sim q$	$r \wedge \sim p$	$(r \wedge \sim p) \vee \sim q$
T	T	T	F	F	F	F
T	T	F	F	F	F	F
T	F	T	F	T	F	T
T	F	F	F	T	F	T
F	T	T	T	F	T	T
F	T	F	T	F	F	F
F	F	T	T	T	T	T
F	F	F	T	T	F	T

41.

p	q	r	$p \vee q$	$\sim(p \vee q)$	$\sim r$	$\sim(p \vee q) \wedge \sim r$
T	T	T	T	F	F	F
T	T	F	T	F	T	F
T	F	T	T	F	F	F
T	F	F	T	F	T	F
F	T	T	T	F	F	F
F	T	F	T	F	T	F
F	F	T	F	T	F	F
F	F	F	F	T	T	T

43. a. p: You did the dishes.; q: You left the room a mess.; $\sim p \wedge q$ **b.** See truth table for Exercise 19. **c.** The statement is true when p is false and q is true.

45. a. p: I bought a meal ticket.; q: I used it.; $\sim(p \wedge \sim q)$

b.

p	q	$\sim q$	$p \wedge \sim q$	$\sim(p \wedge \sim q)$
T	T	F	F	T
T	F	T	T	F
F	T	F	F	T
F	F	T	F	T

c. Answers will vary; an example is: The statement is true when p and q are true.

47. a. p: The student is intelligent.; q: The student is an overachiever.; $(p \vee q) \wedge \sim q$

b.

p	q	$\sim q$	$p \vee q$	$(p \vee q) \wedge \sim q$
T	T	F	T	F
T	F	T	T	T
F	T	F	T	F
F	F	T	F	F

c. The statement is true when p is true and q is false.

49. a. p: Married people are healthier than single people.; q: Married people are more economically stable than single people.; r: Children of married people do better on a variety of indicators.; $(p \wedge q) \wedge r$

b.

p	q	r	$p \wedge q$	$(p \wedge q) \wedge r$
T	T	T	T	T
T	T	F	T	F
T	F	T	F	F
T	F	F	F	F
F	T	T	F	F
F	T	F	F	F
F	F	T	F	F
F	F	F	F	F

c. The statement is true when p, q, and r are all true.

51. a. p: I go to office hours.; q: I ask questions.; r: My professor remembers me.; $(p \wedge q) \vee \sim r$

b.

p	q	r	$\sim r$	$p \wedge q$	$(p \wedge q) \vee \sim r$
T	T	T	F	T	T
T	T	F	T	T	T
T	F	T	F	F	F
T	F	F	T	F	T
F	T	T	F	F	F
F	T	F	T	F	T
F	F	T	F	F	F
F	F	F	T	F	T

c. Answers will vary; an example is: The statement is true when p, q, and r are all true.

53. false **55.** true **57.** true **59.** false **61.** true

63.

p	q	$\sim[\sim(p \wedge \sim q) \vee \sim(\sim p \vee q)]$
T	T	F
T	F	F
F	T	F
F	F	F

65.

p	q	r	$[(p \wedge \sim r) \vee (q \wedge \sim r)] \wedge \sim(\sim p \vee r)$
T	T	T	F
T	T	F	T
T	F	T	F
T	F	F	T
F	T	T	F
F	T	F	F
F	F	T	F
F	F	F	F

67. p: You notice this notice.; q: You notice this notice is not worth noticing.; $(p \vee \sim p) \wedge q$

p	q	$\sim p$	$p \vee \sim p$	$(p \vee \sim p) \wedge q$
T	T	F	T	T
T	F	F	T	F
F	T	T	T	T
F	F	T	T	F

The statement is true when q is true.

69. $p: x \le 3$; $q: x \ge 7$; $\sim (p \vee q) \wedge (\sim p \wedge \sim q)$

p	q	$\sim p$	$\sim q$	$p \vee q$	$\sim (p \vee q)$	$\sim p \wedge \sim q$	$\sim (p \vee q) \wedge (\sim p \wedge \sim q)$
T	T	F	F	T	F	F	F
T	F	F	T	T	F	F	F
F	T	T	F	T	F	F	F
F	F	T	T	F	T	T	T

The statement is true when both p and q are false.

71. The chance of divorce peaks during the fourth year of marriage and the chance of divorce does not decrease after four years of marriage.; false **73.** The chance of divorce does not peak during the fourth year of marriage and more than 2% of all divorces occur during the 25th year of marriage.; false **75.** The chance of divorce peaks during the fourth year of marriage or the chance of divorce does not decrease after four years of marriage.; true **77.** The chance of divorce does not peak during the fourth year of marriage or more than 2% of all divorces occur during the 25th year of marriage.; false **79.** The chance of divorce peaks during the fourth year of marriage and the chance of divorce decreases after four years of marriage, or more than 2% of all divorces occur during the 25th year of marriage.; true **81.** p: In 2004, 29.5% of college freshman were liberal.; q: In 2004, 25.1% of college freshman were conservative.; $\sim (p \wedge q)$; true **83.** p: From 1984 through 2004, the percentage of liberal college freshman increased.; q: From 1984 through 2004, the percentage of conservative college freshman decreased.; r: From 1984 through 2004, the percentage of moderate college freshman increased.; $(p \vee q) \wedge \sim r$; true **85. a.** Hora Gershwin **b.** Bolera Mozart does not have a master's degree in music. Cha-Cha Bach does not either play three instruments or have five years experience playing with a symphony orchestra.

97.

p	q	$p \veebar q$
T	T	F
T	F	T
F	T	T
F	F	F

Section 3.4

Check Point Exercises

1.

p	q	$\sim p$	$\sim q$	$\sim p \to \sim q$
T	T	F	F	T
T	F	F	T	T
F	T	T	F	F
F	F	T	T	T

2. The table shows that $[(p \to q) \wedge \sim q] \to \sim p$ is always true; therefore, it is a tautology.

p	q	$\sim p$	$\sim q$	$p \to q$	$(p \to q) \wedge \sim q$	$[(p \to q) \wedge \sim q] \to \sim p$
T	T	F	F	T	F	T
T	F	F	T	F	F	T
F	T	T	F	T	F	T
F	F	T	T	T	T	T

3. a. p: You use Hair Grow.; q: You apply it daily.; r: You go bald.

p	q	r	$\sim r$	$p \wedge q$	$(p \wedge q) \to \sim r$
T	T	T	F	T	F
T	T	F	T	T	T
T	F	T	F	F	T
T	F	F	T	F	T
F	T	T	F	F	T
F	T	F	T	F	T
F	F	T	F	F	T
F	F	F	T	F	T

b. no

4.

p	q	$p \vee q$	$\sim p$	$\sim p \to q$	$(p \vee q) \leftrightarrow (\sim p \to q)$
T	T	T	F	T	T
T	F	T	F	T	T
F	T	T	T	T	T
F	F	F	T	F	T

Because all cases are true, the statement is a tautology.

5. true

Exercise Set 3.4

1.

p	q	$\sim q$	$p \rightarrow \sim q$
T	T	F	F
T	F	T	T
F	T	F	T
F	F	T	T

3.

p	q	$q \rightarrow p$	$\sim (q \rightarrow p)$
T	T	T	F
T	F	T	F
F	T	F	T
F	F	T	F

5.

p	q	$p \wedge q$	$p \vee q$	$(p \wedge q) \rightarrow (p \vee q)$
T	T	T	T	T
T	F	F	T	T
F	T	F	T	T
F	F	F	F	T

7.

p	q	$p \rightarrow q$	$\sim q$	$(p \rightarrow q) \wedge \sim q$
T	T	T	F	F
T	F	F	T	F
F	T	T	F	F
F	F	T	T	T

9.

p	q	r	$p \vee q$	$(p \vee q) \rightarrow r$
T	T	T	T	T
T	T	F	T	F
T	F	T	T	T
T	F	F	T	F
F	T	T	T	T
F	T	F	T	F
F	F	T	F	T
F	F	F	F	T

11.

p	q	r	$p \wedge q$	$r \rightarrow (p \wedge q)$
T	T	T	T	T
T	T	F	T	T
T	F	T	F	F
T	F	F	F	T
F	T	T	F	F
F	T	F	F	T
F	F	T	F	F
F	F	F	F	T

13.

p	q	r	$\sim q$	$\sim r$	$\sim q \rightarrow p$	$\sim r \wedge (\sim q \rightarrow p)$
T	T	T	F	F	T	F
T	T	F	F	T	T	T
T	F	T	T	F	T	F
T	F	F	T	T	T	T
F	T	T	F	F	T	F
F	T	F	F	T	T	T
F	F	T	T	F	F	F
F	F	F	T	T	F	T

15.

p	q	r	$\sim q$	$p \wedge r$	$\sim (p \wedge r)$	$\sim q \vee r$	$\sim (p \wedge r) \rightarrow (\sim q \vee r)$
T	T	T	F	T	F	T	T
T	T	F	F	F	T	F	F
T	F	T	T	T	F	T	T
T	F	F	T	F	T	T	T
F	T	T	F	F	T	T	T
F	T	F	F	F	T	F	F
F	F	T	T	F	T	T	T
F	F	F	T	F	T	T	T

17.

p	q	$\sim q$	$p \leftrightarrow \sim q$
T	T	F	F
T	F	T	T
F	T	F	T
F	F	T	F

19.

p	q	$p \leftrightarrow q$	$\sim (p \leftrightarrow q)$
T	T	T	F
T	F	F	T
F	T	F	T
F	F	T	F

21.

p	q	$p \leftrightarrow q$	$(p \leftrightarrow q) \rightarrow p$
T	T	T	T
T	F	F	T
F	T	F	T
F	F	T	F

23.

p	q	$\sim p$	$\sim p \leftrightarrow q$	$\sim p \rightarrow q$	$(\sim p \leftrightarrow q) \rightarrow (\sim p \rightarrow q)$
T	T	F	F	T	T
T	F	F	T	T	T
F	T	T	T	T	T
F	F	T	F	F	T

25.

p	q	$p \wedge q$	$q \rightarrow p$	$(p \wedge q) \wedge (q \rightarrow p)$	$[(p \wedge q) \wedge (q \rightarrow p)] \leftrightarrow (p \wedge q)$
T	T	T	T	T	T
T	F	F	T	F	T
F	T	F	F	F	T
F	F	F	T	F	T

27.

p	q	r	$\sim r$	$p \leftrightarrow q$	$(p \leftrightarrow q) \rightarrow \sim r$
T	T	T	F	T	F
T	T	F	T	T	T
T	F	T	F	F	T
T	F	F	T	F	T
F	T	T	F	F	T
F	T	F	T	F	T
F	F	T	F	T	F
F	F	F	T	T	T

29.

p	q	r	$p \wedge r$	$q \vee r$	$\sim (q \vee r)$	$(p \wedge r) \leftrightarrow \sim (q \vee r)$
T	T	T	T	T	F	F
T	T	F	F	T	F	T
T	F	T	T	T	F	F
T	F	F	F	F	T	F
F	T	T	F	T	F	T
F	T	F	F	T	F	T
F	F	T	F	T	F	T
F	F	F	F	F	T	F

31.

p	q	r	$\sim q$	$\sim q \wedge p$	$r \vee (\sim q \wedge p)$	$\sim p$	$[r \vee (\sim q \wedge p)] \leftrightarrow \sim p$
T	T	T	F	F	T	F	F
T	T	F	F	F	F	F	T
T	F	T	T	T	T	F	F
T	F	F	T	T	T	F	F
F	T	T	F	F	T	T	T
F	T	F	F	F	F	T	F
F	F	T	T	F	T	T	T
F	F	F	T	F	F	T	F

33. neither

p	q	$p \rightarrow q$	$(p \rightarrow q) \wedge q$	$[(p \rightarrow q) \wedge q] \rightarrow p$
T	T	T	T	T
T	F	F	F	T
F	T	T	T	F
F	F	T	F	T

35. tautology

p	q	$\sim p$	$\sim q$	$p \rightarrow q$	$(p \rightarrow q) \wedge \sim q$	$[(p \rightarrow q) \wedge \sim q] \rightarrow \sim p$
T	T	F	F	T	F	T
T	F	F	T	F	F	T
F	T	T	F	T	F	T
F	F	T	T	T	T	T

37. neither

p	q	$\sim q$	$p \vee q$	$(p \vee q) \wedge p$	$[(p \vee q) \wedge p] \rightarrow \sim q$
T	T	F	T	T	F
T	F	T	T	T	T
F	T	F	T	F	T
F	F	T	F	F	T

39. tautology

p	q	$\sim p$	$p \to q$	$\sim p \vee q$	$(p \to q) \to (\sim p \vee q)$
T	T	F	T	T	T
T	F	F	F	F	T
F	T	T	T	T	T
F	F	T	T	T	T

41. self-contradiction

p	q	$\sim p$	$\sim q$	$p \wedge q$	$\sim p \vee \sim q$	$(p \wedge q) \wedge (\sim p \vee \sim q)$
T	T	F	F	T	F	F
T	F	F	T	F	T	F
F	T	T	F	F	T	F
F	F	T	T	F	T	F

43. neither

p	q	$\sim p$	$\sim q$	$p \wedge q$	$\sim (p \wedge q)$	$\sim p \wedge \sim q$	$\sim (p \wedge q) \leftrightarrow (\sim p \wedge \sim q)$
T	T	F	F	T	F	F	T
T	F	F	T	F	T	F	F
F	T	T	F	F	T	F	F
F	F	T	T	F	T	T	T

45. neither

p	q	$p \to q$	$q \to p$	$(p \to q) \leftrightarrow (q \to p)$
T	T	T	T	T
T	F	F	T	F
F	T	T	F	F
F	F	T	T	T

47. tautology

p	q	$\sim p$	$p \to q$	$\sim p \vee q$	$(p \to q) \leftrightarrow (\sim p \vee q)$
T	T	F	T	T	T
T	F	F	F	F	T
F	T	T	T	T	T
F	F	T	T	T	T

49. tautology

p	q	$p \leftrightarrow q$	$p \to q$	$q \to p$	$(q \to p) \wedge (p \to q)$	$(p \leftrightarrow q) \leftrightarrow [(q \to p) \wedge (p \to q)]$
T	T	T	T	T	T	T
T	F	F	F	T	F	T
F	T	F	T	F	F	T
F	F	T	T	T	T	T

51. neither

p	q	r	$\sim p$	$p \wedge q$	$\sim p \vee r$	$(p \wedge q) \leftrightarrow (\sim p \vee r)$
T	T	T	F	T	T	T
T	T	F	F	T	F	F
T	F	T	F	F	T	F
T	F	F	F	F	F	T
F	T	T	T	F	T	F
F	T	F	T	F	T	F
F	F	T	T	F	T	F
F	F	F	T	F	T	F

53. tautology

p	q	r	$p \to q$	$q \to r$	$(p \to q) \wedge (q \to r)$	$p \to r$	$[(p \to q) \wedge (q \to r)] \to (p \to r)$
T	T	T	T	T	T	T	T
T	T	F	T	F	F	F	T
T	F	T	F	T	F	T	T
T	F	F	F	T	F	F	T
F	T	T	T	T	T	T	T
F	T	F	T	F	F	T	T
F	F	T	T	T	T	T	T
F	F	F	T	T	T	T	T

55. neither

p	q	r	$[(q \to r) \wedge (r \to \sim p)] \leftrightarrow (q \wedge p)$
T	T	T	F
T	T	F	F
T	F	T	T
T	F	F	F
F	T	T	F
F	T	F	T
F	F	T	F
F	F	F	F

57. a. p: You do homework right after class.; q: You fall behind.; $(p \to \sim q) \wedge (\sim p \to q)$

b.

p	q	$\sim p$	$\sim q$	$p \to \sim q$	$\sim p \to q$	$(p \to \sim q) \wedge (\sim p \to q)$
T	T	F	F	F	T	F
T	F	F	T	T	T	T
F	T	T	F	T	T	T
F	F	T	T	T	F	F

c. Answers will vary; an example is: The statement is true when p and q have opposite truth values.

59. a. p: You cut and paste from the Internet.; q: You cite the source.; r: You are charged with plagiarism.; $(p \wedge \sim q) \to r$

b.

p	q	r	$\sim q$	$p \wedge \sim q$	$(p \wedge \sim q) \to r$
T	T	T	F	F	T
T	T	F	F	F	T
T	F	T	T	T	T
T	F	F	T	T	F
F	T	T	F	F	T
F	T	F	F	F	T
F	F	T	T	F	T
F	F	F	T	F	T

c. Answers will vary; an example is: The statement is true when p, q, and r are all true.

61. a. p: You are comfortable in your room.; q: You are honest with your roommate.; r: You enjoy the college experience.; $(p \leftrightarrow q) \vee \sim r$

b.

p	q	r	$\sim r$	$p \leftrightarrow q$	$(p \leftrightarrow q) \vee \sim r$
T	T	T	F	T	T
T	T	F	T	T	T
T	F	T	F	F	F
T	F	F	T	F	T
F	T	T	F	F	F
F	T	F	T	F	T
F	F	T	F	T	T
F	F	F	T	T	T

c. Answers will vary; an example is: The statement is true when p, q, and r are all true.

63. a. p: I enjoy the course.; q: I choose the class based on the professor.; r: I choose the class based on the course description.; $p \leftrightarrow (q \wedge \sim r)$

b.

p	q	r	$\sim r$	$q \wedge \sim r$	$p \leftrightarrow (q \wedge \sim r)$
T	T	T	F	F	F
T	T	F	T	T	T
T	F	T	F	F	F
T	F	F	T	F	F
F	T	T	F	F	T
F	T	F	T	T	F
F	F	T	F	F	T
F	F	F	T	F	T

c. Answers will vary; an example is: The statement is true when p, q, and r are all false.

65. false **67.** true **69.** false **71.** true **73.** true

75. $(p \rightarrow q) \leftrightarrow [(p \wedge q) \rightarrow \sim p]$

p	q	$(p \rightarrow q) \leftrightarrow [(p \wedge q) \rightarrow \sim p]$
T	T	F
T	F	F
F	T	T
F	F	T

77. $[p \rightarrow (\sim q \vee r)] \leftrightarrow (p \wedge r)$

p	q	r	$[p \rightarrow (\sim q \vee r)] \leftrightarrow (p \wedge r)$
T	T	T	T
T	T	F	T
T	F	T	T
T	F	F	F
F	T	T	F
F	T	F	F
F	F	T	F
F	F	F	F

79. p: You love a person.; q: You marry that person.; $(q \rightarrow p) \wedge (\sim p \rightarrow \sim q)$

p	q	$\sim p$	$\sim q$	$q \rightarrow p$	$\sim p \rightarrow \sim q$	$(q \rightarrow p) \wedge (\sim p \rightarrow \sim q)$
T	T	F	F	T	T	T
T	F	F	T	T	T	T
F	T	T	F	F	F	F
F	F	T	T	T	T	T

Answers will vary; an example is: The statement is true when both p and q are true.

81. p: You are happy.; q: You live contentedly.; r: You are wealthy.; $\sim [r \rightarrow (p \wedge q)]$

p	q	r	$p \wedge q$	$r \rightarrow (p \wedge q)$	$\sim [r \rightarrow (p \wedge q)]$
T	T	T	T	T	F
T	T	F	T	T	F
T	F	T	F	F	T
T	F	F	F	T	F
F	T	T	F	F	T
F	T	F	F	T	F
F	F	T	F	F	T
F	F	F	F	T	F

Answers will vary; an example is: The statement is true when p is false and both q and r are true.

83. p: Men averaged more hours than women for every year shown.; q: Men averaged more hours than women in 2002 through 2005.; r: Women averaged more hours than men in 2001.; $(\sim p \wedge q) \rightarrow r$; true **85.** p: Men averaged 2.4 hours more than women in 2005.; q: Men averaged 1.2 hours more than women in 2004.; r: Men averaged fewer hours in 2005 than in 2002.; $(p \leftrightarrow q) \vee r$; true **87.** false **89.** false **97.** no; Answers will vary. **99.** Answers will vary; examples are: $p \vee q$, $p \wedge q$, $\sim(p \wedge q)$, and $(p \vee q) \rightarrow \sim(p \wedge q)$.

Section 3.5

Check Point Exercises

1. a.

p	q	$\sim q$	$p \vee q$	$\sim q \rightarrow p$
T	T	F	T	T
T	F	T	T	T
F	T	F	T	T
F	F	T	F	F

The statements are equivalent since their truth values are the same.

b. If I don't lose my scholarship, then I attend classes.

2.

p	$\sim p$	$\sim(\sim p)$	$\sim[\sim(\sim p)]$
T	F	T	F
F	T	F	T

Since the truth values are the same, $\sim[\sim(\sim p)] \equiv \sim p$.

3. c **4. a.** If you're not driving too closely, then you can't read this. **b.** If it's not time to do the laundry, then you have underwear. **c.** If supervision during exams is required, then some students are not honest. **d.** $q \to (p \vee r)$ **5.** Converse: If you don't see a Club Med, then you are in Iran.; Inverse: If you are not in Iran, then you see a Club Med.; Contrapositive: If you see a Club Med, then you are not in Iran. **6.** You do not have a fever and you have the flu. **7.** Bart Simpson is not a cartoon character or Tony Soprano is not a cartoon character. **8.** You do not leave by 5 P.M. and you arrive home on time. **9. a.** Some horror movies are not scary or none are funny. **b.** Your workouts are not strenuous and you get stronger. **10.** If we cannot swim or we can sail, it is windy.

Exercise Set 3.5

1. a.

p	q	$\sim p$	$p \vee q$	$\sim p \to q$
T	T	F	T	T
T	F	F	T	T
F	T	T	T	T
F	F	T	F	F

b. The United States supports the development of solar-powered cars or it will suffer increasing atmospheric pollution.

3. not equivalent **5.** equivalent **7.** equivalent **9.** not equivalent **11.** not equivalent **13.** equivalent **15.** a **17.** c **19.** Converse: If I am in Illinois, then I am in Chicago.; Inverse: If I am not in Chicago, then I am not in Illinois.; Contrapositive: If I am not in Illinois, then I am not in Chicago. **21.** Converse: If I cannot hear you, then the stereo is playing.; Inverse: If the stereo is not playing, then I can hear you.; Contrapositive: If I can hear you, then the stereo is not playing. **23.** Converse: If you die, you don't laugh.; Inverse: If you laugh, you don't die.; Contrapositive: If you don't die, you laugh. **25.** Converse: If all troops were withdrawn, then the president is telling the truth.; Inverse: If the president is not telling the truth, then some troops were not withdrawn.; Contrapositive: If some troops were not withdrawn, then the president was not telling the truth. **27.** Converse: If some people suffer, then all institutions place profit above human need.; Inverse: If some institutions do not place profit above human need, then no people suffer.; Contrapositive: If no people suffer, then some institutions do not place profit above human need. **29.** Converse: $\sim r \to \sim q$; Inverse: $q \to r$; Contrapositive: $r \to q$ **31.** I am in Los Angeles and not in California. **33.** It is purple and it is a carrot. **35.** He doesn't and I won't. **37.** There is a blizzard and some schools are not closed. **39.** $\sim q \wedge r$ **41.** Australia is not an island or China is not an island. **43.** My high school did not encourage creativity or it did not encourage diversity. **45.** Jewish scripture does not give a clear indication of a heaven and it does not give a clear indication of an afterlife. **47.** The United States has eradicated neither poverty nor racism. **49.** $p \vee \sim q$ **51.** If you do not succeed, you did not attend lecture or did not study. **53.** If his wife does not cook and his child does not cook, then he does. **55.** $(\sim q \wedge r) \to \sim p$ **57.** I'm going to neither Seattle nor San Francisco. **59.** I do not study and I pass. **61.** I am going or he is not going. **63.** A bill does not become law or it receives majority approval. **65.** $\sim p \wedge q$ **67.** $\sim p \vee (\sim q \wedge \sim r)$ **69.** none **71.** none **73.** none **75.** a and b **77.** If there is no pain, there is no gain.; Converse: If there is no gain, then there is no pain.; Inverse: If there is pain, then there is gain.; Contrapositive: If there is gain, then there is pain.; Negation: There is no pain and there is gain. **79.** If you follow Buddha's "Middle Way," then you are neither hedonistic nor ascetic.; Converse: If you are neither hedonistic nor ascetic, then you follow Buddha's "Middle Way."; Inverse: If you do not follow Buddha's "Middle Way," then you are either hedonistic or ascetic.; Contrapositive: If you are either hedonistic or ascetic, then you do not follow Buddha's "Middle Way."; Negation: You follow Buddha's "Middle Way" and you are either hedonistic or ascetic. **81.** $p \wedge (\sim r \vee s)$ **83.** $\sim p \vee (r \wedge s)$ **85. a.** false **b.** Smith does not comprise 1.006% or Johnson does not comprise 0.699%. **c.** true **87. a.** true **b.** Brown does not comprise 0.699% and Williams comprises 0.621%. **c.** false **89. a.** true **b.** Brown does not comprise 0.621% and Jones comprises 0.621%. **c.** false **91. a.** true **b.** Smith is not the top name or does not comprise 1.006%, and Johnson comprises 0.810%. **c.** false **103.** We will replace or repair the roof, or we will not sell the house.

Section 3.6

Check Point Exercises

1. valid **2.** valid **3.** invalid **4. a.** valid **b.** invalid **c.** valid **5.** valid **6.** Some schools across the country are not reexamining their educational objectives.

Exercise Set 3.6

1. invalid **3.** valid **5.** valid **7.** invalid **9.** invalid **11.** valid **13.** valid

15. $\begin{array}{r} p \to \sim q \\ q \\ \hline \therefore \sim p \end{array}$ valid **17.** $\begin{array}{r} p \vee q \\ q \\ \hline \therefore \sim p \end{array}$ invalid **19.** $\begin{array}{r} p \to q \\ q \\ \hline \therefore p \end{array}$ invalid **21.** $\begin{array}{r} p \to q \\ \sim p \to q \\ \hline \therefore q \end{array}$ valid **23.** $\begin{array}{r} p \vee q \\ \sim q \\ \hline \therefore p \end{array}$ valid **25.** $\begin{array}{r} p \to q \\ \sim p \\ \hline \therefore \sim q \end{array}$ invalid **27.** $\begin{array}{r} p \to q \\ q \to r \\ \hline \therefore p \to r \end{array}$ valid **29.** $\begin{array}{r} p \to q \\ q \to r \\ \hline \therefore r \to p \end{array}$ invalid

31. $\begin{array}{r} (p \wedge q) \to r \\ p \wedge \sim r \\ \hline \therefore \sim q \end{array}$ valid **33.** $\begin{array}{r} (p \vee q) \to r \\ \sim r \\ \hline \therefore \sim p \wedge \sim q \end{array}$ valid **35.** $\begin{array}{r} (p \vee q) \to r \\ r \\ \hline \therefore p \vee q \end{array}$ invalid **37.** $\begin{array}{r} (p \wedge q) \to r \\ \sim p \vee \sim q \\ \hline \therefore \sim r \end{array}$ invalid **39.** $\begin{array}{r} p \to q \\ \sim p \to r \\ \hline \therefore q \vee r \end{array}$ valid **41.** $\begin{array}{r} p \to q \\ q \to \sim r \\ r \\ \hline \therefore \sim p \end{array}$ valid

43. My best friend is not a chemist. **45.** They were dropped from prime time. **47.** Some electricity is not off. **49.** If I vacation in Paris, I gain weight.

51. $\begin{array}{r} p \to q \\ \sim p \\ \hline \therefore \sim q \end{array}$ invalid **53.** $\begin{array}{r} p \vee q \\ \sim p \\ \hline \therefore q \end{array}$ valid **55.** $\begin{array}{r} p \to q \\ q \\ \hline \therefore p \end{array}$ invalid **57.** $\begin{array}{r} p \to q \\ \sim q \\ \hline \therefore \sim p \end{array}$ valid **59.** $\begin{array}{r} p \to q \\ q \to r \\ \hline \therefore p \to r \end{array}$ valid **61.** $\begin{array}{r} p \to q \\ \sim q \\ \hline \therefore \sim p \end{array}$ valid **63.** h **65.** i **67.** c **69.** a **71.** j **73.** d

83. People sometimes speak without being spoken to. **85.** The doctor either destroys the base on which the placebo rests or jeopardizes a relationship built on trust.

Section 3.7

Check Point Exercises

1. valid **2.** invalid **3.** valid **4.** invalid **5.** invalid **6.** invalid

Exercise Set 3.7

1. valid **3.** invalid **5.** valid **7.** invalid **9.** invalid **11.** valid **13.** valid **15.** invalid **17.** invalid **19.** valid **21.** valid **23.** valid **25.** invalid **27.** invalid **29.** valid **31.** invalid **33.** invalid **35.** invalid **37.** valid **39.** valid **43.** b **45.** Some teachers are amusing people.

Chapter 3 Review Exercises

1. $(p \wedge q) \rightarrow r$; If the temperature is below 32° and we have finished studying, we will go to the movies. **2.** $\sim r \rightarrow (\sim p \vee \sim q)$; If we do not go to the movies, then the temperature is not below 32° or we have not finished studying. **3.** The temperature is below 32°, and if we finish studying, we will go to the movies. **4.** We will go to the movies if and only if the temperature is below 32° and we have finished studying. **5.** It is not true that both the temperature is below 32° and we have finished studying. **6.** We will not go to the movies if and only if the temperature is not below 32° or we have not finished studying. **7.** $(p \wedge q) \vee r$ **8.** $(p \vee \sim q) \rightarrow r$ **9.** $q \rightarrow (p \leftrightarrow r)$ **10.** $r \leftrightarrow (p \wedge \sim q)$ **11.** $p \rightarrow r$ **12.** $q \rightarrow \sim r$ **13.** Some houses are not made with wood. **14.** Some students major in business. **15.** No crimes are motivated by passion. **16.** All Democrats are registered voters. **17.** Some new taxes will not be used for education.

18. neither

p	q	$\sim p$	$\sim p \wedge q$	$p \vee (\sim p \wedge q)$
T	T	F	F	T
T	F	F	F	T
F	T	T	T	T
F	F	T	F	F

19. neither

p	q	$\sim p$	$\sim q$	$\sim p \vee \sim q$
T	T	F	F	F
T	F	F	T	T
F	T	T	F	T
F	F	T	T	T

20. neither

p	q	$\sim p$	$\sim p \vee q$	$p \rightarrow (\sim p \vee q)$
T	T	F	T	T
T	F	F	F	F
F	T	T	T	T
F	F	T	T	T

21. neither

p	q	$\sim q$	$p \leftrightarrow \sim q$
T	T	F	F
T	F	T	T
F	T	F	T
F	F	T	F

22. tautology

p	q	$\sim p$	$\sim q$	$p \vee q$	$\sim (p \vee q)$	$\sim p \wedge \sim q$	$\sim (p \vee q) \rightarrow (\sim p \wedge \sim q)$
T	T	F	F	T	F	F	T
T	F	F	T	T	F	F	T
F	T	T	F	T	F	F	T
F	F	T	T	F	T	T	T

23. neither

p	q	r	$\sim r$	$p \vee q$	$(p \vee q) \rightarrow \sim r$
T	T	T	F	T	F
T	T	F	T	T	T
T	F	T	F	T	F
T	F	F	T	T	T
F	T	T	F	T	F
F	T	F	T	T	T
F	F	T	F	F	T
F	F	F	T	F	T

24. neither

p	q	r	$p \wedge q$	$p \wedge r$	$(p \wedge q) \leftrightarrow (p \wedge r)$
T	T	T	T	T	T
T	T	F	T	F	F
T	F	T	F	T	F
T	F	F	F	F	T
F	T	T	F	F	T
F	T	F	F	F	T
F	F	T	F	F	T
F	F	F	F	F	T

25. neither

p	q	r	$r \to p$	$q \vee (r \to p)$	$p \wedge [q \vee (r \to p)]$
T	T	T	T	T	T
T	T	F	T	T	T
T	F	T	T	T	T
T	F	F	T	T	T
F	T	T	F	T	F
F	T	F	T	T	F
F	F	T	F	F	F
F	F	F	T	T	F

26. a. p: I'm in class.; q: I'm studying.; $(p \vee q) \wedge \sim p$

b.

p	q	$\sim p$	$p \vee q$	$(p \vee q) \wedge \sim p$
T	T	F	T	F
T	F	F	T	F
F	T	T	T	T
F	F	T	F	F

c. The statement is true when p is false and q is true.

27. a. p: You spit from a truck.; q: It's legal.; r: You spit from a car.; $(p \to q) \wedge (r \to \sim q)$

b.

p	q	r	$\sim q$	$p \to q$	$r \to \sim q$	$(p \to q) \wedge (r \to \sim q)$
T	T	T	F	T	F	F
T	T	F	F	T	T	T
T	F	T	T	F	T	F
T	F	F	T	F	T	F
F	T	T	F	T	F	F
F	T	F	F	T	T	T
F	F	T	T	T	T	T
F	F	F	T	T	T	T

c. The statement is true when p and q are both false.

28. false **29.** true **30.** true **31.** false **32.** p: \$60.0 million was spent in 2002.; q: Spending decreased from 2002 to 2003.; $p \wedge \sim q$; false **33.** p: More money was spent in 2003 than 2004.; q: \$67.9 million was spent in 2003.; r: \$53.6 million was spent in 2004.; $p \to (q \vee r)$; true **34.** p: \$55.8 million was spent in 2001.; q: \$60.0 million was spent in 2002.; r: \$67.9 million was spent in 2004.; $(p \leftrightarrow q) \vee \sim r$; true

35. a.

p	q	$\sim p$	$\sim p \vee q$	$p \to q$
T	T	F	T	T
T	F	F	F	F
F	T	T	T	T
F	F	T	T	T

b. If the triangle is isosceles, then it has two equal sides.

36. c **37.** not equivalent **38.** equivalent **39.** Converse: If I am in the South, then I am in Atlanta.; Inverse: If I am not in Atlanta, then I am not in the South.; Contrapositive: If I am not in the South, then I am not in Atlanta. **40.** Converse: If today is not a holiday, then I am in class.; Inverse: If I am not in class, then today is a holiday.; Contrapositive: If today is a holiday, then I am not in class. **41.** Converse: If I pass all courses, then I worked hard.; Inverse: If I don't work hard, then I don't pass some courses.; Contrapositive: If I do not pass some course, then I did not work hard. **42.** Converse: $\sim q \to \sim p$; Inverse: $p \to q$.; Contrapositive: $q \to p$ **43.** An argument is sound and it is not valid. **44.** I do not work hard and I succeed. **45.** $\sim r \wedge \sim p$ **46.** Chicago is not a city or Maine is not a city. **47.** Ernest Hemingway was neither a musician nor an actor. **48.** If a number is not 0, the number is positive or negative. **49.** I do not work hard and I succeed. **50.** She is using her car or she is not taking a bus. **51.** $p \wedge \sim q$ **52.** a and c **53.** a and b **54.** a and c **55.** none **56.** invalid **57.** valid

58. $\begin{array}{l} p \to q \\ \underline{\quad q \quad} \\ \therefore p \end{array}$ invalid

59. $\begin{array}{l} p \vee q \\ \underline{\quad q \quad} \\ \therefore \sim p \end{array}$ invalid

60. $\begin{array}{l} p \vee q \\ \underline{\quad \sim p \quad} \\ \therefore q \end{array}$ valid

61. $\begin{array}{l} p \to q \\ \underline{\quad \sim q \quad} \\ \therefore \sim p \end{array}$ valid

62. $\begin{array}{l} p \to \sim q \\ \underline{\sim p \to q} \\ \therefore p \leftrightarrow \sim q \end{array}$ valid

63. $\begin{array}{l} p \to \sim q \\ \underline{\quad r \to q \quad} \\ \therefore \sim r \to p \end{array}$ invalid

64. invalid **65.** valid **66.** valid **67.** invalid **68.** invalid **69.** valid

Chapter 3 Test

1. If I'm registered and I'm a citizen, then I vote. **2.** I don't vote if and only if I'm not registered or I'm not a citizen. **3.** I'm neither registered nor a citizen. **4.** $(p \wedge q) \vee \sim r$ **5.** $(\sim p \vee \sim q) \to \sim r$ **6.** $r \to q$ **7.** Some numbers are not divisible by 5. **8.** No people wear glasses.

9.

p	q	$\sim p$	$\sim p \vee q$	$p \wedge (\sim p \vee q)$
T	T	F	T	T
T	F	F	F	F
F	T	T	T	F
F	F	T	T	F

10.

p	q	$\sim p$	$\sim q$	$p \wedge q$	$\sim (p \wedge q)$	$(\sim p \vee \sim q)$	$\sim (p \wedge q) \leftrightarrow (\sim p \vee \sim q)$
T	T	F	F	T	F	F	T
T	F	F	T	F	T	T	T
F	T	T	F	F	T	T	T
F	F	T	T	F	T	T	T

11.

p	q	r	$q \vee r$	$p \leftrightarrow (q \vee r)$
T	T	T	T	T
T	T	F	T	T
T	F	T	T	T
T	F	F	F	F
F	T	T	T	F
F	T	F	T	F
F	F	T	T	F
F	F	F	F	T

12. p: You break the law.; q: You change the law.; $(p \wedge q) \rightarrow \sim p$

p	q	$\sim p$	$p \wedge q$	$(p \wedge q) \rightarrow \sim p$
T	T	F	T	F
T	F	F	F	T
F	T	T	F	T
F	F	T	F	T

Answers will vary; an example is: The statement is true when p is false.

13. true **14.** true **15. a.** p: There was a decrease in the percentage of students who considered "being very well off financially" essential.; q: There was a decrease in the percentage of students who considered "developing a meaningful philosophy of life" essential.; r: There was a decrease in the percentage of students who considered "raising a family" essential.; $\sim p \vee (q \wedge r)$ **b.** true **16.** b **17.** If it snows, then it is not August. **18.** Converse: If I cannot concentrate, then the radio is playing.; Inverse: If the radio is not playing, then I can concentrate. **19.** It is cold and we use the pool. **20.** The test is not today and the party is not tonight. **21.** The banana is not green or it is ready to eat. **22.** a and b **23.** a and c **24.** invalid **25.** valid **26.** invalid **27.** invalid **28.** valid **29.** invalid

CHAPTER 4

Section 4.1

Check Point Exercises

1. a. 49 **b.** 125 **c.** 1 **d.** 100,000 **e.** 1,000,000 **f.** 18 **2. a.** $(4 \times 10^3) + (0 \times 10^2) + (2 \times 10^1) + (6 \times 1)$ or $(4 \times 1000) + (0 \times 100) + (2 \times 10) + (6 \times 1)$ **b.** $(2 \times 10^4) + (4 \times 10^3) + (2 \times 10^2) + (3 \times 10^1) + (2 \times 1)$ or $(2 \times 10{,}000) + (4 \times 1000) + (2 \times 100) + (3 \times 10) + (2 \times 1)$ **3. a.** 6073 **b.** 80,900 **4.** 12,031 **5.** 80,293

Exercise Set 4.1

1. 25 **3.** 8 **5.** 81 **7.** 100,000 **9.** $(3 \times 10^1) + (6 \times 1)$ **11.** $(2 \times 10^2) + (4 \times 10^1) + (9 \times 1)$ **13.** $(7 \times 10^2) + (0 \times 10^1) + (3 \times 1)$ **15.** $(4 \times 10^3) + (8 \times 10^2) + (5 \times 10^1) + (6 \times 1)$ **17.** $(3 \times 10^3) + (0 \times 10^2) + (7 \times 10^1) + (0 \times 1)$ **19.** $(3 \times 10^4) + (4 \times 10^3) + (5 \times 10^2) + (6 \times 10^1) + (9 \times 1)$ **21.** $(2 \times 10^8) + (3 \times 10^7) + (0 \times 10^6) + (0 \times 10^5) + (0 \times 10^4) + (7 \times 10^3) + (0 \times 10^2) + (0 \times 10^1) + (4 \times 1)$ **23.** 73 **25.** 385 **27.** 528,743 **29.** 7002 **31.** 600,002,007 **33.** 23 **35.** 1262 **37.** 11,523 **39.** 2,416,271 **41.** 14 **43.** 6846 **45.** 3048 **47.** 14,411 **49.** 75,610 **51.** $(4 \times 10^4) + (6 \times 10^3) + (2 \times 10^2) + (2 \times 10^1) + (5 \times 1)$ **53.** $(2 \times 10^3) + (2 \times 10^2) + (9 \times 10^1) + (9 \times 1)$ **55.** 0.4759 **57.** 0.700203 **59.** 5000.03 **61.** 30,700.05809 **63.** 9734 **65.** 8097 **67.** 365 is the number of days in a non-leap year. **77.** <<<<VVVV <<VVVVVVV

Section 4.2

Check Point Exercises

1. 487 **2.** 51 **3.** 2772 **4.** 11_{five} **5.** 1031_{seven} **6.** 42023_{five}

Exercise Set 4.2

1. 23 **3.** 42 **5.** 30 **7.** 11 **9.** 455 **11.** 28,909 **13.** 8342 **15.** 53 **17.** 44,261 **19.** 12_{five} **21.** 14_{seven} **23.** 10_{two} **25.** 31_{four} **27.** 101_{six} **29.** 322_{five} **31.** 1230_{four} **33.** 10011_{two} **35.** 12010_{three} **37.** 1442_{six} **39.** 4443_{seven}
41. <<<<<   <<<<<VV **43.** VVVVVV   <<<VV   <<VVVVVV
45.  **47.** 

49. 25_{seven} **51.** 623_{eight} **53.** 1000110 **55.** 1101101 **57.** PAL **59.** 10011011101111111101101 **65.** $EC4_{\text{sixteen}}$; $EC6_{\text{sixteen}}$

Section 4.3

Check Point Exercises

1. 131_{five} **2.** 1110_{two} **3.** 13_{five} **4.** 1605_{seven} **5.** 201_{seven} **6.** 23_{four}

Exercise Set 4.3

1. 102_{four} **3.** 110_{two} **5.** 1310_{five} **7.** 1302_{seven} **9.** 15760_{nine} **11.** 23536_{seven} **13.** 13_{four} **15.** 4_{five} **17.** 206_{eight} **19.** 366_{seven} **21.** 10_{two} **23.** 111_{three} **25.** 152_{six} **27.** 11_{two} **29.** 4011_{seven} **31.** 3114_{eight} **33.** 312_{four} **35.** 20_{four} **37.** 41_{five} remainder of 1_{five} **39.** 1000110_{two} **41.** 110000_{two} **43.** 110111_{two} **45.** $71BE_{\text{sixteen}}$ **47.** 01100; 11101 **49.** 10001; 11001 **51.** 01100; 00110; 00100; 11011 **53.** The circuit in Exercise 47 **57.** 56_{seven}

Section 4.4

Check Point Exercises

1. 300,222 **2.**  **3.** 1361 **4.** 1447 **5.** CCCXCIX **6.**
二
千
六
百
九
十
三
7. 885

Exercise Set 4.4

1. 322 **3.** 300,423 **5.** 132 **7.**  **9.** 
11.  **13.** 11 **15.** 16 **17.** 40 **19.** 59 **21.** 146 **23.** 1621 **25.** 2677
27. 9466 **29.** XLIII **31.** CXXIX **33.** MDCCCXCVI **35.** $\overline{\text{VI}}$DCCCXCII **37.** 88 **39.** 527 **41.** 2776
43.
四
十
三

45.
五
百
八
十
三

47.
四
千
八
百
七
十

49. 12 **51.** 234 **53.** $\mu\gamma$ **55.** $\upsilon\pi\gamma$

57. MMCCCXXIV;
二
千
三
百
二
十
四

59. a.  **b.**
一
千
七
百
四
十
一

61. 3104_{five} **63.** 1232_{five} **65.**  **67.** 1776; Declaration of Independence

69. 4,640,224; $\overline{\text{MMMMDCXL}}\text{CCXXIV}$ **77.** Preceding: 𓍢𓍢𓎆𓎆𓎆𓎆𓎆𓎆𓎆𓎆𓎆𓏺𓏺𓏺𓏺𓏺𓏺𓏺𓏺𓏺
Following: 𓍢𓍢𓍢

Chapter 4 Review Exercises

1. 121 **2.** 343 **3.** $(4 \times 10^2) + (7 \times 10^1) + (2 \times 1)$ **4.** $(8 \times 10^3) + (0 \times 10^2) + (7 \times 10^1) + (6 \times 1)$ **5.** $(7 \times 10^4) + (0 \times 10^3) + (3 \times 10^2) + (2 \times 10^1) + (9 \times 1)$ **6.** 706,953 **7.** 740,000,306 **8.** 673 **9.** 8430 **10.** 2331 **11.** 65,536 **12.** Each position represents a particular value. The symbol in each position tells how many of that value are represented. **13.** 19 **14.** 6 **15.** 325 **16.** 805 **17.** 4051 **18.** 560 **19.** 324_{five} **20.** 10101_{two} **21.** 122112_{three} **22.** 26452_{seven} **23.** 111140_{six} **24.** $3A2_{\text{twelve}}$ **25.** 132_{seven} **26.** 1401_{eight} **27.** 110000_{two} **28.** $AD0_{\text{sixteen}}$ **29.** 5_{six} **30.** 345_{seven} **31.** 11_{two} **32.** 2304_{five} **33.** 222_{four} **34.** 354_{seven} **35.** 1102_{five} **36.** 133_{four} **37.** 12_{five} **38.** 1246 **39.** 12,432
40. 𓆼𓆼𓍢𓍢𓍢𓍢𓎆𓎆𓎆𓎆𓎆𓎆𓎆𓎆𓏺𓏺𓏺𓏺𓏺𓏺 **41.** 𓂭𓂭𓂭𓆼𓆼𓆼𓆼𓍢𓍢𓍢𓍢𓍢𓎆𓎆𓎆𓎆𓎆𓎆𓎆𓏺𓏺𓏺 **42.** 2314
43. DDDDDCCCBBBBBBBBBAA **44.** Answers will vary. **45.** 163 **46.** 1034 **47.** 1990 **48.** XLIX **49.** MMCMLXV
50. If symbols increase in value from left to right, subtract the value of the symbol on the left from the symbol on the right. Answers will vary.
51. 554 **52.** 8253

53. 二
百
七
十
四

54. 三
千
五
百
八
十
七

55. 365 **56.** 4520

57. G
Y
I
X
C

58. F
Z
H
Y
E
X
D

59. Answers will vary.

60. 653 **61.** 678 **62.** *υνγ* **63.** ∏*β* **64.** 357 **65.** 37,894 **66.** 80,618 **67.** WRG **68.** lfVQC **69.** Answers will vary.

Chapter 4 Test

1. 729 **2.** $(5 \times 10^2) + (6 \times 10^1) + (7 \times 1)$ **3.** $(6 \times 10^4) + (3 \times 10^3) + (0 \times 10^2) + (2 \times 10^1) + (8 \times 1)$ **4.** 7493 **5.** 400,206 **6.** A number represents "How many?" whereas a numeral is a symbol used to write a number. **7.** A symbol for zero is needed for a place holder when there are no values for a position. **8.** 72,731 **9.** 1560 **10.** 113 **11.** 223 **12.** 53 **13.** 2212_{three} **14.** 111000_{two} **15.** 24334_{five} **16.** 1212_{five} **17.** 414_{seven} **18.** 250_{six} **19.** 221_{five} **20.** 20,303 **21.** 𓂭𓂭𓂭𓆼𓆼𓍢𓍢𓍢𓍢𓍢𓍢𓎆𓎆𓎆𓏺𓏺𓏺𓏺
22. 1994 **23.** CDLIX **24.** Answers will vary.

CHAPTER 5

Section 5.1

Check Point Exercises

1. b **2.** $2^3 \cdot 3 \cdot 5$ **3.** 75 **4.** 96 **5.** 90 **6.** 5:00 P.M.

Exercise Set 5.1

1. a. yes **b.** no **c.** yes **d.** no **e.** no **f.** yes **g.** no **h.** no **i.** no **3. a.** yes **b.** yes **c.** yes **d.** no **e.** yes **f.** yes **g.** no **h.** no **i.** yes **5. a.** yes **b.** no **c.** yes **d.** no **e.** no **f.** no **g.** no **h.** no **i.** no **7. a.** yes **b.** yes **c.** yes **d.** no **e.** yes **f.** yes **g.** yes **h.** no **i.** yes **9. a.** yes **b.** yes **c.** yes **d.** yes **e.** yes **f.** yes **g.** yes **h.** yes **i.** yes **11.** true; $5 + 9 + 5 + 8 = 27$ which is divisible by 3. **13.** true; the last two digits of 10,612 form the number 12 and 12 is divisible by 4. **15.** false **17.** true; 104,538 is an even number so it is divisible by 2. $1 + 0 + 4 + 5 + 3 + 8 = 21$ which is divisible by 3 so it is divisible by 3. Any number divisible by 2 and 3 is divisible by 6. **19.** true; the last three digits of 20,104 form the number 104 and 104 is divisible by 8. **21.** false **23.** true; $5 + 1 + 7 + 8 + 7 + 2 = 30$ which is divisible by 3 so it is divisible by 3. The last two digits of 517,872 form the number 72 and 72 is divisible by 4 so it is divisible by 4. Any number divisible by 3 and 4 is divisible by 12. **25.** $3 \cdot 5^2$ **27.** $2^3 \cdot 7$ **29.** $3 \cdot 5 \cdot 7$ **31.** $2^2 \cdot 5^3$ **33.** $3 \cdot 13 \cdot 17$ **35.** $3 \cdot 5 \cdot 59$ **37.** $2^5 \cdot 3^2 \cdot 5$ **39.** $2^2 \cdot 499$ **41.** $3 \cdot 5^2 \cdot 7^2$ **43.** $2^3 \cdot 3 \cdot 5^2 \cdot 11 \cdot 13$ **45.** 14 **47.** 2 **49.** 12 **51.** 24 **53.** 38 **55.** 15 **57.** 168 **59.** 336 **61.** 540 **63.** 360 **65.** 3420 **67.** 4560 **69.** 8 **71.** 6 **73.** 2, 6 **75.** perfect **77.** not perfect **79.** not an emirp **81.** emirp **83.** not a Germain prime **85.** not a Germain prime **87.** 648; 648; Answers will vary. An example is: The product of the greatest common divisor and least common multiple of two numbers equals the product of the two numbers. **89.** The numbers are the prime numbers between 1 and 97. **91.** 12 **93.** 10 **95.** July 1 **97.** 90 min or $1\frac{1}{2}$ hr **111.** GCD: $2^{14} \cdot 3^{25} \cdot 5^{30}$; LCM: $2^{17} \cdot 3^{37} \cdot 5^{31}$ **113.** 2:20 A.M. on the third day **115.** yes **117.** yes

Section 5.2

Check Point Exercises

1.
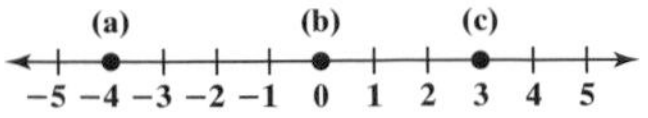

2. a. > **b.** < **c.** < **d.** < **3. a.** 8 **b.** 6 **4. a.** 37 **b.** −4 **c.** −24
5. $15 billion **6. a.** 25 **b.** −25 **c.** −64 **d.** 81 **7.** 36 **8.** 82

Exercise Set 5.2

1. 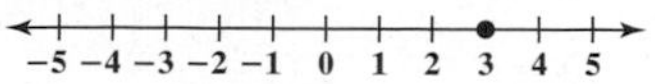 **3.** 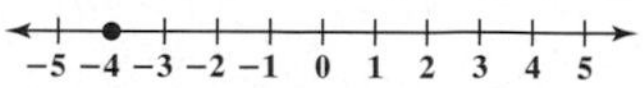 **5.** $<$ **7.** $<$ **9.** $>$ **11.** $<$ **13.** 14 **15.** 14 **17.** 300,000 **19.** -12 **21.** 4 **23.** -3 **25.** -5 **27.** -18 **29.** 0 **31.** 5 **33.** -7 **35.** 14 **37.** 11 **39.** -9 **41.** -28 **43.** -54 **45.** 21 **47.** -12 **49.** 13 **51.** 0 **53.** 25 **55.** 25 **57.** 64 **59.** -125 **61.** 625 **63.** -81 **65.** 81 **67.** -3 **69.** -7 **71.** 30 **73.** 0 **75.** undefined **77.** -20 **79.** -31 **81.** 25 **83.** 13 **85.** 13 **87.** 33 **89.** 32 **91.** -24 **93.** 0 **95.** -32 **97.** 45 **99.** 14 **101.** -36 **103.** 88 **105.** $-10 - (-2)^3; -2$ **107.** $[2(7 - 10)]^2; 36$ **109.** \$389 billion **111.** \$25 billion **113.** 19,757 ft **115.** $-$\$158 billion; deficit **117.** \$554 billion **119.** 7°F **121.** -2°F **133.** $(8 - 2) \cdot 3 - 4 = 14$ **135.** -36

Section 5.3

Check Point Exercises

1. $\frac{4}{5}$ **2.** $\frac{21}{8}$ **3.** $1\frac{2}{3}$ **4. a.** 0.375 **b.** $0.\overline{45}$ **5. a.** $\frac{9}{10}$ **b.** $\frac{43}{50}$ **c.** $\frac{53}{1000}$ **6.** $\frac{2}{9}$ **7.** $\frac{79}{99}$ **8. a.** $\frac{8}{33}$ **b.** $\frac{3}{2}$ or $1\frac{1}{2}$ **c.** $\frac{51}{10}$ or $5\frac{1}{10}$ **9. a.** $\frac{36}{55}$ **b.** $-\frac{4}{3}$ or $-1\frac{1}{3}$ **c.** $\frac{3}{2}$ or $1\frac{1}{2}$ **10. a.** $\frac{2}{3}$ **b.** $\frac{3}{2}$ or $1\frac{1}{2}$ **c.** $-\frac{9}{4}$ or $-2\frac{1}{4}$ **11.** $\frac{19}{20}$ **12.** $-\frac{17}{60}$ **13.** $\frac{5}{12}$ **14.** $2\frac{4}{5}$ eggs; 3 eggs

Exercise Set 5.3

1. $\frac{2}{3}$ **3.** $\frac{5}{6}$ **5.** $\frac{4}{7}$ **7.** $\frac{5}{9}$ **9.** $\frac{9}{10}$ **11.** $\frac{14}{19}$ **13.** $\frac{19}{8}$ **15.** $-\frac{38}{5}$ **17.** $\frac{199}{16}$ **19.** $4\frac{3}{5}$ **21.** $-8\frac{4}{9}$ **23.** $35\frac{11}{20}$ **25.** 0.75 **27.** 0.35 **29.** 0.875 **31.** $0.\overline{81}$ **33.** $3.\overline{142857}$ **35.** $0.\overline{285714}$ **37.** $\frac{3}{10}$ **39.** $\frac{2}{5}$ **41.** $\frac{39}{100}$ **43.** $\frac{41}{50}$ **45.** $\frac{29}{40}$ **47.** $\frac{5399}{10{,}000}$ **49.** $\frac{7}{9}$ **51.** 1 **53.** $\frac{4}{11}$ **55.** $\frac{257}{999}$ **57.** $\frac{21}{88}$ **59.** $-\frac{7}{120}$ **61.** $\frac{3}{2}$ **63.** 6 **65.** $\frac{10}{3}$ **67.** $-\frac{14}{15}$ **69.** 6 **71.** $\frac{5}{11}$ **73.** $\frac{2}{3}$ **75.** $\frac{2}{3}$ **77.** $\frac{7}{10}$ **79.** $\frac{9}{10}$ **81.** $\frac{53}{120}$ **83.** $\frac{1}{2}$ **85.** $\frac{7}{12}$ **87.** $-\frac{71}{150}$ **89.** $1\frac{5}{12}$ **91.** $\frac{4}{15}$ **93.** $\frac{7}{24}$ **95.** $\frac{7}{12}$ **97.** $-\frac{3}{4}$ **99.** Both are equal to $\frac{169}{36}$. **101.** $-\frac{9}{40}$ **103.** $-1\frac{1}{36}$ **105.** $-19\frac{3}{4}$ **107.** $\frac{1}{2^2 \cdot 3}$ **109.** $-\frac{289}{2^4 \cdot 5^4 \cdot 7}$ **111.** $0.5\overline{4}; 0.58\overline{3}$; $<$ **113.** $-0.8\overline{3}; -0.\overline{8}$; $>$ **115.** $\frac{86}{192}; \frac{43}{96}$ **117.** $\frac{1}{3}$ cup butter, $\frac{5}{2} = 2.5$ ounces unsweetened chocolate, $\frac{3}{4}$ cup sugar, 1 teaspoon vanilla, 1 egg, $\frac{1}{2}$ cup flour **119.** $\frac{5}{6}$ cup butter, $\frac{25}{4} = 6.25$ ounces unsweetened chocolate, $\frac{15}{8} = 1\frac{7}{8}$ cups sugar, $\frac{5}{2} = 2\frac{1}{2}$ teaspoons vanilla, $\frac{5}{2} = 2\frac{1}{2}$ eggs, $\frac{5}{4} = 1\frac{1}{4}$ cups flour **121.** 24 brownies **123.** $3\frac{2}{3}$ c **125.** $\frac{4}{5}$ yr **127.** $-\frac{9}{10}$ yr **129.** $\frac{1}{3}$ of the business **131.** $1\frac{3}{20}$ mi; $\frac{7}{20}$ mi **133.** $\frac{1}{10}$

147.

149. a. 0.24625 **b.** 1.45248 **c.** 0.00112

Section 5.4

Check Point Exercises

1. a. $2\sqrt{3}$ **b.** $2\sqrt{15}$ **c.** cannot be simplified **2. a.** $\sqrt{30}$ **b.** 10 **c.** $2\sqrt{3}$ **3. a.** 4 **b.** $2\sqrt{2}$ **4. a.** $18\sqrt{3}$ **b.** $-5\sqrt{13}$ **c.** $8\sqrt{10}$ **5. a.** $3\sqrt{3}$ **b.** $-13\sqrt{2}$ **6. a.** $\frac{5\sqrt{10}}{2}$ **b.** $\frac{\sqrt{14}}{7}$ **c.** $\frac{5\sqrt{2}}{6}$

Exercise Set 5.4

1. 3 **3.** 5 **5.** 8 **7.** 11 **9.** 13 **11. a.** 13.2 **b.** 13.15 **c.** 13.153 **13. a.** 133.3 **b.** 133.27 **c.** 133.270 **15. a.** 1.8 **b.** 1.77 **c.** 1.772 **17.** $2\sqrt{5}$ **19.** $4\sqrt{5}$ **21.** $5\sqrt{10}$ **23.** $14\sqrt{7}$ **25.** $\sqrt{42}$ **27.** 6 **29.** $3\sqrt{2}$ **31.** $2\sqrt{13}$ **33.** 3 **35.** $3\sqrt{5}$ **37.** $-4\sqrt{3}$ **39.** $13\sqrt{3}$ **41.** $-2\sqrt{13}$ **43.** $2\sqrt{5}$ **45.** $7\sqrt{2}$ **47.** $3\sqrt{5}$ **49.** $2\sqrt{2}$ **51.** $34\sqrt{2}$ **53.** $-\frac{3}{2}\sqrt{3}$ **55.** $11\sqrt{3}$ **57.** $\frac{5\sqrt{3}}{3}$ **59.** $3\sqrt{7}$ **61.** $\frac{2\sqrt{30}}{5}$ **63.** $\frac{5\sqrt{3}}{2}$ **65.** $\frac{\sqrt{10}}{5}$ **67.** $20\sqrt{2} - 5\sqrt{3}$ **69.** $-7\sqrt{7}$ **71.** $\frac{43\sqrt{2}}{35}$ **73.** $\frac{5\sqrt{6}}{6}$ **75.** $6\sqrt{3}$ miles; 10.4 miles **77.** 70 mph; He was speeding. **79. a.** 41 in. **b.** 40.6 in.; quite well **81. a.** 36 cm **b.** 44.7 cm **c.** 46.9 cm **d.** The model describes healthy children. **83.** $0.6R_f$; 60 weeks **93.** $<$ **95.** $>$ **97.** -7 and -6 **99.** Answers will vary.; An example is $(3 + \sqrt{2}) - (1 + \sqrt{2}) = 2$.

Section 5.5

Check Point Exercises

1. a. $\sqrt{9}$ **b.** $0, \sqrt{9}$ **c.** $-9, 0, \sqrt{9}$ **d.** $-9, -1.3, 0, 0.\overline{3}, \sqrt{9}$ **e.** $\frac{\pi}{2}, \sqrt{10}$ **f.** $-9, -1.3, 0, 0.\overline{3}, \frac{\pi}{2}, \sqrt{9}, \sqrt{10}$
2. a. associative property of multiplication **b.** commutative property of addition **c.** distributive property of multiplication over addition **d.** commutative property of multiplication **3. a.** yes **b.** no

Exercise Set 5.5

1. a. $\sqrt{100}$ **b.** $0, \sqrt{100}$ **c.** $-9, 0, \sqrt{100}$ **d.** $-9, -\frac{4}{5}, 0, 0.25, 9.2, \sqrt{100}$ **e.** $\sqrt{3}$ **f.** $-9, -\frac{4}{5}, 0, 0.25, \sqrt{3}, 9.2, \sqrt{100}$
3. a. $\sqrt{64}$ **b.** $0, \sqrt{64}$ **c.** $-11, 0, \sqrt{64}$ **d.** $-11, -\frac{5}{6}, 0, 0.75, \sqrt{64}$ **e.** $\sqrt{5}, \pi$ **f.** $-11, -\frac{5}{6}, 0, 0.75, \sqrt{5}, \pi, \sqrt{64}$
5. 0 **7.** Answers will vary; an example is: $\frac{1}{2}$. **9.** Answers will vary; an example is: 1. **11.** Answers will vary; an example is: $\sqrt{2}$.
13. 4 **15.** 6 **17.** 4; 3 **19.** 7 **21.** $30 + 5\sqrt{2}$ **23.** $3\sqrt{7} + \sqrt{14}$ **25.** $5\sqrt{3} + 3$ **27.** $2\sqrt{3} + 6$
29. commutative property of addition **31.** associative property of addition **33.** commutative property of addition
35. distributive property of multiplication over addition **37.** associative property of multiplication **39.** Answers will vary; an example is: $1 - 2 = -1$. **41.** Answers will vary; an example is: $4 \div 8 = \frac{1}{2}$. **43.** Answers will vary; an example is: $\sqrt{2} \cdot \sqrt{2} = 2$. **45.** true **47.** false
49. distributive property; commutative property of addition; associative property of addition; distributive property; commutative property of addition
51. vampire **53.** vampire **55.** narcissistic **57.** narcissistic **59. a.** distributive property **b.** approximately 108 mg; Answers will vary.
69. c

Section 5.6

Check Point Exercises

1. a. 1 **b.** 1 **c.** 1 **d.** −1 **2. a.** $\frac{1}{81}$ **b.** $\frac{1}{216}$ **c.** $\frac{1}{12}$ **3. a.** 7,400,000,000 **b.** 0.000003017 **4. a.** 7.41×10^9
b. 9.2×10^{-8} **5.** $\$5.19 \times 10^{11}$ **6.** 520,000 **7.** 0.0000023 **8. a.** 1.872×10^4 **b.** 18,720 **9.** \$2500

Exercise Set 5.6

1. $2^5 = 32$ **3.** $4^3 = 64$ **5.** $2^6 = 64$ **7.** $1^{20} = 1$ **9.** $4^2 = 16$ **11.** $2^4 = 16$ **13.** 1 **15.** 1 **17.** −1 **19.** $\frac{1}{4}$ **21.** $\frac{1}{64}$
23. $\frac{1}{32}$ **25.** $3^2 = 9$ **27.** $3^{-2} = \frac{1}{9}$ **29.** $2^{-4} = \frac{1}{16}$ **31.** 270 **33.** 912,000 **35.** 80,000,000 **37.** 100,000 **39.** 0.79
41. 0.0215 **43.** 0.000786 **45.** 0.00000318 **47.** 3.7×10^2 **49.** 3.6×10^3 **51.** 3.2×10^4 **53.** 2.2×10^8 **55.** 2.7×10^{-2}
57. 3.7×10^{-3} **59.** 2.93×10^{-6} **61.** 8.2×10^7 **63.** 4.1×10^5 **65.** 2.1×10^{-6} **67.** 600,000 **69.** 60,000 **71.** 0.123
73. 30,000 **75.** 3,000,000 **77.** 0.03 **79.** 0.0021 **81.** $(8.2 \times 10^7)(3.0 \times 10^9) = 2.46 \times 10^{17}$ **83.** $(5.0 \times 10^{-4})(6.0 \times 10^6) = 3 \times 10^3$
85. $\frac{9.5 \times 10^6}{5 \times 10^2} = 1.9 \times 10^4$ **87.** $\frac{8 \times 10^{-5}}{2 \times 10^2} = 4 \times 10^{-7}$ **89.** $\frac{4.8 \times 10^{11}}{1.2 \times 10^{-4}} = 4 \times 10^{15}$ **91.** $\frac{11}{18}$ **93.** $\frac{99}{25} = 3\frac{24}{25}$ **95.** 2.5×10^{-3}
97. 8×10^{-5} **99.** $\$4.65 \times 10^{10}$ **101.** $\$1 \times 10^8$ **103.** approximately 67 hot dogs per person **105.** $2.5 \times 10^2 = 250$ chickens
107. a. $\$1.0813 \times 10^4$; \$10,813 **b.** \$901 **109.** Medicare; \$3242 **111.** 1.06×10^{-18} gram **113.** 3.1536×10^7 **125.** d **127.** $\frac{1}{4}$

Section 5.7

Check Point Exercises

1. 100, 120, 140, 160, 180, and 200 **2.** 8, 5, 2, −1, −4, and −7 **3.** −34 **4. a.** $a_n = 1.16n + 10.84$ **b.** 68.8 million
5. $12, -6, 3, -\frac{3}{2}, \frac{3}{4}$, and $-\frac{3}{8}$ **6.** 3645 **7.** $a_n = 3(2)^{n-1}$; 384

Exercise Set 5.7

1. 8, 10, 12, 14, 16, and 18 **3.** 200, 220, 240, 260, 280, and 300 **5.** −7, −3, 1, 5, 9, and 13 **7.** −400, −100, 200, 500, 800, and 1100
9. 7, 4, 1, −2, −5, and −8 **11.** 200, 140, 80, 20, −40, and −100 **13.** $\frac{5}{2}, 3, \frac{7}{2}, 4, \frac{9}{2}$, and 5 **15.** $\frac{3}{2}, \frac{7}{4}, 2, \frac{9}{4}, \frac{5}{2}$, and $\frac{11}{4}$
17. 4.25, 4.55, 4.85, 5.15, 5.45, and 5.75 **19.** 4.5, 3.75, 3, 2.25, 1.5, and 0.75 **21.** 33 **23.** 252 **25.** 67 **27.** 955 **29.** 82 **31.** −142
33. −43 **35.** −248 **37.** $\frac{23}{2}$ **39.** 1.75 **41.** $a_n = 1 + (n-1)4$; 77 **43.** $a_n = 7 + (n-1)(-4)$; −69 **45.** $a_n = 9 + (n-1)2$; 47
47. $a_n = -20 + (n-1)(-4)$; −96 **49.** 4, 8, 16, 32, 64, and 128 **51.** 1000, 1000, 1000, 1000, 1000, and 1000 **53.** 3, −6, 12, −24, 48, and −96
55. 10, −40, 160, −640, 2560, and −10,240 **57.** 2000, −2000, 2000, −2000, 2000, and −2000 **59.** −2, 6, −18, 54, −162, and 486
61. −6, 30, −150, 750, −3750, and 18,750 **63.** $\frac{1}{4}, \frac{1}{2}$, 1, 2, 4, and 8 **65.** $\frac{1}{4}, \frac{1}{8}, \frac{1}{16}, \frac{1}{32}, \frac{1}{64}$, and $\frac{1}{128}$ **67.** $-\frac{1}{16}, \frac{1}{4}$, −1, 4, −16, and 64

69. 2, 0.2, 0.02, 0.002, 0.0002, and 0.00002 **71.** 256 **73.** 2,324,522,934 $\approx 2.32 \times 10^9$ **75.** 50 **77.** 320 **79.** -2 **81.** 486
83. $\frac{3}{64}$ **85.** $-\frac{2}{27}$ **87.** $\approx -1.82 \times 10^{-9}$ **89.** 0.1 **91.** $a_n = 3(4)^{n-1}$; 12,288 **93.** $a_n = 18\left(\frac{1}{3}\right)^{n-1}$; $\frac{2}{81}$ **95.** $a_n = 1.5(-2)^{n-1}$; 96
97. $a_n = 0.0004(-10)^{n-1}$; 400 **99.** arithmetic; 18 and 22 **101.** geometric; 405 and 1215 **103.** arithmetic; 13 and 18
105. geometric; $\frac{3}{16}$ and $\frac{3}{32}$ **107.** arithmetic; $\frac{5}{2}$ and 3 **109.** geometric; 7 and -7 **111.** arithmetic; -49 and -63
113. geometric; $25\sqrt{5}$ and 125 **115.** arithmetic; 310 **117.** geometric; 59,048 **119.** geometric; -1023 **121.** arithmetic; 80 **123.** 5050
125. a. $a_n = 23.08 + 0.12n$ **b.** 27.88 years old **127.** Company A; \$1400 **129.** \$16,384 **131.** \$3,795,957
133. a. 1.013, 1.013, 1.013, 1.013, 1.013, 1.013, 1.013; the population is increasing geometrically with $r \approx 1.013$. **b.** $a_n = 29.76(1.013)^{n-1}$
c. ≈ 33.86; very well **143.** d

Chapter 5 Review Exercises

1. 2: yes; 3: yes; 4: yes; 5: no; 6: yes; 8: yes; 9: no; 10: no; 12: yes **2.** 2: yes; 3: yes; 4: no; 5: yes; 6: yes; 8: no; 9: yes; 10: yes; 12: no **3.** $3 \cdot 5 \cdot 47$
4. $2^6 \cdot 3 \cdot 5$ **5.** $3 \cdot 5^2 \cdot 7 \cdot 13$ **6.** GCD: 6; LCM: 240 **7.** GCD: 6; LCM: 900 **8.** GCD: 2; LCM: 27,432 **9.** 12 **10.** 11:48 A.M.
11. $<$ **12.** $>$ **13.** 860 **14.** 53 **15.** 0 **16.** -3 **17.** -11 **18.** -15 **19.** 1 **20.** 99 **21.** -15 **22.** 9 **23.** -4
24. -16 **25.** -16 **26.** 10 **27.** -2 **28.** 17 **29.** \$658 billion **30.** $\frac{8}{15}$ **31.** $\frac{6}{25}$ **32.** $\frac{11}{12}$ **33.** $\frac{64}{11}$ **34.** $-\frac{23}{7}$ **35.** $5\frac{2}{5}$
36. $-1\frac{8}{9}$ **37.** 0.8 **38.** $0.\overline{428571}$ **39.** 0.625 **40.** 0.5625 **41.** $\frac{3}{5}$ **42.** $\frac{17}{25}$ **43.** $\frac{147}{250}$ **44.** $\frac{21}{2500}$ **45.** $\frac{5}{9}$ **46.** $\frac{34}{99}$
47. $\frac{113}{999}$ **48.** $\frac{21}{50}$ **49.** $\frac{35}{6}$ **50.** $\frac{8}{3}$ **51.** $-\frac{1}{4}$ **52.** $\frac{2}{3}$ **53.** $\frac{43}{36}$ **54.** $\frac{37}{60}$ **55.** $\frac{11}{15}$ **56.** $\frac{5}{16}$ **57.** $\frac{15}{112}$ **58.** $\frac{27}{40}$
59. $11\frac{1}{4}$ or about 11 pounds **60.** $\frac{5}{12}$ of the tank **61.** $2\sqrt{7}$ **62.** $6\sqrt{2}$ **63.** $5\sqrt{6}$ **64.** $10\sqrt{3}$ **65.** $4\sqrt{3}$ **66.** $5\sqrt{2}$
67. $2\sqrt{3}$ **68.** 3 **69.** $5\sqrt{5}$ **70.** $-6\sqrt{11}$ **71.** $7\sqrt{2}$ **72.** $-17\sqrt{3}$ **73.** $12\sqrt{2}$ **74.** $6\sqrt{5}$ **75.** $\frac{\sqrt{6}}{3}$
76. $8\sqrt{3} \approx 13.9$ feet per second **77. a.** $\sqrt{81}$ **b.** 0, $\sqrt{81}$ **c.** $-17, 0, \sqrt{81}$ **d.** $-17, -\frac{9}{13}, 0, 0.75, \sqrt{81}$ **e.** $\sqrt{2}, \pi$
f. $-17, -\frac{9}{13}, 0, 0.75, \sqrt{2}, \pi, \sqrt{81}$ **78.** Answers will vary; an example is: 0. **79.** Answers will vary; an example is: $\frac{1}{2}$.
80. Answers will vary; an example is: $\sqrt{2}$. **81.** commutative property of addition **82.** associative property of multiplication
83. distributive property of multiplication over addition **84.** commutative property of multiplication **85.** commutative property of multiplication
86. commutative property of addition **87.** Answers will vary; an example is: $2 \div 6 = \frac{1}{3}$. **88.** Answers will vary; an example is: $0 - 2 = -2$.
89. 216 **90.** 64 **91.** 16 **92.** 729 **93.** 25 **94.** 1 **95.** 1 **96.** $\frac{1}{216}$ **97.** $\frac{1}{16}$ **98.** $\frac{1}{49}$ **99.** 27 **100.** 460
101. 37,400 **102.** 0.00255 **103.** 0.0000745 **104.** 7.52×10^3 **105.** 3.59×10^6 **106.** 7.25×10^{-3} **107.** 4.09×10^{-7}
108. 4.2×10^{13} **109.** 9.7×10^{-5} **110.** 390 **111.** 1,150,000 **112.** 0.023 **113.** 40 **114.** $(6.0 \times 10^4)(5.4 \times 10^5) = 3.24 \times 10^{10}$
115. $(9.1 \times 10^4)(4 \times 10^{-4}) = 3.64 \times 10^1$ **116.** $\frac{8.4 \times 10^6}{4 \times 10^3} = 2.1 \times 10^3$ **117.** $\frac{3 \times 10^{-6}}{6 \times 10^{-8}} = 5 \times 10^1$ **118.** 1000 yr **119.** $\$4.5 \times 10^{10}$
120. 1.3×10^{10} people **121.** 7, 11, 15, 19, 23, and 27 **122.** $-4, -9, -14, -19, -24$, and -29 **123.** $\frac{3}{2}, 1, \frac{1}{2}, 0, -\frac{1}{2}$, and -1 **124.** 20
125. -30 **126.** -38 **127.** $a_n = -7 + (n-1)4$; 69 **128.** $a_n = 200 + (n-1)(-20)$; -180 **129.** 3, 6, 12, 24, 48, and 96
130. $\frac{1}{2}, \frac{1}{4}, \frac{1}{8}, \frac{1}{16}, \frac{1}{32}$, and $\frac{1}{64}$ **131.** 16, -8, 4, -2, 1, and $-\frac{1}{2}$ **132.** 54 **133.** $\frac{1}{2}$ **134.** -48 **135.** $a_n = 1(2)^{n-1}$; 128
136. $a_n = 100\left(\frac{1}{10}\right)^{n-1}$; $\frac{1}{100{,}000}$ **137.** arithmetic; 24 and 29 **138.** geometric; 162 and 486 **139.** geometric; $\frac{1}{256}$ and $\frac{1}{1024}$
140. arithmetic; -28 and -35 **141. a.** $a_n = 32.04 - 0.54n$ **b.** 22.32% **c.** potatoes: $a_n = 19.27 - 0.27n$; 14.41%; salads: $a_n = 13.99 - 0.29n$; 8.77%; bread: $a_n = 10.06 - 0.26n$; 5.38% **142. a.** $\frac{5.9}{4.2} \approx 1.4$; $\frac{8.3}{5.9} \approx 1.4$; $\frac{11.6}{8.3} \approx 1.4$; $\frac{16.2}{11.6} \approx 1.4$; $\frac{22.7}{16.2} \approx 1.4$ **b.** $4.2(1.4)^{n-1}$ **c.** 62.0 million

Chapter 5 Test

1. 2, 3, 4, 6, 8, 9, and 12 **2.** $2^2 \cdot 3^2 \cdot 7$ **3.** GCD: 24; LCM: 144 **4.** 1 **5.** -4 **6.** -32 **7.** $0.58\overline{3}$ **8.** $\frac{64}{99}$ **9.** $\frac{1}{5}$ **10.** $\frac{37}{60}$
11. $-\frac{19}{2}$ **12.** $\frac{7}{12}$ **13.** $5\sqrt{2}$ **14.** $9\sqrt{2}$ **15.** $3\sqrt{2}$ **16.** $-7, -\frac{4}{5}, 0, 0.25, \sqrt{4}$, and $\frac{22}{7}$ **17.** commutative property of addition
18. distributive property of multiplication over addition **19.** 243 **20.** 64 **21.** $\frac{1}{64}$ **22.** 7500 **23.** $\frac{4.9 \times 10^4}{7 \times 10^{-3}} = 7 \times 10^6$
24. \$7267 **25.** 1, -4, -9, -14, -19, and -24 **26.** 22 **27.** 16, 8, 4, 2, 1, and $\frac{1}{2}$ **28.** 320

CHAPTER 6

Section 6.1

Check Point Exercises

1. 608 **2.** -2 **3.** -94 **4.** Model 3 **5.** $3x - 21$ **6.** $38x^2 + 23x$ **7.** $2x + 36$

Exercise Set 6.1

1. 27 **3.** 23 **5.** 29 **7.** -2 **9.** 140 **11.** 217 **13.** 176 **15.** 30 **17.** 44 **19.** 22 **21.** 27 **23.** -12 **25.** 69 **27.** -33 **29.** -8 **31.** 10°C **33.** 60 ft **35.** $17x$ **37.** $-3x^2$ **39.** $3x + 15$ **41.** $8x - 12$ **43.** $15x + 16$ **45.** $27x - 10$ **47.** $29y - 29$ **49.** $8y - 12$ **51.** $16y - 25$ **53.** $12x^2 + 11$ **55.** $-2x^2 - 9$ **57.** $x - (x + 4); -4$ **59.** $6(-5x); -30x$ **61.** $5x - 2x; 3x$ **63.** $8x - (3x + 6); 5x - 6$ **65.** 313; very well **67.** 1348 **69.** Model 1 **71.** very well **73. a.** \$32,000 **b.** \$32,616; reasonably well **c.** \$32,597; reasonably well **75.** Model 1 **83.** d **85. a.** \$50.50, \$5.50, and \$1.00 per clock, respectively **b.** no; Answers will vary.

Section 6.2

Check Point Exercises

1. $\{6\}$ **2.** $\{-2\}$ **3.** $\{2\}$ **4.** $\{5\}$ **5.** $\{-2\}$ **6.** 3.7; shown as the point (3.7, 10) **7.** $w = \frac{P - 2l}{2}$ **8.** $m = \frac{T - D}{p}$ **9.** $\varnothing$ **10.** $\{x \mid x \text{ is a real number}\}$

Exercise Set 6.2

1. $\{10\}$ **3.** $\{-17\}$ **5.** $\{12\}$ **7.** $\{9\}$ **9.** $\{-3\}$ **11.** $\left\{-\frac{1}{4}\right\}$ **13.** $\{3\}$ **15.** $\{11\}$ **17.** $\{-17\}$ **19.** $\{11\}$ **21.** $\left\{\frac{7}{5}\right\}$ **23.** $\left\{\frac{25}{3}\right\}$ **25.** $\{8\}$ **27.** $\{-3\}$ **29.** $\{2\}$ **31.** $\{-4\}$ **33.** $\left\{-\frac{1}{5}\right\}$ **35.** $\{-4\}$ **37.** $\{5\}$ **39.** $\{6\}$ **41.** $\left\{-\frac{7}{2}\right\}$ **43.** $\{1\}$ **45.** $\{24\}$ **47.** $\{20\}$ **49.** $\{5\}$ **51.** $L = \frac{A}{W}$ **53.** $b = \frac{2A}{h}$ **55.** $P = \frac{I}{rt}$ **57.** $m = \frac{E}{c^2}$ **59.** $m = \frac{y - b}{x}$ **61.** $a = 2A - b$ **63.** $r = \frac{S - P}{Pt}$ **65.** $x = \frac{C - By}{A}$ **67.** $n = \frac{a_n - a_1}{d} + 1$ or $n = \frac{a_n - a_1 + d}{d}$ **69.** $\varnothing$ **71.** $\{x \mid x \text{ is a real number}\}$ **73.** $\left\{\frac{2}{3}\right\}$ **75.** $\{x \mid x \text{ is a real number}\}$ **77.** $\varnothing$ **79.** $\{0\}$ **81.** $\varnothing$ **83.** $\{0\}$ **85.** 2 **87.** 161 **89.** $\{-2\}$ **91.** $\varnothing$ **93.** $\{10\}$ **95.** $\{-2\}$ **97.** 2013 **99.** 120 chirps per minute **101.** 409.2 ft **103.** 2011 **105.** 2014 **107.** 2022 **117.** c

Section 6.3

Check Point Exercises

1. 12 **2.** 2011 **3.** basketball: 1.6 million; bicycle riding: 1.3 million; football: 1 million **4.** 300 min

Exercise Set 6.3

1. 6 **3.** 19 and 45 **5.** 2050 **7.** 2008 **9.** 2025; 9,900,000 **11.** births: 375 thousand; deaths: 146 thousand **13.** race: 3844; sexual orientation: 1239 **15.** after 5 months; \$165 **17.** 30 times **19.** \$600 of merchandise; \$580 **21.** 11 hr **23.** \$1350 **29.** 5 ft 7 in. **31.** uncle: 60 yr old; woman: 20 yr old **33.** \$4000 for the mother; \$8000 for the boy; \$2000 for the girl

Section 6.4

Check Point Exercises

1. a. $\{15\}$ **b.** $\{140\}$ **2.** \$1500 **3.** 720 deer **4.** 66 gal **5.** 556 ft **6.** $\approx$ 4.36 lb per in^2

Exercise Set 6.4

1. $\{14\}$ **3.** $\{27\}$ **5.** $\left\{-\frac{9}{4}\right\}$ **7.** $\{-15\}$ **9.** $\left\{\frac{7}{2}\right\}$ **11.** $\{10\}$ **13.** 156 **15.** 30 **17.** $x = \frac{ab}{c}$ **19.** $x = \frac{(a + b)d}{c}$ **21.** $x = \frac{ab}{c}$ **23.** \$1115.38 **25.** $\approx$ 20,489 fur seal pups **27.** \$950 **29.** 31 lb **31.** 154.1 in. or $\approx$ 12.8 ft **33.** $\approx$ 607 lb **35.** 120 ft **37.** 0.88°C **39.** 6.4 lb **41.** 112 decibels **49.** The front sprocket can be replaced by a 100-tooth sprocket, or the rear sprocket can be replaced with a 12-tooth sprocket. **51.** The destructive power is 4 times as strong.

Section 6.5

Check Point Exercises

1. a.

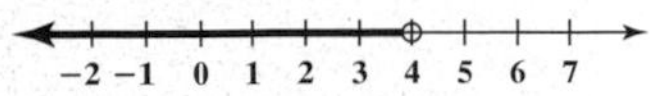

b.

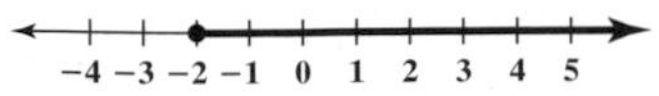

c.

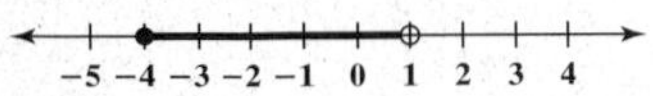

2. $\{x \mid x \leq 4\}$;

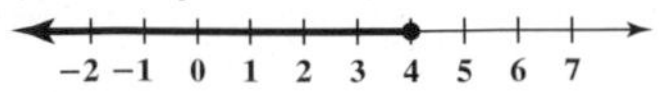

3. a. $\{x \mid x < 8\}$;

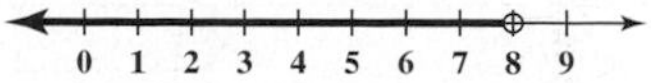

b. $\{x \mid x > -3\}$;

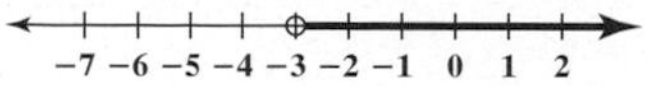

4. $\{x \mid x < -6\}$;

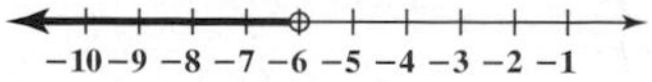

5. $\{x \mid x \geq 1\}$;

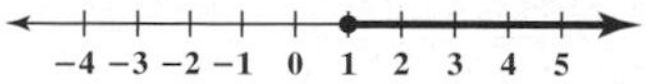

6. $\{x \mid -1 \leq x < 4\}$;

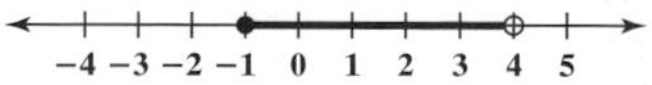

7. at least 83%

Exercise Set 6.5

1.

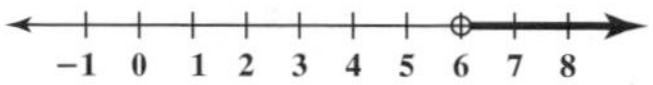

3.

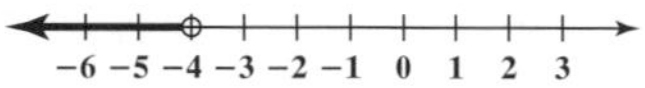

5.

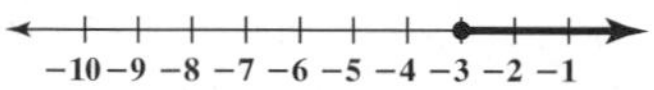

7.

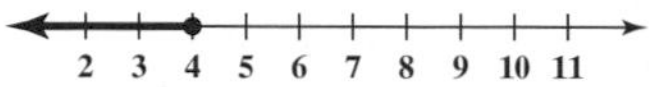

9.

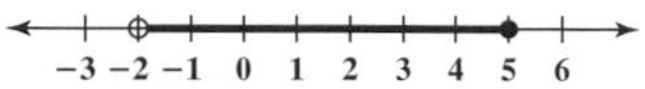

11.

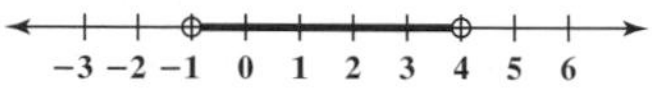

13. $\{x \mid x > 5\}$;

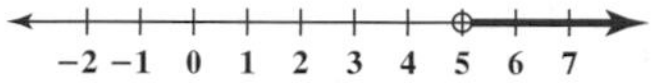

15. $\{x \mid x \leq 5\}$;

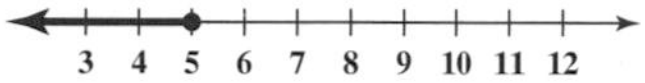

17. $\{x \mid x < 3\}$;

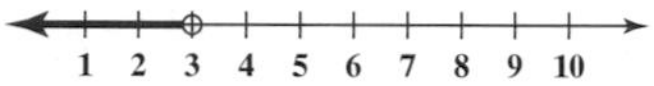

19. $\{x \mid x < 5\}$;

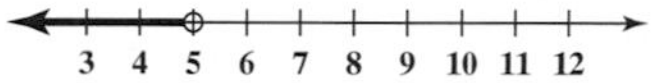

21. $\{x \mid x \geq -5\}$;

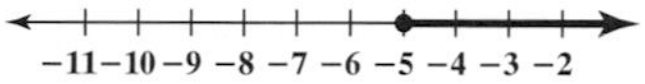

23. $\{x \mid x > 5\}$;

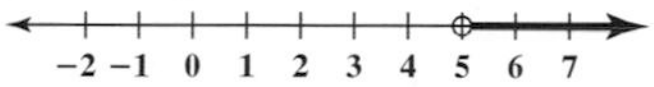

25. $\{x \mid x < 5\}$;

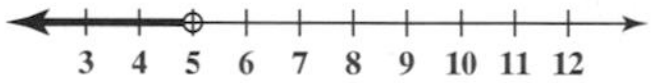

27. $\{x \mid x < 8\}$;

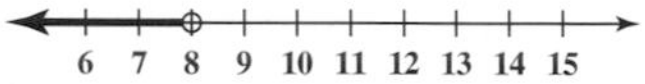

29. $\{x \mid x > -6\}$;

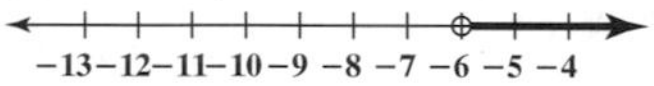

31. $\{x \mid x > -5\}$;

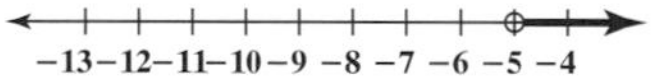

33. $\{x \mid x \leq 5\}$;

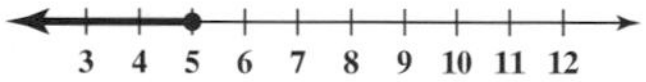

35. $\{x \mid x \leq 3\}$;

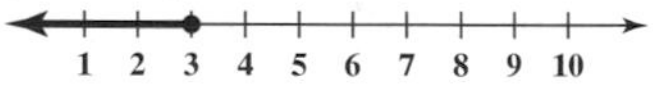

37. $\{x \mid x < 16\}$;

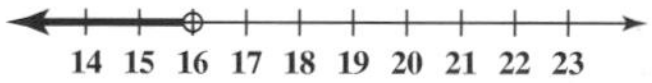

39. $\{x \mid x > -3\}$;

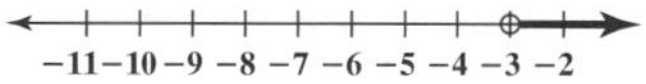

41. $\{x \mid x \geq -2\}$;

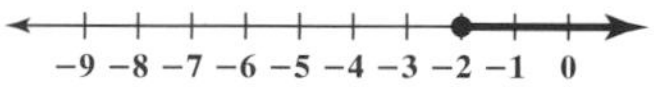

43. $\{x \mid x > -4\}$;

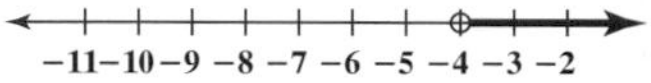

45. $\{x \mid x \geq 4\}$;

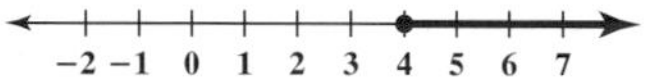

47. $\left\{x \middle| x > \frac{11}{3}\right\}$;

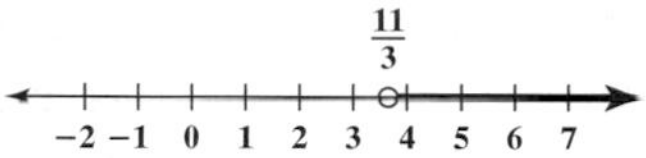

49. $\{x \mid x > 2\}$;

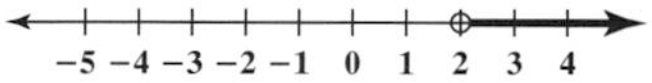

51. $\{x \mid x < 3\}$;

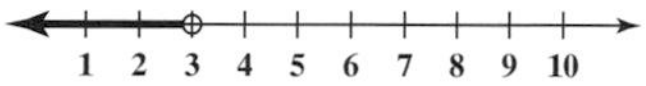

53. $\left\{x \middle| x > \frac{5}{3}\right\}$;

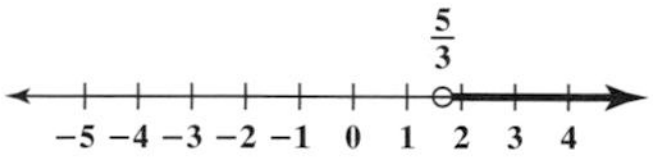

55. $\{x \mid x \geq -10\}$;

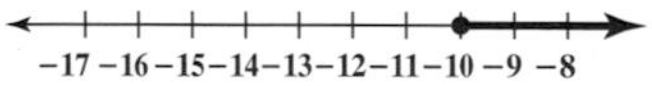

57. $\{x \mid x < -6\}$;

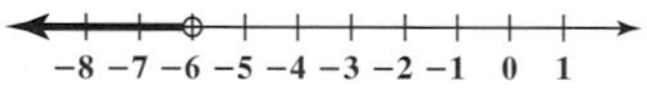

59. $\{x \mid 3 < x < 5\}$;

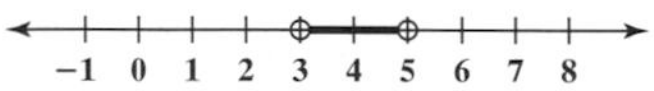

61. $\{x \mid -1 \leq x < 3\}$;

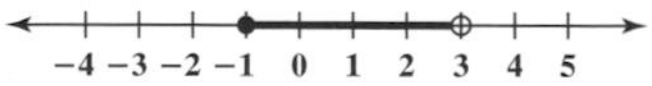

63. $\{x \mid -5 < x \leq -2\}$;

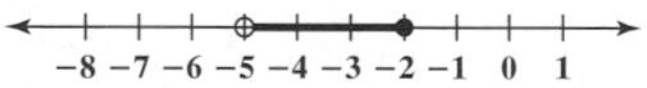

65. $\{x \mid 3 \leq x < 6\}$;

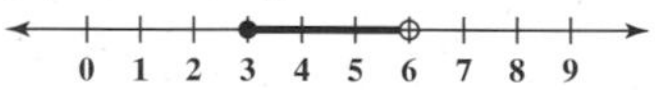

67. $x > \frac{C - By}{A}$ **69.** $x < \frac{C - By}{A}$ **71.** $\{x \mid x + 5 \geq 2x\}$ **73.** $\{x \mid 2(4 + x) \leq 36\}$ **75.** $\left\{x \middle| \frac{3x}{5} + 4 \leq 34\right\}$ **77.** $\{x \mid 0 < x < 4\}$

79. intimacy ≥ passion or passion ≤ intimacy **81.** commitment > passion or passion < commitment **83.** 9; after 3 years **85.** more than 28 years; years after 2012 **87. a.** 88; no **b.** at least 68 **89.** at most 1280 mi **91.** at most 29 bags **93.** between 80 and 110 minutes, inclusive **99.** more than 1200 packages

Section 6.6

Check Point Exercises

1. $x^2 + 11x + 30$ **2.** $28x^2 - x - 15$ **3.** $(x + 2)(x + 3)$ **4.** $(x + 5)(x - 2)$ **5.** $(5x - 4)(x - 2)$ **6.** $(3y - 1)(2y + 7)$ **7.** $\{-6, 3\}$ **8.** $\{-2, 8\}$ **9.** $\left\{-4, \frac{1}{2}\right\}$ **10.** $\left\{-\frac{1}{2}, \frac{1}{4}\right\}$ **11.** $\left\{\frac{3 + \sqrt{7}}{2}, \frac{3 - \sqrt{7}}{2}\right\}$ **12.** approximately 26 years old

Exercise Set 6.6

1. $x^2 + 8x + 15$ **3.** $x^2 - 2x - 15$ **5.** $2x^2 + 3x - 2$ **7.** $12x^2 - 43x + 35$ **9.** $(x + 2)(x + 3)$ **11.** $(x - 5)(x + 3)$ **13.** $(x - 5)(x - 3)$ **15.** $(x - 12)(x + 3)$ **17.** prime **19.** $(x + 1)(x + 16)$ **21.** $(2x + 1)(x + 3)$ **23.** $(2x - 5)(x - 6)$ **25.** $(3x + 2)(x - 1)$ **27.** $(3x - 28)(x + 1)$ **29.** $(3x - 4)(2x - 1)$ **31.** $(2x + 3)(2x + 5)$ **33.** $\{-3, 8\}$ **35.** $\left\{-\frac{5}{4}, 2\right\}$ **37.** $\{-5, -3\}$ **39.** $\{-3, 5\}$ **41.** $\{-3, 7\}$ **43.** $\{-8, -1\}$ **45.** $\{6\}$ **47.** $\left\{-\frac{1}{2}, 4\right\}$ **49.** $\left\{-2, \frac{9}{5}\right\}$ **51.** $\left\{-\frac{7}{2}, -\frac{1}{3}\right\}$ **53.** $\{-5, -3\}$ **55.** $\left\{\frac{-5 + \sqrt{13}}{2}, \frac{-5 - \sqrt{13}}{2}\right\}$ **57.** $\{-2 + \sqrt{10}, -2 - \sqrt{10}\}$ **59.** $\{-2 + \sqrt{11}, -2 - \sqrt{11}\}$ **61.** $\{-3, 6\}$ **63.** $\left\{-\frac{2}{3}, \frac{3}{2}\right\}$ **65.** $\{1 + \sqrt{11}, 1 - \sqrt{11}\}$ **67.** $\left\{\frac{1 + \sqrt{57}}{2}, \frac{1 - \sqrt{57}}{2}\right\}$ **69.** $\left\{\frac{-3 + \sqrt{3}}{6}, \frac{-3 - \sqrt{3}}{6}\right\}$ **71.** $\left\{\frac{3}{2}\right\}$ **73.** $\left\{-\frac{2}{3}, 4\right\}$ **75.** $\{-3, 1\}$ **77.** $\left\{1, -\frac{5}{2}\right\}$ **79.** $\{\pm\sqrt{6}\}$ **81.** $1 + \sqrt{7}$ **83.** 9 teams **85.** exactly **87.** 2014 **89.** 33-yr-olds and 58-yr-olds; The formula models the trend in the data quite well. **97.** 8 and 16 **99.** $(x^n + 9)(x^n + 11)$

Chapter 6 Review Exercises

1. 33 **2.** 15 **3.** -48 **4.** 805 million; fairly well, but slight overestimation **5.** $17x - 15$ **6.** $5y - 13$ **7.** $14x^2 + x$ **8.** $\{6\}$ **9.** $\{2\}$ **10.** $\{12\}$ **11.** $\left\{-\frac{13}{3}\right\}$ **12.** $\{2\}$ **13.** $\varnothing$ **14.** $\{x \mid x \text{ is a real number}\}$ **15.** $x = \frac{By + C}{A}$ **16.** $h = \frac{2A}{b}$ **17.** $B = 2A - C$ **18.** $g = \frac{s - vt}{t^2}$ **19.** 2012 **20.** $7x - 1 = 5x + 9; 5$ **21.** Chicken Caesar: 495; Express Taco: 620; Mandarin Chicken: 590 **22.** 2013 **23.** 500 min **24.** United States: 20.5 million barrels per day; China: 6.5 million barrels per day **25.** $\{5\}$ **26.** $\{-65\}$ **27.** $\left\{\frac{2}{5}\right\}$ **28.** $\{3\}$ **29.** 324 teachers **30.** 287 trout **31.** \$154 **32.** 1600 ft **33.** 5 hr

34. $\{x \mid x < 4\}$;

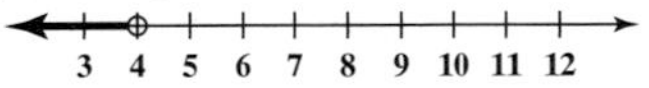

35. $\{x \mid x > -8\}$;

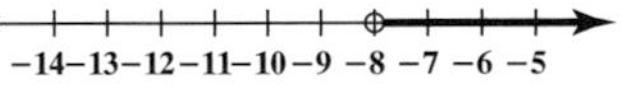

36. $\{x \mid x \geq -3\}$;

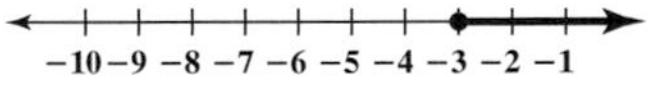

37. $\{x \mid x > 6\}$;

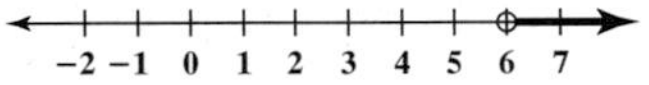

38. $\{x \mid x \geq 4\}$;

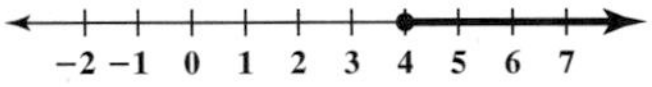

39. $\{x \mid x \leq 2\}$;

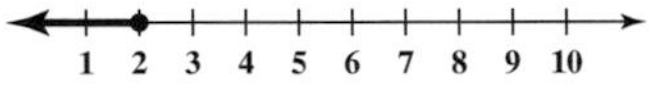

40. $\left\{x \,\middle|\, -\frac{3}{4} < x \leq 1\right\}$;

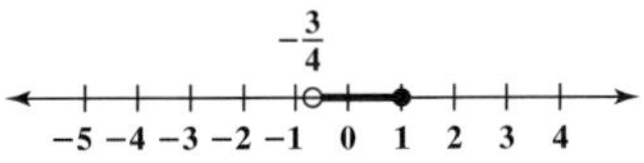

41. at least 64 **42.** $x^2 + 4x - 45$ **43.** $12x^2 - 13x - 14$ **44.** $(x - 4)(x + 3)$ **45.** $(x - 5)(x - 3)$ **46.** prime **47.** $(3x - 2)(x - 5)$ **48.** $(2x - 5)(3x + 2)$ **49.** prime **50.** $\{-7, 2\}$ **51.** $\{-4, 8\}$ **52.** $\left\{-8, \frac{1}{2}\right\}$ **53.** $\{-5, -2\}$ **54.** $\{1, 3\}$ **55.** $\left\{\frac{5 + \sqrt{41}}{2}, \frac{5 - \sqrt{41}}{2}\right\}$ **56.** $\left\{-3, \frac{1}{2}\right\}$ **57.** $\left\{\frac{3 + 2\sqrt{6}}{3}, \frac{3 - 2\sqrt{6}}{3}\right\}$ **58.** 2012

Chapter 6 Test

1. -44 **2.** $14x - 4$ **3.** 616 convictions **4.** $\{-5\}$ **5.** $\{2\}$ **6.** $\varnothing$ **7.** $\{-15\}$ **8.** $y = \frac{Ax + A}{B}$ **9.** 2008 **10.** 63.8 **11.** fitness trainer: \$50,950; teacher: \$28,080 **12.** 5 years **13.** 20 prints; \$3.80 **14.** $\left\{\frac{15}{2}\right\}$ **15.** $\{3\}$ **16.** 6000 tule elk **17.** 137.5 lb per in^2 **18.** 4 hours

19. $\{x \mid x \leq -3\}$;

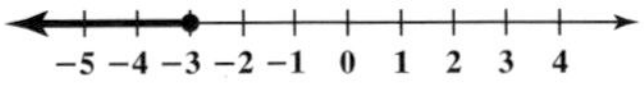

20. $\{x \mid x > 7\}$;

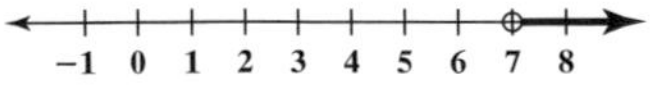

21. $\left\{x \,\middle|\, -2 \leq x < \frac{5}{2}\right\}$;

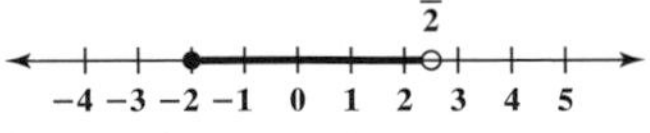

22. at least 92 **23.** $6x^2 - 7x - 20$ **24.** $(2x - 5)(x - 2)$ **25.** $\{-9, 4\}$ **26.** $\left\{\frac{-2 + \sqrt{2}}{2}, \frac{-2 - \sqrt{2}}{2}\right\}$ **27.** 2018 **28.** 2018 **29.** quite well

CHAPTER 7

Section 7.1

Check Point Exercises

1.

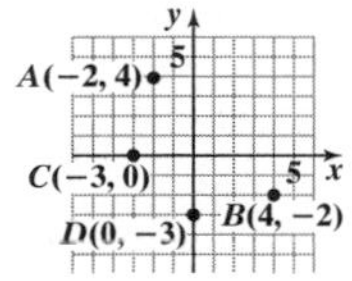

2.

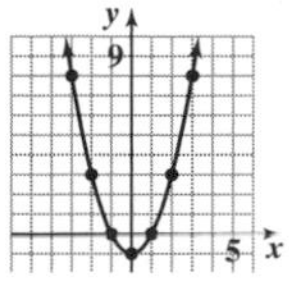

3. a. $y = 2x$

x	(x, y)
0	(0, 0)
2	(2, 4)
4	(4, 8)
6	(6, 12)
8	(8, 16)
10	(10, 20)
12	(12, 24)

$y = 10 + x$

x	(x, y)
0	(0, 10)
2	(2, 12)
4	(4, 14)
6	(6, 16)
8	(8, 18)
10	(10, 20)
12	(12, 22)

b.

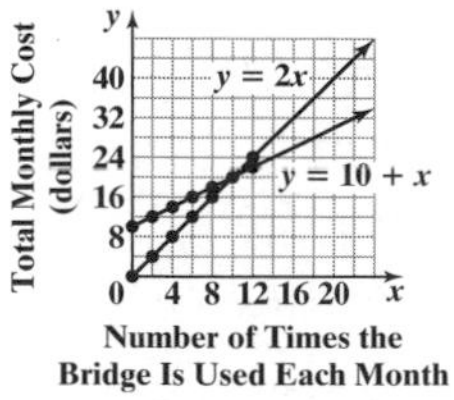

c. (10, 20); When the bridge is used 10 times during a month, the cost is $20 with or without the coupon book.

4. a. 73% **b.** 72.8%

5.

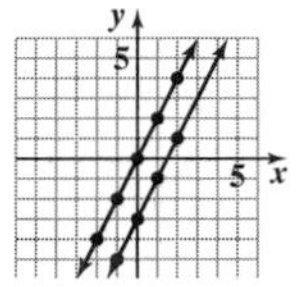

; The graph of g is the graph of f shifted down 3 units.

6. a. function **b.** function **c.** not a function **7. a.** 0 to 3 hours **b.** 3 to 13 hours **c.** 0.05 mg per 100 ml; after 3 hours **d.** None of the drug is left in the body. **e.** No vertical line intersects the graph in more than one point.

Exercise Set 7.1

1.

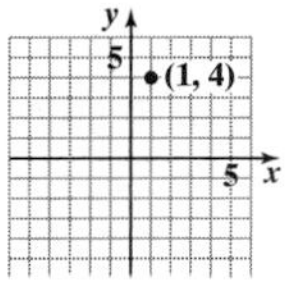

3.

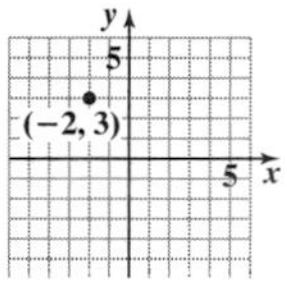

5.

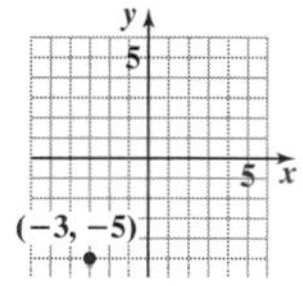

7.

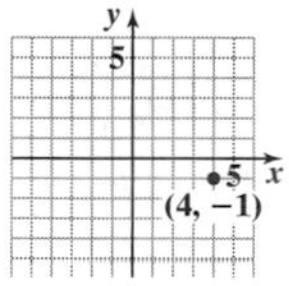

9.

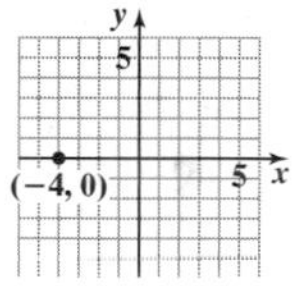

11.

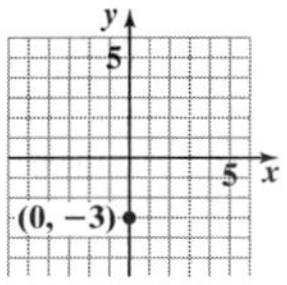

13.

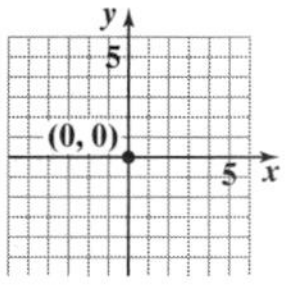

15.

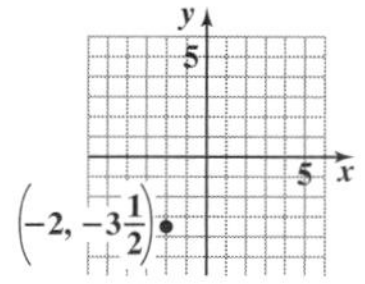

17.

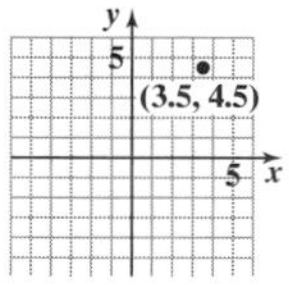

19.

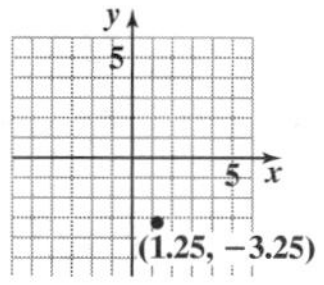

21.

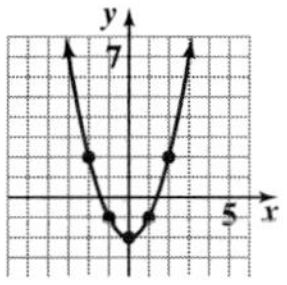

23.

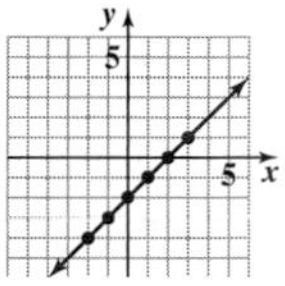

25.

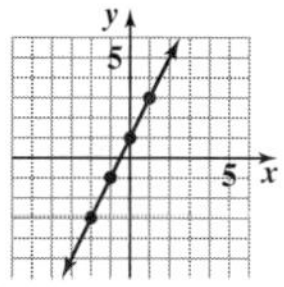

27.

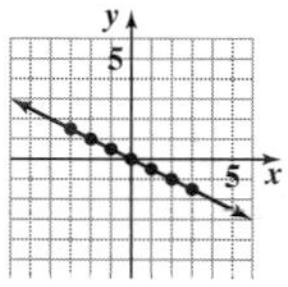

29.

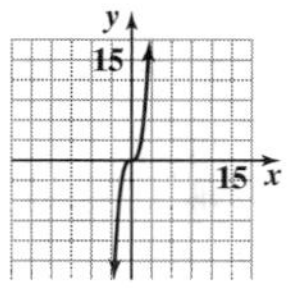

31.

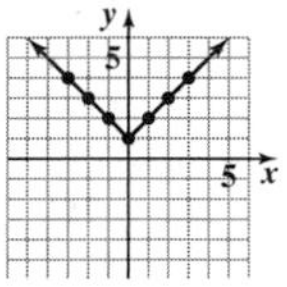

33. a. 4 **b.** −3 **35. a.** 19 **b.** −2 **37. a.** 5 **b.** 5 **39. a.** 53 **b.** 8 **41. a.** 26 **b.** 19

43.

x	$f(x) = x^2 - 1$
−2	3
−1	0
0	−1
1	0
2	3

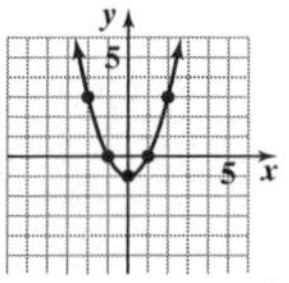

45.

x	$f(x) = x - 1$
−2	−3
−1	−2
0	−1
1	0
2	1

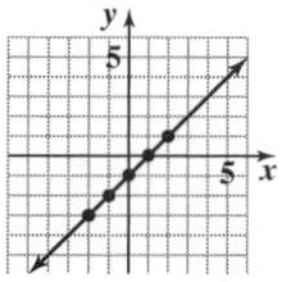

47.

x	$f(x) = (x - 2)^2$
0	4
1	1
2	0
3	1
4	4

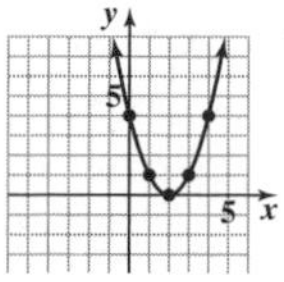

49.

x	$f(x) = x^3 + 1$
−3	−26
−2	−7
−1	0
0	1
1	2

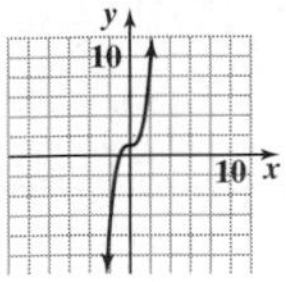

51. function **53.** function **55.** not a function **57.** function **59.** −2; 10 **61.** −38

63. $y = 2x + 4$

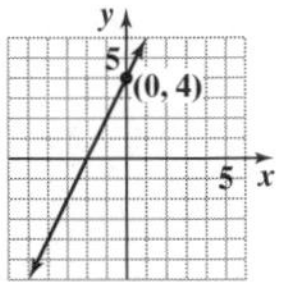

65. $y = 3 - x^2$

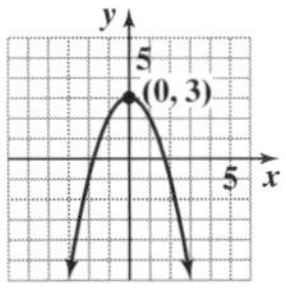

67. (91, 125); In 1991, 125 thousand acres were used for cultivation. **69.** 2000 and 2003 **71.** 2001; 25 thousand acres **73.** 1991 and 1992 **75. a.** 707; Approximately 707,000 bachelor's degrees were awarded to women in 2000.; (20, 707) **b.** a slight overestimation **77. a.** 68; Approximately 68,000 more bachelor's degrees were awarded to women than to men in 1990.; The points on the graphs with first coordinate 10 are 68 units apart. **b.** not very well **79. a.** 2001; 9200 hate crimes **b.** 9191 hate crimes **81.** 8123; (2, 8123) **89.** −2 **91.** 1

Section 7.2

Check Point Exercises

1.

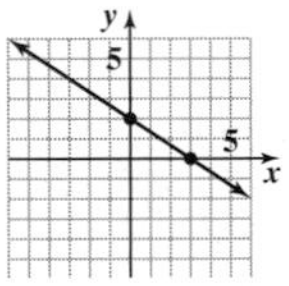

2. a. $m = 6$ **b.** $m = -\frac{7}{5}$

3.

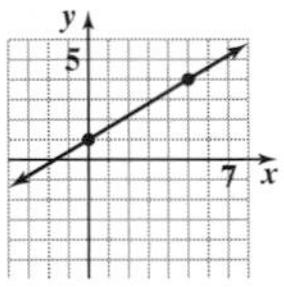

4.

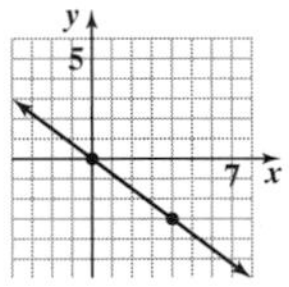

5.

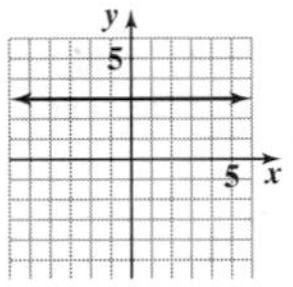

6.

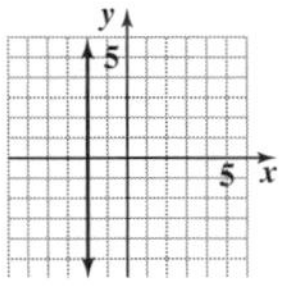

7. $\frac{3.5}{13} = \frac{7}{26} \approx 0.27$; The slope indicates that the number of men living alone is projected to increase by 0.27 million each year. **8.** $S(x) = 0.22x + 1$

Exercise Set 7.2

1.

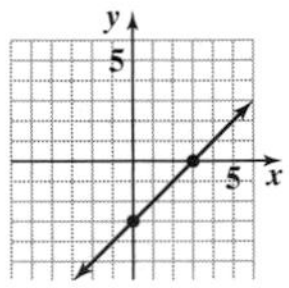

3.

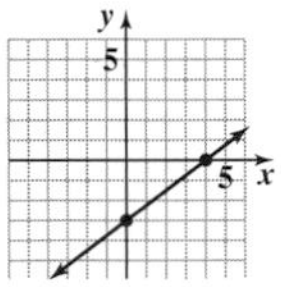

5.

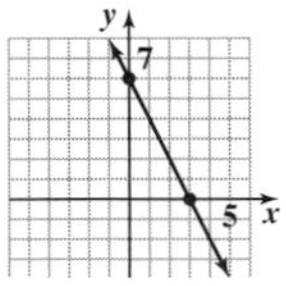

7.

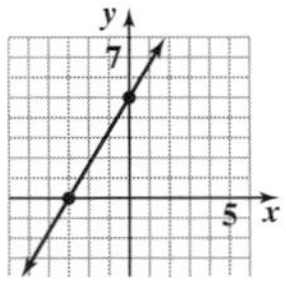

9. −1; falls **11.** $\frac{1}{4}$; rises **13.** −5; falls **15.** undefined; vertical **17.** −4; falls **19.** 0; horizontal

21.

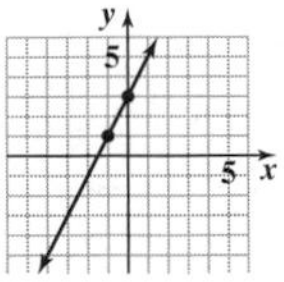

23.

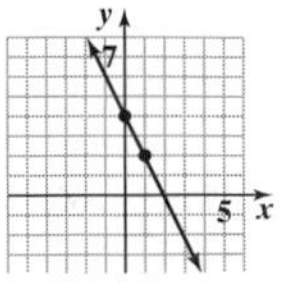

25.

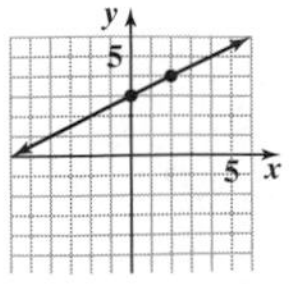

27.

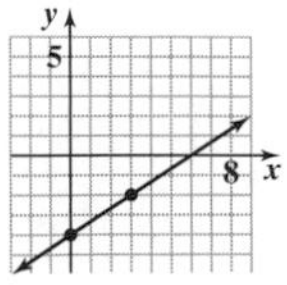

29.

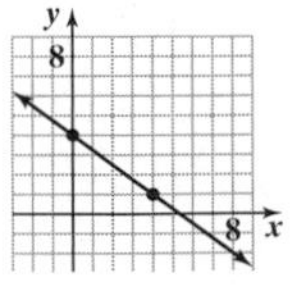

31. 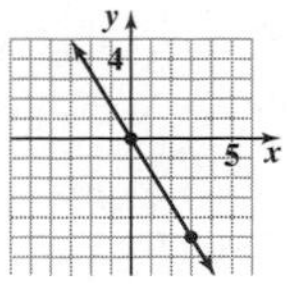

33. a. $y = -3x$ or $y = -3x + 0$ **b.** slope $= -3$; y-intercept $= 0$ **c.** 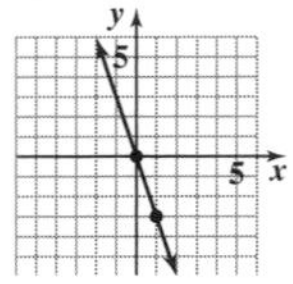

35. a. $y = \frac{4}{3}x$ or $y = \frac{4}{3}x + 0$ **b.** slope $= \frac{4}{3}$; y-intercept $= 0$ **c.** 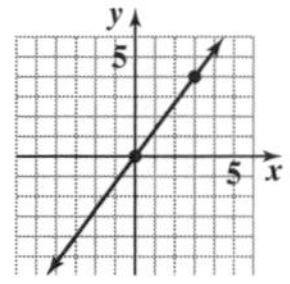

37. a. $y = -2x + 3$ **b.** slope $= -2$; y-intercept $= 3$ **c.** 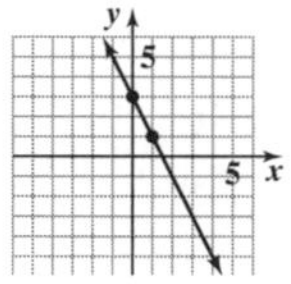

39. a. $y = -\frac{7}{2}x + 7$ **b.** slope $= -\frac{7}{2}$; y-intercept $= 7$ **c.** 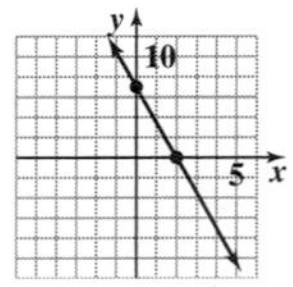

41. 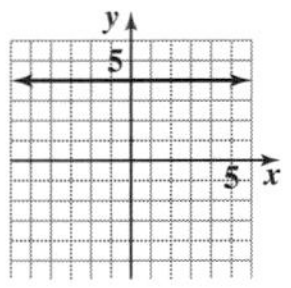 **43.** 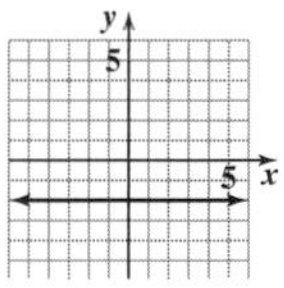 **45.** 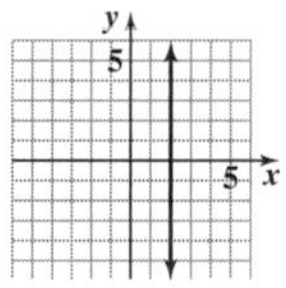 **47.** 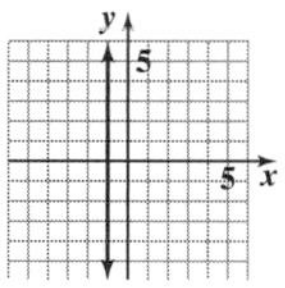

49. $m = -\frac{a}{b}$; falls **51.** undefined slope; vertical **53.** $m = -\frac{A}{B}$; $b = \frac{C}{B}$ **55.** -2 **57.** m_1, m_3, m_2, m_4 **59. a.** -0.075; Between 2000 and 2002, the average price decreased 7.5 cents per year. **b.** 0.24; Between 2002 and 2005, the average price increased 24 cents per year. **61. a.** 33; In 1999 (0 years after 1999), there were 33 million HIV/AIDS cases. **b.** 2; The number of HIV/AIDS cases increased by 2 million each year. **c.** $y = 2x + 33$ **d.** 55 million HIV/AIDS cases **73.** $F = \frac{9}{5}C + 32$

Section 7.3

Check Point Exercises

1. not a solution **2.** 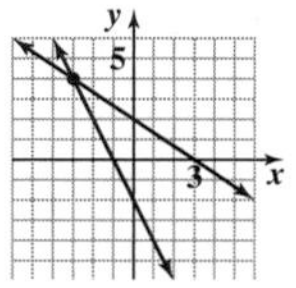 ; $\{(-3, 4)\}$ **3.** $\{(6, 11)\}$ **4.** $\{(1, -2)\}$ **5.** $\{(2, -1)\}$ **6.** $\{(2, -1)\}$ **7.** $\varnothing$

8. $\{(x,y) \mid y = 4x - 4\}$ or $\{(x,y) \mid 8x - 2y = 8\}$ **9. a.** $C(x) = 300{,}000 + 30x$ **b.** $R(x) = 80x$ **c.** (6000, 480,000); The company will break even if it produces and sells 6000 pairs of shoes.

Exercise Set 7.3

1. solution **3.** not a solution

5. 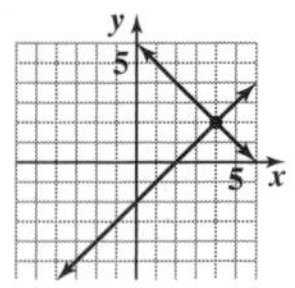 $\{(4, 2)\}$ **7.** 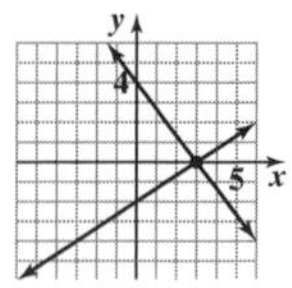 $\{(3, 0)\}$ **9.** 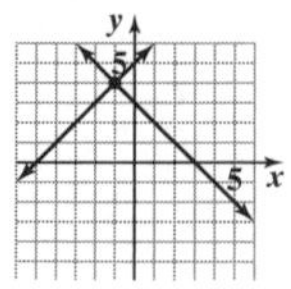 $\{(-1, 4)\}$ **11.** 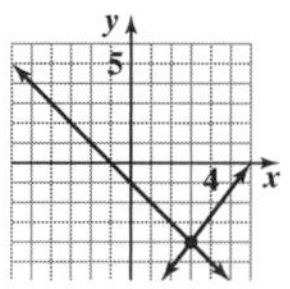 $\{(3, -4)\}$

13. $\{(1, 3)\}$ **15.** $\{(5, 1)\}$ **17.** $\{(2, 1)\}$ **19.** $\{(-1, 3)\}$ **21.** $\{(4, 5)\}$ **23.** $\left\{\left(-4, \frac{5}{4}\right)\right\}$ **25.** $\{(2, -1)\}$ **27.** $\{(3, 0)\}$ **29.** $\{(-4, 3)\}$ **31.** $\{(3, 1)\}$ **33.** $\{(1, -2)\}$ **35.** $\{(-5, -2)\}$ **37.** $\varnothing$ **39.** $\{(x,y) \mid y = 3x - 5\}$ or $\{(x,y) \mid 21x - 35 = 7y\}$ **41.** $\{(1, 4)\}$

43. $\{(x,y) \mid x + 3y = 2\}$ or $\{(x,y) \mid 3x + 9y = 6\}$ **45.** $y = x - 4$; $y = -\frac{1}{3}x + 4$ **47.** $\left\{\left(\frac{1}{a}, 3\right)\right\}$ **49.** $m = -4, b = 3$ **51.** 500 radios **53.** −6000; When the company produces and sells 200 radios, the loss is $6000. **55. a.** $P(x) = 20x - 10{,}000$ **b.** $190,000 **57. a.** $C(x) = 18{,}000 + 20x$ **b.** $R(x) = 80x$ **c.** (300, 24,000); When 300 canoes are produced and sold, both revenue and cost are $24,000. **59. a.** $C(x) = 30{,}000 + 2500x$ **b.** $R(x) = 3125x$ **c.** (48, 150,000); For 48 sold-out performances, both cost and revenue are $150,000. **61. a.** $y = -0.75x + 38$ **b.** $y = -x + 40$ **c.** 1993; 32% **63.** Pan pizza: 1120 calories; beef burrito: 430 calories **65.** Scrambled eggs: 366 mg cholesterol; Double Beef Whopper: 175 mg cholesterol **67.** 50 rooms with kitchen facilities, 150 rooms without kitchen facilities **79.** downstairs: 3 people; upstairs: 5 people

Section 7.4

Check Point Exercises

1.

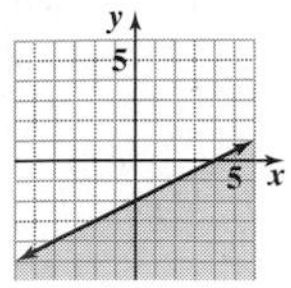

2. $y > -\frac{3}{4}x$

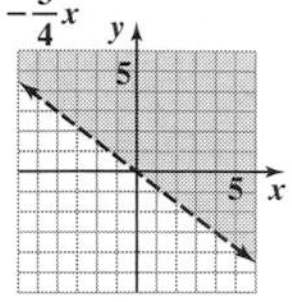

3. a. $y > 1$

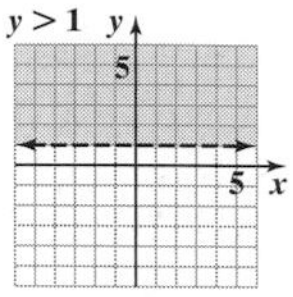

b. $x \le -2$

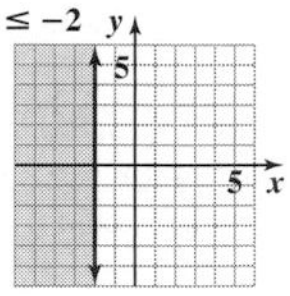

4. $B = (60, 20)$; Using $T = 60$ and $P = 20$, each of the three inequalities for grasslands is true: $60 \ge 35$, true; $5(60) - 7(20) \ge 70$, true; $3(60) - 35(20) \le -140$, true.

5. $x + 2y > 4$, $2x - 3y \le -6$

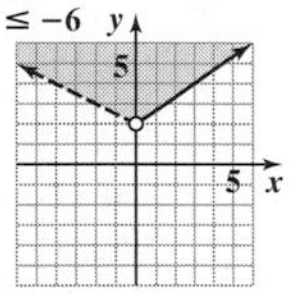

6.

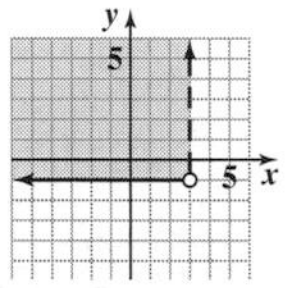

Exercise Set 7.4

1. $x + y \ge 2$

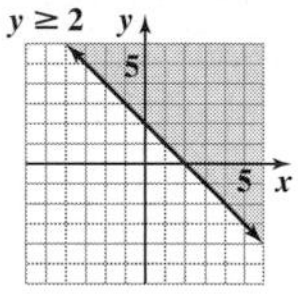

3.

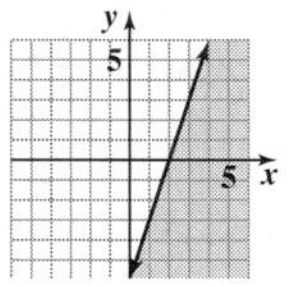

5.

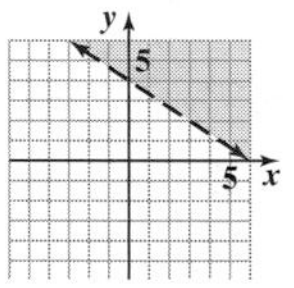

7.

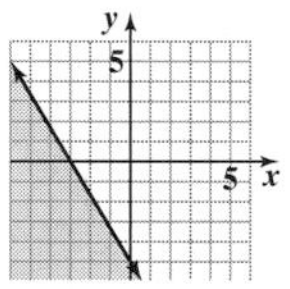

9.

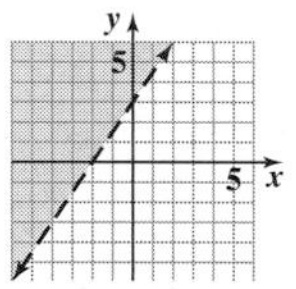

11. $y > \frac{1}{3}x$

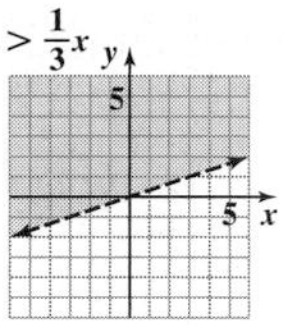

13. $y \le 3x + 2$

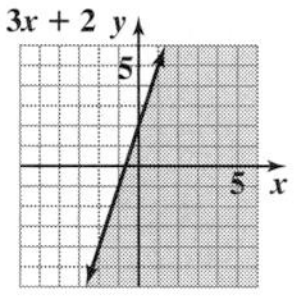

15. $y < -\frac{1}{4}x$

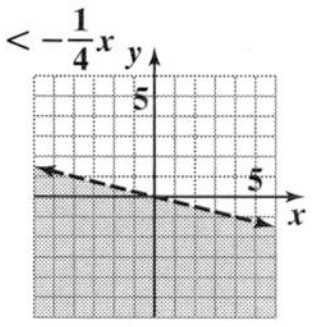

17. $x \le 2$

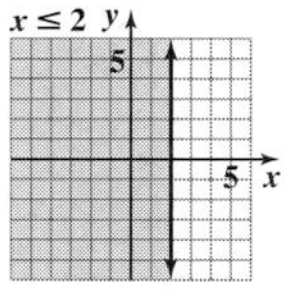

19. $y > -4$

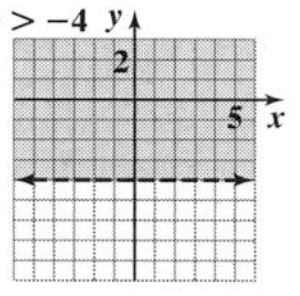

21. $y \ge 0$

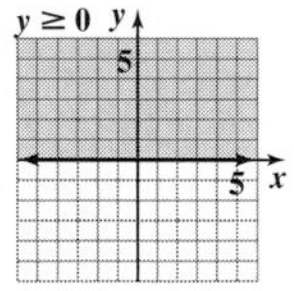

23. $3x + 6y \le 6$, $2x + y \le 8$

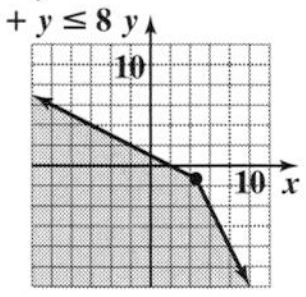

25.

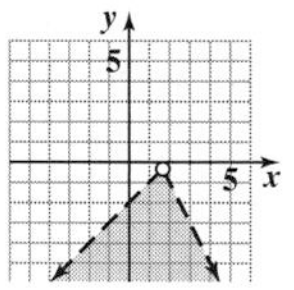

27.

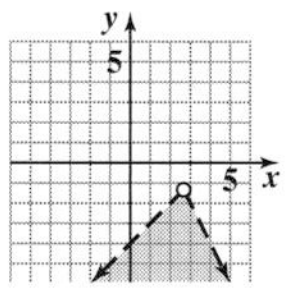

29.

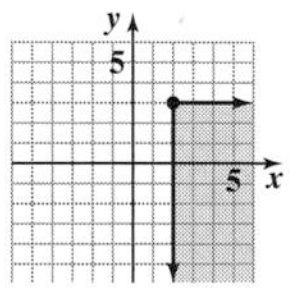

31.

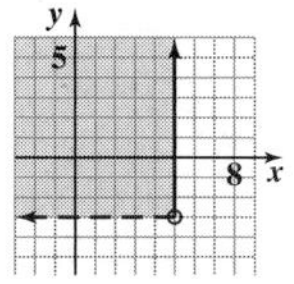

33.

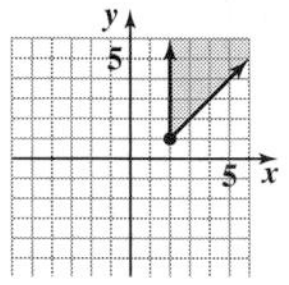

35. $y > 2x - 3$, $y < -x + 6$

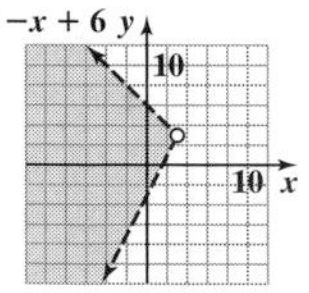

37. $x + 2y \le 4$, $y \ge x - 3$

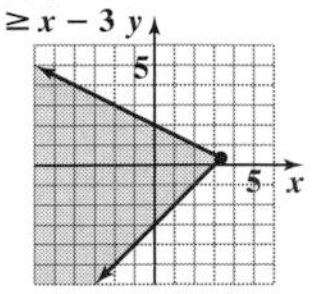

39. $y \ge -2x + 4$

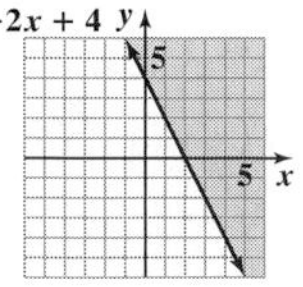

41. $x + y \le 4$, $3x + y \le 6$

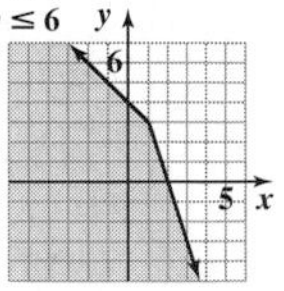

43. $y > \frac{3}{2}x - 2$ or $y < 4$

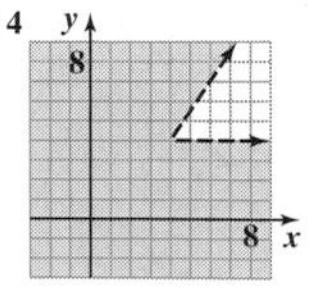

45. a. $A = (20, 150)$; A 20-year-old with a heart rate of 150 beats per minute is within the target range. **b.** $10 \le 20 \le 70$, true; $150 \ge 0.7(220 - 20)$, true; $150 \le 0.8(220 - 20)$, true **47.** $10 \le a \le 70$; $H \ge 0.6(220 - a)$; $H \le 0.7(220 - a)$
49. a. $50x + 150y > 2000$
b.
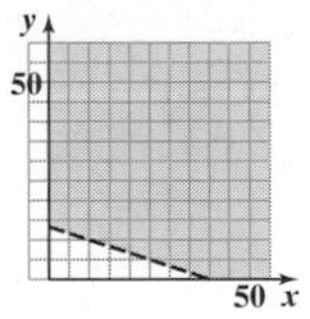

$50x + 150y > 2000$

51. a. 27.1 **b.** overweight **59.** $y > x - 3$; $y \le x$ **61.** no solution **63.** infinitely many solutions

Section 7.5

Check Point Exercises

1. $z = 25x + 55y$ **2.** $x + y \le 80$ **3.** $30 \le x \le 80$; $10 \le y \le 30$; objective function: $z = 25x + 55y$; constraints: $x + y \le 80$; $30 \le x \le 80$; $10 \le y \le 30$ **4.** 50 bookshelves and 30 desks; $2900

Exercise Set 7.5

1. (1, 2): 17; (2, 10): 70; (7, 5): 65; (8, 3): 58; maximum: $z = 70$; minimum: $z = 17$
3. (0, 0): 0; (0, 8): 400; (4, 9): 610; (8, 0): 320; maximum: $z = 610$; minimum: $z = 0$

5. a.
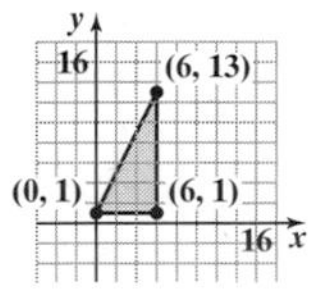

b. (0, 1): 1; (6, 13): 19; (6, 1): 7
c. maximum of 19 at $x = 6$ and $y = 13$; minimum of 1 at $x = 0$ and $y = 1$

7. a.
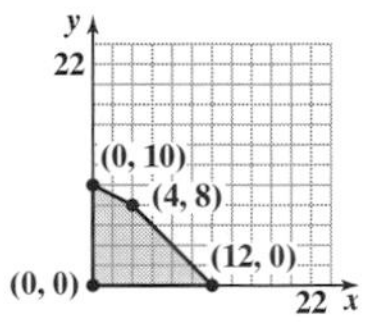

b. (0, 10): 100; (4, 8): 104; (12, 0): 72; (0, 0): 0
c. maximum of 104 at $x = 4$ and $y = 8$; minimum of 0 at $x = 0$ and $y = 0$

9. a.
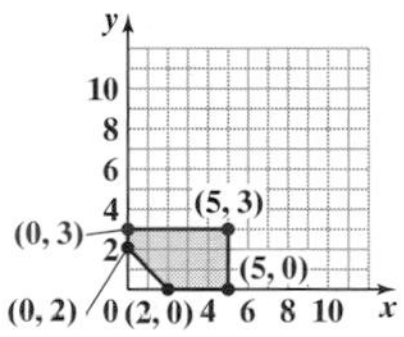

b. (0, 3): −6; (0, 2): −4; (2, 0): 10; (5, 0): 25; (5, 3): 19
c. maximum value: 25 at $x = 5$ and $y = 0$

11. a.
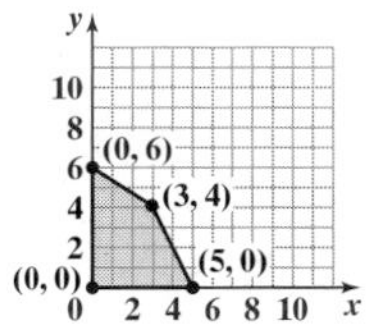

b. (0, 6): 72, (0, 0): 0; (5, 0): 50; (3, 4): 78
c. maximum value: 78 at $x = 3$ and $y = 4$

13. a. $z = 10x + 7y$
b. $x + y \le 20$; $x \ge 3$; $x \le 8$
c.
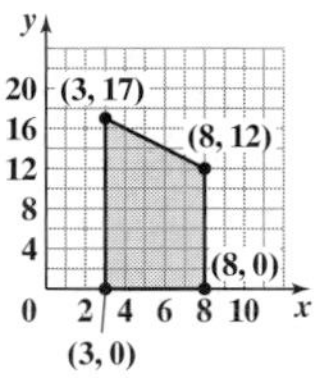

d. (3, 0): 30; (8, 0): 80; (3, 17): 149; (8, 12): 164
e. 8; 12; $164

15. 300 cartons of food and 200 cartons of clothing **17.** 50 students and 100 parents

Section 7.6

Check Point Exercises

1.
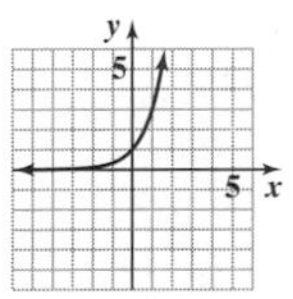

$f(x) = 3^x$

2. a. the exponential function g **b.** f: fairly well; g: not very well **3.** 6.8%

4. $x = 3^y$;
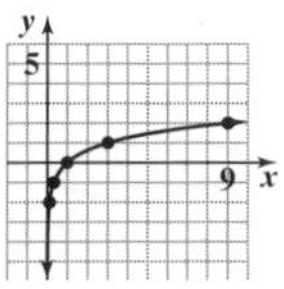

5. 34°; extremely well **6.**
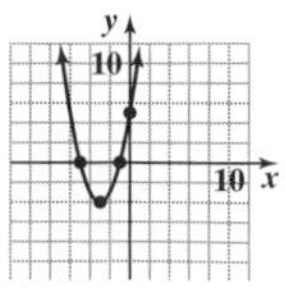

7. 45 years old; 190 accidents per 50 million miles driven

Exercise Set 7.6

1.
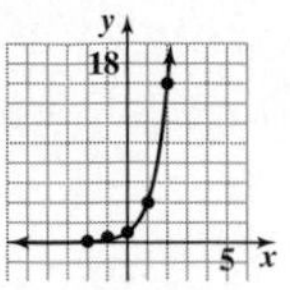

3.
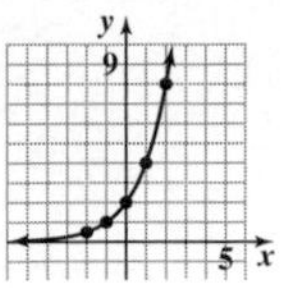

5.
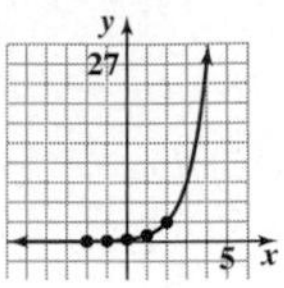

7. $x = 4^y$;
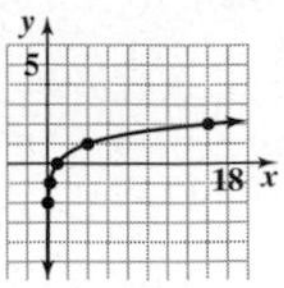

9. a. upward **b.** $(-4, -9)$ **c.** $(-7, 0)$ and $(-1, 0)$ **d.** $(0, 7)$ **e.**
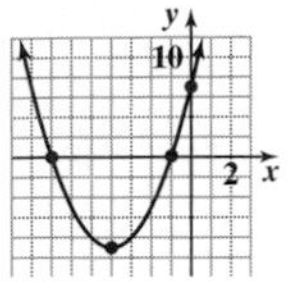

11. a. upward **b.** $(1, -9)$ **c.** $(-2, 0)$ and $(4, 0)$ **d.** $(0, -8)$ **e.**
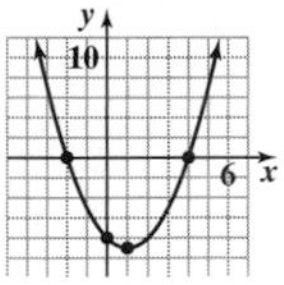

13. a. downward **b.** $(2, 1)$ **c.** $(1, 0)$ and $(3, 0)$ **d.** $(0, -3)$ **e.**
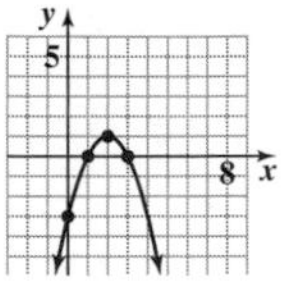

15. a.
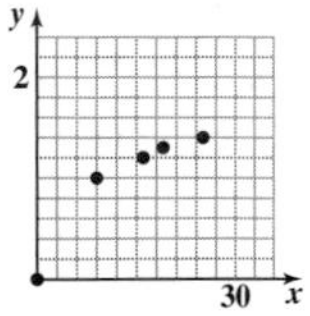

b. logarithmic

17. a.
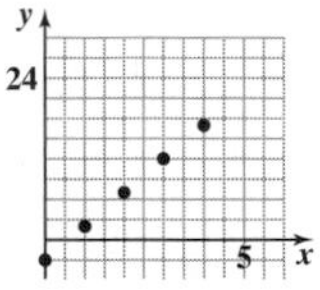

b. linear

19. a.
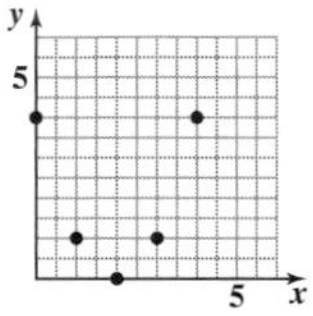

b. quadratic

21. a.
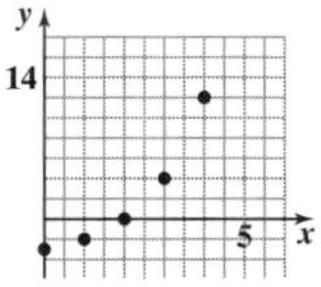

b. exponential

23.
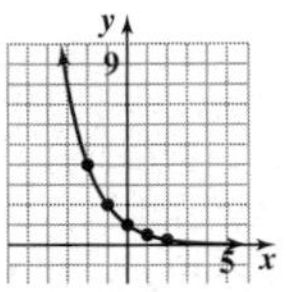

decreasing, although rate of decrease is slowing down

25.
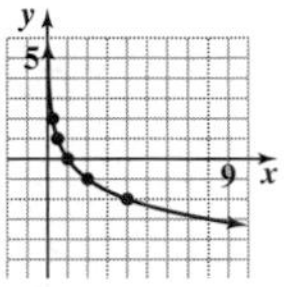

decreasing, although rate of decrease is slowing down

27. a. downward **b.** $(1, 7)$ **c.** $(-0.9, 0)$ and $(2.9, 0)$ **d.** $(0, 5)$ **e.**
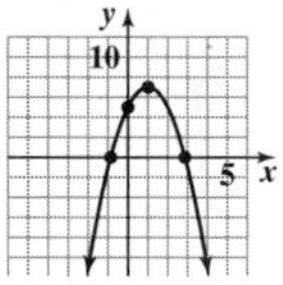

29. $(3, 2)$ **31. a.** increasing more and more rapidly **b.** $f(x) = 1.402(1.078)^x$ **c.** 22.6%; fairly well, small overestimation **33.** linear **35.** 64%; slight overestimation **37. a.** 95.3% **b.** Height increases rapidly at first and then more slowly. **39. a.** The data decrease then increase. **b.** $f(x) = 0.22x^2 - 0.49x + 7.68$ **c.** 2000; 7.4 million; extremely well **47.** c **49.** 1

Chapter 7 Review Exercises

1.
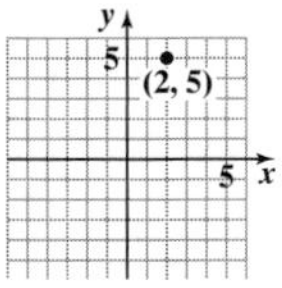

2.
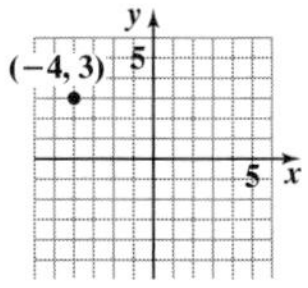

3.
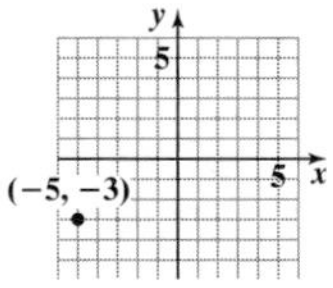

4.
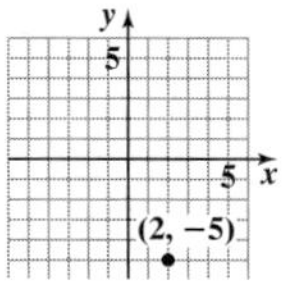

5.
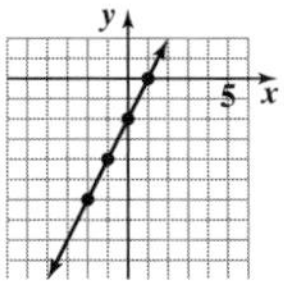

6.
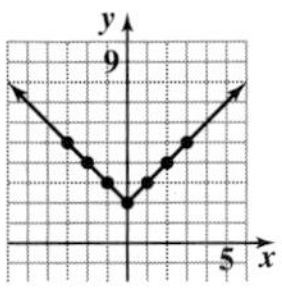

7.
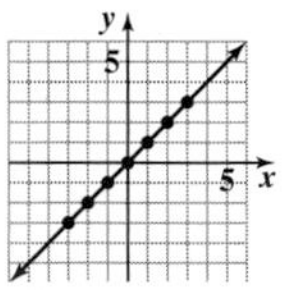

8. 3 **9.** 26 **10.** 30 **11.** −64 **12.**

x	$f(x) = \frac{1}{2}\lvert x \rvert$
−6	3
−4	2
−2	1
0	0
2	1
4	2
6	3

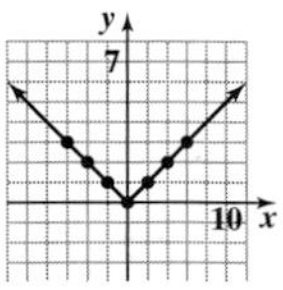

13.

x	$f(x) = x^2 - 2$
−2	2
−1	−1
0	−2
1	−1
2	2

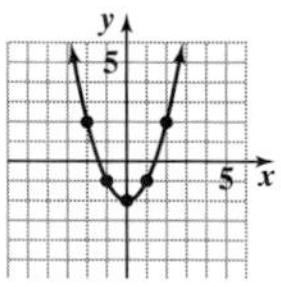

14. y is a function of x. **15.** y is not a function of x. **16. a.** 3.1; In 1960, Jewish Americans comprised about 3.1% of the U.S. population. **b.** 1940; 3.7% **c.** 1900; 1.4% **d.** No vertical line intersects the graph in more than one point. **e.** The percentage of Jewish Americans in the U.S. population was increasing until 1940 and has been decreasing ever since.

17. 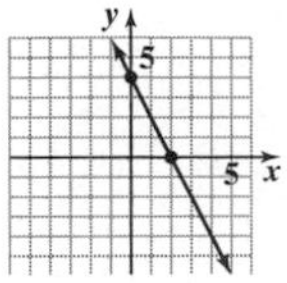

18. 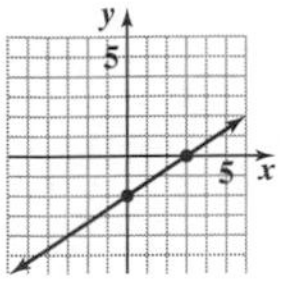

19. 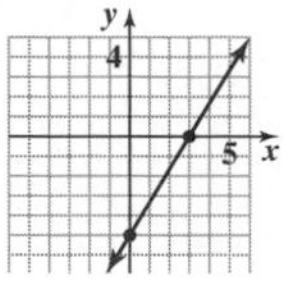

20. $-\frac{1}{2}$; falls **21.** 3; rises **22.** 0; horizontal **23.** undefined; vertical

24. 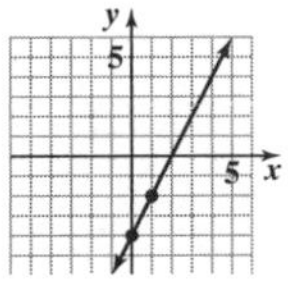

25. 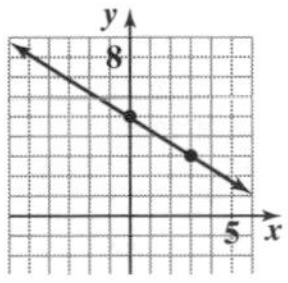

26. 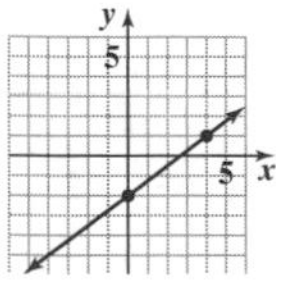

27. 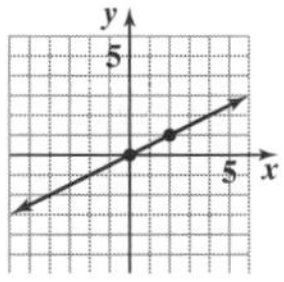

28. a. $y = -2x$

b. slope: -2; y-intercept: 0

c. 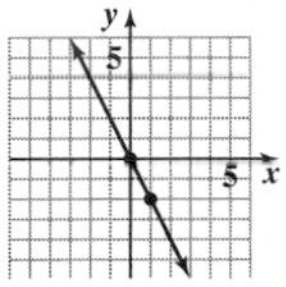

29. a. $y = \frac{5}{3}x$

b. slope: $\frac{5}{3}$; y-intercept: 0

c. 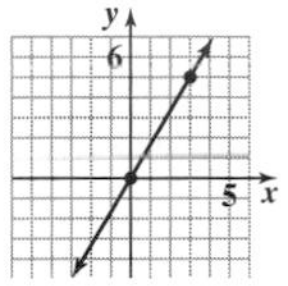

30. a. $y = -\frac{3}{2}x + 2$

b. slope: $-\frac{3}{2}$; y-intecept: 2

c. 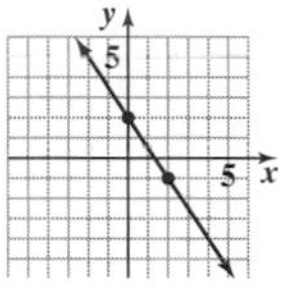

31. 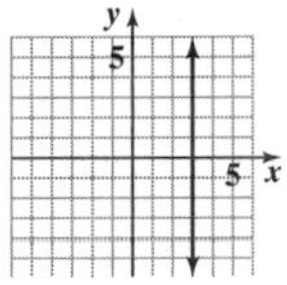

32. 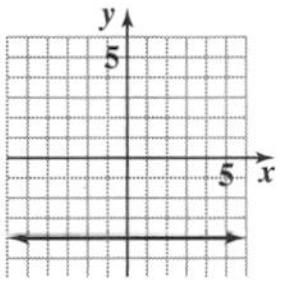

33. 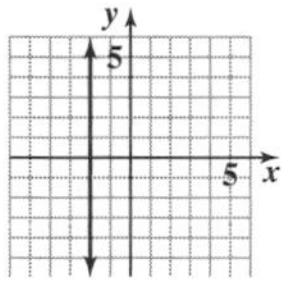

34. a. 2970; In 1990 (0 years after 1990), the average credit card debt was \$2970. **b.** 453; The average credit card debt increased \$453 per year. **c.** $y = 453x + 2970$ **d.** \$12,030 **35.** $\{(2, 3)\}$ **36.** $\{(-2, -3)\}$ **37.** $\{(3, 2)\}$ **38.** $\{(4. -2)\}$ **39.** $\{(1, 5)\}$ **40.** $\{(2, 3)\}$ **41.** $\{(-9, 3)\}$ **42.** $\{(3, 4)\}$ **43.** $\{(2, -3)\}$ **44.** $\varnothing$ **45.** $\{(3, -1)\}$ **46.** $\{(x,y)|3x - 2y = 6\}$ or $\{(x,y)|6x - 4y = 12\}$ **47. a.** $C(x) = 60{,}000 + 200x$ **b.** $R(x) = 450x$ **c.** (240, 108,000); This means the company will break even if it produces and sells 240 desks. **48.** Japan: 73.6 yr; Switzerland: 72.8 yr

49. 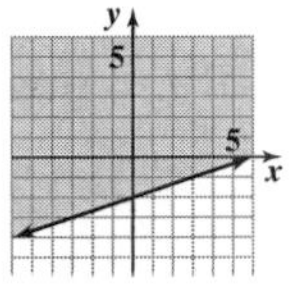

50. 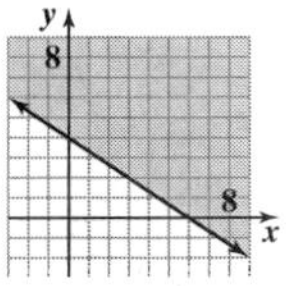

51. 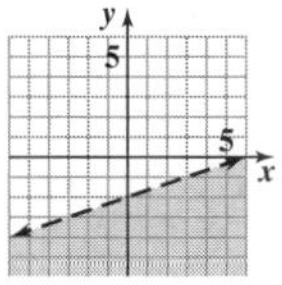

52. 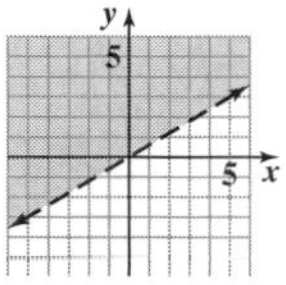

53. 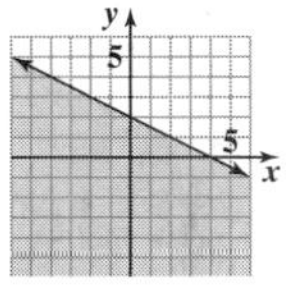

54. 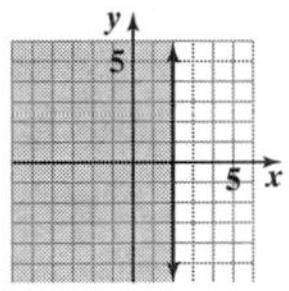

55. 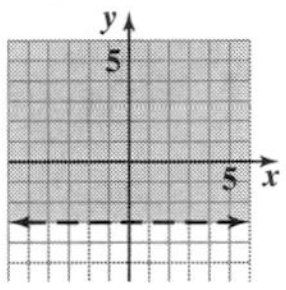

56. 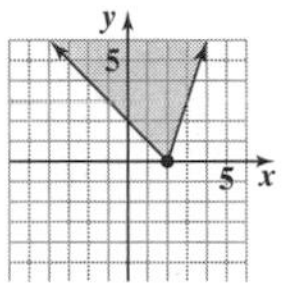

57. 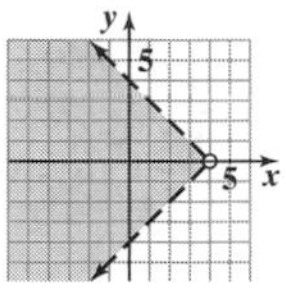

58. 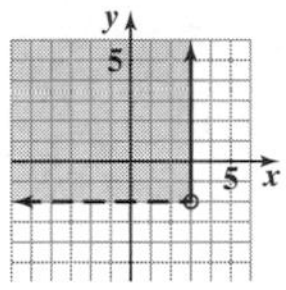

59. 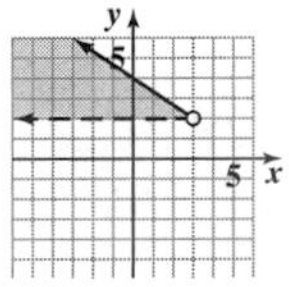

60. 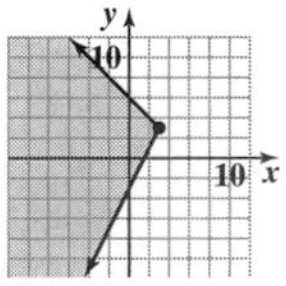

61. 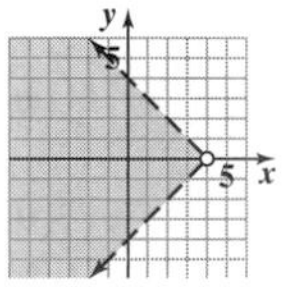

62. (1, 0): 2; $\left(\frac{1}{2}, \frac{1}{2}\right)$: $\frac{5}{2}$; (2, 2): 10; (4, 0): 8; maximum: 10; minimum: 2

63. a. 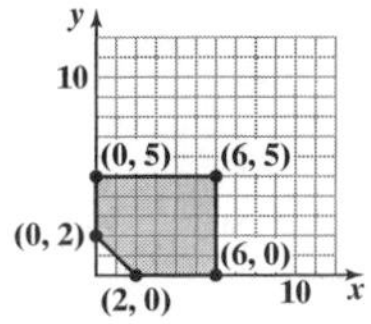

b. (0, 2): 6; (0, 5): 15; (6, 5): 27; (6, 0): 12; (2, 0): 4
c. maximum of 27 at $x = 6$ and $y = 5$; minimum of 4 at $x = 2$ and $y = 0$

64. a. $z = 500x + 350y$
b. $x + y \le 200$; $x \ge 10$; $y \ge 80$
c. 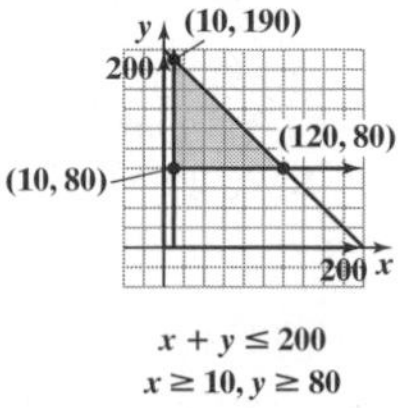

d. (10, 80): 33,000; (10, 190): 71,500; (120, 80): 88,000
e. 120; 80; 88,000

65.
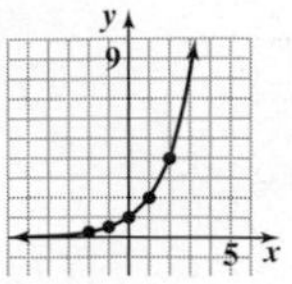

66.
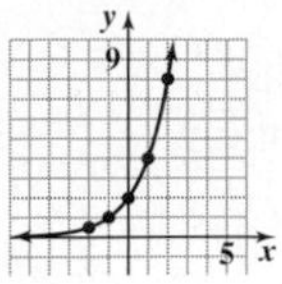

67. $x = 2^y$;
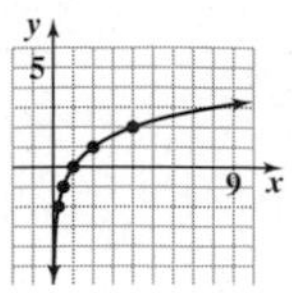

68. a. upward
b. $(3, -16)$
c. $(-1, 0)$ and $(7, 0)$
d. $(0, -7)$
e.
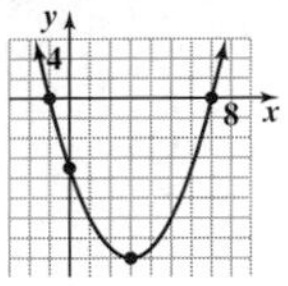

69. a. downward
b. $(-1, 4)$
c. $(-3, 0)$ and $(1, 0)$
d. $(0, 3)$
e.
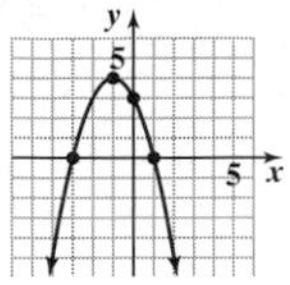

70. a.
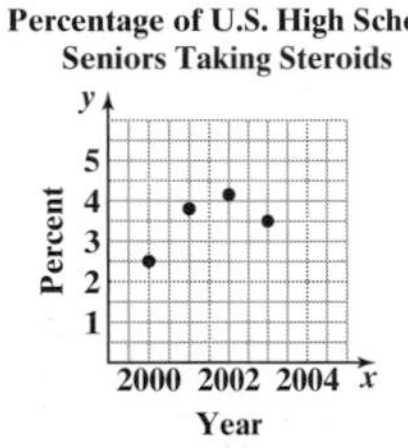

b. quadratic

71. a.

b. exponential

72. a.
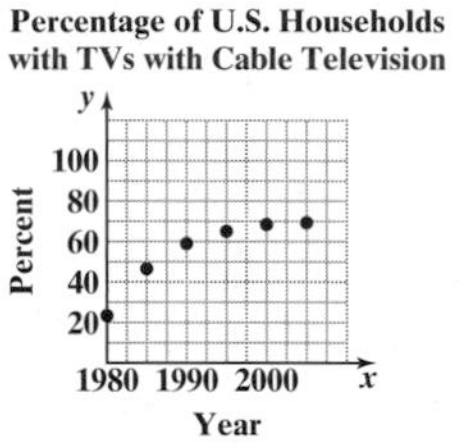

b. logarithmic

73. a.
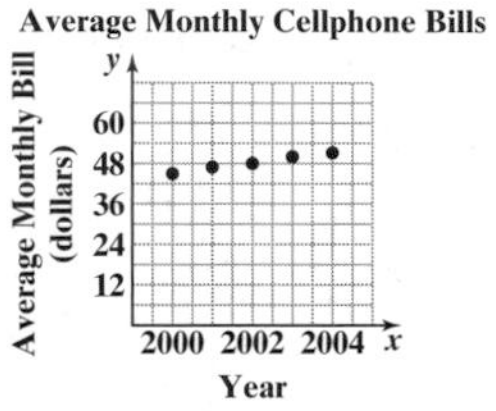

b. linear

74. 559 ppm; nearly double **75.** 210.6 million; slightly more than twice the 2003 population **76. a.** -1.7; The percentage of companies performing drug tests is decreasing by 1.7 each year. **b.** logarithmic model

Chapter 7 Test

1.
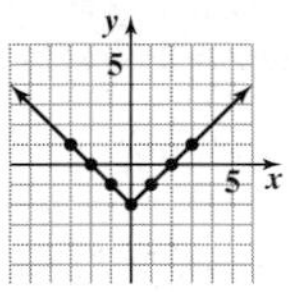

2. 21
3. y is not a function of x. **4.** y is a function of x.
5. a. Yes; no vertical line intersects the graph in more than one point. **b.** 0; The eagle was on the ground after 15 seconds. **c.** 45 meters **d.** between 3 and 12 seconds

6.
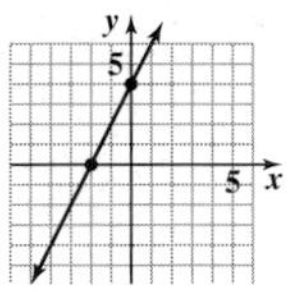

7. $m = 3$

8.
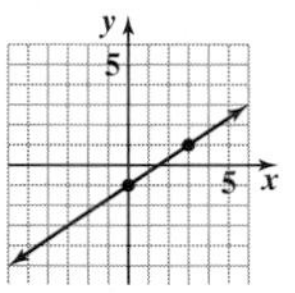

9.
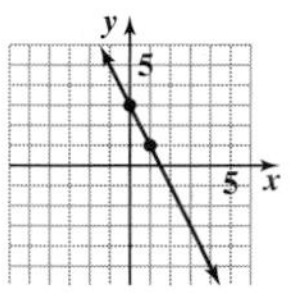

10. a. 180; In 2000 (0 years after 2000), an American adult read a newspaper an average of 180 hours per year. **b.** -2; The average number of hours decreased 2 hours per year. **c.** $y = -2x + 180$ **d.** 156 hours **11.** $\{(2, 4)\}$ **12.** $\{(1, -3)\}$ **13.** $\{(6, -5)\}$
14. a. $C(x) = 360{,}000 + 850x$ **b.** $R(x) = 1150x$ **c.** (1200, 1,380,000); The company will break even if it produces and sells 1200 computers.

15.
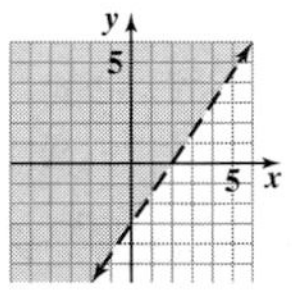

16.
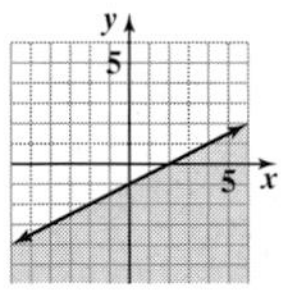

17.
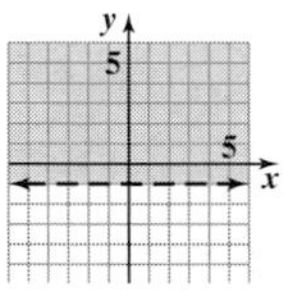

18.
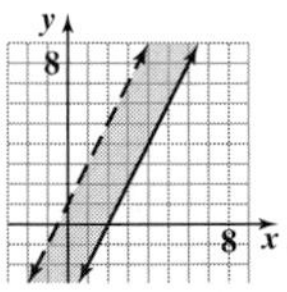

19. (2, 0): 6; (2, 6): 18; (6, 3): 24; (8, 0): 24; maximum: 24; minimum: 6 **20.** 26 **21.** 50 regular skis, 100 deluxe skis; $35,000

22.
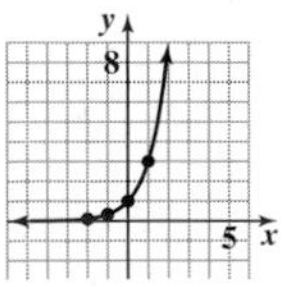

23. $x = 3^y$;
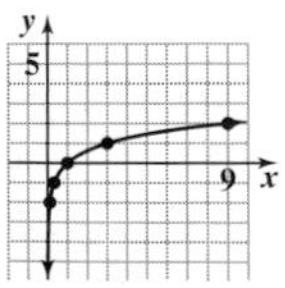

24.
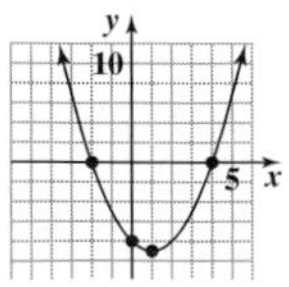

25. linear **26.** logarithmic **27.** exponential **28.** quadratic **29. a.** 159 million; extremely well. **b.** 375 million **30. a.** 15.3; The number of Internet users is increasing by 15.3 million each year. **b.** logarithmic model **c.** f: 137.3 million; g: 141.3 million; logarithmic model; yes

CHAPTER 8

Section 8.1

Check Point Exercises

1. 12.5% **2.** 2.3% **3. a.** 0.67 **b.** 2.5 **4. a.** \$75.60 **b.** \$1335.60 **5. a.** \$133 **b.** \$247 **6.** \$4365 **7. a.** $66\frac{2}{3}\%$ **b.** 40% **8.** 35% **9.** 20% **10. a.** \$1152 **b.** 4% decrease

Exercise Set 8.1

1. 40% **3.** 25% **5.** 37.5% **7.** 2.5% **9.** 11.25% **11.** 59% **13.** 38.44% **15.** 287% **17.** 1487% **19.** 10,000% **21.** 0.72 **23.** 0.436 **25.** 1.3 **27.** 0.02 **29.** 0.005 **31.** 0.00625 **33.** 0.625 **35.** 6 **37.** 7.2 **39.** 5 **41.** 170 **43.** 20% **45.** 12% **47. a.** \$1008 **b.** \$17,808 **49. a.** \$103.20 **b.** \$756.80 **51.** \$4815 **53.** \$2442.50 **55.** \$7030 **57.** \$15,220 **59. a.** \$1530 **b.** \$1405 **c.** 14.7% **61.** 56.1% **63.** 50% **65.** 15% **67.** no; 2% decrease **77.** \$2588.93

Section 8.2

Check Point Exercises

1. \$150 **2.** \$336 **3.** \$2091 **4.** 18% **5.** \$3846.16 **6. a.** \$1200 **b.** \$3800 **c.** 15.8%

Exercise Set 8.2

1. \$240 **3.** \$10.80 **5.** \$318.75 **7.** \$426.25 **9.** \$3420 **11.** \$38,350 **13.** \$9390 **15.** 7.5% **17.** 9% **19.** 31.3% **21.** \$5172.42 **23.** \$8917.20 **25.** \$4509.59 **27. a.** \$93.33 **b.** \$1906.67 **c.** 7.3% **29. a.** \$1560 **b.** \$10,440 **c.** 7.5% **31.** $r = \frac{A - P}{Pt}$ **33.** $P = \frac{A}{1 + rt}$ **35. a.** \$247.50 **b.** \$4247.50 **37.** 21.4% **39.** \$2654.87 **45. a.** $A = 275t + 5000$ **b.** Answers will vary; an example is: The rate of change of the future value per year is \$275.

Section 8.3

Check Point Exercises

1. a. \$1216.65 **b.** \$216.65 **2. a.** \$6253.23 **b.** \$2053.23 **3. a.** \$14,859.47 **b.** \$14,918.25 **4.** \$6189.55 **5. a.** \$6628.28 **b.** 10.5% **6.** ≈ 8.24%

Exercise Set 8.3

1. a. \$10,816 **b.** \$816 **3. a.** \$3655.21 **b.** \$655.21 **5. a.** \$12,795.12 **b.** \$3295.12 **7. a.** \$5149.12 **b.** \$649.12 **9. a.** \$1855.10 **b.** \$355.10 **11. a.** \$49,189.33 **b.** \$29,189.33 **13. a.** \$13,116.51 **b.** \$13,140.67 **c.** \$13,157.04 **d.** \$13,165.31 **15.** 7% compounded monthly **17.** \$8374.84 **19.** \$7528.59 **21. a.** \$10,457.65 **b.** 4.6% **23.** 6.1% **25.** 6.2% **27.** 6.2% **29.** 8.3%; 8.25%; 8% compounded monthly **31.** 5.6%; 5.5%; 5.5% compounded semiannually **33.** 22.5 yr **35.** 4.3 yr **37.** 8.3 yr **39. a.** ≈ \$4,117,800,000 **b.** ≈ \$4,277,900,000 **41.** \$65,728.51 **43.** \$21,679.39 **51.** \$8544.49

Section 8.4

Check Point Exercises

1. a. \$6620 **b.** \$620 **2. a.** \$777,170 **b.** \$657,170 **3. a.** \$333,946 **b.** \$291,946 **4. a.** \$187 **b.** deposits: \$40,392; interest: \$59,608 **5. a.** high: \$63.38; low: \$42.37 **b.** \$2160 **c.** 1.5%; This is much lower than a bank account paying 3.5%. **d.** 7,203,200 shares **e.** high: \$49.94; low: \$48.33 **f.** \$49.50 **g.** The closing price is up \$0.03 from the previous day's closing price. **h.** ≈ \$1.34

Exercise Set 8.4

1. a. \$66,132 **b.** \$26,132 **3. a.** \$702,528 **b.** \$542,528 **5. a.** \$50,226 **b.** \$32,226 **7. a.** \$9076 **b.** \$4076 **9. a.** \$28,850 **b.** \$4850 **11. a.** \$4530 **b.** deposits: \$81,540; interest: \$58,460 **13. a.** \$1323 **b.** deposits: \$158,760; interest: \$41,240 **15. a.** \$356 **b.** deposits: \$170,880; interest: \$829,120 **17. a.** \$920 **b.** deposits: \$18,400; interest: \$1600 **19. a.** high: \$73.25; low: \$45.44 **b.** \$840 **c.** 2.2%; Answers will vary. **d.** 591,500 shares **e.** high: \$56.38; low: \$54.38 **f.** \$55.50 **g.** \$1.25 increase **h.** ≈ \$3.26 **21. a.** \$30,000 **b.** \$30,000 **23. a.** \$287 **b.** with: \$6254; without: \$7115 **c.** with: 12.5%; without: 14.2% **25.** $P = \frac{Ar}{(1 + r)^t - 1}$; the deposit at the end of each year that yields A dollars after t years with interest rate r compounded annually **27. a.** \$11,617 **b.** \$1617 **29. a.** \$87,052 **b.** \$63,052 **31. a.** \$693,031 **b.** \$293,031 **33. a.** \$401 **b.** deposits: \$3208; interest: \$292 **35.** \$641; \$3,653,860

Section 8.5

Check Point Exercises

1. a. \$13,720 **b.** \$19,180 **c.** \$5180 **2.** ≈ 13.5% **3. a.** ≈ \$2057.85 **b.** \$9597.15 **4. a.** ≈ \$1885.18 **b.** \$9769.82 **5. a.** \$59.52 **b.** \$4849.52 **c.** \$135 **6.** unpaid balance method: \$113.40; previous balance method: \$122.40; average daily balance method: \$115.43

Exercise Set 8.5

1. a. \$22,000 **b.** \$29,600 **c.** \$2600 **3. a.** \$1000 **b.** \$1420 **c.** \$320 **5.** 12.5% **7.** 14.5% **9.** 13.0% **11. a.** \$17,000

b. $22,133 **c.** $4633 **d.** 10.0% **13. a.** $1805.73 **b.** $11,534.62 **c.** $1686.11 **d.** $11,654.24 **15. a.** $11.05 **b.** $1013.05 **c.** ≈ $28 **17. a.** $4.96 **b.** $618.61 **c.** $61.86 **19. a.** $7.50 **b.** $45 **c.** $13.75 **31.** b **33.** Answers will vary. **35. a.** 31 days; $376.26 **b.** $4.89 **c.** $471.04

Section 8.6

Check Point Exercises

1. a. $1627 **b.** $117,360 **c.** $148,860

2.

Payment Number	Interest Payment	Principal Payment	Balance of Loan
1	$1166.67	$383.33	$199,616.67
2	$1164.43	$385.57	$199,231.10

3. a. payment: $367; interest: $2616 **b.** payment: $278; interest: $5016 **c.** Monthly payments are less with the longer-term loan, but there is more interest with this loan.

Exercise Set 8.6

1. a. $44,000 **b.** $176,000 **c.** $5280 **d.** $1171 **e.** $245,560 **3.** $60,120 **5.** 20-year at 7.5%; $106,440 **7.** Mortgage A; $11,300 **9. a.** $210 **b.** $840 **11. a.** $137; lower monthly payment **b.** $732; less interest **13.** monthly payment: $386; total interest: $432; $176 more each month; $408 less interest

15. a. monthly payment: $244.13; total interest: $1718.24

b.

Payment Number	Interest	Principal	Loan Balance
1	$66.67	$177.46	$9822.54
2	$65.48	$178.65	$9643.89
3	$64.29	$179.84	$9464.05

17. a. monthly payment: $347.13; total interest: $43,311.20

b.

Payment Number	Interest	Principal	Loan Balance
1	$283.33	$63.80	$39,936.20
2	$282.88	$64.25	$39,871.95
3	$282.43	$64.70	$39,807.25

c. $148.81 more each month; $23,798.40 less interest

27.

$$P\left(1+\frac{r}{n}\right)^{nt} = \frac{\text{PMT}\left[\left(1+\frac{r}{n}\right)^{nt}-1\right]}{\frac{r}{n}}$$

$$P\left(\frac{r}{n}\right)\left(1+\frac{r}{n}\right)^{nt} = \text{PMT}\left[\left(1+\frac{r}{n}\right)^{nt}-1\right]$$

$$\frac{P\left(\frac{r}{n}\right)\left(1+\frac{r}{n}\right)^{nt}}{\left(1+\frac{r}{n}\right)^{nt}-1} = \text{PMT}$$

$$\frac{P\left(\frac{r}{n}\right)}{1-\left(1+\frac{r}{n}\right)^{-nt}} = \text{PMT}$$

Chapter 8 Review Exercises

1. 80% **2.** 12.5% **3.** 75% **4.** 72% **5.** 0.35% **6.** 475.6% **7.** 0.65 **8.** 0.997 **9.** 1.50 **10.** 0.03 **11.** 0.0065 **12.** 0.0025 **13.** 9.6 **14. a.** $1.44 **b.** $25.44 **15. a.** $297.50 **b.** $552.50 **16.** $3535 **17.** 12.5% increase **18.** 35% decrease **19.** no; $9900; 1% decrease **20.** $180 **21.** $2520 **22.** $1200 **23.** $900 **24. a.** $122.50 **b.** $3622.50 **25.** $12,738 **26.** 7.5% **27.** $13,389.12 **28.** $9287.93 **29.** 40% **30. a.** $94.50 **b.** $1705.50 **c.** 7.4% **31. a.** $8114.92 **b.** $1114.92 **32. a.** $38,490.80 **b.** $8490.80 **33. a.** $5556.46 **b.** $3056.46 **34.** 7% compounded monthly; $362 **35.** $16,653.64 **36.** $13,175.19 **37. a.** $2122.73 **b.** 6.1% **38.** 5.6%; Answers will vary; an example is: The same amount of money would earn 5.6% in a simple interest account for a year. **39.** 6.25% compounded monthly **40. a.** $19,129 **b.** $8729 **41. a.** $91,361 **b.** $55,361 **42. a.** $1049 **b.** $20,980; $4020 **43.** high: $64.06; low: $26.13 **44.** $144 **45.** 0.3% **46.** 545,800 shares **47.** high: $61.25; low: $59.25 **48.** $61.00 **49.** $1.75 increase **50.** $1.49 **52. a.** $16,000 **b.** $21,500 **c.** $5000 **d.** 11.5% **53. a.** $250.40 **b.** $4229.60 **54. a.** $213.11 **b.** $4336.89

55. Answers will vary. **56. a.** \$16.50 **b.** \$1756.50 **c.** \$49 **57. a.** \$28.80 **b.** \$64.80 **c.** \$34.61 **58. a.** \$48,000 **b.** \$192,000 **c.** \$3840 **d.** \$1277 **e.** \$267,720 **59.** 20-year at 8%; \$53,040; Answers will vary. **60. a.** option A: \$769; option B: \$699; Answers will vary. **b.** Mortgage A: \$20,900 **61. a.** monthly payment: \$465; total interest: \$1740 **b.** monthly payment: \$305; total interest: \$3300 **c.** Longer term has lower monthly payment but greater total interest.

62. a. \$464.89
b. \$1845.36
c.

Payment Number	Interest	Principal	Loan Balance
1	\$139.68	\$325.21	\$8986.79
2	\$134.80	\$330.09	\$8656.70
3	\$129.85	\$335.04	\$8321.66

Chapter 8 Test

1. a. \$18 **b.** \$102 **2.** \$3430 **3.** 75% **4.** \$72; \$2472 **5.** 25% **6.** \$6698.57 **7.** 4.58%; Answers will vary; an example is: The same amount of money would earn 4.58% in a simple interest account for a year. **8. a.** \$8297 **b.** \$2297 **9. a.** \$7067 **b.** \$1067 **c.** Only part of the \$6000 is invested for the entire five years.; Answers will vary. **10.** \$2070 **11.** \$704 per month; \$1,162,080 interest **12.** high: \$25.75; low: \$25.50 **13.** \$2030 **14.** \$386.25 **15.** \$13,000 **16.** \$21,000 **17.** \$5000 **18.** 13.5% **19.** \$819.67 **20.** \$6680.33 **21.** \$15.60 **22.** \$1335.60 **23.** \$37 **24.** \$16.80 **25.** \$12,000 **26.** \$108,000 **27.** \$2160 **28.** \$830.52 **29.** \$190,987.20

30. a. monthly payment: \$230; total interest: \$7600
b.

Payment Number	Interest	Principal	Loan Balance
1	\$113.33	\$116.67	\$19,883.33
2	\$112.67	\$117.33	\$19,766.00

CHAPTER 9

Section 9.1

Check Point Exercises

1. a. 6.5 ft **b.** 3.25 mi **c.** $\frac{1}{12}$ yd **2. a.** 8 km **b.** 53,000 mm **c.** 0.0604 hm **d.** 6720 cm **3. a.** 243.84 cm **b.** ≈ 22.22 yd **c.** ≈ 1181.1 in. **4.** 37.5 mi/hr

Exercise Set 9.1

1. 2.5 ft **3.** 360 in. **5.** $\frac{1}{6}$ yd ≈ 0.17 yd **7.** 216 in. **9.** 18 ft **11.** 2 yd **13.** 4.5 mi **15.** 3960 ft **17.** 500 cm **19.** 1630 m **21.** 0.03178 hm **23.** 0.000023 m **25.** 21.96 dm **27.** 35.56 cm **29.** ≈ 5.51 in. **31.** 424 km **33.** 165.625 mi **35.** ≈ 13.33 yd **37.** ≈ 55.12 in. **39.** 0.4064 dam **41.** 1.524 m **43.** ≈ 16.40 ft **45.** 60 mi/hr **47.** 72 km/hr **49.** 457.2 cm **51.** $8\frac{1}{3}$ yd **53.** 48.28032 km **55.** 176 ft/sec **57.** meter **59.** millimeter **61.** meter **63.** millimeter **65.** millimeter **67.** b **69.** a **71.** c **73.** a **75.** 0.216 km **77.** 148.8 million km **87.** 9 hm **89.** 11 m or 1.1 dam

Section 9.2

Check Point Exercises

1. 8 square units **2.** 219.3 people per square mile **3. a.** 0.72 ha **b.** ≈ \$576,389 per hectare **4.** 9 cubic units **5.** 74,800 gal **6.** 220 L

Exercise Set 9.2

1. 16 square units **3.** 8 square units **5.** ≈ 2.15 in.^{2} **7.** 37.5 yd^2 **9.** 25.5 acres **11.** 91 cm^2 **13.** 24 cubic units **15.** 74,800 gal **17.** 1600 gal **19.** 9 gal **21.** 13.5 yd^3 **23.** 45 L **25.** 17 mL **27.** 1500 cm^3 **29.** 150 cm^3 **31.** 12,000 dm^3 **33. a.** 1900: 25.6 people per square mile; 2000: 79.6 people per square mile **b.** 210.9% **35.** 17.0 people per square kilometer **37. a.** 20 acres **b.** \$12,500 per acre **39.** square centimeters **41.** square kilometers **43.** b **45.** b **47.** 336,600 gal **49.** 4 L **57.** 12,139.4 people per square mile **59.** Answers will vary. **61.** 6.5 liters; Answers will vary.

Section 9.3

Check Point Exercises

1. a. 420 mg **b.** 6.2 g **2.** 145 kg **3. a.** 83.7 kg **b.** 100.44 mg **4.** 122°F **5.** 15°C

Exercise Set 9.3

1. 740 mg **3.** 0.87 g **5.** 800 cg **7.** 18,600 g **9.** 0.000018 g **11.** 50 kg **13.** 4200 cm^3 **15.** 1100 t **17.** 40,000 g **19.** 2.25 lb **21.** 1008 g **23.** 243 kg **25.** 36,000 g **27.** 1200 lb **29.** ≈ 222.22 T **31.** 50°F **33.** 95°F **35.** 134.6°F **37.** 23°F

39. 20°C **41.** 5°C **43.** 22.2°C **45.** −5°C **47.** 176.7°C **49.** −30°C **51. a.** $\frac{9}{5}$; Fahrenheit temperature increases by $\frac{9}{5}$° for each 1° change in Celsius temperature. **b.** $F = \frac{9}{5}C + 32$ **53.** true **55.** false **57.** false **59.** milligram **61.** gram **63.** kilogram **65.** kilogram **67.** b **69.** a **71.** c **73.** 13.28 kg **75.** $1.06 **77.** Purchasing the regular size is more economical. **79.** 90 mg **81. a.** 43 mg **b.** 516 mg **83.** a **85.** c **87.** 19.4°F **95.** b

Chapter 9 Review Exercises

1. 5.75 ft **2.** 0.25 yd **3.** 7 yd **4.** 2.5 mi **5.** 2280 cm **6.** 70 m **7.** 1920 m **8.** 0.0144 hm **9.** 0.0005 m **10.** 180 mm **11.** 58.42 cm **12.** ≈ 7.48 in. **13.** 528 km **14.** 375 mi **15.** ≈ 15.56 yd **16.** ≈ 39.37 ft **17.** ≈ 28.13 mi/hr **18.** 96 km/hr **19.** 0.024 km, 24,000 cm, 2400 m **20.** 4.8 km **21.** 24 square units **22.** 84.5 people per square mile; In the United States, there is an average of 84.5 people for each square mile. **23.** 18 acres **24.** ≈ 333.33 ft^2 **25.** 31.2 km^2 **26.** a **27.** 24 cubic units **28.** 251,328 gal **29.** 76 L **30.** c **31–32.** Answers will vary. **33.** 1240 mg **34.** 1200 cg **35.** 0.000012 g **36.** 0.00045 kg **37.** 50,000 cm^3 **38.** 4000 dm^3, 4,000,000 g **39.** 94.5 kg **40.** 14 oz **41.** kilograms; Answers will vary. **42.** 2.25 lb **43.** a **44.** c **45.** 59°F **46.** 212°F **47.** 41°F **48.** 32°F **49.** −13°F **50.** 15°C **51.** 5°C **52.** 100°C **53.** 37°C **54.** ≈ −17.8°C **55.** −10°C **56.** more; Answers will vary.

Chapter 9 Test

1. 0.00807 hm **2.** 250 in. **3.** 4.8 km **4.** mm **5.** cm **6.** km **7.** 128 km/hr **8.** 9 times **9.** 200.8 people per square mile; In Spain, there is an average of 200.8 people for each square mile. **10.** 45 acres **11.** b **12.** Answers will vary.; 1000 times **13.** 74,800 gal **14.** b **15.** 0.137 kg **16.** 40.5 kg **17.** kg **18.** mg **19.** 86°F **20.** 80°C **21.** d

CHAPTER 10

Section 10.1

Check Point Exercises

1. 30° **2.** 71° **3.** 46°, 134° **4.** $m\measuredangle 1 = 57°$, $m\measuredangle 2 = 123°$, and $m\measuredangle 3 = 123°$
5. $m\measuredangle 1 = 29°$, $m\measuredangle 2 = 29°$, $m\measuredangle 3 = 151°$, $m\measuredangle 4 = 151°$, $m\measuredangle 5 = 29°$, $m\measuredangle 6 = 151°$, and $m\measuredangle 7 = 151°$

Exercise Set 10.1

1. 150° **3.** 90° **5.** 20°; acute **7.** 160°; obtuse **9.** 180°; straight **11.** 65° **13.** 146° **15.** 42°; 132° **17.** 1°; 91° **19.** 52.6°; 142.6° **21.** $x + x + 12° = 90°$; 39°, 51° **23.** $x + 3x = 180°$; 45°, 135° **25.** $m\measuredangle 1 = 108°$; $m\measuredangle 2 = 72°$; $m\measuredangle 3 = 108°$ **27.** $m\measuredangle 1 = 50°$; $m\measuredangle 2 = 90°$; $m\measuredangle 3 = 50°$ **29.** $m\measuredangle 1 = 68°$; $m\measuredangle 2 = 68°$; $m\measuredangle 3 = 112°$; $m\measuredangle 4 = 112°$; $m\measuredangle 5 = 68°$; $m\measuredangle 6 = 68°$; $m\measuredangle 7 = 112°$ **31.** $m\measuredangle 1 = 38°$; $m\measuredangle 2 = 52°$; $m\measuredangle 3 = 142°$ **33.** 60°, 30° **35.** 112°, 112° **37.** $\overline{BC}$ **39.** $\overline{AD}$ **41.** $\overleftrightarrow{AD}$ **43.** $\overline{AD}$ **45.** 45° **47.** When two parallel lines are intersected by a transversal, corresponding angles have the same measure. **57.** d

Section 10.2

Check Point Exercises

1. 49° **2.** $m\measuredangle 1 = 90°$; $m\measuredangle 2 = 54°$; $m\measuredangle 3 = 54°$; $m\measuredangle 4 = 68°$; $m\measuredangle 5 = 112°$ **3.** 32 in. **4.** 32 yd **5.** 25 ft **6.** 120 yd

Exercise Set 10.2

1. 67° **3.** 32° **5.** $m\measuredangle 1 = 50°$; $m\measuredangle 2 = 130°$; $m\measuredangle 3 = 50°$; $m\measuredangle 4 = 130°$; $m\measuredangle 5 = 50°$
7. $m\measuredangle 1 = 50°$; $m\measuredangle 2 = 50°$; $m\measuredangle 3 = 80°$; $m\measuredangle 4 = 130°$; $m\measuredangle 5 = 130°$
9. $m\measuredangle 1 = 55°$; $m\measuredangle 2 = 65°$; $m\measuredangle 3 = 60°$; $m\measuredangle 4 = 65°$; $m\measuredangle 5 = 60°$; $m\measuredangle 6 = 120°$; $m\measuredangle 7 = 60°$; $m\measuredangle 8 = 60°$; $m\measuredangle 9 = 55°$; $m\measuredangle 10 = 55°$ **11.** 5 in. **13.** 6 m **15.** 16 in. **17.** 5 **19.** 9 **21.** 17 m **23.** 39 m **25.** 12 cm **27.** 50°, 50°, 80° **29.** 40°, 80°, 60° **31.** If $a^2 + b^2 = c^2$, then the triangle is a right triangle. **33.** not a right triangle **35.** 71.7 ft **37.** $4\sqrt{5} \approx 8.9$ ft **39.** $5\sqrt{7}$ ft ≈ 13.2 ft **41.** $70\sqrt{2} \approx 99.0$ ft **43.** $2\sqrt{5} \approx 4.5$ mi **45. a.** 3.3 m; 10.8 ft; no **b.** 3.32 m; 2 cm; 1 in.; no **c.** 19.7 ft; Answers will vary. **55.** 70° **57.** 5 ft by 12 ft

Section 10.3

Check Point Exercises

1. $3120 **2. a.** 1800° **b.** 150° **3.** Each angle of a regular octagon measures 135°. 360° is not a multiple of 135°.

Exercise Set 10.3

1. quadrilateral **3.** pentagon **5.** a: square; b: rhombus; d: rectangle; e: parallelogram **7.** a: square; d: rectangle **9.** c: trapezoid **11.** 30 cm **13.** 28 yd **15.** 1000 in. **17.** 27 ft **19.** 18 yd **21.** 84 yd **23.** 32 ft **25.** 540° **27.** 360° **29.** 108°; 72° **31. a.** 540° **b.** $m\measuredangle A = 140°$; $m\measuredangle B = 40°$ **33. a.** squares, hexagons, dodecagons (12-sided polygons) **b.** 3 angles; 90°, 120°, 150° **c.** The sum of the measures is 360°. **35. a.** triangles, hexagons **b.** 4 angles; 60°, 60°, 120°, 120° **c.** The sum of the measures is 360°. **37.** no; Each angle of the polygon measures 140°. 360° is not a multiple of 140°. **39.** 50 yd by 200 yd **41.** 160 ft by 360 ft **43.** 115°, 115°, 120°, 120° **45.** If the polygons were all regular polygons, the sum would be 363°. The sum is not 360°. **47.** $5600 **49.** 48 **59.** 6*a*

Section 10.4

Check Point Exercises

1. 66 ft^2; yes **2.** \$672 **3.** 60 $in.^2$ **4.** 30 ft^2 **5.** 105 ft^2 **6.** 10π in.; 31.4 in. **7.** 49.7 ft **8.** large pizza

Exercise Set 10.4

1. 18 m^2 **3.** 16 $in.^2$ **5.** 2100 cm^2 **7.** 56 $in.^2$ **9.** 20.58 yd^2 **11.** 30 $in.^2$ **13.** 91 m^2 **15.** C: 8π cm, $\approx$ 25.1 cm; A: 16π cm^2, $\approx$ 50.3 cm^2 **17.** C: 12π yd, $\approx$ 37.7 yd; A: 36π yd^2, $\approx$ 113.1 yd^2 **19.** 72 m^2 **21.** 300 m^2 **23.** $100 + 50\pi$; 257.1 cm^2 **25.** 192 cm^2 **27.** perimeter: 54 ft; area: 168 ft^2 **29.** length: 20 ft; width: 15 ft **31.** base: 5 cm; height: 6 cm **33.** \$556.50 **35.** 148 ft^2 **37. a.** 23 bags **b.** \$575 **39. a.** 3680 ft^2 **b.** 15 cans of paint **c.** \$404.25 **41.** \$933.40 **43.** 40π m; 125.7 m **45.** 377 plants **47.** large pizza **55.** by a factor of $\frac{9}{4}$ **57.** \$13,032.73

Section 10.5

Check Point Exercises

1. 105 ft^3 **2.** 8 yd^3 **3.** 48 ft^3 **4.** 302 $in.^3$ **5.** 101 $in.^3$ **6.** no **7.** 632 yd^2

Exercise Set 10.5

1. 36 $in.^3$ **3.** 64 cm^3 **5.** 175 yd^3 **7.** 56 $in.^3$ **9.** 150π cm^3, 471 cm^3 **11.** 3024π $in.^3$, 9500 $in.^3$ **13.** 48π m^3, 151 m^3 **15.** 15π yd^3, 47 yd^3 **17.** 288π m^3, 905 m^3 **19.** 972π cm^3, 3054 cm^3 **21.** 62 m^2 **23.** 96 ft^2 **25.** 324π cm^3, 1018 cm^3 **27.** surface area: 186 yd^2; volume: 148 yd^3 **29.** 666 yd^2 **31.** $\frac{1}{8}$ **33.** 9 times **35.** \$40 **37.** no **39. a.** 3,386,880 yd^3 **b.** 2,257,920 blocks **41.** yes **43.** \$27 **47.** The volume is multiplied by 8. **49.** 168 cm^3 **51.** 84 cm^2

Section 10.6

Check Point Exercises

1. $\sin A = \frac{3}{5}$; $\cos A = \frac{4}{5}$; $\tan A = \frac{3}{4}$ **2.** 263 cm **3.** 298 cm **4.** 994 ft **5.** 54°

Exercise Set 10.6

1. $\sin A = \frac{3}{5}$; $\cos A = \frac{4}{5}$; $\tan A = \frac{3}{4}$ **3.** $\sin A = \frac{20}{29}$; $\cos A = \frac{21}{29}$; $\tan A = \frac{20}{21}$ **5.** $\sin A = \frac{5}{13}$; $\cos A = \frac{12}{13}$; $\tan A = \frac{5}{12}$ **7.** $\sin A = \frac{4}{5}$; $\cos A = \frac{3}{5}$; $\tan A = \frac{4}{3}$ **9.** 188 cm **11.** 182 in. **13.** 7 m **15.** 22 yd **17.** 40 m **19.** $m\measuredangle B = 50°$, $a = 18$ yd, $c = 29$ yd **21.** $m\measuredangle B = 38°$, $a = 43$ cm, $b = 33$ cm **23.** 37° **25.** 28° **27.** 653 units **29.** 39 units **31.** 298 units **33.** 257 units **35.** 529 yd **37.** 2879 ft **39.** 2059 ft **41.** 695 ft **43.** 36° **45.** 1376 ft **47.** 15.1° **59. a.** 357 ft **b.** 394 ft

Section 10.7

Check Point Exercises

1. Answers will vary.

Exercise Set 10.7

1. a. traversable **b.** sample path: D, A, B, D, C, B **3. a.** traversable **b.** sample path: A, D, C, B, D, E, A, B **5.** not traversable **7.**

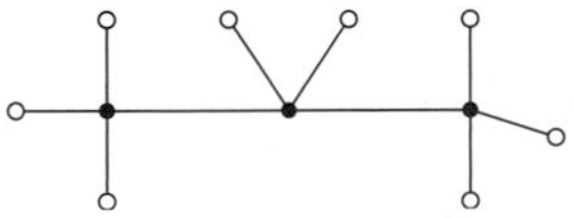

9. no **11.** 2 **13.** sample path: $B, E, A, B, D, C, A, E, C, E, D$ **15.** 2 **17.** 4 **19.** Answers will vary. **21.** The sum of the angles of such a quadrilateral is greater than 360°. **23.** yes

Chapter 10 Review Exercises

1. $\measuredangle 3$ **2.** $\measuredangle 5$ **3.** $\measuredangle 4$ and $\measuredangle 6$ **4.** $\measuredangle 1$ and $\measuredangle 6$ **5.** $\measuredangle 4$ and $\measuredangle 1$ **6.** $\measuredangle 2$ **7.** $\measuredangle 5$ **8.** 65° **9.** 49° **10.** 17° **11.** 134° **12.** $m\measuredangle 1 = 110°$; $m\measuredangle 2 = 70°$; $m\measuredangle 3 = 110°$ **13.** $m\measuredangle 1 = 138°$; $m\measuredangle 2 = 42°$; $m\measuredangle 3 = 138°$; $m\measuredangle 4 = 138°$; $m\measuredangle 5 = 42°$; $m\measuredangle 6 = 42°$; $m\measuredangle 7 = 138°$ **14.** 72° **15.** 51° **16.** $m\measuredangle 1 = 90°$; $m\measuredangle 2 = 90°$; $m\measuredangle 3 = 140°$; $m\measuredangle 4 = 40°$; $m\measuredangle 5 = 140°$ **17.** $m\measuredangle 1 = 80°$; $m\measuredangle 2 = 65°$; $m\measuredangle 3 = 115°$; $m\measuredangle 4 = 80°$; $m\measuredangle 5 = 100°$; $m\measuredangle 6 = 80°$ **18.** 5 ft **19.** 3.75 ft **20.** 10 ft **21.** 7.2 in. **22.** 10.2 cm **23.** 12.5 ft **24.** 15 ft **25.** 12 yd **26.** rectangle, square **27.** rhombus, square **28.** parallelogram, rhombus, trapezoid **29.** 30 cm **30.** 4480 yd **31.** 44 m **32.** 1800° **33.** 1080° **34.** $m\measuredangle 1 = 135°$; $m\measuredangle 2 = 45°$ **35.** \$132 **36. a.** triangles, hexagons **b.** 5 angles; 60°, 60°, 60°, 60°, 120° **c.** The sum of the measures is 360°. **37.** yes; Each angle of a regular hexagon measures 120°, and 360° is a multiple of 120°. **38.** 32.5 ft^2 **39.** 20 m^2 **40.** 50 cm^2 **41.** 135 yd^2 **42.** $C = 20\pi$ m $\approx$ 62.8 m; $A = 100\pi$ m^2 $\approx$ 314.2 m^2

43. 192 in.^{2} **44.** 28 m^2 **45.** $787.50 **46.** $650 **47.** 31 yd **48.** 60 cm^3 **49.** 960 m^3 **50.** 128π yd^3, 402 yd^3
51. $\frac{44{,}800\pi}{3}$ in.^{3}, 46,914 in.^{3} **52.** 288π m^3, 905 m^3 **53.** 126 m^2 **54.** 4800 m^3 **55.** 651,775 m^3 **56.** $80
57. $\sin A = \frac{3}{5}$; $\cos A = \frac{4}{5}$; $\tan A = \frac{3}{4}$ **58.** 42 mm **59.** 23 cm **60.** 37 in. **61.** 58° **62.** 772 ft **63.** 31 m **64.** 56°
65. not traversable **66.** traversable; sample path: $A, B, C, D, A, B, C, D, A$ **67.** 0 **68.** 2 **69.** 1 **70.** 2 **71.** Answers will vary.
72. Answers will vary.

Chapter 10 Test

1. 36°; 126° **2.** 133° **3.** 70° **4.** 35° **5.** 3.2 in. **6.** 10 ft **7.** 1440° **8.** 40 cm **9.** d **10. a.** triangles, squares
b. 5 angles; 60°, 60°, 60°, 90°, 90° **c.** The sum of the measures is 360°. **11.** 517 m^2 **12.** 525 in.^{2} **13. a.** 12 cm **b.** 30 cm **c.** 30 cm^2
14. $C{:} = 40\pi$ m, 125.7 m; $A{:}\ 400\pi$ m^2, 1256.6 m^2 **15.** 108 tiles **16.** 18 ft^3 **17.** 16 m^3 **18.** 175π cm^3, 550 cm^3 **19.** 85 cm **20.** 70 ft
21. traversable; sample path: B, C, A, E, C, D, E **22.** Answers will vary.

CHAPTER 11

Section 11.1

Check Point Exercises

1. 150 **2.** 40 **3.** 30 **4.** 160 **5.** 729 **6.** 90,000

Exercise Set 11.1

1. 80 **3.** 12 **5.** 6 **7.** 40 **9.** 144; Answers will vary. **11.** 8 **13.** 96 **15.** 243 **17.** 144 **19.** 676,000 **21.** 2187 **27.** 720 hr

Section 11.2

Check Point Exercises

1. 2 **2.** 120 **3. a.** 504 **b.** 524,160 **c.** 100 **4.** 840 **5.** 15,120 **6.** 420

Exercise Set 11.2

1. 720 **3.** 120 **5.** 120 **7.** 362,880 **9.** 6 **11.** 4 **13.** 504 **15.** 570,024 **17.** 3,047,466,240 **19.** 600 **21.** 10,712 **23.** 5034
25. 24 **27.** 6 **29.** 42 **31.** 1716 **33.** 3024 **35.** 6720 **37.** 720 **39.** 1 **41.** 720 **43.** 8,648,640 **45.** 120 **47.** 15,120
49. 180 **51.** 831,600 **53.** 105 **55.** 280 **65.** 360 **67.** 14,400 **69.** $\frac{n(n-1)\cdots 3\cdot 2\cdot 1}{2} = n(n-1)\cdots 3$

Section 11.3

Check Point Exercises

1. a. combinations **b.** permutations **2.** 35 **3.** 1820 **4.** 23,049,600

Exercise Set 11.3

1. combinations **3.** permutations **5.** 6 **7.** 126 **9.** 330 **11.** 8 **13.** 1 **15.** 4060 **17.** 1 **19.** 7 **21.** 0 **23.** $\frac{3}{4}$
25. -9499 **27.** $\frac{3}{68}$ **29.** 20 **31.** 495 **33.** 24,310 **35.** 22,957,480 **37.** 360 ways **39.** 1716 ways **41.** 1140 ways
43. 840 passwords **45.** 2730 cones **47.** 735 **49.** 4,516,932,420 **51.** 720 **53.** 20 **55.** 24 **57.** 12 **63.** The 5/36 lottery is easier to win.; Answers will vary. **65.** 570 sec or 9.5 min; 2340 sec or 39 min

Section 11.4

Check Point Exercises

1. a. $\frac{1}{6}$ **b.** $\frac{1}{2}$ **c.** 0 **d.** 1 **2. a.** $\frac{1}{13}$ **b.** $\frac{1}{2}$ **c.** $\frac{1}{26}$ **3.** $\frac{1}{2}$ **4. a.** 0.24 **b.** 0.48

Exercise Set 11.4

1. $\frac{1}{6}$ **3.** $\frac{1}{2}$ **5.** $\frac{1}{3}$ **7.** 1 **9.** 0 **11.** $\frac{1}{13}$ **13.** $\frac{1}{4}$ **15.** $\frac{3}{13}$ **17.** $\frac{1}{52}$ **19.** 0 **21.** $\frac{1}{4}$ **23.** $\frac{1}{2}$ **25.** $\frac{1}{2}$ **27.** $\frac{3}{8}$ **29.** $\frac{3}{8}$
31. $\frac{7}{8}$ **33.** 0 **35.** $\frac{1}{4}$ **37.** $\frac{1}{9}$ **39.** 0 **41.** $\frac{3}{10}$ **43.** $\frac{1}{5}$ **45.** $\frac{1}{2}$ **47.** 0 **49.** $\frac{1}{4}$ **51.** $\frac{1}{4}$ **53.** $\frac{1}{2}$ **55.** 0.43 **57.** 0.13
59. 0.03 **61.** 0.38 **63.** 0.78 **65.** 0.12 **75.** $\frac{3}{8} = 0.375$

Section 11.5

Check Point Exercises

1. $\frac{1}{60}$ **2.** $\frac{1}{13{,}983{,}816} \approx 0.0000000715$ **3. a.** $\frac{1}{6}$ **b.** $\frac{1}{2}$

Exercise Set 11.5

1. a. 120 **b.** 6 **c.** $\frac{1}{20}$ **3. a.** $\frac{1}{6}$ **b.** $\frac{1}{30}$ **c.** $\frac{1}{720}$ **d.** $\frac{1}{3}$ **5. a.** 84 **b.** 10 **c.** $\frac{5}{42}$ **7.** $\frac{1}{18{,}009{,}460} \approx 0.0000000555$; $\frac{100}{18{,}009{,}460} \approx 0.00000555$ **9. a.** $\frac{1}{177{,}100} \approx 0.00000565$ **b.** $\frac{27{,}132}{177{,}100} \approx 0.153$ **11.** $\frac{3}{10} = 0.3$ **13. a.** 2,598,960 **b.** 1287 **c.** $\frac{1287}{2{,}598{,}960} \approx 0.000495$ **15.** $\frac{11}{1105} \approx 0.00995$ **17.** $\frac{36}{270{,}725} \approx 0.000133$ **23.** $9,004,730 **25.** $\frac{1}{10}$

Section 11.6

Check Point Exercises

1. $\frac{3}{4}$ **2. a.** $\frac{160}{191}$ **b.** $\frac{182}{191}$ **3.** $\frac{1}{3}$ **4.** $\frac{27}{50}$ **5.** $\frac{3}{4}$ **6. a.** 0.99 **b.** 0.65 **7. a.** 2:50 or 1:25 **b.** 50:2 or 25:1 **8.** 199:1 **9.** 1:15; $\frac{1}{16}$

Exercise Set 11.6

1. $\frac{12}{13}$ **3.** $\frac{3}{4}$ **5.** $\frac{10}{13}$ **7.** $\frac{2{,}598{,}924}{2{,}598{,}960} \approx 0.999986$ **9.** $\frac{2{,}595{,}216}{2{,}598{,}960} \approx 0.998559$ **11. a.** 0.10 **b.** 0.90 **13.** $\frac{23}{28}$ **15.** $\frac{95}{112}$ **17.** $\frac{2}{13}$ **19.** $\frac{1}{13}$ **21.** $\frac{1}{26}$ **23.** $\frac{9}{22}$ **25.** $\frac{5}{6}$ **27.** $\frac{7}{13}$ **29.** $\frac{11}{26}$ **31.** $\frac{3}{4}$ **33.** $\frac{5}{8}$ **35.** $\frac{33}{40}$ **37.** $\frac{4}{5}$ **39.** $\frac{7}{10}$ **41.** $\frac{8}{11}$ **43.** $\frac{108}{187}$ **45.** $\frac{122}{187}$ **47.** 3:8; 8:3 **49.** $\frac{93}{143}$ **51.** $\frac{127}{143}$ **53.** $\frac{5}{13}$ **55.** 38:105; 105:38 **57.** 1:142; 142:1 **59.** 11:2; 2:11 **61.** 2:1 **63.** 1:2 **65. a.** 9:91 **b.** 91:9 **67.** 1:3 **69.** 1:1 **71.** 12:1 **73.** 25:1 **75.** 47:5 **77.** 49:1 **79.** 9:10 **81.** 14:5 **83.** 14:5 **85.** 9:10 **87.** $\frac{3}{7}$ **89.** $\frac{4}{25}$; 84 **91.** $\frac{1}{1000}$ **101.** 0.06

Section 11.7

Check Point Exercises

1. $\frac{1}{361} \approx 0.00277$ **2.** $\frac{1}{16}$ **3. a.** $\frac{625}{130{,}321} \approx 0.005$ **b.** $\frac{38{,}416}{130{,}321} \approx 0.295$ **c.** $\frac{91{,}905}{130{,}321} \approx 0.705$ **4.** $\frac{1}{221} \approx 0.00452$ **5.** $\frac{11}{850} \approx 0.0129$ **6.** $\frac{1}{2}$ **7. a.** $\frac{9}{10} = 0.9$ **b.** $\frac{45}{479} \approx 0.094$

Exercise Set 11.7

1. $\frac{1}{6}$ **3.** $\frac{1}{36}$ **5.** $\frac{1}{4}$ **7.** $\frac{1}{36}$ **9.** $\frac{1}{8}$ **11.** $\frac{1}{36}$ **13.** $\frac{1}{3}$ **15.** $\frac{3}{52}$ **17.** $\frac{1}{169}$ **19.** $\frac{1}{4}$ **21.** $\frac{1}{64}$ **23.** $\frac{1}{6}$ **25. a.** $\frac{1}{256} \approx 0.00391$ **b.** $\frac{1}{4096} \approx 0.000244$ **c.** ≈ 0.524 **d.** ≈ 0.476 **27.** 0.0144 **29.** 0.008 **31.** 0.4686 **33.** $\frac{7}{29}$ **35.** $\frac{5}{87}$ **37.** $\frac{2}{21}$ **39.** $\frac{4}{35}$ **41.** $\frac{11}{21}$ **43.** $\frac{1}{57}$ **45.** $\frac{8}{855}$ **47.** $\frac{11}{57}$ **49.** $\frac{1}{5}$ **51.** $\frac{2}{3}$ **53.** $\frac{3}{4}$ **55.** $\frac{3}{4}$ **57.** $\frac{412{,}368}{412{,}878} \approx 0.999$ **59.** $\frac{412{,}368}{574{,}895} \approx 0.717$ **61.** 0.898 **63.** 0.168 **65.** 0.542 **67.** 0.415 **69.** 0.103 **71.** 0.886 **81.** 0.59049 **83. a.** Answers will vary. **b.** $\frac{365}{365} \cdot \frac{364}{365} \cdot \frac{363}{365} \approx 0.992$ **c.** ≈ 0.008 **d.** 0.411 **e.** 23 people

Section 11.8

Check Point Exercises

1. 2.5 **2.** 2 **3. a.** $8000; In the long run, the average cost of a claim is $8000. **b.** $8000 **4.** 0; no; Answers will vary. **5.** table entries: $998, $48, and −$2; expected value: −$0.90; In the long run, a person can expect to lose an average of $0.90 for each ticket purchased.; Answers will vary. **6.** −$0.20; In the long run, a person can expect to lose an average of $0.20 for each card purchased.

Exercise Set 11.8

1. 1.75 **3. a.** $29,000; In the long run, the average cost of a claim is $29,000. **b.** $29,000 **c.** $29,050 **5.** $0; Answers will vary. **7.** $0.73 **9.** $\frac{1}{16} = 0.0625$; yes **11.** the second mall **13. a.** $140,000 **b.** no **15.** ≈ −$0.17; In the long run, a person can expect to lose an average of about $0.17 for each game played. **17.** ≈ −$0.05; In the long run, a person can expect to lose an average of about $0.05 for each game played. **19.** −$0.50; In the long run, a person can expect to lose an average of $0.50 for each game played. **27.** $160

Chapter 11 Review Exercises

1. 800 **2.** 20 **3.** 9900 **4.** 125 **5.** 243 **6.** 60 **7.** 720 **8.** 120 **9.** 120 **10.** 240 **11.** 800 **12.** 114 **13.** 990 **14.** 151,200 **15.** 9900 **16.** 32,760 **17.** 1,860,480 **18.** 420 **19.** 60 **20.** combinations **21.** permutations **22.** combinations

23. 330 **24.** 2002 **25.** 210 **26.** 1287 **27.** 1140 **28.** 55,440 **29.** $\frac{1}{6}$ **30.** $\frac{2}{3}$ **31.** 1 **32.** 0 **33.** $\frac{1}{13}$ **34.** $\frac{3}{13}$ **35.** $\frac{3}{13}$ **36.** $\frac{1}{52}$ **37.** $\frac{1}{26}$ **38.** $\frac{1}{2}$ **39.** $\frac{1}{3}$ **40.** $\frac{1}{6}$ **41. a.** $\frac{1}{2}$ **b.** 0 **42.** 0.623 **43.** 0.518 **44.** 0.149 **45.** $\frac{1}{24}$ **46.** $\frac{1}{6}$ **47.** $\frac{1}{30}$ **48.** $\frac{1}{720}$ **49.** $\frac{1}{3}$ **50. a.** $\frac{1}{15,504} \approx 0.0000645$ **b.** $\frac{100}{15,504} \approx 0.00645$ **51. a.** $\frac{1}{14}$ **b.** $\frac{3}{7}$ **52.** $\frac{3}{26}$ **53.** $\frac{5}{6}$ **54.** $\frac{1}{2}$ **55.** $\frac{1}{3}$ **56.** $\frac{2}{3}$ **57.** 1 **58.** $\frac{10}{13}$ **59.** $\frac{3}{4}$ **60.** $\frac{2}{13}$ **61.** $\frac{1}{13}$ **62.** $\frac{7}{13}$ **63.** $\frac{11}{26}$ **64.** $\frac{5}{6}$ **65.** $\frac{5}{6}$ **66.** $\frac{1}{2}$ **67.** $\frac{2}{3}$ **68.** 1 **69.** $\frac{5}{6}$ **70.** $\frac{4}{5}$ **71.** $\frac{3}{4}$ **72.** $\frac{18}{25}$ **73.** $\frac{6}{7}$ **74.** $\frac{3}{5}$ **75.** $\frac{12}{35}$ **76.** in favor: 1:12; against: 12:1 **77.** 99:1 **78.** $\frac{3}{4}$ **79.** $\frac{2}{9}$ **80.** $\frac{1}{36}$ **81.** $\frac{1}{9}$ **82.** $\frac{1}{36}$ **83.** $\frac{8}{27}$ **84.** $\frac{1}{32}$ **85. a.** 0.04 **b.** 0.008 **c.** 0.4096 **d.** 0.5904 **86.** $\frac{1}{9}$ **87.** $\frac{1}{12}$ **88.** $\frac{1}{196}$ **89.** $\frac{1}{3}$ **90.** $\frac{3}{10}$ **91. a.** $\frac{1}{2}$ **b.** $\frac{2}{7}$ **92.** $\frac{27}{29}$ **93.** $\frac{4}{29}$ **94.** $\frac{144}{145}$ **95.** $\frac{11}{20}$ **96.** $\frac{11}{135}$ **97.** $\frac{1}{125}$ **98.** $\frac{1}{232}$ **99.** $\frac{19}{1044}$ **100.** $\frac{26,098}{30,242} \approx 0.863$ **101.** $\frac{11,586}{30,242} \approx 0.383$ **102.** $\frac{27,818}{30,242} \approx 0.920$ **103.** $\frac{15,892}{30,242} \approx 0.525$ **104.** $\frac{4186}{30,242} \approx 0.138$ **105.** $\frac{3887}{26,098} \approx 0.149$ **106.** $\frac{2225}{2424} \approx 0.918$ **107.** 3.125 **108. a.** \$0.50; In the long run, the average cost of a claim is \$0.50. **b.** \$10.00 **109.** \$4500; Answers will vary. **110.** −\$0.25; In the long run, a person can expect to lose an average of \$0.25 for each game played.

Chapter 11 Test

1. 240 **2.** 24 **3.** 720 **4.** 990 **5.** 210 **6.** 420 **7.** $\frac{6}{25}$ **8.** $\frac{17}{25}$ **9.** $\frac{11}{25}$ **10.** $\frac{5}{13}$ **11.** $\frac{1}{210}$ **12.** $\frac{10}{1001} \approx 0.00999$ **13.** $\frac{1}{2}$ **14.** $\frac{1}{16}$ **15.** $\frac{1}{8000} = 0.000125$ **16.** $\frac{8}{13}$ **17.** $\frac{3}{5}$ **18.** $\frac{1}{19}$ **19.** $\frac{1}{256}$ **20.** 3:4 **21. a.** 4:1 **b.** $\frac{4}{5}$ **22.** $\frac{3}{5}$ **23.** $\frac{39}{50}$ **24.** $\frac{3}{5}$ **25.** $\frac{9}{19}$ **26.** $\frac{7}{150}$ **27.** \$1000; Answers will vary. **28.** −\$12.75; In the long run, a person can expect to lose an average of \$12.75 for each game played.

CHAPTER 12

Section 12.1

Check Point Exercises

1. a. the set containing all the city's homeless **b.** no: People already in the shelters are probably less likely to be against mandatory residence in the shelters. **2.** By selecting people from a shelter, homeless people who do not go to the shelters have no chance of being selected. An appropriate method would be to randomly select neighborhoods of the city and then randomly survey homeless people within the selected neighborhood.

3.

Grade	Frequency
A	3
B	5
C	9
D	2
F	1
	20

4.

Class	Frequency
40–49	1
50–59	5
60–69	4
70–79	15
80–89	5
90–99	7
	37

5.

Stem	Leaves
4	1
5	8 2 8 0 7
6	8 2 9 9
7	3 5 9 9 7 5 5 3 3 6 7 1 7 1 5
8	7 3 9 9 1
9	4 6 9 7 5 8 0

Exercise Set 12.1

1. a. population: all American men aged 18 or older; sample: those men actually polled **b.** each man's impression of his own health; qualitative **3.** c **5.** 7; 31 **7.** 151

9.

Time Spent on Homework (in hours)	Number of Students
15	4
16	5
17	6
18	5
19	4
20	2
21	2
22	0
23	0
24	2
	30

11. 0, 5, 10, . . . , 40, 45 **13.** 5 **15.** 13 **17.** the 5–9 class

19.

Age at Inauguration	Number of Presidents
41–45	2
46–50	8
51–55	15
56–60	9
61–65	7
66–70	2
	43

21. a.

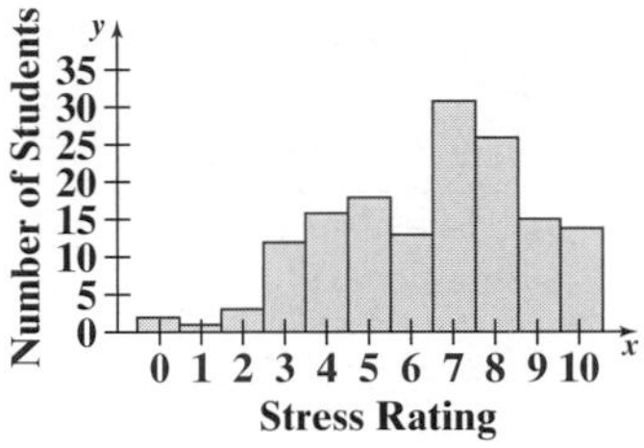

b.

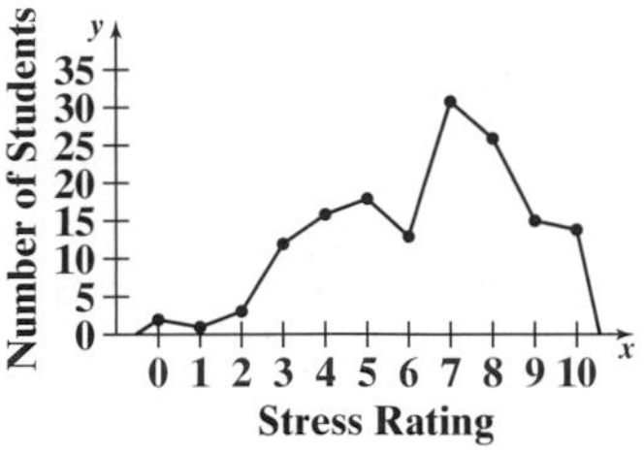

23.

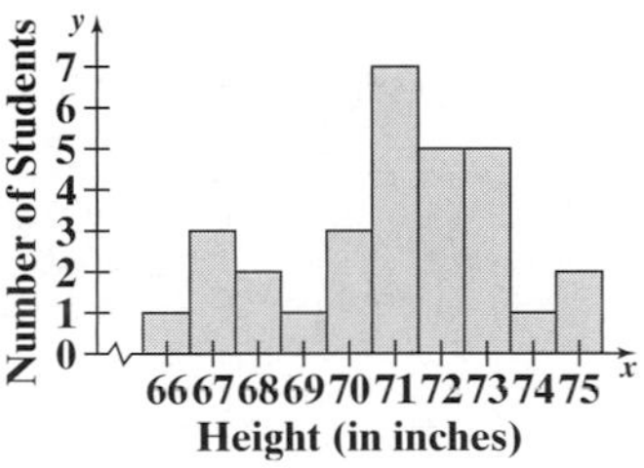

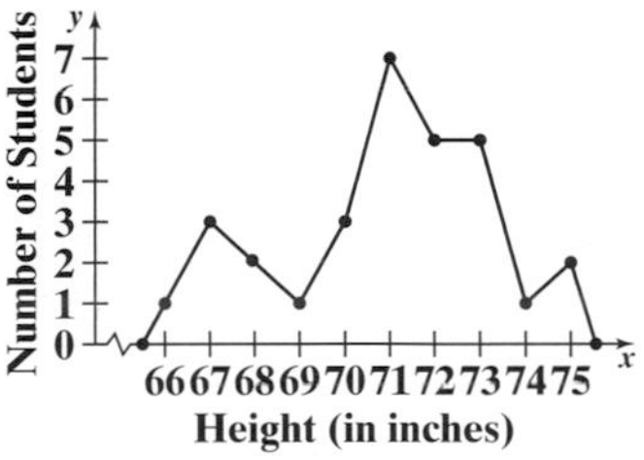

25. b **27.**

Stem	Leaves
2	8 8 9 5
3	8 7 0 1 2 7 6 4 0 5
4	8 2 2 1 4 5 4 6 2 0 8 2 7 9
5	9 4 1 9 1 0
6	3 2 3 6 6 3

The greatest number of college professors are in their 40s.

29. Time intervals on the horizontal axis do not represent equal amounts of time. **31.** Percentages do not add up to 100%.
33. It is not clear whether the lengths of the bars represent the percentage or the loan amount.

45.

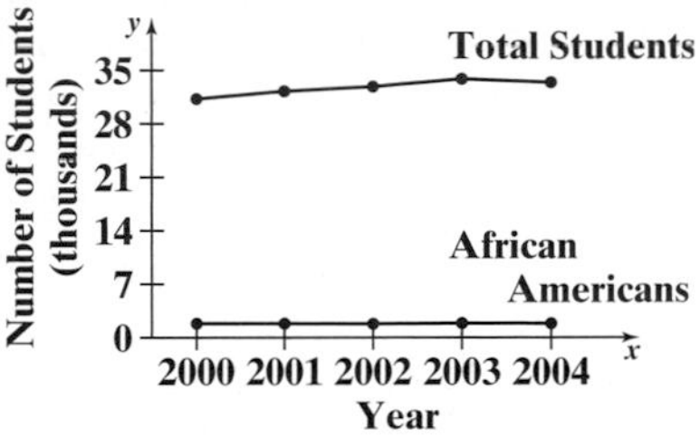

Section 12.2

Check Point Exercises

1. a. 30 **b.** 30 **2.** 36 **3. a.** 35 **b.** 82 **4.** 5 **5.** 162.5 **6.** 54.5 **7. a.** \$66.94 billion **b.** \$30 billion **c.** One data items is much greater than the other items. **8.** 8 **9.** \$124,500 **10.** mean: 158.6 cal; median: 153 cal; mode: 138 cal; midrange: 151 cal

Exercise Set 12.2

1. 4.125 **3.** 95 **5.** 62 **7.** ≈ 3.45 **9.** ≈ 4.71 **11.** ≈ 6.26 **13.** 3.5 **15.** 95 **17.** 60 **19.** 3.6 **21.** 5 **23.** 6 **25.** 3 **27.** 95 **29.** 40 **31.** 2.5, 4.2 (bimodal) **33.** 5 **35.** 6 **37.** 4.5 **39.** 95 **41.** 70 **43.** 3.3 **45.** 4.5 **47.** 5.5 **49.** mean: 30; median: 30; mode: 30; midrange: 30 **51.** mean: approximately 12.4; median: 12.5; mode: 13; midrange: 12.5 **53.** mean: approximately 31.3; median: 31; mode: 31; midrange: 33 **55. a.** 67.4 **b.** 69 **c.** 71 **d.** 69.5 **57. a.** approximately 19.2 **b.** 18 **c.** 19 **d.** 24 **59. a.** ≈ 17.27 **b.** 17 **c.** 7, 12, 17 **d.** 24.5 **61.** 175 lb **63.** 177.5 lb **65.** ≈ 2.76 **77.** All 30 students had the same grade.

Section 12.3

Check Point Exercises

1. 9 **2.** mean: 6;

Data item	Deviation
2	–4
4	–2
7	1
11	5

3. ≈ 3.92 **4.** sample A: 3.74; sample B: 28.06 **5. a.** stocks **b.** stocks; Answers will vary.

Exercise Set 12.3

1. 4 **3.** 8 **5.** 2

7. a.

Data item	Deviation
3	–9
5	–7
7	–5
12	0
18	6
27	15

b. 0

9. a.

Data item	Deviation
29	–20
38	–11
48	–1
49	0
53	4
77	28

b. 0

11. a. 91
b.

Data item	Deviation
85	–6
95	4
90	–1
85	–6
100	9

c. 0

13. a. 155
b.

Data item	Deviation
146	–9
153	–2
155	0
160	5
161	6

c. 0

15. a. 2.70
b.

Data item	Deviation
2.25	–0.45
3.50	0.80
2.75	0.05
3.10	0.40
1.90	–0.80

c. 0

17. ≈ 1.58 **19.** ≈ 3.46 **21.** ≈ 0.89 **23.** 3 **25.** ≈ 2.14
27. *Sample A*: mean: 12; range: 12; standard deviation: ≈ 4.32
Sample B: mean: 12; range: 12; standard deviation: ≈ 5.07
Sample C: mean: 12; range: 12; standard deviation: 6
The samples have the same mean and range, but different standard deviations.
29. 0 **31.** 1 **33.** 7.91 **35.** 1.55 **37. a.** Best Actor; Most of the ages for Best Actor are in the upper 30s and lower 40s while all of the ages for Best Actress are in the upper 20s and lower 30s. **b.** Best Actor: 38.57; Best Actress: 30.71 **c.** Best Actor; There is greater spread in the ages for Best Actor, since one age, 29, is much lower than the other ages. **d.** Best Actor: 5.68; Best Actress: 3.77 **47.** a **51.** The mean is increased by 2.; The standard deviation is unaffected.

Section 12.4

Check Point Exercises

1. a. 75.5 in. **b.** 58 in. **2. a.** 95% **b.** 47.5% **c.** 16% **3. a.** 2 **b.** 0 **c.** -1 **4.** ACT **5. a.** 64 **b.** 128
6. 75% of the scores on the SAT are less than this student's score. **7.** 88.49% **8.** 8.08% **9.** 83.01% **10. a.** $\pm 4.5\%$
b. We can be 95% confident that between 49.5% and 58.5% of American adults support physician-assisted suicide. **c.** The percentage of American adults who support physician-assisted suicide may be less than 50%.

Exercise Set 12.4

1. 120 **3.** 160 **5.** 150 **7.** 60 **9.** 90 **11.** 68% **13.** 34% **15.** 47.5% **17.** 49.85% **19.** 16% **21.** 2.5% **23.** 95% **25.** 47.5% **27.** 16% **29.** 2.5% **31.** 0.15% **33.** 1 **35.** 3 **37.** 0.5 **39.** 1.75 **41.** 0 **43.** -1 **45.** -1.5 **47.** -3.25 **49.** 1.5 **51.** 2.25 **53.** -1.25 **55.** -1.5 **57.** The person who scores 127 on the Wechsler has the higher IQ. **59.** 500 **61.** 475 **63.** 250 **65.** 275 **67. a.** 72.57% **b.** 27.43% **69. a.** 88.49% **b.** 11.51% **71. a.** 24.2% **b.** 75.8% **73. a.** 11.51% **b.** 88.49% **75.** 33.99% **77.** 15.74% **79.** 86.64% **81.** 28.57% **83.** 91.92% **85.** 27.43% **87.** 88.49% **89.** 6.69% **91.** 45.14% **93.** 6.68% **95.** 24.17% **97. a.** $\pm 2.1\%$ **b.** We can be 95% confident that between 15.9% and 20.1% of parents in the population consider a doctor as the dream job for their child. **99. a.** $\pm 1.6\%$ **b.** We can be 95% confident that between 58.6% and 61.8% of all TV households watched the final episode of "M*A*S*H". **101.** 0.2% **103. a.** skewed to the right **b.** 5.6 murders per 100,000 residents **c.** 5 murders per 100,000 residents **d.** yes; The mean is greater than the median which is consistent with a distribution skewed to the right. **e.** 6.3; yes; For a normal distribution, almost 100% of the z-scores are between -3 and 3. **119.** 630

Section 12.5

Check Point Exercises

1. This indicates a moderate relationship. **2.** −0.84 **3.** $y = -22.97x + 260.56$; 30.86 deaths per 100,000 people **4.** yes

Exercise Set 12.5

1.

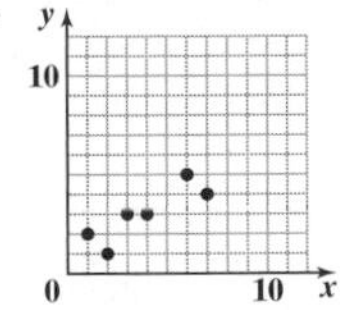

There appears to be a positive correlation.

3.

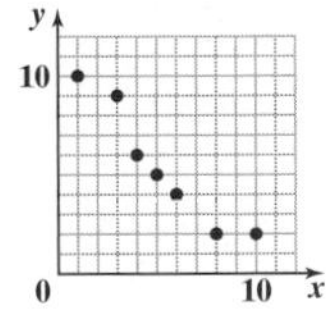

There appears to be a negative correlation.

5.

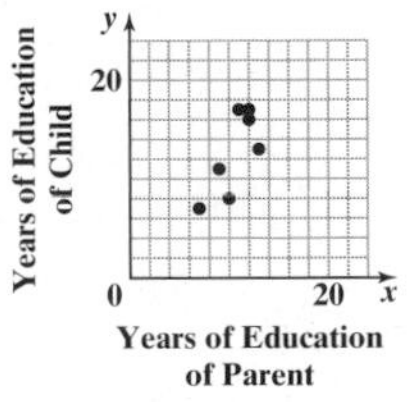

There appears to be a positive correlation.

7.

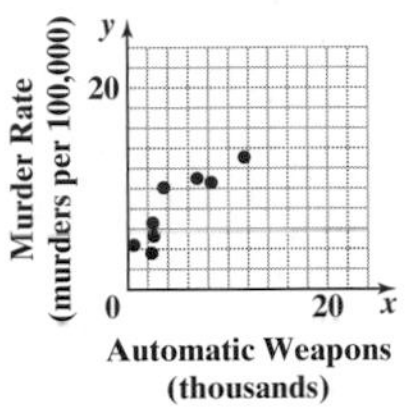

There appears to be a positive correlation.

9. false **11.** true **13.** true **15.** false **17.** true **19.** false **21.** true **23.** false **25.** false **27.** a **29.** d **31.** 0.855 **33.** −0.954 **35.** **a.** 0.75 **b.** $y = 1.52x - 3.38$ **c.** 21 years **37.** **a.** 0.885 **b.** $y = 0.85x + 4.05$ **c.** 16 murders per 100,000 people **39.** A correlation does exist. **41.** A correlation does not exist. **43.** A correlation does exist. **45.** A correlation does not exist.

Chapter 12 Review Exercises

1. population: American women ages 25 through 60; sample: 1511 women randomly selected from the population **2.** how often she entertains guests for dinner **3.** a

4.

Time Spent on Homework (in hours)	Number of Students
6	1
7	3
8	3
9	2
10	1
	10

5.

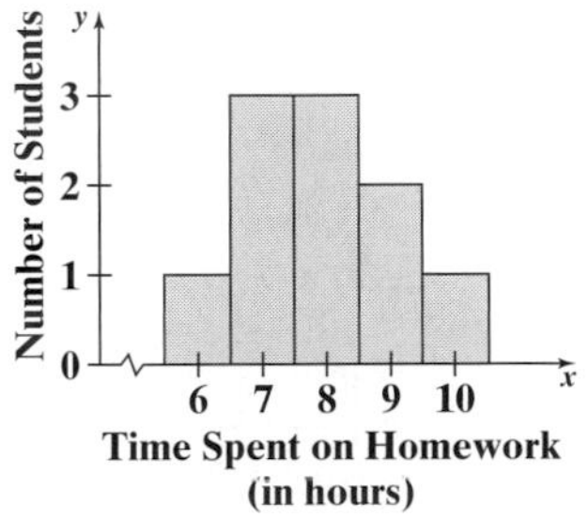

6.

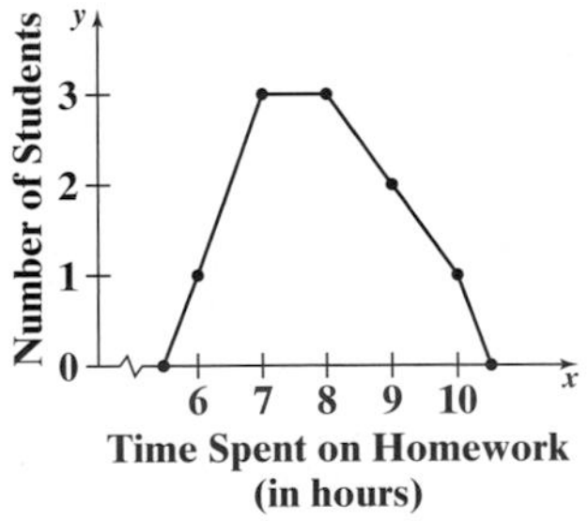

7.

Grades	Number of Students
0–39	19
40–49	8
50–59	6
60–69	6
70–79	5
80–89	3
90–100	3
	50

8.

Stem	Leaves
1	8 4 3 3 7 1
2	4 6 9 9 2 7
3	4 9 6 1 5 1 1
4	4 7 9 1 2 2 0 5
5	4 7 9 0 6 1
6	3 7 0 8 3 9
7	2 5 4 0 3
8	1 7 6
9	1 0 5

9. Sizes of barrels are not scaled proportionally in terms of the data they represent. **10.** 91.2 **11.** 17 **12.** 2.3 **13.** 11 **14.** 28 **15.** 2 **16.** 27 **17.** 585, 587 (bimodal) **18.** 2 **19.** 91 **20.** 19.5 **21.** 2.5

24. a.

Age at First Inauguration	Number of Presidents
42	1
43	1
44	0
45	0
46	2
47	1
48	1
49	2
50	1
51	5
52	2
53	0
54	5
55	4
56	3
57	4
58	1
59	0
60	1
61	3
62	1
63	0
64	2
65	1
66	0
67	0
68	1
69	1
	43

b. mean: ≈ 54.84 yr; median: 55 yr; mode: 51 yr, 54 yr (bimodal); midrange: 55.5 yr **25.** 18 **26.** 564

27. a.

Data item	Deviation
29	–6
9	–26
8	–27
22	–13
46	11
51	16
48	13
42	7
53	18
42	7

b. 0

28. a. 50

b.

Data item	Deviation
36	–14
26	–24
24	–26
90	40
74	24

c. 0

29. ≈ 4.05 **30.** ≈ 5.13 **31.** mean: 49; range: 76; standard deviation: ≈ 24.32 **32.** Set A: mean: 80; standard deviation: 0; Set B: mean: 80; standard deviation: ≈ 11.55; Answers will vary. **33.** Answers will vary. **34.** 86 **35.** 98 **36.** 60 **37.** 68% **38.** 95% **39.** 34% **40.** 99.7% **41.** 16% **42.** 84% **43.** 2.5% **44.** 0 **45.** 2 **46.** 1.6 **47.** −3 **48.** −1.2 **49.** vocabulary test **50.** 38,000 miles **51.** 41,000 miles **52.** 22,000 miles **53.** 91.92% **54.** 96.41% **55.** 88.33% **56.** 10.69% **57.** 75% **58.** 14% **59.** 11% **60. a.** ±2.2% **b.** We can be 95% confident that between 12.8% and 17.2% of executives of American companies have careers not related to their college degrees. **61. a.** skewed to the right **b.** mean: 2.1 syllables; median: 2 syllables; mode: 1 syllable **c.** yes; The mean is greater than the median which is consistent with a distribution skewed to the right.

62.

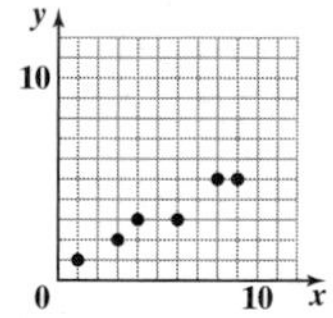

There appears to be a positive correlation.

63.

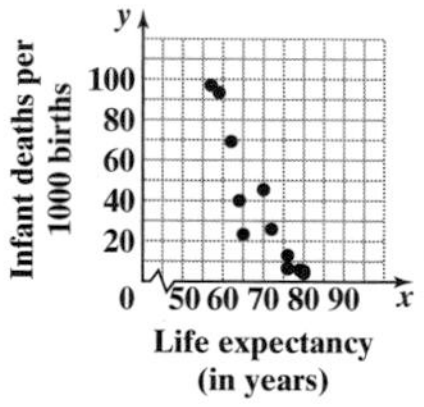

There appears to be a negative correlation.

64. false **65.** true **66.** false **67.** false **68.** true **69.** false **70.** true **71.** c **72. a.** 0.972 **b.** $y = 0.509x + 0.537$ **73. a.** 0.99 **b.** There is a correlation.

Chapter 12 Test

1. d **2.**

Score	Frequency
3	1
4	2
5	3
6	2
7	2
8	3
9	2
10	1
	16

3.

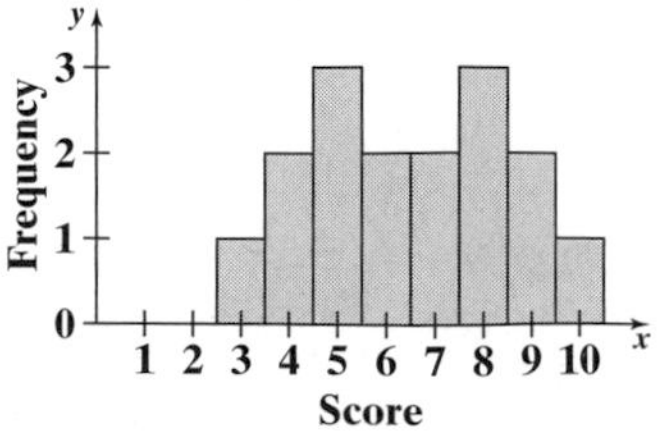

4.

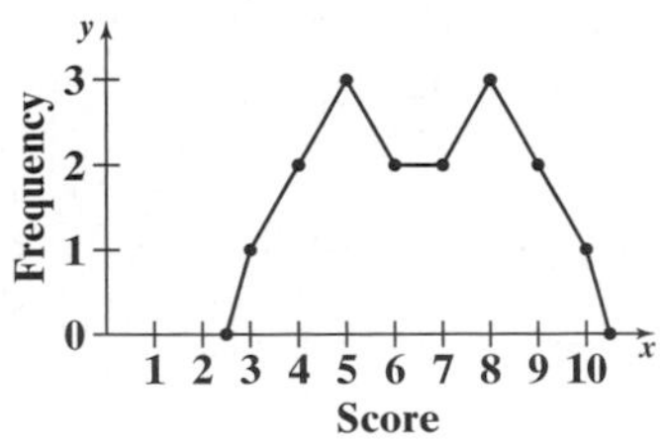

5.

Class	Frequency
40–49	3
50–59	6
60–69	6
70–79	7
80–89	6
90–99	2
	30

6.

Stem	Leaves
4	8 1 6
5	1 0 5 0 9 0
6	7 2 0 3 1 1
7	9 8 3 1 9 1 5
8	9 3 0 8 9 1
9	3 0

7. The roofline gives the impression that the percentage of home-schooled students grew at the same rate each year between the years shown which might not have happened. **8.** ≈ 3.67 **9.** 3 **10.** 4 **11.** ≈ 2.34 **12.** 2.25 **13.** 2 **14.** 2 **15.** Answers will vary. **16.** 34% **17.** 2.5% **18.** student **19.** 8.08% **20.** 41%
21. a. $\pm 10\%$ **b.** We can be 95% confident that between 50% and 70% of all students are very satisfied with their professors.
22.

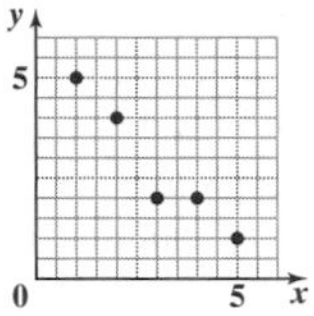

; There appears to be a strong negative correlation. **23.** false **24.** false **25.** true **26.** Answers will vary.

CHAPTER 13

Section 13.1

Check Point Exercises

1. *E*; The sum of two odd numbers is an even number. **2.** not closed **3.** closed **4.** not closed

5. $(1 \oplus 3) \oplus 2 = 1 \oplus (3 \oplus 2)$
$0 \oplus 2 = 1 \oplus 1$
$2 = 2$

6. *g* **7.** -12 **8.** $\frac{1}{12}$ **9. a.** *k* **b.** *l* is the inverse of *j*; *k* is its own inverse; *j* is the inverse of *l*; *m* is its own inverse.

Exercise Set 13.1

1. $\{e, a, b, c\}$ **3.** *c* **5.** *a* **7.** *e* **9.** *b* **11.** *e* **13.** *a* **15.** not closed; Answers will vary. **17.** closed; The sum of any two natural numbers is a natural number. **19.** not closed; Answers will vary. **21.** not closed; $b * a = c$ is not an element of the set $\{a, b\}$. **23.** Both sides of the equality equal 1. **25.** Both sides of the equality equal 0. **27.** commutative property; The entries in the table are mirror images about the diagonal line that extends from the upper left corner to the lower right corner. **29.** Both sides of the equality equal 4. **31.** Both sides of the equality equal 0. **33. a.** *b* **b.** *a* **c.** not associative; When the grouping changes, the answer changes. **35.** Answers will vary. Sample answer: $(5 - 2) - 1 = 3 - 1 = 2$ but $5 - (2 - 1) = 5 - 1 = 4$. **37.** -29 **39.** $\frac{1}{29}$ **41.** *a* **43.** *c* **45.** *e* **47.** *c* **49.** *e* **51.** *a*
53. *d* **55.** *b* **57.** 0 **59.** 4 **61.** 2 **63. a.** *d* **b.** *d* is its own inverse.; *a*, *b*, and *c* do not have inverses.
65. a. $e \triangle (c \sqcap d) = e \triangle a = a$; $(e \triangle c) \square (e \triangle d) = d \square c = a$ **b.** distributive property
67. *c* **69.** *b* **71.** *d*
73. The mathematical system shows all possible starting and ending position for the four-way switch. The starting positions are shown in the left column. The number of clockwise turns are shown across the top. The 25 entries in the table represent the final position of the switch for each starting position and number of clockwise turns.

75.–79.

×	E	O
E	E	E
O	E	O

75. closed; All entries in the body of the table are elements of the set $\{E, O\}$.
77. Answers will vary. Sample answer: $(O \times E) \times O = E \times O = E$ and $O \times (E \times O) = O \times E = E$.
79. *E* does not have an inverse.

89. a. $\begin{bmatrix} 15 & 20 \\ 35 & 46 \end{bmatrix}$ **b.** $\begin{bmatrix} 4 & 7 \\ 34 & 57 \end{bmatrix}$ **c.** This multiplication is not commutative.

Section 13.2

Check Point Exercises

1. a. 1. All entries in the table are elements of the set $\{E, O\}$; thus, the system is closed.
2. Two examples of the associative property follow. Answers will vary.
$(O \circ E) \circ O = O \circ O = E$ and $O \circ (E \circ O) = O \circ O = E$
$(E \circ O) \circ E = O \circ E = O$ and $E \circ (O \circ E) = E \circ O = O$
3. *E* is the identity element.
4. *E* is its own inverse, and *O* is its own inverse. Each element has an inverse. Since the system meets the four requirements, the system is a group.
b. Since $E \circ O = O$ and $O \circ E = O$, the order does not matter. Thus, the group is commutative.
2. a. $(8 + 5) + 11 = 1 + 11 = 0$ and $8 + (5 + 11) = 8 + 4 = 0$ **b.** Both sides of the equality equal 1.
3. a. true **b.** true **c.** false **4. a.** 4 (mod 5) **b.** 2 (mod 7) **c.** 5 (mod 13) **5.** Tuesday

Exercise Set 13.2

1. 8-fold rotational symmetry **3.** 18-fold rotational symmetry **5.** All entries in the body of the table are elements of the set $\{e, p, q, r, s, t\}$. **7.** $(r \circ t) \circ q = p \circ q = e$ and $r \circ (t \circ q) = r \circ r = e$ **9.** e **11.** q **13.** r **15.** t **17.** t **19.** The operation is not commutative. **21.** Answers will vary. Sample answer: The element 2 does not have an inverse.

23. a.

+	0	1	2	3	4	5
0	0	1	2	3	4	5
1	1	2	3	4	5	0
2	2	3	4	5	0	1
3	3	4	5	0	1	2
4	4	5	0	1	2	3
5	5	0	1	2	3	4

b. 1. Since all entries in the body of the table are elements of the set, the closure property is satisfied. **2.** Since the result of using clock addition to add 3 elements is the same regardless of whether the first two elements are grouped or the last two elements are grouped, the associative property is satisfied.
Example 1:
$(1 + 2) + 3 = 3 + 3 = 0$
$1 + (2 + 3) = 1 + 5 = 0$
Example 2:
$(2 + 4) + 5 = 0 + 5 = 5$
$2 + (4 + 5) = 2 + 3 = 5$
3. Since 0 is an element of the set and $0 + e = e$ and $e + 0 = e$ for all elements e in the set, the identity property is satisfied. **4.** Since each element has an inverse within the set, the inverse property is satisfied. **5.** Since the entries in the table are symmetric about the diagonal from the upper left corner to the lower right corner, we know that the order of clock addition does not matter. The commutative property is satisfied.
Since all 5 properties are satisfied, this mathematical system is a commutative group.

25. true **27.** true **29.** false; $84 \equiv 0 \pmod 7$ **31.** false; $23 \equiv 3 \pmod 4$ **33.** true **35.** 5 (mod 6) **37.** 3 (mod 6) **39.** 4 (mod 7) **41.** 48 (mod 50) **43.** 11 (mod 12) **45. a.** 6 (mod 7) **b.** 6 (mod 7) **c.** distributive property **47.** 2 **49.** 1, 3, and 5 **51.** none **53.** 1800 **55.** 0020 **57.** Sunday **59.** *beam me up* **61.** valid **63.** not valid **65.** valid **67.** valid **69.** not valid

79. Answers will vary. In general,

$$\begin{aligned}(a \cdot b) \cdot c &= (a - b + ab) \cdot c \\ &= a - b + ab - c + (a - b + ab)c \\ &= a - b + ab - c + ac - bc + abc \\ &= a - b - c + ab + ac - bc + abc \\ a \cdot (b \cdot c) &= a \cdot (b - c + bc) \\ &= a - (b - c + bc) + a(b - c + bc) \\ &= a - b + c - bc + ab - ac + abc\end{aligned}$$

Since $(a \cdot b) \cdot c \neq a \cdot (b \cdot c)$, the associative property is not satisfied. Thus the mathematical system is not a group.

81. 8:00 A.M.

Chapter 13 Review Exercises

1. $\{e, c, f, r\}$ **2.** closed; All entries in the body of the table are elements of the set $\{e, c, f, r\}$. **3.** r **4.** f **5.** c **6.** Both expressions equal e. **7.** Both expressions equal c. **8.** Both expressions equal f. **9.** commutative property **10.** The entries in the table are mirror images about the diagonal from the upper left corner to the lower right corner. **11.** Both expressions equal f. **12.** Both expressions equal e. **13.** associative property **14.** e **15.** e **16.** r **17.** f **18.** c **19.** not closed; $1 + 1 = 2$ which is not in the set. **20.** closed; All products result in either 0 or 1. **21.** not closed; $1 \div 2 = \frac{1}{2}$ which is not in the set. **22.** -123 **23.** $\frac{1}{123}$

24. a.

∘	0	1	2	3	4
0	0	1	2	3	4
1	1	1	2	3	4
2	2	2	2	3	4
3	3	3	3	3	4
4	4	4	4	4	4

b. 0 **c.** no inverse; No element combined with 2 results in 0.

25. 3-fold rotational symmetry **26.** 18-fold rotational symmetry

27. a.

+	0	1	2	3	4
0	0	1	2	3	4
1	1	2	3	4	0
2	2	3	4	0	1
3	3	4	0	1	2
4	4	0	1	2	3

b. 1. Since all entries in the body of the table are elements of the set, the closure property is satisfied. **2.** Since the result of using clock addition to add 3 elements is the same regardless of whether the first two elements are grouped or the last two elements are grouped, the associative property is satisfied.
Example:
$(1 + 2) + 3 = 3 + 3 = 1$
$1 + (2 + 3) = 1 + 0 = 1$
3. Since 0 is an element of the set and $0 + e = e$ and $e + 0 = e$ for all elements e in the set, the identity property is satisfied. **4.** Since each element has an inverse within the set, the inverse property is satisfied. **5.** Since the entries in the table are symmetric about the diagonal from the upper left corner to the lower right corner, we know that the order of clock addition does not matter. The commutative property is satisfied.
Since all 5 properties are satisfied, this mathematical system is a commutative group.

28. false; $17 \equiv 1 \pmod 8$ **29.** false; $37 \equiv 2 \pmod 5$ **30.** true **31.** 1 (mod 6) **32.** 6 (mod 8) **33.** 7 (mod 9) **34.** 1 (mod 20)

Chapter 13 Test

1. closed; All entries in the body of the table are elements of the set $\{x, y, z\}$. **2.** Both expressions equal x.; commutative property **3.** Both expressions equal y.; associative property **4.** x **5.** x is its own inverse. z is the inverse of y. y is the inverse of z. **6.** not closed; $1 + 1 = 2$ which is not in the set. **7.** $\frac{1}{5}$; $5 \times \frac{1}{5} = 1$ **8.** 6-fold rotational symmetry; Since it takes 6 equal turns to restore the design to its original position and each of these turns is a design that is identical to the original, the design has 6-fold rotational symmetry.

9.

+	0	1	2	3
0	0	1	2	3
1	1	2	3	0
2	2	3	0	1
3	3	0	1	2

10. Check that all properties are satisfied:
1. Since all entries in the body of the table are elements of the set, the closure property is satisfied. **2.** Since the result of using clock addition to add 3 elements is the same regardless of whether the first two elements are grouped or the last two elements are grouped, the associative property is satisfied.
Example:
$(1 + 2) + 3 = 3 + 3 = 2$
$1 + (2 + 3) = 1 + 1 = 2$
3. Since 0 is an element of the set and $0 + e = e$ and $e + 0 = e$ for all elements e in the set, the identity property is satisfied. **4.** Since each element has an inverse within the set, the inverse property is satisfied. **5.** Since the entries in the table are symmetric about the diagonal from the upper left corner to the lower right corner, we know that the order of clock addition does not matter. The commutative property is satisfied.
Since all 5 properties are satisfied, this mathematical system is a commutative group.

11. true **12.** false; $14 \equiv 0 \pmod 7$ **13.** 10 (mod 11) **14.** 5 (mod 10)

CHAPTER 14

Section 14.1

Check Point Exercises

1. a. 4210 **b.** 40 **c.** 2865 **2.** Donna **3.** Bob **4.** Carmen **5.** Bob

Exercise Set 14.1

1. 7; 5; 4 **3.**

Number of Votes	5	1	4	2
First Choice	A	B	C	C
Second Choice	B	D	B	B
Third Choice	C	C	D	A
Fourth Choice	D	A	A	D

5. a. 26 **b.** 8 **c.** 22 **d.** 3 **7.** musical **9.** Darwin **11.** Comedy **13.** Freud **15.** Comedy **17.** Einstein **19.** 10 **21.** 28 **23.** Comedy **25.** Hawking **27.** A **29.** B **31.** Rent **33.** Rent **35. a.** C **b.** A **37.** C **49.** b

Section 14.2

Check Point Exercises

1. a. A **b.** B **2. a.** B **b.** A **3. a.** A **b.** C **c.** yes **4. a.** A **b.** D **c.** yes

Exercise Set 14.2

1. a. D **b.** A **c.** no **3. a.** A **b.** V **c.** no **5. a.** A **b.** C **c.** no **7. a.** C **b.** B **c.** no
9. a. S **b.**

Number of Votes	15	8
First Choice	S	L
Second Choice	L	S

; S **c.** yes

11. a. A **b.** no **13. a.** C **b.** no **15. a.** B **b.** no **c.** no **d.** A; no **17. a.** B **b.** no **c.** no
19. a. A **b.** yes **c.** yes **d.**

Number of Votes	7	3	2
First Choice	A	B	A
Second Choice	B	C	C
Third Choice	C	A	B

; A **e.** yes **f.** no

Section 14.3

Check Point Exercises

1. a. 50 **b.** 22.24; 22.36; 26.4; 30.3; 98.7 **2.** 22; 22; 27; 30; 99 **3.** 22; 22; 26; 30; 100 **4.** 22; 23; 27; 30; 98 **5.** 22; 22; 27; 30; 99

Exercise Set 14.3

1. a. 20; 20,000 **b.** 6.9; 13.3; 26.7; 33.1 **c.**

State	Lower Quota	Upper Quota
A	6	7
B	13	14
C	26	27
D	33	34

3. 7; 13; 27; 33 **5.** 30; 41; 53; 73; 103 **7.** 3; 5; 12; 15; 22 **9.** 17; 55; 24; 54 **11.** 28; 33; 53; 15; 22; 29 **13.** 12; 10; 8 **15.** 4; 10; 6 **17.** 20; 24; 29; 29; 98 **19.** 57; 81; 68; 44 **21.** 57; 81; 68; 44 **23.** 7; 2; 2; 2; 8; 14; 4; 5; 10; 10; 13; 2; 6; 2; 18 **25.** 7; 2; 2; 2; 8; 14; 4; 5; 10; 10; 12; 2; 6; 3; 18

Section 14.4

Check Point Exercises

1. B's apportionment decreases from 11 to 10. **2. a.** 10; 19; 71 **b.** State A: 1.005%; State B: 0.998% **c.** State A loses a seat to State B, even though the population of State A is increasing at a faster rate. **3. a.** 21; 79 **b.** With North High added to the district, West High loses a counselor to East High.

Exercise Set 14.4

1. a. 16; 8; 6 **b.** 17; 9; 5; Liberal Arts Math loses a teaching assistant when the total number of teaching assistants is raised from 30 to 31. This is an example of the Alabama paradox. **3.** State A loses a seat when the total number of seats increases from 40 to 41. **5. a.** 4; 6; 14 **b.** 28.3%; 26.3%; 14.7% **c.** 3; 7; 14; A loses a seat while B gains, even though A has a faster increasing population. The population paradox does occur. **7.** C loses a truck to B even though C increased in population faster than B. **9. a.** 10; 90 **b.** Branch B loses a promotion when branch C is added. This means the new-states paradox has occurred. **11. a.** 9; 91 **b.** State B loses a seat when state C is added. **13. a.** 6; 13; 31 **b.** The new-states paradox does not occur. As long as the modified divisor, *d*, remains the same, adding a new state cannot change the number of seats held by existing states.

Chapter 14 Review Exercises

1.

Number of Votes	4	3	3	2
First Choice	A	B	C	C
Second Choice	B	D	B	B
Third Choice	C	C	D	A
Fourth Choice	D	A	A	D

2. 23 **3.** 4 **4.** 16 **5.** 14 **6.** Musical **7.** Comedy **8.** Musical **9.** Musical **10.** A **11.** B **12.** A **13.** A **14.** B **15.** A; no **16.** A; no **17.** B **18.** B; yes **19.** A **20.** B **21.** A **22.** A **23.** A; Borda count method **24.** B **25.** A; no **26.** A

27.

Number of Votes	400	450
First Choice	A	C
Second Choice	C	A

; C; no

28. B **29.** B still wins. The irrelevant alternatives criterion is satisfied. **30.** 50.05 **31.** 5.49; 7.83; 12.21; 14.47 **32.** A: 5, 6; B: 7, 8; C: 12, 13; D: 14, 15 **33.** 6; 8; 12; 14 **34.** 5; 8; 12; 15 **35.** 6; 8; 12; 14 **36.** 6; 8; 12; 14 **37.** 14; 42; 62; 82 **38.** 13; 42; 63; 82 **39.** 14; 42; 63; 81 **40.** 14; 42; 62; 82 **41. a.** 8; 67; 75 **b.** The Alabama paradox occurs. **42. a.** 72; 20; 8 **b.** 0.8%; 1.3% **c.** The population paradox occurs. **43. a.** 7; 26 **b.** The new-states paradox does not occur. **44.** False. Answers will vary.

Chapter 14 Test

1. 3600 **2.** 600 **3.** 1500 **4.** 1500 **5.** B **6.** B **7.** A **8.** A **9.** A **10.** A; yes **11.** A **12.** B; no **13.** C **14.** B; no **15.** no **16.** 50 **17.** 2.38; 3.3; 4.32 **18.** A: 2, 3; B: 3, 4; C: 4, 5 **19.** 3; 3; 4 **20.** 2; 3; 5 **21.** 3; 3; 4 **22.** 2; 3; 5 **23.** yes **24.** The new-states paradox does not occur. **25.** Answers will vary.

CHAPTER 15

Section 15.1

Check Point Exercises

1. The two graphs have the same number of vertices connected to each other in the same way.

2.

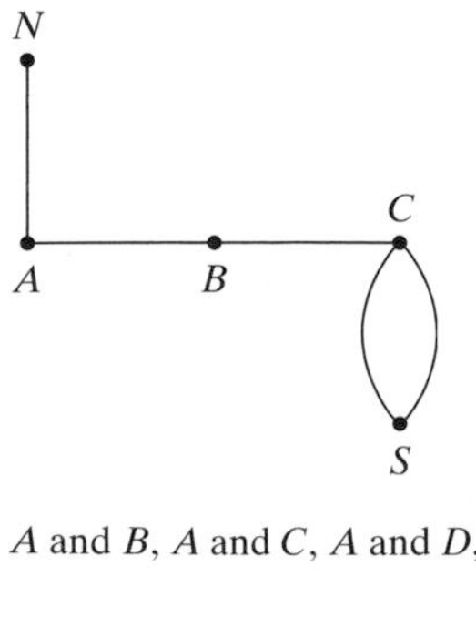

3.

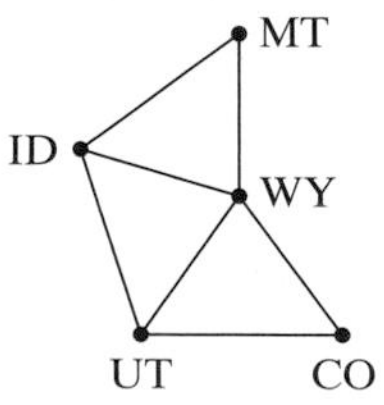

4.

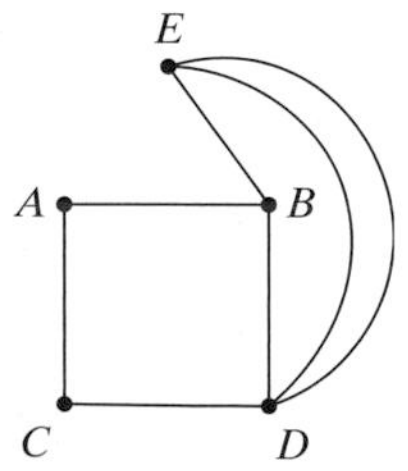

5.

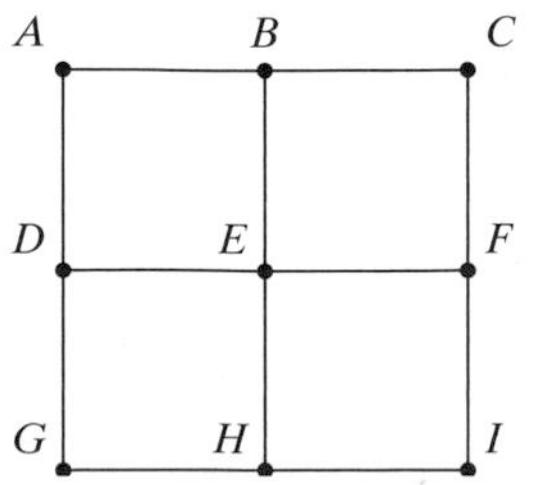

6. *A* and *B*, *A* and *C*, *A* and *D*, *A* and *E*, *B* and *C*, and *E* and *E*

Exercise Set 15.1

1. 6; St. Louis, Chicago, Philadelphia, Montreal; 1, 1, 2, 2 **3.** No; no; Answers will vary.

5. Possible answers:

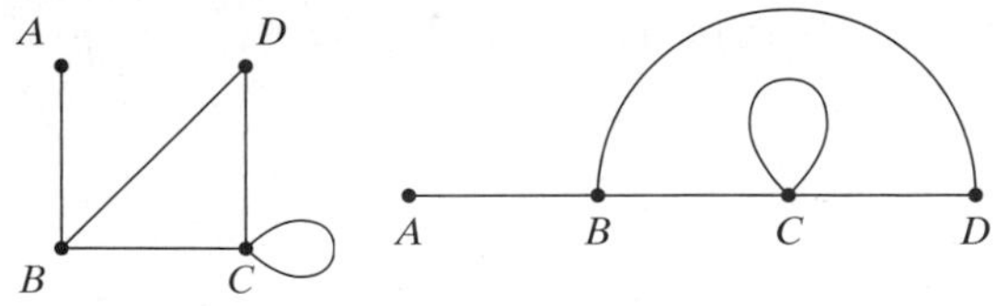

7. The two graphs have the same number of vertices connected in the same way, so they are the equivalent. Possible answer:

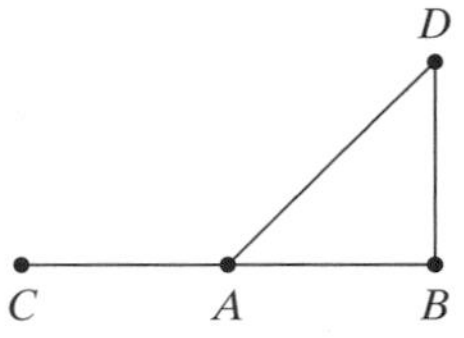

9.

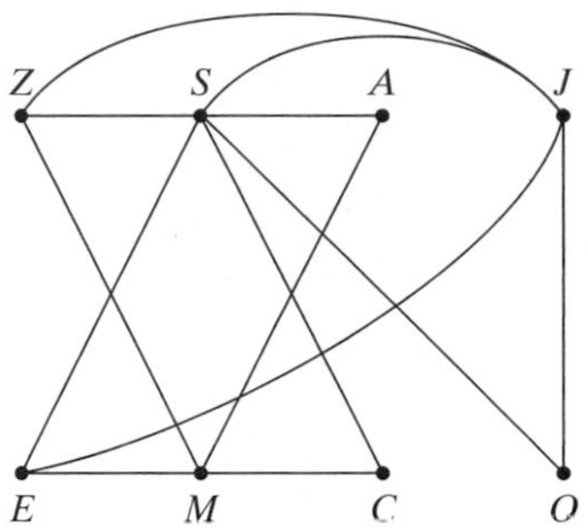

11.

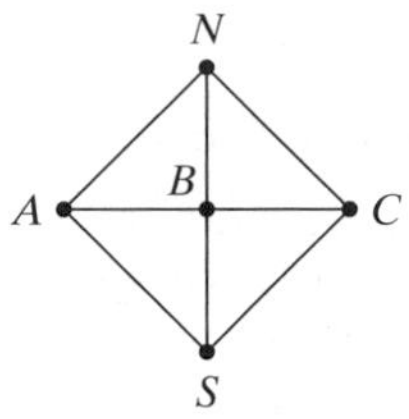

13.

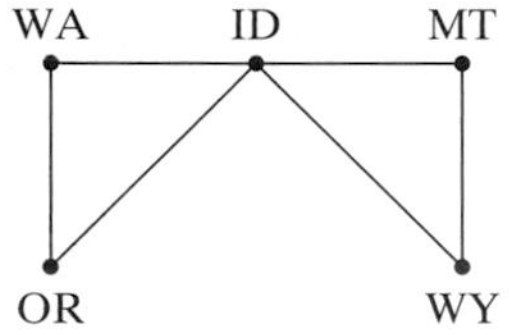

15.

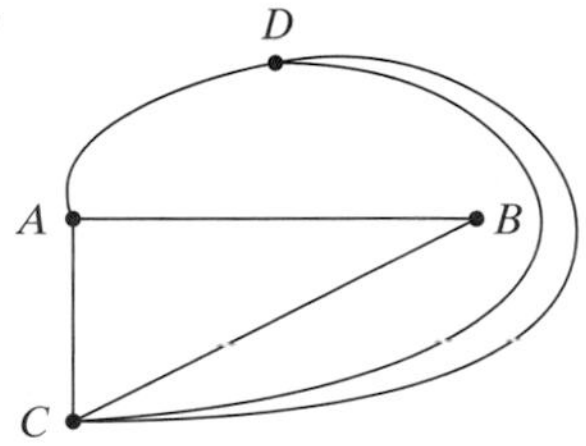

17.

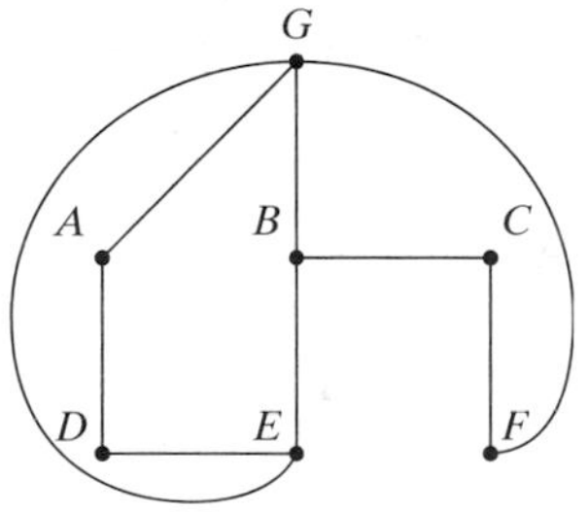

19.

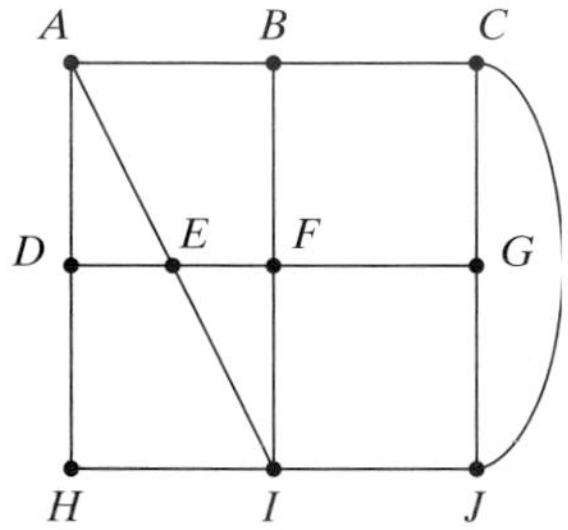

21.

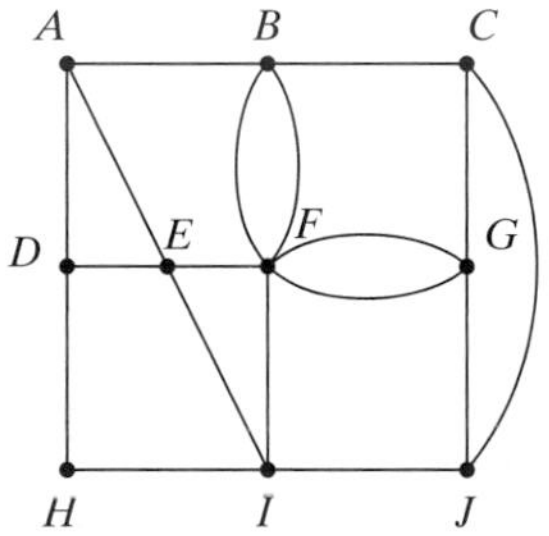

23. *A*: 2; *B*: 2; *C*: 3; *D*: 3; *E*: 3; *F*: 1 **25.** *B* and *C* **27.** *A, C, D*; *A, B, C, D* **29.** *AC* and *DF* **31.** While edge *CD* is included, the graph is connected. If we remove *CD*, the graph will be disconnected. **33.** *DF* **35.** Even: *A, B, G, H, I*; odd: *C, D, E, F* **37.** *D, G*, and *I* **39.** Possible answers: *B, C, D, F*; *B, A, C, D, F* **41.** *G, F, I, H, G* **43.** *A, B, C, C, D, F, G, H, I* **45.** *G, F, D, E, D* requires that edge *DE* be traversed twice. This is not allowed within a path. **47.** No edge connects *F* and *E*.

49. Possible answer:

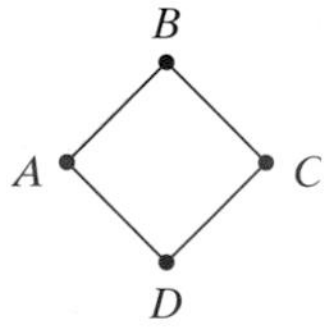

51. Possible answer:

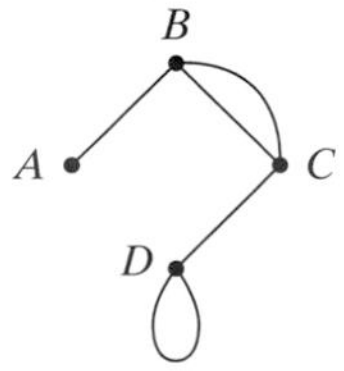

67.

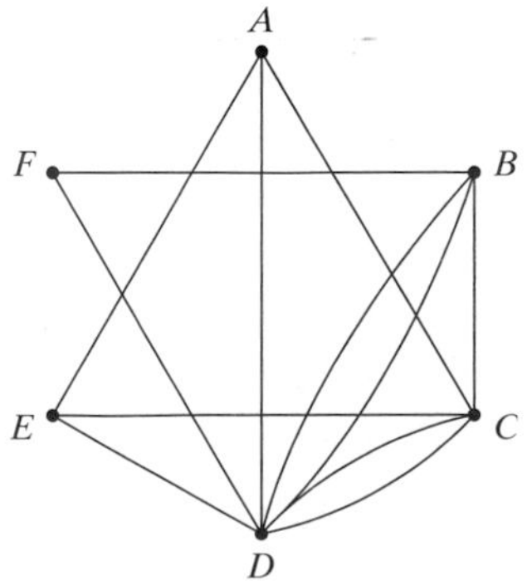

Section 15.2

Check Point Exercises

1.

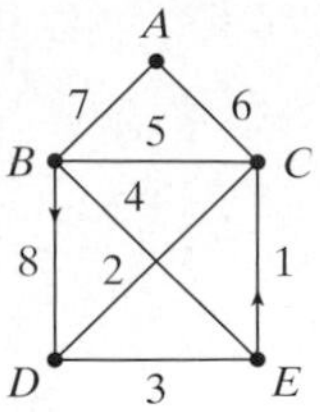

; *E, C, D, E, B, C, A, B, D*

2.

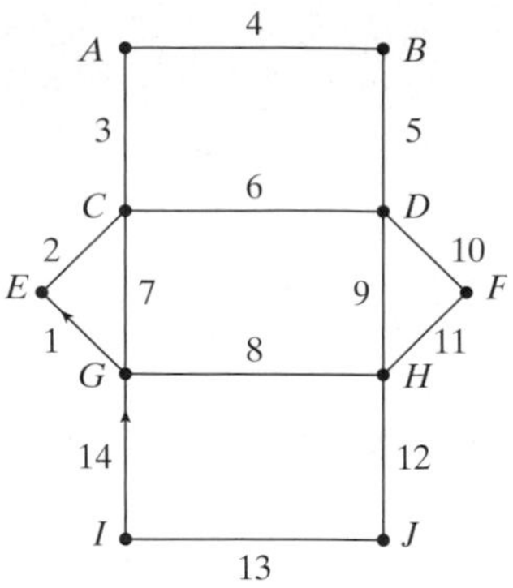

; *G, E, C, A, B, D, C, G, H, D, F, H, J, I, G*

3. a. yes **b.**

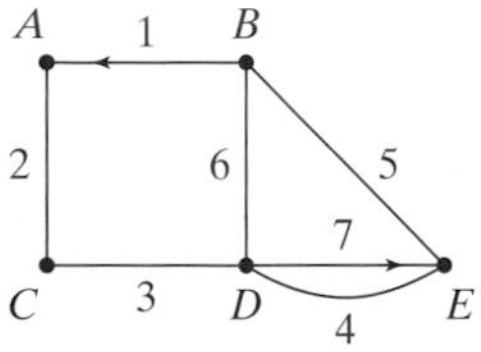

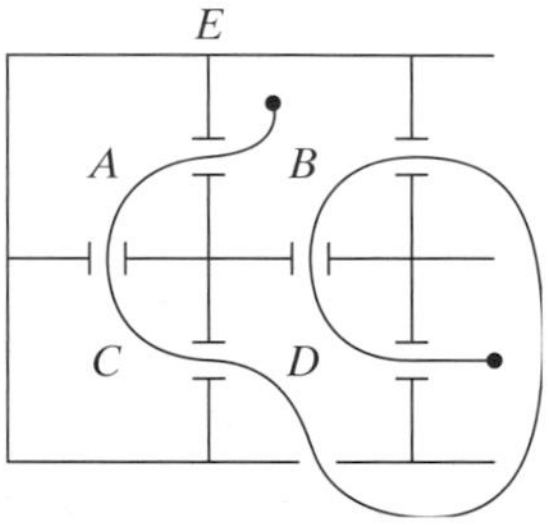

4.

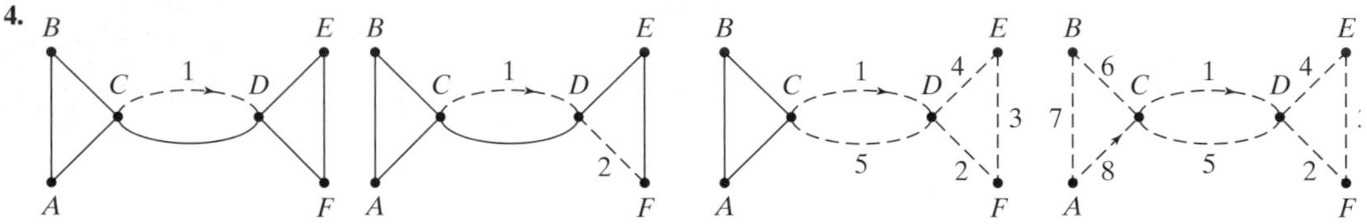

Exercise Set 15.2

1.

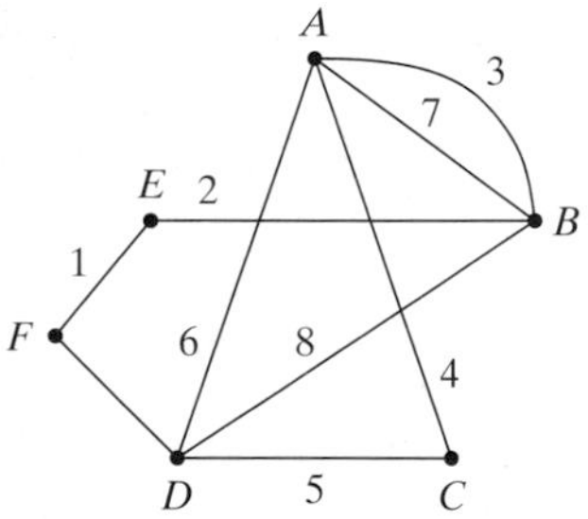

neither

3.

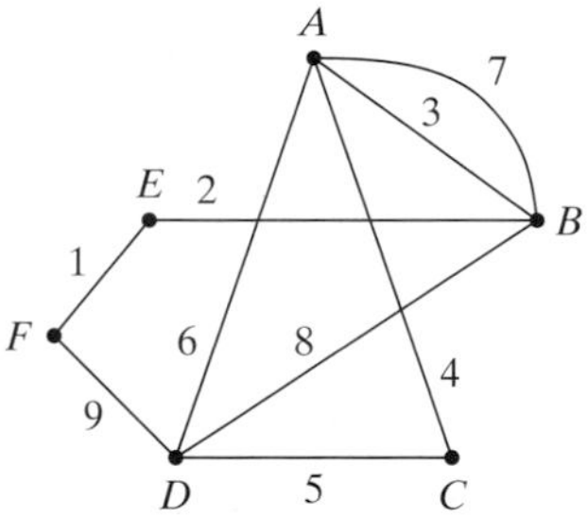

Euler circuit

5.

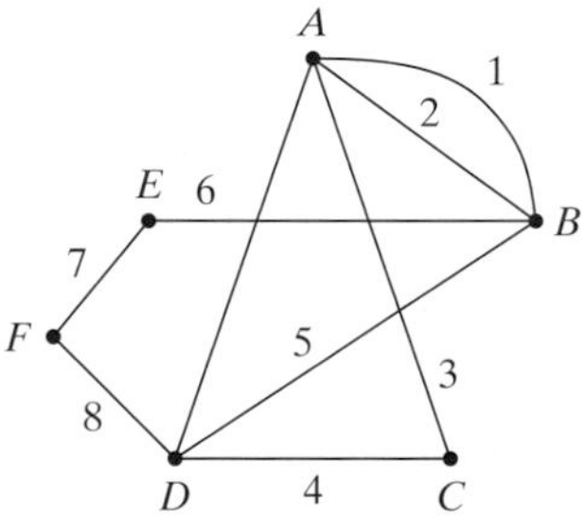

neither

7. a. There are two odd vertices.
b. Possible answer:

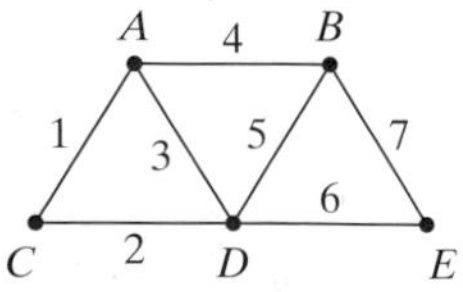

9. a. There are no odd vertices.
b. Possible answer:

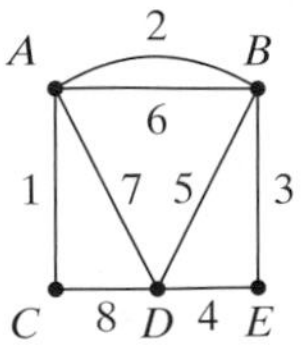

11. There are more than two odd vertices. **13.** Euler circuit **15.** Euler path, but no Euler circuit **17.** neither an Euler path nor an Euler circuit

19. a. Euler circuit
b. Possible answer:

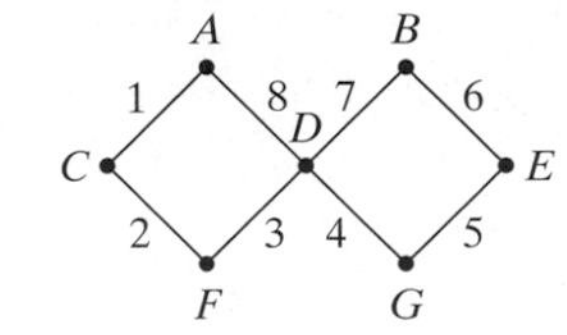

21. a. Euler path
b. Possible answer:

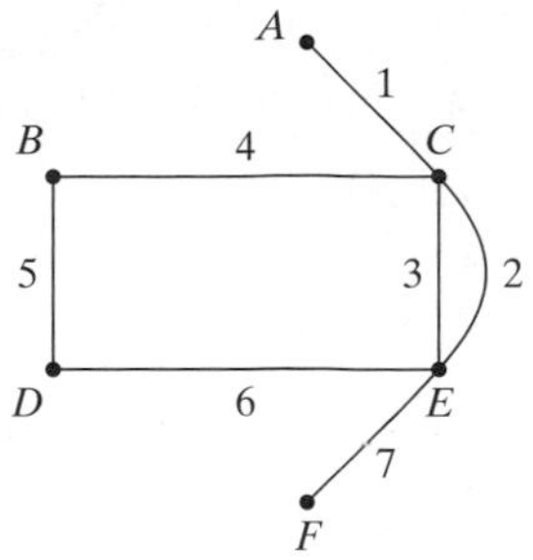

23. a. neither

25. a. Euler path
b. Possible answer:

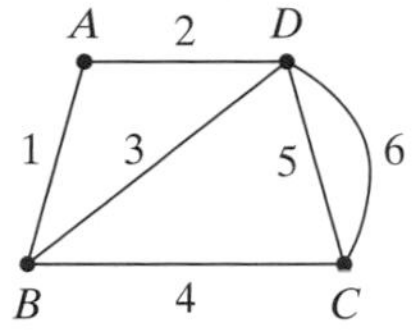

27. a. Euler circuit
b. Possible answer:

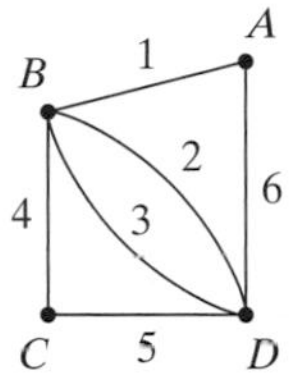

29. a. neither

31. a. Euler path
b. Possible answer:

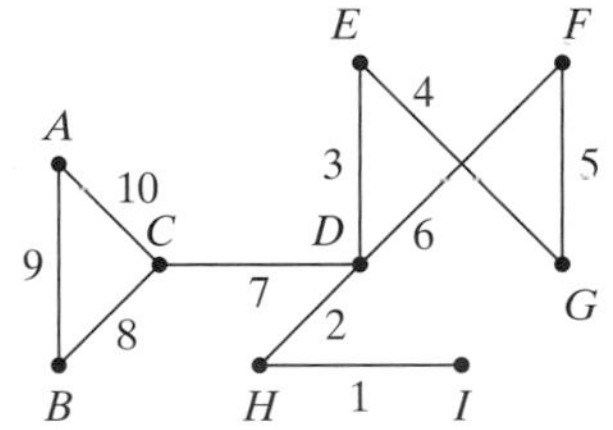

33. Possible answer:

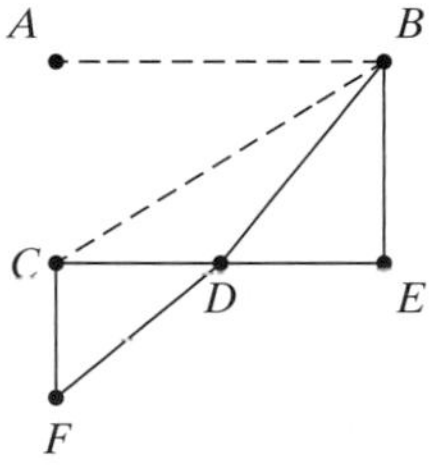

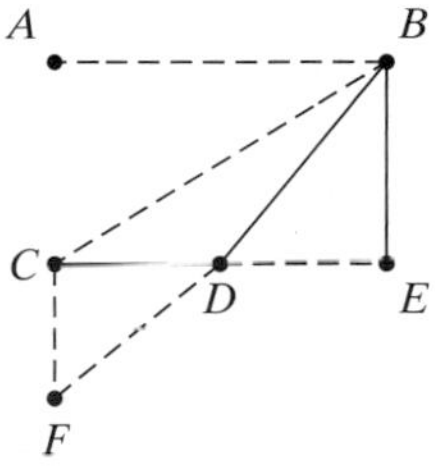

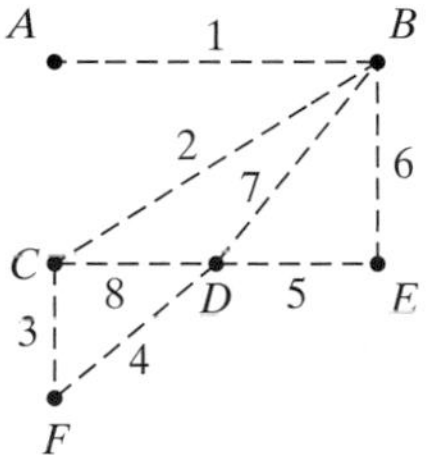

35. Possible answer:

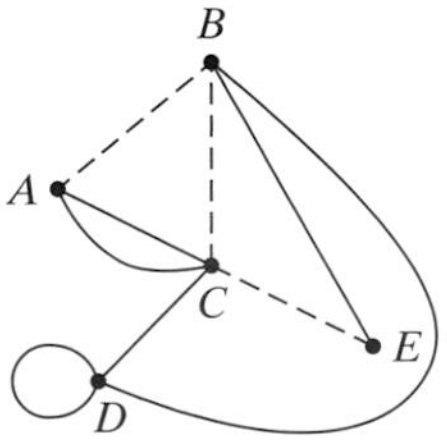

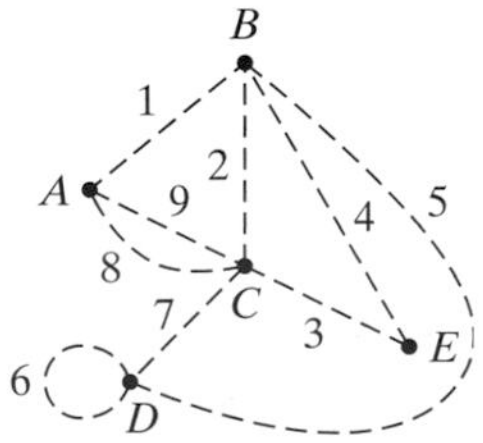

37. Possible answer:

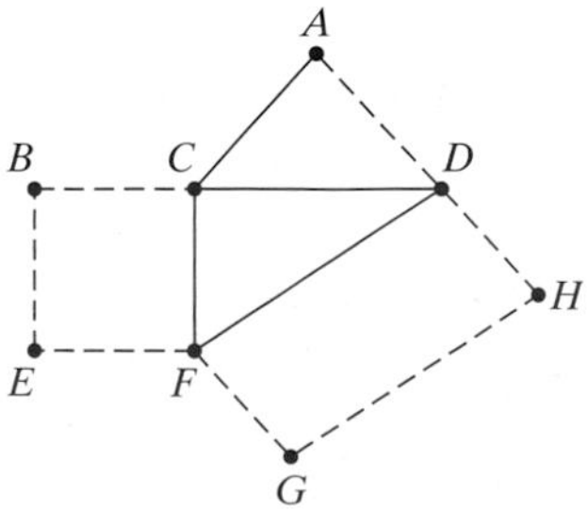

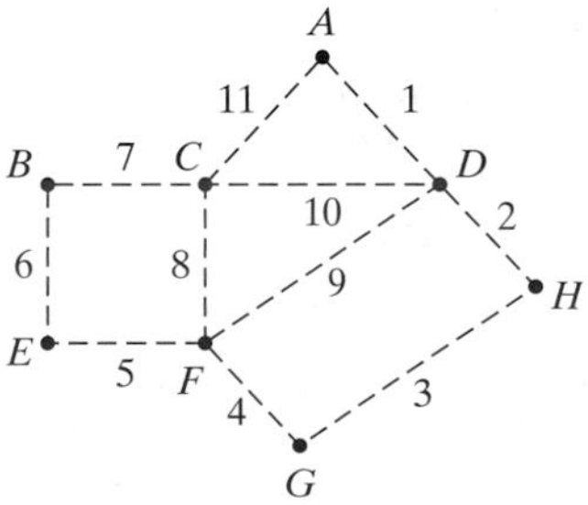

39. Possible answer:

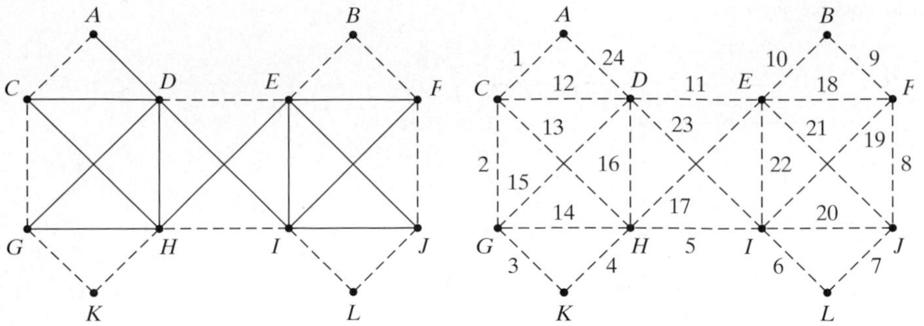

41. a. Remove *FG*. **b.** Sample answer: *EC*, *CB*, *BD*, *DF*, *FA*, *AD*, *DG*, *GH*, *HC*, *CG*, *GB*, *BH*, *HE*

43. a. Remove *BA* and *FJ*. **b.** Sample answer: *CA*, *AD*, *DI*, *IH*, *HG*, *GF*, *FC*, *CD*, *DE*, *EH*, *HJ*, *JG*, *GB*, *BC*

45. The graph has an Euler circuit.

47.

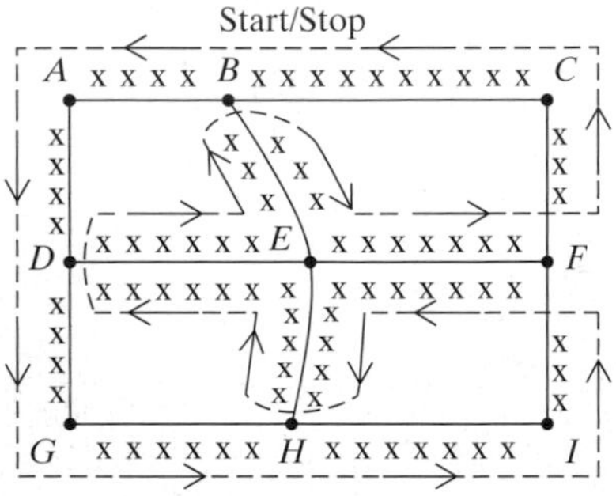

49. a.

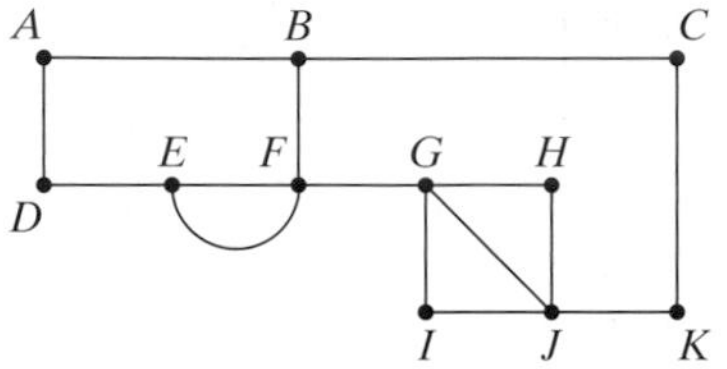

b. Yes; begin at *B* or *E*.

51. a.

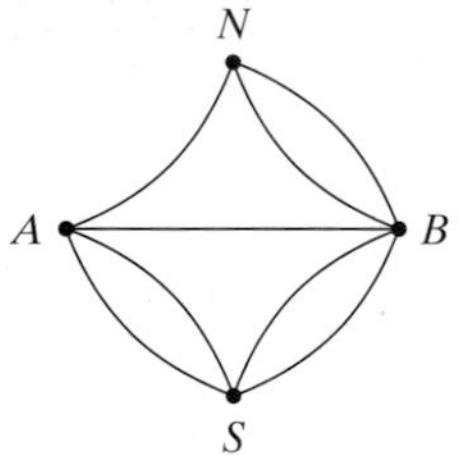

b. Yes, they can.

c. Possible answer:

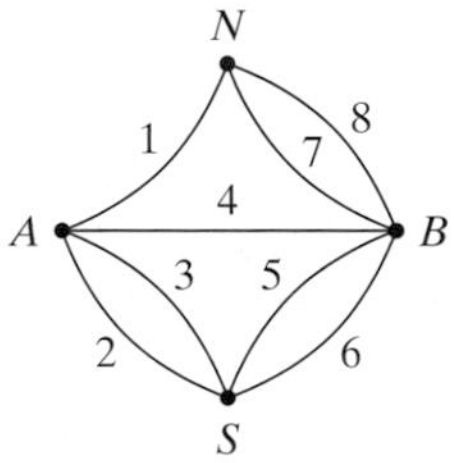

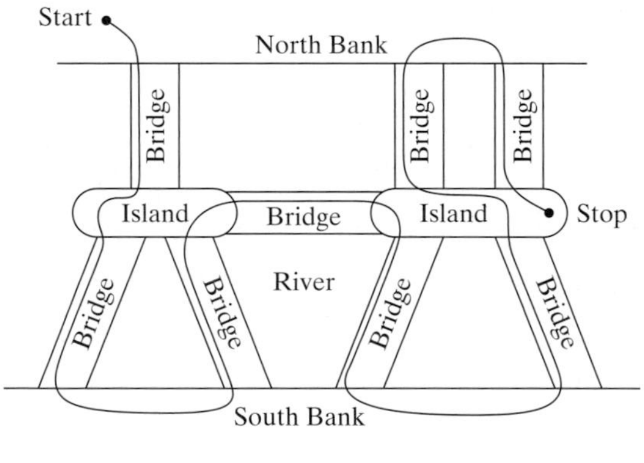

53.

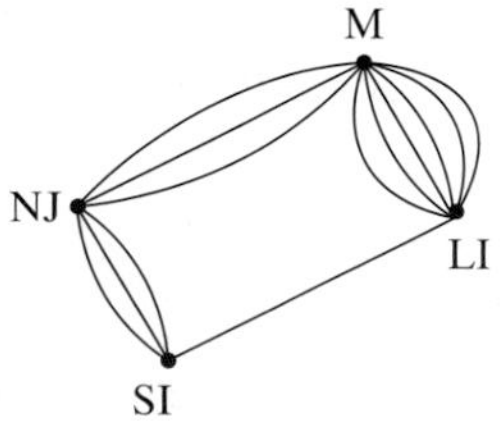

; It is possible.

55. a.

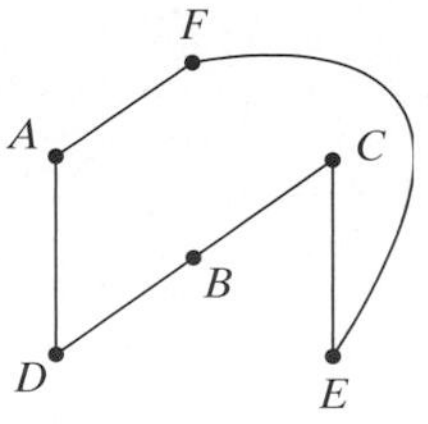

b. It is possible.
c. Possible answer:

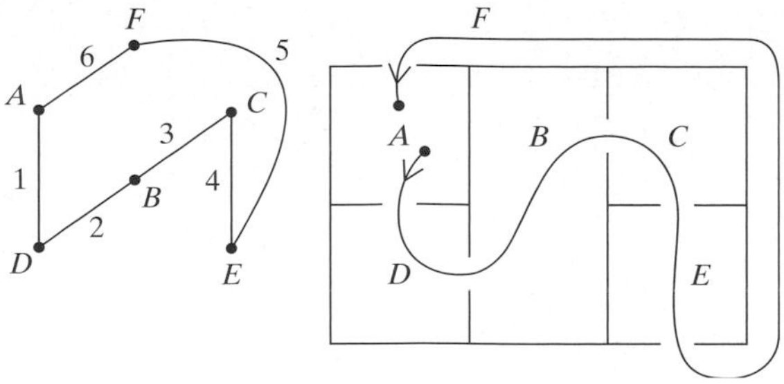

57. Possible answer:

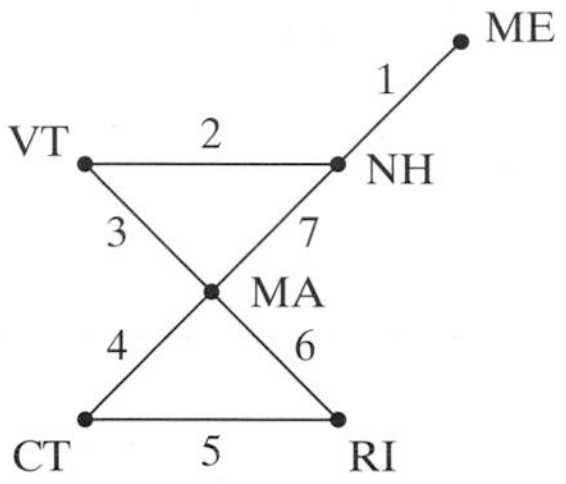

59. a.

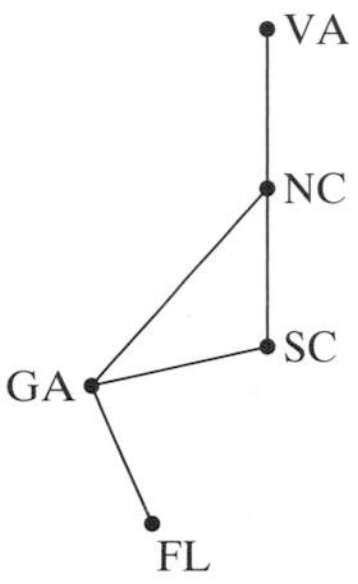

b. not possible
d. not possible

Section 15.3

Check Point Exercises

1. a. Possible answer: E, C, D, G, B, A, F **b.** Possible answer: E, C, D, G, B, F, A, E **2. a.** 2 **b.** 120 **c.** 362,880 **3.** $562

4.

Hamilton Circuit	Sum of the Weights of the Edges	=	Total Cost
A, B, C, D, A	20 + 15 + 50 + 30	=	$115
A, B, D, C, A	20 + 10 + 50 + 70	=	$150
A, C, B, D, A	70 + 15 + 10 + 30	=	$125
A, C, D, B, A	70 + 50 + 10 + 20	=	$150
A, D, B, C, A	30 + 10 + 15 + 70	=	$125
A, D, C, B, A	30 + 50 + 15 + 20	=	$115

A, B, C, D, A; A, D, C, B, A

5. A, B, C, D, E, A; 198

Exercise Set 15.3

1. Possible answer: A, G, C, F, E, D, B **3.** Possible answer: A, B, G, C, F, E, D, A **5.** Possible answer: A, F, G, E, C, B, D
7. Possible answer: A, B, C, E, G, F, D, A **9. a.** no **11. a.** yes **b.** 120 **13. a.** no **15.** 2 **17.** 39,916,800 **19.** 11 **21.** 36
23. 36 **25.** 88 **27.** 70 **29.** 70 **31.** A, C, B, D, A and A, D, B, C, A **33.** B, D, C, A, B; 82 **35. a.** Add AB.; 6
b. Sample answers: AD, DB, BC, CA; CA, AB, BD, DC **c.** Remove CD. **d.** Sample answer: AC, CB, BD, DA
37. a. Add AB, AC, BC, and DE.; 24 **b.** Sample answers: AB, BC, CE, ED, DA; AB, BC, CD, DE, EA **c.** Remove BD and BE.
d. Sample answer: AE, EC, CD, DA **39.** A, D, B, C, E, A

41.

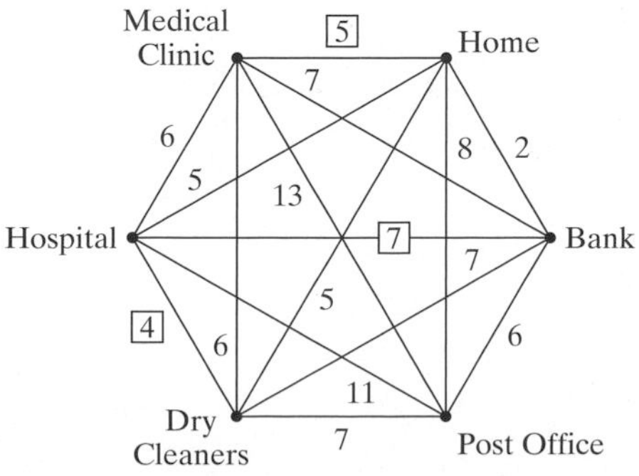

43. 30 **45.**

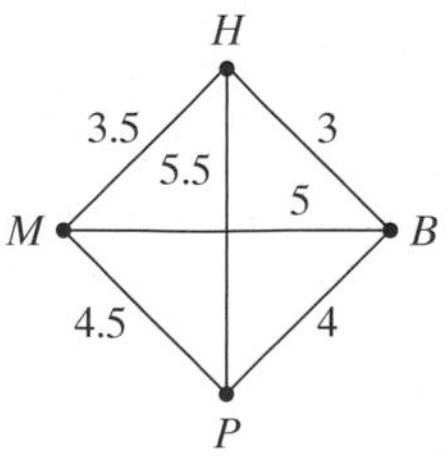

47. H, B, P, M, H; 15 mi; same

Section 15.4

Check Point Exercises

1. Figure 15.51(c) **2.** Possible answer:

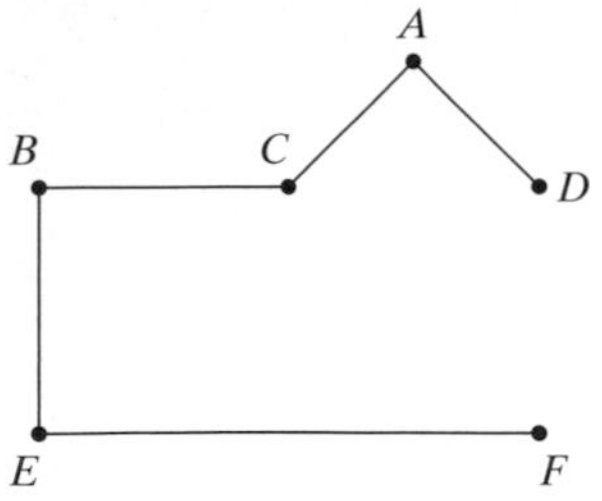

3.

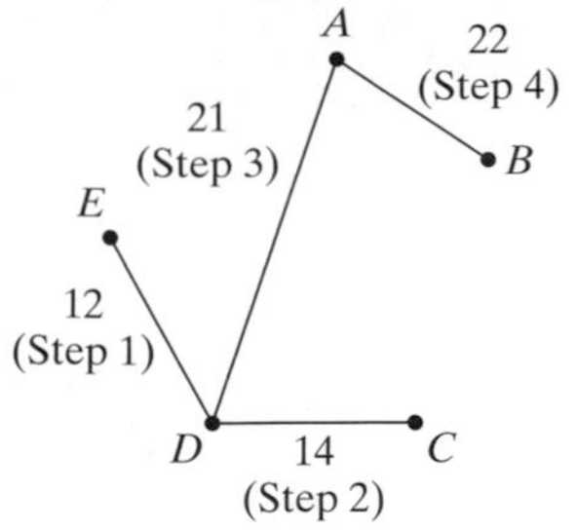

; 69

Exercise Set 15.4

1. yes **3.** no **5.** yes **7.** no **9.** yes **11.** i. **13.** ii. **15.** ii. **17.** iii.

19.

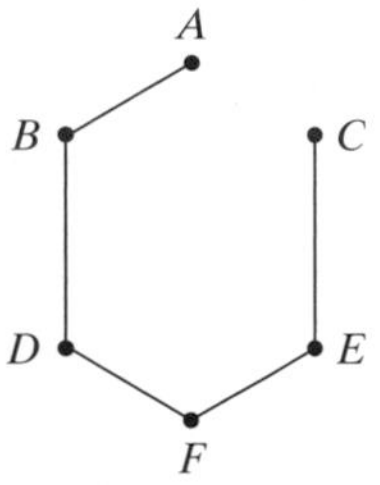

21.

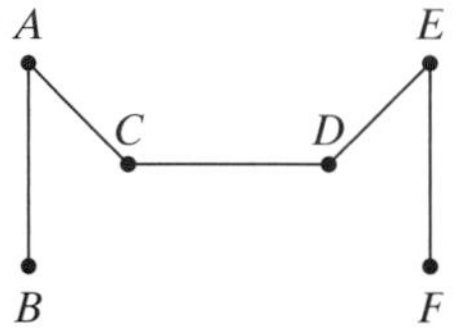

23.

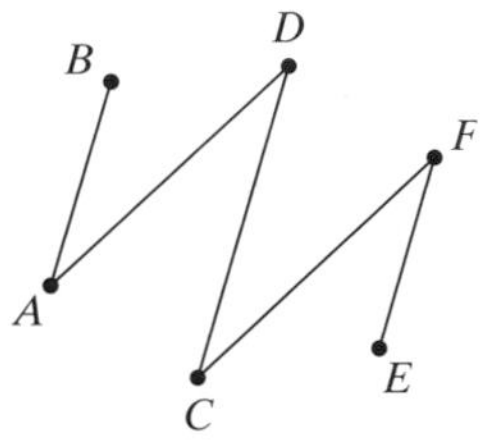

25.

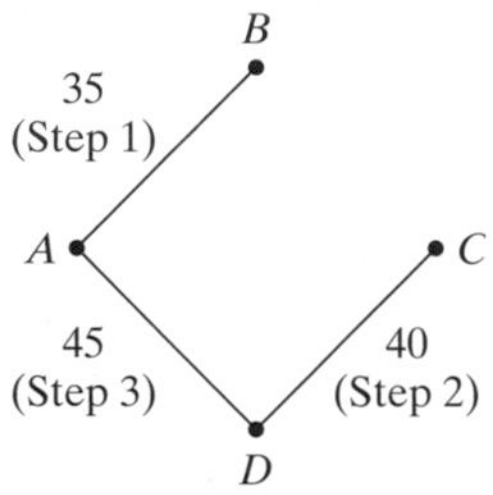

; 120

27.

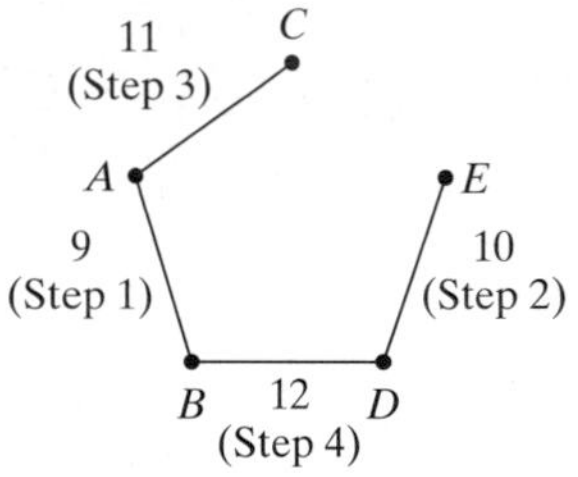

; 42

29.

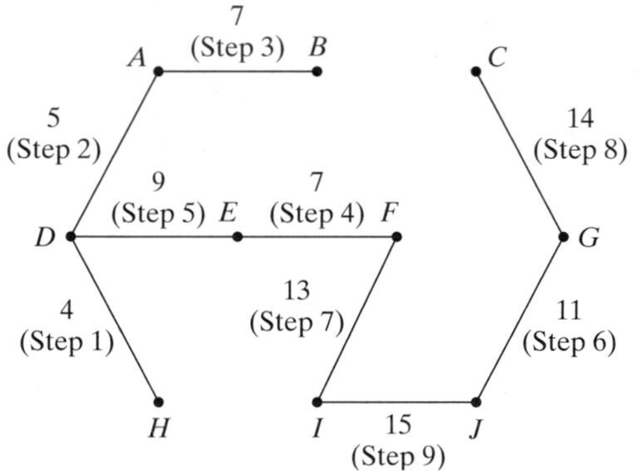

; 85

31.

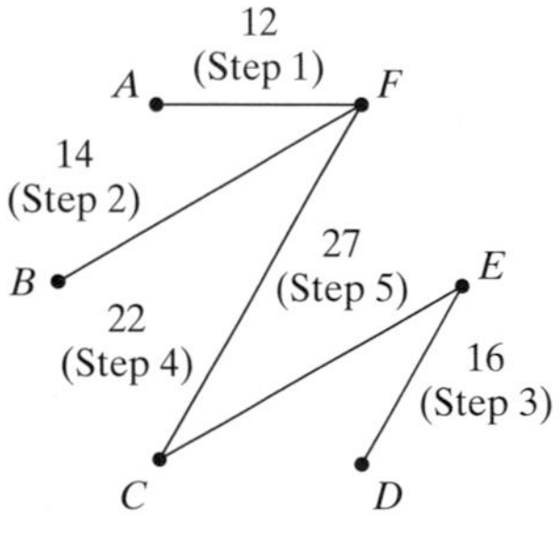

; 91

33. Sample answers: AB, AC, CD; AB, BC, CD; AB, AD, CD; AB, AD, BC **35.** AE, BC, CD, CE; 64

37. Sample answer: AE, BC, BE, CF, DE, EH, FG, FJ, HI; 141

39.

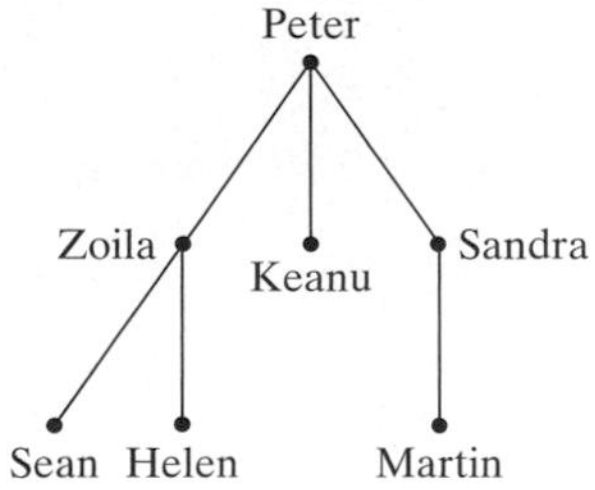

41. a.

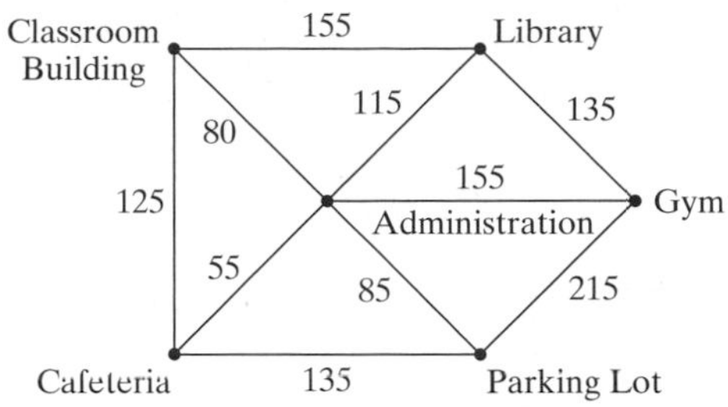

b.

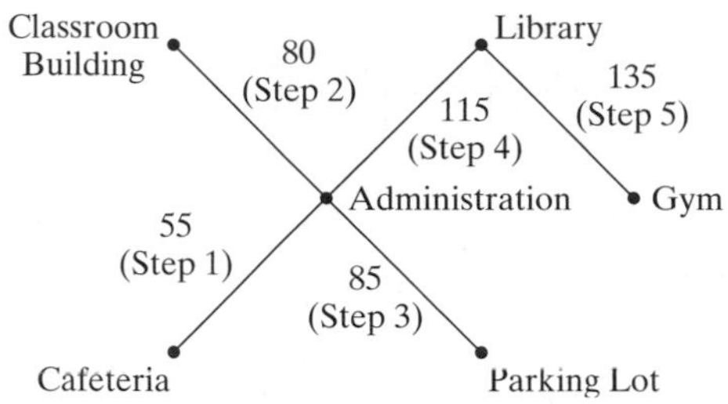

; 470 ft

43.

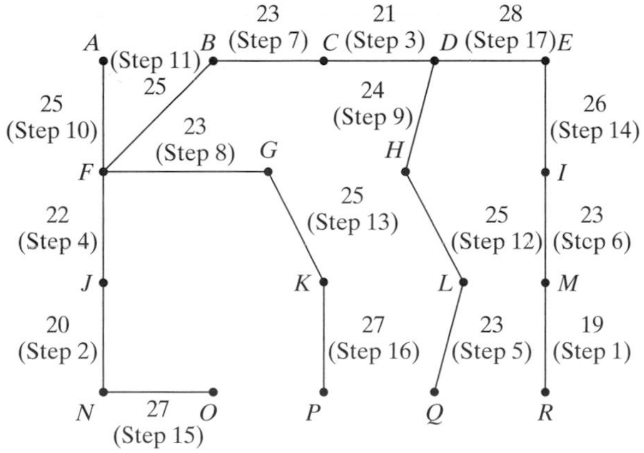

; 406 mi

Chapter 15 Review Exercises

1. Both graphs have the same number of vertices, and these vertices are connected in the same ways. Possible answer:

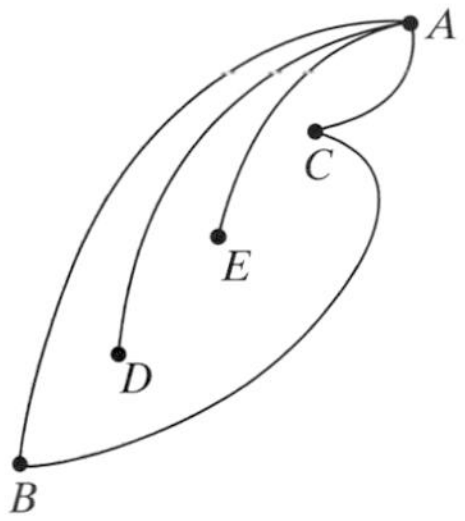

2. *A*: 5; *B*: 4; *C*: 5; *D*: 4; *E*: 2 **3.** Even: *B*, *D*, *E*; odd: *A*, *C*
4. *B*, *C*, and *E* **5.** Possible answer: *E*, *D*, *B*, *A* and *E*, *C*, *A*
6. Possible answer: *E*, *D*, *C*, *E* **7.** yes **8.** no **9.** *AD*, *DE*, and *DF*

10.

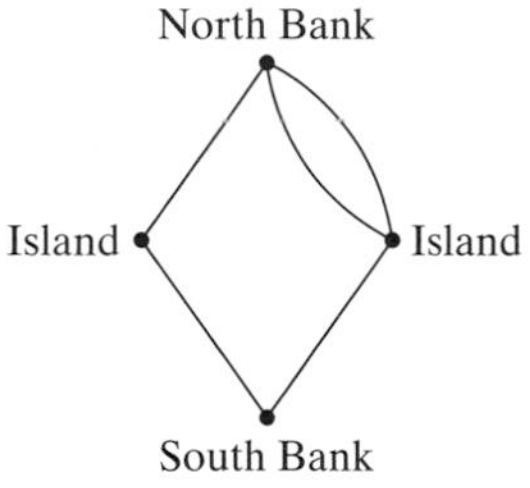

11.

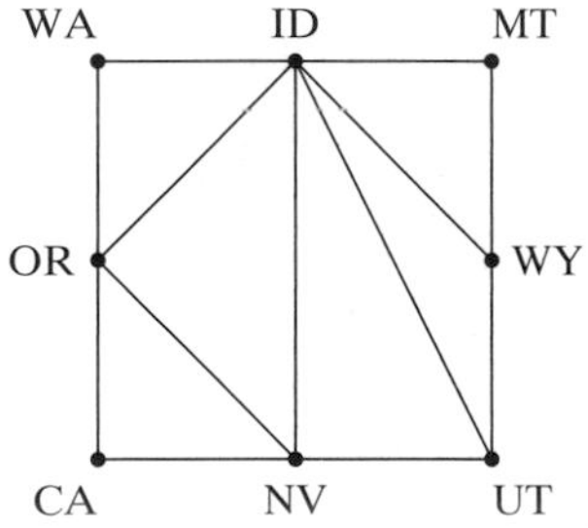

12.

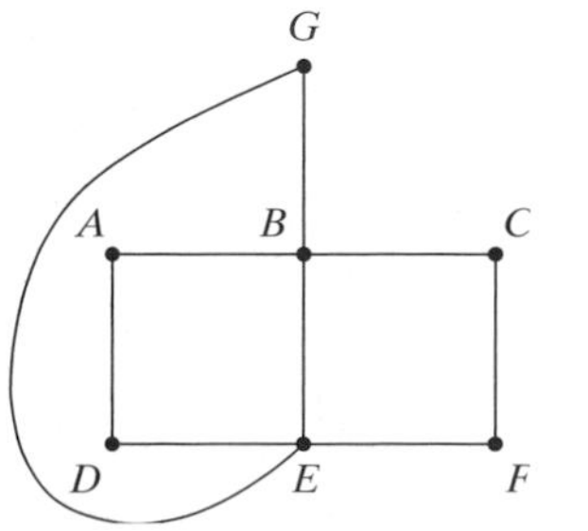

13. a. neither

14. a. Euler circuit
b. Possible answer:

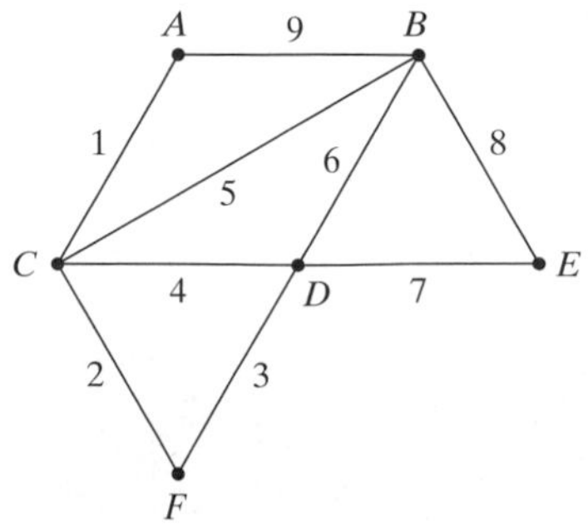

15. a. Euler path
b. Possible answer:

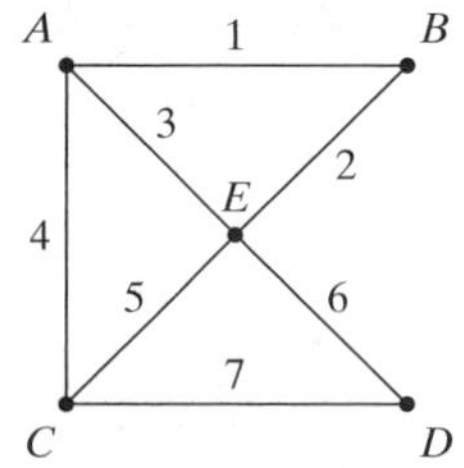

16.

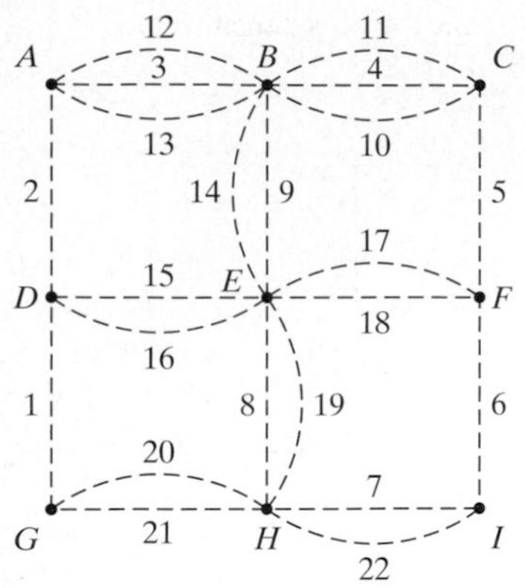

17.

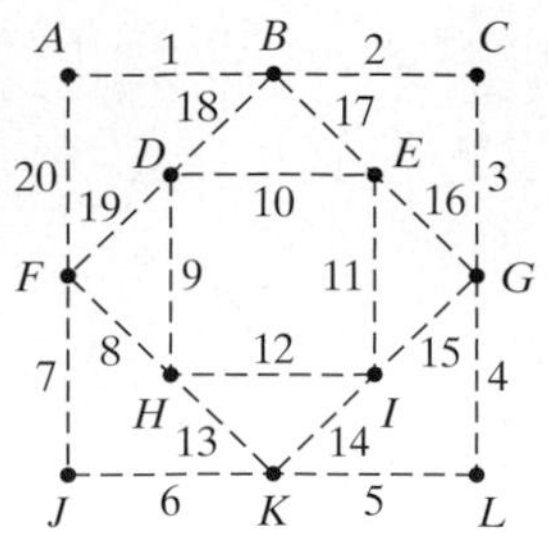

18. a. yes **b.**

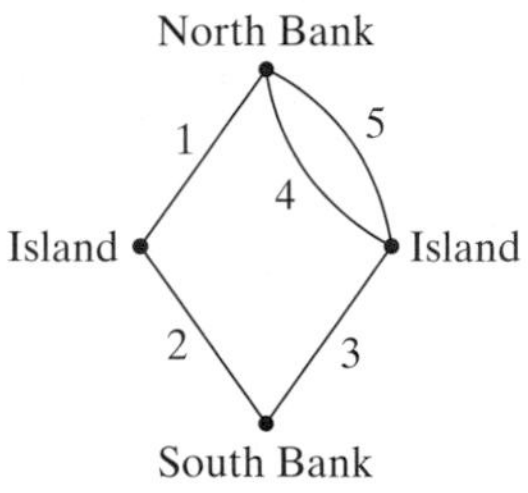

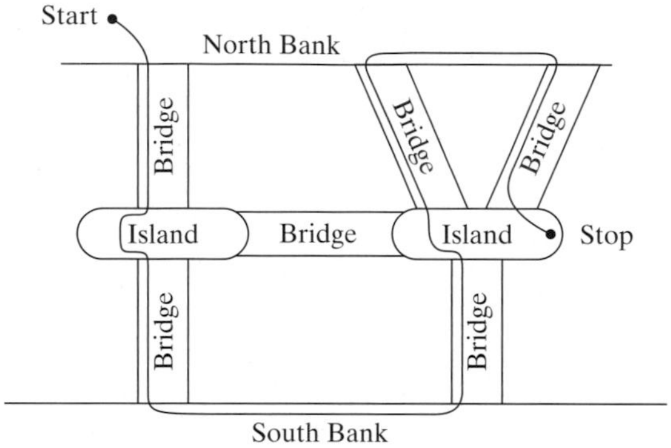

c. no

19. It is possible. **20. a.** yes **b.** Possible answer:

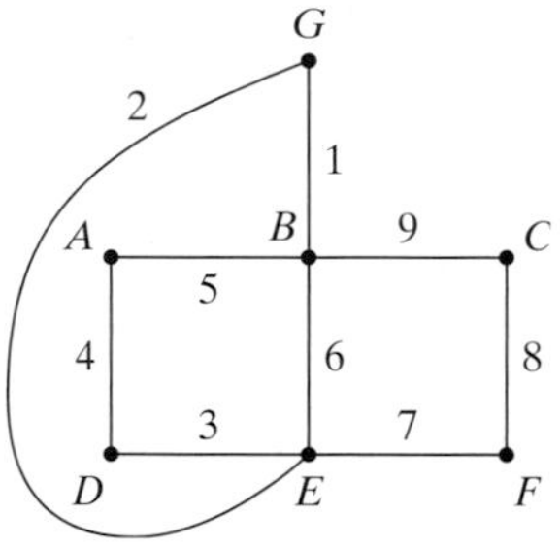

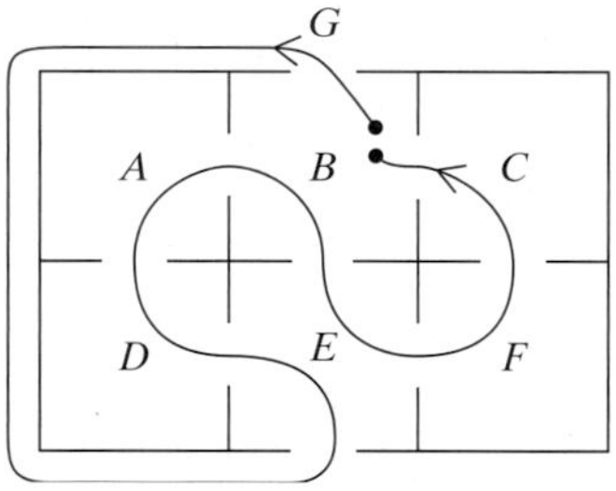

21. a.

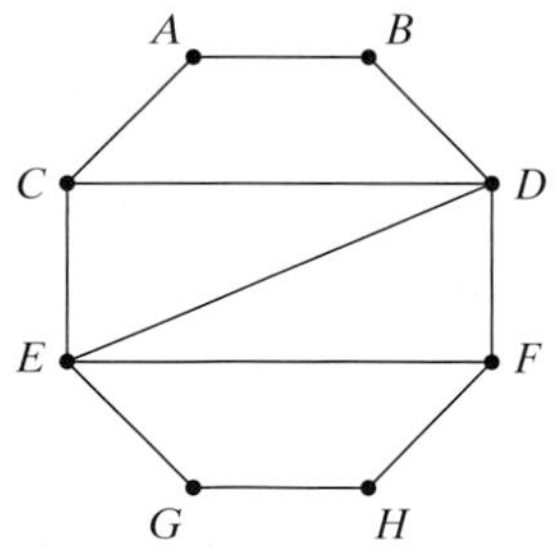

b. yes
c. The guard should begin at *C* and end at *F*, or vice versa.

22. Possible answer: *A*, *E*, *C*, *B*, *D*, *A*
23. Possible answer: *D*, *B*, *A*, *E*, *C*, *D*
24. a. no
25. a. yes **b.** 6
26. a. no
27. a. yes **b.** 24

28. *A*, *B*, *C*, *D*, *A*: 19; *A*, *B*, *D*, *C*, *A*: 18; *A*, *C*, *B*, *D*, *A*: 19; *A*, *C*, *D*, *B*, *A*: 18; *A*, *D*, *B*, *C*, *A*: 19; *A*, *D*, *C*, *B*, *A*: 19
29. *A*, *B*, *D*, *C*, *A* and *A*, *C*, *D*, *B*, *A* **30.** *A*, *C*, *D*, *B*, *A*; 18 **31.** *A*, *B*, *E*, *D*, *C*, *A*; 24

32.

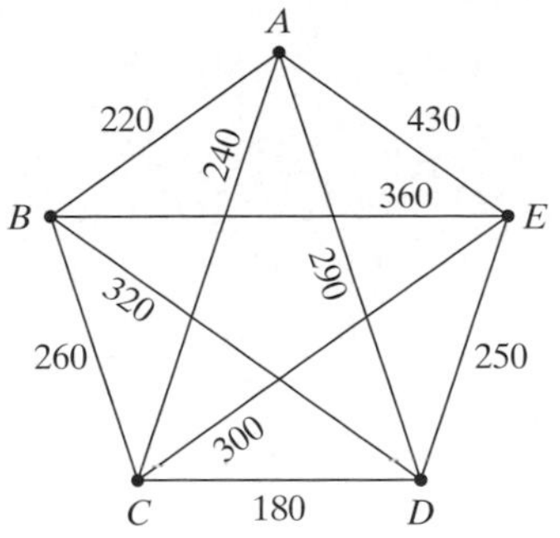

33. *A*, *B*, *C*, *D*, *E*; $1340 **34.** yes **35.** No. It has a circuit. **36.** No. It is disconnected.

37. Possible answer:

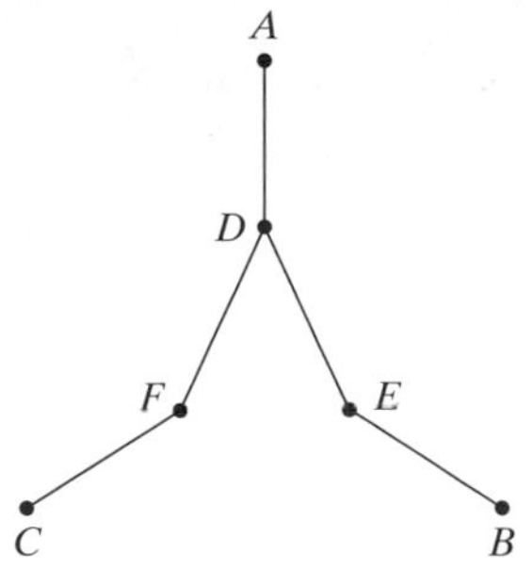

38. Possible answer:

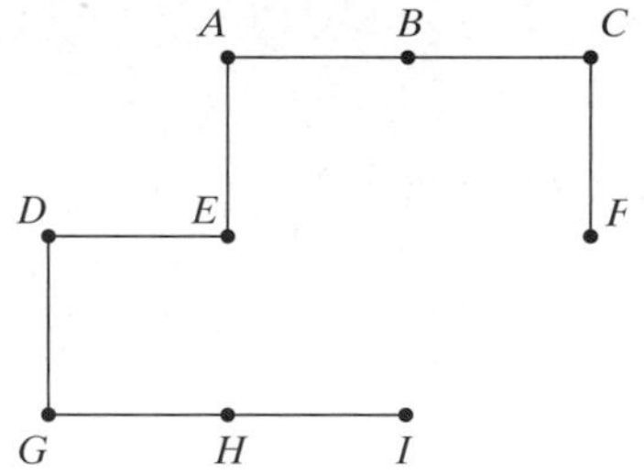

39.

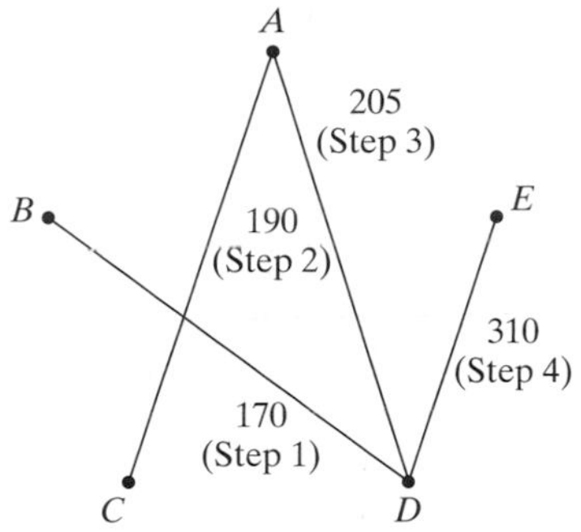

; 875

40.

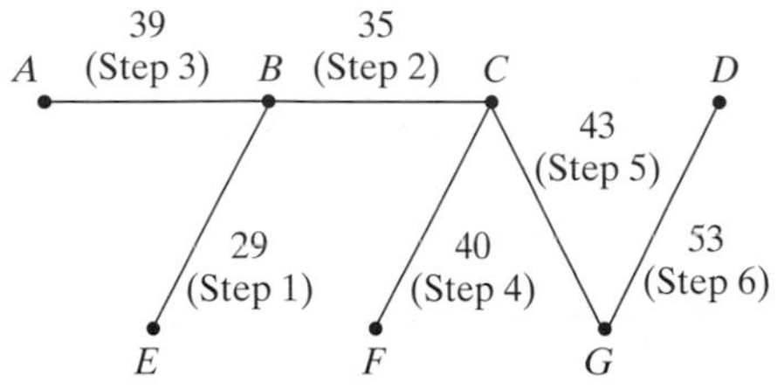

; 239

41.

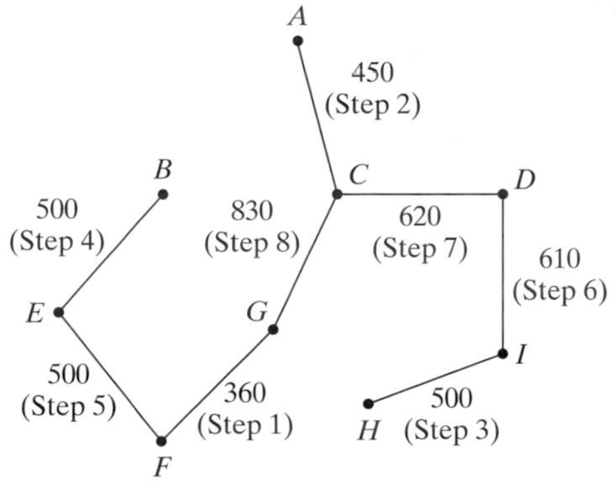

; 4370 mi

Chapter 15 Test

1. *A*: 2; *B*: 2; *C*: 4; *D*: 3; *E*: 2; *F*: 1 **2.** Possible answer: *A*, *D*, *E* and *A*, *B*, *C*, *E* **3.** *B*, *A*, *D*, *E*, *C*, *B* **4.** *CF*

5.

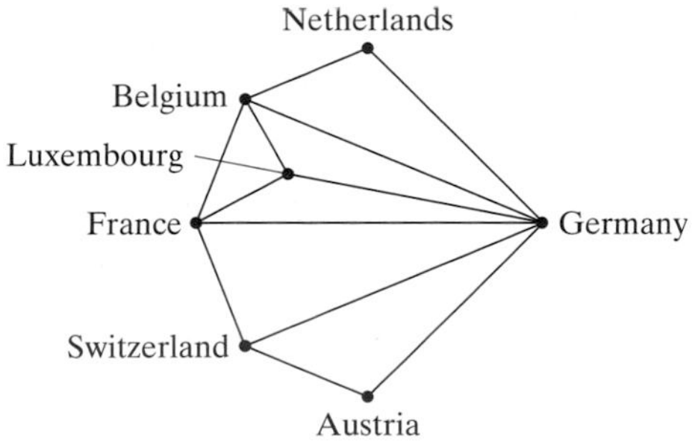

6. a. Euler path **b.** Possible answer:

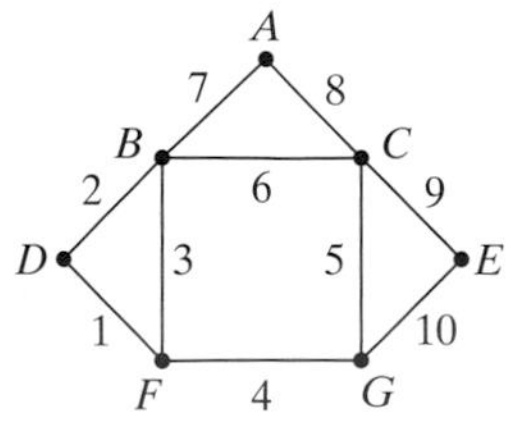

7. a. neither

8. a. Euler circuit **b.** Possible answer:

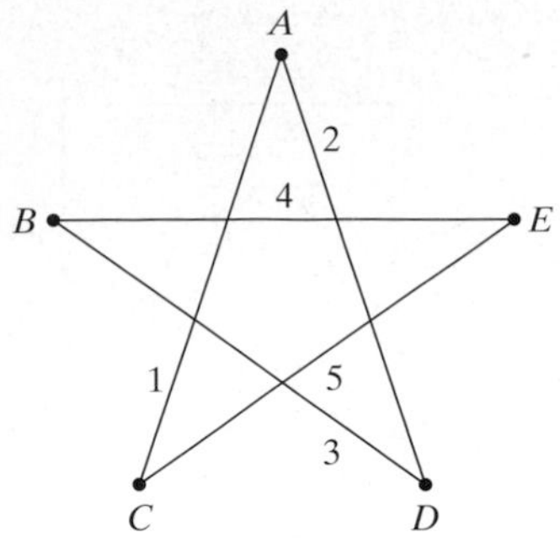

9.

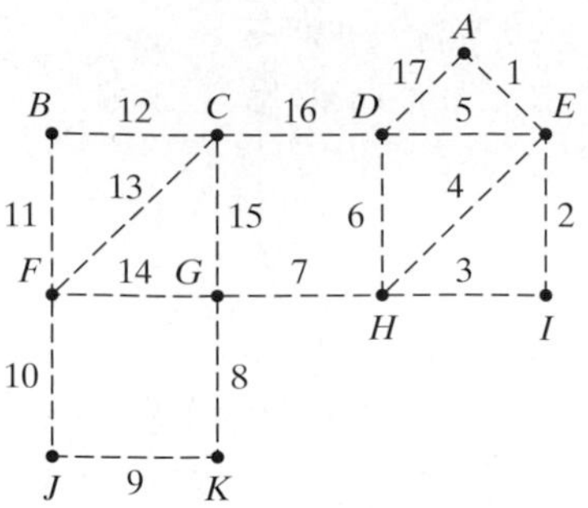

10. a.

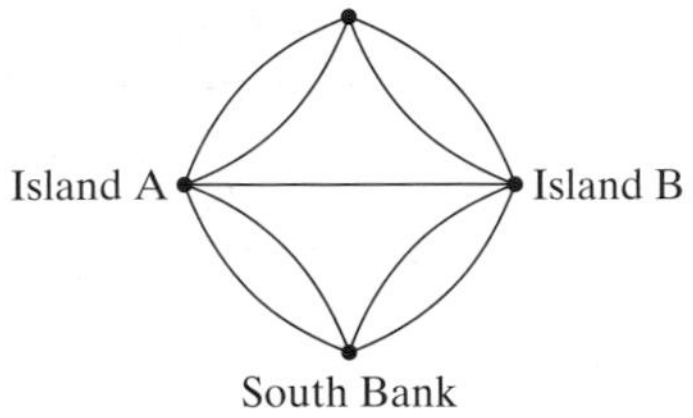

b. yes **c.** at one of the islands

11. a.

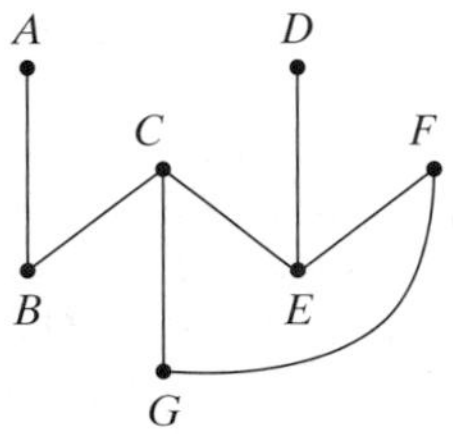

b. no

12. a.

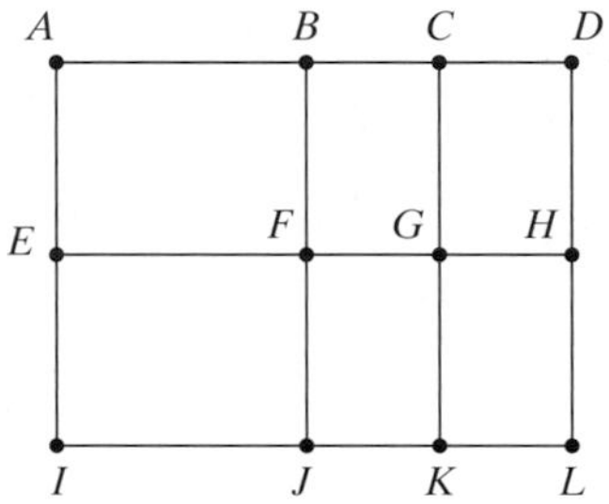

b. no

13. *A, B, C, D, G, F, E, A* and *A, F, G, D, C, B, E, A* **14.** 24

15.

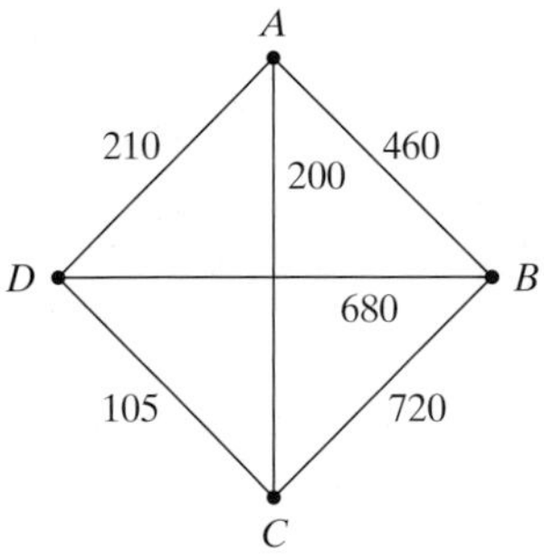

16. *A, B, D, C, A* or *A, C, D, B, A*; \$1445
17. *A, E, D, C, B, A*; 33
18. no

19. Possible answer:

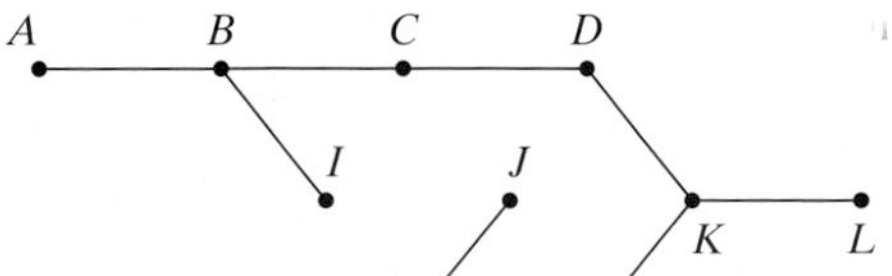

20.

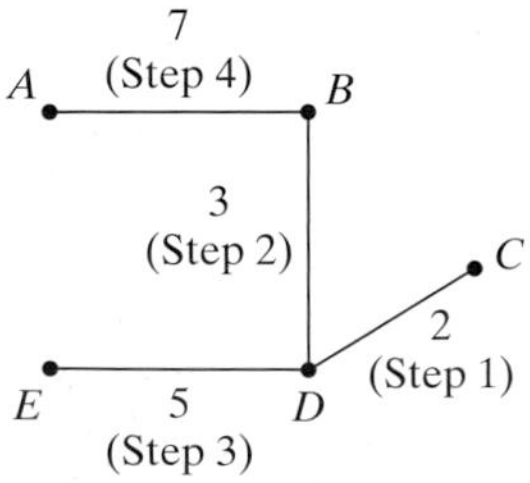

; 17

Photo Credits

CHAPTER 1 **CO** Foreground: JFPI Studios, Inc./Corbis/Bettmann; Background: Jason Reed/Getty Images, Inc.-Photodisc **p. 2** King Features Syndicate **p. 6** LSHTM/Getty Images, Inc.-Stone Allstock **p. 9** Richard F. Voss **p. 13** (left) Ken Fisher/Getty Images, Inc.-Stone Allstock; (right) Martin Bydalek/Getty Images, Inc.-Stone Allstock **p. 15** Ken Fisher/Getty Images, Inc.-Stone Allstock **p. 26** Phil Jason/Getty Images, Inc.-Taxi **p. 27** Harry Harris/AP Wide World Photos **p. 31** Jim Cummins/Jim Cummins Studio, Inc.

CHAPTER 2 **CO** Foreground: Courtesy of John Christiana; Background: Keith Brofsky/Getty Images, Inc.-Photodisc **p. 46** Jay Brousseau/Getty Images, Inc.-Image Bank **p. 47** Globe Photos, Inc. **p. 48** Illustration by John Tenniel, colored by Fritz Kredel. Discoveries®. Gallimard Jeunesse Publishers **p. 58** Frederick M. Brown/Getty Images, Inc. **p. 63** (1) Bob London/Agence France Presse/Getty Images, Inc. (2) Jerry Young © Dorling Kindersley (3) Labat J.M. Jacana/Scientific Control/Photo Researchers, Inc. (4) Donna Svennevik/Getty Images, Inc.-Liaison **p. 64** P. J. Crook **p. 67** Si´ TV, Inc. **p. 79** Victor Habbick Visions/Science Photo Library/Photo Researchers, Inc. **p. 91** (left) Bill Brooks/Alamy Images; (right) Mark Edwards/Peter Arnold, Inc.

CHAPTER 3 **CO** Foreground: Robert Fried/Robert Fried Photography; Background: Willie Maldonado/Riser/Getty Images, Inc. **p. 108** Brian King/eStock Photography LLC **p. 112** Paramount Pictures/Picture Desk, Inc./Kobal Collection **p. 115** Jonathan Kitchen/Getty Images/Digital Vision **p. 127** Mike Powell/Corbis/Bettmann **p. 128** (top) Gala/SuperStock, Inc.; (bottom) Carole Elies/Getty Images, Inc.-Stone Allstock **p. 152** Columbia Pictures/ZUMA/Corbis/Bettmann **p. 161** AP Wide World Photos **p. 163** Phototheque R. Magritte/ADAGP/ Art Resource, N.Y. **p. 166** Ted Soqui/Corbis/Sygma **p. 168** Paramount/The Kobal Collection **p. 174** AP Wide World Photos **p. 177** (top) United Media/United Feature Syndicate, Inc.; (bottom) United Media/United Feature Syndicate, Inc. **p. 179** (left) Martin Droeshout (British) "William Shakespeare" (1564–1616). National Portrait Gallery, London/SuperStock; (right) Image Works/Mary Evans Picture Library Ltd **p. 186** Scala/Art Resource, N.Y.

CHAPTER 4 **CO** Foreground: Fujitsu/Handout/Corbis/Reuters America LLC; Background: Haruyoshi Yamaguchi/Corbis/Sygma **p. 196** Bill Brooks/Masterfile Corporation **p. 198** M. Beck-Coppola/RMN/Art Resource/Reunion des Musees Nationaux **p. 199** Christie's Images Inc. **p. 201** William Munoz **p. 203** Jeff Greenberg/PhotoEdit Inc. **p. 205** Image Works/Mary Evans Picture Library Ltd **p. 209** Kathryn Hollinrake/Masterfile Corporation **p. 211** Phil Degginger/Getty Images, Inc.-Stone Allstock **p. 212** IBM Corporate Archives **p. 214** David Scharf/Getty Images, Inc.-Science Faction **p. 216** Scott Halleran/Allsport/Getty Images, Inc.-Allsport Photography **p. 219** Lee Snider/The Image Works

CHAPTER 5 **CO** Foreground: Corbis Royalty Free; Background: Corbis Royalty Free **p. 228** Peter Tenzer/ImageState/International Stock Photography Ltd. **p. 237** Sanford/Agliolo/Photo Researchers, Inc. **p. 249** Michael Newman/PhotoEdit Inc. **p. 262** Scala/Art Resource, N.Y. **p. 264** Telegraph Colour Library/Getty Images, Inc.-Taxi **p. 266** Photofest **p. 268** John G. Ross/Photo Researchers, Inc. **p. 271** Everett Collection **p. 272** Robert F. Blitzer **p. 275** The Cartoon Bank **p. 277** AFP Photo/Stand Honda/Getty Images, Inc.-Agence France Presse **p. 280** (top) The Gallery/Stratford; (bottom) David Weintraub/Photo Researchers, Inc. **p. 285** Charles Rex Arbogast/AP Wide World Photos **p. 288** Dick Morton **p. 294** Richard Lord/The Image Works

CHAPTER 6 **CO** Foreground: ©Bettmann/CORBIS; Background: Archive Holdings, Inc./Getty Images, Inc.-Image Bank **p. 304** Dana Edmunds/PacificStock.com **p. 311** Warner Bros. TV/Bright/Kauffman/Crane Pro/Picture Desk, Inc./Kobal Collection **p. 322** Kurt Amsler/Photo-Cine-Sub **p. 323** Michael Agliolo/Grant Heilman Photography, Inc. **p. 326** Martin Harvey/©318/Gallo Images/CORBIS **p. 331** Doc White/TCL/ SeaPics.com **p. 334** Frans Lanting/Minden Pictures **p. 336** Tom Sanders/ImageState/International Stock Photography Ltd. **p. 339** UPI/Corbis/Bettmann **p. 340** Ron Kimball Photography **p. 349** Mauro Fermariello/Photo Researchers, Inc. **p. 357** Corbis/Bettmann

CHAPTER 7 **CO** Foreground: Getty Images/Digital Vision; Background: Steve Bloom/Taxi/Getty Images **p. 368** Globe Photos, Inc. **p. 379** (left) Spantrans/AGE Fotostock America, Inc.; (right) LWA-Stephen/Corbis/Bettmann **p. 391** Gareth Cattermole/Getty Images **p. 400** NBC/Everett Collection **p. 405** Frank Clarkson **p. 414** AP Wide World Photos **p. 415** Pascal Parrot/Corbis/Sygma **p. 420** David Schmidt/Masterfile Corporation **p. 427** Copyright © 1981 Scott Kim, scottkim.com. All rights reserved.

CHAPTER 8 **CO** Foreground: Man sitting: Photodisc/Getty Images; Coins: Andreas Koerner/Stock4B/Getty Images; Background: MedioImages/Getty Images-MedioImages **p . 444** Erlendur Berg/SuperStock, Inc. **p. 452** SuperStock, Inc. **p. 454** The Granger Collection, New York **p. 460** Getty Images, Inc.-Stone Allstock **p. 467** Nati Harnik/AP Wide World Photos **p. 480** George Doyle/Getty Images, Inc.-Stockdisc **p. 488** AP Wide World Photos **p. 491** Paul Barton/Corbis/Stock Market **p. 495** Mel Yates/Getty Images, Inc.-Taxi

CHAPTER 9 **CO** Foreground: W. Perry Conway/CORBIS-NY; Background: Gail Shumway/Getty Images, Inc.-Taxi **p. 507** Joe McDonald/CORBIS–NY **p. 508** Index Stock Imagery, Inc. **p. 510** Bills: U.S. Bureau of Engraving and Printing; Coins: Frank LaBua/Pearson Education/PH Collge **p. 517** Robert Brenner/PhotoEdit, Inc. **p. 519** Peter Langone/ Getty Images, Inc.-Stone Allstock **p. 525** Image Source/Getty Images, Inc.-Image Source **p. 530** Roland Seitre

CHAPTER 10 **CO** Foreground: Darrell Gulin/Photodisc/Getty Images; Background: Jh Pete Carmichael/Riser/Getty Images **p. 538** San Francisco MOMA/Olivier Laude Photography **p. 545** Creators Syndicate, Inc. **p. 546** VAGA **p. 549** Robert Ginn/PhotoEdit, Inc. **p. 555** "That's Dancing!" from MGM/UA Entertainment Co. Courtesy The Kobal Collection **p. 556** Omni-Photo Communications, Inc. **p. 557** Tim Eagan/Woodfin Camp & Associates **p. 561** The M. C. Escher Company BV **p. 564** Bart Geerligs/Getty Images, Inc.-Taxi **p. 568** Benjamin Shearn/Getty Images, Inc.-Taxi **p. 570** J. Silver/SuperStock, Inc. **p. 574** Paramount TV/Everett Collection **p. 576** Doug Armand/Getty Images, Inc.-Stone Allstock **p. 582** Chris Noble/Getty Images, Inc.-Stone Allstock **p. 586** Janet Foster/Masterfile Corporation **p. 590** (top) Hugh Sitton/Getty Images, Inc.-Stone Allstock; (bottom left) J. A. Kraulis/Masterfile Corporation; (bottom right) Gregory Sams/Photo Researchers, Inc. **p. 594** Ari Lehtonen **p. 595** M. C. Escher's "Circle Limit III" © 2006 The M.C. Escher Company – Holland. All rights reserved. www.mcescher.com **p. 597** (top) Daryl Hepting, Ph.D.; (middle left and right) Gregory Sams/Science Photo Library/Photo Researchers, Inc. **p. 598** SuperStock, Inc.

CHAPTER 11 **CO** Abraham Lincoln: © Bettmann/CORBIS. All Rights Reserved. John F. Kennedy: © Bettmann/CORBIS. All Rights Reserved. **p. 608** AP Wide World Photos **p. 609** SuperStock, Inc. **p. 613** (left) ©2001 by Vaughn Youtz; (middle) AP Wide World Photos; (right) AP Wide World Photos **p. 614** Corbis/Sygma **p. 621** Marilyn Monroe: Picture Desk, Inc./Kobal Collection. James Dean: Imapress/Globe Photos, Inc. Jim Morrison: Michael Ochs Archives.com. Kurt Cobain: S.I.N./Corbis/Bettmann. Selena: AP Wide World Photos **p. 627** Larry Kolvoord/The Image Works **p. 630** Paul S. Howell/Getty Images, Inc.-Liaison **p. 632** Ron Avery/SuperStock, Inc. **p. 635** Greg Heins/Addison Gallery of American Art **p. 636** Sue Klemen/Stock Boston **p. 637** Corrado Giambalvo/AP Wide World Photos **p. 641** Grant V. Faint/Getty Images-Iconica **p. 645** Manoj Shah/Getty Images, Inc.-Stone Allstock **p. 649** Alec Pytlowany/Masterfile Corporation **p. 653** Jerry Driendl/Getty Images, Inc.-Taxi **p. 654** UPI/Corbis/Bettmann **p. 663** Tom Le Goff/Getty Images/Digital Vision **p. 667** Miro Vintoniv/Stock Boston **p. 668** Bob Daemmrich/Stock Boston

CHAPTER 12 **CO** Foreground left: Rob Goldman/Getty Images, Inc. Foreground right: Tim Macpherson/Getty Images, Inc.-Stone Allstock. Background: Ingram Publishing/Getty Images **p. 680** CBS-TV/Picture Desk, Inc./Kobal Collection **p. 681** Art Resource/The New York Public Library **p. 692** King Features Syndicate **p. 705** Getty Images, Inc.-Photodisc **p. 712** Robert Brenner/PhotoEdit, Inc. **p. 714** Simon Warner, Photographer **p. 717** Michael Newman/PhotoEdit, Inc. **p. 721** Norbert Schafer/Corbis/Stock Market **p. 730** Culver Pictures, Inc. **p. 733** Stuart Westmorland/Getty Images, Inc.-Stone Allstock

CHAPTER 13 **CO** Foreground: Gail Shumway; Background: joSon/Getty Images, Inc.-Stone Allstock **p. 757** Gerben Oppermans/Getty Images, Inc.-Stone Allstock **p. 758** (top) Ben Davidson; (bottom) Dr. Gerald D. Carr, PhD. **p. 759** (top) Joyce Photographics/Photo Researchers, Inc.; (bottom) Golt/Rapho/Photo Researchers, Inc. **p. 760** U.S. Postal Service

CHAPTER 14 **CO** Foreground: Jupiter Images-PictureArts Corporation; Background: Jupiter Images Picturerequest-Royalty Free **p. 772** Photofest **p. 777** Archive Photos/Jupiter Images-FoodPix-Creatas-Brand X-Banana Stock-PictureQuest **p. 779** AP Wide World Photos **p. 784** AFP Photo/Adrian Dennis/Getty Images, Inc.-Agence France Presse **p. 787** The Granger Collection, New York **p. 791** AFP Photo/Rhona Wise/Getty Images, Inc.-Agence France Presse **p. 792** Michael Schuman/Corbis/SABA Press Photos, Inc. **p. 796** The Granger Collection **p. 799** The Granger Collection, New York **p. 801** The Granger Collection, New York **p. 802** The Granger Collection, New York **p. 804** The Granger Collection, New York **p. 809** (left) Ohio Historical Society; (right) The Granger Collection, New York **p. 811** Benelux Press, b.v./eStock Photography/Jupiter Images-FoodPix-Creatas-Brand X-Banana Stock-PictureQuest **p. 813** The Granger Collection, New York

CHAPTER 15 **CO** Foreground: Businessman running: Emmanuel Faure/Taxi/Getty Images; Train station: Will & Deni McIntyre/Photodisc/Getty Images; Family: Baerbel Schmidt/Getty Images, Inc.-Stone Allstock; Background: Alan & Sandy Carey/Photodisc/Getty Images **p. 824** Oprah Winfrey: Stephane Cardinale/CORBIS-NY; George W. Bush: Folio/Omni-Photo Communications, Inc.; Bono: Chris Wattie/Corbis/Reuters America LLC; Steve Jobs: James Leynse/Corbis/Bettmann **p. 834** Bernard Boutrit/Woodfin Camp & Associates **p. 845** AP Wide World Photos **p. 855** Gary Harwood/Corbis/Reuters America LLC **p. 859** Japan Society

Subject Index

Q

R

S

Index of Applications